CW00816173

THE COMPLETE ILLUSTRATED CHECK LIST OF THE BIRDS OF THE WORLD

THE COMPLETE ILLUSTRATED CHECK LIST OF THE BIRDS OF THE WORLD

TIM WESTOLL

Glinger Publications
Carlisle

Dykeside, Longtown, Carlisle, Cumbria CA6 5ND

First published by Tim Westoll 1998

A catalogue record for this book is available from The British Library

ISBN 0 9533367 0 0

Designed and produced by Geoff Green Book Design, Cambridge

Printed in Hong Kong by Midas Ltd.

CONTENTS

Introduction xiv

THE CHECKLIST 1

Plate 1. Family 1. *Struthionidae.* Ostriches. (l)
Family 2. *Rheidae,* Rheas. (1–3)
Family 3. *Casuaridae.* Cassowaries. (1–3)
Family 4. *Dromaiidae.* Emus. (l)
Family 5. *Apterygidae.* Kiwis. (1–3)
Plate 2. Family 6. *Tinamidae.* (l) *Tinamous.* (1–26)
Plate 3. *Tinamidae.* (2) *Tinamous;* (27–48)
Plate 4. Family 7. *Spheniscidae.* Penguins. (1–18)
Plate 5. Family 8. *Gaviidae.* Divers or Loons. (1–15)
Family 9. *Podicipedidae.* Grebes. (1–21)
Plate 6. Family 10. *Diomedeidae.* Albatrosses. (1–14)
Plate 7. Family 11. *Procellariidae.* (1) Fulmars, Large Petrels. (1–18)
Plate 8. *Procellariidae.* (2) Shearwaters. (19–41)
Plate 9. *Procellariidae.* (3) Petrels. (42–77)
Plate 10. Family 12. *Hydrobatidae.* Storm Petrels. (1–21). Family 13. *Pelicanoididae.* Diving Petrels. (1–4)
Plate 11. Family 14. *Phaethontidae.* Tropicbirds. (1–4)
Family 15. *Pelicanidae.* Pelicans. (1–8)
Family 16. *Sulidae.* Gannets & Boobies. (1–9)
Plate 12. Family 17, *Phalacrocoracidae.* (1) Cormorants & Shags. (1–33)
Plate 13. *Phalacrocoracidae.* (2), Cormorants & Shags. (34–39)
Family 18. *Anhingidae.* Snakebirds or Darters. (1–4)
Family 19. *Fregatidae.* Frigate Birds. (1–5)
Plate 14. Family 20. *Ardeidae.* (1) Herons. (1–21)
Plate 15. *Ardeidae.* (2) Egrets ,Night Herons, (22–45)
Plate 16. *Ardeidae.* (3) Night Herons, Bitterns. (46–66)
Plate 17. Family 21. *Balaenicipitidae.* Whale headed Stork. (1)
Family 22 *Scopidae.* Hammerkop. (1) Family 23. *Ciconiidae.* (1) Storks.1–19.
Plate 18. Family 24. *Threskiornithidae.* (1) Ibises. (1–22).
Plate 19. *Threskiornithidae.* (2) Ibises, Spoonbills. (23–33)
Family 25. *Phoenicopteridae.* Flamingos. (1–6)
Plate 20. Family 26. *Anhimidae.* Screamers. (1–3)
Family 27. *Anatidae.* (1) Tree Ducks, Swans. (1–18)
Plate 21. *Anatidae.* (2) Geese, (19–39)
Plate 22. *Anatidae.* (3) Geese, Shelducks. Steamer Ducks. (40–54)
Plate 23. *Anatidae.* (4) Surface feeding Ducks, (55–88)
Plate 24. *Anatidae.* (5) Dabbling, Torrent Ducks, Eiders. (89–113)
Plate 25. *Anatidae.* (d) Diving Ducks. (114–139)
Plate 26. *Anatidae.* (7) Scoters ,Mergansers ,etc (140–166)

Plate 27. Family 28. *Cathartidae*. New·world Vultures. (1–7)
Family 29. *Sagittariidae*. Secretary Bird, (1)
Plate 28. Family 30. *Accipitridae*. (1) Lizard Hawks, Honey Buzzards, Kites. (1–27)
Plate 29. *Accipitridae*. (2) Kites, Sea Eagles. (28–44)
Plate 30. *Accipitridae*. (3) Old world Vultures. (45–59)
Plate 31. *Accipitridae*. (4) Snake Eagles, Harriers. (60–91)
Plate 32. *Accipitridae*. (5) Goshawks, Sparrow Hawks (92–124)
Plate 33. *Accipitridae*. (6) Goshawks, Sparrow hawks (125–157)
Plate 34. *Accipitridae*. (7) Hawks, Buzzards, Eagles, (158–182)
Plate 35. *Accipitridae*. (8) Buzzards. (183–211)
Plate 36. *Accipitridae*, (9) Eagles. (212–229)
Plate 37. *Accipitridae*. (10) Eagles. (230–251)
Plate 38. Family 31, *Pandionidae*, Osprey. (1)
Family 32, *Falconidae*(1), Caracaras, Falcons(1)
Plate 39. *Falconidae*(2). Falcons. (2)
Plate 40. Family 33, *Megapodiidae* Mound builders. (1–19)
Plate 41. Family 34, *Cracidae*. (1) Guans & Curassows, (1–27)
Plate 42. *Cracidae*, (2) Guans & Curassows, (28–49)
Plate 43. Family 35, *Tetraonidae*. Grouse.
Plate 44. Family 36, *Phasianidae*. (1) Wood Partridges, Quails. (1–36)
Plate 45. *Phasianidae*, (2) Partridges, Francolins. (37–68)
Plate 46. *Phasianidae*, (3) Francolins, Partridges. (69–103)
Plate 47. *Phasianidae*. (4) Quails, Partridges, (104–145a)
Plate 48. *Phasianidae*. (5) Pheasants. (146–155)
Plate 49. *Phasianidae*, (6) Pheasants. (156–167)
Plate 50. *Phasianidae*. (7) Pheasants. (168–182)
Plate 51. *Phasianidae*. (8) Pheasants, Peafowl, (183–197)
Plate 52. Family 37, *Numididae*. Guineafowl. (1–8)
Family 38, *Meleagrididae*, Turkeys. (1–2)
Family 39, *Opisthocomidae*. Hoatzin, (1)
Plate 53, Family 40. *Mesitornithidae*. Mesites, (1–3)
Family 41, *Turnicidae*. Button Quails, (1–18)
Family 42. *Pedionomidae*. Plains Wanderer. (1)
Plate 54. Family 43. *Gruidae*. Cranes. (1–15)
Family 44. *Aramidae*. Limpkin, (1)
Family 45. *Psophiidae*. Trumpeters. (1–3)
Plate 55. Family 46. *Rallidae*. (1). Rails. (1–42)
Plate 56. *Rallidae*. (2). Rails. (43–64)
Plate 57. *Rallidae*. (3). Crakes, (65–113)
Plate 58. *Rallidae*. (4). Gallinules, Moorhens. (114–136)
Plate 59. *Rallidae*. (S). Coots, (137–147)
Family 47. *Heliornithidae*, Finfoots. (1–3)
Family 48. *Rhynochetidae*, Kagu. (1)
Family 49, *Eurypygidae*, Sun Bittern. (1)
Family 50. *Cariamidae*, Seriamas, (1–2)
Plate 60. Family 51. *Otidae*. (1), Bustards, (1–12)
Plate 61. *Otidae*. (2). Bustards. (13–2).
Plate 62. Family 52. *Jacanidae*. Jacanas. (1–8)
Family 53, *Rostratulidae*. Painted Snipe. (1–2)
Family 54. *Haematopodidae*. Oystercatchers. (1–10)
Family 55, *Charadriidae*. (1) Plovers, (1–10)
Plate 63. *Charadriidae*, (2) Plovers. (11–44),
Plate 64. *Charadriidae*. (3) Plovers. (45–68)

Family 56. *Scolopacidae.* (1) Curlews, (1–9)
Plate 65. *Scolopacidae.* (2) Godwits, Sandpipers. (10–30)
Plate 66. *Scolopacidae.* (3) Snipe, Woodcock, (31–60)
Plate 67. *Scolopacidae.* (4) Sandpipers. (61–85)
Family 57 *Recurvirostridae.* Stilts, Avocets, (1–14)
Plate 68. Family 58, *Phalaropidae.* Phalaropes,
Family 59. *Dromadidae.* Crab Plover, (1)
Family 60. *Burhinidae.* Stone Curlews, (1–9)
Family 61. *Glareolidae.* Coursers & Pratincoles, (1–18)
Family 62. *Thinocoridae.* Seedsnipe. (1–4)
Plate 69. Family 63. *Chionididae.* Sheathbills, (1–2)
Family 64, *Stercorariidae,* Skuas, (1–8)
Family 65. *Laridae,* (1) Gulls. (1–14)
Plate 70. *Laridae.* (2) Gulls. (15–31)
Plate 71. *Laridae.* (3) Gulls. (32–52)
Plate 72. *Laridae.* (4) Terns. (53–75)
Plate 73. *Laridae.* (5) Terns, (7–96)
Family 66 *Rynchopidae.* Skimmers. (1–3)
Plate 74. Family 67. *Alcidae.* Auks. (1–24)
Plate 75. Family 68. *Pteroclididae.* Sandgrouse. (1–16)
Plate 76. Family 69. *Columbidae.* (1) Pigeons. (1–26)
Plate 77. *Columbidae.* (2) Pigeons. (27–53).
Plate 78. *Columbidae.* (3) Doves. (54–87).
Plate 79. *Columbidae.* (4) Doves & Pigeons. (88–118)
Plate 80. *Columbidae.* (5) Doves. (119–146)
Plate 81. *Columbidae.* (6) Doves. (147–176).
Plate 82. *Columbidae.* (7) Doves & Pigeons. (177–91)
Plate 83. *Columbidae.* (8) Green Pigeons. (192–215)
Plate 84. *Columbidae.* (9) Fruit Doves. (216–243)
Plate 85. *Columbidae.* (10) Fruit Doves, Blue Pigeons. (245–272)
Plate 86. *Columbidae.* (11) Imperial Pigeons. (273–294)
Plate 87. *Columbidae.* (12) Pigeons. (295–314)
Plate 88. Family 70. *Psittacidae.* (1) Lories. (1–32)
Plate 89. *Psittacidae.* (2) Lories, Lorikeets. (33–59)
Plate 90. *Psittacidae.* (3) Cockatoos. (60–66)
Plate 91. *Psittacidae.* (4) Cockatoos, etc. (67–81)
Plate 92. *Psittacidae.* (S) Pygmy, Fig, Racquet Parrots. (82–110.
Plate 93. *Psittacidae.* (6) Parrots, King Parrots. (111–126)
Plate 94, *Psittacidae.* (7) Australasian Parrots, Rosellas. (127–147)
Plate 95. *Psittacidae.* (8) Australasian Parrots. (148–167)
Plate 96. *Psittacidae.* (9) Lovebirds, Hanging Parrots. (168–200)
Plate 97. *Psittacidae,* (10) Asian Parakeets. (201–214)
Plate 98. *Psittacidae.* (11) Macaws. (215–222)
Plate 99. *Psittacidae.* (12) Macaws, (223–232)
Plate 100. *Psittacidae.* (13) Conures. (233–259)
Plate 101. *Psittacidae.* (14) Conures. (260–289)
Plate 102. *Psittacidae.* (15) Amazons. (290–320)
Plate 103. *Psittacidae.* (16) Amazons. (321–342)
Plate 104. *Psittacidae.* (17) Amazons. (343–366)
Plate 105. Family 71. *Musophagidae.* Touracos, Go-away Birds. (1–22)
Plate 106. Family 72. *Cuculidae.* (1) Cuckoos. (1–34)
Plate 107. *Cuculidae.* (2) Cuckoos. (35–68).
Plate 108. *Cuculidae,* (3) Cuckoos, Malcohas. (69–90)

Plate 109. *Cuculidae*. (4) Anis, Roadrunners, Couas. (91–110)
Plate 110. *Cuculidae*. (5) Couas, Coucals. (111–129).
Plate 111. *Cuculidae*. (6) Coucals. (130–148)
Plate 112. Family 73. *Tytonidae*, Barn Owls. (1–16)
Family 74. *Strigidae*. (1). Typical Owls. (1–17)
Plate 113. *Strigidae*. (2). Typical Owls. (18–66)
Plate 114 *Strigidae*. (3), Typical Owls. (67–84)
Plate 115 *Strigidae*. (4). Typical Owls. (85–116)
Plate 116 *Strigidae*. (5). Typical Owls. (117–146.)
Plate 117 *Strigidae*. (6). Typical Owls. (147–172)
Plate 118 Family 75. *Steatornithidae*. Oilbird. (1)
Family 76. *Podargidae*. Frogmouths. (1–14)
Family 77. *Nyctibiidae*. Potoos. (1–7)
Family 78. *Aegothelidae*. Owlet Nightjars. (1–8)
Plate 119. Family 79. *Caprimulgidae*. (1) Nightjars. (1–27)
Plate 120 *Caprimulgidae*. (2) Nightjars. (28–56)
Plate 121 *Caprimulgidae*. (3) Nightjars. (57–89)
Plate 122. Family 80. *Hemiprocnidae*. Tree Swifts. (1)
Family 81. *Apodidae*. (1) Swifts. (1–42)
Plate 123. *Apodidae*. (2) Swifts. (43–73)
Plate 124 *Apodidae*. (3) Swifts. (74–105)
Plate 125. Family 82, *Trochilidae*. (1) Hummingbirds, (1–42)
Plate 126. *Trochilidae*, (2) Hummingbirds, (43–75)
Plate 127. *Trochilidae*. (3) Hummingbirds. (76–118)
Plate 128. *Trochilidae*. (4) Hummingbirds. (119–157)
Plate 129. *Trochilidae*, (5) Hummingbirds, (158–207)
Plate 130. *Trochilidae*. (6) Hummingbirds, (208–234)
Plate 131. *Trochilidae*, (7) Hummingbirds. (235–279)
Plate 132. *Trochilidae*, (8) Hummingbirds, (280–306)
Plate 133. *Trochilidae*, (9) Hummingbirds. (307–329)
Plate 134. *Trochilidae*, (10) Hummingbirds. (330–357)
Plate 135. Family 83, *Coliidae*. Mousebirds. (1–6)
Family 84, *Trogonidae*. (1) American Trogons, (1–11)
Plate 136. *Trogonidae*. (2) American Trogons. (12–25)
Plate 137. *Trogonidae*. (3) African & Asian Trogons. (26–39)
Plate 138. Family 85, *Alcedinidae*. (1) Kingfishers. (*1*–9)
Plate 139. *Alcedinidae*. (2) Kingfishers. (10–41)
Plate 140. *Alcedinidae*, (3) Kingfishers. (42–50)
Plate 141. *Alcedinidae*. (4) Kingfishers, (51–75)
Plate 142. *Alcedinidae*. (5) Kingfishers. (76–92)
Plate 143. *Alcedinidae*. (6) Kingfishers. (93–108)
Plate 144. Family 86, *Todidae*. Todies. (1–5)
Family 87. *Momotidae*. Motmots. (1–l0)
Plate 145. Family 88. *Meropidae*. (1) Bee–eaters, (1–13)
Plate 146. Family 89. *Meropidae*. (2) Bee– eaters, (14–26)
Family 90, *Leptosomatidae*, Courols, (1)
Plate 147. Family 90. *Brachypteraciidae*. Ground Rollers, (1–5)
Family 91, *Coraciidae*. Rollers, (1–12)
Plate 148. Family 92, *Upupidae*, Hoopoes. (1–2)
Family 93, *Phoeniculidae* Wood Hoopoes, (1–9)
Plate 149. Family 94. *Bucerotidae*, (1) Hornbills. (1–18)
Plate 150. *Bucerotidae*. (2) Hornbills, (19–33)
Plate 151. Bucerotidae. (3) Hornbills. (34–43)

Plate 152. Bucerotidae. (4) Hornbills. (44–52)
Plate 153. Bucerotidae. (5) Hornbills. (53–58)
Plate 154. Family 95. *Galbulidae*. Jacamars. (1–15)
Family 96. *Bucconidae*. (1) Puffbirds. (1–8)
Plate 155. *Bucconidae*. (2) Puffbirds, Nunbirds. (9–33)
Plate 156. Family 97. *Capitonidae*. (1) Barbets. (1–18)
Plate 157. *Capitonidae*. (2) Barbets. (19–40)
Plate 158. *Capitonidae*. (3) Barbets. (41–73)
Plate 159. *Capitonidae*. (4) Barbets. (74–88)
Family 98. *Indicatoridae*. Honeyguides. (1–18)
Plate 160. Family 99. *Ramphastidae*. (1) Toucans. (1–18)
Plate 161. *Ramphastidae*. (2) Toucans. (19–33)
Plate 162. *Ramphastidae*. (3) Toucans. (34–46)
Plate 163. Family 100. *Picidae*. (1) Woodpeckers. (1–38)
Plate 164. *Picidae*. (2) Woodpeckers. (39–51)
Plate 165. *Picidae*. (3) Woodpeckers. (52–76)
Plate 166. *Picidae*. (4) Woodpeckers. (77–95)
Plate 167. *Picidae*. (5) Woodpeckers. (95–105)
Plate 168. *Picidae*. (6) Woodpeckers. (106–118)
Plate 169. *Picidae*. (7) Woodpeckers. (119–128)
Plate 170. *Picidae*. (8) Woodpeckers. (124–142)
Plate 171. *Picidae*. (9) Woodpeckers. (143–161)
Plate 172. *Picidae*. (10) Woodpeckers. (162–186)
Plate 173. *Picidae*. (11) Woodpeckers. (187–208)
Plate 174. Family 100. *Picidae*. (12) Woodpeckers. (209–228)
Plate 175. *Picidae*. (13) Woodpeckers. (229–236) Order *Passeriformes*: Perching Birds.
Plate 176. Family 101. *Eurylaimidae*. Broadbills. (1–15)
Family 102. *Dendrocolaptidae*. (1) Woodcreepers. (1–8)
Plate 177. *Dendrocolaptidae*. (2) Woodcreepers. (9–31)
Plate 178. *Dendrocolaptidae*. (3) Woodcreepers. (32–53)
Plate 179. Family 103. *Furnariidae*. (1) Ovenbirds. (1–35)
Plate 180. *Furnariidae*. (2) Ovenbirds. (36–77)
Plate 181. *Furnariidae*. (3) Ovenbirds. (78–122)
Plate 182. *Furnariidae*. (4) Ovenbirds. (123–162)
Plate 183. *Furnariidae*. (5) Ovenbirds. (163–207)
Plate 184. *Furnariidae*. (6) Ovenbirds. (208–240)
Plate 185. Family 104. *Formicariidae*. (1) Antbirds. (1–16)
Plate 186. *Formicariidae*. (2) Antbirds. (17–37
Plate 187. *Formicariidae*. (3) Antbirds. (38–61)
Plate 188. *Formicariidae*. (4) Antbirds. (62–88)
Plate 189. *Formicariidae*. (5) Antbirds. (89–119)
Plate 190. *Formicariidae*. (6) Antbirds. (120–143)
Plate 191. *Formicariidae*. (7) Antbirds. (144–164)
Plate 192. *Formicariidae*. (8) Antbirds. (165–190)
Plate 193. *Formicariidae*. (9) Antbirds. (191–225)
Plate 194. *Formicariidae*. (10) Antpittas. (226–248)
Family 105. *Conopophagidae*. Gnateaters. (1–9)
Plate 195. Family 106. *Rhinocryptidae*. Tapaculos. (1–31)
Plate 196. Family 107. *Tyrannidae*. (1) Tyrant Flycatchers. (1–35)
Plate 197. *Tyrannidae*. (2) Tyrant Flycatchers. (36–67)
Plate 198. *Tyrannidae*. (3) Tyrant Flycatchers. (68–100)
Plate 199. *Tyrannidae*. (4) Tyrant Flycatchers. (101–129)
Plate 200. *Tyrannidae*. (5) Tyrant Flycatchers. (130–167).

Plate 201. *Tyrannidae.* (6) Tyrant Flycatchers. (168–222)
Plate 202. *Tyrannidae.* (7) Tyrant Flycatchers. (223–282)
Plate 203. *Tyrannidae.* (8) Tyrant Flycatchers. (283–340)
Plate 204. *Tyrannidae,* (9) Tyrant Flycatchers, (341–391)
Plate 205. *Tyrannidae,* (10) Tyrant Flycatchers, (392–408)
Family 108, *Oxyruncidae.* Sharpbill, (1).
Family 109. *Phytotomidae.* Plantcutters. (1–3)
Plate 206. Family 110. *Pipridae,* (1) Manikins. (1–27)
Plate 207. *Pipridae,* (2) Manikins. (28–6l)
Plate 208. Family 111. *Cotingidae.* (1) Cotingas. (1–19)
Plate 209. *Cotingidae.* (2) Cotingas. (20–43)
Plate 210. *Cotingidae,* (3) Cotingas. (44–72)
Plate 211. *Cotingidae.* (4) Cotingas. (73–86)
Plate 212. Family 112. *Pittidae,* (1) Pittas. (1–20)
Plate 213. *Pittidae,* (2) Pittas. (21–32),
Family 113, *Philepittidae,* Asities, (1–4)
Plate 214. Family 114. *Acanthisitidae.* New Zealand Wrens, (1–4)
Family 115, *Menuridae,* Lyre Birds, (1–2)
Family 116. *Atrichornithidae.* Scrub Birds. (1–2)
Plate 215. Family 117, *Alaudidae.* (1). Larks. (1–46)
Plate 216. *Alaudidae,* (2), Larks. (47–88)
Plate 217. Family 118. *Hirundinidae.* (1) Swallows, & Martins. (1–40)
Plate 218. *Hirundinidae.* (2) Swallows & Martins, (41–90)
Plate 219. Family 119. *Motacillidae.* (1) Wagtails & Pipits. (1–33)
Plate 220. *Motacillidae.* (2) Pipits, (34–72)
Plate 221. Family 120. *Campephagidae,* (1) Cuckoo Shrikes. (1–18)
Plate 222. *Campephagidae.* (2) Cuckoo Shrikes. (19–34)
Plate 223. *Campephagidae,* (3) Cuckoo Shrikes, (35–52)
Plate 224. *Campephagidae.* (4) Cuckoo Shrikes. (53–71)
Plate 225. *Campephagidae,* (5) Cuckoo Shrikes. (72–88)
Plate 226. Family 121. *Pycnonotidae.* (1) Bulbuls. (1–42)
Plate 227. *Pycnonotidae.* (2) Bulbuls. (43–80)
Plate 228. *Pycnonotidae,* (3) Bulbuls, (81–112)
Plate 229. *Pycnonotidae.* (4) Bulbuls. (113–139)
Plate 230. Family 122. *Irenidae.* Leafbirds, Ioras. (1–24)
Plate 231. Family 123, *Prionopidae.* Helmet Shrikes. (1–11)
Family 124. *Laniidae.* (1) Shrikes, (1–17)
Plate 232. *Laniidae,* (2) Shrikes. (18–43)
Plate 233. *Laniidae.* (3) Shrikes. (44–l)
Plate 234. *Laniidae.* (4) Shrikes. (62–80)
Plate 235. Family 125. *Vangidae.* Vanga Shrikes, (1–12)
Family 126. *Hypposittadae.* Coral Nuthatch. (1)
Family 127. *Bombycillidae.* Waxwings. (1–3)
Family 128. *Ptilogonatidae,* Silky Flycatchers. (1–5)
Family 129. *Dulidae.* Palmchat. (1)
Plate 236. Family 130. *Cinclidae,* Dippers, (1–5)
Family 131, *Troglodytidae,* (1) Wrens. (1–28)
Plate 237. *Troglodytidae.* (2) Wrens. (29–81)
Plate 238. Family 132. *Mimidae.* (1) Thrashers, Mocking Birds. (1–27)
Plate 239. *Mimidae.* (2) Thrashers, Mocking Birds. (28–36)
Family 133. *Prunellidae.* Accentors. (1–13)
Plate 240. Family 134, *Muscicapidae.* Sub Fam. Turdidae. (1). Robins. (1–30)
Plate 241. *Turdidae,* (2) African Robins, Robin Chats. (31–70)

Plate 242. *Turdidae.* (3) Alethes, Shamas, Redstarts. (71–96).
Plate 243. *Turdidae,* (4) Redstarts, Forktails.
Plate 244. *Turdidae.* (5) Cochoas, Bluebirds. etc. (120–143)
Plate 245. *Turdidae, (*6) Chats, (144–173)
Plate 246. *Turdidae,* (7) Wheatears, (174–201)
Plate 247. *Turdidae.* (8) Rock & Whistling Thrushes. (202–221)
Plate 248. *Turdidae,* (9) Zoothera Thrushes. (222–249)
Plate 249. *Turdidae,* (10) Zoothera, Old World Thrushes. (250–279)
Plate 250. *Turdidae.* (11) Old World Thrushes. (280–300)
Plate 251. *Turdidae.* (12) New World Thrushes. (301–328)
Plate 252. *Turdidae.* (13) New World Thrushes, (329–354)
Plate 253. Sub Fam. 135. *Orthonychinae,* Logrunners. (1–20).
Plate 254. Sub Fam. 136. *Timaliinae.* (1) Babblers. (1–51)
Plate 255. *Timaliinae,* (2) Babblers, (52–101)
Plate 256. *Timaliinae,* (3) Babblers. (102–143)
Plate 257. *Timaliinae,* (4) Babblers, (144–176)
Plate 258. *Timaliinae.* (5) Babblers. (177–204)
Plate 259. *Timaliinae.* (6) Babblers. (205–236)
Plate 260. *Timaliinae.* (7) Babblers. (237–277)
Plate 261 Sub Fam, 137, *Picathartidae,* Rockfowl/Bald Crows, (1–2)
Sub Fam,138, *Paradoxornithinae,* Parrotbills, (1–21)
Sub Fam,139, *Chamaeidae,* Wrentit, (1)
Sub Fam, l40, *Polioptilinae.* Gnatcatchers (1–l6)
Plate 262. Sub Fam,l41. *Sylviinae.* (1) Old World Warblers. (1–67)
Plate 263. *Sylviinae.* (2) Reed & Sylvia Warblers. (68–130)
Plate 264. *Sylviinae.* (3) Leaf Warblers. (131–197)
Plate 265. *Sylviinae.* (4) Prinias, Tailorbirds. (198–251)
Plate 266. *Sylviinae.* (5) Cisticolas, (252–302)
Plate 267. Sub Fam, 141. *Sylviinae.* (6) Apalis, Cameroptera etc, (303–356)
Plate 268. *Sylviinae,* (7) Eremomela etc, (357–410) Sub Fam, 142. *Regulidae.* Goldcrests, Kinglets, (1–8)
Plate 269. Sub Fam, 143. *Malurinae.* Blue Wrens, Wren Warblers. (1–33)
Plate 270. Sub Fam. 144. *Acanthizinae.* (1) Australasian Warblers. (1–6l)
Plate 271. *Acanthizinae,* (2) Australasian Warblers, (62–85)
Sub Fam, 145. *Ephthianuridae.* Australian Chats. (1–5)
Plate 272. Sub Fam, 146, *Eopsaltriidae,* (1) Australian Robins etc, (1–49)
Plate 273. *Eopsaltriidae,* (2) Thicket Flycatchers, (50–57)
Sub Fam. 147. *Muscicapinae,* (1) Old World Flycatchers, (1–29)
Plate 274. *Muscicapinae,* (2) Old World Flycatchers. (28–56)
Plate 275. *Muscicapinae,* (3) Niltava Flycatchers, (57–82)
Plate 276. *Muscicapinae,* (4) Old World Flycatchers. (83–119)
Plate 277. Sub Fam,148. *Rhipidurinae,* Fantail Flycatchers. (1–46)
Plate 278. Sub Fam,149, *Platysteirinae.* Puffback, Wattled Flycatchers, (1–31)
Plate 279. Sub Fam.l50, *Monarchinae.* (1) Paradise Flycatchers, (1–25)
Plate 280. *Monarchinae.* (2) Monarch Flycatchers, (26–59)
Plate 281. *Monarchinae,* (3) Monarch Flycatchers. (60–94)
Plate 282. Sub Fam, 151, *Pachycephalinae,* (1) Whistlers, (1–28)
Plate 283. *Pachycephalinae,* (2) Whistlers, (29–49)
Plate 284. *Pachycephalinae,* (3) Shrike Thrushes, (50–69)
Plate 285. Family 152, *Aegithalidae.* Long tailed Tits, (1–10)
Family 153, *Remizidae,* Penduline Tits, (1–12)
Family 154. *Paridae,* (1) Titmice, Chickadees, (1–26)
Plate 286. *Paridae,* (2) Titmice Chickadees, (27–56)

Family 155, *Sittidae*, Nuthatches, (1–24)
Plate 287. Family 156, *Daphoenosittinae*. Australian Nuthatches, (1–7)
Family 157, *Tichadromadinae*, Wallcreeper, (1)
Family 158. *Certhiidae*, Tree creepers, (1–7)
Family 159, *Rhabdornithidae*, Philippine Creepers. (1–3)
Family 160, *Climacteridae*, Australian Creepers, (1–10)
Plate 288. Family 161, *Dicaeidae*. (1) Flowerpeckers, (1–28)
Plate 289. *Dicaeidae*, (2) Flowerpeckers, Pardalotes, (29–62)
Plate 290. Family 162, *Nectariniidae*, (1) Sunbirds, (1–30)
Plate 291. *Nectariniidae*, (2) Sunbirds. (31–58)
Plate 292. *Nectariniidae*, (3) Sunbirds. (59–82)
Plate 293. *Nectariniidae*, (4) Sunbirds, (83–109)
Plate 294. *Nectariniidae*, (5) Sunbirds, Spiderhunters. (110–135)
Plate 295. Family 163, *Zosteropidae*, (1) White–eyes, (1–52)
Plate 296. *Zosteropidae*, (2) White–eyes, (53–102)
Plate 297. Family 164, *Meliphagidae*. (1) Honeyeaters, (1–44)
Plate 298. *Meliphagidae*, (2) Honeyeaters, (45–80)
Plate 299. *Meliphagidae*, (3) Honeyeaters. (81–113)
Plate 300. *Meliphagidae*. (4) Friar Birds, (114–136)
Plate 301. *Meliphagidae*, (5) Honeyeaters, (137–160)
Plate 302. *Meliphagidae*, (6) Honeyeaters, Miners, (161–190)
Family 165, *Ptromeropidae*. Sugarbirds, (1–2)
Plate 303. Family 166, *Emberizidae*, (1) Buntings, (1–26)
Plate 304. *Emberizidae*, (2) Buntings, (27–48)
Plate 305. *Emberizidae*. (3) American Sparrows, (49–89)
Plate 306. *Emberizidae*, (4) American Sparrows, (90–129)
Plate 307. *Emberizidae*, (5) American Finches, (130–157)
Plate 308. *Emberizidae*, (6) American Finches, (158–195)
Plate 309. *Emberizidae*, (7) Seedeaters. (196–237)
Plate 310. *Emberizidae*, (8) Towhees, Finches. (278–273)
Plate 311. *Emberizidae*, (9) Brush Finches, Sparrows. (274–318)
Plate 312. Family 166. *Emberizidae*. (10) Finches, Cardinals, (319–330)
Family 167, *Catamblyrhynchinae*, Plush capped Finch. (1)
Family 168. *Cardinalinae*, (1) Cardinal Grosbeaks. (1–15)
Plate 313. *Cardinalinae*. (2) Grosbeaks, Saltators. (16–42),
Plate 314. Family 169. *Thraupinae*. (1) Tanagers. (1–37)
Plate 315. *Thraupinae*. (2) Tanagers. (38–69)
Plate 316. *Thraupinae*. (3) Tanagers, (70–95)
Plate 317. *Thraupinae*. (4) Tanagers. (96–126)
Plate 318. *Thraupinae*. (5) Tanagers. (127–168)
Plate 319. *Thraupinae*. (6) Tanagers, (169–214)
Plate 320. *Thraupinae*. (7) Tanagers. (215–229)
Family 170. *Coeribidae*. (1) Dacnis, Honeycreepers. (1–15)
Plate 321. *Coeribidae*. (2) Flowerpiercers, Conebills. (16–47)
Family 171. *Tersinae*. Swallow Tanager. (1)
Family 172. *Zeledoniidae*. Wren Thrush. (1)
Plate 322. Family 173. *Parulidae*. (1) American Wood Warblers. (1–33)
Plate 323. *Parulidae*. (2) American Wood Warblers, (34–66)
Plate 324. *Parulidae*. (3) American Redstarts, Warblers, (67–122)
Plate 325. Family 174. *Drepanididae*. Hawaiian Honeycreepers. (1–38)
Plate 326. Family 175. *Vireonidae*, Peppershrikes, Vireos. (1–56)
Plate 327. Family 176. *Icteridae*. (1) Oropendolas. (1–12)
Plate 328. *Icteridae*. (2) Caciques, Orioles, (13–43)

Plate 329. *Icteridae.* (3) Orioles, Blackbirds, (44–67)
Plate 330. *Icteridae.* (4) Blackbirds, Meadow Larks. (68–90)
Plate 331. *Icteridae.* (5) Grackles, Cowbirds. (91–105)
Plate 332. Family 177. *Fringillidae.* Chaffinches. (1–3)
Sub Fam 178. *Carduelinae,* (*1*) Canaries ,Goldfinches, (1–44)
Plate 333. *Carduelinae.* (2) Goldfinches, Linnets. (45–78)
Plate 334. *Carduelinae.* (3) Redpolls ,Rose Finches, (79–103)
Plate 335. *Carduelinae.* (4) Rosefinches. (104–124)
Plate 336. *Carduelinae.* (5) Bullfinches, Grosbeaks. (125–146)
Plate 337. Family 179. *Estrildidae.* (1) Waxbills. (1–30)
Plate 338. *Estrildidae.* (2) Waxbills. (31–64)
Plate 339. *Estrildidae.* (3) Avadavats, Australian Finches. (65–97)
Plate 340. *Estrildidae.* (4) Parrot Finches, Mannikins. (98–149)
Plate 341. Family 180. *Ploceidae.* (Viduinae) (1), Whydahs, Indigo Birds. (1–15)
Family 181. *Ploceinae.* (1) Buffalo Weavers. (1–3)
Plate 342. *Ploceinae.* (2) Sparrows, (4–40)
Plate 343. *Ploceinae.* (3) Snow Finches, Weavers. (41–73)
Plate 344. *Ploceinae.* (4) Weavers. (74–97)
Plate 345. *Ploceinae.* (5) Weavers. (98–121)
Plate 346. *Ploceinae.* (6) Malimbes, Fodies. (122–144)
Plate 347. *Ploceinae.* (7) Bishops, Widow–Birds, (145–165).
Plate 348. Family 182. *Sturnidae.* (1:) Starlings. (1–24)
Plate 349. *Sturnidae.* (2) Starlings. (25–38)
Plate 350. *Sturnidae.* (3) Starlings. (39–68)
Plate 351. *Sturnidae.* (4) Starlings. (65–90)
Plate 352. *Sturnidae.* (5) Mynas, Oxpeckers. (91–115)
Plate 353. Family 183. *Oriolidae.* (1) Old World Orioles. (1–22)
Plate 354. *Oriolidae.* (2) Orioles, Figbirds. (23–30)
Family 184. *Artamidae.* Wood Swallows. (1–11)
Plate 355. Family 185. *Dicruridae.* Drongos. (1–24)
Plate 356. Family 186. *Callaeidae.* New Zealand Wattle Birds. (1–5)
Family 187. *Grallinidae,* Magpie Larks, (1–4)
Family 188. *Cracticidae.* (1) Bell Magpies. (1–5)
Plate 357. *Cracticidae.* (2) Currawongs, Butcherbirds, (4–14)
Family 189. *Ptilorhynchidae.* (1) Catbirds. Bowerbirds. (1–8)
Plate 358. *Ptilorhynchidae,* (2) Bowerbirds, (9–22)
Family 190. *Paradisaeidae.* (1) Birds of Paradise, (1–6)
Plate 359. *Paradisaeidae,* (2) Birds of Paradise. (7–20)
Plate 360. *Paradisaeidae.* (3) Birds of Paradise. (21–29)
Plate 361. *Paradisaeidae,* (4) Birds of Paradise, (28–37)
Plate 362. *Paradisaeidae.* (5) Birds of Paradise. (38–44)
Plate 363. Family 191. *Corvidae,* (1) Magpies. (1–24)
Plate 364. *Corvidae,* (2) Jays, (25–58)
Plate 365. *Corvidae.* (3) Jays, Choughs. (59–87)
Plate 366. *Corvidae,* (4) Crows, (88–113)
Plate 367. *Corvidae* 5) Crows, Ravens. (114–131)

INTRODUCTION

I have always been a keen watcher of British Birds but, apart from the war years, I had never been abroad until 1970 when I started taking foreign holidays. I immediately became interested in the birds of the country I was visiting. This was before Field Guides started to spring up and, for instance, when I went to the Seychelles there was no illustrated book of Seychelles birds. It seemed to me there must be many travellers like myself who would welcome a concise illustrated check list of all the birds of the world which they could pack with their luggage wherever they went and I decided to try and produce such a book myself. This is the reason for the book's appearance, a task which has taken me nearly thirty years. I have seen rather less than a third of the ten thousand birds I have painted in the wild and for the rest have had to rely on museum specimens, illustrations and occasionally, when no illustration appeared to exist, on a written description alone.

The starting off point was to find or compile a list of all the Birds. Peter's Birds of the World in 15 volumes was and still is about the most widely recognised publication but two volumes had still to appear and Volume 1 was already in need of revision. Its listing begins with Ostrich and ends with Crows (some listings end with Buntings) and I believe it is properly known as the "Basel sequence of families". In 1976 Edward Gruson produced "A Check List of Birds of the World", a concise work which closely followed Peter's sequence which listed the species in each family alphabetically and is now somewhat out of date. I decided to base my work on this check list and within a few months I had set out 367 plates, with a space for every bird therein listed, and painted in a few hundred birds. The search to fill in the gaps then began.

In 1980-81 three new checklists appeared in the shops by Walters, Clements, and Howard & Moore, the latter listing, in addition to the species, every subspecies (about 40,000). It would clearly be impracticable to paint all of these, but I had already decided that in addition to the species listed by Gruson, I would include a number of subspecies e.g. the Hooded Crow as well as the Carrion Crow, as the two birds are very dissimilar. I have finally included some 500 subspecies whose selection is not based on any firm rule, but includes several subspecies formerly regarded as species and vice versa.

I felt I was getting near the end when from America there arrived "Distribution and Taxonomy of Birds of the World" by Sibley and Monro, (a monster volume) together with a smaller "World Check List". This contained over a hundred "new" species which I had obviously got to squeeze in. It also listed the families in a completely new sequence based on scientific research. I feel this sequence may well be universally adopted in due course, but I decided to stick to the "Basel" sequence, especially as it seems it is to be followed in the mammoth "ICBP Handbook of Birds" of which four volumes have appeared.

I am not qualified to join the argument as to what is or is not a true species. I think it is generally agreed that there are between 9,000 and 10,000 full species in the world and I have painted some 10,300 different birds on the 367 plates contained herein. In every case I have painted the male in full breeding plumage and also some 2,500 females when these differ substantially from the male in size or colour. When both male and female appear, the male faces to the left and the female to the right of the page. I have also shown about 150 birds in eclipse or non breeding plumage (no ducks, as the eclipse drake nearly always resembles the duck): a random selection of about 120 immature birds (marked JUV or IMM) and shown either head-on or back-on: and rough sketches of about 200 birds in flight. Since I completed the plates a few months ago I have added only new species discovered, which have been described in the ornithological press up to the end of 1997. To the best of my belief I have included every species listed by Howard and Moore and by Sibley and Monroe and a few others

Apart from this introduction, the list of contents which follows it and the index at the end, the entire text is contained on the pages which face the plates and gives the following information about each bird illustrated:

(1) *The numerical identification of the bird illustrated on the facing page.* This is self-evident. Birds added at a later date may be numbered, as e.g. 18A opposed to 18. Letters are also used to distinguish between colour phases of a single species, e.g. 7(a), 7(b).

(2) *The scientific (Latin) name of each bird.* It will be generally known that every bird has a Latin name which is recognised internationally. This consists of two or sometimes three words, generic, specific and sometimes subspecific. So the Order Passeriformes (Perching Birds) includes the family of Corvidae (Crows and Jays) which contains the genus Corvus which in turn contains the species Corone (Carrion Crow) which has a subspecies Corvus corone corvix (Hooded Crow). The Carrion Crow should strictly be Corvus corone corone.

(3) *The English name or names of each bird.* Attempts have been made to find an agreed English name for every bird, but agreement has not been reached and many suggested names are unpopular. I have frequently listed two or even three widely used English names, but even so I am sure I will not have satisfied everybody as to what I should have called them.

(4) *The number of subspecies.* This number is constantly changing as new discoveries are made and arguments about the status of various birds are solved. The number of subspecies varies enormously. e.g. the Bananaquir has 42 subspecies of which I have only painted two. The Common Jay has 36 subspecies and I have painted 7, in order to show the sort of variation which can occur. The difference between some is very slight indeed and can be vocal and not visual. It should be helpful to know roughly how many variations occur in the single species, in that it is known that a picture of a species can be quite different from one of its subspecies.

(5) *Length in Centimetres.* This is of course variable and approximate measured

from the tip of the bill to the end of the tail. Generally males are slightly larger than females except in the case of raptors where the female is larger as a general rule. In some cases I have given the length of both sexes.

At the top of each plate there is a bar which represents the length of a bird of 15cm (the size of a sparrow) and this should give an idea of the actual size of the bird. I have tried to draw all the birds of one family to the same scale.

(6) *Where the bird is to be found.* This is straightforward when the bird is endemic to a single island, but in general, consideration of space rations the description of its range throughout the world to a very few words, e.g. 'S. E. Asia' or 'N. America, winters Caribbean'. It is perhaps wise not to be too precise: rarities occur everywhere and become more frequent as skill in identification increases. Where individual countries are listed, I may well have failed to keep up to date. Since I started the work Celebes has become Sulaweri, Zaire Congo and Madagascar was going to be Malagasy.

Considerations of space has prevented an index in English and Latin. I have chosen Latin as Latin names are recognised throughout the world whereas English names are only used in English speaking countries.

As I reach the end of the work (which paradoxically happens to be the Foreword), I have obtained a copy of "World Species Checklist" recently published by M.G. Wells: a most impressive work with a scientific basis for its list of 9951 species: as compared to 9236 by Howard & Moore: and 9702 by Sibley and Monroe. My own list of 10300 "varieties" includes about 500 subspecies, and it could be argued that it is not "complete" because for example I have not illustrated two species of Ostrich, but (like Howard and Moore) have treated the bird as a single species with 5 subspecies. In my opinion it is unlikely to be possible to reach a precise count of species at any time because the processes of 'splitting' and 'lumping' create or remove species and bring constant change to the recognised total.

There are so many people who have helped and encouraged me in the production of this book I cannot possibly thank them all here: but I must single out Mrs F.E. Warr, the Librarian of the Natural History Museum at Tring who never failed to produce any information requested: and thank my wife for her support and forbearance in seeing her sitting room turned into a sort of office cum library cum studio: and my family for their great help, especially in trying to educate me in the mysteries of word processing.

Dykeside
April 1998
TW

THE CHECKLIST

RATITES
Ostriches, Rheas, Cassowaries, Emus, Kiwis.

Family 1. STRUTHIONIDAE. Ostriches.

1. *Struthio camelus.*Ostrich. 5ss. 200+ E, W, & S Africa, formerly Arabia, Asia.

Family 2. RHEIDAE. Rheas.

1. *Rhea americana.* Greater/Common Rhea. 5ss 130. E & C Brazil to N & C Argentina.
2. *Rhea/Pterocnemia pennata.* Lesser/Darwin's Rhea. 3ss 96. Peru, Chile, Bolivia. Argentina
3. incl. *R. p. tarapacensis.* Puna Rhea. 100 Chile, Sometimes considered separate species

Family 3. CASUARIIDAE. Cassowaries.

1. *Casuarius bennetti.* Dwarf Cassowary. 7ss, 100. New Guinea, Pacifis Is.
2. *Casuarius casuarius.* Southern/ Double wattled Cassowary. 8ss, 150. Queensland. New Guinea & Is,
3. *Casuarius unappendiculatus.* Northern/Single wattled Cassowary. 6ss. 135. New Guinea,

Family 4. DROMAIIDAE, Emu.

1. Dromaius novaehollandiae, Emu, 3ss, 190. Australia except NE,

Family 5. APTERYGIDAE. Kiwis.

1. *Apteryx australis.* Brown/Common Kiwi. 4ss 50. New Zealand.
2. *Apteryx haasti,* Great spotted Kiwi 50. New Zealand. South Island
3. *Apteryx owenii.* Little spotted Kiwi. 40. New Zealand. South Island.

STRUTHIONIDAE
1
RHEIDAE
1
2
3
CASUARIDAE
1
2
3
DROMAIIDAE
APTERYGIDAE
1
2
3

TINAMIDAE (1)
Tinmaous

1. *Tinamus guttatus.*White throated Tinamou.32. Venezuela, Colombia to Brazil, Bolivia.
2. *Tinamus major.* Great Tinamou.12ss 45. As for 1. Also Mexico to Guyanas.
3. *Tinamus osgoodi.* Black Tinamou.2ss 45. Colombia to Peru.
4. *Tinamus solitarius.* Solitary Tinamou. 2ss 45. Brazil, Paraguay, Argentina
5. *Tinamus tao.* Grey Tinamou.4ss 45. Colombia, Venezuela to Brazil, Bolivia.
6. *Nothocercus bonapartei.* Highland Tinamou. 5ss 32. Costa Rica to Peru.
7. Nothocercus julius.Tawny breasted Tinamou.38. Venezuela. Colombia, Ecuador.
8. *Nothocercus nigrocapillus.* Hooded Tinamou. 2ss 32. Peru, Bolivia.
9. *Crypturellus erythropus.* Red footed Tinamou. 7ss. 30. Colombia, Venezuela, Guyanas.
10. *Crypturellus atrocapillus.* Black capped Tinamou. 2ss 30. Peru, Bolivia.
11. *Crypturellus bartletti.* Bartlett's Tinamou.30. Brazil, Peru, Bolivia.
12. *Crypturellus boucardi.* Slaty breasted Tinamou. 2ss 27. Mexico to Colombia.
13. *Crypturellus brevirostris.* Rusty Tinamou. 30. French Guyana. Brazil, Peru.
14. Crypturellus casiquiare. Barred Tinamou. 25. Colombia, Venezuela.
15. *Crypturellus cinereus.* Cinereous Tinamou.30. Guyanas & Amazonia.
16. *Crypturellus cinnamomeus.* Thicket Tinamou.9ss. 27. Mexico to Venezuela.
17. *Crypturellus duidae.* Grey legged Tinamou.30. Colombia, Venezuela.
18. *Crypturellus kerriae.* Choco Tinamou. 27. W. Colombia. E Panama.
19. *Crypturellus noctivagus.* Yellow legged Tinamou. 2ss 45. E Brazil.
20. *Crypturellus obsoletus.* Brown Tinamou.8ss. 27. Venezuela to Argentina.
21. *Crypturellus parvirostris.* Small billed Tinamou.20. Brazil, Peru, Bolivia to Paraguay Argentina
22. *Crypturellus ptaritepui.* Tepui Tinamou. 27. Venezuela.
23. *Crypturellus saltuarius.* Magdalena Tinamou.27. N C Colombia.
24. *Crypturellus soui.* Little Tinamou.14ss 23. Mexico to Brazil, Bolivia.
25. *Crypturellus strigulosus.* Brazilian Tinamou.27. Brazil. Peru, Bolivia.
26. *Crypturellus tataupa.* Tataupa Tinamou. 4ss 25. Amazon basin to Argentina.

1
2
3
4
5
6
7
8
14
9
13
11
10
12
15
16
18
19
17
20
22
24
26
23
21
25

TINAMIDAE
Tinamous

27. *Crypturellus transfasciatus.* Pale browed Tinamou. 27. Ecuador, Peru.
28. *Crypturellus undulatus.* Undulated Tinamou. 6ss. 30. Guyanas to N Argentina.
29. incl. *C. u. yapura.* Banded Tinamou. 30. Colombia, Ecuador, Peru, Brazil,
30. *Crypturellus variegatus.* Variegated Tinamou. 32. Venezuela to Bolivia, Brazil,
31. *Crypturellus berlepschi.* Berlepsch's Tinamou. 28. Colombia, Ecuador.
32. *Rhynchotus rufescens.* Red winged Tinamou. 4ss. 40. Brazil, Peru to Argentina,
33. *Nothoprocta cinerascens.* Brushland Tinamou. 2ss. 30. Bolivia, Paraguay, Argentina.
34. *Nothoprocta curvirostris.* Curve billed Tinamou. 2ss. 25. Ecuador, Peru.
35. *Nothoprocta kalinowskii.* Kalinowski's Tinamou. 35. Peru.
36. *Nothoprocta ornata.* Ornate Tinamou. 3ss. 35. Peru, Bolivia, Chile, Argentina
37. *Nothoprocta pentlandi.* Andean Tinamou. 7ss 27. Ecuador to Chile Argentina.
38. *Nothoprocta perdicaria.* Chilean Tinamou. 2ss. 30. Chile.
39. *Nothoprocta taczanowskii.* Taczanowski's Tinamou. 32. Peru.
40. *Nothura boraquira.* White bellied Nothura. 25. Brazil, Paraguay, Bolivia.
41. *Nothura chacoensis*, Chaco Nothura. 25. Paraguay, N Argentina.
42. *Nothura darwinii.* Darwin's Nothura, 5ss 25. Peru, Bolivia, N Argentina.
43. *Nothura maculosa.* Spotted Nothura. 9ss. 25. Brazil, Paraguay, Uruguay, Argentina
44. *Nothura minor.* Lesser Nothura. 17. E & C Brazil.

45 *Taoniscus nanus*, Dwarf Tinamou, 17. E Brazil,

46 *Eudromia elegans.* Elegant crested Tinamou. 8ss. 40. Chile, Argentina,

47. *Eudromia formosa.* Quebracho Tinamou. 2ss 40. Paraguay, Argentina.
48. *Tinamotis ingoufi*, Patagonian Tinamou. 38. Argentina, S Chile.
49. *Tinamotis pentlandi.* Puna Tinamou. 45. Peru, Bolivia, Chile, Argentina.

27
28
30
32
31
29
35
36
33
34
37
38
39
40
41
42
43
44
45
46
47
48
49

SPHENISCIDAE
Penguins

1. *Pygoscelis adeliae.* Adelie Penguin. 76. Antarctica.
2. *Pygoscelis antarctica.* Chinstrap Penguin. 76. Antarctica.
3. *Pygoscelis papua.* Gentoo Penguin. 3ss 76. Antarctica.
4. *Aptenodytes forsteri.* Emperor Penguin. 122. Antarctica.
5. *Aptenodytes patagonicus.* King Penguin. 2ss 94. Antarctic & Southern Oceans.
6. *Eudyptes chrysolophus.* Macaroni Penguin. 71. Islands in Southern Oceans.
7. *Eudyptes schlegeli.* Royal Penguin. 71. Macquarie Island.
8. *Eudyptes robustus.* Snares Island' Penguin. 73. Snares Island & New Zealand waters.
9. *Eudyptes chrysocome.* Rockhopper Penguin. 3ss. 63. All Southern Oceans.
10. *Eudyptes pachyrhynchus.* Fiordland Crested Penguin3ss 71. South Is., New Zealand, Adjacent Islands
11. *Eudyptes sclateri.* Erect / Big Crested Penguin. 71. Australasian region.
12. *Megadyptes antipodes.* Yellow eyed Penguin. 76. Auckland, Stewart, Campbell, & S.I, N. Zealand.
13. *Eudyptula albosignata.* White flippered Penguin. 42. South Is. New Zealand.
14. *Eudyptula minor.* Little (Blue) Penguin. 40. Australia, New Zealand. Pacific.
15. *Spheniscus demersus.* Jackass Penguin. 65. Coasts & Islands of Namibia & S Africa.
16. *Spheniscus humboldti.* Humboldt Penguin. 68. Coastal Peru & Chile.
17. *Spheniscus magellanicus.* Magellanic Penguin. 71. Patagonian coasts, Falklands.
18. *Spheniscus mendiculus.* Galapagos Penguin. 50. Galapagos Is.

1
2
3
4
5
6
7
8
9
10
11
12
13
14
15
16
12 JUV
JUV
17
18

GAVIDAE, PODICIPEDIDAE
Divers or Loons, Grebes

1. *Gavia adamsii*. White billed Diver / Yellow billed Loon. 90. Holarctic region.
2. Gavia arctica, Black throated Diver / Arctic Loon. 2ss. 64. Holarctic to India, C America,
3. incl. *G.a. pacifica*. Pacific Loon. 62. Alaska, NW America.
4. *Gavia immer*. Great Northern Diver / Common Loon. 80. Holarctic to C. America.
5. *Gavia stellata*. Red throated Diver / Loon. 60. Holarctic, India, C. America.

Family 9. PODICIPEDIDAE. Grebes

1. *Podiceps auritus*. Horned / Slavonian Grebe. 2ss 33. Eurasia, N America.
2. *Podiceps cristatus*. Great Crested grebe. 3ss. 46. Palearctic, Africa, Australasia,
3. *Tachybaptus dominicus*. Least Grebe. 4ss. 24. Southern USA to Argentina, W Indies.
4. *Podiceps grisegena*. Red necked Grebe. 2ss 44. Holarctic. Winters S. Eurasia, C America,
5. *Podiceps gallardoi*. Hooded Grebe. 28. W Argentina.
6. *Podiceps major*. Great Grebe. 60. Peru, Brazil to Chile, Argentina.
7. *Podiceps nigricollis*. Black necked Grebe. 4ss. 30. All world except Australia.
8. *Tachybaptus novaehollandiae*. Australasian Grebe. 7ss. 28. Indonesia. Oceania Australasia
9. *Podiceps occipitalis*. Silvery Grebe. 2ss 27. Colombia to Tierra del Fuego.
10. *Tachybaptus pelzelnii*. Madagascar little Grebe. 25. Malagasy.
11. *Poliocephalus poliocephalus*. Hoary headed Grebe. 29. Australasia.
12. *Rollandia rolland*. White tufted Grebe. 3ss. 31. Peru, Brazil to T. del Fuego. Falkland Is.
13. *Tachybaptus ruficollis*. Little Grebe / Dabchick. 10ss. 26. Eurasia, India to New Guinea,
14. *Tachybaptus rufolavatus*. Delacouer's / Alaotra Grebe. 25. Malagasy. (extinct?)
15. *Podiceps rufopectus*, New Zealand Dabchick. 27. New Zealand.
16. *Podiceps taczanowskii*. Puna Grebe. 35. Lake Junin (Peru).
17. *Aechmophorus occidentalis*. Western Grebe. 2ss. 62. Alaska to N Mexico.
18. *Aechmophorus clarkii*. Clark's Grebe. 2ss. 62. Western N. America, Mexico.
19. *Rollandia microptera*. Short winged Grebe. 27. Lake Titicaca, Peru, Bolivia.
20. Podilymbus gigas. Atitlan Grebe. 27. Guatemala. (extinct?)
21. *Podilymbus podiceps*. Pied billed Grebe. 3ss. 34. Alaska to Chile, West Indies.

GAVIIDAE
1 Br
NB
2 Br
NB
3 B
4 B
NB
5 B
NB
PODIDICEPIDAE
Br
1
NB
2
NB
3
NB
4
NB
5
NB
6
NB
7
NB
8
NB
9
NB
10
NB
11
NB
12
NB
13
NB
14
NB
15
NB
16
NB
17
NB
18
NB
19
NB
20
NB
21
NB

DIOMEDEIDAE
Albatrosses or Mollymawks

1. *Diomedea albatrus.* Short tailed Albatross. 94. Tori Shima (Izu Is). N Pacific.
2. *Diomedea bulleri.* Buller's Albatross. 86. New Zealand ranges to Western. S America.
3. *Diomedea cauta.* Shy Albatross. 3ss. 99. Tasmania, New Zealand. Southern oceans.

3A. inc. *D. c. eremita.* Chatham Island Albatross. 99. Chatham, Oceans East of New Zealand.

3B. *D. c. salvini.* Grey backed Albatross. 99. Snares, Bounty Is. South Pacific.

4. *Diomedea chlororhynchos.* Yellow nosed Albatross. 80. Tristan, Gough Is. Southern Oceans,
5. *Diomedea chrysostoma.* Grey headed Albatross. 76. Islands of S Hemisphere.
6. *Diomedea epomophora.* Royal Albatross. 122. Islands near New Zealand.
7. *Diomedea exulans.* Wandering Albatross. 3ss. 117. Circumpolar Southern Oceans.
8. *Diomedea fusca.* Sooty Albatross. 81. S. Atlantic & Indian Ocean Islands.
9. *Diomedea immutabilis.* Laysan Albatross. 81. Hawaii, N Pacific.
10. *Diomedea irrorata,* Waved Albatross. 89. Galapagos Islands. E Pacific.
11. Diomedea melanophris. Black browed Albatross. 2ss. 83. Southern Ocean Islands to N Atlantic.
12. *Diomedea nigripes.* Black footed Albatross. 71. Hawaii, Izu Is, N Pacific.
13. *Diomedea palpebrata.* Light mantled Albatross, 71. South Georgia, Southern Oceans.

14, *Diomedea amsterdamensis,* Amsterdam Island Albatross, ll2. Amsterdam Island, Indian Ocean.

1
14
2
3
4
5
3A
3B
6
7
8
10
9
11
12
13

PROCELLARIIDAE (1)
Tubbed nosed swimmers, Fulmars, Petrels. (1)

1. *Macronectes giganteus.* Giant Fulmar / Petrel. 88. All southern Oceans. (a) Dark (b) pale phase.
2. *Macronectes halli*, Hall's Giant Petrel. 88. Range overlaps with 1.
3. *Daption capense.* Cape Petrel. 2ss. 36. Southern oceans. 4. Fulmarus glacialis. Northern Fulmar. 3ss. 50. Atlantic & N. Pacific (a) Light phase. (b) dark phase illustrated only in flight.
5. *Fulmarus glacialoides*, Southern Fulmar. 46. Antarctica, Southern Oceans.
6. *Halobaena caerulea.* Blue Petrel. 28. Falkland Islands & Antarctic.
7. *Pachyptila belcheri.* Slender billed Prion28. Crozert, Kerguelen, Falklands. S. Oceans.
8. *Pachyptila desolata.* Dove / Antarctic Prion. 3ss. 28. Sub-Antarctic Islands.
9. *Pachyptila vittata.* Broad billed Prion. 2ss. 28. Tristan, & N. Zealand Islands. S. Oceans.
10. *Pachyptila salvini.* Medium billed Prion. 28. Islands in S, SW Indian Ocean.
11. *Pachyptila turtur.* Fairy Prion. 26. Sub – Antarctic Islands.
12. *Pachyptila crassirostris.* Thick billed / Fulmar Prion. 26. Chatham Island. Southern Oceans.
13. *Thalassoica antarctica.* Antarctic Petrel. 43. Antarctic Islands. Southern Oceans.
14. *Procellaria cinerea.* Grey / Brown Petrel / Shearwater. 48. Tristan, Sub – Antarctic Islands & Seas,
15. *Procellaria aequinoctalis.* White chinned Petrel. 2ss. 53. New Zealand S. I, Southern Oceans & Is.
16. *Procellaria parkinsoni.* Black Petrel. 46. New Zealand, Pacific to S America.
17. *Procellaria westlandica.* Westland Petrel. 50. New Zealand to Australia,
18. *Pagodroma nivea.* (Lesser) Snow Petrel. 32. South Georgia & Antarctica.

18a. *Pagodroma confusa.* Greater Snow Petrel. 40. Balleny Is, Adelieland, Antarctica,

1 (a)
1(b)
2
1
JUV
1(a)
3
4(a)
4(b)
5
4
5
6
7
8
9
6
7
9
11
13
13
10
11
12
14
15
18
18A
14
16
17
15

PROCELLARIIDAE (1)
Tube nosed swimmers Fulmars, Petrels (2)

19. *Calonectris diomedia.* Cory's Shearwater. 4ss. 50. Mediterranean, N & S Atlantic.
20. *Calonectris leucomelas* . Streaked Shearwater. 48. Islands of Japan, NW Pacific .
21. *Puffinus pacificus.* Wedge tailed Shearwater 4ss. 39. Indian Ocean Islands, Pacific
22. *Puffinus bulleri.* Buller's Shearwater. 42. New Zealand North Island, South Pacific,
23. *Puffinus carneipes.* Flesh footed Shearwater. 2ss. 45. Australia, New Zealand to North Pacific,
24. *Puffinus creatopus.* Pink footed Shearwater, 48. J Fernandez Island to N Pacific
25. *Puffinus gravis,* Great Shearwater. 50. S. Atlantic Islands to Arctic.
26. *Puffinus griseus.* Sooty Shearwater. 46. Australia to N Atlantic & Pacific.
27. *Puffinus tenuirostris.* Short tailed Shearwater. 39. Australia to N Pacific .
28. *Puffinus nativitatis.* Christmas Island Shearwater. 36. Christmas Island to whole Pacific.
29. *Puffinus lherminieri.* Audubon's Shearwater. 9ss. 30. W Atlantic, Indian & Pacific Oceans.
30. *Puffinus bannermanni.* Bannerman's Shearwater, 34. Bonin & Volcano Islands.
31. *Puffinus Bailloni.* Baillon's Shearwater, 31. Mascarene Island.
32. *Puffinus persicus.* Persian Shearwater. 32. Arabian Sea.
33. *Puffinus heinrothi.* Heinroth's Shearwater. 27. Bismarck Archipelago.
34. *Puffinus assimilis.* Little Shearwater, 8ss. 28. Atlantic, Indian, Pacific Oceans,
35. *Puffinus puffinus.* Manx Shearwater. 4ss. 34. North Atlantic. 35a.Puffinus atrodorsalis. Mascarene Shearwater 31. Indian Ocean
36. *Puffinus auricularis.* Townsend's Shearwater. 33. Revillagigido Island (Mexico), Pacific
37. *Puffinus gavia.* Fluttering Shearwater. 33. New Zealand Islands to Tasman Sea.
38. *Puffinus huttoni.* Hutton's Shearwater. 38. New Zealand South Island to Tasmania.
39. *Puffinus newelli.* Newell's Shearwater. 32. Hawaii & adjacent seas.
40. *Puffinus opisthomelas.* Black vented Shearwater, 34. Baja, California Islands.
41. *Puffinus mauritanicus,* Balearic Shearwater, 37. W Mediterranean,
42. *Puffinus yelkouan.* Levantine Shearwater. 34. E Mediterranean.(conspf. 41)

19
19
20
22
21
21 (a)
21 (b)
22
24
23
24
25
26
27
28
29
25
26
30
29
35
33
31
32
33
34
35A
35
36
37
38
39
40
41
42

PROCELLARIIDAE (3)
Tube nosed swimmers, Petrels

43. *Pterodroma macroptera*. Great winged Petrel.2ss. 40. Southern Oceans.
44. *Pterodroma lessonii*. White headed Petrel. 43. Southern Oceans.
45. *Pterodroma incerta*. Atlantic Petrel. 43. Tristan, South Atlantic.
46. *Pterodroma solandri*. Providence Petrel. 41. Lord Howe Island, Pacific.
47. *Pterodroma magentae*. Magenta Petrel. 36. Chatham Islands, S Pacific.
48. *Pseudobulweria rostrata*. Tahiti Petrel. 3ss. 39. Oceania, Pacific.
49. *Pseudobulweria becki*. Beck's Petrel. 28. Solomon Islands.
50. *Pterodroma aterrima*. Mascarene Black Petrel. 36. Reunion, Indian Ocean.
51. *Pterodroma neglecta*. Kermadec's Petrel. 2ss. 36. S Pacific Islands, NZ to Chile. a. Pale. b. Dark morphs.
52. *Pterodroma arminjoniana*. Trinidade Petrel. 3ss. 38. S Atlantic, Indian Ocean. a. Pale. b. Dark morphs.
53. *Pterodroma heraldica*. Herald Petrel. 35. Tonga, Pacific.
54. *Pterodroma alba*. Phoenix Petrel. 36. Oceania, S Pacific.
55. *Pterodroma ultima*. Murphy's Petrel. 38. S Polynesia.
56. *Lugensa brevirostris*. Kerguelen Petrel. 33. Islands in S Atlantic, Indian Ocean.
57. *Pterodroma mollis*. Soft plumaged Petrel. 35. Islands in S Atlantic, Indian Ocean. a. Pale. b. Dark phases.
58. *Pterodroma feae*. Cape Verde Petrel. 36. Cape Verde Islands, E Atlantic.
59. *Pterodroma madeira*. Madeira Petrel. 34. Madeira, E Atlantic.
60. *Pterodroma inexpectata*. Mottled Petrel. 34. Stewart, Snares Islands to N. Pacific.
61. *Pterodroma cahow*. Bermuda Petrel / Cahow. 37. Bermuda.
62. *Pterodroma hasitata*. Black capped Petrel / Diablotin. 41. W Indies, N Atlantic.
63. *Pterodroma externa*. Juan Fernandez Petrel. 43. J. Fernandez Island, Pacific.
64. *Pterodroma cervicalis*. White necked Petrel. 43. Kermadec Island, S Pacific.
65. *Pterodroma baraui*. Barau's Petrel. 38. Mascarene Islands, Indian Ocean.
66. *Pterodroma phaeopygia*. Dark rumped / Galapagos Petrel. 43. Galapagos, Pacific.

66A. *Pterodroma sandwichensis*. Hawaiian Petrel . 43. Hawaii, Pacific.

67. *Pterodroma cookii*. Cook's/Blue footed Petrel. 27. New Zealand. Pacific.
68. *Pterodroma dephilippiana*. Defilippe's Petrel. 28. Mas a Tierra Island, off Chile, S Pacific.
69. *Pterodroma leucoptera*. Gould's Petrel. 2ss. 30. E Australia to S Pacific.
70. *Pterodroma brevipes*. Collared Petrel. 30. Fiji, Samoa, S Pacific,
71. *Pterodroma longirostris*. Stejneger's Petrel. 26. Mas Afuera to S Pacific.
72. *Pterodroma pycrofti*. Pycroft's Petrel. 26. Islands off N New Zealand.
73. *Pterodroma hypoleuca*. Bonin Petrel. 32. Islands in N Pacific.
74. *Pterodroma nigripennis*. Black winged Petrel. 31. South West to Central Pacific.
75. *Pterodroma axillaris*. Chatham Islands Petrel. 30. Chatham Island.
76. *Pseudobulweria macgillivrayi*. Fiji Petrel. 29. Fiji area.
77. *Bulweria bulwerii*. Bulwer's Petrel . 27. Tropical Atlantic & Pacific Oceans.
78. *Bulweria fallax*. Jouanin's Petrel. 32. Arabian Sea, NW Indian Ocean.

50
43
44
45
46
47
48
49
51 (a)
51 (b)
43
44
45
46
48
51
52
52 (a)
52 (b)
53
54
55
56
57 (a)
57 (b)
60
61
62
54
55
56
57
60
62
63
59
63
64
65
58
66
66A
67
68
69
70
65
66
67
68
73
75
77
71
72
73
74
75
76
77
78

OCEANINITIDAE
Petrels

Family 12. HYDROBATIDAE Storm Petrels

1. *Oceanites gracilis*. White vented Storm Petrel. 2ss. 15. Pacific coast South America, Galapagos Is.
2. *Oceanites oceanicus*. Wilson's Storm Petrel. 2ss. 18, Antarctic. Worldwide .
3. *Pelagodroma marina*. White faced Storm Petrel. 6ss. 20. S & tropical oceans.
4. *Fregetta grallaria*. White bellied Storm Petrel. 4ss. 21. Southern oceans.
5. *Fregetta tropica*. Black bellied Storm Petrel. 2ss, 20. Southern oceans.
6. *Garrodia nereis*. Grey backed Storm Petrel. 17. Sub-Antarctic circumpolar region.

7(a) *Nesofregetta fuliginosa*. White throated / Polynesian Storm Petrel. 22. Tropical C. W. Pacific.

7(b) melanistic phase. formerly considered distinct (N. moestissima) Samoan Storm Petrel. 22.Tropical C & W Pacific. Incl. Samoa.

8. *Hydrobates pelagicus*. Storm Petrel. 17. Atlantic, Mediterranean to India.
9. *Oceanodroma castro*. Band rumped Storm Petrel. 19. Eastern North Atlantic, N Pacific.
10. *Oceanodroma macrodactyla*. Guadeloupe Storm Petrel. 22. Guadeloupe, extinct.
11. *Oceanodroma furcata*. Fork tailed Storm Petrel. 2ss. 20. Bering Sea, N Pacific.
12. *Oceanodroma homochroa*. Ashy Storm Petrel. 19. Californian coast.
13. *Oceanodroma hornbyi*. Ringed Storm Petrel. 21. W coast of S. America.
14. *Oceanodroma leucorhoa*. leach's Storm Petrel. 4ss, 22. Almost world-wide.
15. *Oceanodroma markhami*. Markham's / Sooty Storm Petrel. 24. Coast of Peru.
16. *Oceanodroma matsudairae*. Matsudaira's Storm Petrel. 25. Volcano Is (Japan) to Indian Ocean.
17. *Oceanodroma melania*. Black Storm Petrel. 23. E Pacific, California to Peru.
18. *Oceanodroma monorhis*. Swinhoe's Storm Petrel. 2ss. 18. Japan to Indian Ocean.
19. *Oceanodroma tethys*. Wedge rumped Storm Petrel. 2ss. 17. Galapagos region.
20. *Oceanodroma tristrami*. Tristram's Storm Petrel. 24. Hawaii to Japan.
21. *Oceanodroma microsoma*. Least Storm Petrel. 15. California to Ecuador.

Family 13. PELECANOIDIDAE, Diving Petrels.

1. Pelecanoides garnot. Peruvian Diving Petrel. 21. Peruvian, Chilean Is.
2. Pelecanoides georgicus. South Georgia Diving Petrel. 19. Circumpolar Sub-Antarctic,
3. Pelecanoides magellani. Magellanic Diving Petrel. 21. Chile, Argentina, Islands.
4. Pelecanoides urinator. Common Diving Petrel. 6ss. 19. Southern oceans.

8
2
13
10
1
2
3
4
7(a)
5
6
8
7(b)
10
9
11
12
13
14
15
16
17
18
19
20
21
PELECANOIDIDAE
4
1
2
3
4

PHAETHONTIDAE, PELECANIDAE, SULIDAE
Tropicbirds, Pelicans, Gannets and Boobies

Family 14. PHAETRONYTIDAE Tropic Birds

1. *Phaethon aethereus*. Red billed Tropicbird. 3ss. 61. Tropical Atlantic, Indian, & Pacific Oceans.
2. *Phaethon lepturus*. White tailed / Yellow billed Tropicbird. 5ss. 41. Tropical Atlantic, Indian & Pacific Oceans.
3. incl. *P. l. fulvus*. Golden Bosun bird. 41. Christmas Island.
4. *Phaethon rubricauda*. Red tailed Tropicbird. 4ss. 46. S Indian & Pacific Oceans.

Family 15. PELECANIDAE. Pelicans.

1. *Pelecanus conspicillatus*. Australian Pelican. 152. Australia, New Guinea.
2. *Pelecanus crispus*. Dalmatian Pelican. 160. S Eurasia, Winters to India.
3. *Pelecanus erythrorhynchos*. American White Pelican. 160. Canada to Texas, Winters to Costa Rica.
4. *Pelecanus occidentalis*. Brown Pelican. 5ss. 110. US coasts to Galapagos.
5. *Pelecanus thagus*. Peruvian Pelican. 150. Ecuador to Chile.
6. *Pelecanus onocrotalus*. (Syn.P roseus. Rosy P.)Great White Pelican. 160. S. Central Eurasia to India & Africa.
7. *Pelecanus philippensis*. Spot billed / Grey Pelican. 140. India to Philippines & SE Asia.
8. *Pelecanus rufescens*. Pink backed Pelican. 145. Arabia, Africa, Malagasy.

Family 16. SULIDAE. Gannets & Boobies.

1. *Sula abbotti*. Abbott's Booby. 71. Christmas Island, Indian Ocean.
2. *Morus bassanus*. (Northern) Gannet. 92. N Atlantic, Mediterranean.
3. *Morus capensis*. Cape Gannet. 87. Coasts of Southern Africa.
4. *Morus serrator*. Australian Gannet. 2ss. 92. Australia,New Zealand.
5. *Sula dactylatra*. Blue faced / Masked Booby. 6ss. 87. All tropical oceans.
6. *Sula leucogaster*. Brown Booby. 5ss. 73. All tropical oceans.
7. *Sula nebouxii*. Blue footed Booby 2ss. 88. Pacific coast, California to Peru, Galapagos Is.
8. *Sula sula*. Red footed Booby. 3ss. 70. All tropical oceans. A. White phase. B. Brown phase
9. *Sula variegata*. Peruvian Booby. 74. E Pacific Islands off Peru & Chile.

PHAETHONTIDAE
2
1
4
3
PELICANIDAE
1
2
3
5
4
6
7
8
SULIDAE
2
1
2
JUV
3
5
4
8
(a)
6
7
8
(b)
9

PHALACROCORACIDAE
Cormorants and Shags (1)

1. *Phalacrocorax harrisi*. Galapagos Flightless Cormorant. 87. Galapagos Islands.
2. *Phalacrocorax africanus*. Long tailed / Reed Cormorant. 3ss. 59. Most of Africa.
3. *Phalacrocorax albiventer*. King Cormorant. 3ss. 70. Argentina, Falkland Islands.
4. *Phalacrocorax aristotelis*. European Shag. 3ss. 70. NW Europe, Mediterranean.
5. *Phalacrocorax atriceps*. Imperial Shag / Blue eyed Cormorant. 3ss. 70. Antarctica, S America.
6. *Phalacrocorax bransfieldensis*. Antarctic Shag. 77. S Shetland Is, Antarctic. 3,5,6,&21 may be conspecific or hybrid.
7. *Phalacrocorax auritus*. Double Crested Cormorant. 4ss 85. N America. Bahamas.
8. *Phalacrocorax bougainvilliei*. Guanay Cormorant. 75. Peru, Chile.
9. *Phalacrocorax campbelli*. Campbell Shag. 63. Campbell Island.(off NZ).
10. *Phalacrocorax ranfurly*. Bounty Shag. 71. Bounty Island.
11. *Phalacrocorax capensis*. Cape Cormorant. 63. Coasts of S & SW Africa.
12. *Phalacrocorax capillatus*. Japanese Cormorant. 0. Coast of E Asia.
13. *Phalacrocorax carbo*. Common/Great Cormorant. 5ss. 90. N Atlantic Islands & coasts. a. normal b. sinensis Breeding plumage.
14. *Phalacrocorax lucidus*. White breasted Cormorant. 90. African Coasts, Lakes.
15. *Phalacrocorax carunculatus*. Rough faced Shag. 3ss. 75. New Zealand.
16. *Phalacrocorax chalconotus*. Bronze Shag. 3ss. 75. New Zealand.
17. *Phalacrocorax onslowi*, Chatham Shag. 63. Chatham Island.
18. *Phalacrocorax colensoi*. Auckland Shag. 63. Auckland Island, (conspecific 9?)
19. *Phalacrocorax coronatus*. Crowned Cormorant. 54. African coast, Angola to RSA. (conspf 2?)
20. *Phalacrocorax fuscescens*. Black faced Cormorant. 65. S Australia, Tasmania, Islands in Bass Str.
21. *Phalacrocorax georgianus*. South Georgia Shag. 70. South Georgia.
22. *Phalacrocorax verrucosus*. Kerguelen Shag. 70. Kerguelen Is.
23. *Phalacrocorax fuscicollis*. Indian Cormorant. 63. India, SE Asia.
24. *Phalacrocorax gaimardi*. Red legged Cormorant. 70. Peru, Chile, Argentina.
25. *Phalacrocorax magellanicus*. Rock Shag. 65. Chile, Argentina, Falkland Islands.
26. *Phalacrocorax melanoleucos*. Little Pied Cormorant. 3ss. 58. Indonesia, Oceania, Australasia.
27. *Phalacrocorax neglectus*. Bank Cormorant. 75. Namibia to Cape.
28. *Phalacrocorax niger*. Little Cormorant, 56. India to SE Asia & Java.
29. *Phalacrocorax pygmaeus*. Pygmy Cormorant. 50. SE Europe to Central Asia, Tunisia.
30. *Phalacrocorax nigrogularis*. Socotra Cormorant. 80. Persian Gulf area.
31. *Phalacrocorax brasilianus/olivaceus*. Neptropic Cormorant. 4ss. 70. Southern USA to Tierra del Fuego.
32. *Phalacrocorax pelagicus*. Pelagic Cormorant. 2ss. 68. N Pacific coasts, Asia & America.
33. *Phalacrocorax penicillatus*. Brandt's Cormorant. 85. Pacific coast of N America.

Several of above 'Cormorants' are known as 'shags' and Vice versa.

1
2
3
4
5
6
7
8
9
10
11
12
13
13 Br
14
15
16
17
18
13 JUV
20
21
22
23
19
24
25
26
27
30
28
29
31
32
33

PHALACROCORACIDAE (2), ANHINGIDAE, FREGATIDAE
Cormorants, Snake Birds or Darters, Frigate Birds

Family 17. Cormaorants (2)

34. *Phalacrocorax punctatus*. Spotted Shag. 3ss. 59. New Zealand.
35. *Phalacrocorax featherstoni*. Pitt island Shag. 59. Chatham Is.
36. *Phalacrocorax sulcirostris*. Little Black Cormorant. 61. Malaysia to Australia, New Zealand.
37. *Phalacrocorax perspicillatus*. Spectacled / Pallas' Cormorant. 87. Bering Strait, (extinct).
38. *Phalacrocorax urile*. Red faced Cormorant. 80. Bering Sea. Aleutian Islands.
39. *Phalacrocorax varius*. Pied Cormorant. 2ss. 80. Australia. New Zealand.

Family 18. ANHINGIDAE. Snake Birds or Darters.

1. *Anhinga anhinga*. Anhinga. 85. Southern USA to Brazil & Argentina.
2. *Anhinga melanogaster*. Asian Darter. 90. India, SE Asia.
3. *Anhinga novaehollandiae*. Australian Darter. 87. SE Asia to Australia.
4. *Anhinga rufa*. African Darter. 78. Africa South of Sahara, Malagasy.

Family 19. FREGATIDAE. Frigate Birds.

1. *Fregata andrewsi*. Christmas island Frigatebird. 96. Some Indian ocean Islands.
2. *Fregata aquila*. Ascension island Frigatebird. 95. South Atlantic.
3. *Fregata ariel*. Lesser Frigatebird. 80. Widely scattered in Tropical Oceans.
4. *Fregata magnificens*. Magnificent Frigatebird.114/89. Tropical American Coasts.
5. Fregata minor. Great Frigatebird. l0l/93. Atlantic, Indian & Pacific Oceans.

34
35
36
37
38
39
ANHINGIDAE
1 ♀
2 JUV ♀
3 ♀
4 ♀
1 ♂
2 ♂
3 ♂
4 ♂
FREGATIDAE
1
2
3
4
5 JUV

ARDEIDAE (1)
Herons

1. *Ardea cinerea.* Grey Heron. 5ss. 90. Europe, Asia, Africa.
2. *Ardea cocoi.* Cocoi Heron. 125. Panama to Chile & Argentina.
3. *Ardea goliath.* Goliath Heron. 146. Most of Africa to India, Sri Lanka.
4. *Ardea herodias.* Great Blue Heron. 4ss. 123. Canada to West Indies, North of S America
5. incl. *A. h. occidentalis.* Great White Heron. 123. Florida, Cuba, Jamaica.
6. *Ardea humbloti.* Madagascar Heron. 95. Malagasy.
7. *Ardea insignis.* White bellied / Imperial Heron. 127. Nepal to Assam.
8. *Ardea melanocephala.* Black headed Heron. 87. Gambia to Sudan, Cape Province.
9. *Ardea/Egretta novaehollandiae.* White faced Heron. 2ss. 65. Indonesia, Australasia,
10. *Ardea pacifica.* White necked / Pacific Heron. 90. Australasia.
11. *Ardea picata.* Pied Heron. 2ss. 48. New Guinea, Indonesia, Australia.
12. *Ardea purpurea.* Purple Heron. 4ss. 78. Europe. Africa. S Asia, Indonesia.
13. *Ardea sumatrana.* Great billed Heron. 113. Malaysia, Philippines, New Guinea, Australia.
14. *Ardeola rufiventris.* Rufous bellied Heron. 38. E & SE Africa.
15. *Butorides striatus.* Striated, Mangrove, Little Green Heron. 34ss.40. Cosmopolitan except Europe, S America.
16. *Butorides virescens.* Green Heron. 50. Canada to Colombia, Venezuela.
17. *Butorides Sundevallii.* Lava Heron. 40. Galapagos Islands.
18. *Ardeola bacchus.* Chinese Pond Heron. 45. Bangladesh to China & Borneo.
19. *Ardeola grayii.* Indian Pond Heron 2ss. 45. Persian Gulf, India, Andaman Islands.
20. *Ardeola idae.* Madagascar Pond Heron. 48. Malagasy to SE Africa.
21. *Ardeola ralloides.* Squacco Heron. 45. S Europe, W Asia, Africa, Malagasy.
22. *Ardeola speciosa.* Javanese Pond Heron. 45. SE Asia, Philippines, Indonesia.

1
2
3
4
5
6
7
8
9
10
11
12
13
14
15
-16-
JUV
17
18
19
JUV
NB
22
JUV
NB
-20-
NB
21

ARDEIDAE (2)
Egrets and Night Herons

23. *Bubulcus ibis.* Cattle Egret / Buff backed Heron.3ss 50. Almost world wide in warm climates.
24. *Casmmerodius albus.* Great Egret. 5ss. 87. Cosmopolitan.
25. *Egretta ardesiaca.* Black Heron. 60. Local Africa S of Sahara.
26. *Egretta caerulea.* Little Blue Heron. 58. Canada to Brazil, Uruguay. W Indies.
27. *Egretta dimorpha.* Mascarene/Dimorphic Heron. 55. E Africa coast. Madagascar. (a) White phase (b) Dark phase. (Consp 30 ?).
28. *Egretta eulophotes.* Chinese Egret. 68. Korea, Japan, China to Indonesia.
29. *Egretta garzetta.* Little Egret. 2ss. 55. Most of world except C. South America.
30. *Egretta gularis.* Western Reef-Egret. West Africa to Persian Gulf area. India, Sri Lanka.(Also dark phase)
31. *Egretta/Mesophoyx intermedia.* Intermediate Egret. 3ss. 70. Africa,S Asia to Australia.
32. *Egretta rufescens.* Reddish Egret. 3ss. 79. USA to W Indies, Venezuela. (Also White Phase).
33. *Egretta sacra.* Eastern Reef-Heron. 2ss. 54. SE Asia to Oceania, Australia, New Zealand. (Also Dark phase).
34. *Egretta vinaceigula.* Slaty Egret. 60. Botswana.
35. *Egretta thula.* Snowy Egret. 2ss. 63. Central USA to Argentina, West Indies.
36. *Egretta tricolor.* Tricoloured / Louisiana Heron. 3ss. 57. Southern USA to Brazil.
37. *Agamia agami.* Agami Heron. 75. Mexico to Peru, Brazil.
38. *Pilherodius pileatus.* Capped Heron. 55. Panama to Brazil & Paraguay.
39. *Sirigma sibilatrix.* Whistling Heron. 2ss. 55. Colombia, Venezuela to Argentina.
40. *Cochlearius cochlearius.* Boat billed Heron. 5ss. 48. Mexico To Brazil, Argentina.
41. *Nycticorax caledonicus.* Rufous Night Heron. 7ss. 57. SW Pacific, Australasia.
42. *Nycticorax leuconotus.* White backed Night Heron. 53. Zimbabwe, W, C Africa.
43. *Gorsachius magnificus.* White eared Night Heron. 53. Hainan, S China.
44. *Nycticorax nycticorax.* Black crowned Night Heron. 4ss. 60. Cosmopolitan except Australasia.
45. *Nyctanassa violacea.* Yellow crowned Night Heron. 6ss. 60. USA to Peru, Brazil.

23
NB
-24-
NB
25
-26-JUV
30
31
-27-
(a)
(b)
28
29
37
34
35
36
32
33
JUV
40
41
JUV
39
38
42
43
44
JUV
45

ARDEIDAE (0)
Night and Tiger Herons, Bitterns

46. *Gorsachius goisagi.* Japanese Night Heron. 48. Japan. Winters S China to Indonesia.
47. *Gorsachius melanolophus.* Malaysian Night Heron. 48. India, SE Asia. Winters Philippines Greater Sundas.
48. *Zonerodius heliosylus.* Forest Bittern. 93. New Guinea & Islands.
49. *Tigrisoma fasciatum.* Fasciated Tiger Heron. 4ss.65. Costa Rica to Argentina.
50. *Tigriornis leucolophus.* White crested Tiger Heron.65. Sierra Leone to Zaire.
51. *Tigrisoma lineatum.* Rufescent Tiger Heron. 2ss.73. Honduras to Argentina.
52. *Tigrisoma mexicanum.* Bare throated Tiger Heron. 2ss.75. Mexico to Colombia.
53. *Zebrilus undulatus.* Zigzag Heron. 31. Amazon basin.
54. Ixobrychus cinnamomeus. Cinnamon Bittern. 38. India, China, SE Asia, Indonesia.
55. *Ixobrychus eurhythmus.* Schrenck's Bittern. 35. E Asia. W. Philippines, Sundas.
56. *Ixobrychus exilis.* Least Bittern. 6ss 27/35. S Canada to Argentina, West Indies.
57. *Ixobrychus involucris.* Stripe backed Bittern. 32. Colombia to Argentina.
58. Ixobrychus minutus. Little Bittern. 5ss. 35. Palearctic, Afro-tropical regions.
59. *Ixobrychus novaezelandiae.* Black backed Bittern. 53. New Zealand. Australia.
60. *Ixobrychus sinensis.* Yellow Bittern. 30. E.S Asia, Indonesia, Oceania.
61. *Ixobrychus sturmii.* Dwarf Bittern. 25. Africa South of Sahara.
62. *Botaurus lentiginosus.* American Bittern. 85. Newfoundland to Mexico. Winters to Panama, West Indies.
63. *Botaurus pinnatus.* Pinnated Bittern. 2ss. 63. Mexico to Brazil, Argentina.
64. *Botaurus poiciloptilus.* Australasian Bittern. 70. S. Australia, New Zealand, New Caledonia.
65. *Botaurus stellaris.* Great / Eurasian Bittern. 2ss 95.
66. *Ixobrychus flavicollis.* Black Bittern. 3ss. 55. India, China, SE Asia, Sulawesi New Guinea. Solomon Islands, Australia.

46
47
48
49
50
-51-
JUV
JUV
-52-
53
54
55
56
57
58
60
61
62
59
65
63
64
66

BALAENICIPITIDAE, SCOPODAE, CICONIIDAE
Whale Headed Stork, Hammerhead Stork, Storks

Family 21 BALAENICIPIDIDAE. Whale Headed Stork

1. *Balaeniceps rex*. Shoebill. 119.White Nile to Uganda.

Family 22. SCOPIDAE. Hammerhead Stork.

1. *Scopus umbretta*. Hammerkop. 2ss. 50. Africa South of Sahara, Arabia, Malagasy.

Family 23 CICONIIDAE. Storks.

1. *Mycteria americana*. Wood Stork. 120. Southern. USA to Argentina, Cuba, Hispaniola.
2. *Mycteria cinerea*.. Milky Stork. 96. Indo-China, Malaya, Sumatra, Java.
3. *Mycteria ibis*. Yellow billed Stork. 96. Africa South of Sahara, Malagasy.
4. *Mycteria leucocephala*. Painted Stork. 101. India to China, SE Asia.
5. *Anastomus lamelligerus*. African Openbill. 2ss. 93. Africa South of Sahara.
6. *Anastomus oscitans*. Asian Openbill. 80. India to Cambodia, Thailand.
7. *Ciconia abdimii*. Abdim's Stork. 75. SW Arabia, Africa South of Sahara.
8. *Ciconia ciconia*. White Stork. 2ss. 100. W Palearctic, Winters SE Asia, India, Africa.
9. *Ciconia boyciana*. Oriental Stork. 112. NE Asia, Winters China, India.
10. *Ciconia episcopus*. Woolly necked Stork. 3ss. 88. Africa, S Asia, Indonesia.
11. *Ciconia stormi*. Storm's Stork. 85. Borneo.12. Ciconia nigra. Black Stork. 96. Europe to China. Winters Africa, India.
13. *Ciconia maguari*. Maguari Stork. 108. Guyanas to Chile, Argentina.
14. *Ephippiorhynchus asiaticus*. Black necked Stork. 2ss. 132. India , SE Asia to New Guinea, Australia.
15. *Ephippiorhynchus senegalensis*. Saddlebill Stork. 132. Africa, South of Sahara.
16. *Jabiru mycteria*. Jabiru. 140. Mexico to Brazil & Argentina.
17. *Leptoptilus crumeniferus*. Marabou Stork. 120/150. Africa, South of Sahara.
18. *Leptoptilus dubius*. Greater Adjutant Stork. 145. India, SE Asia.
19. *Leptoptilus javanicus*. Lesser Adjutant Stork. 114. India, China, SE Asia, Greater Sundas.

CICONIIDAE
BALAENICIPITIDAE
1
SCOPIDAE
1
1
2
3
4
5
6
7
8
9
13
8
JUV
10
11
12
14
15
16
17
18
19

THRESKIORNITHIDAE (1) Ibises

1. *Threskiornis aethiopicus*. Sacred Ibis. 3ss. 87. All of Africa to W Asia.
2. incl. *T. a. bernieri*. Madagascar Ibis. 87. Malagasy.
3. *Threskiornis melanocephalus*. Black headed Ibis. 75. India, China, SE Asia. W Philippines, Sumatra.
4. *Threskiornis molucca*. Australian Ibis. 2ss. 70. Indonesia, New Guinea, Australia, New Zealand.
5. *Threskiornis spinicollis*. Straw necked Ibis. 70. Australia to New Guinea.
6. *Pseudibis davisoni*. White shouldered Ibis. 75. China, SE Asia, Borneo.
7. *Pseudibis gigantea*. Giant Ibis. 104. Thailand, Indo-China.
8. *Pseudibis papillosa*. Red naped Ibis. 2ss. 68. Pakistan, India.
9. *Geronticus calvus*. Bald Ibis. 78. South African mountains.
10. *Geronticus eremita*. Waldrapp. 68. Morocco. Red Sea area.
11. *Nipponia nippon*. Japanese crested Ibis. 74. Japan, formerly China.
12. *Bostrychia caruncularta*. Wattled Ibis. 81. Ethiopia, Eritrea.
13. *Bostrychia hagadech*. Hadada Ibis. 3ss. 75. Africa South of Sahara.
14. *Bostrychia olivacea*. Olive Ibis. 5ss 60. Equatorial Africa.
15. *Bostrychia rara*. Spot breasted Ibis. 50. West & Central Africa.
16. *Theristicus caerulescens*. Plumbeous Ibis. 80. Brazil to Argentina.
17. *Theristicus caudatus*. Buff necked Ibis. 73. Guyanas, Venezuela to Brazil, Argentina
18. *Theristicus melanopis*. Black faced Ibis. 73. Peru, Chile, Argentina.
19. *Theristicus branickii*. Andean Ibis. 74. Ecuador, Peru.
20. *Mesembrinibis cayennensis*. Green Ibis. 57. Costa Rica to Brazil, Argentina.
21. *Phimosus infuscatus*. Bare faced Ibis. 3ss. 49. Venezuela to Brazil, Argentina.
22. *Eudocimus albus*. White Ibis. 60. Southern USA to Peru, Bahamas, Gr. Antilles.
23. *Eudocimus ruber*. Scarlet Ibis. 57. Colombia, Venezuela, Trinidad to Brazil.

1
2
3
4
5
6
7
8
10
11
12
9
16
13
14
15
18
17
19
20
21
22
JUV
-23-

THRESKIORNITHIDAE (2)
Ibises and Spoonbills

Family 24 Ibises (2)

24. *Cercibis oxycerca*. Sharp tailed Ibis. 73. Guyana, Venezuela, Colombia, Brazil .
25. *Plegadis chihi*. White faced Ibis. 54. South C. USA to Brazil & Argentina.
26. *Plegadis falcinellus*. Glossy Ibis. 50.Tropical Eurasia to Australia. America.
27. *Plegadis ridgwayi*. Puna Ibis. 55. Peru, Bolivia, Chile, Argentina.
28. *Lophotibis cristata*. Crested/White winged Ibis.50. Malagasy.

Subfamily Plataleinae. Spoonbills.

29. *Platalea ajaja*. Roseate Spoonbill. 80. Southern USA to Brazil, Argentina, West Indies.
30. *Platalea alba*. African Spoonbill. 82. Africa South of Sahara.
31. *Platalea leucorodia*. (Eurasian)Spoonbill. 4ss. 82. S Palearctic. West Africa, SE Asia.
32. *Platalea minor*. Black faced Spoonbill. 2ss.75. China, Korea Winters SE Asia.
33. *Platalea regia*. Royal Spoonbill. 75. Australia, New Zealand. W. Indonesia, New Guinea.

Family 25. PHOENICOPTERIDAE. (Flamingos.).

1. *Phoenicopterus minor*. Lesser Flamingo. 100. Africa to NW India.
2. *Phoenicopterus ruber*. American/Caribbean Flamingo. 125. Central South America, West Indies.
3. *Phoenicopterus chilensis*. Chilean Flamingo. 106. Chile, Peru.
4. *Phoenicopterus roseus*. Greater Flamingo. 150. Europe, Asia, Africa.(consp. 1)
5. *Phoenicopterus andinus*. Andean Flamingo 120. Peru to Chile & Argentina.
6. *Phoenicopterus jamesi*. Puna Flamingo. 100. Peru to Chile & Argentina.

24
25
JUV
26
27
28
29
30
31
32
PHOENICOPTERIDAE
33
34
1
3
2
4
6
5

ANHIMIDAE, ANATIDAE
Screamers, Swans, Geese and Ducks

Family 26. ANHIMIDAE. Screamers.

1. *Anhima cornuta*. Horned Screamer. 92. Venezuela to Bolivia, Brazil.
2. *Chauna chavaria*. Northern Screamer. 70. Colombia, Venezuela.
3. *Chauna torquata*. Southern / Crested Screamer. 70. South Brazil to Argentina.

Family 27. ANATIDAE. (I). Swans, Geese & Ducks.

1. *Anseranas semipalmata*. Magpie Goose. 85. Australia, New Guinea.
2. *Dendrocygna arborea*. West Indian Whistling Duck. 55. West Indies .
3. *Dendrocygna arcuata*. Wandering Whistling Duck. 57. East Indies to Australia.
4. *Dendrocygna autumnalis*. Red billed Whistling Duck.or Black bellied Whistling Duck. 2ss.50. Texas to Argentina.
5. *Dendrocygna bicolor*. Fulvous Whistling Duck. 2ss. 49. South USA to Argentina, E Africa, Malagasy, S Asia.
6. *Dendrocygna eytoni*. Plumed Whistling Duck. 53. Australia, Tasmania.
7. *Dendrocygna guttata*. Spotted Whistling Duck. 49. Sulawesi to New Guinea, Philippines.
8. *Dendrocygna javanica*. Lesser Whistling Duck. 42. India to SE Asia and Java.
9. *Dendrocygna viduata*. White faced Whistling Duck. 38. Costa Rica to Brazil, Africa South of Sahara.
10. *Thalassornis leuconotus*. White backed Duck. 2ss. 43. Africa, Malagasy.
11. *Coscoroba coscoroba*. Coscoroba Swan. 87. Brazil to Falklands. Winters Northward.
12. *Cygnus atratus*. Black Swan. 116. Australia. Introduced in many countries.
13. *Cygnus columbianus*. Tundra/Whistling Swan. 3ss. 118. Arctic Canada, Winters USA.
14. incl. *C. c. bewickii*. Bewick's Swan. 118. N Russia, Siberia, Winters Eurasia.
15. *Cygnus cygnus*. Whooper Swan. 150. N Palearctic. Winters Eurasia, UK to China.
16. *Cygnus buccinator*. Trumpeter Swan. 150. Western N America.
17. *Cygnus melanocoryphus*. Black necked Swan. 99. S Brazil to Argentina, Falklands, W & N to Tropic of Capricorn.
18. *Cygnus olor* Mute Swan 50 Eurasian widely introduced and domesticated.

1
2
3
ANATIDAE
1
2
3
4
5
6
7
8
9
10
11
12
13
14
15
16
17
18
18
JUV

ANATIDAE (2)
Geese

19. *Anser albifrons*. White fronted Goose. 5ss. 70. N Eurasia, Greenland, N America, Winters Europe, W USA, E Asia.
20. *Anser anser.* Grey Lag Goose. 2ss. 80. Iceland, most of Eurasia. Winters N. Africa, India, SE Asia.
21. *Anser caerulescens atlanticus*. Greater Snow Goose. 80. Greenland, Winters USA, Atlantic coast.
21a. *A c. caerulescens*. Lesser Snow Goose. 2ss. 70. Canada, Winters California, Mexico. Morphs. snowy & blue Goose. Blue phase formerly considered distinct species (A. hyperboreus, Blue Goose,).
22. *Anser canagicus*. Emperor Goose. 75. Siberia & Alaska.
23. *Anser cygnoides*. Swan Goose. 90. C Asia to Japan. Winters China.
24. *Anser erythropus*. Lesser White fronted Goose. 67. Arctic Eurasia. Winters Eurasia.
25. *Anser fabalis*. Bean Goose. 5ss. 78. Arctic Eurasia. Winters Eurasia.
26. *Anser brachyrhynchus*. Pink footed Goose. 75. Iceland, Greenland, Winters Europe.
27. *Anser indicus*. Bar headed Goose. 73. Central Asia, Winters India, Burma.
28. *Anser Rossii*. Ross' Goose. 60. N Canada, Winters California.
29. *Branta bernicla*. Brent Goose/Brant. 4ss. 57. N America, NW Palearctic. Winters USA, W Europe, E Asia.
30. *Branta canadensis*. Canada Goose. 100/60. Arctic Canada to Mexico. 10ss.incl (a)canadensis.(b)minima. Introduced W Europe, New Zealand.
31. *Branta leucopsis*. Barnacle Goose. 63. N Palearctic, Winters UK, W Europe.
32. *Branta ruficollis*. Red breasted Goose. 54. Siberia, Winters S Russia.
33. *Branta sandviensis*. Nene, Hawaiian Goose. 57. Hawaii.
34. *Ceropsis novaehollandiae*. Cape Barren Goose. 99. SE Australian Islands.
35. *Chloephaga hybrida*. Kelp Goose. 2ss. 57. Chile, Argentina, Falkland Islands.
36. *Chloephaga melanoptera*. Andean Goose. 68. Andes, Peru to Chile, Argentina.
37. *Chloephaga picta*. Upland Goose. 2ss. 57. Chile, Argentina.
38. *Chloephaga poliocephala*. Ashy headed Goose. 55. Chile, Argentina.
39. *Chloephaga rubidiceps*. Ruddy headed Goose. 55. Argentina, Falkland Islands.

19
20
21
21A
22
23
24
25
27
28
29
26
30(a)
32
31
33
34
35
30 (b)
37
36
38
39

ANATIDAE (3)
Shelduck, Steamer Duck

40. *Cyanochen cyanoptera*. Blue winged Goose. 57. Ethiopian highlands.
41. *Neochen jubata*. Orinoco Goose. 63. Orinoco, Amazon basins to Argentina.
42. *Alopochen aegyptiacus*. Egyptian Goose. 69. Most of Africa except Sahara.
43. *Tadorna cana*. South African Shelduck. 63. S Africa.
44. *Tadorna cristata*. Crested Shelduck. 67. Russia, Korea, Japan,(extinct).
45. Tadorna ferruginea. Ruddy Shelduck. 63. Mediterranean to E Asia, Winters India, Africa.
46. *Tadorna radjah*. Radjah Shelduck. 64. Moluccas, NE Australia, New Guinea.
47. *Tadorna tadorna*. Common Shelduck. 60. Palearctic. Winters N Africa, Near East, India, SE Asia,
48. *Tadorna tadornoides*. Australian Shelduck. 71. S & SW Australia, Tasmania.
49. *Tadorna variegata*. Paradise Shelduck. 62. New Zealand.
50. *Anas/Lophonetta specularioides*. Crested Duck. 58. Peru, Chile, Argentina, Falklands.
51. *Tachyeres brachypterus*. Falkland Islands Flightless Steamer Duck. 68. Falklands.
52. *Tachyeres patachonicus*. Flying Steamer Duck. 61. Chile, Argentina, Falklands.
53. *Tachyeres pteneres*. (Magellanic)Flightless Steamer Duck. 68. S Chile.
54. *Tachyeres leucocephalus*. Chubut Steamer Duck. 68. Argentine coast.

40
41
42
43
44
45
46
47
48
49
50
-51-
54
-52-
-53-

ANATIDAE (4)
Surface feeding Ducks

55. *Anas specularis.* Spectacled Duck. 46. Andes, Chile, Argentina.
56. *Anas sparsa.* African Black Duck. 3ss. 54. Africa South of Sahara.
57. *Anas platyrhynchos.* Mallard. 7ss. 58. Eurasia, N Africa, N America.
58. incl. *A.. P. laysanensis.* Laysan Duck. 37. Laysan Island, (Hawaii).
59. *A. p. wyvilliana.* Hawaiian Duck. 46. Hawaiian Islands.
60. *A. p. fulvigula.* Florida/Mottled Duck. 55. SE USA.
61. *A. p. diazi.* Mexican Duck. 52. N C Mexico.
62. *A. p. oustaleti.* Mariana Duck. 52. Mariana Islands. (extinct).
63. *Anas rubripes.* American Black Duck. 55. Canada to S E USA .
64. *Anas poecilorhyncha.* Spotbill. 6ss. 60. India & E Asia.
65. *Anas superciliosa.* Pacific Black Duck. 55. Australasia, Indonesia, Micronesia, Polynesia.
66. *Anas undulata.* African Yellowbill Duck. 54. Ethiopia to South Africa.
67. *Anas melleri.* Meller's Duck. 65. Malagasy.
68. *Anas luzonica.* Philippine Duck. 53. Philippines .
69. *Anas gibberifrons.* Sunda Teal. 3ss. 42. Indonesia.
70. incl. *A. g. albogularlis.* Andaman Teal. 42. Andaman Islands.
71. *Anas gracilis.* Australian Grey Teal. 42. Australia, New Zealand, New Guinea.
72. *Anas castanea.* Chestnut Teal. 40. Australia, Tasmania.
73. *Anas aucklandica.* Brown Teal. 3ss. 40. New Zealand.
74. *Anas bernieri.* Madagascar Teal. 40. Malagasy.
75. *Anas flavirostris.* Speckled Teal. 4ss. 40. Venezuela to Tierra del Fuego.
76. incl. *A. f. andinum.* Andean Teal. 40. Colombia, Ecuador.
77. *A. f. oxyptera.* Sharp winged Teal. 40. Peru to Chile, Argentina.
78. *Anas crecca.* Teal. 3ss. 35. Eurasia, N Africa, N America.
79. *Anas formosa.* Baikal Teal. 40. Siberia, Winters China, Japan.
80. *Anas falcata.* Falcated Duck. 48. N Asia, Winters Iran, India, Burma.
81. *Anas strepera.* Gadwall. 50. Palearctic, N America.
82. *Anas penelope.* Wigeon. 45. N C Eurasia, Winters Africa, S Asia.
83. *Anas americana.* American Wigeon. 50. N America, Winters Caribbean, N South America.
84. *Anas sibilatrix.* Chloe Wigeon. 48. Chile, Argentina, Falkland Islands.
85. *Anas bahamensis.* White cheeked Pintail. 3ss. 43. S America, Galapagos, Bahamas.
86. *Anas acuta.* Pintail. 3ss. 55. N Eurasia, N America. Winters South America, S Eurasia.
87. *Anas eatoni.* Eaton's Pintail. 3ss. 55. Crozet & Kerguelen Islands.
88. *Anas georgica.* Yellow billed Pintail. 3ss. 50. S Georgia, Colombia to Tierra del Fuego.

55
56
57
59
JUV
62
63
58
61
64
60
65
66
68
67
74
75♀
72
71
70
77
-73-
76
69
75♂
78
80
79
81
82
JUV
JUV
83
84
85
88
86
87

ANATIDAE (5)
Surface feeding Ducks, Torrent Ducks, Eiders

89. *Anas erythrorhyncha*. Red billed Teal. 47. E & S Africa, Malagasy.
90. *Anas/Marmaronetta angustirostris*. Marbled Teal. 40. Spain to India.
91. *Anas capensis*. Cape Teal. 46. Ethiopia to Botswana, Cape.
92. *Anas versicolor*. Silver Teal. 3ss. 40. Bolivia to Argentina.
93. incl. *A. v. puna*. Puna Teal. 40. Peru to Chile.
94. *Anas hottentota*. Hottentot Teal. 35. Local, Uganda to Cape, Malagasy.
95. *Anas querquedula*. Garganey. 38. Eurasia, Winters to S Africa, Australasia.
96. *Anas discors*. Blue winged Teal. 2ss. 58. Canada to S America.
97. *Anas cyanoptera*. Cinnamon Teal. 5ss. 42. S Canada to Tierra del Fuego, Falkland Is.
98. *Anas/Callonetta leucophrys*. Ringed Teal. 35. Brazil, Bolivia to Argentina.
99. *Anas clypeata*. Northern Shoveler. 50. Eurasia, N America, Winters Africa, Indonesia, S America.
100. *Anas platalea*. Red Shoveler. 45. Peru, Brazil to Tierra del Fuego.
101. *Anas smithii*. Cape Shoveler. 52. Angola, Transvaal to Cape.
102. *Anas rhynchotis*. Australian Shoveler. 2ss. 52. Australia, New Zealand.
103. *Anas/Salvadorina waigiuensis*. Salvadori's. Teal. 42. New Guinea.
104. *Malacorhynchus membranaceus*. Pink eared Duck. 40. Australia.
105. *Hymenolaimus malacorhynchus*. Blue Duck. 52. New Zealand.
106. *Merganetta armata*. Chilean Torrent Duck.7ss. 38. Chile.
107. incl. *M. a. leucogenis*. Peruvian Torrent Duck. 38. Peru, Ecuador.
108. *Rhodonessa caryophyllacea*. Pink headed Duck. 60. India, Burma. (extinct).
109. *Stictonetta naevosa*. Freckled Duck. 55. S Australia, Tasmania.
110. *Polysticta stelleri*. Steller's Eider. 45. Siberia, Alaska, Aleutian Is.
111. *Somateria mollissima*. Common Eider. 6ss. 57. NW Palearctic, N American coasts.
112. *Somateria fischeri*. Spectacled Eider. 53. Siberia, Alaska.
113. *Somateria spectabilis*. King Eider. 55. N Eurasia, N Canada.

89
90
91
92
94
95
96
93
98
99
97
103
101
100
104
105
102
106
107
108
109
110
JUV
111
112
113

ANATIDAE (6)
Pochards, Pygmy Geese

114. *Aythya valisineria*. Canvasback. 50. NW America. Winters SE USA, Mexico.
115. *Aythya ferina*. Common Pochard. 45. Palearctic, Winters Africa, India, SE. Asia.
116. *Aythya americana*. Redhead. 50. Alaska to S. USA. Winters Mexico, West Indies.
117. *Aythya innotata*. Madagascar Pochard. 42. Malagasy. (extinct?)
118. *Aythya australis*. White eyed Duck/Hardhead. 3ss. 55. Australasia, Oceania
119. *Aythya ayroca*. Ferruginous Duck. 40. Palearctic, Winters Africa to SE Asia.
120. *Aythya baeri*. Baer's Pochard. 46. E Palearctic, Winters India, SE Asia.
121. *Aythya collaris*. Ring necked Duck. 42. Canada, NW USA, Winters Panama, West Indies.
122. *Aythya fuligula*. Tufted Duck. 42. Eurasia. Winters Africa, S Asia, Philippines.
123. *Aythya Novaeseelandiae*. New Zealand Scaup. 40. New Zealand.
124. *Aythya affinis*. Lesser Scaup. 40. Alaska to S. USA, S America, Hawaii.
125. *Aythya marila*. Scaup. 3ss. 48. Holarctic. Winters S. Europe, S Asia, S. USA.
126. *Netta erythrophthalma*. Southern Pochard. 2ss. 42. S America, S Africa.
127. *Netta peposaca*. Rosy billed Pochard. 50. Paraguay, Chile, Argentina.
128. *Netta rufina*. Red crested Pochard. 55. E Europe to Central Asia, Winters India, Africa.
129. *Chenonetta jubata*. Maned Goose/Duck. 50. Australia.
130. *Amazonetta brasiliensis*. Brazilian Teal. 2ss. 39. Venezuela to Argentina.
131. *Aix galericulata*. Mandarin Duck. 41. NE Asia, widely introduced elsewhere.
132. *Aix sponsa*. Carolina Wood Duck. 43. Canada to Mexico to Cuba, West Indies.
133. *Nettapus auritus*. African Pygmy Goose. 33. Most of Tropical Africa.
134. *Nettapus coromandelianus*. Cotton Pygmy Goose. 2ss. 33. India, China to NE Australia.
135. *Nettapus pilchellus*. Green Pygmy Goose. 33. Sulawesi, Moluccas, New Guinea, Australia.
136. *Sarkidiornis melanotos*. Comb Duck. 3ss. 49. Africa to SE Asia, S America.
137. *Cairina moschata*. Muscovy Duck. 73. Mexico to Peru, Uruguay.
138. *Cairina scutulata*. White winged Wood Duck. 74. Burma, Vietnam to Indonesia .
139. *Pteronetta hartlaubi*. Hartlaub's Duck. 2ss. 65. West & Central Africa.

114
115
116
117
118
119
120
121
122
123
124
125
126
127
128
129
130
131
132
133
134
135
136
137
138
139

ANATIDAE (7)
Scoters, Mergansers, Stifftails

140. *Plectropterus gambensis*. Spur winged Goose. 93. Africa South of Sahara.
141. *Camptorhynchus labradorius*. Labrador Duck. 54. North Atlantic.(extinct.)
142. *Melanitta fusca*. Velvet/White winged Scoter. 4ss. 55. N,America,Eurasia.
143. *Melanitta nigra*. Black/Common Scoter. 2ss. 48. Holarctic. Winters far south.
144. *Melanitta perspicillata*. Surf Scoter. 53. N American Lakes. Winters at sea to Mexico.
145. *Histrionicus histrionicus*. Harlequin Duck. 2ss. 42. Greenland, Iceland, Siberia, Alaska. Winters S USA, E Asia, N Europe.
146. *Clangula hyemalis*. Long tailed Duck, Old Squaw. 40/53. Arctic circle. Winters Europe, USA, Japan.
147. *Bucephala albeola*. Bufflehead. 35. N America Winters to Mexico, West Indies.
148. *Bucephala clangula*. Goldeneye. 2ss. 45. Canada,N Eurasia. Winters India, S Europe California.
149. *Bucephala islandica*. Barrow's Goldeneye. 53. Alaska to Iceland. Winters coasts of USA.
150. *Mergus albellus*. Smew. 42. N Europe, N Asia, Winters to Africa, India, China.
151. *Mergus cucullatus*. Hooded Merganser. 42. N America. Winters to Mexico, W Indies.
152. *Mergus Australis*. Auckland Islands Merganser. 57. Auckland Island. (extinct.)
153. *Mergus merganser*. Goosander / Common Merganser. 3ss.65. Eurasia, N America.
154. *Mergus octosetaceus*. Brazilian Merganser. 55. Brazil, Paraguay, Argentina.
155. *Mergus serrator*. Red breasted Merganser. 2ss. 57. N Palearctic, N America, Winters S Palearctic, Mexico.
156. *Mergus squamatus*. Chinese / Scaly sided Merganser. 58. Siberia, Winters to China.
157. *Oxyura australis*. Blue billed Duck. 40. Australia.
158. *Oxyura dominica*. Masked Duck. 36. Texas to N Argentina, West Indies.
159. *Oxyura jamaicensis*. Ruddy Duck. 2ss. 40. Alaska to El Salvador , West Indies.
160. incl. *O. i. andina*. Colombian Ruddy Duck. 40. Andes of Colombia.
161. *O. j. ferruginea*. Peruvian Ruddy Duck. 40. Peru, Chile.
162. *Oxyura leucocephala*. White headed Duck / Stifftail. 45. Mediterranean to Central Asia.
163. *Oxyura maccoa*. Maccoa Duck. 49. E & S Africa.
164. *Oxyura vittata*. Lake Duck. 43. S Argentina, Chile, Winters Paraguay, Brazil.
165. *Biziura lobata*, Musk Duck. 65. S Australia, Tasmania.
166. *Heteronetta atricapilla*. Black headed Duck. 36. Brazil, Bolivia, Paraguay, Uruguay, Argentina, Chile.

140
141
142
143
144
145
146
Br
NB
147
148
149
150
151
152
153
154
155
156
157
158
162
163
164
159
160
161
165
166

CATHARTIDAE
New World Vultures

Family 28. CATHARTIDAE. New world Vultures.

1. *Cathartes aura.* Turkey Vulture. 4ss. 75. S Canada to Tierra del Fuego.
2. *Cathartes burrovianus.* Lesser Yellow headed Vulture. 70. Mexico to Brazil.
3. *Cathartes melambrotus.* Greater Yellow headed Vulture. 82. Guyanas to Brazil, Peru, Bolivia.
4. *Coragyps atratus.* Black Vulture. 3ss. 60. S. USA, Trinidad to Argentina.
5. *Sarcoramphus papa.* King Vulture. 75. Central & South America.
6. *Vultur/Gymnogyps californicus.* Californian Condor. 125. California.
7. *Vultur gryphus.* Andean Condor. 106. Andes, Venezuela to Argentina.

Family 29. SAGITTARIIDAE. Secretary Bird.

1. *Sagittarius serpentarius.* Secretary Bird. 116. Africa South of Sahara.

1
2
3
4
5
6
7
4
2
3
1
5
6
7
SAGITTARIIDAE
1

Plate 28 Family 30.

ACCIPITRIDAE (1)
Cuckoo Falcons, Honeu Buzzards, Kites

1. *Aviceda cuculoides*. African Cuckoo Hawk. 4ss. 40. Africa South of Sahara.
2. *Aviceda Jordan*. Jerdon's Baza. 5ss. 45. India, SE Asia, Philippines, Borneo, Sulawesi.
3. *Aviceda leuphotes*. Black Baza. 5ss. 32. India, China, SE Asia, Andaman Is.
4. *Aviceda madagascarensis*. Madagascar Cuckoo Hawk. 44. Malagasy.
5. *Aviceda subcristata*. Crested Baza. 16ss. 38. Lesser Sundas, New Guinea, Solomon Islands, Australia.
6. *Leptodon cayanensis*. Grey Headed Kite. 47. Mexico to Brazil & Argentina.
7. *Leptodon forbesi*. White collared Kite. 47. E Brazil.(4 specimens.)
8. *Chondrohierax uncinatus*. Hook billed Kite. 4ss. 42. Mexico to Argentina.
9. *Henicopernis infuscatus*. Black Honey Buzzard. 50. New Britain.
10. *Henicopernis longicauda*. Long tailed Honey Buzzard. 3ss. 60. New Guinea.
11. *Pernis apivorus*. Honey Buzzard. 55. W Palearctic, Winters Iran to S Africa.
12. *Pernis celebensis*. Barred Honey Buzzard. 2ss. 56. Sulawesi.
13. *Pernis ptilorhynchus*. Oriental Honey Buzzard. 6ss. 50. E, S, SE Asia to Java.
14. *Elanoides forficatus*. Swallow tailed Kite. 2ss. 56. S USA to Argentina.
15. *Macheirhamphus alcinus*. Bat Hawk. 3ss. 45. Africa, SE Asia, Sumatra, Borneo, New Guinea.
16. *Gampsonyx swainsonii*. Pearl Kite. 3ss. 20. Nicaragua to Brazil, Argentina.
17. *Elanus caeruleus*. Black winged Kite. 4ss. 32. S Eurasia, Africa.
18. *Elanus leucurus*. White tailed Kite. 2ss. 38. SW USA to Brazil & Argentina.
19. *Elanus axillaris/notatus*. Australian Kite. 35. Australia. 17,18,&19 are all sometimes called "Black shouldered Kite".
20. *Chilectina riocourii*. Scissor tailed Kite. 30. Senegal, Gambia to Kenya, Somalia.
21. *Elanus scriptus*. Letter winged Kite. 36. Interior Australia.
22. *Rostrhamus hamatus*. Slender billed Kite. 36. Panama to Bolivia, Brazil.
23. *Rostrhamus sociabilis*. Snail Kite. 4ss. 45. Florida, Cuba, Mexico to Argentina.
24. *Harpagus bidentatus*. Double toothed Kite. 2ss. 32. Mexico to Bolivia, Brazil.
25. *Harpagus diodon*. Rufous thighed Kite. 32. Guyanas to Brazil, Argentina.
26. *Ictinia misisippiensis*. Mississippi Kite. 35. S USA, Winters S America.
27. *Ictinia plumbea*. Plumbeous Kite. 35. Mexico to Paraguay, Argentina.

1
2
3
4
7
5
6
8
9
10
11
JUV
12
13
17
18
14
15
16
23
19
20
21
22
24
25
26
27

ACCIPITRIDAE (2)
Kites, Sea Eagles

28. *Lophoictinia isura.* Square tailed Kite. 49. Australia.
29. *Hamirostra melanosternon.* Black breasted Buzzard Kite. 55. N. Australia.
30. *Milvus migrans.* Black Kite. 55. Europe, Asia, Africa, Australia.
31. *Milvus milvus.* Red Kite. 60. Europe, W Asia, NW Africa,Cape Verde Is.
32. *Haliastur indus.* Brahminy Kite. 45. India, SE Asia to Australia.
33. *Haliastur sphenurus.* Whistling Kite. 53. Australia, New Guinea, New Caledonia.
34. *Milvus lineatus.* Black eared Kite. 53. C Asia, Japan, Winters Iraq to SE Asia.
35. *Haliaeetus albicilla.* White Tailed Eagle / Erne. 90. Local N Eurasia, Alaska.
36. *Haliaeetus leucocephalus.* Bald Eagle. 85. N America, NE Siberia.
37. *Haliaeetus leucogaster.* White bellied Sea Eagle. 67. India, Indonesia, Australia.
38. *Haliaeetus leucorhyphus.* Pallas' Fish Eagle. 75. Asia, mainly inland waters.
39. *Haliaeetus pelagicus.* Steller's Sea Eagle. 105. Siberia, Winters E Asian coasts.
40. *Haliaeetus sanfordi.* Sanford's Eagle. 65. Solomon Islands.
41. *Haliaeetus vocifer.* African Fish Eagle. 67. Africa South of Sahara.
42. *Haliaeetus vociferoides.* Madagascar Fish Eagle. 62. Malagasy.
43. *Ichthyophaga ichthyatus.* Grey headed Fish Eagle. 66. India, SE Asia, Borneo, Java, Philippines.
44. *Ichthyaetus humilis/nanus.* Lesser Fish Eagle. 56. India, SE Asia, Sumatra, Sulawesi, Borneo.

28
29
30
31
32
33
35
36
36
38
37
39
34
40
43
44
41
42

Plate 30 Family 30.

ACCIPITRIDAE (3)
Old World Vultures

45. *Gypohierax angolensis*. Palm-nut Vulture. 58. Tropical Africa.
46. *Necrisyrtes monachus*. Hooded Vulture. 62. Africa South of Sahara.
47. *Neophron percnopterus*. Egyptian Vulture. 65. S Europe, NE Africa, S Asia.
48. *Gypaetus barbatus*. Lammergeyer. 100. S Europe to Himalayas, E & S Africa.
49. *Gyps bengalensis*. White rumped Vulture. 75. Iran to India, China, SE Asia.
50. *Gyps africanus*. White backed Vulture. 75. Africa South of Sahara.
51. *Gyps coprotheres*. Cape (Griffon) Vulture. 100. Southern Africa.
52. *Gyps fulvus*. (Eurasian) Griffon Vulture. 103. S Europe, SW Asia, N Africa.
53. *Gyps himalayensis*. Himalayan Griffon. 104. C. Asia, India, Tibet to China.
54. *Gyps indicus/tenuirostris*. Long billed Vulture. 82. India, Burma, Malaysia.
55. *Gyps rueppellii*. Ruppell's Griffon. 102. Senegal to Somalia, Tanzania.
56. *Sarcogyps calvus*. Red headed Vulture. 76. India, SE Asia.
57. *Aegypius monachus*. Cinereous Vulture. 109. Spain, SE Europe, SW Asia.
58. *Torgos tracheliotus*. Lappet faced Vulture. 108. Israel to Ethiopia & Cape.
59. *Trigonoceps occipitalis*. White headed Vulture. 82. Senegal to Sudan, Cape.

45
46
47
48
49
50
51
52
53
54
55
56
57
58
59

ACCIPITRIDAE (4)
Snake Eagles, Harriers

60. *Circaetus cinerascens.* Banded Snake Eagle. 63. Africa South of Sahara.
61. *Circaetus cinereus.* Brown Snake Eagle. 75. Africa South of Sahara.
62. *Circaetus fasciolatus.* Southern Banded / Fasciated Snake Eagle. 58. E Africa.
63. *Circaetus gallicus.* Short toed Snake Eagle. 4ss. 73. Palearctic to Wallacea.
64. incl. *C. g. beaudouini.* Beaudouin's Snake Eagle. 73. Africa South of Sahara.
65. *C. g. pectoralis.* Black breasted Snake Eagle. 73. Most of Africa.
66. *Terathropius ecaudatus.* Bateleur. 60. Arabia, Africa South of Sahara.
67. *Spilornis holospilus.* Philippine Serpent Eagle. 62. Philippines.
68. *Spilornis kinabaluensis.* Mountain Serpent Eagle. 65. NE Borneo.
69. *Spilornis cheela.* Crested Serpent Eagle. 2lss. 75. India, China to Great Sundas.
70. *Spilornis minimus/klossi.* Nicobar Serpent Eagle. 46. Nicobar Island.
71. *Spilornis elgini.* Andaman Serpent Eagle. 56. Andaman Islands.
72. *Spilornis rufipectus.* Sulawesi Serpent Eagle. 2ss. 43. Sulawesi.
73. *Dryotriorchis spectabilis.* Congo Serpent Eagle. 2ss. 55. Liberia to Cameroon, Gabon & Zaire.
74. *Eutriorchis astur.* Madagascar Serpent Eagle. 57. Malagasy.
75. *Polyboroides typus.* Gymnogene / African Harrier Hawk. 2ss. 60. Africa South of Sahara.
76. *Polyboroides radiatus.* Madagascar Harrier Hawk. 60. Malagasy.
77. *Geranospiza caerulescens.* Crane Hawk. 6ss. 45. Central & South America.
78. incl. *G. c. nigra.* Blackish Crane Hawk. 45. Mexico to Panama.
79. *Circus aeruginosus.* Marsh Harrier / Western Swamp Hawk. 8ss. 53. Europe, N. Africa.
80. *Circus approximans.* Pacific Marsh/Swamp Harrier. 53. Australasia, Oceania.
81. *Circus maillardi.* Madagascar Marsh Harrier. 53. Malagasy.
82. *Circus spilonotus.* Asian/Eastern Marsh Harrier. 53. E. Asia. Winters to Sundas.
83. *Circus ranivorus.* African Marsh Harrier. 48. Kenya, Angola, Cape.
84. *Circus assimilis.* Spotted Harrier. 54. Australia to Sulawesi.
85. *Circus buffoni.* Long winged Harrier. 53.Colombia to Argentina, Trinidad & Tobago.
86. *Circus cinereus.* Cinereous Harrier. 48. Winters S America, Falkland Is.
87. *Circus cyaneus.* Hen Harrier/Marsh Hawk. 2ss. 50/60. Eurasia, N.C America.
88. *Circus macrourus.* Pallid Harrier. 45. E Europe, C Asia. Winters Africa India.
89. *Circus maurus.* Black Harrier. 49. Namibia, Botswana, RSA.
90. *Circus melanoleucos.* Pied Harrier. 48. E Asia. Winters to S Asia, Philippines, Sundas.
91. *Circus pygargus.* Montagu's Harrier 42. Palearctic. Winters India, Iran, S Africa.

64
65
60
61
62
63
66
67
68
69
70
72
71
73
74
75
76
77
78
79
83
84
85
80
81
82
86
87
88
89
90
91

ACCIPITRIDAE (5) GOSHAWKS & SPARROWHAWKS

92. *Melierax canorus.* Pale Chanting Goshawk. 46/54. Southern Africa.
93. *Melierax poliopterus.* Eastern Chanting Goshawk. 42/50. Ethiopia to Tanzania.
94. *Melierax metabates.* Dark Chanting Goshawk. 5ss. 43/51. Africa South of Sahara. Arabia.
95. *Melierax gabar.* Gabar Goshawk. 28/36. Senega1 to Ethiopia & Arabia. (a) normal, (b) melanistic.
96. *Megatriorchis doriae.* Doria's Goshawk. 58/69. New Guinea.
97. *Erythrotriorchis radiatus.* Red Goshawk. 51/58. N & E Australia.
98. *Accipiter gentilis.* Goshawk. 9ss. 45/60. Eurasia, N Africa.
99. incl. *A. g. albidus.* Pale Goshawk. 45/60. Siberia.
100. *A. g. atricapillus.* Black capped Goshawk. 42/48. N America.
101. *Accipiter melanoleucus.* Great Sparrowhawk. 2ss. 48/58. Africa, South of Sahara.
102. *Accipiter henstii.* Henst's Goshawk. 48/58. Malagasy.
103. *Accipiter meyerianus.* Meyer's Goshawk. 51/61. Moluccas, New Guinea, Solomon Is.
104. *Erythrotriorchis buergersi.* Chestnut shouldered Goshawk. 48/58. also melanistic form, New Guinea.
105. *Accipiter madagascariensis.* Madagascar Sparrowhawk. 29/38. Malagasy.
106. *Accipiter ovampensis.* Ovampo Sparrowhawk. 33/38. Africa South of Sahara. (a) normal, (b) melanistic.
l07. *Accipiter gularis.* Japanese Sparrowhawk. 25/30. E Asia. Winters Philippines, Indonesia.
108. *Accipiter virgatus.* Besra Sparrowhawk. 7ss 28/36. SE Asia, Philippines, Sundas.
109. *Accipiter rhodogaster.* Vinous breasted Goshawk. 28/33. Sulawesi.
110. *Accipiter nanus.* Small Sparrowhawk. 23/28. Sulawesi.
111. *Accipiter cirrhocephalus.* Collared Sparrowhawk. 25/33. Australia, Molucca, New Guinea.
112. *Accipiter erythrauchen.* Rufous necked Sparrowhawk. 2ss 28/35. Moluccas.
113. *Accipiter brachyurus.* New Britain Sparrowhawk. 28/33. New Britain.
114. *Accipiter nisus.* European Sparrowhawk. 6ss. 27/37. Eurasia.
115. *Accipiter rufiventris.* Rufous chested Sparrowhawk. 2ss. 33/40. Ethiopia to S Africa.
116. *Accipiter striatus.* Sharp shinned Hawk. 10ss. 25/35. Alaska to Mexico, Hispaniola, Winters to Panama.
117. incl. *A .s. chionogaster* . White breasted Hawk. 25 /35. Mexico to Nicaragua.
118. *A. s. erythronemius.* Rufous thighed Hawk. 25/35. Brazil to Argentina.
119. *A. s. ventralis.* Plain breasted Hawk. 25/35. Venezuela to Bolivia.
120. *Accipiter erythropus.* Red legged Sparrowhawk. 2ss. 23/28. Gambia to Togo, Cameroon, Angola, Uganda.
121. *Accipiter minullus.* little Sparrowhawk. 23/28. Ethiopia to Angola, Cape.
122. *Accipiter castanilius.* Chestnut flanked Goshawk. 2ss. 28/35. Nigeria to Zaire.
123. *Accipiter tachiro.* African Goshawk. 6ss. 35/43. Africa South of Sahara.
124, *Accipiter toussenellii.* Red chested Goshawk. 32/40. Sierra Leone to East Cameroon, Gabon, Zaire.

92
93
94
Juv
95
(a)
(b)
96
97
99
Juv
98
100
101
102
103
104
105
106
(a)
(b)
107
108
109
110
111
112
113
114
115
117
118
119
116
120
121
122
123
124

ACCIPITRIDAE (6)
Goshawks, Sparrowhawks

125. *Accipiter trivirgatus*. Crested Goshawk. 10ss. 40/46. India to Philippines, Borneo.
126. *Accipiter griseiceps*. Sulawesi Goshawk. 33/38. Sulawesi.
127. *Accipiter trinotatus*. Spot tailed Goshawk. 29/31. Sulawesi.
128. *Accipiter luteoschistaceus*. Slaty mantled / Blue & grey Sparrowhawk. 31/38. New Britain.
129. *Accipiter henicogrammus*. Moluccan / Gray's Goshawk. 38/48. Moluccas.
130. *Accipiter fasciatus* . Brown/Australian Goshawk. 12ss. 33/51. Australia, New Guinea, Lesser Sundas.
131. *Accipiter n. albiventris*. Variable Goshawk. Grey & vinous form. Kei Island.
132. (a). *Accipiter novaehollandiae*. White phase. White Goshawk. Australia. (b). *Accipiter novaehollandiae*. Grey phase. Grey Goshawk. Australia.
133. incl. *A. n. rubianae*. Vinous chested form. 33/51. New Georgia.
134. *A. n. leucosomus*. Grey & rufous form. 19ss. New Guinea.
135. *Accipiter griseogularis*. Grey throated Goshawk. 3ss. 43/48. Moluccas.
136. *Accipiter melanochlamys*. Black mantled Goshawk. 33/38. New Guinea.
137. *Accipiter imitator*. Imitator Sparrowhawk. 26/33. Solomon Islands.
(a) normal.(b) pale phase (also melanistic.)
138. *Accipiter albogularis*. Pied Hawk. 5ss. 33/41. Solomon Islands. (a) normal (b) chestnut phase.
139. *Accipiter haplochrous*. White bellied Goshawk. 35/41. New Caledonia.
140. *Accipiter rufitorques*. Fiji Goshawk. 33/41. Fiji.
141. *Accipiter soloensis*. Chinese Goshawk. 25/30. China, Korea. Winters to Indonesia.
142. *Accipiter princeps*. New Britain Goshawk. 38/45. New Britain.
143. *Accipiter poliocephalus*. Grey Headed Goshawk. 33/38. New Guinea.
144. *Accipiter brevipes*. Levant Sparrowhawk. 33/38. Balkans to Russia. Winters Arabia, NE Africa.
145. *Accipiter radius*. Shikra. 6ss. 28/35. S Asia, Arabia, Africa South of Sahara.
146. *Accipiter butleri*. Nicobar Sparrowhawk. 2ss. 28/33. Nicobar Is.
147. *Accipiter francesii*. France 's Sparrowhawk. 4ss. 28/33. Malagasy, Comoros.
148. *Accipiter collaris*. Semi collared Hawk. 28/31. Venezuela to Peru.
149. *Accipiter superciliosus*. Tiny Hawk. 23/30. Nicaragua to Brazil, Argentina.
150. *Accipiter gundlachi*. Gundlach's Hawk. 41/48. Cuba.
151. *Accipiter cooperi*. Cooper's Hawk. 39/48. S Canada to Costa Rica.
152. *Accipiter b.bicolor*. Bi-coloured Hawk. 5ss. 33/40. Mexico.
153. incl. *A. b. chilensis*. Andean form. 33/40. Andes, Chile, Argentina.
154 *A. b. guttifer.* South American form. 38/40. Bolivia, Paraguay, Argentina.
155. *A. b. pileatus*. Brazilian form. 38/40. Brazil.
156. *Accipiter poliogaster*. Grey bellied Hawk. 43/48. Local through S America.
157. *Urotriorchis macrourus*. Long tailed Hawk. 60. Ghana to Zaire. (also melanistic form.)

125
126
127
128
129
130
131
132
(a)
(b)
133
134
135
136
137
(a)
(b)
(a)
138
(b)
139
140
141
142
143
144
145
146
147
148
149
150
151
152
153
154
Juv
155
156
157

ACCIPITRIDAE (7) Hawks

158. *Butastur indicus*. Grey faced Buzzard Eagle. 42. China, Japan. Winters to New Guinea,
159. *Butastur liventer*. Rufous winged Buzzard Eagle. 40. Burma to Sula Island, Java.
160. *Butastur rufipennis*. Grasshopper Buzzard. 38. Senegal to Ethiopia, Tanzania.
161. *Butastur teesa*. White eyed Buzzard Eagle. 40. Iran to India, Burma.
162. *Kaupifalco monogrammicus*. Lizard Buzzard. 2ss. 31. Africa, South of Sahara.
163. *Leucopternis albicollis*. White Hawk. 5ss. 53. Mexico to Peru, Bolivia, Brazil.
164. *Leucopternis kuhli*. White browed Hawk. 38. Amazon basin.
165. *Leucopternis lacernulata*. White necked Hawk. 39. SE Brazil.
166. *Leucopternis melanops*. Black faced Hawk. 40. Venezuela to Ecuador, Brazil.
167. *Leucopternis occidentalis*. Grey backed Hawk. 48. Ecuador.
168. *Leucopternis plumbea*. Plumbeous Hawk. 38. Panama to Peru.
169. *Leucopternis polionota*. Mantled Hawk. 50. Brazil, Paraguay, Argentina.
170. *Leucopternis princeps*. Barred Hawk. 47. Costa Rica to Ecuador.
171. *Leucopternis schistacea*. Slate coloured Hawk. 43. Venezuela, Bolivia, Brazil.
172. *Leucopternis semiplumbea*. Semi-Plumbeous Hawk. 38. Honduras to Ecuador.
173. *Buteogallus aequinoctialis*. Rufous Crab Hawk. 44. Venezuela to Brazil.
174. *Buteogallus anthracinus*. Common Black Hawk. 4ss. 52. SW USA, West Indies, Guyana.
175. *Buteogallus subtilis*. Mangrove Black Hawk. 52. El Salvador to Peru.
176. *Buteogallus urubitinga*. Great Black Hawk. 2ss. 55. Mexico to Argentina.
177. *Harpyhaliaetus coronatus*. Crowned Eagle. 75. Bolivia to Argentina.
178. *Harpyhaliaetus solitarius*. Solitary Eagle. 70. Mexico to Peru.
179. *Buteogallus meridionalis*. Savannah Hawk. 85. Panama to Argentina.
180. *Busarellus nigricollis*. Black collared Hawk. 2ss. 50. Mexico to Argentina.
181. *Geranoaetus melanoleucus*. Black chested Buzzard Eagle. 2ss. 67. Venezuela to Tierra del Fuego.
182. *Parabuteo unicinctus*. Harris' Hawk. 3ss. 51. SW USA to Chile, Argentina.

158
159
160
161
162
163
164
165
166
167
168
169
170
171
172
173
174
175
176
177
178
179
180
181
182

ACCIPITRIDAE (8)
Buzzards

183. *Buteo albicaudatus.* White tailed Hawk. 3ss. 58. S. USA to Argentina.
184. *Buteo albonotatus.* Zone tailed Hawk. 49. SW USA to Brazil & Bolivia.
185. *Buteo auguralis.* Red necked Buzzard. 42. Sierra Leone to Ethiopia, Angola.
186. *Buteo brachypterus.* Madagascar Buzzard. 42. Malagasy.
187. *Buteo brachyurus.* Short tailed Hawk. 2ss. 40. Florida to Brazil, Argentina.
188. *Buteo albigula.* White throated Hawk. 40. Andes ,Venezuela to Argentina.
189. *Buteo buteo.* Common Buzzard. 5ss. 53. Europe. Winters Africa (a) normal, (b) pale.
190. incl. *B. b. vulpinus.* Steppe Buzzard. 53. Russia to E Asia. Winters Africa, S. Asia.
191. *Buteo galapagoensis* . Galapagos Hawk. 51. Galapagos .
192. *Buteo hemilasius.* Upland Buzzard. 64. Central Asia.
193. *Buteo jamaicensis.* Red tailed Hawk. 14ss. 62. N & C America, West Indies.
194. *Buteo lagopus.* Rough legged Buzzard. 4ss. 55. N Eurasia, N America.
195. *Buteo leucorrhous.* White rumped Hawk. 36. Venezuela to Brazil, Argentina.
196. *Buteo lineatus.* Red shouldered Hawk. 5ss. 45. Canada to Mexico.
197. *Buteo magnirostris.* Roadside Hawk. 12ss. 31. S Mexico to N Argentina.
198. incl. *B. m. stauratus.* Large billed Hawk. 31. Bolivia, W Argentina.
199. *Asturina nitida.* Grey lined Hawk. 40. Costa Rica to Argentina, Trinidad.
199a. *Asturina plagiata.* Grey Hawk. 40. S. USA to N. Costa Rica.
200. *Buteo oreophilus.* (African)Mountain Buzzard. 2ss. 42. E & S Africa.
201. *Buteo platypterus.* Broad winged Hawk. 6ss. 40. E. USA.
202. *Buteo poecilochrous.* Variable/Puna Hawk. 53. Andes, Colombia to Chile.
203. *Buteo polyosoma.* Red backed Hawk. 2ss. 50. Colombia to Tierra del Fuego.
204. *Buteo regalis.* Ferruginous Hawk. 63. Canada, Winters USA to Mexico.
205. *Buteo ridgwayi.* Ridgway's Hawk. 36. Hispaniola.
206. *Buteo rufinus.* Long legged Buzzard. 2ss. 61. Eastern. Mediterranean to C Asia.
207. *Buteo augur.* Augur Buzzard. 51. Ethiopia to Mozambique, Angola.
207a. *Buteo archeri.* Archer's Buzzard. 51. Somalia.
208. *Buteo rufofuscus.* Jackal Buzzard. 51. S Africa.
209. *Buteo solitarius.* Hawaiian Hawk. 40. Hawaii. (a) normal,(b) dark phases.
210. *Buteo swainsoni.* Swainson's Hawk. 49. N America. Winters to Argentina. (a)&(b).
211. *Buteo ventralis.* Rufous tailed Hawk. 50. Chile, Argentina. (normal & black phases.)

202 is slightly Larger than 203, otherwise almost indistinguishable. Both have identical range of colour types including Melanistic, which are worn by both sexes. But plain Grey birds are apparently always male.

183
184
185
186
187
188
189
(a)
(b)
190
191
192
193
194
195
196
197
198
199
199
A
200
201
202
203
204
205
206
(a)
(b)
207A
207
208
209
(a)
(b)
210
(a)
(b)
211
(a)
(b)

ACCIPITRIDAE (9)
Eagles

212. *Morphnus guianensis*. Crested Eagle. 85. Honduras to Argentina. (also dark morph.)
213. *Harpia harpyja*. Harpy Eagle. 97. S Mexico to Argentina.
214. *Harpyopsis novaeguineae*. New Guinea Harpy Eagle. 80. New Guinea.
215. *Pithecophaga jefferyi*. Great Philippine / Monkey eating Eagle. 82. Philippines.
216. *Ictinaetus malayensis*. (Indian) Black Eagle. 68. Himalayas to Gr. Sundas & Moluccas.
217. *Aquila audax*. Wedge tailed Eagle. 2ss. 93. Australia, Tasmania, New Guinea.
218. *Aquila chrysaetos*. Golden Eagle. 5ss. 83. Holarctic. Winters Mexico, N. Africa.
219. *Aquila clanga*. Greater Spotted Eagle. 69. Finland to NW India.
220. *Aquila gurneyi*. Gurney's Eagle. 70. Moluccas to W New Guinea & Islands.
221. *Aquila heliaca*. Imperial Eagle. 2ss. 75. Balkans to India & Indo-China.
222. *Aquila adalberti*. Spanish Eagle. 81. Iberian peninsula.
223. *Aquila pomarina*. (European) Lesser Spotted Eagle.2ss.62. Europe, Caucasus.
224. incl. *A. p. hastata*. (Asian) Lesser Spotted Eagle. 62. India. Burma.
225. *Aquila rapax*. African Tawny Eagle. 3ss. 70. Africa.
226. *Aquila nipalensis*. Steppe Eagle. 70. C Asia. Winters India, Burma.
227. *Aquila vindhiana*. Eurasian Tawny Eagle. 70. SE Europe to Asia.
228. *Aquila verreauxii*. Verreaux's Eagle. 75. E Africa, Arabia.
229. *Aquila wahlbergi*.. Wahlberg's Eagle. 57. Africa South of Sahara. (also dark & intermediate morphs)

Adult 219/223 indistinguishable In the field, but juvenile 223 lacks spots.
227 is unlikely to be a valid species.

212
213
214
215
216
217
218
219
Juv
220
221
222
223
224
225
226
227
228
229

ACCIPITRIDAE (10) Hawk Eagles

230. *Hieraaetus fasciatus*. Bonelli's Eagle. 3ss. 67. W. Palearctic, Asia, Sundas.
231. *Hieraaetus spilogaster*. African Hawk Eagle. 66-79. Gambia to Ethiopia & Cape.
232. *Hieraaetus kienerii*. Rufous bellied Eagle. 2ss. 48. India to Philippines & Java.
233. *Hieraaetus morphnoides*. Little Eagle. 2ss. 49. New Guinea & Australia.
234. *Hieraaetus pennatus*. Booted Eagle. 2ss. 55. S Europe, SW Asia, N Africa.
235. *Hieraaetus ayresii*. Ayre's Hawk Eagle. 50. Togo & Ethiopia to South Africa.
236. *Spizaetus occipitalis*. Long crested Eagle. 54. Africa South of Sahara.
237. *Spizaetus africanus*. Cassin's Hawk Eagle. 57. West & Central Africa.
238. *Spizaetus alboniger*. Blyth's Hawk Eagle. 54. Burma, Malaya, Sumatra, Borneo.
239. *Spizaetus bartelsi*. Javan Hawk Eagle. 57. Java.
240. *Spizaetus cirrhatus*. Crested Hawk Eagle. 56/81. India.
241. incl. *S. c. limnaetus*. Changeable Hawk Eagle. 69. S Asia to Philippines. Indonesia. (a) Pale, (b) dark phase.
242. *Spizaetus lanceolatus*. Celebes Hawk Eagle. 58. Sulawesi.
243. *Spizaetus nanus*. Wallace's Hawk Eagle. 2ss.48. Malaya, Borneo, Sumatra.
244. *Spizaetus nipalensis*. Mountain Hawk Eagle. 3ss.72. Sri Lanka, India to China & Japan. Winters to SE Asia.
245. *Spizaetus ornatus*. Ornate Hawk Eagle. 2ss. 60. Mexico to Argentina.
246. *Spizaetus philippensis*. Philippine Hawk Eagle. 65. Philippines.
247. *Spizaetus tyrannus*. Black Hawk Eagle. 66. Mexico to Brazil & Argentina.
248. *Spizastur melanoleucus*. Black & White Hawk Eagle.56. Mexico to Argentina.
249. *Spizaetus coronatus*. Crowned Eagle. 85. Africa South of Sahara.
250. *Oroaetus isidori*. Black & Chestnut Eagle. 68.Andes,Venzla to Argentina.
251. *Polemaetus bellicosus*. Martial Eagle. 87.Africa South of Sahara.

230
231
232
233
(a)
234
(b)
235
236
237
238
239
240
241
(a)
(b)
242
244
245
246
248
243
247
249
250
251

PANDIONIDAE, FALCONIDAE
Osprey, Caracas & Falcons

Family 31. PANDIONIDAE. Osprey.

1. Pandion haliaetus. Osprey. 6ss. 60. Worldwide except Polar regions & S America.

Family 32. FALCONIDAE. Caracaras & Falcons.

1. *Daptrius americanus.* Red throated Caracara. 48. Mexico to Brazil.
2. *Daptrius ater.* Black Caracara. 42. Guyanas, Venezuela, Brazil, Bolivia.
3. *Phalcoboenus albogularis.* White throated Caracara. 50. Chile & Argentina.
4. *Phalcoboenus australis.* Striated Caracara. 65. Tierra del Fuego, Falklands.
5. *Phalcoboenus carunculatus.* Carunculated Caracara. 50. Colombia, Ecuador.
6. *Phalcoboenus megalopterus.* Mountain Caracara. 50. Peru, Bolivia N Chile.
7. *Polyborus plancus.* Southern Caracara. 4ss. 60. USA to south of S America.
8. incl. *P. p. auduboni.* Crested Caracara. 60. N America to Panama.
9. *Polyborus lutosus.* Guadeloupe Caracara. 62. Guadeloupe Islands. (extinct.)
10. *Milvago chimachima.* Yellow headed Caracara. 41. Panama to Argentina.
11. *Milvago chimango.* Chimango Caracara. 2ss. 39. Southern S America.
12. *Herpetotheres cachinnans.* Laughing Falcon. 2ss. 46. Mexico to Argentina.
13. *Micrastur buckleyi.* Buckley's Forest Falcon. 42. Ecuador, Peru.
14. *Micrastur mirandollei.* Slaty backed Forest Falcon. 43. Costa Rica to Amazonia.
15. *Micrastur plumbeus.* Plumbeous Forest Falcon. 32. Colombia, Ecuador.
16. *Micrastur ruficollis.* Barred Forest Falcon. 7ss. 33. Mexico to Argentina.
17. incl. *M. r. interstes.* 33. Costa Rica to Ecuador.
18. *M. r. zonothorax.* 33. Colombia, Venezuela.
19. *M. r. gilvicollis.* Lined Forest Falcon. Guyanas, Amazonia.
20. *Micrastur semitorquatus.* Collared Forest Falcon. 53. Mexico to Argentina. (a) Light phase. (b) Dark phase. (c) Tawny phase. (d) Juvenile.
21. *Spiziapteryx circumcinctus.* Spot winged Falconet. 28/31. N Argentina.
22. *Polihierax insignis.* White rumped Falcon. 3ss. 25/28. Burma to Cambodia.
23. *Polihierax semitorquatus.* Pygmy Falcon. 2ss. 19/24. NE & S Africa.
24. *Microhierax caerulescens.* Collared Falconet. 2ss. 14/19. SE Asia, India.
25. *Microhierax erythrogonys.* Philippine Falconet. 15/18. Philippine Islands.
26. *Microhierax fringillarius.* Black legged Falconet. 14/15. Malaya, Great Sundas.
27. *Microhierax latifrons.* White fronted Falconet. 16. N Borneo.
28. *Microhierax melanoleucos.* Pied Falconet. 15/18. Assam to S China.

1
1
2
6
7
11
FALCONIDAE
9
10
15
16
19
1
2
3
4
5
6
8
7
9
10
11
12
13
14
15
17
JUV
20
(a)
(b)
(c)
16
18
(d)
19
21
22
23
24
25
26
27
28

FALCONIDAE (2)
Falcons

29. *Falco naumanni*. Lesser Kestrel. 28/31. Mediterranean to Asia. Winters Africa, India.
30. *Falco rupicoloides*. Greater Kestrel . 3ss. 33/35. E & S Africa.
31. *Falco alopex*. Fox Kestrel. 36/38. Ghana to Sudan & Ethiopia.
32. *Falco sparverius*. American Kestre1. 16ss. 23/31. N & C America. West Indies.
33. incl. *F. s. sparveroides*. Caribbean form. Cuba, Bahamas.
34. *F. s. cinnamominus*. S. American form. Peru to Chile &Argentina.
35. *Falco tinnunculus*. Common Kestrel. 12ss. 31/35. Europe,N Africa, S Asia.
36. *Falco newtoni*. Madagascar Kestre1. 2ss. 25/28. Malagasy, Aldabra, Comor.
37. *Falco punctatus*. Mauritius Kestre1. 28/33. Mauritius.
38. *Falco araea*. Seychelles Kestrel. 23/25. Seychelles.
39. *Falco ardosiaceus*. Grey Kestrel. 33/35. Africa South of Sahara.
40. *Falco zoniventris*. Barred Kestrel. 31/33. Malagasy.
41. *Falco moluccensis*. Spotted Kestrel. 5ss. 29/31. Moluccas.
42. *Falco cenchrroides*. Australian Kestre1. 2ss. 28/31. Australia. Winters Indonesia.
43. *Falco dickinsoni*. Dickinson's Kestrel. 28/31. Tanzania, Mozambique, Angola.
44. *Falco vespertinus*. Red footed Falcon. 28/31. C Eurasia, Winters Africa.
45. *Falco amurensis*. Amur Falcon. 28/31. E Siberia, China. Winters India, Africa.
46. *Falco chicquera*. Red necked Falcon. 3ss. 28/36. Africa South of Sahara, Iran to India.
47. *Falco colombarius*. Merlin. 8ss. 25/33. Worldwide except Australasia.
48. *Falco berigora*. Brown Falcon. 3ss. 38/46. Australia,New Guinea. (a) light (b) dark phase.
49. *Falco novaeseelandiae*. New Zealand Falcon. 38/46. New Zealand.
50. *Falco longipennis*. Australian Hobby. 28/33. Australia.
51. *Falco subbuteo*. Hobby. 2ss. 31/35. Palearctic. Winters S Africa, Asia, Indonesia.
52. *Falco cuvieri*. African Hobby. 25/31. Africa South of Sahara.
53. *Falco severus*. Oriental Hobby. 2ss. 28/33. Himalayas to New Guinea.
54. *Falco eleoneora*. Eleonora's Falcon. 33/38. Mediterranean. (a) normal. (b) dark phase.
55. *Falco concolor*. Sooty Falcon. 31/33. NE Africa. Winters S. Africa, Malagasy.
56. *Falco rufigularis*. Bat Falcon. 2ss. 23/31. Mexico to Brazil, Argentina.
57. incl. *F. r. albigularis/petrophilus*. White throated Falcon. Mexico.
58. *Falco femoralis*. Aplomado Falcon. 3ss. 33/43. S. USA to Tierra del Fuego.
59. *Falco hypoleucos*. Grey Falcon. 31/41. Australia.
60. *Falco subniger*. Black Falcon. 43/48. Australia.
61. *Falco mexicanus*. Prairie Falcon. 41/46. Canada to Mexico.
62. *Falco biarmicus*. Lanner Falcon. 5ss. 38/46. W Palearctic & Africa, deserts.
63. *Falco jugger*. Laggar Falcon. 38/43. Iran to India & Burma.
64. *Falco cherrug*. Saker Falcon. 3ss. 46/58. C Eurasia. Winters NE Africa, N India.
65. *Falco altaicus*. Altai Falcon. 46/58. C Asia.
66. *Falco deiroleucus*. Orange breasted Falcon. 33/38. Mexico to Brazil, Argentina.
67. *Falco fasciinucha*. Taita Falcon. 28/43. Ethiopia to Mozambique.
68. *Falco rusticolus*. Gyr Falcon. 51/58. N Holarctic Winters N Europe, C Asia, (a) white, (b) grey phase. N. America.
69. *Falco kreyenburgi*. Pallid Falcon. 38/43. Argentina, Chile.
70. *Falco peregrinus*. Peregrine Falcon. 36/48. Nearly world-wide.
71. *Falco pelegrinoides*. Barbary Falcon. 36/48. Form of 70?.North Africa, Middle East.

29
30
31
32
33
34
35
36
37
38
39
40
41
42
43
44
45
46
47
48
(a)
(b)
49
50
51
52
53
54
(a)
(b)
55
56
57
58
59
60
61
62
63
64
65
66
67
68
(a)
(b)
69
70
71
29
31
28
36
38
44
41
40
47
51
50
52
53
54
56
68
70
30
29

MEGAPODIIDAE
Megapodes or Mound builders

1. *Megapodius freycinet.* Dusky Scrubfowl. 2ss. 30-40. E. Wallacea, NW New Guinea.
2. *Megapodius laperouse.* Micronesian Scrubfowl. 2ss. 38. Palau, Mariana Islands.
3. *Megapodius pritchardi.* Polynesian Scrubfowl. 38. Tonga.
4. *Megapodius wallacei.* Moluccan Scrubfowl. 30. Moluccas, W Papuan Islands.
5. *Megapodius nicobariensis.* Nicobar Scrubfowl. 2ss. 40. Nicobar Islands.
6. *Megapodius reinwardt.* Orange footed Scrubfowl / 10ss. 38. Australia, Moluccas, Incubator Bird. Lesser Sundas, New Guinea.
7. *Megapodius eremita.* Bismarck Scrubfowl. 2ss. 30-40. Bismarck Archipelago.
8. *Megapodius affinis.* New Guinea Scrubfowl. 38. N New Guinea.
9. *Megapodius cumingi.* Tabon Scrubfowl. 4ss. 40. Philippines, Borneo, Sulawesi.
10. *Megapodius bernsteinii.* Sula Scrubfowl. 40. Banggai, Sula Island.
11. *Megapodius layardi.* New Hebrides Scrubfowl. 40. Vanuatu.
12. *Leipoa ocellata.* Malleefowl. 60. Southern Australia.
13. *Alectura lathami.* Brush Turkey. 2ss. 70. Eastern Australia.
14. *Talegalla cuvieri.* Red billed Brush Turkey. 56. New Guinea.
15. *Talegalla fuscirostris.* Black billed Brush Turkey. 2ss. 53. New Guinea.
16. *Talegalla jobiensis.* Brown collared Brush Turkey. 2ss. 58. New Guinea.
17. *Aepypodius arfakianus.* Wattled Brush Turkey. 2ss. 42, New Guinea & Islands.
18. *Aepypodius bruijni.* Bruijn's Brush Turkey. 43. New Guinea.
19. *Macrocephalon maleo.* Maleo Fowl. 50. Sulawesi.

1
5
6
7
8
2
3
4
9
12
11
13
10
14
15
16
17
18
19

CRACIDAE (1)
Chacalacas, Guans

1. *Ortalis canicollis*. Chaco Chachalaca. 2ss. 55. Bolivia, Brazil, Paraguay.
2. *Ortalis cinereiceps*. Grey headed Chachalaca. 50. Honduras to Colombia.
3. *Ortalis erythroptera*. Rufous headed Chachalaca. 55. Ecuador, Peru.
4. *Ortalis garrula*. Chestnut winged Chachalaca. 3ss. 52. Colombia.
5. *Ortalis leucogastra*. White bellied Chachalaca. 50. Mexico to Costa Rica.
6. *Ortalis motmot*. Little Chachalaca. 7ss. 45. Guyanas, Venezuela, Brazil.
7. *Ortalis guttata*. Speckled Chachalaca. 52. Colombia, Bolivia, Brazil.
8. *Ortalis superciliaris*. Buff browed Chachalaca. 52. N Brazil.
9. *Ortalis ruficauda*. Rufous vented Chachalaca. 4ss. 52. Colombia, Venezuela, Tobago.
10. *Ortalis poliocephala*. West Mexican Chachalaca. 3ss. 60. W Mexico.
11. *Ortalis wagleri*. Rufous bellied Chachalaca. 60. W Mexico.
12. *Ortalis vetula*. Plain Chachalaca. 4ss. 55. Texas to Belize & Honduras.
13. *Penelope albipennis*. White winged Guan. 60. Peru.
14. *Penelope barbata*. Bearded Guan. 60. Ecuador.
15. *Penelope argyrotis*. Band tailed Guan 5ss. 60. Colombia, Venezuela.
16. *Penelope dabbeni*. Red faced Guan. 77. Bolivia, NW Argentina.
17. *Penelope jacquacu*. Spix's Guan. 4ss. 87. Guyanas, Venezuela to Bolivia, Brazil.
18. *Penelope jacucaca*. White browed Guan. 70. NE Brazil.
19. *Penelope marail*. Marail Guan. 2ss. 82. Guyanas, Venezuela, Brazil.
20. *Penelope montagnii*. Andean Guan. 5ss. 60. Andes, Venezuela to Argentina.
21. *Penelope obscura*. Dusky legged Guan. 3ss. 87. Brazil, Uruguay, Argentina.
22. *Penelope ochrogaster*. Chestnut bellied Guan. 70. EC Brazil.
23. *Penelope ortoni*. Baudo Guan. 65. Colombia, Ecuador.
24. *Penelope perspicax*. Cauca Guan. 87. Colombia.
25. *Penelope pileata*. White crested Guan. 70. Brazil.
26. *Penelope purpurascens*. Crested Guan. 3ss. 90. Mexico to Ecuador, Venezuela.
27. *Penelope superciliaris*. Rusty margined Guan. 3ss. 67. Brazil, Bolivia, Paraguay, Argentina.

1
2
6
3
4
5
7
8
10
9
11
12
13
14
15
16
17
18
19
20
21
24
22
23
25
26
27

CRACIDAE (2)
Piping Guans & Curassows

28. *Aburria aburri*. Wattled Guan. 70. Venezuela to Peru.
29. *Pipile jacutinga*. Black fronted Piping Guan. 60. Brazil, Paraguay, Argentina.
30. *Pipile pipile*. Trinidad Piping Guan. 60. Trinidad.
31. *Pipile cumanensis*. Blue throated Piping Guan. 2ss. 60. Guyanas, Venezuela to Bolivia, Brazil.
32. *Pipile cujubi*. Red throated Piping Guan. 2ss. 60. Brazil, Bolivia.
33. *Chamaepetes goudotii*. Sickle winged Guan. 5ss. 60. Colombia to Peru, Bolivia.
34. *Chamaepetes unicolor*. Black Guan. 70. Costa Rica, Panama.
35. *Penelopina nigra*. Highland Guan. 56. Mexico to Nicaragua.
36. *Oreophasis derbianus*. Horned Guan. 80. S. Mexico, Guatemala.
37. *Nothocrax urumutum*. Nocturnal Curassow. 65. Venezuela to Peru, Brazil.
38. *Crax alberti*. Blue knobbed Curassow. 90. Colombia.
39. *Crax alector*. Black Curassow. 88. Guyanas, Venezuela, Colombia to Brazil.
40. *Crax blumenbachii*. Red billed Curassow. 80. Brazil.
41. *Crax daubentoni*. Yellow knobbed Curassow. 90. Venezuela, Colombia.
42. *Crax fasciolata*. Bare faced Curassow. 3ss. 83. Brazil, Bolivia, Paraguay, Argentina.
43. *Crax globulosa*. Wattled Curassow. 88. Colombia, Peru, Bolivia, Brazil.
44. *Mitu tuberosa*. Razor billed Curassow. 89. Colombia to Bolivia, Brazil.

44a. *Mitu mitu*. Alagoas Curassow. 89. E. Brazil. (Extinct in wild?)

45. *Pauxi pauxi*. Helmeted Curassow. 2ss. 90. Venezuela, Colombia. (a) normal, (b) rufous, female only
46. *Crax rubra*. Great Curassow. 2ss. 95. Mexico to Colombia.
47. *Mitu salvini*. Salvin' s Curassow. 87. Colombia, Peru.
48. *Mitu tomentosa*. Crestless Curassow. 82. Guyana, Venezuela, Colombia, Brazil.
49. *Pauxi unicornis*. Horned Curassow. 90. Bolivia, Peru.

28
29
30
32
31
33
34
35
36
37
38
39
40
41
42
43
44
44A
45 (b)
45 (a)
46
47
48
49

TETRAONIDAE
Grouse

1. *Tetrao parvirostris.* Black billed Capercaillie. 5ss. 50/75. Siberia, Mongolia.
2. *Tetrao urogallus.* Capercaillie. 10ss. 60/85. Scotland, Central Europe to N C Asia.
3. *Tetrao mlokosiewiczi.* Caucasian Black Grouse. 40/48. Caucasus Mountains.
4. *Tetrao/Lyrurus tetrix.* Black Grouse. 7ss. 40/52. UK, N Eurasia.
5. *Lagopus lagopus.* Willow Ptarmigan. 11ss. 38. N America, N Palearctic.
6. incl. *L.L. scoticus.* Red Grouse. 35. Northern Britain.
7. *Lagopus leucurus.* White tailed Ptarmigan. 5ss. 30. Alaska to New Mexico.
8. *Lagopus mutus.* (Rock) Ptarmigan. 27ss. 35. Northern Holarctic.
9. *Dendragapus canadensis.* Spruce Grouse. 5ss. 37/43. Canada, N USA.
10. *Dendragapus falcipennis.* Siberian / Sharp winged Grouse. NE Asia.
11. *Dendragapus obscurus.* Blue Grouse.. 7ss. 48. Northern N America. incl. ss. Dusky & Sooty Grouse.
12. *Bonasa/Tetrastes bonasia.* Hazel Grouse. 35. N Europe to Siberia, Japan.
13. *Bonasa sewerzowi.* Chinese (Black breasted) Grouse. 2ss. 35. WC China.
14. *Bonasa umbellus.* Ruffed Grouse. 14ss. 40/47. North America. (a)Grey, (b)Rufous Phase.
15. *Tympanuchus cupido.* Greater Prairie Chicken. 2ss. 45. Local.Canada to Texas.
16. *Tympanuchus pallidicinctus.* Lesser Prairie Chicken. 40. SC USA.
17. *Tympanuchus phasianellus.* Sharp tailed Grouse. 5ss. 43. Alaska to New Mexico.
18. *Centrocercus urophasianus.* Sage Grouse. 55/65, S. Canada to SW USA.

1
2
3
4
5
6
7
8
W
W
W
9
10
11
12
13
14
(a)
(b)
15
16
17
18

PHASIANIDAE (1)
Wood Partridges, Quails

1. *Dendrortyx barbatus*. Bearded Wood Partridge/Tree Quail. 20. Mexico.
2. *Dendrortyx leucophrys*. Buffy crowned Wood Partridge. 3ss. 23. Mexico to Costa Rica.
3. *Dendrortyx macroura*. Long tailed Wood Partridge. 5ss. 28. Mexico.
4. *Oreortyx pictus*. Mountain Quail. 4ss. 25. W USA to Baja California.
5. *Callipepla squamata*. Scaled Quail. 4ss. 20. SW USA, Mexico.
6. *Callipepla californica*. Californian Quail. 6ss. 21. British Columbia to Mexico.
7. *Callipepla douglasii*. Elegant Quail. 5ss. 21. W Mexico.
8. *Callipepla gambelii*. Gambel's Quail. 5ss. 23. S USA deserts.
9. *Philortyx fasciatus*. Banded Quail. 18. SE Mexico.
10. *Colinus cristatus*. Crested Bobwhite. 14ss. 22. Guatemala to Brazil.
11. incl. *C. c. leucopogon*. Spot bellied Bobwhite. 22.Pacific coast C America.
12. *Colinus nigrogularis*. Black throated Bobwhite. 4ss. 20. Mexico to Nicaragua.
13. *Colinus virginianus*. Northern Bobwhite. 18ss. 21. Canada to Guatemala.
14. incl. *C. v. pectoralis*. Rufous bellied Bobwhite. 21. Mexico.
15. *C. v. atriceps*. Black headed Bobwhite. 21. Mexico.
16. *C. v. ridgwayi*. Masked Bobwhite. 21. Mexico.
17. *Odontophorus atrifrons*. Black fronted Wood Quail. 3ss. 30. Colombia.
18. *Odontophorus balliviani*. Stripe faced Wood Quail. 27. Peru, Bolivia.
19. *Odontophorus capueira*. Spot winged Wood Quail. 26. Brazil, Paraguay.
20. *Odontophorus columbianus*. Venezuelan Wood Quail. 24. Venezuela.
21. *Odontophorus dialeucos*. Tacarcuna Wood Quail. 23. Panama, Colombia.
22. *Odontophorus erythrops*. Rufous fronted Wood Quail. 5ss. 26. Colombia, Ecuador.
23. *Odontophorus melanotis*. Black eared Wood Quail. 26. Honduras to Panama.
24. *Odontophorus gujanensis*. Marbled Wood Quail. 9ss. 25. Costa Rica to Bolivia, Brazil.
25. *Odontophorus guttatus*. Spotted Wood Quail. 23. Mexid co to Panama.
26. *Odontophorus hyperythrus*. Chestnut Wood Quail. 26. Colombia.
27. *Odontophorus leucolaemus*. Black breasted Wood Quail. 20. Costa Rica, Panama.
28. *Odontophorus melanonotus*. Dark backed Wood Quail. 26. Ecuador.
29. *Odontophorus speciosus*. Rufous breasted Wood Quail. 3ss. 27. Ecuador, Peru.
30. *Odontophorus stellatus*. Starred Wood Quail. 25. Ecuador, Peru.
31. *Odontophorus strophium*. Gorgeted Wood Quail. 25. Colombia.
32. *Dactylortyx thoracicus*. Singing Quail. 11ss. 20. Mexico to Honduras.
33. *Cyrtonyx montezumae*. Montezuma/Harlequin Quail. 3ss. 23. S. USA, Mexico.
34. incl. *C. m. sallei*. Salle's Quail. 20. Mexico.
35. *Cyrtonyx ocellatus*. Ocellated Quail. 2ss. 18. Mexico to Nicaragua.
36. *Rhynchortyx cinctus*. Tawny faced Quail. 4ss. 19. Honduras to Ecuador.

The above (1-36) are often treated as a separate Family "ODONTOPHORIDAE" distinct from "PHASIANIDAE".

1
2
3
4
5
6
7
8
9
10
11
12
13
14
15
16
17
18
19
20
21
22
23
24
25
26
27
28
29
30
31
32
33
34
35
36

PHASIANIDAE (2)
Partridges, Francolins

37. *Lerwa lerwa*. Snow Partridge. 35/38. Afghanistan & Himalayas.
38. *Ammoperdix griseogularis*. See-see Partridge. 2ss. 26. Turkey & Middle East to Pakistan.
39. *Ammoperdix heyi*. Sand Partridge. 4ss. 24. Egypt, Arabia, Palestine.
40. *Tetraogallus altaicus*. Altai Snowcock. 2ss. 58. Central Asia.
41. *Tetraogallus caspius*. Caspian Snowcock. 2ss. 58/61. Asia minor to Iran.
42. *Tetraogallus caucasicus*. Caucasian Snowcock. 56. Caucasus.
43. *Tetraogallus himalayensis*. Himalayan Snowcock. 5ss. 54/72. Himalayas.
44. *Tetraogallus tibetanus*. Tibetan Snowcock. 6ss. 51. Tibet, China.
45. Tetraophasis obscurus. Verreaux's Partridge. 46. W China.
46. *Tetraophasis szechenyii*. Buff throated Partridge. 43. Tibet, SW China.
47. *Alectoris barbara*. Barbary Partridge. 5ss. 32. N Africa, Canary Is.
48. *Alectoris chukar*. Chukar Partridge. 6ss. 38. Balkans to Himalayas, China.
49. *Alectoris graeca*. Rock Partridge. 16ss. 35. Alps, SE Europe to Himalayas.
50. *Alectoris philbyi* . Philby's Partridge. 32. SW Arabia.
51. *Alectoris magna*. Rusty necklaced Partridge. 38. NE China.
52. *Alectoris melanocephala*. Arabian Partridge. 2ss. 36. Arabia.
53. *Alectoris rufa*. Red legged Partridge. 5ss. 34. France, SW Europe. Intr.UK.
54. *Anurophasis monorthonyx*. Snow Mountain Quail. 26. New Guinea.
55. *Francolinus adspersus*. Red billed Francolin. 38. SC Africa.
56. *Francolinus afer*. Red necked/Bare throated Greywing/Francolin. 18ss. 35/41. E, C, & S Africa.
57. *Francolinus africanus*. Grey Winged Francolin. 9ss. 33. Somalia to RSA.
58. *Francolinus ahantensis*. Ahanta Francolin. 2ss. 33. Senegambia to Nigeria.
59. *Francolinus albogularis*. White throated Francolin. 4ss. 23. W & WC Africa.
60. *Francolinus bicalcaratus*. Double spurred Francolin. 5ss. 33. W Africa.
61. *Francolinus camerunensis*. Cameroon Francolin. 33. Cameroon mountains.
62. *Francolinus capensis*. Cape Francolin. 43. Cape province, RSA.
63. *Francolinus castaneicollis*. Chestnut naped Francolin. 6ss. 40. Ethiopia.
64. *Francolinus clappertoni*. Clapperton's Francolin. 7ss. 40. Africa South of Sahara
65. *Francolinus coqui*. Coqui Francolin. 11ss 28. Most of Africa South of Sahara.
66. *Francolinus erckelii*. Erckel's Francolin. 2ss. 40. Sudan, Ethiopia.
67. *Francolinus finschi*. Finsch's Francolin. 34. Angola, Gabon, Zaire.
68. *Francolinus francolinus*. Black Francolin/Partridge. 7ss. 32. Cyprus, Near & M. East to India.

37
38
39
40
41
42
43
44
45
46
47
48
49
50
51
52
53
54
55
56
57
58
59
60
61
62
63
64
65
66
67
68

PHASIANIDAE (3) Francolins, Partridges

69. *Francolinus griseostriatus*. Grey striped Francolin. 36. Angola.
70. *Francolinus gularis*. Swamp Partridge/Kyah. 37. E Bengal to Assam.
71. *Francolinus hartlaubi*. Hartlaub's Francolin. 3ss. 28. Angola, Namibia.
72. *Francolinus harwoodi*. Harwood's Francolin. 36. Ethiopia.
73. *Francolinus hildebrandti*. Hildebrandt's Francolin. 6ss. 40. Kenya to Malawi.
74. *Francolinus icterorhynchus*. Heuglin's/Yellow billed Francolin. 3ss.31. Uganda.
75. *Francolinus jacksoni*. Jackson's Francolin. 3ss. 39. Kenya.W Uganda.
76. *Francolinus lathami*. Forest Francolin. 2ss. 30. Sierra Leone to Zaire, Uganda.
77. *Francolinus leucoscepus*. Yellow necked Spurfowl. Ethiopia to Tanzania.
78. *Francolinus levaillantii*. Red winged Francolin. 5ss. 38. E, C, S Africa.
79. *Francolinus levaillantoides*. Orange River Francolin. 9ss. 36. S Africa.
80. *Francolinus nahani*. Nahan's Francolin. 30. Zaire, Uganda.
81. *Francolinus natalensis*. Natal Francolin. 2ss. 38. Zambia, Mozambique to Cape.
82. *Francolinus nobilis*. Handsome Francolin. 2ss. 40. Uganda, Zaire, Rwanda.
83. *Francolinus ochropectus*. Pale bellied Francolin. 30. Somalia.
84. *Francolinus pictus*. Painted Francolin. 3ss. 31. India, Sri Lanka.
85. *Francolinus pintadeanus*. Chinese Francolin. 2ss. 33. China, SE Asia & Islands.
86. *Francolinus pondicerianus*. Grey Francolin. 4ss. 33. Iran to India, Sri Lanka.
87. *Francolinus psilolaemus*. Moorland Francolin. 3ss. 31. Ethiopia, E Africa.
88. *Francolinus elgonensis*. Mt Elgon Francolin. 31. Kenya, Uganda. (ss of 93?)
89. *Francolinus rufopictus*. Grey breasted Francolin. 40. S E Lake Victoria.
90. *Francolinus schlegelii*. Schlegel's Francolin. 25. Bongo River. W Africa.
91. *Francolinus rovuma*. Kirk's Francolin. 36. Tanzania to Mozambique.
92. *Francolinus sephaena*. Crested Francolin. 5ss. 36. E Africa, Sudan to RSA.
93. *Francolinus shelleyi*. Shelley's Francolin. 5ss. 33. Kenya to Transvaal.
94. *Francolinus squamatus*. Scaly Francolin. 8ss. 33. Central Africa.
95. *Francolinus streptophorus*. Ring necked Francolin. 28. Cameroon to E Africa.
96. *Francolinus swainsoni*. Swainson's Francolin. 4ss. 41. SE & SW Africa.
97. *Francolinus swierstrai*. Swierstra's Francolin. 33. Angola.
98. *Perdix dauuricae*. Daurian Partridge. 5ss. 30. Turkestan to Mongolia.
99. *Perdix hodgsoniae*. Tibetan Partridge. 4ss. 31. Tibet.
100. *Perdix Perdix*. Grey / Common Partridge. 10ss. 30. W Eurasia.
101. *Rhizothera longirostris*. Long billed Partridge. 2ss. 35. Thailand, Malaya to Sumatra, Borneo.
102. *Margaroperdix madagascariensis*. Madagascar Partridge. 30. Malagasy.
103. *Melanoperdix nigra*. Black Wood Partridge. 2ss. 24. Malaya, Borneo, Sumatra.

69
70
71
72
73
74
75
76
77
78
79
80
81
82
83
84
85
86
87
88
89
90
91
92
93
94
95
96
97
98
99
100
101
102
103

PHASIANIDAE (4)
Partridges, Quail

104. *Coturnix / excalfactoria chinensis*. Asian Blue (breasted) Quail. 9ss. 14. Asia & Australia.
105. *Coturnix adansonii*. African Blue Quail. 14. Africa South of Sahara.
106. *Coturnix coromandelica*. Rain Quail. 18. India, Sri Lanka. Burma.
107. *Coturnix coturnix*. Common Quail. 6ss. 19 Eurasia, Africa.
108. *Coturnix delegorguei*. Harlequin Quail. 3ss. 18. Africa South of Sahara, Arabia.
109. *Coturnix japonica*. Japanese Quail. 18. E Asia. Winters SE Asia.
110. *Coturnix novaezelandiae*. New Zealand Quail. 15. New Zealand (extinct?)
111. *Coturnix pectoralis*. Stubble Quail. 18/19. Australia, Tasmania.
112. *Coturnix australis*. Brown Quail. 12ss. 18. Australia, New Guinea, Sundas.
113. *Coturnix ypsilophora*. Swamp/Tasmanian Brown Quail. 20. Tasmania, SE Australia.
114. *Perdicula asiatica*. Jungle Bush Quail. 17. India, Sri Lanka.
115. *Perdicula argoondah*. Rock Bush Quail. 17. India.
116. *Perdicula erythrorhyncha*. Painted Bush Quail. 2ss. 18. India.
117. *Perdicula manipurensis*. Manipur Bush Quail. 2ss. 20. Assam.
118. *Arborophila ardens*. Hainan Partridge. 25. Hainan.
119. *Arborophila atrogularis*. White cheeked Partridge. 28. Assam, Burma.
120. *Arborophila brunneopectus*. Bar backed Brown breasted Partridge. 3ss. 28. Yunnan, Assam. Thailand, Vietnam.
121. *Arborophila cambodiana*. Chestnut headed Partridge. 2ss. 29. Cambodia, Thailand.
122. *Arborophila charltonii*. Chestnut necklaced Partridge. 4ss. 30. SE Asia.
123. *Arborophila chloropus*. Green legged Partridge. 3ss. 30. Burma,Vietnam.
124. *Arborophila crudigularis*. Formosan Partridge. 28. Taiwan.
125. *Arborophila davidi*. Orange necked Partridge. 28. Cochin-China. 1 specimen.
126. *Arborophila gingica*. White necklaced/Collared Partridge.30. SE China.
127. *Arborophila hyperythra*. Red breasted Tree Partridge. 25. Borneo.
128. *Arborophila javanica*. Chestnut bellied Partridge. 3ss. 28. Java.
129. *Arborophila mandellii*. Chestnut breasted Partridge. 28. Sikkim, Bhutan.
130. *Arborophila merlini*. Annamese Partridge. 2ss. 30. Annam.
131. *Arborophila orientalis*. Grey breasted Partridge. 4ss. 28. Malaya, Sumatra.
132. *Arborophila rubrirostris*. Red billed Partridge. 28. Sumatra.
133. *Arborophila rufipectus*. Boulton's/Sichuan Partridge. 29. Szechwan, China.
134. *Arborophila rufogularis*. Rufous throated Partridge. 6ss. 27. India,China.
135. *Arborophila torqueola*. Hill Partridge. 4ss. 28. India, Tibet, China, Burma.
136. *Caloperdix oculea*. Ferruginous Partridge. 3ss. 26. Thailand to Indonesia.
137. *Haematortyx sanguiniceps*. Crimson headed Partridge. 25. North Borneo.
138. *Rollulus roulroul*. Crested Partridge. 25. Thailand to Borneo & Sumatra.
139. *Ptilopachus petrosus*. Stone Partridge. 5ss. 26. E & W Africa.
140. *Bambusicola fytchii*. Mountain Bamboo Partridge. 2ss. 35. China, Assam, Burma.
141. *Bambusicola thoracica*. Chinese Bamboo Partridge. 2ss. 31. Taiwan, China.
142. *Galloperdix bicalarata*. Ceylon Spurfowl. 34. Sri Lanka.
143. *Galloperdix lunulata*. Painted Spurfowl. 32. India.
144. *Galloperdix spadicea*. Red Spurfowl. 3ss. 36. India.
145. *Ophrysia superciliosa*. Himalayan Quail. 25. NW Himalayas.(extinct.)

145a. *Xenoperdix udzungwensis*. Udzungwa Forest Partridge. 29. Ndundula (Tanzania).

104
105
106
107
108
109
110
111
112
113
114
115
116
117
118
119
120
121
122
123
124
125
126
127
128
129
130
131
132
133
134
135
136
137
138
139
140
141
145A
142
143
144
145

PHASINIDAE (5) Pheasants

146. *Ithaginis cruentus.* Blood Pheasant. 14ss. 40/45. Nepal, Tibet, China, Burma.
147. *Tragopan blythii.* Blyth's Tragopan. 2ss. 59/68. Tibet to Burma.
148. *Tragopan caboti.* Cabot's Tragopan. 50/60. SE China.
149. *Tragopan melanocephalus.* Western Tragopan. 60/71. NW India, Pakistan, Tibet.
150. *Tragopan satyra.* Satyr Tragopan. 59/68. Nepal, Tibet.
151. *Tragopan temminckii.* Temminck's Tragopan. 55/64. Tibet, Assam, Yunnan, Tonkin.
152. *Lophophorus impejanus.* Himalayan Monal. 63/70. Afghanistan to Tibet.
153. *Lophophorus lhuysii.* Chinese Monal. 76/80. Kansu, Sichuan, Tsinghai.
154. *Lophophorus sclateri.* Sclater's Monal. 2ss. 63/68. Bhutan, Tibet, Yunnan, Burma.
155. *Crossoptilon auritum.* Blue eared Pheasant. 96. China.
156. *Crossoptilon Crossoptilon.* White eared Pheasant. 5ss. 92. Tibet, Assam, Sichuan, Yunnan.
157. *Crossoptilon mantchuricum.* Brown eared Pheasant. 100. NE China.
158. *Crossoptilon harmani.* Tibetan eared Pheasant. 85. Tibet & adj. India .

146
147
148
149
150
151
152
153
154
155
156
157
158

PHASIANIDAE (6)
Pheasants

159. *Lophura bulweri.* Bulwer's Pheasant. 55/77. Borneo.
160. *Lophura diardi.* Siamese Fireback. 60/80. Thailand, Indo-China.
161. *Lophura edwardsi.* Edward's Pheasant. 60. Annam.
162. *Lophura erythrophthalma.* Crestless Fireback. 2ss. 50. Malaya, Sumatra, Borneo.
163. *Lophura ignita.* Crested Fireback. 4ss. 55/68. Malaya, Sumatra, Borneo.
164. incl. *L. i. rufa.* Malaysian Fireback. 55/70. Thailand to Sumatra.
165. *Lophura imperialis.* Imperial Pheasant. 60/75. C Vietnam, Laos.
166. *Lophura inornata.* Salvadori's Pheasant. 2ss. 50. Sumatra.
167. *Lophura hoogerswerfi.* Sumatran Pheasant. 50. N W Sumatra.
168. *Lophura leucomanos.* Kalij Pheasant. 9ss. 60/68. Himalayas.
169. incl. *L. l. hamiltoni.* White crested Kalij. 60/68. Western Himalayas.
170. *Lophura nycthemera.* Silver Pheasant. 14ss. 70/125. Yunnan, Tonkin, Hainan China, Burma Vietnam.
171. *Lophura swinhoei.* Swinhoe's Pheasant. 50/79. Taiwan.
172. *Lophura haitiensis.* Vo Quy's Pheasant. 60. N C Vietnam.

Female 167 un-described. Probably similar to 166.

159
160
161
162
163
164
165
166
167
♂
♀
169
168
170
172
171

PHASIANIDAE (7) Pheasants

173. *Gallus gallus*. Red Junglefowl. 5ss. 44/70. Java to Kashmir. Philippines. introduced elsewhere. Ancestor of domestic fowl.
174. *Gallus lafayetii*. Ceylon Junglefowl. 35/70. Sri Lanka.
175. *Gallus sonnerata*. Grey Junglefowl. 38/75. S & W India.
176. *Gallus varius*. Green Junglefowl. 40/70. Java, Bali, Lesser Sundas.
177. *Pucrasia macrolopha*. Koklass Pheasant. 10ss. 52/60. Afghanistan to China.
178. *Catreus wallichii*. Cheer Pheasant. 90/100. Pakistan, India, Nepal.
179. *Phasianus colchicus*. Common Pheasant. 31ss. 55/85. Originally Asia, introduced most of world.
180. Incl. *P. c. torquatus*. Chinese ring necked form.
181. *P. c. tenebrosus*. Melanistic mutant form.
182. *Phasianus versicolor*. Green / Japanese Pheasant. 3ss. 55/85. Japan.
183. *Syrmaticus ellioti*. Elliot's Pheasant. 50/80. SE China.
184. *Syrmaticus humiae*. Mrs Hume's / Bar tailed Pheasant.2ss.60/90. Assam China, Burma ,Thailand.
185. *Syrmaticus mikado*. Mikado Pheasant. 52/105. Taiwan.
186. *Syrmaticus reevesii*. Reeves' Pheasant. 75/200. N & C China.
187. *Syrmaticus soemmerringii*. Copper Pheasant. 5ss. 52/110. Japan.

173
174
175
176
177
178
179
180
181
182
183
184
185
186
187

PHASIANIDAE
Pheasants & Peafowl

188. *Chrysolophus amherstiae*. Lady Amherst's Pheasant. 67/150. Tibet, China, Burma.
189. *Chrysolophus pictus*. Golden Pheasant. 65/105. C & S China.
190. *Polyplectron bicalcaratum*. Grey Peacock Pheasant. 5ss. 48/65. Sikkim, Bhutan, Assam, Burma, Thailand, Tonkin, Laos, Hainan.
191. *Polyplectron inopinatum*. Rothschild's/Mountain Peacock Pheasant.46/65. Malay Peninsula.
192. *Polyplectron emphanum*. Palawan Peacock Pheasant. 40/50. Palawan Island.
193. *Polyplectron germaini*. Germain's Peacock Pheasant. 48/55. S Vietnam.
194. *Polyplectron chalcurum*. Bronze tailed Peacock Pheasant. 2ss.45/56. Sumatra.
195. *Polyplectron malacense*. Malay Peacock Pheasant. 40/50. Burma. Thailand. Malaysia.
196. *Polyplectron schleiermacheri*. Bornean Peacock Pheasant. 40/50. Borneo.
197. *Rheinardia ocellata*. Crested Argus. 2ss. 75/220. Vietnam.
198. incl. *R. o. nigrescens*. Malay Crested Argus. 75/220. C Malaysia.
199. *Argusianus argus*. Great Argus. 2ss. 75/180. Thailand, Malaya, Sumatra.
200. *Pavo cristatus*. Indian Peafowl. 95/205. India & Sri Lanka.
201. *Pavo muticus*. Green Peafowl. 3ss. 105/240. Assam, Burma,Thailand, Malaysia, Java.
202. *Afropavo congensis*. Congo Peafowl. 61/67. Zaire.

188
189
190
191
192
193
194
195
196
197
198
199
200
201
202

NUMIDAE, MELEAGRIDIDAE, OPISTHOCOMIDAE
Guinea Fowl, Turkeys, Hoatzin

Family 57. NUMIDAE, Guinea Fowl

1. *Phasidus/Agelastes niger*. Black Guineafowl. 42. Cameroon & Gabon to Zaire.
2. *Agelastes meliagrides*. White breasted Guineafowl. 42. West Africa.
3. *Numida meleagris*. Helmeted Guineafowl. 2lss. 55. Most of Africa, SW Arabia.
4. incl. *N. m. reichenowi*. Reichenow's Guineafowl. 57. Kenya, Tanzania.
5. *Guttera edouardi*. Crested Guineafowl. 9ss. 47. Africa South of Sahara.
6. *Guttera plumifera*. Plumed Guineafowl. 2ss. 44. Cameroon, Gabon to Angola, Zaire.
7. *Guttera pucherani*. Kenya crested Guineafowl. 47. Coastal Kenya.
8. *Acryllium vulturinum*. Vulturine Guineafowl. 70. East Africa.

Family 38. MELEAGRIDIDAE, Turkeys.

1. *Meleagris gallopavo*. Wild Turkey. 7ss. 90/120. C S USA, Mexico.
2. *Agriocharis ocellata*. Ocellated Turkey. 88/105. Yucatan, Guatemala, Belize.

Family 39. OPISTHOCOMIDAE, Hoatzin.

1. *Opisthocomus hoazin*. Hoatzin. 57. Amazonia.

NUMIDAE
2
1
3
4
5
6
7
8
MELIAGRIDIDAE
1
2
OPISTHOCOMIDAE
1

MESITORNITHIDAE, TURNICIDAE, PEDIONOMIDAE
Mesites, Button Quails, Plains Wanderer

1. *Mesitornis unicolor*. Brown Mesite. 30. E Malagasy.
2. *Mesitornis variegata*. White breasted Mesite. 31. E Malagasy.
3. *Monias benschi*. Subdesert Mesite, Bensch's Monia. 32. SW Malagasy.

Family 41. TURNICIDAE. Button Quails.

1. *Turnix castanota*. Chestnut backed Buttonquail. 2ss. 18. Coastal N Australia.
2. *Turnix everetti*. Sumba Buttonquail. 15. Sumba.(Lesser Sundas.) 3 specimens.
3. *Turnix nana*. Black rumped Buttonquail. 15. Africa S of Sahara.
4. *Turnix hottentotta*. Hottentot Buttonquail. 15. Cape Province RSA.
5. *Turnix maculosa*. Red backed Buttonquail. 15. Philippines. Indonesia to Australia.
6. *Turnix melanogaster*. Black breasted Buttonquail. 18. E Australia.
7. *Turnix nigricollis*. Madagascar Buttonquail. 15. Malagasy.
8. *Turnix ocellata*. Spotted Buttonquail. 19. Philippines.
9. *Turnix powelli*. Sunda Buttonquail. 15. Lesser Sunda Is.
10. *Turnix pyrrhothorax*. Red chested Buttonquail. 14. E Australia.
11. *Turnix suscitator*. Barred Buttonquail/Bustard Quail. 17ss.l6. Asia, Indonesia.
12. *Turnix sylvatica*. Small Buttonquail/Andalusian Hemipode. 10ss. l5. Mediterranean, Africa, S Asia to Indonesia.
13. *Turnix tanki*. Yellow legged Buttonquail. 2ss. 16. S & SE Asia.
14. *Turnix olivii*. Buff breasted Buttonquail. 19.N Queensland.
15. *Turnix varia*. Painted Buttonquai1. 3ss. 20/16. Australia. New Caledonia.
16. *Turnix velox*. Little Buttonquail. 13/11. Australia.
17. *Turnix worcesteri*. Worcester's/Luzon Buttonquail. l5/14. Philippines.
18. *Ortyxelos meiffrenii*. Quail Plover/Lark Buttonquail. 12. Sub-saharan Africa.

Family 42. PEDIONOMIDAE. Plains Wanderer,

1. *Pedionomus torquatus*. Plains Wanderer/Collared Hemipode. l5/18. SE Australia.

1
2
3
TURNICIDAE
1
2
3
4
5
6
7
8
9
10
11
12
13
15
14
16
PEDIONOMIDAE
1
17
18

GRUIDAE, ARAMIDAE, PSOPHIIDAE
Cranes, Limpkin, Trumpeters

Family 43. GRUIDAE. Cranes.

1. *Grus americana*. Whooping Crane. 120. Canada. Winters to Texas, Mexico.
2. *Grus antigone*. Sarus Crane. 2ss. 160. India to SE Asia, Philippines, Australia.
3. *Grus canadensis*. Sandhill Crane. 105. Siberia, N America. Winters S USA, Cuba, Mexico
4. *Grus/Bugeranus carunculatus*. Wattled Crane. 115. N E & S Africa.
5. *Grus grus*. Crane. 2ss. 114. N Eurasia. Winters to N Africa, India, SE Asia.
6. *Grus japonensis*. Red crowned Crane. 125. Siberia, Mongolia, Japan. Winters Korea, China.
7. *Grus leucogeranus*. Siberian Crane. 140. Siberia Winters India, China.
8. *Grus monacha*. Hooded Crane. 87. Siberia, Manchuria. Winters to China, N India.
9. *Grus nigricollis*. Black necked Crane. 105. S C Asia, Winters S China, NE India.
10. *Grus rubicunda*. Brolga / Australian Crane. 105. NE Australia, S. New Guinea.
11. *Grus vipio*. White naped Crane. 105. Siberia, Manchuria. Winters China, Japan, Korea.
12. *Grus/Anthropoides paradisea*. Blue Crane. 102. Namibia, Zimbabwe, S Africa.
13. *Grus/Anthropoides virgo*. Demoiselle Crane. 95. Eurasia. Winters N Africa, SE Asia.
14. *Balearica pavonina*. (Black) Crowned Crane. 3ss. 102. E & W Africa.
15. *Balearica regulorum*. South African/Grey Crowned Crane.102. S Africa.

Family 44, ARAMIDAE, Limpkin.

1. *Aramus guaruna*. Limpkin. 4ss. 66. SE USA to Brazil, Argentina, West Indies.

Family 45. PSOPHIIDAE. Trumpeters.

1. *Psophia crepitans*. Grey winged Trumpeter. 2ss. 52. Amazon basin.
2. *Psophia leucoptera*. Pale winged Trumpeter. 2ss. 52. Peru, Bolivia, Brazil.
3. *Psophia viridis*. Dark winged Trumpeter. 4ss. 52. Brazil.

1
2
3
4
5
6
7
8
9
10
11
12
13
14
15
ARAMIDAE
1
PSOPHIIDAE
1
2
3

RALLIDAE (1)
Rails & Crakes

1. *Rallus antarcticus*. Austral Rail. 22. Chile & Argentina.
2. *Rallus aquaticus*. Water Rail. 4ss. 28. Eurasis,N Africa. Winters to SE Asia, Borneo.
3. *Rallus caerulescens*. Kaffir Rai1. 26. E & S Africa.
4. *Rallus elegans*. King Rail. 35. E USA to Mexico, Cuba.
5. *Rallus limicola*. Virginia Rail. 3ss. 22. Local Canada, USA. Colombia to Argentina.
6. *Rallus longirostris*. Clapper Rai1. 24ss. 37. USA to Peru, Brazil, West Indies.
7. *Rallus maculatus*. Spotted Rail. 2ss. 25. Mexico & Cuba to Argentina.
8. *Rallus madagascariensis*. Madagascar Rail. 25. Malagasy.
9. *Pardirallus nigricans*. Blackish Rai1. 2ss. 27. Colombia to Brazil, Argentina.
10. *Gallirallus owstoni*. Guam Rail. 28. Guam, (Mariana Islands).
11. *Lewinia muelleri*. Mueller's Rail. 21. Auckland Islands.
12. *Gallirallus okinawae*. Okinawa Rai1. 30. Okinawa.
13. *Lewinia mirificus*. Brown banded Rail, 20. Luzon.
14. *Lewinia/Rallus pectoralis*. Lewin's Rail. 8ss. 20. New Guinea to Australia.
15. *Rallus philippensis*. Buff banded Rai1. 24ss. 30. Philippines, Australasia, Polynesia.

15a. *Gallirallus rovianae*. Rovianna Rail. 30. C Solomon Is.

16. *Gallirallus dieffenbachii*. Chatham banded Rail. 30. Chatham Island. (extinct.)
17. *Gallirallus ecaudatus*. Tonga Rail. 30. Tonga.(extinct).
18. *Rougetius/Rallus rougetii*. Rouget's Rail. 30. Ethiopia.
19. *Pardirallus sanguinolentus*. Plumbeous Rail. 6ss. 27. Peru, Brazil to Argentina.
20. *Rallus semiplumbeus*. Bogota Rail. 25. Colombia.
21. *Gallirallus striatys*. Slaty breasted Rail. 7ss. 25. India,China to Philippines.
22. *Gallirallus torquatus*. Barred Rail. 5ss. 32. Sulawesi, Philippines, New Guinea.
23. *Rallus wetmorei*. Plain flanked Rail. 32. Venezuela.
24. *Gallirallus modestus*. Chatham Island Rail. 21. Chatham Is. (extinct).
25. *Gallirallus wakensis*. Wake Island Rail. 22. Wake Island.(extinct).
26. *Gallirallus pacificus*. Tahitian Rail. 23. Tahiti.
27. *Atlantisia rogersi*. Inaccessible Island Rail. 13. Tristan da Cunha.
28. *Tricholimnas/Gallinula silvestris*. Lord Howe Rai1. 37. Lord Howe I.
29. *Tricholimnas lafresnayanus*. New Caledonian Rail. 42. New Caledonia. (extinct?)
30. *Dryolimnas cuvieri*. White throated Rail. 2ss. 24. Malagasy, Aldabra.
31. *Amaurolimnas concolor*. Uniform Crake. 3ss. 22. Mexico to Brazil, Bolivia.
32. *Rallina canningi*. Andaman Crake. 34. Andaman Is.
33. *Rallina eurizonoides*. Banded Crake. 6ss. 25. S Asia to Indonesia, Micronesia.
34. *Rallina fasciata*. Red legged Crake. 23. SE Asia, Indonesia.
35. *Rallina tricolor*. Red necked Crake. 3ss. 28. Indonesia.New Guinea, Australia.
36. *Rallina forbesi*. Forbes' Rail. 2ss. 22. New Guinea.
37. *Rallina leucospila*. White striped Forest Rail. 23.New Guinea.
38. *Rallina mayri*. Mayr's Rai1. 2ss. 22. New Guinea.
39. *Rallina rubra*. Chestnut Forest Rai1.3ss. 21. New Guinea.
40. *Cyanolimnas cerverai*. Zapata Rail. 29. SW Cuba.
41. *Porzana sandwichensis*. Hawaiian Rail. 14. Hawaii, (extinct)
42. *Porzana palmeri*. Laysan Crake. 15. Hawaii.(extinct)

1
2
3
4
JUV
5
6
7
8
11
13
9
10
14
15
12
16
15A
19
20
21
18
27
28
22
23
24
25
29
26
30
31
32
33
17
34
35
36
38
41
42
37
39
40

RALIDAE (2)
Rails

43. *Aramides axillaris.* Rufous necked Wood Rail. 30. Mexico to Ecuador, Trinidad.
44. *Aramides cajanea.* Grey necked Wood Rail. 8ss. 37. Mexico to Argentina.
45. *Aramides calopterus.* Red winged Wood Rail. 35. Ecuador, Peru, Brazil.
46. *Aramides mangle.* Little Wood Rail. 32. Brazil.
47. *Aramides saracura.* Slaty breasted Wood Rail. 40. Brazil, Paraguay, Argentina.
48. *Aramides wolfi.* Brown Wood Rail. 32. Colombia, Ecuador.
49. *Aramides ypecaha.* Giant Wood Rail. 47. Brazil, Paraguay, Uruguay, Argentina.
50. *Aramidopsis plateni.* Snoring/Platen's Rail. 30. Sulawesi.
51. *Nesoclopeus woodfordi.* Woodford's Rail. 35. Solomon Is. (extinct ?)
52. *Nesoclopeus poecilopterus.* Bar winged Rail. 35. Fiji. (extinct ?)
53. *Gymnocrex plumbeiventris.* Bare eyed Rail. 2ss. 33. Moluccas,New Guinea, Aru, New Ireland.
54. *Gymnocrex rosenbergi.* Bare faced Rail. 30. Sulawesi.
55. *Gallinula/Edithornis silvestris.* 25. San Cristobal. (l specimen 1929.)
56. *Gallirallus australis.* South Island Weka. 4ss. 47. N. Zealand. South Is. A. Pale, B. Dark phases.
57. Incl. *G. a. greyi.* North Island Weka. 47. New Zealand. North Island.
58. *Gallirallus insignis.* New Britain Rail. 38. New Britain.
59. *Habroptila wallacii.* Invisible Rail. 50. Halmahera (Moluccas).
60. *Megacrex inepta.* New Guinea flightless Rail. 2ss. 37. New Guinea.
61. *Eulabeornis castaneoventris.* Chestnut Rail. 2ss. 55. Aru, N Australian coast.
62. *Himantornis haematopus.* Nkulengu Rail. 3ss. 43. Liberia to Zaire.
63. *Canirallus kioloides.* Madagascar Wood Rail. 2ss. 28. Malagasy.
64. *Canirallus oculeus.* Grey throated Rail. 2ss. 30. Liberia to Uganda, Zaire.

43
44
45
46
47
48
49
50
52
51
53
54
56
(b)
57
58
(a)
55
59
60
61
62
63
64

RALLIDAE (3)
Crakes

65. *Crex crex*. Corncrake / Landrail 26. Eurasia, Winters Africa, Australia.
66. *Crecopsis egregia*. African Crake. 23. Africa south of Sahara.
67. *Coturnicops lugens*. Chestnut headed Crake. 2ss 22. Colombia, Peru.
68. *Amaurornis flavirostra*. African Black Crake. 20. Africa South of Sahara.
69. *Porzana albicollis*. Ash throated Crake. 2ss. 25. Venezuela to Argentina.
70. *Amaurornis bicolor*. Black tailed Crake. 25. NE India, SW China, SE Asia.
71. *Porzana carolina*. Sora. l9. Alaska to Mexico. Winters W Indies, Northern .S America.
72. *Neocrex colombianus*. Colombian Crake. 2ss. 20. Colombia.
73. *Amaurornis olivieri*. Sakalava Rail. 18. Malagasy.
74. *Coturnicops exquisitus*. Swinhoe's Rail. 13. Siberia, E Asia. Winters China, Japan.
75. *Porzana flaviventer*. Yellow breasted Crake. 5ss. 14. Mexico to Argentina.
76. *Porzana fliminea*. Australian spotted Crake. 20. Australia, Tasmania.
77. *Porzana fusca*. Ruddy breasted Crake. 4ss. 17. SE Asia, Philippines, Indonesia.
78. *Aenigmatolimnas marginalis*. Striped Crake. 16. Local Africa, south of Sahara.
79. *Porzana parva*. Little Crake. 19. Eurasia. Winters N Africa, India.
80. *Porzana paykullii*. Band bellied Crake. 22. E Asia, Winters t o Gr. Sundas.
81. *Porzana porzana*. Spotted Crake. 22. Eurasia. Winters to S Africa, SE Asia.
82. *Porzana pusilla*. Baillon 's Crake. 7ss 18. S Eurasia o S Africa, Australasia.
83. *Porzana tabuensis*. Spotless Crake. 4ss. 20. Philippines to Australasia, Oceania.
84. *Porzana atra*. Henderson Island Crake. 22. Paumotu group, Pitcairn Island.
85. *Laterallus exilis*. Grey breasted Crake. 15. Belize to Brazil & Bolivia.
86. *Laterallus fasciatus*. Black banded Crake. 17. Colombia, Peru, Brazil.
87. *Laterallus jamaicensis*. Black Rail. 4ss. 12. Local USA to Chile, Argentina.
88. *Laterallus leucopyrrhus*. Red & white Crake. 17. Brazil, Paraguay, Uruguay, Argentina.
89. *Laterallus levraudi*. Rusty flanked Crake. 17. Venezuela.
90. *Laterallus melanophaius*. Rufous sided Crake. 2ss. 17. Guyanas to Argentina.
91. *Laterallus albigularis*. White throated Crake. 3ss. 17. Honduras to Ecuador.
92. *Laterallus ruber*. Ruddy Crake. 15. Yucatan to Costa Rica.
93. *Laterallus spilonotus*. Galapagos Rail. 15. Galapagos Is.
94. *Porzana spiloptera*. Dot winged Crake. 15. Uruguay, Argentina.
95. *Anurolimnas viridis*. Russet crowned Crake. 2ss. 16. Venezuela to Peru, Brazil.
96. *Laterallus xenopterus*. Rufous faced Crake. 17. Paraguay, SE Brazil.
97. *Porzana monasa*. Kosrae Crake. 17. Kosrae I (Kusaie Is). Probably extinct.
98. *Micropygia schomburgkii*. Ocellated Crake. 2ss. 14. Guyanas to Bolivia, Brazil.
99. *Coturnicops notatus*. Speckled Rail. 14. Guyana to Uruguay, Argentina.
100. *Coturnicops noveboracensis*. Yellow Rail. 2ss. 18. Canada, USA. Winters to Mexico.
101. *Neocrex erythrops*. Paint billed Crake. 2ss. 20. Venezuela to Argentina, Galapagos Islands.
102. *Sarothrura affinis*. Striped Flufftail. 2ss. 15. E & S Africa.
103. *Sarothrura ayresii*. White winged Flufftail. 16. Ethiopia to eastern S Africa.
104. *Sarothrura boehmi*. Streaky breasted Flufftail. 15. Cameroon to Kenya.
105. *Sarothrura elegans*. Buff spotted Flufftail. 2ss. 16. Africa South of Sahara.
106. *Sarothrura insularis*. Madagascar Crake. 14. Malagasy.
107. *Sarothrura lugens*. Chestnut headed Flufftail. 15. Central Africa.
108. incl. *S. l. lynesii*. Lynes' F1ufftail. 14. Zambia.
109. *Sarothrura pulchra*. White spotted Flufftail. 4ss. 14. Senegambia, C Africa.
110. *Sarothrura rufa*. Red chested Flufftail. 3ss. 13. Africa South of Sahara.
111. *Sarothrura watersi*. Slender billed Flufftail. 14. Malagasy.
112. *Porzana cinerea*. White browed Crake. 6ss. 17. SE Asia to Samoa, Australasia.
113. *Gallinula melanops*. Spot flanked Gallinule. 3ss. 27. Colombia to Chile, Brazil, Argentina.

65
66
67
68
69
70
71
72
73
74
75
76
77
78
JUV
79
80
81
82
83
84
90
85
86
87
88
89
91
92
93
94
95
96
97
98
99
100
101
102
103
104
105
106
107
108
109
110
111
112
113

RALLIDAE (4)
Moorhens, Gallinules

114. *Gallinula mortierii.* Tasmanian Native Hen. 42. Tasmania.
115. *Gallinula ventralis.* Black tailed Native Hen. 32. Australia.
116. *Maaurornis akool.* Brown Crake. 2ss. 25. India, SE Asia, SE China.
117. *Amaurornis isabellinus.* Isabelline Waterhen. 35. Sulawesi.
118. *Amaurornis olivaceus.* Plain Bush Hen. 25. Philippines.
119. *Amaurornis moluccanus.* Rufous tailed Bush Hen. 4ss. 25. Indonesia, Australia.
120. *Gallinula pacifica.* Samoan Wood Rail. 15. Samoa. (extinct).
121. *Amaurornis phoenicurus.* White breasted Waterhen. 3ss. 30. S,SE Asia.
122. *Gallicrex cinerea.* Watercock / Kora. 42. India, SE Asia.
123. *Gallinura angulata.* Lesser Moorhen. 28. Ethiopian region.
124. *Gallinura chloropus.* Moorhen/Common Gallinule. 12ss. 32. Almost worldwide.
125. *Gallinula tenebrosa.* Dusky Moorhen. 3ss. 37. Indonesia, Australia, New Guinea.
126. *Gallinula nesiotis.* South Atlantic Rail. 32. Gough I. (extinct on Tristan.)
127. *Porphyrio alleni.* Allen's Gallinule. 25. Sub-saharan Africa, Malagasy.
128. *Porphyrio flavirostris.* Azure Gallinule. 25. Venezuela to Argentina.
129. *Porphyrio martinicus.* American Purple Gallinule. 33. S. USA to Argentina.
130. *Porphyrio albus.* White Swamphen. 55. Lord Howe I.(extinct).
131. *Porphyrio porphyrio.* Purple Swamphen/Gallinule. 13ss. 47. Mediterranean, Middle East, NE & NW Africa.
132. Incl. *P. p. madagascariensis.* King Reed Hen. 43. Africa, Malagasy.
133. *P. p. melanotus.* Eastern Swamphen. 42. Australia (except SW).
134. *P. p. poliocephalus.* Indian/Grey headed Swamphen. 42. Iraq to Thailand, SE Asia, Oceania.
135. *P. p. pulverulentus.* Philippine Swamphen. 42. Philippines.
136. *Porphyrio/Notornis mantelli.* Takahe. 2ss. 49. New Zealand.

114
115
116
117
118
119
121
122
120
123
124
125
124
JUV
124
NB
IMM
126
128
129
127
130
131
132
133
134
136
135

RALLIDAE (5), HELIORNITHIDAE, EURYPHYGIDAE, RHYNOCHETIDAE, CARIAMIDAE
Coots, Sungrebes, Sun Bitterns, Kagu, Seriemas

Family 46. RALLIDAE. (5). Coots.

137. *Fulica americana*. American Coot. 3ss. 44. N America, West Indies.
138. *Fulica alai*. Hawaiian Coot. 44. Hawaii.
139. *Fulica ardesiaca*. Slate coloured Coot. 40. Colombia, Peru.
140. *Fulica armillata*. Red gartered Coot. 42. Paraguay, Uruguay. Brazil. Argentina.
141. *Fulica atra*. Coot. 4ss. 37. Palearctic, S Asia, Australasia.
142. *Fulica caribaea*. Caribbean Coot. 37. Venezuela, West Indies.
143. *Fulica cornuta*. Horned Coot. 60. Bolivia, Argentina.
144. *Fulica cristata*. Red knobbed/Crested Coot. 40. Spain, Morocco, Ethiopia to Cape, Malagasy.
145. *Fulica gigantea*. Giant Coot. 67. Peru, Bolivia, Chile, Argentina.
146. *Fulica leucoptera*. White winged Coot. 32. Brazil, Bolivia, Chile.
147. *Fulica rufifrons*. Red fronted Coot. 47. Brazil, Paraguay, Uruguay , Argentina.

Family 47. HELIORNITHIDAE. Sungrebes.

1. *Podica senegalensis*. African Finfoot. 4ss. 60. Africa, South of Sahara.
2. *Heliopais personata*. Masked Finfoot. 53. Bangladesh, SE Asia, Winters Java, Sumatra.
3. *Heliornis fulica*. Sungrebe. 27. Mexico to Brazil & Argentina.

Family 48 EURYPYGIDAE, Sun Bittern.

1. *Eurypyga helias*. Sun Bittern. 3ss. 50. Guatemala to Brazil.

Family 49. RHYNOCHETIDAE. Kagu.

1. *Rhynochetos jubatus*. Kagu. 55. New Caledonia.

Family 50. CARPAMIDAE. Seriemas.

1. *Cariama cristata*. Red legged Seriema. 85. Brazil, Paraguay, Argentina.
2. *Chunga burmeisteri*. Black legged Seriema. 75. Argentina.

137
138
140
141
139
142
143
144
146
145
147
HELIORNITHIDAE
1
2
3
EURYPYGIDAE
1
RHYNOCHETIDAE
1
CARIAMIDAE
1
2

OYIDIDAE (1)
Bustards

1. *Otis tarda.* Great Bustard. 3ss. 75/100. Discontinuous Palearctic. Winters S Asia.
2. *Otis tetrax.* Little Bustard. 2ss 44. Europe, Middle East. Winters N. Africa, India, N Africa.
3. *Neotis denhami.* Denham's Bustard.3ss. 70/90. Senegal to Sudan Ethiopia, Zaire.
4. incl. *N. d. stanleyi.* Stanley's Bustard. 70/90. S Africa.
5. *Neotis heuglini.* Heuglin's Bustard. 87. Ethiopia, Somalia, Kenya.
6. *Neotis burchelli.* Burchell's Bustard. 80. Sudan.(1 specimen only).
7. *Neotis ludwigi.* Ludwig's Bustard. 65/84. Angola, Namibia, Botswana, RSA.
8. *Neotis nuba.* Nubian Bustard. 60/75. W Africa, Sudan.
9. *Ardeotis arabs.* Arabian Bustard. 74/90. NW Africa to Red Sea, SW Arabia.
10. *Ardeotis australis.* Australian Bustard. 85/112. Australia , New Guinea.
11. *Ardeotis kori.* Kori Bustard. 110/130. North east & Southern Africa.
12. *Ardeotis nigriceps.* Indian Bustard. 93/122. India, Pakistan.

1
2
3
4
5
6
7
8
9
10
11
12

OTIDIDAE (2)
Bustards

13. *Chlamydotis undulata.* Houbara Bustard. 3ss. 66/73. Canary Islands .Deserts from Sahara to W Asia.
14. *Eupodotis afraoides.* White quilled Bustard. 52. Botswana.
15. *Eupodotis afra.* Black Bustard. 3ss. 52. Namibia, RSA.
16. *Eupodotis bengalensis.* Bengal Florican. 2ss. 68/66. N India, Cambodia, Cochin – China.
17. *Eupodotis caerulescens.* Blue Bustard. 55. South Africa.
18. *Eupodotis hartlaubi.* Hartlaub' s Bustard. 60. Sudan to Tanzania.
19. *Eupodotis humilis.* Little Brown Bustard. 35. Somalia, Ethiopia.
20. *Eupodotis melanogaster.* Black bellied Bustard. 2ss. 60. Africa South of Sahara.
21. *Eupodotis/Lophotis ruficrista.* Red crested Bustard. 2ss. 50. Southern Africa.

2la. *Eupodotis grindiana.* Buff crested Bustard. 50. NE Africa.

22. *Eupodotis Savilei.* Savile's Bustard. 40. Senegal, Nigeria to Sudan.
23. *Eupodotis senegalensis.* Senegal Bustard. 3ss. 55. Senegal to Sudan. E Africa.
24. incl. *E. s. canicollis.* White bellied Bustard. 55. Ethiopia to Tanzania.
25. *Eupodotis vigorsi.* Karoo, Black throated Bustard. 6ss. 57. Namibia, RSA.
26. *Eupodotis rueppellii.* Ruppell's Bustard/Korhaan. 8ss. 56. Angola, Namibia.
27. *Eupodotis/Sypheotides indica.* Lesser Florican. 51/46. Indian Sub-continent.

13
14
15
16
23
24
18
19
21
22
20
21A
17
25
26
27

JACANIDAE, ROSTRATULIDAE, HAEMATOPPDIDAE, CHARADRIIDAE
Jacanas, Painted Snipe, Oystercatchers, Lapwings, Plovers

Family 52. JACANIDAE. Jacanas.

1. *Microparra capensis*. Smaller Jacana. 18. Africa South of Sahara.
2. *Actophilornis africanus*. African Jacana / Lily-trotter. 28. Africa sub – Sahara.
3. *Actophilornis albinucha*. Madagascar Jacana. 28. Malagasy.
4. *Irediparra gallinacea*. Lotusbird/Comb crested Jacana. 3ss.23. Indonesia, Philippines, Australasia.
5. *Hydrophasianus chirurgus*. Pheasant tailed Jacana. 48. India to Indonesia.
6. *Metopidius indicus*. Bronze winged Jacana. 28. India. E & SE Asia, Sumatra, Java.
7. *Jacana spiniosa*. Northern Jacana. 3ss. 24. Texas to Panama.
8. *Jacana jacana*. Wattled Jacana. 6ss. 24. Panama to Argentina.

Family 53. ROSTRATULIDAE. Painted Snipe.

1. *Rostratula benghalensis*. Painted Snipe. 2ss. 26/24. S Asia, Africa, Australia.
2. *Rostratula semicollaris*. American Painted Snipe. 20. Brazil to Argentina.

Family 54. HAEMATOPODIDAE. Oystercatchers.

1. *Haematopus ater*. Blackish Oystercatcher. 47. Peru to Uruguay & Argentina.
2. *Haematopus bachmani*. Black Oystercatcher. 2ss. 43. Aleutian Is to Mexico.
3. *Haematopus fuliginosus*. Sooty Oystercatcher. 2ss. 47. Australia & Islands.
4. *Haematopus unicolor*. Variable Oystercatcher. 2ss. 48. New Zealand, Chatham Island. Black & Pied forms exist.
5. *Haematopus leucopodus*. Magellanic Oystercatcher. 43. Southern South America.
6. *Haematopus ostralegus*. Eurasian Oystercatcher. 10ss. 43. Eurasia.
7. *Haematopus moquini*. African Oystercatcher. 50. African Coast, Gabon to Natal.
8. *Haematopus meadewaldoi*. Canary Island Oystercatcher. 45. E Canary Is.(extinct).
9. *Haematopus palliatus*. American Oystercatcher. 43. USA, S America inc. West Indies, Galapagos Is.
10. *Haematopus chathamensis*. Chatham Is Oystercatcher. 48. Chatham Is.
11. *Haematopus finschi*. South Island Oystercatcher. 48. New Zealand.
12. *Haematopus longirostris*. Pied Oystercatcher. 50. Wallacea, Australasia. New Guinea.

Family 55. CHARADRIIDAE (1). Lapwings, Plovers.

1. *Vanellus albiceps*. White headed Lapwing. 30. Africa South of Sahara.
2. *Vanellus armatus*. Blacksmith Plover. 28. Kenya to South Africa.
3. *Vanellus chilensis*. Southern Lapwing. 4ss. 33. Most of S America.
4. *Vanellus cinereus*. Grey headed Lapwing. 35. China, Japan. Winters India, SE Asia.
5. *Vanellus coronatus*. Crowned Lapwing. 2ss. 28. E & S Africa.
6. *Vanellus macropterus*. Javanese Wattled Lapwing. 28. Java. Last seen 1920.
7. *Vanellus crassirostris*. Long toed Lapwing. 3ss. 30. E, C, & S Africa.
8. *Vanellus gregarius*. Sociable Lapwing. 29. S Russia, Winters to N Africa, India, SE Asia.
9. *Vanellus indicus*. Red wattled Lapwing. 3ss. 32. S, SE Asia. Winters to Sumatra.
10. *Vanellus leucura*. White tailed Lapwing. 28. India, Russia, Turkey, Winters to NE. Africa,

JACANIDAE
1
2
3
4
Br
5
NB
6
7
8
ROSTRATULIDAE
1
2
HAEMATOPODIDAE
1
2
3
5
8
4
10
6
JUV
W
7
9
11
12
CHARADRIIDAE
1
2
3
4
5
6
7
8
9
10

CHARADRIIDAE (2)
Plover

11. *Vanellus lugubris*. Senegal Plover. 23. Africa South of Sahara.
12. *Vanellus malabaricus*. Yellow wattled Lapwing. 27. India Pakistan, Sri Lanka.
13. *Vanellus melanocephalus*. Spot breasted Lapwing. 34. Ethiopia.
14. *Vanellus melanopterus*. Black winged Lapwing. 2ss. 27. S & E Africa,
15. *Vanellus miles*. Masked Lapwing . 35. Australia, New Zealand, New Guinea.
16. incl. *V. m. novaehollandiae*. Australian Lapwing. 35. Australia, New Zealand.
17. *Vanellus resplendens*. Andean Lapwing . 32. Colombia to Chile & Argentina.
18. *Vanellus senegallus*. Wattled Lapwing. 3ss. 34. Africa South of Sahara.
19. *Vanellus duvaucelii*. River Lapwing. 30. India, S E Asia.
20. *Vanellus spinosus*. Spur-winged Plover. 28. N. Africa to Tanzania, Red Sea, Mediterranean.
21. *Vanellus superciliosus*. Brown chested Lapwing. 25. Ghana, Cameroon, Winters E. Africa.
22. *Vanellus tectus*. Black headed Lapwing. 2ss. 27. Africa South of Sahara.
23. *Vanellus tricolor*. Banded Lapwing. 25. Australia & New Zealand.
24. *Vanellus vanellus*. Lapwing / Green Plover. 31. N Eurasia, N Africa, S Asia.
25. *Vanellus cayanus*. Pied Lapwing. 23. Peru, Bolivia, Paraguay, Argentina.
26. *Pluvialis apricaria altifrons*. Eurasian Golden Plover. Northern form. 27
27. *Pluvialis apricaria*. Southern form 27. N. Eurasia, Winters to Mediterranean.
28. *Pluvialis dominica*. American Golden Plover. 25. Arctic America. Winters S. America.
29. *Pluvialis fulva*. Asian/Pacific Golden Plover. 24. Siberia. Winters to Australasia.
30. *Pluvialis squatarola*. Grey/Black bellied Plover. 31. Holarctic. Winters World-wide.
31. *Charadrius alexandrinus*. Kentish Plover. 4ss. 16. Palearctic, Winters Africa, Philippines.

31a. incl. *C. a. javanicus*. Javan Plover. 16. Java.

32. *C. a. nivosus*. Snowy Plover. 16. S. USA, Caribbean, Northern S America.
33. *Charadrius alticola*. Puna Plover. 18. Peru, Bolivia, Argentina, Chile.
34. *Charadrius asiaticus*. Caspian Plover. 19. Central Asia, Winters Arabia, N Africa.
35. *Charadrius bicinctus*. Double banded Plover. 20. New Zealand, Winters Australia.
36. *Charadrius/Erythrogonys cinctus*. Red kneed Dotterel. 18. Australia, New Guinea.
37. *Charadrius collaris*. Collared Plover. 17. Mexico to Chile, Argentina.
38. *Charadrius rubricollis*. Hooded Dotterel / Plover. 20. S Australia, Tasmania.
39. *Charadrius dubius*. Little Ringed Plover. 4ss. 17. Palearctic, Winters Africa, Australia.
40. *Charadrius falklandicus*. Two banded Plover. 18. Chile, Argentina. Winters Brazil.
41. *Charadrius forbesi*. Forbes' Plover. 20. W & C Africa.
42. *Charadrius hiaticula*. Ringed Plover. 3ss. 19. Palearctic, Winters Africa, Australia.
43. *Charadrius leschenaultii*. Greater Sandplover. 22. S C Asia, Winters Africa, New Zealand.
44. *Charadrius marginatus*. White fronted Plover. 3ss. 17. E to S Africa.

28/29 Formerly known as Lesser Golden Plover.

11
12
13
14
15
19
16
17
18
20
21
22
23
24
25
NB
26
Br
Br
28
30
Br
NB
27
Br
NB
29
Br
31
32
-33-
Br
NB
Br
34
NB
35
NB
36
37
38
42
Br
NB
39
-31A-
40
Br
NB
41
43
44

CHARADRIIDAE (3), SCOLOPACIDAE PLOVER, CURLEWS

Family 55. CHARADRIIDAE (3). Plover.

45. *Elseyornis/Chorardrius melanops*. Black fronted Dotterel. 17. Australia, New Zealand.
46. *Charadrius melodus*. Piping Plover. 18. Canada, USA, Winters Bahamas, Greater Antilles.
47. *Charadrius mongolus*. Mongolian Plover. 3ss. 19. NE Asia, Winters Africa, Asia, Australia .
48. *Charadrius montanus*. Mountain Plover. 22. Canada to SW USA, Winters to Mexico.
49. *Charadrius novaeseelandiae*. New Zealand Shore Plover. 20. Chatham Is.
50. *Charadrius obscurus*. Red breasted Dotterel. 26. New Zealand.
51. *Charadrius pallidus/venustus*. Chestnut banded Sand Plover. 2ss. 15. S Africa.
52. *Charadrius pecuarius*. Kittlitz's Sand Plover. 2ss. 17. Africa S of Sahara.
53. *Charadrius sanctaehelenae*. St Helena Wirebird. 15. St Helena.
54. *Charadrius peronii*. Malaysian Plover. 15. Malaysia, Philippines, Sulawesi.
55. *Charadrius placidus*. Long billed Plover. 21. E Asia, Winters India, SE Asia.
56. *Charadrius ruficapillus*. Red capped Dotterel. 15. Australia.
57. *Charadrius semipamatus*. Semi-palmated Plover. 19. N America, Winters. S America, Hawaii.
58. *Charadrius thoracicus*. Black banded Sand/Madagascar Plover.14. Malagasy.
59. *Charadrius tricollaris*. Three banded Plover. 2ss. 18. Africa S of Sahara.
60. *Charadrius veredus*. Oriental Plover. 25. NE Asia, Winters Sulawesi, Australia.
61. *Charadrius vociferus*. Killdeer. 3ss. 25. N America, W Indies. Winters S America.
62. *Charadrius wilsonia*. Wilson's Plover. 4ss. 20. S USA to Peru, Brazil, West Indies.
63. *Oreopholus ruficollis*. Tawny throated Dotterel. 2ss. 28. Ecuador to Argentina.
64. *Eudromias morinellus*. Dotterel. 22. N Eurasia, Alaska, Winters to Mediterranean.
65. *Charadrius modestus*. Rufous chested Dotterel. 20. Argentina, Falkland Is.
66. *Anarhynchus frontalis*. Wrybill. 20. New Zealand South Is., Winters North Is.
67. *Pluvianellus socialis*. Magellanic Plover. 20. Chile Argentina.
68. *Phegornis mitchelli*. Diademed Sandpiper Plover. 18. Peru, Chile, Argentina.

(for Peltohyas australis, Australian Dotterel, see Plate 68.)

Family 56. SCOLOPACIDAE (1). Curlews,

1. *Bartramia longicauda*. Upland/Bartram's Sandpiper. 28. N America, Winters S America.
2. *Numenius americanus*. Long billed Curlew. 2ss. 57. Canada,USA.Winters C America.
3. *Numenius arquata*. (Eurasian) Curlew. 2ss. 57. Palearctic to S Africa, Indonesia.
4. *Numenius borealis*. Eskimo Curlew. 32. Arctic Canada. Winters to S America.
5. *Numenius madagascariensis*. Far Eastern Curlew. 37. NE Asia. Winters to Australia.
6. *Numenius minutus*. Little Curlew. 30. Siberia, Winters to Australasia.
7. *Numenius phaeopus*. Whimbrel. 3ss. 41. Northern Hemisphere, Winters world-wide.
8. *Numenius tahitiensis*. Bristle thighed Curlew. 42. Alaska, Winters Hawaii, S Pacific.
9. *Numenius tenuirostris*. Slender billed Curlew. 40. Siberia Winters to Mediterranean.

45
46
Br
47 NB
Br
48
NB
49
50
51
52
54
55
56
53
58
59
61
57
Br
60
NB
63
Br
Br
62 NB
64
65
NB
NB
66
67
68
1
SCOLOPACIDAE
2
3
4
5
6
7
8
9

SCOLOPACIDAE (2)
Godwits & Sandpipers

10. *Limosa fedoa*. Marbled Godwit. 44. Plains of N America, Winters to Chile, Argentina.
11. *Limosa haemastica*. Hudsonian Godwit. 38. Canadian Arctic, Winters to S America.
12. *Limosa lapponica*. Bar tailed Godwit. 2ss. 37. Arctic Eurasia, Alaska, Winters S Africa, Australasia.
13. *Limosa limosa*. Black tailed Godwit. 2ss. 40. N Palearctic, Winters Africa, S Asia, Australia.
14. *Tringa brevipes*. Grey tailed Tattler. 25. Siberia, Winters to Australia.
15. *Prosoboria cancellata*. Tuamotu Sandpiper. 14. Tuamotu archipelago.
16. *Tringa cinerea*. Terek Sandpiper. 25. N Eurasia. Winters Africa, SE Asia Australia.
17. *Tringa erythropus*. Spotted Redshank. 30. N. Eurasia, Winters to Africa & SE Asia.
18. *Tringa flavipes*. Lesser Yellowlegs. 24. N America Winters S America, Occasional Europe.
19. *Tringa glareola*. Wood Sandpiper. 22. N Eurasia. Winters Africa, Asia, Australia.
20. *Tringa guttifer*. Nordmann's Greenshank. 33. Siberia. Winters to SE Asia, Philippines.
21. *Tringa hypoleucos*. Common Sandpiper. 20. Eurasia, Winters Africa, Asia Australia.
22. *Tringa incana*. Wandering Tattler. 25. Siberia, Alaska. Winters Pacific Is, S America.
23. *Tringa macularia*. Spotted Sandpiper. 19. N America Winters S America.
24. *Tringa melanoleuca*. Greater Yellowlegs. 33. Alaska to Labrador. Winters S America.
25. *Tringa nebularia*. Greenshank. 35. N Eurasia. Winters to Africa, s Asia, Australia.
26. *Tringa ochrophus*. Green Sandpiper. 24. Eurasia, Winters to S Africa, Asia, Australia.
27. *Tringa solitaria*. Solitary Sandpiper. 2ss. 18. Alaska Canada, Winters S America.
28. *Tringa stagnatilis*. Marsh Sandpiper. 25. Palearctic, Winters Africa, Asia, Pacific, Australia.
29. *Tringa totanus*. Redshank. 4ss, 28. Eurasia, Winters Africa, SE Asia.
30. *Catoptrophorus semipalmatus*. Willet. 2ss. 40. E & W USA, Winters to Brazil, Chile.

10
Br
NB
11
Br
NB
12
Br
NB
13
Br
NB
Br
14
NB
Br
NB
15
Br
NB
16
Br
17
NB
18
19
Br
NB
20
21
22
Br
NB
23
NB
Br
24
25
26
27
28
Br
NB
29
30

SCOLOPACIDAE (3)
Snipe, Dowitchers, Woodcock

31. *Gallinago andina*. Puna Snipe. 22. Peru to Chile, Argentina.
32. *Gallinago gallinago*. Common Snipe. 3ss. 27. Most of world except Australasia.
33. *Gallinago hardwickii*. Latham's Snipe. 25. Japan, Winters Australasia.
34. *Gallinago imperialis* . Imperial/Banded Snipe. 30. Colombia, Peru.
35. *Gallinago paraguia*. South America Snipe. 3ss. 25. Uruguay, Argentina, Falklands.
36. *Gallinago macrodactyla*. Madagascar Snipe. 30. Malagasy.
37. *Gallinago media*. Great Snipe. 29. N Europe to India. Winters E & S Africa.
38. *Gallinago megala*. Swinhoe's Snipe. 29. Siberia Winters India, SE Asia, Australia.
39. *Gallinago nemoricola*. Wood Snipe. 30. China ,Tibet. Winters India, SE Asia.
40. *Gallinago jamesoni*. Andean Snipe. 29. Venezuela to Bolivia.
41. *Gallinago nigripennis*. African Snipe. 2ss. 27. E C & S Africa.
42. *Gallinago nobilis*, Noble Snipe. 30. Venezuela, Colombia, Ecuador.
43. *Gallinago solitaria*, Solitary Snipe. 2ss. 30. C Asia to Japan, China, Burma.
44. *Gallinago stenura*. Pintail Snipe. 25. Siberia, Winters China, India to Indonesia.
45. *Gallinago stricklandii*. Cordilleran/Fuegan Snipe. 35. Argentina Chile.
46. *Gallinago undulata*. Giant Snipe. 42. Guyanas, Venezuela to Brazil, Paraguay.
47. *Arenaria interpres*. (Ruddy)Turnstone. 2ss. 23. Arctic. Winters most of world.
48. *Arenaria melanocephala*. Black Turnstone. 23. Alaska. Winters to Mexico.
49. *Limnodromus griseus*. Short billed Dowitcher/Red breasted Snipe. 2ss. 28. Alaska, Canada. Winters to S USA. Straggle Europe.
50. *Limnodromus scolopaceus*. Long billed Dowitcher. 30. Alaska. Winters to Brazil.
51. *Limnodromus semipalmatus*. Asian Dowitcher. 35. Siberia. Winters to S Asia, Sumatra.
52. *Coenocorypha aucklandica*. Sub-Antarctic Snipe. 4ss. 23. New Zealand.
53. *Coenocorypha pusilla*. Chatham Snipe. 20. Chatham Is.
54. *Scolopax celebensis*. Sulawesi Woodcock. 2ss. 31. Sulawesi.
55. *Scolopax minor*. American Woodcock. 29. Canada, N. USA. Winters to Florida.
56. *Scolopax mira*. Amami Woodcock. 35. Amami-O-Shima. Ryukyu Is.
57. *Scolopax rochussenii*. Obi Woodcock. 33. Obi Island. (N Moluccas.)
58. *Scolopax rusticola*. (Eurasian) Woodcock. 35. C & N Eurasia.
59. *Scolopax saturata*. Dusky/Rufous Woodcock. 2ss.29. Sumatra, Java New Guinea.
60. *Lymnocryptes minimus*. Jack Snipe. 20. Eurasia, Winters Africa, SE Asia.

31
32
33
34
35
36
37
38
39
40
41
42
43
44
45
46
Br
47
NB
48
49
50
51
Br
NB
52
53
54
56
57
58
55
59
60

SCOLOPACIDAE (4), RECURVIROSTRIDAE
Shorebirds, Ibisbill, Stilts, Avocets

Family 56. SCOLOPACIDAE. (4) Shorebirds.

61. *Aphriza virgata*. Surfbird. 25. Alaska. Winters West coast to S America.
62. *Calidris acuminata*. Sharp tailed Sandpiper. 21. Siberia. Winters Australia, Polynesia.
63. *Calidris alba*. Sanderling. 21. Arctic circle. Winters world-wide.
64. *Calidris alpina*. Dunlin. 5ss. 18. Holarctic. Winters world-wide.
65. *Calidris bairdii*. Baird's Sandpiper. 18. Siberia, Alaska. Winters S America.
66. *Calidris canutus*. (Red) Knot. 25. Arctic Circle, Winters Africa, Australia, S America.
67. *Calidris ferruginea*. Curlew Sandpiper. 18. N Asia. Africa, Asia, Australia.
68. *Calidris fuscicollis*. White rumped / Bonaparte's Sandpiper. 18. Arctic. Winters S America.
69. *Calidris maritima*. Purple Sandpiper. 20. Arctic circle. Winters W Europe, E.USA.
70. *Calidris mauri*. Western Sandpiper. 16. Alaska. Siberia Winters to Northern S America.
71. *Calidris melanotos*. Pectoral Sandpiper. 20. Siberia. N America, Winters S America.
72. *Calidris paramelanotos*. Cox's Sandpiper. 19. Australia, Status uncertain.
73. *Calidris minuta*. Little Stint. 12. Arctic Eurasia. Winters Africa, Sri Lanka.
74. *Calidris minutilla*. Least Sandpiper. 15. Northern N America. Winters S America.
75. *Calidris ptilocnemis*. Rock Sandpiper. Siberia, Alaska, Winters California, Japan.
76. *Calidris pusillus*. Semi-palmated Sandpiper. 17. Arctic ,Winters mainly S America.
77. *Calidris ruficollis*. Rufous necked Sandpiper. 16. Siberia, Winters to Australia.
78. *Calidris subminuta*. Long toed Stint. 15. E Siberia. Winters E & S Asia.
79. *Calidris temminckii*. Temminck's Stint. 15. Arctic Eurasia. Winters SE Asia, Africa
80. *Calidris tenuirostris*. Great Knot. 27. Siberia, Winters E Asia to Australia.
81. *Eurynorhynchus pygmeus*. Spoonbilled Sandpiper. 15. Siberia. Winters E Asia.
82. *Limicola falcinellus*. Broad billed Sandpiper. 2ss.15. Arctic, Winters Africa, Australia.
83. *Micropalama himantopus*. Stilt Sandpiper. 20. Arctic, Winters to S America.
84. *Tryngites subruficollis*. Buff breasted Sandpiper. 20. Arctic ,Winters to S America.
85. *Philomachus pugnax*. Ruff. 29.N Palearctic, Winters to Africa. SE Asia, Australia.

Family 57, RECURVIROSTRIDAE. Ibisbill, Stilts, Avocets.

1. *Ibidorhyncha struthersii*. Ibisbill. 40. C Asia.
2. *Himantopus himantopus*. Black winged Stilt. 37. Mediterranean, Asia, Africa.
3. *Himantopus meridionalis*. South African Stilt. 38. South Africa.
4. *Himantopus leucocephalus*. Australian Pied Stilt. 37. Philippines to Australia.
5. *Himantopus knudseni*. Hawaiian Stilt. 37. Hawaii.
6. *Himantopus ceylonensis*. Sri Lankan Stilt. 35. Sri Lanka.
7. *Himantopus melanurus*. Black-tailed Stilt. 35. Peru, Brazil to Chile, Argentina.
8. *Himantopus mexicanus*. Black-necked Stilt. 35. USA to Northern S America. West Indies.
9. *Himantopus novaezelandiae*. Black Stilt. 38. New Zealand. (Rare,) hybrids common.
10. *Cladorhynchus leucocephalus*. Banded Stilt. 40. Australia.
11. *Recurvirostra americana*. American Avocet. 44. Canada to C America.
12. *Recurvirostra andina*. Andean Avocet. 42. Peru, Bolivia, Chile, Argentina.
13. *Recurvirostra avosetta*. Avocet. 42. NW Europe, Middle East, Winters SE Asia, Africa.
14. *Recurvirostra novaehollandiae*. Red necked Avocet. 42. Australia, Tasmania.

2-9 now all given specific status, formerly regarded as single species.

61
Br
NB
62
Br
NB
63
Br
NB
64
Br
NB
66
Br
NB
67
Br
NB
65
68
Br
NB
73
Br
NB
69
Br
NB
72
70
71
74
75
Br
NB
76
77
Br
NB
78
79
83
Br
NB
80
Br
NB
81
Br
NB
82
5
6
85
Br
NB
84
2
3
4
RECURVIROSTRIDAE
1
10
7
8
11
2 ♀
9
12
13
14

PHALAROPIDAE, DROMADIDAE, BURHINIDAE, GLAREOLIDAE, THINOCORIDAE
Phalaropes, Crab Plover, Courses & Pratincoles, Seedsnipe

Family 58. PHALAROPIDAE. Phalaropes.

1. *Phalaropus fulicarius*. Red / Grey Phalarope. 17. Holarctic. Winters S Hemisphere.
2. *Phalaropus lobatus*. Red necked Phalarope. 15. Arctic circle. Winters S Oceans.
3. *Steganopus tricolor*. Wilson's Phalarope. 22. Canada, USA, Winters to S America.

Family 59. DROMADIDAE. Crab Plover.

1. *Dromas ardeola*. Crab Plover. 36. E African coast. Indian Ocean, Persian Gulf.

Family 60. BURHINIDAE. Stone Curlews.

1. *Burhinus bistriatus*. Double striped Thick-knee. 4ss. 47. Mexico to Brazil,
2. *Burhinus capensis*. Spotted Thick-knee/Cape Dikkop. 6ss.42. C & S Africa.
3. *Burhinus magnirostris/grallarius*. Bush Curlew. 55. Australia ,New Guinea,
4. *Burhinus oedicnemus*. Stone Curlew. 8ss. 41. Eurasia & N Africa,
5. *Burhinus senegalensis*. Senegal Thick-knee. 2ss. 38. Africa S of Sahara.
6. *Burhinus superciliaris*. Peruvian Thick-knee. 40. Ecuador to Chile.
7. *Burhinus vermiculatus*. Water Dikkop. 2ss. 38. Africa S of Sahara.
8. *Burhinus giganteus*. Beach Thick-knee. 50. Malaysia & Is to Australia,
9. *Burhinus recurvirostris*. Great Stone Plover. 50. India, SE Asia.

Family 61, GLAREOLIDAE. Coursers & Pratincoles.

1. *Pluvianus aegyptius*. Crocodile Bird/Egyptian Plover. 2ss.20. Egypt to W. Africa.
2. *Rhinoptilus africanus*. Two banded Courser. 8ss.21. E & S Africa.
3. *Rhinoptilus bitorquatus*. Jerdon's Courser. 27. Bengal. (Extinct?)
4. *Rhinoptilus chalcopterus*. Bronze winged Courser.2ss.25. Africa S of Sahara.
5. *Rhinoptilus cinctus*. Heuglin's/Three banded Courser. 3ss.28. E & S Africa.
6. *Cursorius coromandelicus*. Indian Courser. 26. India, Pakistan, Sri Lanka.
7. *Cursorius rufus*. Burchell's Courser. 23. S Africa.
8. *Cursorius cursor*. Cream coloured Courser. 23. N Africa, Atlantic Islands to India.
9. *Cursorius temminckii*. Temminck's Courser. 2ss.20. Africa S of Sahara.
10. *Peltohyas australis*. Australian Courser / Dotterel.20. Australia. (Family 55?)
11. *Glareola cinerea*. Grey Pratincole. 2ss.19. W & C Africa.
12. *Stiltia isabella*. Australian Pratincole. 23. Australia, New Guinea, Indonesia.
13. *Glareola lactea*. Small Pratincole. 17. India ,S & E Asia.
14. *Glareola maldivarum*. Oriental Pratincole. 24. E Asia, Indian Ocean. Philippines to Australia.
15. *Glareola nordmanni*. Black winged Pratincole. 25. SE Europe, W Asia. Winters Africa.
16. *Glareola nuchalis*. Rock Pratincole. 2ss.19. Tropical Africa South to Zambesi.
17. *Glareola ocularis*. Madagascar Pratincole. 20. Malagasy, Winters E Africa.
18. *Glareola pratincola*. Collared Pratincole.5ss.25. Mediterranean to India.

Family 62. THINOCORIDAE. Seedsnipe.

1. *Attagis gayi*. Rufous bellied Seedsnipe. 3ss. 30. Ecuador to Chile, Argentina.
2. *Attagis malouinus*. White bellied Seedsnipe. 2ss. 27. Argentina.
3. *Thinocorus orbignyianus*. Grey breasted Seedsnipe. 2ss. 23. Peru to Chile, Argentina.
4. *Thinocorus rumicovorus*.Least Seedsnipe. 5ss. 19. Ecuador to Argentina.

PHALAROPIDAE
1
Br
NB
Br
NB
2
Br
NB
3
DROMADIDAE
1
BURHINIDIDAE
1
2
3
4
5
6
7
GLAREOLIDAE
1
8
9
2
3
4
5
6
7
8
9
10
11
12
13
14
15
16
17
18
THINOCORIDAE
1
2
3
4

CHIONIDIDAE, STARCORARIIDAE, LARIDAE
Sheathbills, Skuas or Jaegers, Gulls

Family 63. CHIONIDIDAE, SheathbilLs,

1. *Chionis alba.* Snowy Sheathbill. 41. South Georgia & Antarctic Is, Argentina & Chile.
2. *Chionis minor.* Black faced Sheathbill. 4ss. 41. Antarctica, S Indian Ocean Islands.

Family 64, STERCORARIIDAE, Skuas or Jaegers.

1. *Stercorarius longicaudus.* Long tailed Jaegar. 52. Arctic Tundra, Winters S Oceans.
2. *Stercorarius parasiticus.* Parasitic Jaegar/Arctic/Richardson's Skua.47. (a) Dark morph. (b)light morph. Arctic circle, Scotland, Scandinavia, Canada. Winters S Oceans.
3. *Stercorarius pomarinus.* Pomarine Skua. 0. (a)Dark morph. (b)light. morph. Arctic coasts Eurasia, America, Greenland, Winters S Oceans.
4. *Catharacta skua.* Great Skua/Bonxie. 57. Arctic NW Eurasia, Winters South.
5. *Catharacta antarctica.* Antarctic Skua. 63. Falkland Is, Argentina, Winters South,
6. *Catharacta lonnbergi.* Brown Skua. 63. Antarctic Is. to New Zealand. Winters North.
7. *Catharacta maccormicki.*South Polar Skua. 53. Antarctica, Winters North.
8. *Catharacta chilensis.* Chilean Skua. 58. Coasts of Chile &Argentina.

Family 65, LARIDAE. (1) Gulls.

1. *Larus argentatus.* Herring Gull. 8ss.55. N European, N American, Arctic coasts.
2. *Larus cachinnans.* Yellow legged Herring Gull. 60. Mediterranean, Middle-East.
3. *Larus armenicus.* Armenian Gull. 60. Armenia, Turkey. Winters Israel.
4. *Larus atricilla.* Laughing Gull. 40. Atlantic coast N America, Caribbean.
5. *Larus audouinii.* Audouin's Gull, 50. Mediterranean.
6. *Larus belcheri.* Band tailed Gull. 50. Coasts Peru & Chile.
7. *Larus atlanticus.* Olrog's Gull. 48. NE Argentina, Winters Uruguay.
8. R*issa brevirostris.* Red Legged Kittiwake. 37. Bering Sea, Winters N Pacific.
9. *Larus Brunnicephalus.* Brown headed Gull. 45. C Asia, Winters Arabia to SE Asia.
10. *Larus bulleri.* Black billed Gull. 36. South Island ,New Zealand.
11. *Larus californicus.* California Gull. 53. N American coasts, Winters to Guatemala.
12. *Larus kamtschatschensis.* Eastern Common Gull. 45. NE Asian coast.
13. *Larus canus.* Mew / Common Gull. 2ss. 40. NW America, N Europe, Siberia.
14. *Larus cirrocephalus.* Grey headed Gull. 2ss. 40. Africa, Malagasy, Southern S. America.

CHIONIDIDAE
1
2
STERCORARIIDAE
1
2
(a)
(b)
(a)
3
(b)
6
4
5
7
8
LARIDAE
JUV
1
1
2
4
5
6
NB
6
7
8
9
10
11
12
13
13 JUV
14

LARIDAE (2)
Gulls

15. *Larus crassirostris.* Black tailed Gull. 45. Siberia, Kurile Is. to Korea, China ,Japan.
16. *Larus delawerensis.* Ring billed Gull. 45. N America, Winters to N of S America, West Indies.
17. *Larus dominicanus.* Kelp Gull. 53. Antarctic, S Africa, S America, Australasia.
18. *Pagophila eburnea.* Ivory Gull. 42. Arctic Circle.
19. *Larus fuliginosus.* Lava Gull. 52. Galapagos Islands.
20. *Larus fuscus.* Lesser Black backed Gull. 2ss. 54. N Eurasia. Winters Africa, USA.
21. *Larus genei.* Slender billed Gull. 43. Mediterranean, SW Asia, Pakistan.
22. *Larus glaucescens.* Glaucous winged Gull. 62. Bering Sea, Winters Japan, Mexico.
23. *Larus glaucoides.* Iceland Gull. 60. Arctic, N America, Iceland, Greenland. Winters to N Europe, N USA.
24. *Larus kumlieni.* Kumlien's Gull. 61. NE Canada, Winters E. USA.
25. *Larus heermanni.* Heermann's Gull. 43. Mexico, NW coast of N America.
26. *Larus hemprichii.* Sooty Gull. 42. NE Africa to Persian Gulf.
27. *Larus hyperboreus.* Glaucous Gull. 70. N Holarctic, Winters Eurasia, N America.
28. *Larus ichthyaetus.* Great Black headed Gull. 66. S C Asia, Winters Africa, Middle East, SE Asia.
29. *Larus leucophthalmus.* White eyed Gull. 41. Red Sea, Somali coast.
30. *Larus maculipennis.* Brown hooded Gull. 35. Patagonia, Falkland Islands.
31. *Larus marinus.* Great Black backed Gull. 73. Palearctic, NE N America.

15
16
17
19
18
20
JUV
JUV
JUV
21
23
22
24
25
28
26
27
31
29
JUV
30

LARIDAE (3)
Gulls

32. *Larus melanocephalus*. Mediterranean Gu11. 39. SE Europe, SW Asia.
33. *Larus minutus*. Little Gull. 28. N Eurasia & NE N America.
34. *Larus modestus*. Grey Gull. 44. Peru, Chile.
34a. *Larus scopulinus*. Red billed Gull. 37. New Zealand, Chatham Is.
35. *Larus novaehollandiae*. Silver Gull. 3ss. 40. Australia, New Caledonia.
36. *Larus hartlaubi*. Hartlaub's Gull. 38. Namibia, South Africa.
37. *Larus occidentalis*. Western Gull 2ss. 62. Pacific coast of N America.
38. *Larus livens*. Yellow footed Gull. 69. Gulf of California.
39. *Larus pacificus*. Pacific Gull. 62. S Australia, Tasmania.
40. *Larus Philadelphia*. Bonaparte's Gull. 33. N America, Mexico, W Indies vagrant to Europe.
41. *Larus pipixcan*. Franklin's Gull. 34. N America, Winters Pacific coast S America.
42. *Larus relictus*. Relict Gull. 45. Mongolia.
43. *Larus ridibundus*. Black headed Gull. 37. Widespread Europe into Asia.
44. *Rhodostethia rosea*. Ross's Gull. 32. N America, N Eurasia.
45. *Xema sabini*. Sabine's Gull. 33. Arctic Circle.
46. *Larus saundersi*. Saunder's Gull. 33. China & E Asia. Breeding area unknown.
47. *Larus schistisagus*. Slaty backed Gull. 60. E & NE Asia.
48. *Larus scoresbii*. Dolphin Gull. 41. Chile, Argentina, Falkland Is.
49. *Larus serranus*. Andean Gull. 45. Ecuador, Chile, Argentina.
50. *Larus thayeri*. Thayer's Gull. 57. Arctic Canada. Winters Pacific Coast N America.
51. *Rissa tridactyla*. Black legged Kittiwake. 41. Atlantic coasts Europe &America. Winters Mexico, Mediterranean.
52. *Creagrus furcatus*. Swallow tailed Gull. 50. Galapagos,WintersColombia to Chile.

32
NB
33
Br
34
J
34
A
36
35
38
39
-37-
40
43
Br
JUV
NB
41
42
-44-
NB
45
Br
47
46
48
49
50
52
51
JUV

LARIDAE (4)
Terns (1)

53. *Chlidonias hybridus.* Whiskered Tern. 6ss. 25. "Old world".
54. *Chlidonias leucoptera.* White winged Black Tern. 24. SE Europe, C Asia, Winters Africa. India, China, Australia.
55. *Chlidonias nigra.* Black Tern. 2ss. 23. Europe,W Asia, N America. Winters tropical Africa & S America.
56. *Phaetusa simplex.* Large billed Tern. 2ss. 37. S America E. of Andes.
57. *Sterna acuticauda.* Black bellied Tern. 30. S & SE Asia.
58. *Chlidonias albistriatus.* Black fronted Tern. 31. New Zealand.
59. *Sterna albifrons.* Little Tern. 9ss. 24. Palearctic, SE Asia, Australasia.
60. *Sterna antillarum.* Least Tern. 23. N American coasts, W Indies. Winters S America.
61. *Sterns aleutica.* Aleutian Tern. 37. Alaska to Japan.
62. *Sterna anaethetus.* Bridled Tern. 7ss. 35. Most tropical ocean Islands.
63. *Sterna aurantia.* Indian River Tern. 35. S & SE Asia.
64. *Sterna balaenarum.* Damara Tern. 24. W coast Africa, Lagos to Cape.
65. *Sterna bengalensis.* Lesser Crested Tern. 3ss. 36. Most Oceans except America.
66. *Sterns bergii.* (Greater) Crested Tern. 5ss. 48. Indian Ocean to Australasia.
67. *Sterna caspia.* Caspian Tern. 2ss. 52. N America, Europe, C, SE Asia. Africa, Australasia.
68. *Sterna dougallii.* Roseate Tern. 5ss. 37. All continents but not S America.
69. *Sterna elegans.* Elegant Tern. 41. California to Chile.
70. *Sterna eurygnatha.* Cayenne Tern. 40. Coasts of Eastern S America. (ss. of 82?)
71. *Sterna forsteri.* Forster's Tern. 38. W Canada, Winters to S. USA & C America.
72. *Sterna fuscata.* Sooty Tern. 7ss. 42. Tropical Oceans.
73. *Sterna hirundinacea.* South American Tern. 42. Brazil, Peru to Cape Horn.
74. *Sterna hirundo.* Common Tern. 4ss. 35. Nearctic, Palearctic, Winters S America, Africa ,Australia.
75. *Sterna lorata.* Peruvian Tern. 33. Pacific coast, Ecuador to Chile.

53
Br
NB
54
Br
NB
55
Br
NB
56
57
Br
NB
59
Br
NB
58
Br
NB
60
61
62
63
64
65
66
67
68
69
70
71
72
73
74
NB
Br
75

LARIDAE (5)
Terns (2)

Family 65 LARIDAE (5). Terns.

76. *Sterna lunata*. Grey backed Tern. 35. Oceania from Hawaii to Fiji.
77. *Sterna maxima*. Royal Tern. 2ss. 47. E American coast, W Indies, W Africa.
78. *Sterns nereis*. Fairy Tern. 4ss. 25. Australia, New Zealand, New Caledonia.
79. *Sterna nilotica*. Gull billed Tern. 6ss. 37. Europe, W Asia, N Africa.
80. *Sterna paradisaea*. Arctic Tern. 38. Arctic Circle, Winters to Antarctica.
81. *Sterna repressa*. White cheeked Tern. 33. Islands & coasts of Indian Ocean.
82. *Sterna sandvicensis*. Sandwich Tern. 2ss. 40. Atlantic coasts of America, Europe & Africa.
83. *Sterna saundersi*. Saunders' Tern. 22. Red Sea to Pakistan, Winters to Malaya.
84. *Sterns striata*. White fronted Tern. 3ss. 41. New Zealand & Is, Tasmania.
85. *Sterna sumatrana*. Black naped Tern. 2ss. 30. Indian Ocean Islands, SE Asia, SW Oceania, Australasia.
86. *Sterna superciliaris*. Amazon/Yellow billed Tern. 25. South America.
87. *Sterna trudeaui*. Snowy crowned Tern. 35. South of S America, Winters Brazil.
88. *Sterna virgata*. Kerguelen Tern. 5ss. 37. Kerguelen Islands, S Indian Ocean.
89. *Sterna vittata*. Antarctic Tern. 5ss. 37. Antarctica, Winters South America.
90. *Sterna bernsteini*. Chinese crested Tern. 38. E China, Winters SE Asia, Moluccas.
91. *Larosterna inca*. Inca Tern. 38. West coast of S America.
92. *Procelsterna cerulea*. Blue/Grey Noddy. 7ss. 28. Pacific Is.
93. *Anous stolidus*. Brown / Common Noddy. 5ss. 40. Southern Ocean Islands.
94. *Anous tenuirostris*. Lesser Noddy. 2ss. 30. Indian Ocean Islands to W Australia.
95. *Anous minutus*. Black/White capped Noddy. 7ss. 34. S Atlantic & Pacific Islands.
96. *Gygis alba*. White/Fairy Tern. 7ss. 31. Tropical Ocean Islands.
97. *Gygis microrhyncha*. Little White Tern. 28. Marquesas Is.

Family 66. RYNCHOPIDAE Skimmers.

1. *Rynchops albicollis*. Indian Skimmer. 39. S & SE Asia.
2. *Rynchops flavirostris*. African Skimmer. 38. Africa S of Sahara.
3. *Rynchops nigra*. Black Skimmer. 3ss. 47. E coast of Americas, W coast S. America.

76
77
78
79
80
81
82
83
84
85
86
87
88
89
90
91
92
93
94
95
96
97
RYNCHOPIDAE
66/1
2
3

ALCIDAE
Auks

1. *Pinguinus impennis*. Great Auk. 75. N Atlantic. (Extinct.)
2. *Alle alle*. Little Auk/Dovekie. 2ss. 20. Arctic, Winters to S of N Atlantic.
3. *Alca torda*. Razorbill. 3ss. 40. N Atlantic.
4. Uria aalge. Guillemot/Common Murre. 7ss. 40. N Atlantic, N Pacific.
5. incl. *Uria Ringvie*. Bridled Guillemot. 40. Atlantic & Arctic only. Not now considered separate species, merely morph. of 4.
6. *Uria lomvia*. Brunnich's Guillemot / Thick billed Murre. 2ss. 44. Oceans of Northern Hemisphere.
7. *Cepphus carbo*. Spectacled Guillemot. 37. Japan & NW Pacific.
8. *Cepphus columba*. Pigeon Guillemot. 2ss. 32. Bering Sea. Japan to California.
9. *Cepphus grylle*. Black Guillemot. 3ss. 32. Arctic Eurasia, N Atlantic.
10. *Brachyramphus brevirostris*. Kittlitz's Murrelet. 23. NW Pacific, Alaska.
11. *Brachyramphus hypoleucus*. Xantus' Murrelet. 25. California. Winters W coast America, from Canada to Baja California.
12. *Synthliboramphus craveri*. Craveri's Murrelet. 21. Islands in Gulf of California.
13. *Brachyramphus marmoratus*. Marbled Murrelet. 24. Siberia, NW America.
14. *Synthliboramphus antiquus*. Ancient Murrelet. 25. Bering Sea, N Pacific.
15. *Synthliboramphus wumizusume*. Japanese Murrelet. 26. Japan.
16. *Ptychoramphus aleuticus*. Cassin's Auklet. 21. Alaska to California.
17. *Cyclorrhynchus psittacula*. Parakeet Auklet. 25. N Pacific, Winters Japan, California.
18. *Aethia cristatella*. Crested Auklet. 23. NE Asia, W Alaska.
19. *Aethia pusilla*. Least Auklet. 15. Alaska, Siberia. Winters to Japan.
20. *Aethia pygmaea*. Whiskered Auklet. 18. Siberia, Aleutians. Winters to Japan.
21. *Cerorhinca monocerata*. Rhinoceros Auklet. 37. Both sides of N Pacific.
22. *Fratercula arctica*. Puffin. 3ss. 30. Coasts NW Palearctic & NE America.
23. *Fratercula corniculata*. Horned Puffin. 36. Siberia, Alaska. Winters to Japan & California.
24. *Lunda cirrhata*. Tufted Puffin. 39. Bering Sea & N Pacific.

2
Br
NB
NB
Br
4
1
5
6
3
NB
8
Br
9
7
NB
-10-
11
Br
12
13
Br
NB
15
16
18
Br
JUV
NB
NB
14
Br
17
Br
NB
19
NB
Br
23
Br
NB
20
JUV
Br
NB
Br
21
NB
22
JUV
24
NB
Br

PTEROCLIDAE
Sandgrouse

1. *Syrrhaptes paradoxus*. Pallas' Sandgrouse. 37. C Asia, Winters to Europe, China.
2. *Syrrhaptes tibetanus*. Tibetan Sandgrouse. 48. Tibet Mountains. Winters lower ground.
3. *Pterocles alchata*. Pin-tailed Sandgrouse. 2ss. 37. Iberia, NW Africa, Israel, to C. Asia & India.
4. *Pterocles bicinctus*. Double banded Sandgrouse. 5ss. 26. Southern Africa.
5. *Pterocles burchelli*. Variegated Sandgrouse. 2ss. 25. S Africa.
6. *Pterocles coronatus*. Coroneted Sandgrouse. 5ss. 28. N Africa, Middle East. to India.
7. *Pterocles decoratus*. Black faced Sandgrouse. 4ss. 25. Somalia, Kenya, Tanzania.
8. *Pterocles exustus*. Chestnut bellied Sandgrouse.6ss. 29. Senegal to Ethiopia. NE Africa, Arabia, Iraq, India.
9. *Pterocles gutturalis*. Yellow throated Sandgrouse.3ss. 31. E & S Africa.
10. *Pterocles indicus*. Painted Sandgrouse. 27. India.
11. *Pterocles lichtensteinii*. Lichtenstein's Sandgrouse. 5ss. 25. Kenya, N Africa, Arabia to Pakistan.
12. *Pterocles namaqua*. Namaqua Sandgrouse. 28. Southern Africa.
13. *Pterocles orientalis*. Black bellied Sandgrouse. 3ss. 35. Mediterranean Canary Is to India, China, SE Asia.
14. *Pterocles personatus*. Madagascar Sandgrouse. 35. Malagasy.
15. *Pterocles quadricinctus*. Four banded Sandgrouse. 2ss. 25. Africa S of Sahara.
16. *Pterocles senegallus*. Spotted Sandgrouse. 34. NE Africa, Middle East, India.

1
2
3
4
5
6
7
8
9
10
11
12
13
14
15
16

COLUMBIDAE (1).
Pigeons & Doves

1. *Columba albinucha*. White naped Pigeon. 34. Cameroon, Zaire, Uganda, Rwanda.
2. *Columba albitorques*. White collared Pigeon. 31. Ethiopia, Eritrea.
3. *Columba araucana*. Chilean Pigeon. 37. Chile, Argentina.
4. *Columba argentina*. Silvery Wood Pigeon. 38. Sumatra, Borneo & adjacent Islands.
5. *Columba arquatrix*. African Olive Pigeon. 40. Ethiopia, Arabia to S Africa.
6. *Columba sjoestedti*. Cameroon Pigeon. 40. Cameroon, Nigeria.
7. *Columba thomensis*. Sao Tome Olive Pigeon. 40. Sao Tome Island.
8. *Columba bollii*. Bolle's Pigeon. 39. Canary Is.
9. *Columba caribaea*. Ring tailed Pigeon. 40. Jamaica.
10. *Columba cayennensis*. Pale vented Pigeon. 5ss. 30. Mexico to Brazil, Argentina.
11. *Columba chiriquensis*. Chiriqui Pigeon. 29. Panama, Unique. Probably Hybrid.
12. *Columba corensis*. Bare eyed Pigeon. 33. Colombia, Venezuela & adjacent Islands.
13. *Columba delagorguei*. Eastern Bronze naped Pigeon. 2ss. 29. E & S Africa.
14. *Columba elphinstonii*. Nilgiri Wood Pigeon. 42. S W India.
15. *Columba eversmanni*. Pale backed Pigeon. 30. Iran to NW India.
16. *Columba fasciata*. Band tailed Pigeon. 8ss. 35. West of America, Canada to Argentina.
17. *Columba flavirostris*. Red billed Pigeon. 4ss. 33. Texas to Costa Rica.
18. *Columba goodsoni*. Dusky Pigeon. 26. Colombia, Ecuador.
19. *Columba guinea*. Speckled Pigeon. 3ss. 37. Africa S of Sahara.
20. *Columba hodgsonii*. Speckled Wood Pigeon. 38. India, Burma, China.
21. *Columba inornata*. Plain Pigeon. 3ss. 37. Cuba, Hispaniola, Jamaica, Puerto Rico.
22. *Columba janthina*. Japanese Wood Pigeon. 3ss. 40. Ryukyu, Bonin & Volcano Is.
23. *Columba jouyi*. Ryukyu Pigeon. 40. Ryukyu Islands (extinct.)
24. *Columba junoniae*. Laurel Pigeon. 38. Canary Is.
25. *Columba leucocephala*. White crowned Pigeon. 35. Florida. W Indies. Panama.
26. *Columba leucomela*. White headed Pigeon. 40. E Australia.

1
2
3
4
5
6
7
8
9
10
11
12
13
14
15
16
17
18
19
20
21
22
23
24
25
26

COLUMBIDAE (2)
Pigeons & Doves

27. *Columba leuconota*. Snow Pigeon. 2ss. 34. Himalayas to China.
28. *Columba livia*. Rock Dove. 14ss. 33. Europe, N Africa, Middle East.
 A & B are examples of Feral (Domestic) Pigeons, incl. in 28.
29. *Columba maculosa*. Spot-winged Pigeon. 2ss. 33. Peru, Brazil, Argentina.
30. *Columba malherbii*. Sao Tome Pigeon. 32. Sao Tome.
31. *Columba iriditorques*. Western Bronze naped Pigeon. 29. W & WC Africa.
32. *Columba mayeri*. Pink Pigeon. 35. Mauritius. (extinct ?)
33. *Columba nigrirostris*. Short billed Pigeon. 30. Mexico to Colombia.
34. *Columba oenas*. Stock Dove/Pigeon. 3ss. 33. Europe,W Asia. Winters to N Africa.
35. *Columba oenops*. Peruvian Pigeon. 30. Peru.
36. *Columba oliviae*. Somali Pigeon. 31. Somaliland.
37. *Columba pallidiceps*. Yellow legged Pigeon. 40. Bismarck Archipelago. Solomon Islands.
38. *Columba palumboides*. Andaman Wood Pigeon. 41. Andaman, Nicobar Islands.
39. *Columba palumbus*. Wood Pigeon. 6ss. 41. Western Palearctic.
40. *Columba picazuro*. Picazuro Pigeon. 2ss. 35. Brazil, Bolivia, Argentina.
41. *Columba plumbea*. Plumbeous Pigeon. 6ss. 30. N E &C South America.
42. *Columba pollenii*. Comoro Olive Pigeon. 40. Comoro Is.
43. *Columba pulchricollis*. Ashy Wood Pigeon. 36. Tibet, Nepal, Taiwan, SE Asia.
44. *Columba punicea*. Pale capped Pigeon. 40. India, Tibet, Hainan. SE Asia.
45. *Columba rupestris*. Hill/Eastern Rock Pigeon. 2ss. 33. C Asia, Manchuria.
46. *Columba speciosa*. Scaled Pigeon. 30. Mexico to Brazil & Argentina.
47. *Columba squamosa*. Scaly naped Pigeon. 37. West Indies, Venezuela.
48. *Columba subvinacea*. Ruddy Pigeon. 8ss. 28. Costa Rica to Bolivia & Brazil.
49. *Columba torringtoni*. Ceylon Wood Pigeon. 39. Sri Lanka.
50. *Columba trocaz*. Trocaz Pigeon. 39. Madeira.
51. *Columba unicincta*. African Wood Pigeon. 40. W & C Africa.
52. *Columba versicolor*. Bonin Wood Pigeon. 42. Bonin Island.(extinct.)
53. *Columba vitiensis*. Metallic Wood Pigeon. 9ss. 40. Malaysia, New Guinea, SW Oceania.

27
A
28
B
29
30
31
32
33
34
35
37
38
36
39
40
41
42
43
44
45
46
47
48
49
50
51
52
53

COLUMBIDAEE (3)
Turtle Doves, Cuckoo Doves

54. *Streptopelia bitorquata*. Island Collared Dove. 2ss. 27. Sundas to Philippines.
55. *Streptopelia capicola*. Ring necked Dove. 10ss. 25. E & S Africa, Comoros.
56. *Streptopelia chinensis*. Spotted Dove. 8ss. 30. India to SE Asia, Australia.
57. *Streptopelia decaocto*. Collared Dove. 3ss. 28. Asia, now also most Europe.
58. *Streptopelia decipiens*. African Mourning Dove. 5ss. 30. Africa S of Sahara.
59. *Streptopelia Lugens*. Dusky Turtle Dove. 3ss. 28. E Africa, SW Arabia.
60. *Streptopelia hypopyrrha*. Pink bellied/Adamawa Turtle Dove. 27. Nigeria to Cameroon, Chad.
61. *Streptopelia orientalis*. Eastern Turtle Dove. 6ss. 33. C & E Asia.
62. *Stretopelia picturata*. Madagascar Turtle Dove. 8ss. 32. Malagasy, Indian Ocean islands.
63. *Streptopelia reichenowi*. White winged Collared Dove. 25. East Africa.
64. *Streptopelia risoria*. Barbary Dove. 28. World-wide.(Domesticated form 65).
65. *Streptopelia Roseogrisea*. Pink headed/African Collared Dove. 3ss. 26. Africa S of Sahara, Arabia.
66. *Streptopelia semitorquata*. Red eyed Dove. 3ss. 32. Africa S of Sahara, Arabia.
67. *Streptopelia senegalensis*. Laughing Dove. 8ss. 24. E, SE Africa to India.
68. *Streptopelia tranquebarica*. Red collared Dove. 3ss. 24. India, SE Asia.
69. *Streptopelia turtur*. Turtle Dove. 4ss. 26. Europe, Asia. Winters to S Africa.
70. *Streptopelia vinacea*. Vinaceous Dove. 3ss. 24. Senegal to Sudan & Zaire.
71. *Geopelia cuneata*. Diamond Dove. 20. N C Australia, domesticated elsewhere.
72. *Geopelia humeralis*. Bar shouldered Dove. 2ss. 29. N E Australia.
73. *Geopelia striata*. Zebra Dove. 4ss. 20. SE Asia to Australia. introduced elsewhere.
74. *Geopelia maugeus*. Barred Dove. 2ss. 20. Sumbawa to Timor. Kai Is & Tanimbar.
75. *Geopelia placida*. Peaceful Dove. 20. N Australia, S New Guinea.
76. *Aplopelia larvata*. Lemon Dove. 6ss. 25. Africa S of Sahara.
77. *Turacoena manadensis*. White faced Pigeon. 2ss. 32. Sulawesi.
78. *Turacoena modesta*. Slaty Cuckoo Dove / Timer Black Pigeon. 33. Timor, Wetar.
79. *Macropygia amboinensis*. Slender billed / Pink breasted Cuckoo Dove. 15ss. 40. East Indies, New Guinea, Bismarck Arch.

79a. *Macropygia emiliana*. Indonesian/Ruddy Cuckoo Dove. 40. Sumatra to Flores.

80. *Macropygia m. arossi*. Mackinlay's Cuckoo Dove. (Chestnut form)30. Solomons.
81. *Macropygia Mackinlayi*. Mackinlay's Cuckoo Dove. (Grey forms) 3ss 30 Vanuatu & other Pacific islands.

81a. *Macropygia cinnamomea*. Enggano Cuckoo Dove. 40. Enggano I.

82. *Macropygia magna*. Large/Dusky Cuckoo Dove. 4ss. 40. Wallacea.
83. *Macropygia nigrirostris*. Black billed Cuckoo Dove. 30. New Guinea, Bismarck Archipelago.
84. *Macropygia phasianella*. Brown Cuckoo Dove. 9ss. 40. N, E Australia & Islands.

84a. *Macropygia tenuirostris*. Philippine Cuckoo Dove. 40. Philippines.

85. *Macropygia ruficeps*. Little Cuckoo Dove. 8ss. 30. China, SE Asia, Sundas.
86. *Macropygia rufipennis*. Andaman Cuckoo Dove. 40. Andaman & Nicobar Is.
87. *Macropygia unchall*. Barred Cuckoo Dove. 3ss. 38. Himalayas to SE Asia, Sundas.

54
55
56
57
58
59
60
61
62
63
64
65
68
♀
♂
66
67
69
70
71
72
73
74
75
76
77
78
79
79
A
80
81
82
83
81A
84
85
86
84A
87

COLUMBIDAE (4)
Pigeons & Doves

88. *Reinwardtoena browni.* Pied Cuckoo Dove. 40. New Britain, Duke of York Island.
89. *Reinwardtoena crassirostris.* Crested Cuckoo Dove. 40. Solomon Islands.
90. *Reinwardtoena reinwardtsi.* Great Cuckoo Dove. 3ss. 40. Moluccas, New Guinea.
91. *Oena capensis.* Namaqua Dove. 2ss. 22. Africa S of Sahara.
92. *Turtur abyssinicus.* Black billed Wood Dove. 18. Senegal to Ethiopia.
93. *Turtur afer.* Blue spotted Wood Dove. 20. Africa S of Sahara.
94. *Turtur brehmeri.* Blue headed Wood Dove. 2ss. 25. W Africa.
95. *Turtur chalcospilus.* Emerald spotted Wood Dove. 2ss. 18. E & S Africa.
96. *Turtur tympanistria.* Tambourine Dove. 2ss. 19. Africa S of Sahara.
97. *Chalcophaps indica.* Emerald Dove. 13ss. 25. India,SE Asia to Australia.
98. *Chalcophaps stephani.* Stephan's/Brown backed Dove. 3ss. 23. Sulawesi, New Guinea to Solomon Islands.
99. *Henicophaps albifrons.* New Guinea Bronzewing. 2ss. 32. New Guinea & Islands.
100. *Henicophaps foersteri.* New Britain Bronzewing. 32. New Britain.
101. *Petrophassa albipennis.* White quilled Rock Pigeon. 2ss. 28. NW Australia.
102. *Geophaps plumifera.* Spinifex / Plumed Pigeon. 4ss. 22. N,C Australia.
103. Incl. *G. p. ferruginea.* Red plumed Pigeon. 21. NW Australia.
104. *Petrophassa rufipennis.* Chestnut quilled Rock Pigeon. 33. N Australia.
105. *Geophaps scripta.* Squatter Pigeon. 2ss. 28. NE Australia.
106. *Geophaps smithii.* Partridge Pigeon. 25. NW Australia.
107. *Phaps chalcoptera.* Common Bronzewing. 3ss. 30. Australia.
108. *Phaps elegans.* Brush Bronzewing. 2ss. 28. SE, E, SW Australia.
109. *Phaps histrionica.* Flock Bronzewing. 2ss. 27. C N Australia.
110. *Geophaps lophotes.* Crested Pigeon. 2ss. 31. Interior of Australia.
111. *Leucosarcia melanoleuca.* Womga Pigeon. 42. E Australia.
112. *Zenaida asiatica.* White winged Dove. 4ss. 27. SW USA to Chile, West Indies.
113. *Zenaida auriculata.* Eared Dove. 11ss. 25. S America, Lesser Antilles.
114 *Zenaida aurita.* Zenaida Dove. 3ss. 29. Mexico, West Indies.
115. *Zenaida galapagoensis.* Galapagos Dove. 2ss. 28. Galapagos Islands.
116. *Zenaida macroura.* Mourning Dove. 6ss. 27. N & C America. West Indies.
117. *Zenaida graysoni.* Socorro Dove. 30. Socorro Island. (extinct in wild)
118. *Ectopistes migratorius.* Passenger Pigeon. 40. E of N America. (extinct.)

88
89
90
91
92
93
94
95
96
97
98
99
100
101
102
103
104
105
106
107
108
109
110
111
112
113
114
118
115
116
117

COLUMBIDAE (5)
New World Pigeons & Doves

119. *Columbina cruziana*. Croaking Ground Dove. 18. Ecuador, Peru, Chile.
120. *Columbina cyanopis*. Blue eyed Ground Dove. 15. Brazil.
121. *Columbina minuta*. Plain breasted Ground Dove. 3ss. 15. Mexico to Argentina.
122. *Columbina passerina*. Common Ground Dove. 19ss. 16. USA to Brazil, Ecuador.
123. *Columbina picui*. Picui Ground Dove. 2ss. 18. Peru to Brazil, Chile, Argentina.
124. *Columbina squammata*. Scaled Dove. 2ss. 21. Venezuela, Colombia to Brazil, Argentina.
125. *Columbina inca*. Inca Dove. 18. S W USA to Costa Rica.
126. *Columbina talpacoti*. Ruddy Ground Dove. 4ss. 18. Mexico to Brazil, Argentina.
127. *Columbina buckleyi*. Ecuadorian Ground Dove. 18. Ecuador, Peru.
128. *Claravis godefrida*. Purple winged Ground Dove. 22. Brazil, Paraguay.
129. *Claravis mondetoura*. Maroon chested Ground Dove. 22. Mexico to Bolivia.
130. *Claravis pretiosa*. Blue Ground Dove. 21. Mexico to Brazil, Argentina.
131. *Metriopelia aymara*. Golden spotted Ground Dove. 19. Peru, Chile, Argentina.
132. *Metriopelia ceciliae*. Bare faced Ground Dove. 3ss. 19. Peru, Bolivia, Chile.
133. *Metriopelia melanoptera*. Black winged Ground Dove. 2ss. 22. Colombia to Argentina, Chile.
134. *Metriopelia morenoi*. Bare eyed Ground Dove. 18. Argentina.
135. *Uropelia campestris*. Long tailed Ground Dove. 18. Brazil, Bolivia.
136. *Leptotila cassini*. Grey chested Dove. 3ss. 25. Colombia.
137. *Leptotila conoveri*. Tolima Dove. 25. Colombia.
138. *Leptotila jamaicensis*. Caribbean Dove. 31. Jamaica & adjacent Islands.
139. *Leptotila megalura*. White faced Dove. 2ss. 30. Bolivia Argentina.
140. *Leptotila ochraceiventris*. Ochre bellied Dove. 24. Ecuador, Peru.
141. *Leptotila pallida*. Pallid Dove. 25. Colombia, Ecuador.
142. *Leptotila plumbeiceps*. Grey headed Dove. 24. Mexico to Colombia.
143. *Leptotila battyi*. Brown backed Dove. 4ss. 24. Panama & Pacific Is.
144. *Leptotila rufaxilla*. Grey fronted Dove. 7ss. 28. Guyanas, Venezuela to Brazil, Argentina.
145. *Leptotila verreauxi*. White tipped Dove. 7ss. 28. S USA to Brazil, Argentina.
146. *Leptotile wellsi*. Grenada Dove. 30. Grenada.

119
120
121
122
123
124
125
126
127
128
129
130
131
132
133
134
135
136
137
138
139
140
141
142
143
144
145
146

COLUMBIDAE (6)
Quail Doves, Ground Doves

147. *Geotrygon caniceps*. Grey headed Quail Dove. 2ss. 28. Cuba, Dominican Republic.
148. *Geotrygon chrysia*. Key West Quail Dove. 28. Bahamas, Cuba, Hispaniola.
149. *Geotrygon costaricensis*. Buff fronted Quail Dove. 28. Costa Rica, Panama.
150. *Geotrygon frenata*. White throated Quail Dove. 3ss. 33. Colombia to Bolivia.
151. *Geotrygon goldmani*. Russet crowned Quail Dove. 2ss. 27. Panama.
152. *Geotrygon lawrencii*. Purplish backed Quail Dove. 3ss. 33. Mexico to Panama.
153. *Geotrygon linearis*. Lined Quail Dove. 6ss. 30. Colombia, Venezuela.
154. *Geotrygon chiriquensis*. Rufous breasted Quail Dove. 30. Panama.
155. *Geotrygon albifacies*. White faced Quail Dove. 30. Mexico to Nicaragua.
156. *Geotrygon montana*. Ruddy Quail Dove. 2ss. 24. West Indies, Mexico to Argentina.
157. *Geotrygon mystacea*. Bridled Quail Dove. 30. Virgin Is, Lesser Antilles.
158. *Geotrygon sapphirina*. Sapphire Quail Dove. 3ss. 26. Colombia, Ecuador, Peru.
159. *Geotrygon veraguensis*. Olive backed Quail Dove. 24. Costa Rica to Ecuador.
160. *Geotrygon versicolor*. Crested Quail Dove. 30. Jamaica.
161. *Geotrygon violacea*. Violaceous Quail Dove. 2ss. 24. Nicaragua to Argentina.
162. *Gallicolumba beccarii*. Bronze Ground Dove. 6ss. 18. New Guinea to Solomon Islands.
163. *Gallicolumba canifrons*. Palau Ground Dove. 22. Palau.
164. *Gallicolumba erythroptera*. Polynesian Ground Dove. 27. Tuamotu Archipelago.
165. *Gallicolumba luzonica*. Luzon Bleeding Heart. 30. Luzon.
166. *Gallicolumba criniger*. Mindanao Bleeding Heart. 30. Mindanao, Leyte.
167. *Gallicolumba keayi*. Negros Bleeding Heart. 30. Negros.
168. *Gallicolumba menagei*. Sulu Bleeding Heart. 30. Tawitawi.(Sulu Archipelago).
169. *Gallicolumba platenae*. Mindoro Bleeding Heart. 30. Mindoro.
170. *Gallicolumba hoedtii*. Wetar Ground Dove. 30. Wetar.(Lesser Sundas).
171. *Gallicolumba jobiensis*. White bibbed Ground Dove. 2ss. 26. New Guinea, Solomon Islands.
172. *Gallicolumba rubescens*. Marquesan Ground Dove. 22. Marquesas Is.
173. *Gallicolumba rufigula*. Cinnamon Ground Dove / Goldenheart. 5ss. 25. New Guinea & Islands.
174. *Gallicolumba salamonis*. Thick billed Ground Dove. 24. Solomon Islands.
175. *Gallicolumba sanctaecrucis*. Santa Cruz Ground Dove. 24. Santa Cruz, Vanuatu.
176. *Gallicolumba stairi*. Friendly Ground Dove. 26. Fiji, Samoa, Tonga.

147
148
149
150
151
152
153
154
155
156
157
158
159
160
161
162
163
164
165
166
167
168
166
JUV
169
170
171
172
173
174
175
176

COLUMBIDAE (7)
Pigeons

177. *Gallicolumba tristigmata.* Celebes Quail Dove. 3ss. 30. Sulawesi.
178. *Gallicolumba xanthonura.* White throated Ground Dove. 25. Mariana Islands.
179. *Gallicolumba kubaryi.* Truk Island Ground Dove. 28. Caroline Is.
179a. *Gallicolumba ferruginea.* Tanna Ground Dove. 27. Vanuatu.
180. *Starnoenas cyanocephala.* Blue headed Quail Dove. 30. Cuba.
181. *Otidiphaps nobilis.* Pheasant Pigeon. 4ss. 60. New Guinea & Is.
182. *Caloenas nicobarica.* Nicobar Pigeon. 2ss. 36. Nicobar Is. to Palau, Solomon Is.
183. *Trugon terrestris.* Thick billed Ground Dove. 3ss. 34. Papua,New Guinea.
184. *Goura cristata.* Western Ground Pigeon. 2ss. 72. W New Guinea, Papuan Is.
185. *Goura scheepmakeri.* Southern Ground Pigeon. 3ss. 75. Southern New Guinea.
186. *Goura victoria.* Victoria crowned Pigeon. 75. N. New Guinea.
187. *Didunculus strigirostris.* Tooth billed Pigeon. 30. Samoa.
188. *Phapitreron amethystina.* Amethyst Brown Dove. 5ss. 28. Philippines.
189. *Phapitreron leucotis.* White eared Brown Dove. 4ss 26. Philippines.
190. *Phapitreron cinereiceps.* Dark eared Brown Dove. 26. S. Philippines.
191. *Microgoura meeki.* Choiseul Pigeon. 41. Solomon Is. (not seen since 1904.)

177
178
179
180
179A
182
181
183
184
185
186
188
187
189
190
191

COLUMBIDAE (8)
Green Pigeons

192. *Treron apicauda*. Pin tailed Green Pigeon. 3ss. 32. W India to Laos.
193. *Treron australis*. Madagascar Green Pigeon. 3ss. 28. Malagasy,Comoros.
194. *Treron calva*. African Green Pigeon. 18ss. 28. Africa.
195. incl. *T. c. delalandiae*. Delalande's Green Pigeon 28. E. to S. Africa.
196. *Treron pembaensis*. Pemba Island Green Pigeon. 28. Pemba Island.
197. *Treron sanctithomae*. Sao Thome Green Pigeon. 28. Sao Thome.
198. *Treron bicincta*. Orange breasted Green Pigeon. 4ss. 29. India to S E Asia, Java.
199. *Treron capellei*. Large Green Pigeon. 2ss. 35. Malaysia, Indonesia.
200. *Treron curvirostra*. Thick billed Green Pigeon. 10ss. 26. S E Asia, Indonesia.
201. *Treron floris*. Flores Green Pigeon. 29. Lesser Sunda Is.
202. *Treron formosae*. Whistling Green Pigeon. 4ss. 32. Taiwan, Ryukyu Is, Philippines.
203. *Treron fulvicollis*. Cinnamon headed Green Pigeon. 4ss. 25. SE Asia, Borneo, Sumatra.
204. *Treron griseicauda*. Grey cheeked Green Pigeon. 5ss. 26. Sumatra, Java, Bali, to Sulawesi.
205. *Treron olax*. Little Green Pigeon. 21. Malaya, Sumatra, Java, Borneo.
206. *Treron oxyura*. Green spectacled Pigeon. 30. Sumatra Java.
207. *Treron phoenicoptera*. Yellow footed Green Pigeon. 5ss. 32. Pakistan to China & S E Asia.
208. *Treron pompadora*. Pompadour Green Pigeon. 9ss. 25. India, S E Asia, Wallacea.
209. *Treron psittacea*. Timor Green Pigeon. 29. Timor & Lesser Sundas.
210. *Treron seimundi*. Yellow vented Green Pigeon. 2ss. 26. Annam, Malaya.
211. *Treron sieboldii*. (White bellied) Green Pigeon. 32. S E Asia, Japan Taiwan.
212. *Treron sphenura*. Wedge tailed Green Pigeon. 6ss. 32. India. S E Asia to Indonesia.
213. *Treron teysmanni*. Sumba Green Pigeon. 29. Sumba Island.
214. *Treron vernans*. Pink necked Green Pigeon. 8ss. 26. SE Asia, Philippines, Sulawesi, Gr. Sundas.
215. *Treron waalia*. Bruce's Green Pigeon. 28. Senegal to Horn of Africa, Arabia.

192
193
194
195
196
197
198
199
200
201
202
203
204
205
206
207
208
209
210
211
212
213
214
215

COLUMBIDAE (9)
Fruit Doves

216. *Ptilinopus arcanus*. Negros Fruit Dove. 16. Negros Island.(Philippines).
217. *Ptilinopus aurantiifrons*. Orange fronted Fruit Dove. 30. New Guinea.
218. *Ptilinopus cinctus*. Black backed Fruit Dove. 5ss. 33. Lesser Sundas.
219. *Ptilinopus alligator*. Black banded Fruit Dove. 33. N C Australia.
220. *Ptilinopus coronulatus*. Coroneted Fruit Dove. 5ss. 26. New Guinea & Islands.
221. *Ptilinopus dohertyi*. Red naped Fruit Dove. 31. Sumba I.
222. *Ptilinopus dupetithouarsii*. White capped Fruit Dove. 2ss. 26. Marquesas Is.
223. *Ptilinopus eugeniae*. White headed Fruit Dove. 19. Solomon Is.
224. *Ptilinopus fischeri*. Red eared Fruit Dove. 3ss. 34. Sulawesi.
225. *Ptilinopus bernsteinii*. Scarlet breasted Fruit Dove. 26. N Moluccas.
226. *Ptilinopus granulifrons*. Carunculated Fruit Dove. 27. Obi.(Moluccas).
227. *Ptilinopus greyii*. Red bellied Fruit Dove. 20. Vanuatu, New Caledonia.
228. *Ptilinopus huttoni*. Rapa Fruit Dove. 29. Rapa Islands, (Austral group).
229. *Ptilinopus hyogastra*. Grey headed Fruit Dove. 27. N Moluccas.
230. *Ptilinopus insolitus*. Knob billed Fruit Dove. 2ss. 24. Bismarck Archipelago.
231. *Ptilinopus insularis*. Henderson Fruit Dove. 28. Henderson I.(Pitcairns.)
232. *Ptilinopus iozonus*. Orange bellied Fruit Dove. 5ss. 26. New Guinea & Islands.
233. *Ptilinopus jambu*. Jambu Fruit Dove. 26. Malaya, Sumatra, Borneo.
234. *Ptilinopus layardi*. Velvet / Whistling Dove. 29. Fiji.
235. *Ptilinopus leclancheri*. Black chinned Fruit Dove. 2ss. 29. Philippines.
236. *Ptilinopus luteovirens*. Golden Dove. 19. Fiji.
237. *Ptilinopus magnificus*. Wompoo Fruit Dove. 7ss. 35/50. New Guinea.
238. *Ptilinopus marchei*. Flame breasted Fruit Dove. 30. Philippines, E Australia.
239. *Ptilinopus melanospila*. Black naped Fruit Dove. l0ss. 28. Philippines to Sulawesi, Moluccas, Sundas.
240. *Ptilinopus mercieri*. Red moustached Fruit Dove. 2ss. 24. Marquesss Is.
241. *Ptilinopus merrillii*. Cream bellied Fruit Dove. 2ss. 30. Philippines.
242. *Ptilinopus monacha*. Blue capped Fruit Dove. 22. N Moluccas.
243. *Ptilinopus naina*. Dwarf Fruit Dove. 2ss. 15. New Guinea & adjoining Islands.

216
217
218
219
220
221
222
223
224
225
226
227
230
232
228
229
231
233
234
235
236
237
239
240
241
238
242
243

COLUMBIDAE (10)
Fruit Doves, Blue Pigeons

245. *Ptilinopus occipitalis*. Yellow breasted Fruit Dove. 29. Philippines.
246. *Ptilinopus ornatus*. Ornate Fruit Dove. 3ss. 30. New Guinea.
247. *Ptilinopus perlatus*. Pink spotted Fruit Dove. 3ss. 30. New Guinea.
248. *Ptilinopus perousii*. Many coloured Fruit Dove. 2ss. 21. Samoa, Fiji, Tonga.
249. *Ptilinopus porphyraceus*. Crimson crowned Fruit Dove. 4ss. 23. Samoa, Fiji, Tonga & adjoining Islands.
250. *Ptilinopus pelewensis*. Pelew Fruit Dove. 21. Palau Island.
251. *Ptilinopus porphyreus*. Pink headed Fruit Dove. 30. Sumatra, Java, Bali.
252. *Ptilinopus pulchellus*. Beautiful Fruit Dove. 2ss. 24. New Guinea & Islands.
253. *Ptilinopus purpuratus*. Grey-green Fruit Dove. 5ss. 26. Society Island, Tuamotu.
254. *Ptilinopus coralensis*. Atoll Fruit Dove. 26.Tuamotu.
255. *Ptilinopus chalcurus*. Mahatea Fruit Dove. 26. Mahatea I.(Tuamotu).
256. *Ptilinopus rarotongensis*. Rarotonga Fruit Dove. 2ss . 23. Rarotonga.
257. *Ptilinopus regina*. Rose crowned Fruit Dove. 5ss. 23. NE Australia, Lesser Sundas.
258. *Ptilinopus richardsii*. Silver capped Fruit Dove. 2ss. 28. Solomon Is.
259. *Ptilinopus rivoli*. White breasted Fruit Dove. 6ss. 25. Moluccas,New Guinea, Bismarck Archipelago.
260. *Ptilinopus roseicapilla*. Mariana Fruit Dove. 28. Mariana Is.
261. *Ptilinopus solomonensis*. Yellow bibbed Fruit Dove. 9ss. 19. Solomon Is.
262. *Ptilinopus subgularis*. Maroon chinned Fruit Dove. 3ss. 30. Sulawesi.
263. *Ptilinopus superbus*. Superb Fruit Dove. 2ss. 23. Sulawesi, Moluccas to New Guinea & E Australia.
264. *Ptilinopus tannensis*. Tanna Fruit Dove. 30. Vanuatu.
265. *Ptilinopus victor*. Orange Dove. 20. Fiji.
266. *Ptilinopus viridis*. Claret breasted Fruit Dove. 7ss. 26. Moluccas to New Guinea & Solomon Isl.
267. *Ptilinopus wallacii*. Wallace's Fruit Dove. 29. Moluccas, New Guinea, Aru.
268. *Drepanoptila holosericea*. Cloven feathered Dove. 30. New Caledonia.
269. *Alectroenas madagascariensis*. Madagascar Blue Pigeon. 26. Malagasy.
270. *Alectroenas nitidissima*. Mauritius Blue Pigeon. 21. Mauritius.(extinct).
271. *Alectroenas pulcherrima*. Seychelles Blue Pigeon. 25. Seychelles.
272. *Alectroenas sganzini*. Comoro Blue Pigeon. 2ss. 28. Comoro Is.

245
246
247
248
249
250
251
252
253
254
255
256
257
258
259
260
261
262
263
264
265
266
267
268
269
270
271
272

COLUMBIDAE (11)
Imperial Pigeons

273. *Ducula aenea*. Green Imperial Pigeon. 13ss. 45. India, SE Asia, Indonesia.
274. *Ducula aurorae*. Polynesian Imperial Pigeon. 35. Society Is.
275. *Ducula badia*. Mountain Imperial Pigeon. 6ss. 45. India, China, SE Asia, Greater Sundas.
276. *Ducula bakeri*. Baker's Imperial Pigeon. 41. Vanuatu.
277. *Ducula basilica*. Cinnamon bellied Imperial Pigeon. 2ss.35. N Moluccas.
278. *Ducula bicolor*. Pied Imperial Pigeon. 45. SE Asia, Philippines to Indonesia.
278a. *Ducula constans*. Kimberley Imperial Pigeon. 45. NW Australia.
279. *Ducula subflavescens*. Yellow tinted Imperial Pigeon. 45. Bismarck Archipelago.
279a. *Ducula luctuosa*. White Imperial Pigeon. 48. Sulawesi.
280. *Ducula brenchleti*. Chestnut bellied Pigeon. 41. Solomon Is.
281. *Ducula carola*. Spotted Imperial Pigeon. 3ss. 33. Philippines.
282. *Ducula chalconota*. Rufescent Imperial Pigeon. 2ss. 37. New Guinea.
283. *Ducula cineracea*. Timor Imperial Pigeon. 2ss. 45. Timor.Wetar.
284. *Ducula concinna*. Elegant Imperial Pigeon. 4ss. 47. Talaud to Kai, Tanimbar Islands.
285. *Ducula finschii*. Finsch's Imperial Pigeon. 36. Bismarck Archipelago.
286. *Ducula forsteni*. White bellied Imperial Pigeon. 44. Sulawesi.
287. *Ducula galeata*. Marquesas Imperial Pigeon. 48. Nukuhiva.(Marquesas)
288. *Ducula goliath*. New Caledonian Imperial Pigeon. 55. New Caledonia.
289. *Ducula lacernulata*. Dark backed Imperial Pigeon. 3ss. 45. Java, Bali, Lombok, Flores.
290. *Ducula latrans*. Peale's Imperial Pigeon. 41. Fiji.
291. *Ducula melanochroa*. Bismarck Imperial Pigeon. 43. Bismarck Archipelago.
292. *Ducula mindorensis*. Mindoro Imperial Pigeon. 48. Mindoro.
293. *Ducula mullerii*. Collared Imperial Pigeon. 2ss. 40. New Guinea, Aru Is.
294. *Ducula myristicivora*. Spice Imperial Pigeon. 2ss. 40. W Papuan Islands.

273
274
275
276
277
278
279
280
281
282
283
284
285
286
287
288
289
290
291
278 A
292
279 A
293
294

COLUMBIDAE (12) Pigeons

295. *Ducula oceanica.* Micronesian Pigeon. 5ss. 35. Caroline & Marshall Is.
296. *Ducula pacifica.* Pacific Pigeon. 5ss. 37. Widespread over Pacific Islands.
297. *Ducula perspicillata.* White eyed Imperial Pigeon. 2ss 45. Moluccas.
298. *Ducula pickeringi.* Grey Imperial Pigeon. 3ss. 42. Philippines to Borneo.
299. *Ducula pinon.* Pinyon Imperial Pigeon. 4ss. 43. New Guinea & adjacent Islands.
300. *Ducula pistrinaria.* Island Imperial Pigeon. 4ss. 41. Solomon Islands, Bismarck Archipelago.
301. *Ducula rosacea.* Pink headed Imperial Pigeon. 2ss. 41. Lesser Sundas.
302. *Ducula poliocephala.* Pink bellied Imperial Pigeon. 43. Philippines.
303. *Ducula radiata.* Grey headed Imperial Pigeon. 32. Sulawesi.
304. *Ducula rubricera.* Red knobbed Imperial Pigeon. 2ss. 40. Bismarck Archipelago, Solomon Islands.
305. *Ducula rufigaster.* Purple tailed Imperial Pigeon. 3ss. 35. New Guinea.
306. *Ducula spilorrhoa.* Torresian Imperial Pigeon. 4ss. 45. New Guinea to NE Australia.
307. *Ducula whartoni.* Christmas Island Imperial Pigeon. 45. Christmas Island.
308. *Ducula zoeae.* Banded/Zoe Imperial Pigeon. 41. New Guinea & adjacent Islands.
309. *Hemiphaga novaeseelandiae.* New Zealand Pigeon. 2ss. 50. New Zealand.
310. *Lopholaimus antarcticus.* Topknot Pigeon. 42. Queensland to Victoria.
311. *Cryptophaps poecilorrhoa.* Sombre Pigeon. 45. Sulawesi.
312. *Gymnophaps albertisii.* Papuan/Bare eyed Mountain Pigeon. 2ss. 33. Moluccas. New Guinea to Bismarck Archipelago.
313. *Gymnophaps mada.* Long tailed Mountain Pigeon. 2ss. 35. Buru, Ceram.
314. *Gymnophaps solomonensis.* Pale Mountain Pigeon. 35. Solomon Islands.

295
296
297
298
299
300
301
302
303
304
305
306
307
308
309
310
311
312
313
314

PSITTACIDAE (1)
Pacific Lories & Lorikeets

1. *Chalcopsitta atra.* Black Lory. 4ss. 32. New Guinea & Papuan Is.
2. *Chalcopsitta cardinalis.* Cardinal Lory. 31. Solomon Islands & Bismarck Archipelago.
3. *Chalcopsitta duivenbodei.* Brown Lory. 2ss. 31. New Guinea.
4. *Chalcopsitta sintillata.* Yellow streaked Lory. 3ss. 31. Aru Is, New Guinea
5. *Eos bornea.* Red Lory. 4ss. 31. S Moluccas & Kai Is.6. Eos cyanogenia. Black winged Lory. 30. Geelvink Bay Is. (off New Guinea.)
7. *Eos histrio.* Red & blue Lory. 3ss. 31. Sangihe,Talaud Is. (off Sulawesi.)
8. *Eos reticulata.* Blue streaked Lory. 31.Tanimbar Is. (E Sundas).
9. *Eos semilarvata.* Blue eared Lory. 24. Ceram, (S Moluccas).
10. *Eos squamata.* Violet necked Lory. 4ss. 27. N Moluccas, W Papuan Is.
11. *Pseudeos fuscata.* Dusky Lory. 25. New Guinea. Salawati, Yapen Is.
12. *Trichoglossus chloroleoidotus.* Scaly breasted Lorikeet. 23. E Australia.
13. *Trichoglossus euteles.* Olive headed/Perfect Lorikeet.25. Lesser Sundas.
14. *Trichoglossus flavoviridis.* Yellow & green Lorikeet. 2ss. 21. Sulawesi,Sula.
15. *Psitteuteles goldiei.* Goldie's Lorikeet. 19. New Guinea.16. Trichoglossus haematodus. Rainbow Lorikeet. 21ss. 26. Indonesia to Solomons, Australia.
17. incl. *T .h. flavicans.* Admiralty Is. Lorikeet. 26. New Hanover.
18. *T. h. rubritorquis.* Red collared Lorikeet. 26. N. Australia.19. T. h. weberi. Weber's Lorikeet. 24. Flores.
20. *Psitteuteles iris.* Iris Lorikeet. 20.Timor, Wetar.
21. *Trichoglossus johnstoniae.* Mindanao / Johnston's Lorikeet. 20. Mindanao.
22. *Trichoglossus ornatus.* Ornate Lorikeet. 25. Sulawesi & adjacent Islands.
23. *Trichoglossus rubiginosus.* Ponape Lorikeet. 24. Pohnpei Island. (Carolines).
24. *Psitteuteles versicolor.* Varied Lorikeet. 19. N Australia.
25. *Lorius aldibinuchus.* White naped Lory. 26. New Ireland.
26. *Lorius amabilis.* Stresemann's Lory. 26. New Britain. (ss. of 31)
27. *Lorius chlorocercus.* Yellow bibbed Lory. 28. E Solomon Islands.
28. *Lorius domicellus.* Purple naped Lory. 28. Ceram, Amboina.
29. *Lorius tibialis.* Blue thighed Lory. 28. Moluccas. Only female known.
30. *Lorius garrulus.* Chattering Lory. 30. N Moluccas.
31. *Lorius hypoinochrous.* Purple bellied Lory. 26. New Guinea, Bismarck Archipelago. 32. Lorius lory. Black capped Lory. 31. New Guinea.
32. *Lorius Lory* Black capped Lory 31 New Guinea

1
2
3
4
5
6
7
8
9
10
11
12
13
16
17
18
19
20
21
22
23
24
14
15
25
27
26
29
28
30
31
32

PSITTACIDAE (2)
Pacific Lories & Lorikeets

33. *Phygis solitarius*. Collared Lory. 20. Fiji.
34. *Vini australis*. Blue crowned Lorikeet. 19. Niue, Samoa.
35. *Vini kuhlii*. Kuhl's Lorikeet. 19. Rimitara & Kiribati Islands.
36. *Vini peruviana*. Tahitian Lorikeet. 18. Society & Cook Is, W Tuamotu Archipelago.
37. *Vini stepheni*. Stephen's Lorikeet. 19. Henderson I. (Pitcairns).
38. *Vini ultramina*. Ultramarine Lorikeet. 18. Marquesas Is.
39. *Glossopsitta concinna*. Musk Lorikeet. 22. E, SE Australia incl. Tasmania.
40. *Glossopsitta porphyrocephala*. Purple crowned Lorikeet. 15. SE SW Australia.
41. *Glossopsitta pusilla*. Little Lorikeet. 15. E, SE Australia, Tasmania.
42. *Charmosyna amabilis*. Red throated Lorikeet. 18. Fiji.
43. *Charmosyna diadema*. New Caledonian Lorikeet. 18. New Caledonia.
44. *Charmosyna josefinae*. Josephine's Lorikeet. 3ss. 24. New Guinea.
45. *Charmosyna margarethae*. Duchess Lorikeet. 20. Solomon Is.
46. *Charmosyna meeki*. Meek's Lorikeet. 16. Solomon Is.
47. *Charmosyna multistriata*. Striated Lorikeet. 18. New Guinea.
48. *Charmosyna palmarum*. Palm Lorikeet . 17. Vanuatu & other SW Pacific Islands.
49. *Charmosyna papou*. Papuan Lorikeet. 4ss. 42. New Guinea.
50. *Charmosyna papou*. Melanistic form. 42, New Guinea.
51. *Charmosyna placentis*. Red flanked Lorikeet. 5ss. 17. Moluccas, New Guinea To Solomon Is.
52. *Charmosyna pulchella*. Fairy Lorikeet. 3ss. 18. New Guinea.
53. *Charmosyna rubrigularis*. Red chinned Lorikeet. 5ss. 17. New Britain, New Ireland.54. Charmosyna rubronotata. Red spotted Lorikeet. 2ss. 17. New Guinea.
55. *Charmosyna toxopei*. Blue fronted Lorikeet. 16. Buru (Moluccas).
56. *Charmosyna wilhelminae*. Pygmy Lorikeet. 13. New Guinea.
57. *Oreopsittacus arfaki*. Plum faced/Whiskered Lorikeet. 3ss.15. New Guinea.
58. *Neopsittacus musschenbroekii*. Yellow billed Lorikeet. 3ss. 23. New Guinea.
59. *Neopsittacus pullicauda*. Orange billed/Emerald Lorikeet. 3ss.18. New Guinea.

33
34
35
36
37
38
39
40
41
42
43
44
45
46
47
48
49
50
51
52
53
54
55
56
57
58
59

PSITTACIDEA (3)
Cockatoos

60. *Probosciger aterrimus*. Palm Cockatoo. 3ss. 60. New Guinea, Papuan islands, NE Australia.
61. *Calyptorhynchus funereus*. Yellow tailed Black Cockatoo. 3ss. 67. SW & SE Australia incl. Tasmania.
61a. *Calyptorhynchus baudinii*. White tailed Black Cockatoo. 66. SW Australia.
61b. *Calyptorhynchus latirostris*. Slender billed Black Cockatoo. 55. SW Australia.
62. *Calyptorhynchus Lathami*. Glossy Cockatoo. 48. Eastern Australia.
63. *Calyptorhynchus banksii* / magnificus. Red tailed Cockatoo. 4ss. 60. Most of Australia.
64. *Callocephalon fimbriatum*. Gang-gang Cockatoo. 34. SE Australia.
65. *Eolophus roseicapillus*. Galah. 3ss. 35. All Australia.
66. *Nymphicus hollandicus*. Cockatiel. 32. Whole of interior Australia.

60
61A
61
63
62
61B
65
66
64

PSITTACIDAE (4) Cockatoos etc

67. *Cacatua alba.* White Cockatoo. 46. N & C Moluccas.
68. *Cacatua ducorpsii.* Ducorps' Cockatoo. 31. Bougainville to Guadalcanal.
69. *Cacatua galerita.* Sulphur crested Cockatoo. 4ss. 50. New Guinea. N & E Australia.
70. *Cacatua goffini.* Tanimbar Cockatoo. 32. Lesser Sundas.
71. *Cacatua haematuropygia.* Red vented Cockatoo. 31. Philippines.
72. *Cacatua leadbeateri.* Major Mitchell's/Pink Cockatoo. 2ss.35. Internal Australia.
73. *Cacatua moluccensis.* Salmon crested Cockatoo. 52. S Moluccas.
74. *Cacatua ophthalmica.* Blue eyed Cockatoo. 50. New Britain, New Ireland.
75. *Cacatua sanguinea.* Little Corella. 2ss. 38. N, NW, & C Australia.
76. *Cacatua sulphurea.* Yellow crested Cockatoo. 33. Sulawesi, Lesser Sundas.
77. *Cacatua tenuirostris.* Long billed Corella. 2ss. 38. SE Australia.
78. *Cacatua pastinator.* Western Corella. 40. SW Australia.
79. *Nestor meridionalis.* Kaka. 45. New Zealand & Islands.
80. *Nestor productus.* Norfolk Kaka. 45. Norfolk I.(extinct.)
81. *Nestor notabilis.* Kea. 48. New Zealand, South Island.

67
68
69
70
71
72
73
74
75
76
77
78
79
80
81

PSITTACIDAE (5)
Pygmy, Fig. Racquet tailed Parrots

82. *Micropsitta bruijnii.* Red breasted Pygmy Parrot. 4ss. 9. New Guinea to Solomon Is.
83. *Micropsitta finschii.* Finsch's Pygmy Parrot. 5ss. 9. Bismarck Archipelago.
84. *Micropsitta geelvinkiana.* Geelvink Pygmy Parrot. 2ss. 9. Numfor, Biak.
85. *Micropsitta keiensis.* Yellow capped Pygmy Parrot. 3ss. 9. Kai, Aru Is, New Guinea.
86. *Micropsitta meeki.* Meek's Pygmy Parrot. 2ss. 10. St Matthias, Admiralty Is.
87. *Micropsitta pusio.* Buff faced Pygmy Parrot. 4ss. 8. New Guinea, Bismarck Arch.
88. *Opopsitta diophthalma.* Double eyed Fig Parrot. 8ss. 14. New Guinea, N Australia.
89. *Opopsitta gulielmitertii.* Orange breasted Pig Parrot. 7ss. 13. New Guinea.
90. *Psittaculirostris desmarestii.* Large Fig Parrot. 19. Irian Jaya, New Guinea.
91. *Psittaculirostris edwardsii.* Edwards' Fig Parrot. 18. NE New Guinea.
92. *Psittaculirostris salvadorii.* Salvadori's Fig Parrot. 19. Irian Jaya.
93. *Bolbopsittacus lunulatus.* Guaiabero. 4ss. 15. Philippines.
94. *Psittinus cyanurus.* Blue rumped Parrot. 3ss. 18. Thailand to Sumatra, Borneo.
95. *Psittacella brehmii.* Brehm's Tiger Parrot. 4ss. 24. New Guinea.
96. *Psittacella madaraszi.* Madaras's Tiger Parrot. 4ss. 14. New Guinea.
97. *Psittacella modesta.* Modest Tiger Parrot. 3ss. 14. New Guinea, Irian Jaya.
98. *Psittacella picta.* Painted Tiger Parrot. 3ss. 19. New Guinea, Irian Jaya.
99. *Geoffroyus geoffroyi.* Red cheeked Parrot. 16ss. 21. Indonesia, New Guinea, to Australia.
100. *Geoffroyus heteroclitus.* Singing Parrot. 2ss. 25. Bismarck Arch, Solomon Is.
101. *Geoffroyus simplex.* Blue collared Parrot. 2ss. 22. New Guinea.
102. *Prioniturus discurus.* Blue crowned Racquet tail. 4ss. 27. Philippines.
103. *Prioniturus platenae.* Blue headed Racquet tail. 27. Philippines.
104. *Prioniturus flavicans.* Yellow breasted Racquet tail. 37. Sulawesi & Is.
105. *Prioniturus luconensis.* Green Racquet tail. 29. Luzon, Marinduque.
106. *Prioniturus mada.* Buru Racquet tail. 32. Buru. (Moluccas).
107. *Prioniturus montanus.* Luzon Racquet tail. 4ss. 30. Philippines.
108. *Prioniturus verticalis.* Blue winged Racquet tail, 30. Sulu archipelago.
109. *Prioniturus waterstradti.* Mindanao Racquet tail, 30. Mindanao.
110. *Prioniturus platurus.* Golden mantled Racquet tail. 3ss. 28. Sulawesi.

82
83
84
85
86
87
88
89
90
91
92
93
94
95
96
97
98
99
100
103
101
102
104
105
106
110
107
108
109

PSITTACIDAE (6)
Parrots

111. *Tanygnathus gramineus*. Black lored Parrot. 40. Buru. (S Moluccas).
112. *Tanygnathus lucionensis*. Blue naped Parrot. 3ss. 31. Philippines & Is.
113. *Tanygnathus megalorhynchos*. Great billed Parrot. 8ss. 41. Islands of C Indonesia.
114. *Tanygnathus sumatranus*. Blue backed Parrot. 3ss. 32. Philippines to Sulawesi.
115. *Tanygnathus heterurus*. Rufous tailed Parrot. 30. Sulawesi.
116. *Eclectus roratus*. Grand Eclectus Parrot. l0ss. 35. Indonesia to Solomons.
117. incl. *E. r. riedeli*. Eclectus Parrot. 32.Tenimbar Is.
118. *Psittrichas fulgidus*. Pesquet's Parrot. 46. New Guinea.
119. *Prosopeia personata*. Masked Shining Parrot. 47. Fiji.
120. *Prosopeia splendens*. Kandavu / Crimson Shining Parrot. 45. Kandavu, Fiji.
121. *Prosopeia tabuensis*. Red Shining Parrot. 2ss. 45. Fiji.
122. *Alisterus amboinensis*. Moluccan King Parrot. 6ss. 35. Wallacea, New Guinea.
123. *Alisterus chloropterus*. Green winged / Papuan King Parrot.3ss. 36. Irian Jaya, New Guinea.
124. *Alisterus scapularis*. Australian King Parrot. 2ss. 43 E Australia.
125. *Aprosmictus erythropterus*. Red winged Parrot. 3ss. 32. N, E Australia, S New Guinea.
126. *Aprosmictus jonquillaceus*. Olive shouldered Parrot. 2ss. 35. Timor.

-111-
112
113
116
-114-
115
117
120
118
119
121
122
123
124
-125-
126

PSITTACIDAE (7)
Australian Parrots, Rosellas

127. *Polytelis anthopeplus*. Regent Parrot. 2ss. 40. South Australia.
128. *Polytelis alexandrae*. Princess / Alexandra's Parrot. 45. Interior Australia.
129. *Polytelis swainsonii*. Superb Parrot. 40. SE Australia.
130. *Purpureicephalus spurius*. Red capped Parrot. 36. SW Australia.
131. *Barnardius barnardi*. Mallee Ringneck. 3ss. 33. Internal E Australia.
132. *Barnardius zonarius*. Port Lincoln Parrot. 5ss. 38. C & W Australia.
133. *Platycercus adelaidae*. Adelaide Rosella. 36. S Australia.
134. *Platycercus adscitus*. Pale headed Rosella. 4ss. 30. NE & E Australia.
135. *Platycercus caledonicus*. Green Rosella. 36.Tasmania.
136. *Platycercus elegans*. Crimson Rosella. 4ss. 36. NE & SE Australian coasts.
137. *Platycercus eximius*. Eastern Rosella. 3ss. 30. SE Australia, Tasmania.
138. *Platycercus flaveolus*. Yellow Rosella. 33. SE Australia.
139. *Platycercus icterotis*. Western Rosella. 2ss. 25. SW Australia.
140. *Platycercus venustus*. Northern Rosella. 28. N Australia.
141. *Psephotus chrysopterygius*. Golden shouldered Parrot. 26. N Australia.
142. *Psephotus dissimilis*. Hooded Parrot. 26. N C Australia.
143. *Northiella. h. haematogaster.* Bluebonnet. 4ss. 28. S, SE Australia.
144. incl. *N. h. narethae*. Little Bluebonnet. 25. W Australia.
145. *Psephotus haematonotus*. Red rumped Parrot. 2ss. 27. SE Australia.
146. *Psephotus pulcherrimus*. Paradise Parrot. 27. E Australia.
147. *Psephotus varius*. Mulga Parrot. 2ss. 27. Interior S Australia.

-127-
-128-
-129-
130
131
132
133
134
135
136
137
138
-139-
140
-141-
142
143
144
-145-
-146-
-147-

PSITTACIDAE (8)
Australian Parrots

148. *Cyanoramphus auriceps.* Yellow fronted Parakeet. 2ss. 23. New Zealand.
149. *Cyanoramphus malherbi.* Orange fronted Parakeet. 20. New Zealand. South I. (extinct?)
150. *Cyanoramphus novaezelandiae.* Red fronted Parakeet. 6ss. 27. NewZealand.
151. *Cyanoramphus cookii.* Norfolk I. Parakeet. 30. Norfolk Is.
152. *Cyanoramphus unicolor.* Antipodes Parakeet. 30. Antipodes Is.
153. *Cyanoramphus ulietanus.* Society Parakeet. 25. Society Is.(extinct)
154. *Cyanoramphus zeelandicus.* Black fronted Parakeet. 25. Tahiti.(extinct)
155. *Eunymphicus connutus.* Horned Parrot. 2ss. 32. New Caledonia, Loyalty Is.
156. *Neophema bourkii.* Bourke's Parrot. 19. Australian interior.
157. *Neophema chrysogaster.* Orange bellied Parrot. 20. Tasmania.
158. *Neophema chrystostomus.* Blue winged Parrot. 20. E Australia, Tasmania.
159. *Neophema elegans.* Elegant Parrot. 23. SE & SW Australia.
160. *Neophema petrophila.* Rock Parrot. 2ss. 22. Coastal S. Australia.
161. *Neophema pulchella.* Turquoise Parrot. 20. Queensland to Victoria.
162. *Neophema splendida.* Scarlet chested Parrot. 19. Interior Australia.
163. *Lathamus discolor.* Swift Parrot. 25. Tasmania, winters to SE Australia,
164. *Melopsittacus undulatus.* Budgerigar. 18. Most of Australia.

(Various domesticated forms also shown.)

165. *Pezoporus wallicus.* Ground Parrot. 2ss. 30. SE, SW Australia, Tasmania.
166. *Geopsittacus occidentalis.* Night Parrot. 23. Interior Australia.
167. *Strigops habroptilus.* Kakapo. 64. New Zealand. Now only South Island.

Several related parrots have become extinct within the last century. These are not all illustrated.

148
149
150
152
155
156
-157-
-158-
151
159
160
-161-
163
164
162
165
153
166
154
167

PSITTACIDAE (9)
African Parrots, Hanging Parrots

168. *Coracopsis nigra*. Black Parrot. 4ss. 35. Malagasy, Comoro Is, Praslin.
169. *Coracopsis vasa*. Vasa Parrot. 50. Malagasy, Comoro Is.
170. *Psittacus erithacus*. Grey Parrot. 3ss. 33. W & C Africa.
171. *Poicephalus crassus*. Niam Niam Parrot. 25. Cameroon, Chad, Sudan.
172. *Poicephalus cryptoxanthus*. Brown headed Parrot. 3ss. 22. Kenya to Malawi & Mozambique.
173. *Poicephalus flavifrons*. Yellow faced Parrot. 2ss. 28. Ethiopia.
174. *Poicephalus gulielmi*. Jardine's/Red fronted Parrot. 4ss. 28. W C Africa.
175. *Poicephalus meyeri*. Meyer's/Brown Parrot. 6ss. 21. Africa S of Sahara.
176. *Poicephalus robustus*. Brown necked/ Cape Parrot. 3ss.. 33. W, C S Africa.
177. *Poicephalus ruppellii*. Rueppell's Parrot. 22. Angola, Namibia.
178. *Poicephalus rufiventris*. Red bellied Parrot. 2ss. 22. Ethiopia to Tanzania.
179. *Poicephalus senegalus*. Senegal Parrot. 3ss. 23. Senegal to Cameroon, Chad.
180. *Agapornis canus*. Grey headed Lovebird. 2ss. 14. Malagasy.
181. *Agapornis fischeri*. Fischer's Lovebird. 15. Kenya, Tanzania.
182. *Agapornis lilianae*. Lilian's / Nyasa Lovebird. 13. Zambia, Mozambique.
183. *Agapornis nigrigenis*. Black cheeked Lovebird. 13. Zambia, Zimbabwe, Namibia.
184. *Agapornis personatus*. Yellow collared Lovebird. 14. Kenya, Tanzania.
185. *Agapornis pullarius*. Red headed Lovebird. 3ss. 15. C & W C Africa.
186. *Agapornis roseicollis*. Rosy faced Lovebird. 2ss. 15. Angola to Cape.
187. *Agapornis swinderniana*. Black collared Lovebird. 3ss. 13. Liberia to Uganda
188. *Agapornis taranta*. Black winged Lovebird. 16. Ethiopia.
189. *Loriculus amabilis*. Moluccan Hanging Parrot. 4ss. 11. N Moluccas & Islands.
190. *Loriculus catamene*. Sangihe Hanging Parrot. 11. Sangihe Island.
191. *Loriculus aurantiifrons*. Orange fronted Hanging Parrot.3ss. 10. New Guinea, Bismarck Archipelago.
192. *Loriculus tener*. Green fronted Hanging Parrot. 10. Bismarck Archipelago.
193. *Loriculus beryllinus*. Ceylon Hanging Parrot, 13. Sri Lanka.
194. *Loriculus exilis*. Green/Pygmy Hanging Parrot. 10. Sulawesi.
195. *Loriculus flosculus*. Wallace's Hanging Parrot. 12. Flores.(extinct?).
196. *Loriculus galgulus*. Blue crowned Hanging Parrot. 12. Malaya, Sumatra, Borneo.
197. *Loriculus philippensis*. Philippine Hanging Parrot. 11ss. 14. Philippines.
198. *Loriculus pusillus*. Yellow throated Hanging Parrot. 12. Java, Bali.
199. *Loriculus stigmatus*. Celebes Hanging Parrot. 3ss. 15. Sulawesi.
200. *Loriculus vernalis*. Vernal Hanging Parrot. 13. India, China, SE Asia.

168
169
170
171
172
173
174
175
176
177
178
179
180
181
182
183
184
185
186
187
188
189
190
191
192
193
194
195
196
197
198
199
200

PSITTACIDAE (10)
Afro-Asian Parakeets

201. *Psittacula alexandri.* Red breasted Parakeet. 8ss. 33. S, SE Asia, Greater Sundas.
202. *Psittacula calthropae.* Layard's Parakeet. 29. Sri Lanka.
203. *Psittacula caniceps.* Blyth's / Nicobar Parakeet. 36. Nicobar Is.
204. *Psittacula columboides.* Malabar Parakeet . 38. S W India.
205. *Psittacula cyanocephala.* Plum headed Parakeet. 33. India, Sri Lanka.
206. *Psittacula echo.* Mauritius Parakeet. 42. Mauritius.
206a. *Psittacula exsul.* Newton's Parakeet. 40. Rodriguez. (extinct).
207. *Psittacula eupatria.* Alexandrine Parakeet. 58. Afghanistan to Indo-China, S E Asia, Andaman Islands.
208. *Psittacula derbiana.* Derbyan Parakeet. 50. Assam, Tibet, W China.
209. *Psittacula himalayana.* Slaty headed Parakeet. 40. Afghanistan to Assam.
210. *Psittacula finschii.* Grey headed Parakeet. 40. Assam to Indo-China.
211. *Psittacula intermedia.* Intermediate Parakeet. 36. N India.
212. *Psittacula krameri.* Rose ringed Parakeet. 4ss. 40. Sub-saharan Africa to India, China, Burma.
213. *Psittacula longicauda.* Long tailed Parakeet. 5ss. 42. Malaya, Borneo, Sumatra, Andaman & Nicobar Islands.
214. *Psittacula roseata.* Blossom headed Parakeet. 2ss. 30. Assam, Burma, Indo-China, S E Asia.

201
202
203
204
205
206A
207
208
206
211
209
210
212
213
214

PSITTACIDAE (11)
Macaws

215. *Anodorhynchus glaucus.* Glaucous Macaw. 72. Paraguay, Uruguay. (extinct)
216. *Anodorhynchus hyacintinus.* Hyacinthine Macaw. 100.Brazil.
217. *Anodorhynchus leari.* Lear's Macaw. 75. Brazil.
218. *Cyanopsitta spixii.* Spix's Macaw. 56. Brazil.
219. *Ara ambigua.* Great green Macaw. 2ss. 85. Honduras to Ecuador.
220. *Ara ararauna.* Blue & yellow Macaw. 86. Panama to Brazil.
221. *Ara glaucogularis.* Blue throated / Caninde Macaw. 85. Bolivia.
222. *Ara auricollis.* Golden collared Macaw. 38. Bolivia, Paraguay, Brazil, Argentina.

215
216
217
218
220
221
219
222

PSITTACIDAE (12)
Macaws

223. *Ara chloropterus.* Red & green Macaw. 90. Panama to Argentina.
224. *Ara couloni.* Blue headed Macaw. 41. Peru.
225. *Ara macao.* Scarlet Macaw. 85. Mexico to Bolivia, Brazil,
226. *Ara manilata.* Red bellied Macaw. 50. Trinidad, Venezuela, Guyanas, Amazonia.
227. *Ara maracana.* Blue winged Macaw. 43. Brazil, Paraguay, Argentina.
228. *Ara militaris.* Military Macaw. 70. Mexico to Argentina.
229. *Ara nobilis.* Red shouldered Macaw. 30. Guyanas, Venezuela to Brazil, Bolivia.
230. *Ara rubrogenys.* Red fronted Macaw. 60. Bolivia.
231. *Ara severa.* Chestnut fronted Macaw. 46. Panama to Brazil, Bolivia.
232. *Ara tricolor.* Cuban/Hispaniolan Macaw. 50. 2 or more West Indian species, all extinct.

223
224
225
226
227
228
229
230
231
232

PSITTACIDAE (0)
New World Parakeets, Conures

233. *Aratinga acuticaudata*. Blue crowned Parakeet. 4ss. 37. Colombia, Venezuela. Brazil to Argentina.
234. *Aratinga aurea*. Peach fronted Parakeet. 2ss. 26. Peru to Brazil, Argentina.
235. *Aratinga auricapilla*. Golden capped Parakeet. 2ss. 30. E Brazil.
236. *Aratinga cactorun*. Caatinga Parakeet. 2ss 25. N E Brazil.
237. *Aratinga canicularis*. Orange fronted Parakeet. 3ss. 24. Mexico to Costa Rica.
238. *Aratinga chloroptera*. Hispaniolan Parakeet. 32. Hispaniola.
239. *Aratinga erythrogenys*. Red masked Parakeet. 33. Ecuador, Peru.
240. *Aratinga euops*. Cuban Parakeet. 26. Cuba.
241. *Aratinga finschi*. Crimson fronted Parakeet. 28. Nicaragua to Panama.
242. *Aratinga guarouba*. Golden Parakeet. 34. Brazil.
243. *Aratinga holochlora*. Green Parakeet. 5ss. 32. Mexico, Socorro I.
244. *Aratinga Strenua*. Pacific Parakeet. 35. Mexico to Nicaragua.
245. *Aratinga jandaya*. Jandaya Parakeet. 30. N E Brazil.
246. *Aratinga leucophthalmus*. White eyed Parakeet. 4ss. 32. Guyanas, Venezuela to Brazil, Argentina.
247. *Aratinga mitrata*. Mitred Parakeet, 2ss. 38. Peru to Argentina.
248. *Aratinga nana*. Olive throated Parakeet. 3ss. 26. Mexico to Panama, Jamaica.
249. incl. *A. n. astec*. Aztec Parakeet. 25. Mexico to Costa Rica.
250. *Aratinga pertinax*. Brown Throated Parakeet. 14ss. 25. Panama to Guyanas, Brazil.
251. *Aratinga solstitialis*, Sun Parakeet. 30. Guyanas, Venezuela Brazil.
252. *Aratinga wagleri*. Scarlet fronted Parakeet. 4ss. 36. Venezuela to Peru.
253. *Aratinga weddellii*. Dusky headed Parakeet. 28. Northern South America.
254. *Nandayus nenday*. Nanday Parakeet. 30. Brazil, Paraguay, Argentina.
255. *Leptosittaca branickii*. Golden plumed Parakeet. 35. Colombia, Ecuador, Peru.
256. *Rhynchopsitta pachyryncha*. Thick billed Parrot. 38. Mexico.
257. *Rhynchopsitta terrisi*. Maroon fronted Parrot. 38. Mexico.
258. *Cyanoliseus patagonus*. Burrowing Parrot. 3ss. 45. Chile, Argentina.
259. *Ognorhynchus icterotis*. Yellow eared Parrot. 42. Colombia, Ecuador.

233
234
235
236
237
238
239
240
241
242
244
243
245
246
247
250
248
249
251
252
253
254
257
256
258
259
255

PSITTACIDAE (14) South American Parakeets

260. *Pyrrhura albipectus.* White necked Parakeet. 24. Ecuador.
261. *Pyrrhura calliptera.* Flame winged Parakeet. 22. Colombia.
262. *Pyrrhura cruentata.* Blue throated Parakeet. 30. E Brazil.
263. *Pyrrhura devillei.* Blaze winged Parakeet. 26. Bolivia, Paraguay, Brazil.
264. *Pyrrhura egregia.* Fiery shouldered Parakeet. 2ss. 25. Guyana, Surinam, Venezuela.
265. *Pyrrhura frontalis.* Maroon bellied Parakeet. 3ss. 26. Brazil to Argentina.
266. *Pyrrhura hoematotis.* Red eared Parakeet. 2ss. 25. Venezuela.
267, *Pyrrhura hoffmanni.* Sulphur winged Parakeet. 2ss. 24. Costa Rica, Panama.
268. *Pyrrhura hypoxantha.* Yellow sided Parakeet. 25. Brazil. (ss. of 273 ?)
269. *Pyrrhura Leucotis.* White eared Parakeet. 5ss. 23. Venezuela, Brazil.
270. *Pyrrhura melanura.* Maroon tailed Parakeet. 5ss. 24. Venezuela to Peru, Brazil.
271. incl. *P. m. berlepschi.* Huallaga Parakeet. 24. E Peru.
272. *Pyrrhura orcesi.* El Oro Parakeet. 24. Ecuador.
273. *Pyrrhura molinae.* Green cheeked Parakeet. 5ss. 26. Brazil, Bolivia, Argentina.
274. *Pyrrhura perlata.* Pearly Parakeet. 4ss. 24. Brazil.
275. *Pyrrhura picta.* Painted Parakeet. 22. Panama to Amazonian Brazil.
276. incl. *P. p. roseifrons.* Red headed Parakeet. 22. Brazil.
277. *Pyrrhura rhodocephala.* Rose crowned Parakeet. 24. Venezuela.
278. *Pyrrhura rhodogaster.* Crimson bellied Parakeet. 24. Amazonian Brazil.
279. *Pyrrhura rupicola.* Black capped Parakeet. 2ss. 25. Peru.
280. *Pyrrhura viridicata.* Santa Marta Parakeet. 25. Colombia.
281. *Enicognathus ferrugineus.* Austral Parakeet. 2ss. 33. Chile, Argentina.
282. *Enicognathus leptorhynchus.* Slender billed Parakeet. 40. Chile.
283. *Conuropsis carolinensis.* Carolina Parakeet. 30. Formerly E USA. (extinct).
284. *Myiopsitta monachus.* Monk Parakeet. 4ss. 29. Bolivia, Brazil, Argentina.
285. *Bolborhynchus aurifrons.* Mountain Parakeet. 4ss. 18. Peru to Chile, Argentina.
286. *Bolborhynchus aymara.* Grey hooded Parakeet. 20. Bolivia, Argentina, Chile.
287. *Bolborhynchus ferrugineifrons.* Rufous fronted Parakeet. 18. Colombia.
288. *Bolborhynchus lineola.* Barred Parakeet. 2ss. 16. Mexico to Peru.
289. *Bolborhynchus orbygnesius.* Andean Parakeet. 17. Peru, Bolivia.

260
261
262
263
264
265
266
267
268
269
275
270
273
274
276
272
271
277
282
278
279
280
281
283
284
285
286
287
288
289

PSITTACIDAE (15)
New World parrots

290. *Forpus coelestis*. Pacific Parrotlet. 12. Ecuador, Peru.
291. *Forpus conspicillatus*. Spectacled Parrotlet. 3ss. 12. Panama,Colombia.
292. *Forpus cyanopygius*. Mexican / Blue rumped Parrotlet. 3ss.13. Mexico.
293. *Forpus passerinus*. Green rumped Parrotlet. 3ss. 12. Trinidad, Venezuela.
294. *Forpus sclateri*. Dusky billed Parrotlet. 2ss. 12. N & E of S America.
295. *Forpus xanthops*. Yellow faced Parrotlet. 16. Peru.
296. *Forpus xanthopterygius*. Blue winged Parrotlet. 6ss. 12. Colombia to Brazil & Argentina.
297. *Brotoeeris chrysopterus*. Golden winged Parakeet. 5ss. 16. Amazonia.
298. *Brotogeris cyanoptera*. Cobalt winged Parakeet. 2ss. 18. W Amazon basin.
299. *Brotogeris gustavi*. Gustave's Parakeet. 18. Peru.
300. *Brotogeris jugularis*. Orange chinned Parakeet. 2ss. 10. Mexico to Colombia Venezuela.
301. *Brotogeris pyrrhopterus*. Grey cheeked Parakeet. 20. Ecuador, Peru.
302. *Brotogeris sanctithomae*. Tui Parakeet. 2ss. 17. W Amazon basin.
303. *Brotogeris tirica*. Plain Parakeet. 23. E Brazil.
304. *Brotogeris versicolurus*. Canary winged Parakeet. 3ss. 22. N & C S America.
304a. *Brotogeris chiriri*. Yellow chevronned Parakeet. 22. Brazil to Argentina.
305. *Nannopsitta panychlora*. Tepui Parrotlet. 14. Venezuela, Guyana.
305a. *Nannopsitta dachilleae*. Amazonian Parrotlet. 14. Peru, Bolivia.
306. *Touit batavica*. Lilac tailed Parrotlet. 14. Trinidad, Venezuela, Guyana.
307. *Touit dilectissina*. Red winged / Blue fronted Parrotlet. 2ss. 17. Panama, Colombia, Ecuador.
307a. *Touit costaricensis*. Red fronted Parrotlet. 18. Costa Rica, Panama.
308. *Touit huetii*. Scarlet shouldered Parrotlet. 15. Colombia to Bolivia, Brazil.
309. *Touit melanonotus*. Black eared / Brown backed Parrotlet. 15. SE Brazil.
310. *Touit purpurata*. Sapphire rumped Parrotlet.2ss. 17. Venezuela, Guyanas to Ecuador, Brazil.
311. *Touit stictoptera*. Spot winged Parrotlet. 17. Colombia, Ecuador, Peru.
312. *Touit surda*. Golden tailed Parrotlet. 2ss. 16. SE Brazil.
313. *Pionetes leucogaster*. White bellied Parrot. 3ss. 23. Amazonia.
314. *Pionetes melanocephalus*. Black headed Parrot. 2ss. 23. Venezuela, Guyanas to Peru, Brazil.
315. *Pionopsitta barrabandi*. Orange cheeked Parrot. 2ss. 25. Amazon basin.
316. *Pionopsitta caica*. Caica Parrot. 23. Guyanas, Venezuela, Brazil.
317. *Pionopsitta haematotis*. Brown hooded Parrot. 2ss. 21. Mexico to Colombia.
318. *Pionopsitta pileata*. Pileated Parrot. 22. S E Brazil.
319. *Pionopsitta pulchra*. Rose faced Parrot. 23. Colombia, Ecuador.
320. *Pionopsitta pyrilia*. Saffron headed Parrot. 24. Panama, Colombia, Venezuela.

290
291
292
293
294
295
296
297
298
300
301
302
303
304
299
305
306
307
308
309
304 A
305 A
307 A
310
311
312
313
314
315
316
317
- 318 -
319
320

PSITTACIDAE (16)
New World Parrots, Amazons

321. *Gypopsitta vulturina*. Vulturine Parrot. 23. NE Brazil.
322. *Hapalopsittaca fuertesi*. Indigo winged Parrot. 23. Colombia.
323. *Hapalopsittaca amazonina*. Rusty faced Parrot. 2ss. 23. Venezuela, Colombia.
324. *Hapalopsittaca pyrrhops*. Red faced Parrot. 23. Ecuador, Peru.
325. *Hapalopsittaca melanotis*. Black winged Parrot. 2ss. 24. Peru, Bolivia.
326. *Graydidasculus brachyurus*. Short tailed Parrot. 24. Amazon basin.
327. *Pionus chalcopterus*. Bronze winged Parrot. 2ss. 29. Venezuela to Peru.
328. *Pionus fuscus*. Dusky Parrot. 26. Colombia to Guyanas & Brazil.
329. *Pionus maximiliani*. Scaly headed Parrot. 4ss. 29. Brazil, Argentina.
330. *Pionus menstruus*. Blue headed Parrot. 3ss. 28. Costa Rica to Brazil, Bolivia.
331. *Pionus senilis*. White capped Parrot. 24. Mexico to Panama.
332. *Pionus seniloides*. White headed Parrot. 30. Venezuela, Colombia, Ecuador.
333. *Pionus sordidus*. Red billed Parrot. 6ss. 28. Venezuela to Bolivia.
334. *Pionus tumultuosus*. Speckle faced / Plum crowned Parrot.29. Peru, Bolivia.
335. *Amazona aestiva*. Blue fronted Parrot. 2ss. 37. Brazil, Bolivia to Argentina.
336. *Amazona agilis*. Black billed Parrot. 25. Jamaica.
337. *Amazona albifrons*. White fronted Parrot. 3ss. 26. Mexico to Costa Rica.
338. *Amazona amazonica*. Orange winged Parrot. 2ss. 31. Amazonia, Trinidad & Tobago.
339. *Amazona arausiaca*. Red necked Parrot. 40. Dominica.
340. *Amazona autumnalis*. Red lored Parrot. 3ss. 34. Mexico to Ecuador, Brazil.
341. *Amazona barbadensis*. Yellow shouldered Parrot. 2ss. 33. Venezuela & Islands.
342. *Amazona brasiliensis*. Red tailed Parrot. 37. Brazil.

321
322
323
324
325
326
327
328
329
330
331
332
333
334
335
336
337
338
339
340
341
342

PSITTACIDAE (17)
New World Parrots, Amazons

343. *Amazona collaria*. Yellow billed Parrot. 28. Jamaica.
344. *Amazona dufresniana*. Blue cheeked Parrot. 34. Guyanas, Venezuela.
345. *Amazona rhodocoryrhra*. Red browed Parrot. 34. EC Brazil.
346. *Amazona farinosa*. Mealy Parrot. 5ss. 38. Mexico to Bolivia, Brazil.
346a. *Amazona kawalli*. Kawall's Parrot. 38. Brazil.
347. *Amazona festiva*. Festive Parrot. 2ss. 34. Guyana, Brazil, Ecuador, Peru.
348. *Amazona finschi*. Lilac crowned Parrot. 2ss. 33. Mexico.
349. *Amazona guildingii*. St. Vincent Parrot. 40. St Vincent.
350. *Amazona imperialis*. Imperial Parrot. 45. Dominica.
351. *Amazona leucocephala*. Cuban Parrot. 5ss. 32. Cuba, Bahamas.
352. *Amazona mercenaria*. Scaly naped Parrot. 2ss. 34. Venezuela to Peru, Bolivia.
353. *Amazona oratrix*. Yellow headed Parrot. 35. Mexico to Belize.
354. *Amazona ochrocephala*. Yellow crowned Parrot. 35. Honduras to Bolivia, Brazil, Trinidad.
355. *Amazona aureopalliata*. Yellow naped Parrot. 35. Mexico to Costa Rica.
356. *Amazona pretrei*. Red spectacled Parrot. 32. Brazil, Argentina.
357. *Amazona tucumana*. Alder Parrot. 31. Bolivia, Argentina.
358. *Amazona ventralis*. Hispaniolan Parrot. 28. Hispaniola.
359. *Amazona versicolor*. St. Lucia Parrot. 43. St Lucia.
360. *Amazona vinacea*. Vinaceous Parrot. 30. Brazil, Paraguay. Argentina.
361. *Amazona viridigenalis*. Red crowned Parrot. 33. Mexico.
362. *Amazona vittata*. Puerto Rican Parrot. 29. Puerto Rico.
363. *Amazona xantholora*. Yellow lored Parrot. 26. Cozumel, Yucatan to Belize.
364. *Amazona xanthops* yellow faced Parrot 27 Brazil
365. *Deroptyus accipitrinus*. Red-fan Parrot. 2ss. 35. Amazon basin.
366. *Triclaria malachitacea*. Blue bellied Parrot. 28. Brazil.

343
344
345
346
A
346
347
348
349
350
351
352
355
356
354
357
353
359
358
360
361
362
365
366
363
364

MUSOPHAGIDAE
Turacos

1. *Tauraco bannermanni*. Bannerman's Turaco. 40. Cameroon.
2. *Tauraco corythaix*. Knysna Turaco. 8ss. 46. South Africa.
3. *Tauraco erythrolophus*. Red crested Turaco. 42. Angola.
4. *Tauraco fischeri*. Fisher's Turaco. 40. Kenya, Tanzania.
5. *Tauraco hartlaubi*. Hartlaub's Turaco. 40. Kenya, Uganda, Tanzania.
6. *Musophaga johnstoni*. Ruwenzori Turaco. 3ss. 40. Kivu, C Africa.
7. *Tauraco leucolophus*. White crested Turaco. 38. Nigeria to Uganda, Kenya.
8. *Tauraco leucotis*. White cheeked Turaco. 2ss. 39. Ethiopia, Sudan, Somalia.
9. *Tauraco livingstonii*. Livingstone' s Turaco. 3ss. 40. Tanzania to Zaire, Natal.
10. *Tauraco macrorhynchus*. Yellow billed Turaco. 2ss. 42. Sierra Leone to Gabon & Zaire.
11. *Tauraco persa*. Guinea / Green Turaco. 42. Senegal, Zaire, Angola.

11a. *Tauraco schalowi*. Schalow's Turaco. 42. Kenya to Zimbabwe & Angola.

12. *Musophaga porphyreolophus*. Purple crested Turaco. 2ss. 42. E & SE Africa.
13. *Tauraco ruspolii*. Prince Rupert's Turaco. 38. Ethiopia. (hybrid?).
14. *Tauraco schuttii*. Black billed Turaco. 40. Zaire, Uganda, Sudan.
15. *Musophaga rossae*. Ross' Turaco. 50. Cameroon to Zambia.
16. *Musophaga violacea*. Violet Turaco. 50. Gambia to Nigeria.
17. *Corythaeola cristata*. Great Blue Turaco. 72. Guinea to Angola & W Kenya.
18. *Crinifer piscator.* Western Grey Plantain eater. 50. Senegal to Zaire.
19. *Crinifer zonurus*. Eastern Grey Plantain eater. 50. Ethiopia, Tanzania, Zaire.
20. *Corythaixoides concolor*. (Grey) Go-away-bird . 3ss. 50. Tanzania to RSA.
21. *Corythaixoides* / Criniger leucogaster. White bellied Go-away-bird. 50. Ethiopia to Tanzania.
22. *Corythaixoides personata*. Bare faced Go-away-bird. 2ss. 50. Ethiopia,Kenya, to Zaire, Zambia, Malawi.

1
2
3
4
5
6
7
8
9
10
11
12
13
14
11A
17
18
15
16
19
20
21
22

CUCULIDAE (1)
Cuckoos

1. *Clamator coromandus*. Chestnut winged Cuckoo. 47. Himalayas to China, Java, Borneo.
2. *Clamator glandarius*. Great spotted Cuckoo. 39. S Europe to Africa.
3. *Clamator jacobinus*. Pied Cuckoo. 2ss. 33. Africa S of Sahara, Iran to Burma.
4. *Clamator levaillantii*. Levaillant's Cuckoo. 40. Africa S of Sahara.
5. *Pachycoccyx audeberti*. Thick billed Cuckoo. 3ss. 45. Africa S of Sahara.
6. *Cuculus canorus*. Common Cuckoo. 9ss. 33. Palearctic, Winters Africa, India, SE Asia. (a). hepatic race. (b). normal
7. *Cuculus gularis*. African Cuckoo. 32. Africa S of Sahara.
8. *Cuculus clamosus/cafer*. Black Cuckoo. 2ss. 30. Africc S of Sahara.

x9. *Cuculus fugax*. Hodgson's Hawk Cuckoo. 4ss. 29. Himalayas to SE Asia, Sundas.

10. *Cuculus crassirostris*. Sulawesi Hawk Cuckoo. 33. Sulawesi.
11. *Cuculus micropterus*. Indian Cuckoo. 3ss. 33. India to E Asia, Philippines, Sundas.
12. *Cuculus pallidus*. Pallid Cuckoo. 2ss. 30. Australia, Winters New Guinea, Sundas.
13. *Cuculus poliocephalus*. Lesser Cuckoo. 3ss. 26. S & E Asia. Winters SE Asia, India.
14. *Cuculus saturatus*. Oriental Cuckoo. 3ss. 31. C E Asia. Winters to Indonesia, Australasia.
15. *Cuculus solitarius*. Red chested Cuckoo. 30. Africa S of Sahara.
16. *Cuculus sparverioides*. Large Hawk Cuckoo. 2ss. 38. Himalayas to S E Asia, Winters Philippines, Indonesia.
17. *Cuculus vagans*. Moustached Hawk Cuckoo. 30. Malay Peninsula, Gr. Sundas.
18. Cuculus varius. Common Hawk Cuckoo / Brainfever bird. 2ss. 34. Indian sub-continent.
19. *Cuculus rochii*. Madagascar Cuckoo. 28. Malagasy.
20. *Cercococcyx mechowi*. Dusky long tailed Cuckoo. 32. Sierra Leone to Zaire, & Angola.
21. *Cercococcyx montanus*. Barred long tailed Cuckoo. 32. Zaire to Kenya, Zambia, Mozambique.
22. *Cercococcyx olivinus*. Olive long tailed Cuckoo. 32. W & C Africa.
23. *Cacomantis castaneiventris*. Chestnut breasted Cuckoo. 3ss. 22. New Guinea, Queensland.
24. *Cacomantis heinrichi*. Moluccan Brush Cuckoo. 23. Halmahera, Batjan.
25. *Cacomantis querulus*. Burmese Plaintive Cuckoo. 23. Himalayas, China, Indo-China.
26. *Cacomantis passerinus*. Grey breasted Plaintive Cuckoo. 23. Himalayas, India, Sri Lanka.
27. *Cacomantis merulinus*. Plaintive Cuckoo. 5ss. 23. India,SE Asia, Indonesia.
28. *Cacomantis flabelliformis*. Fan tailed Cuckoo. 6ss. 25. Australia, New Guinea. Solomon Islands, Fiji, New Caledonia.
29. *Cacomantis sonneratii*. Banded Bay Cuckoo. 5ss. 24. India, China, S E Asia, Philippines, Gr. Sundas.
30. *Cacomantis sepulcralis*. Indonesian Cuckoo. 4ss. 24. Philippines, Indonesia.
31. incl. *C. s. virescens*. Rusty breasted Cuckoo. 24. Sulawesi.
32. *Cacomantis variolosus*. Brush Cuckoo. 16ss. 23. Indonesia, Australasia.
33. incl. *C. v. infaustus*. Grey headed Brush Cuckoo. 23. New Guinea, Moluccas.
34. *Rhamphomantis megarhynchus*. Long billed Cuckoo. 2ss. 18. New Guinea.

1
2
3
4
(a)
(b)
6
7
8
5
9
10
11
12
13
14
15
16
17
18
20
21
22
23
19
24
25
26
27
28
29
30
31
32
33
34

CUCULIDAE (2)
Cuckoos

35. *Chrysococcyx flavigularis.* Yellow throated Cuckoo. 13. Sierra Leone to Uganda & Zaire.
36. *Chrysococcyx caprius.* Didric Cuckoo. 2ss. 18. Africa S of Sahara.
37. *Chrysococcyx klaas.* Klaas' Cuckoo. 20. Africa S of Sahara.
38. *Chrysococcyx cupreus.* African Emerald Cuckoo. 2ss. 20. Africa S of Sahara.
39. *Chrysococcyx/Chalcites basalis.* Horsfield's Bronze Cuckoo. 18. Australia, Winters New Guinea to Malaya.
40. *Chrysococcyx/Chalcites rufomerus.* Green cheeked Bronze Cuckoo. 18. Lesser Sundas.
41. *Chrysococcyx/Chalcites russatus.* Gould's Bronze Cuckoo. 4ss. 18. Philippines to Australia.
42. *Chrysococcyx/Chalcites crassirostris.* Pied Bronze Cuckoo. 15. Tanimbar, Kai Is.
43. *Chrysococcyx/Chalcites lucidus.* Shining Bronze Cuckoo. 5ss. 15. Australasia, Oceania, Winters to New Guinea.
44. *Chrysococcyx/Chalcites maculatus.* Asian Emerald Cuckoo. 18. India to SE Asia.
45. *Chrysococcyx/Chalcites malayanus.* Malaysian Bronze Cuckoo. 16. Malaysia to Philippines.
46. *Chrysococcyx/Chalcites meyeri.* White eared Bronze Cuckoo. 16. New Guinea.
47. *Chrysococcyx/Chalcites minutillus.* Little Bronze Cuckoo. 15. NW Australia. Conspf. 45 ?
48. *Chrysococcyx/Chalcites osculans.* Black eared Cuckoo. 20. Australia, Winters New Guinea.
49. *Chrysococcyx/Chalcites ruficollis.* Rufous throated Bronze Cuckoo. 16. New Guinea.
50. *Chrysococcyx/Chalcites xanthorhynchus.* Violet Cuckoo. 4ss. 17. India, SE Asia, Philippines, Borneo, Java.
51. *Chrysococcyx poecilurus.* New Guinea Bronze Cuckoo. 15. New Guinea & Is.
52. *Caliechthrus leucolophus.* White crowned Koel. 32. Salawati Is., New Guinea.
53. *Surniculus lugubris.* Drongo Cuckoo. 7ss. 25. India, Sri Lanka to SE Asia.
54. *Microdynamis parva.* Dwarf Koel. 2ss. 20. New Guinea.
55. *Eudynamis scolopacea.* Koel. 18ss. 43. India,Sri Lanka, SE Asia, Andaman Islands.
56. *Eudynamis cyanocephala.* Australian Koel. 2ss. 43. NE Australia.
57. *Eudynamis taitensis.* Long tailed Koel. 38. New Zealand. Winters Pacific Is.
58. *Eudynamis melanorhyncha.* Black billed Koel. 40. Wallacea.
59. *Scythrops novaehollandiae.* Channel billed Cuckoo. 60. Sundas to Australia.
60. *Coccyzus americanus.* Yellow billed Cuckoo. 2ss. 27. N America, Winters S America.
61. *Coccyzus cinereus.* Ash coloured Cuckoo. 24. Brazil, Peru to Argentina.
62. *Coccyzus ferrugineus.* Cocos Island Cuckoo. 33. Cocos Is. (Costa Rica).
63. *Coccyzus erythrophthalmus.* Black billed Cuckoo. 29. N America Winters to Bolivia.
64. *Coccyzus julieni / euleri.* Pearly breasted Cuckoo. 2S. Guyanas to Argentina.
65. *Coccyzus lansbergi.* Grey capped Cuckoo. 25. Venezuela, Colombia, Ecuador, Peru.
66. *Coccyzus melacoryphus.* Dark billed Cuckoo. 26. Venezuela to Argentina, Galapagos Islands.
67. *Coccyzus minor.* Mangrove Cuckoo. 14ss. 31. W Indies, Mexico to Brazil.
68. *Coccyzus pumilus.* Dwarf Cuckoo. 21. Colombia, Venezuela, Brazil.

35
36
37
38
39
42
41
40
43
51
44
45
46
47
48
49
50
52
56
53
54
55
57
59
58
61
62
60
63
64
65
66
67
68

CUCULIDAE (3) Cuckoos

69. *Piaya cayana.* Squirrel Cuckoo. 18ss. 40. C America. to Argentina.
70. *Piaya melanogaster.* Black billed Cuckoo. 2ss. 36. Guyanas to Brazil, Peru.
71. *Piaya minuta.* Little Cuckoo. 4ss. 27. Panama to Brazil.
72. *Hyetornis pluvialis.* Chestnut bellied Cuckoo. 53. Jamaica.
73. *Hyetornis rufigularis.* Bay breasted Cuckoo. 45. Hispaniola, Gonave Is.
74. *Saurothera merlini.* Great Lizard Cuckoo. 4ss. 50. Bahamas, Cuba.
75. *Saurothera longirostris.* Hispaniolan Lizard Cuckoo. 3ss. 42. Hispaniola.
76. *Saurothera vetula.* Jamaican Lizard Cuckoo. 39. Jamaica.
77. *Saurothera vielloti.* Puerto Rican Lizard Cuckoo. 42. Puerto Rico.
78. *Ceuthmochares aureus.* Yellowbill. 4ss. 32. Africa S of Sahara.
79. *Phaenicophaeus calyorhynchus.* Yellow billed Malkoha. 4ss. 45. Sulawesi.
80. *Phaenicophaeus chlorophaeus.* Raffles Malkoha. 3ss. 33. Malaya, Sumatra, Borneo.
81. *Phaenicophaeus cumingi.* Scale feathered Malkoha. 45. Philippines.
82. *Phaenicophaeus curvirostris.* Chestnut breasted Malkoha. 6ss. 45. Palawan, Malaysia, Greater Sundas.
83. *Phaenicophaeus diardi.* Black bellied Malkoha. 2ss. 36. Malaysia, Indonesia.
84. *Phaenicophaeus javanicus.* Red billed Malkoha. 4ss. 45. Malaysia, Gr. Sundas.
85. *Phaenicophaeus leschenaultii.* Sirkeer Malkoha. 4ss. 43. Indian sub-continent.
86. *Phaenicophaeus pyrrocephalus.* Red faced Malkoha. 46. Sri Lanka, India.
87. *Phaenicophaeus sumatranus.* Rufous bellied Malkoha. 2ss. 40. Malaya, Borneo, Sumatra.
88. *Phaenicophaeus superciliosus.* Red crested Malkoha. 45. Philippines.
89. *Phaenicophaeus tristis.* Green billed Malkoha. 6ss. 51. Himalayas, China, SE Asia to Sumatra.
90. *Phaenicophaeus viridirostris.* Blue faced Malkoha. 39. India, Sri Lanka.

69
70
71
72
73
74
75
76
77
78
79
80
81
82
83
84
85
86
87
88
89
90

CUCULIDAE (4)
Cuckoos

Nos. 91-94 may be separate family "CROTOPHAGIDAE."

91. *Crotophaga ani*. Smooth billed Ani. 35. W Indies, Costa Rica to Argentina.
92. *Crotophaga major*. Greater Ani. 48. Panama to Argentina.
93. *Crotophaga sulcirostris*. Groove billed Ani. 2ss. 30. Texas to Argentina.
94. *Guira guira*. Guira Cuckoo. 40. Brazil, Bolivia, Argentina.

Nos. 95-105 may be separate family "NEOMORPHIDAE"

95. *Tapera naevia*. Striped Cuckoo. 3ss. 29. Trinidad, C America to Argentina.
96. *Morococcyx erythropygus*. lesser Ground Cuckoo. 5ss. 26. Mexico to Costa Rica.
97. *Dromococcyx pavoninus*. Pavonine / Peacock Cuckoo. 2ss. 25. Guianas to Argentina.
98. *Dromococcyx phasianellus*. Pheasant Cuckoo. 2ss. 38. Mexico to Argentina.
99. *Geococcyx californiana*. Roadrunner. 55. California, Mexico.
100. *Geococcyx velox*. lesser Roadrunner. 5ss. 45. Mexico & C America.
101. *Neomorphus geoffroyi*. Rufous vented Ground Cuckoo. 5ss.45. Nicaragua to Brazil & Bolivia.
102. *Neomorphus pucheranii*. Red billed Ground Cuckoo. 2ss. 45. Peru, Brazil.
103. *Neomorphus radiolosus*. Banded Ground Cuckoo. 45. Colombia, Ecuador.
104. *Neomorphus rufipennis*. Rufous winged Ground Cuckoo. 2ss.45. Guyana, Venezuela, Brazil.
105. *Neomorphus squamiger*. Scaled Ground Cuckoo. 2ss. 45. Brazil.
106. *Carpococcyx radiceus*. Sunda Ground Cuckoo. 2ss. 60. Borneo, Sumatra.
107. *Carpococcyx renauldii*. Coral billed Ground Cuckoo. 67. Indo-China, Thailand.
108. *Coua caerulea*. Blue Coua. 40. Malagasy.
109. *Coua coquereli*. Coquerel's Coua. 42. Malagasy.
110. *Coua cristata*. Crested Coua. 40. Malagasy.

91
92
93
94
95
96
97
98
99
100
101
102
103
104
105
106
107
108
109
110

CUCULIDAE (5)
Coucals

111. *Coua cursor*. Running Coua. 40. Malagasy.
112. *Coua delalandei*. Snail eating Coua. 58. Malagasy.(Extinct).
113. *Coua gigas*. Giant Coua. 62. Malagasy.
114. *Coua reynaudi*. Red fronted Coua. 40. Malagasy.
115. *Coua ruficeps*. Red capped Coua. 42. Malagasy.
116. *Coua serriana*. Red breasted Coua. 42. Malagasy.
117. *Coua verreauxi*. Verreaux's Coua. 38. Malagasy.

Nos. 118–148 are often considered to be a separate family "CENTROPODIDAE".

118. *Centropus anselli*. Gabon Coucal. 48. Cameroon to Zaire, Angola.
119. *Centropus ateralbus*. Pied Coucal. 40. New Britain, New Ireland.
120. *Centropus bengalensis*. Lesser Coucal. 5ss. 37. Himalayas, India to Indonesia.
121. *Centropus bernsteinii*. Lesser Black Coucal. 2ss. 46. New Guinea.
122. *Centropus celebensis*. Bay Coucal. 2ss. 44. Sulawesi.
123. *Centropus chalybeus*. Biak Coucal. 46. Biak Is.
124. *Centropus chlororhynchus*. Green billed Coucal. 43. Sri Lanka.
125. *Centropus cupreicaudus*. Copper tailed Coucal. 48. Tanzania, Angola, S to Zambesi.
126. *Centropus leucogaster*. Black throated Coucal. 3ss. 45. W & C Africa.
127. *Centropus neumanni*. Neumann's Coucal. 40. Zaire.
128. *Centropus melanops*. Black faced Coucal. 2ss. 45. Philippines.
129. *Centropus menbeki*. Greater Black Coucal. 3ss. 64. New Guinea, Aru & other W Papuan Is.

111
112
113
114
115
116
117
118
119
120
Br
NB
Juv
121
122
123
124
125
126
127
128
129

Plate 111 Family 72.

CUCULIDAE (6)
Coucals

130. *Centropus milo*. Buff headed Coucal. 2ss. 70. Solomon Is.
131. *Centropus monachus*. Blue headed Coucal. 5ss. 50. W & C Africa.
132. *Centropus nigrorufus*. Sunda Coucal. 46. Java, Sumatra.
133. *Centropus phasianus*. Pheasant Coucal. 6ss. 60. Australia, New Guinea.
134. *Centropus rectunguis*. Short toed Coucal. 36. Malaysia, Sumatra, Borneo.
135. *Centropus Senegalensis*. Senegal Coucal. 4ss. 38. Africa S of Sahara.
136. *Centropus epomidis*. Rufous bellied Coucal. 58. Ghana, Nigeria.
137. *Centropus sinensis*. Greater Coucal. 7ss. 50. India, China, SE Asia, Sumatra.
138. *Centropus andamanensis*. Andaman Coucal. 50. Andaman Is.
139. *Centropus spilopterus*. Kai / Moluccan Coucal. 60. Kai Is.
140. *Centropus steeri*. Steere's Coucal. 40. Mindoro.
141. *Centropus superciliosus*. White browed Coucal. 40. Arabia, E & C Africa.
142. *Centropus burchelli*. Burchell's Coucal. 40. SE Africa.
143. *Centropus toulou*. Madagascar Coucal. 3ss. 40. Malagasy, Aldabra.
144. *Centropus grillii*. Black Coucal. 3ss. 40. Guinea to Natal.
145. *Centropus unirufus*. Rufous Coucal. 2ss. 45. Philippines.
146. *Centropus violaceus*. Violet Coucal. 70. New Ireland, New Britain.
147. *Centropus goliath*. Large Coucal. 70. N Moluccas.
148. *Centropus viridis*. Philippine Coucal. 3ss. 45. Philippines.

130
131
132
135
IMM
Br
133
NB
136
138
134
135
137
146
139
140
141
142
144
145
143
147
148

TYTONIDAE, STRIGIDAE
Barn Owls, Owls

TYTONIDAE. Barn Owls.

1. *Tyto soumagnei*. Madagascar Red Owl. 27. Malagasy.
2. *Tyto alba*. Barn Owl. 36ss. 40. Cosmopolitan.
3. *Tyto glaucops*. Ashy faced Owl. 33. Hispaniola.
4. *Tyto rosenbergi*. Sulawesi masked Owl. 2ss. 46. Sulawesi.
5. *Tyto nigrobrunnea*. Taliabu / Sula masked Owl. 30. Taliabu (Sulawesi).
6. *Tyto inexpectata*. Minahassa Masked Owl. 30. Sulawesi.
7. *Tyto novaehollandiae*. Australian Masked Owl. 5ss. 51. Australia, New Guinea..

7a. *Tyto castanops*. Tasmanian Masked Owl. 51. Tasmania.

8. *Tyto sororcula*. Lesser Masked Owl. 2ss. 49. Buru (Moluccas). Tanimba Is.
9. *Tyto manusi*. Manus Owl. 45. Manus Is.(Bismarck Arch.)
10. *Tyto aurantia*. Bismarck Owl. 30. New Britain.
11. *Tyto tenebricosa*. Greater Sooty Owl. 2ss. 35. New Guinea, E & S Australia.
12. *Tyto multipunctata*. Lesser Sooty Owl. 32. Queensland.
13. *Tyto capensis*. African Grass Owl. 4ss. 40. Kenya & Cameroon to Cape.
14. *Tyto longimembris*. Australasian Grass Owl. 6ss. 40. India, SE Asia, Australia.
15. *Phodilus badius*. Oriental Bay Owl. 5ss. 28. Nepal, Indo-China, Indonesia.
16. *Phodilus prigoginae*. Congo Bay Owl. 28. Zaire.

Family 74. STRIGIDAE (1). Owls.

1. *Otus sagittatus*. White fronted Scops Owl. 26. Burma, Thailand
2. *Otus rufescens*. Rufous Scops Owl. 3ss. 17. Malaysia, Indonesia.
3. *Otus bakkamoena*. Indian Scops Owl. 7ss. 21. Arabia to India ,Thailand.
4. *Otus lempiji*. Collared Scops Owl. 13ss. 20. Japan, China to Malaya, Borneo.
5. *Otus elegans*. Ryukyu Scops Owl. 4ss. 21. Ryukyu Is.
6. *Otus sunia*. Oriental Scops Owl. 4ss. 17. Himalayas to Thailand, Sri Lanka.
7. *Otus spilocephalus*. Spotted Scops Owl. 7ss. 18. Himalayas to China, Indonesia.
8. *Otus Balli*. Andaman Scops Owl. 18. Andaman Is.
9. *Otus fuliginosus*. Palawan Scops Owl. 18. Palawan Is.
10. *Otus podarginus*. Palau Scops Owl. 22. Palau Is.
11. *Otus longicornis*. Luzon Scops Owl. 19. Luzon.
12. *Otus mindorensis*. Mindoro Scops Owl. 17. Mindoro.
13. *Otus mirus*. Mindanao Scops Owl. 17. Mindanao.
14. *Otus manadensis*. Sulawesi Scops Owl. 21. Sulawesi.
15. *Otus megalotis*. Philippine Scops Owl. 3ss. 23. Philippine Is.
16. *Otus brookii*. Rajah Scops Owl. 2ss. 23. Sarawak, Java, Sumatra.
17. *Otus alfredi*. Flores Scops Owl. 19. Flores.

TYTONIDAE
1
2
3
4
5
6
7
8
9
10
11
12
13
14
7A
15
16
2
JUV
29
JUV
STRIGIDAE
1
2
3
4
5
6
7
8
9
10
11
12
13
14
15
16
17

STRIGIDAE (2) Owls)

18. *Otus angelinae.* Javan Scope Owl. 20. Java.
19. *Otus vandewateri.* Sumatran Screech Owl. 18. Sumatra.
20. *Otus umbra.* Semulu Scops Owl. 16. Simeulue Is. (Sumatra)
21. *Otus enganensis.* Enggano Scops Owl. 16. Enggano Is. (Sumatra)
22. *Otus mantananensis.* Mantanani Scops Owl. 5ss. 21. S Philippines.
23. *Otus mentawi.* Mentawi Scops Owl. 21. Siberut, Sipura Is. (Sumatra)
24. *Otus magicus.* Moluccan Scops Owl. 9ss. 21. Moluccan Is.
25. *Otus silvicola.* Wallace's Scops Owl. 23. Flores, Sumbawa.
26. *Otus leucotis.* White faced Scops Owl. 3ss. 24. Senegal & Sudan to Cape.
27. *Otus brucei.* Pallid Scops Owl. 3ss. 16. Israel to Pakistan.
28. *Otus beccarii.* Biak / Papuan Scops Owl. 24. Biak I. (New Guinea)
29. *Otus scops.* European Scops Owl. 9ss. 18. Most of Europe & Asia.
30. *Otus insularis.* Seychelles Bare legged Scops Owl. 20. Mahe. (Seychelles.)
31. *Otus rutilus.* Madagascar Scops Owl. 3ss. 21. Malagasy, Anjouan, Mayotte.
32. *Otus pauliani.* Comoro Scops Owl. 20. Comoro Is.
33. *Otus pembaensis.* Pemba Scops Owl. 21. Pemba Is.
34. *Otus senegalensis.* African Scops Owl. 12ss. 19. Senegal, Sudan to Cape.
35. *Otus ireneae.* Sokoke Scops Owl. 17. Kenya.
36. *Otus icterorhynchus.* Sandy Scops Owl. 2ss. 19. Ghana, Cameroon, Zaire.
37. *Otus hartlaubi.* Sao Thome Scops Owl. 18. Sao Thome Is.
38. *Otus flammeolus.* Flammulated Owl. 6ss. 17. Canada to Guatemala.
39. *Otus asio.* Eastern Screech Owl. 8ss. 21. E America, Canada to Mexico.
40. *Otus kennicotti.* Western Screech Owl. 17ss. 20. W America, Alaska to Mexico.
41. *Otus vinaceus.* Vinaceous Screech Owl. 20. Sinaloa.
42. *Otus lawrencii.* Cuban / Bare legged Owl. 2ss. 22. Cuba, Is. of Pines.
43. *Otus nudipes.* Puerto Rican Screech Owl. 3ss. 22. Puerto Rico, Lesser Antilles.
44. *Otus seductus.* Balsas Screech Owl. 2ss. 20. Mexico.
45. *Otus cooperi.* Pacific Screech Owl. 2ss. 23. W Mexico & C America.
46. *Otus clarkii.* Bare shanked Screech Owl. 23. Costa Rica to Colombia.
47. *Otus barbarus.* Bearded Screech Owl. 21. Guatemala, Mexico.
48. *Otus chlodiba.* Tropical Screech Owl. 17ss. 21. Trinidad, Costa Rica to Argentina.
49. *Otus trichopsis.* Whiskered Screech Owl. 7ss. 19. Arizona to Panama.
50. *Otus vermiculatus.* Vermiculated Screech Owl. 23. Costa Rica, Panama.
51. *Otus Guatemalae.* Guatemalan Screech Owl. 17ss. 20. Mexico to Ecuador, Peru.
52. *Otus colombianus.* Colombian Screech Owl. 23. Colombia, Ecuador, Peru.
53. *Otus sanctaecaterinae.* Long tufted Screech Owl. 23. Brazil.
54. *Otus albigularis.* White throated Screech Owl. 3ss. 21. Venezuela to Ecuador.
55. *Otus roboratus.* Peruvian Screech Owl. 21. NW Peru.
56. *Otus watsonii.* Tawny bellied Screech Owl. 5ss. 21. Amazon basin.
57. *Otus koepeckeae.* Maria Koepcke's Screech Owl. 21. Peru, Bolivia.
58. *Otus marshalli.* Cloud forest Screech Owl. 20. S E Peru.
59. *Otus peterseni.* Cinnamon Screech Owl. 21. Peru, Ecuador.
60. *Otus atricapillus.* Variable / Black capped Screech Owl. 2ss. 23. Brazil.
61. *Otus usta.* Austral Screech Owl. 21. Brazil, Argentina.
62. *Otus ingens.* Rufescent Screech Owl. 2ss. 23. Venezuela, Ecuador.
63. *Otus minimus.* Bolivian Screech Owl. 15. Bolivia.
64. *Mimizuku gurneyi.* Giant Scops / Lesser Eagle Owl. 30. Mindanao.
65. *Lophostrix cristata.* Crested Owl. 3ss. 40. Mexico to Brazil.
66. *Jubula lettii.* Maned Owl. 44. Liberia to Zaire.

18
19
20
21
22
23
24
25
26
27
28
29
30
31
32
33
34
35
36
37
38
39
40
41
42
43
44
45
46
47
48
49
50
51
52
53
54
55
56
57
58
59
60
61
62
63
64
65
66

STRIGIDAE (3)
Owls

67. *Bubo africanus*. Spotted Eagle Owl. 3ss. 35. Africa S of Sahara.a. grey morph. b. rufous buff morph.
68. *Bubo bubo*. Eurasian Eagle Owl. 18ss. 68. Palearctic.
69. *Bubo bengalensis*. Indian Eagle Owl. 60. N & C India.
70. *Bubo capensis*. Cape Eagle Owl. 3ss. 49. Ethiopia, E Africa to Cape.
71. *Bubo coromandus*. Dusky Eagle Owl. 2ss. 45. India to SE Asia.
72. *Bubo lacteus*. Verreaux's Eagle Owl. 17ss. 57. Most of Africa S of Sahara.
73. *Bubo leucostictus*. Akun Eagle Owl. 43. Liberia to Zaire & Gabon.
74. *Bubo nipalensis*. Forest Eagle Owl. 2ss. 56. India, Sri Lanka to Indo-China.
75. *Bubo philippensis*. Philippine Eagle Owl. 2ss. 40. Philippines.
76. *Bubo ascalaphus*. Pharaoh Eagle Owl. 50. E Africa, Near East.
77. *Bubo poensis*. Fraser's Eagle Owl. 2ss. 42. W & C Africa.

77a. *Bubo vosseleri*. Usambara Eagle Owl. 42. Tanzania.

78. *Bubo shelleyi*. Shelley's Eagle Owl. 61. W & C Africa.79. Bubo sumatramus. Malay / Barred Eagle Owl.2ss. 43. Malaya to Java, Sumatra, Borneo.
80. *Bubo virginianus*. Great horned Owl. 17ss. 48. Alaska, Canada to Argentina.
81. *Ketupa blakistoni*. Blakiston's Fish Owl. 4ss. 56. Siberia, China.
82. *Ketupa flavipes*. Tawny Fish Owl. 49. C Asia to Indo-China.
83. *Ketupa ketupa*. Buffy Fish Owl. 4ss. 41. S E Asia & Greater Sundas.
84. *Ketupa zeylonensis*. Brown Fish Owl. 4ss. 49. Middle East to India, Sri Lanka to China.

67 (a)
67 (b)
68
70
71
72
69
74
75
76
78
79
77A
77
80
81
82
83
84
73

STRIGIDAE (4)
Owls

85. *Scotopelia bouvieri*. Vermiculated Fishing Owl. 48. Cameroon, Zaire, Angola.
86. *Scotopelia peli*. Pel's Fishing Owl. 56. Local in Africa S of Sahara.
87. *Scotopelia ussheri*. Rufous Fishing Owl. 46. Ghana to Sierra Leone.
88. *Pulsatrix koeniswaldiana*. Tawny browed Owl. 43. C Brazil.
89. *Pulsatrix melanota*. Band bellied Owl. 2ss. 48. Ecuador, Peru.
90. *Pulsatrix perspicillata*. Spectacled Owl. 6ss. 45. Mexico to Brazil, Argentina.
91. *Sceloglaux albifacies*. Laughing Owl. 42. New Zealand. (extinct).
92. *Nyctea scandiaca*. Snowy Owl. 60. Arctic Circle. Winters South.
93. *Surnia ulula*. Northern Hawk Owl. 3ss. 39. Arctic Eurasia, N America.
94. *Glaucidium brasilianum*. Ferruginous Pygmy Owl. 12ss. 14. Arizona to Tierra del Fuego.

94a. *Glaucidium peruanum*. Peruvian Pygmy Owl. 14. Peru.

95. *Glaucidium nanum*. Austral Pygmy Owl. 18. Chile, Argentina.
96. *Glaucidium jardinii*. Andean Pygmy Owl. 2ss. 16. Costa Rica to Bolivia.

96a. *Glaucidium bolivianum*. Yungas Pygmy Owl. 16. Peru, Bolivia, Argentina.

97. *Glaucidium albertinum*. Prigogine's / *Albertine Owlet. 22. Zaire, Rwanda.*
98. *Glaucidium brodiei*. Collared Pygmy Owl. 4ss. 15. Himalayas, China, SE Asia, Sumatra, Borneo.
99. *Glaucidium capense*. Barred Owlet. 2ss. 22. Angola, Southern Africa.
100. *Glaucidium castaneum*. Chestnut Owlet. 20. W Africa.
101. *Glaucidium cuculoides*. Cuckoo / Asian barred Owlet. 10ss. 24. S, SE Asia.
102. *Glaucidium castanopterum*. Chestnut winged Owlet. 20. Java.
103. *Glaucidium gnoma*. Mountain Pygmy Owl. 7ss. 17. Arizona to Honduras.
104. *Glaucidium californicum*. Northern Pygmy Owl. 17. Alaska to Mexico.
105. *Glaucidium minutissimum*. Least Pygmy Owl. 8ss. 13. Mexico to Brazil, Paraguay.

105a. *Glaucidium hardyi*. Amazonian Pygmy Owl. 12. Brazil.

105b. *Glaucidium parkeri*. Subtropical Pygmy Owl. 13. Ecuador, Peru.

106. *Glaucidium scheffleri*. Scheffler's Owlet. 21. Kenya, Tanzania.
107. *Glaucidium passerinum*. Eurasian Pygmy Owl. 2ss. 17. N Eurasia.
108. *Glaucidium perlatum*. Pearl spotted Owlet. 3ss. 18. Africa S of Sahara.
109. *Glaucidium ngamiense*. Ngami Owlet. 21. Tanzania to Angola, Mozambique.
110. *Glaucidium radiatum*. Jungle Owlet. 2ss. 17. India, Burma, Sri Lanka.
111. *Glaucidium siju*. Cuban Pygmy Owl. 2ss. 17. Cuba, Is. of Pines.
112. *Glaucidium castanonotum*. Chestnut backed Owlet. 17. Sri Lanka.
113. *Glaucidium sjostedti*. Sjostedt' s Owlet. 25. Cameroon, Zaire, Gabon.
114. *Glaucidium tephronotum*. Red chested Owlet. 6ss. 18. Liberia to Uganda, Kenya.
115. *Xenoglaus loweryi*. Long whiskered Owlet. 16. Peru.
116. *Micrathene whitneyi*. Elf Owl. 14. S W USA, Mexico.

* Note. Glaucidium Pygmy Owls from S America are very variable. Identification is very difficult
e.g. Yungas Pygmy Owl is found in three distinct colour morphs.- 96a.(a) (b) & (c)

85
86
87
88
89
90
JUV
91
93
92
94A
96
95
96A
(c)
94
96A
(b)
100
96A
(a)
99
97
98
101
102
103
104
105
106
107
108
105A
105
B
110
111
112
113
109
114
115
116

STRIGIDAE (5) Owls

117. *Uroglaux dimorpha*. Papuan Hawk Owl. 32. New Guinea.
118. *Ninox affinis*. Andaman Hawk Owl. 2ss. 23. Andaman Is.
119. *Ninox connivens*. Barking Owl. 7ss. 41. New Guinea, Australia.
120. *Ninox jacquinoti*. Solomon Hawk Owl. 27. Solomon Is.
121. *Ninox meeki*. Manus Hawk Owl. 23. Admiralty Is.
122. *Ninox novaeseelandiae*. Boobook / Morepork. 4ss. 35. New Zealand & Is.
123. *Ninox boobook*. Southern Boobook. 11ss. 35. Australia, New Guinea & Is.
124. *Ninox rudolfi*. Sumba Boobook. 35. Sumba Is.
125. *Ninox odiosa*. New Britain Hawk Owl. 22. New Britain.
126. *Ninox perversa/ochracea*. Ochre bellied Hawk Owl. 23. Sulawesi.
127. *Ninox philippensis*. Philippine Hawk Owl. 3ss. 18. Philippines.
128. incl. *N. p. spilonota*. Mindoro barred Hawk Owl. 20. Mindoro.
129. *N. p. spilocephala*. Mindanao spotted Hawk Owl. 18. Mindanao.
130. *Ninox punctulata*. Speckled Hawk Owl. 23. Sulawesi.
131. *Ninox rufa*. Rufous Owl. 4ss. 45. New Guinea, N E Australia.
132. *Ninox scutulata*. Brown Hawk Owl. 10ss. 23. India, China to Malaya.
133. *Ninox variegata/solomonis*. Bismarck Hawk Owl. 2ss. 27. New Britain, New Ireland.
134. *Ninox squamipila*. Moluccan Hawk Owl. 5ss. 31. Christmas I, Moluccas, Tanimbar.
135. *Ninox strenua*. Powerful Owl. 64. S E Australia.
136. *Ninox superciliaris*. Madagascar/ White browed Hawk Owl. 26. Malagasy.
137. *Ninox theomacha*. Jungle / Sooty backed Hawk Owl. 4ss.23. New Guinea.
138. *Athene blewitti*. Forest Owlet. 22. Central India.(extinct ?)
139. *Athene brama*. Spotted Owlet. 4ss. 20. Iran to India to Indo-China.
140. *Athene cunicularia*. Burrowing Owl. 18ss. 22. Canada to Argentina.
141. *Athene noctua*. Little Owl. 15ss. 21. Palearctic. 142. Strix (Ciccaba) albitarsus. Rufous banded Owl. 30. Venezuela to Bolivia.
143. *Strix (C) huhula*. Black banded Owl. 32. Venezuela, Amazonia.
144. *Strix (C) nigrolineata*. Black & white Owl. 36. Mexico to Peru. 145. Strix (C) virgata. Mottled Owl. 8ss. 33. Mexico to Argentina.
146. *Strix(C)woodfordii*. African Wood Owl. 5ss. 33. Africa S of Sahara.

117
118
119
120
121
122
123
124
127
128
129
130
131
132
133
134
125
135
136
137
126
138
139
141
142
143
140
144
145
146

STRIGIDAE (6)
Owls

147. *Strix aluco*. Tawny Owl. 13ss. 41. Europe, Middle East to China.
148. *Strix butleri*. Hume's Tawny Owl. 33. Deserts, Syria, Sinai, Egypt, Arabia.
149. *Strix hylophila*. Rusty barred Owl. 36. S Brazil.
150. *Strix leptogrammica*. Brown Wood Owl. 15ss. 50. India, China, SE Asia to Indonesia.
151. *Strix nebulosa*. Great grey Owl. 3ss. 72. Northern N America, N Eurasia.
152. *Strix occidentalis*. Spotted Owl. 3ss. 44. British Columbia to Mexico.
153. *Strix ocellata*. Mottled Wood Owl. 3ss. 42. India.
154. *Strix rufipes*. Rufous legged Owl. 36. Chile, Argentina. Falkland Is, S Georgia.
155. *Strix seloputo*. Spotted Wood Owl. 43. SE Asia, Malaysia, Java, Palawan.
156. *Strix uralensis*. Ural Owl. 11ss. 59. Scandinavia to China, Japan.
157. incl. *S. u. davidi*. David's Wood Owl. 59. W Szechwan.
158. *Strix varia*. Barred Owl. 5ss. 51. Canada, E USA to Guatemala.
159. *Strix fulvescens*. Fulvous Owl. 42. Mexico to Honduras.
160. *Asio clamator*. Striped Owl. 3ss. 35. Mexico to Brazil & Bolivia.
161. *Asio capensis*. African Marsh Owl. 3ss. 35. E W & S Africa.
162. *Asio flammeus*. Short eared Owl. 10ss. 38. N Eurasia, N & S America, Hawaii.
163. *Asio madagascariensis*. Madagascar Long eared Owl. 32. Malagasy.
164. *Asio otus*. Long eared Owl. 5ss. 38. Eurasia, N America.
165. *Asio abyssinicus*. Abyssinian Owl. 40. E Africa.
166. *Asio stygius*. Stygian Owl. 6ss. 42. Mexico to Argentina, Gr. Antilles.
167. *Pseudoscops grammicus*. Jamaican Owl. 31. Jamaica.
168. *Nesasio solomonensis*. Fearful Owl. 33. Solomon Is.
169. *Aegolius acadicus*. Saw whet Owl. 2ss. 18. Alaska to Mexico.
170. *Aegolius funereus*. Tengmalm's / Boreal Owl. 8ss. 21. Arctic Circle forests.
171. *Aegolius Harrisii*. Buff fronted Owl. 2ss. 21. Colombia to Brazil, Argentina.
172. *Aegolius ridgwayi*. Unspotted Saw Whet Owl. 3ss. 18. Mexico to Costa Rica.

147
148
150
151
149
152
153
154
159
160
155
156
157
158
161
162
165
163
164
166
167
169
168
170
171
172

STEATORNIYHIDAE, PODARGIDAE, NYCTIBIIDAE AEGOTHELIDAE
Oilbird, Frogmouths, potoos, owlet-nightjars

Family 75. STEATORNITHIDAE. Oilbird.

1. *Steathornis caripensis*. Oilbird. 45. Trinidad, Northern S America, S to Bolivia.

Family 76. PODARGIDAE. Frogmouths

1. *Podargus ocellatus*. Marbled Frogmouth. 5ss. 37. Australia, New Guinea, Solomon Is.
2. *Podargus papuensis*. Papuan Frogmouth. 48. New Guinea to NE Queensland.
3. *Podargus strigoides*. Tawny Frogmouth. 8ss. 40. Most of Australia.
4. *Batrachostomus affinis*. Blyth's Frogmouth. 23. Malaya, Sumatra, Borneo.
5. *Batrachostomus auritus*. Large Frogmouth. 40. Thailand, Malaysia, Borneo, Sumatra.
6. *Batrachostomus harteri*. Dulit Frogmouth. 33. Borneo.
7. *Batrachostomus hodgsoni*. Hodgson's Frogmouth. 2ss. 26. India, China, SE Asia.
8. *Batrachostomus javensis*. Javan Frogmouth. 4ss. 23. Java.
9. *Batrachostomus cornutus*. Sunda Frogmouth. 23. Borneo, Sumatra, Palawan. *
10. *Batrachostomus moniliger*. Ceylon Frogmouth. 23. Sri Lanka, S E India.
11. *Batrachostomus mixtus*. Sharpe's Frogmouth. 20. Borneo.
12. *Batrachostomus poliolophus*. Pale headed Frogmouth. 20. Borneo, Sumatra.
13. *Batrachostomus septimus*. Philippine Frogmouth. 3ss. 25. Philippines.
14. *Batrachostomus stellatus*. Gould's Frogmouth. 21. Malaya, Sumatra, Borneo.

* Both sexes are polymorphic but males are usually grey, females reddish.

Family 77. NYCTIBIIDAE. Potoos.

1. *Nyctibius aethereus*. Long tailed Potoo. 3ss. 45. North of S America.
2. *Nyctibius bracteatus*. Rufous Potoo. 23. Guyana, W Amazon basin.
3. *Nyctibius jamaicensis*. Jamaican Potoo. 40. Jamaica, Mexico.
4. *Nyctibius grandis*. Great Potoo. 50. Guatemala to Brazil, Bolivia.
5. *Nyctibius maculosus*. Andean Potoo. 32.Venezuela to Bolivia.
6. *Nyctibius griseus*. Grey Potoo. 37. Nicaragua to Brazil & Argentina.
7. *Nyctibius leucopterus*. White winged Potoo. 2ss. 30. Brazil.

Family 78. AEGOTHELIDAE. Owlet-Nightjars.

1. *Aegotheles albertisi*. Mountain Owlet-Nightjar. 3ss. 19. New Guinea.
2. *Aegotheles bennettii*. Barred Owlet-Nightjar. 5ss. 24. New Guinea & Is.
3. *Aegotheles crinifrons*. Moluccan Owlet-Nightjar. 28. Halmahera, Batjan.
4. *Aegotheles cristatus*. Australian Owlet-Nightjar. 4ss. 23. Australia. (a.) Grey, (b.) Red phase.
5. *Aegotheles insignis*. Feline Owlet-Nightjar. 28. New Guinea.
6. *Aegotheles savesi*. New Caledonian Owlet-Nightjar. 28. New Caledonia.
7. *Aegotheles wallacei*. Wallace's Owlet-Nightjar. 3ss. 22. New Guinea.
8. *Aegotheles archboldi*. Archbold's Owlet-Nightjar. 20. New Guinea.

Most species in this family have two distinct colour phases (a) and (b)

STEATHORNITHIDAE
PODARGIDAE
NYCTIBIIDAE
AEGOTHELIDAE

CAPRIMULGIDAE (1)
Nightjars

1. *Lurocalis semitorquatus.* Short tailed Nighthawk. 6ss. 25. Nicaragua to Brazil & Argentina.
1a. *Lurocalis rufiventris.* Rufous bellied Nighthawk. 7ss. 25. Andes, S America.
2. *Chordeiles acutipennis.* Lesser Nighthawk. 9ss. 20. W USA to Brazil, Chile.
3. *Chordeiles minor.* Common Nighthawk. 10ss. 23. Canada to Panama, Winters to Argentina.
4. *Chordeiles pusillus.* Least Nighthawk. 3ss. 15. Venezuela to Brazil.
4a. *Chordeiles vielliardi.* Vielliard's Nighthawk. 17. Bahia, Brazil.
5. *Chordeiles rupestris.* Sand coloured Nighthawk. 2ss. 22. Colombia.
6. *Chordeiles gundlachi.* Antillean Nighthawk. 2ss. 23. Bahamas, Gr. Antilles.
7. *Nyctiprogne leucopyga.* Band tailed Nighthawk. 5ss. 18. Guyanas, Amazonia.
8. *Podager nacunda.* Nacunda Nighthawk. 2ss. 28. Colombia to Argentina.
9. *Nyctidromus albicollis.* Pauraque. 6ss. 26. Texas to Brazil, Paraguay.
10. *Phalaenoptilus nuttalli.* Common Poorwill. 5ss. 20. W USA to Mexico.
11. *Siphonorhis brewstoni (americanus).* Least Pauraque. 18. Hispaniola.
12. *Nyctiphrynus mcleodii.* Eared Poorwill. 2ss. 19. Mexico.
13. *Nyctiphrynus yucatanicus.* Yucatan Poorwill. 19. Mexico, Guatemala.
14. *Nyctiphrynus ocellatus.* Ocellated Poorwill. 3ss. 21. Nicaragua to Argentina.
15. *Hydropsalis brasiliana.* Scissor tailed Nightjar. 2ss. 28+22. Bolivia, Peru, Uruguay, Argentina.
16. *Hydropsalis climacocerca.* Ladder tailed Nightjar. 5ss. 28. Venezuela, Amazonia.
17. *Uropsalis lyra.* Lyre tailed Nightjar. 2ss. 31+48. Venezuela to Argentina.
18. *Uropsalis segmentata.* Swallow tailed Nightjar. 2ss. 23+38. Colombia to Bolivia.
19. *Macropsalis creagra.* Long trained Nightjar. 20+50. Brazil to Argentina.
20. *Eleothreptus anomalus.* Sickle winged Nightjar. 19. Brazil, Paraguay, Argentina.
21. *Eurostopodus archboldi.* Archbold's/Mountain Nightjar. 26. New Guinea.
22. *Eurostopodus diabolicus.* Satanic Nightjar. 25. Sulawesi.23. Eurostopodus argus. (guttatus.) Spotted Nightjar. 4ss. 29. Australia, Winters Aru Is.
24. *Eurostopodus macrotis.* Great eared Nightjar. 5ss. 40. India, China, Philippines, S E Asia, Sulawesi.
25. *Eurostopodus mysticalis.* White throated Nightjar. 3ss. 32. E Australia, Winters New Guinea, Solomon Islands.
26. *Eurostopodus papuensis.* Papuan Nightjar. 2ss. 25. New Guinea.
27. *Eurostopodus temmincki.* Malaysian Nightjar. 27. Malaya, Sumatra, Borneo.

21-27 now considered separate family "EUROSTOPIDAE." Eared Nightjars.

1
1A
2
3
3
4
4A
5
5
6
7
8
8
9
9
10
10
11
11
12
13
14
15
16
17
18
19
20
21
22
23
24
25
26
27

CAPRIMULGIDAE (2)
Nightjars

28. *Macrodipteryx longpennis.* Standard winged Nightjar. 26+45. Senegal to Ethiopia.
29. *Macrodipteryx vexillarius.* Pennant winged Nightjar. 28+45. S Africa. W Nigeria to Uganda.
30. *Caprimulgus europaeus.* Eurasian Nightjar. 5ss. 25. Eurasia, W. Africa.
30a. *Caprimulgus solala.* Nechisar Nightjar. 26S. Ethiopia. Unique ? Described from single wing of corpse.
31. *Caprimulgus ruficollis.* Red necked Nightjar. 2ss. 30. Iberia, NW Africa.
32. *Caprimulgus aegyptius.* Egyptian Nightjar. 2ss. 26. N Africa, SW Asia, W Africa.
33. *Caprimulgus nubicus.* Nubian Nightjar. 4ss. 24. Arabia to E Africa.
34. *Caprimulgus eximius.* Golden Nightjar. 2ss. 23. W. Africa.
35. *Caprimulgus pectoralis.* Dusky Nightjar. 2ss. 22. S. Africa.
36. incl. *C. p. fervidus.* Fiery necked Nightjar. 23. Kenya to Angola.
37. *Caprimulgus nigriscapularis.* Black shouldered Nightjar. 24. W & Central Africa.
38. *Caprimulgus rufigena.* Rufous cheeked Nightjar. 2ss. 23. E & S Africa.
39. *Caprimulgus fraenatus.* Sombre Nightjar. 25. Ethiopia to Kenya.
40. *Caprimulgus donaldsoni.* Donaldson Smith's Nightjar. 16. Somalia, Kenya.
41. *Caprimulgus polioceplalus.* Montane Nightjar. 3ss. 24. Ethiopia to Angola.
42. incl. *C. p. guttifer.* Usumbara Nightjar. 24. Tanzania.
43. *Caprimulgus ruwenzorii.* Ruwenzori Nightjar. 24. Zaire, Uganda.
44. *Caprimulgus natalensis.* Swamp Nightjar. 7ss. 25. Africa S. of Sahara.
45. *Caprimulgus inornatus.* Plain Nightjar. 3ss. 23. SW Arabia, Tanzania to Nigeria.
46. *Caprimulgus stellatus.* Star spotted Nightjar. 2ss. 22. Ethiopia to Kenya.
47. *Caprimulgus ludovicianus.* Ethiopian Nightjar. 25. Ethiopia.
48. *Caprimulgus tristigma.* Freckled Nightjar. 3ss. 26. Africa, S of Sahara.
49. *Caprimulgus enarratus.* Collared Nightjar. 24. Malagasy.
50. *Caprimulgus madagascariensis.* Madagascar Nightjar. 2ss. 21. Malagasy.
51. *Caprimulgus batesi.* Bates' Nightjar. 24. Cameroon to Zaire.
52. *Caprimulgus prigoginei.* Itombwe Nightjar. 19. Zaire.
53. *Caprimulgus fossii.* Square tailed Nightjar 25. Gabon, Zaire, Kenya to Natal.
54. *Caprimulgus climacurus.* Long tailed Nightjar. 5ss. 28. Senegal to Sudan.
55. *Caprimulgus clarus.* Slender tailed Nightjar. 23. Ethiopia to Tanzania.
56. *Caprimulgus binotatus.* Brown Nightjar. 20. Ghana to Cameroon.

53, 54, 55 considered a separate genus, "SCOTORNIS".

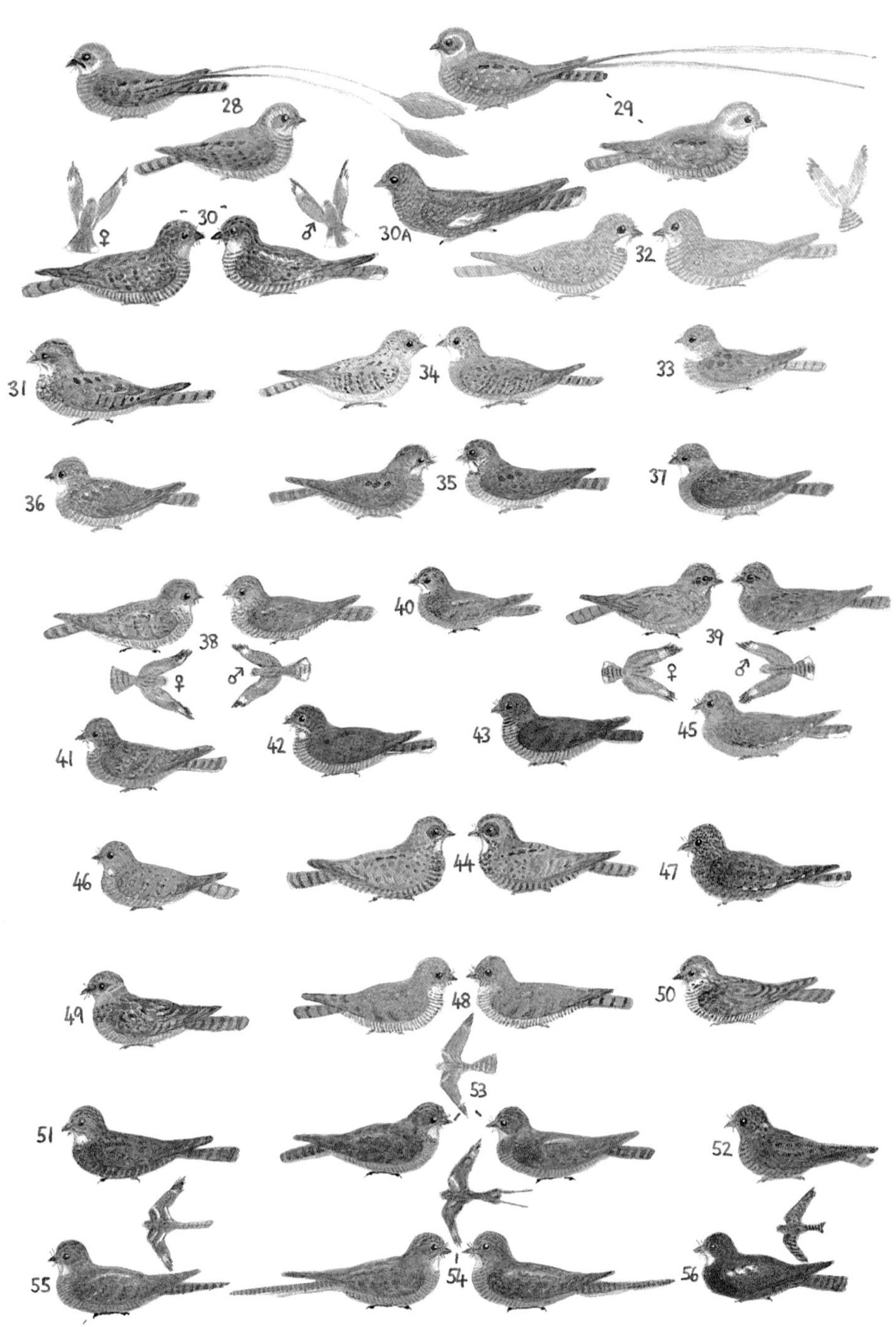
28
29
30
♀
♂
30A
32
31
34
33
36
35
37
38
40
39
♀
♂
♀
♂
41
42
43
45
46
44
47
49
48
50
53
51
52
55
54
56

CAPRIMULGIDAE (3)
Nightjars

57. *Caprimulgus indicus.* Grey / Jungle Nightjar. 5ss. 29. India, E Asia, Philippines.
58. *Caprimulgus asiaticus.* Indian Nightjar. 3ss. 24. Indian subcontinent, SE Asia.
59. *Caprimulgus centralasicus.* Vaurie's Nightjar. 19. W China.
60. *Caprimulgus monticolus.* Franklin's Nightjar. 4ss. 25. India, China, Thailand, Indo-China.
61. *Caprimulgus mahrattensis.* Sykes' Nightjar. 23. Iran to Pakistan, NW India.
62. *Caprimulgus affinis.* Allied / Savannah Nightjar.7ss. 20. S & SE Asia, Philippines, Sulawesi, Sundas.
63. *Caprimulgus concretus.* Bonaparte's Nightjar. 20. Sumatra, Borneo.
64. *Caprimulgus atripennis.* Jerdon's Nightjar. 2ss. 28. India, Sri Lanka.
65. *Caprimulgus manillensis.* Philippine Nightjar. 32. Philippines.
66. *Caprimulgus pulchellus.* Salvadori's Nightjar. 2ss. 24. Java, Sumatra.
67. *Caprimulgus macrurus.* Large tailed Nightjar. 18ss. 32. S Asia to Australia.
67a. *Caprimulgus celebensis.* Sulawesi Nightjar. 30. N Sulawesi.
68. *Caprimulgus carolinensis.* Chuck Will's Widow. 29. SE N America, Northern S America.
69. *Caprimulgus rufus.* Rufous Nightjar. 5ss. 25. Panama to Brazil.
70. *Caprimulgus saltarius.* Salta Nightjar. 28. N W Argentina, Bolivia.
71. *Caprimulgus otiosus.* St. Lucia Nightjar. 28. St. Lucia.
72. *Caprimulgus cubanensis.* Greater Antillean Nightjar. 2ss. 28. Cuba, Hispaniola.
73. *Caprimulgus sericocaudatus.* Silky tailed Nightjar. 2ss. 29. Peru, Argentina.
74. *Caprimulgus salvini.* Tawny collared Nightjar. 25. Mexico.
75. *Caprimulgus badius.* Yucatan Nightjar. 25. Yucatan, Belize.
76. *Caprimulgus ridgwayi.* Buff collared Nightjar. 2ss. 22. Mexico to Honduras.
77. *Caprimulgus vociferus.* Whip poor Will. 6ss. 24. S Canada to Honduras.
78. *Caprimulgus noctitherus.* Puerto Rican Nightjar. 22. Puerto Rico.
79. *Caprimulgus saturatus.* Dusky Nightjar. 23. Costa Rica, Panama.
80. *Caprimulgus longirostris.* Band winged Nightjar. 6ss. 23. Venezuela to Argentina.
81. *Caprimulgus cayannensis.* White tailed Nightjar. 5ss. 22. Costa Rica to Brazil.
82. *Caprimulgus candicans.* White winged Nightjar. 23. Brazil, Paraguay.
83. *Caprimulgus maculicaudus.* Spot tailed Nightjar / Pitsweet. 20. Mexico to Brazil.
84. *Caprimulgus parvulus.* Little Nightjar. 2ss. 20. Colombia to Argentina.
85. *Caprimulgus anthonyi.* Scrub Nightjar. 20. Ecuador, Peru.
86. *Caprimulgus maculosus.* Cayenne Nightjar. 22. French Guyana.
87. *Caprimulgus nigrescens.* Blackish Nightjar. 20. Venezuela, Guyanas, Amazonia.
88. *Caprimulgus whiteleyi.* Roraiman Nightjar. 22. Venezuela.
89. *Caprimulgus hirundinaceus.* Pygmy Nightjar. 2ss. 18. Brazil.

58
57
59
60
61
62
63
64
65
66
67A
67
68
69
71
72
70
73
77
78
74
80
81
75
82
83
76
84
86
85
87
79
88
89

HEMIPROCNIDAE, APONIDAE
Tree Swifts, Swifts

1. *Hemiprocne comata.* Lesser / Whiskered Tree Swift. 4ss. 15. SE Asia.
2. *Hemiprocne longipennis.* Grey rumped Tree Swift. 6ss. 20. Malaya, Indonesia. (ss. of 1 ?)
3. *Hemiprocne coronata.* Moustached Tree Swift. 4ss. 28. India, SE Asia.
4. *Hemiprocne mystacea.* Moustached Tree Swift. 4ss. 28. Moluccas-Solomons.

Family 81. APODIDAE (1). Swifts.

1. *Collocalia escuelenta.* Glossy Swiftlet. 19ss. 10. SE Asia to N Australia.
2. *Collocalia marginata.* Grey rumped Swiftlet. 2ss. 12. Philippines. (ss. of 1?).
3. *Collocalia linchi.* Cave Swiftlet. 4ss. 10. Indonesia.
4. *Collocalia troglodytes.* Pygmy Swiftlet. 8. Philippines.
5. *Collocalia elaphra.* Seychelles Swiftlet. 12ss. 13. Seychelles.
6. *Collocalia francica.* Mascarene Swiftlet. 13. Mascarene Is.
7. *Collocalia unicolor.* Indian Swiftlet. 12.India, Sri Lanka.
8. *Collocalia infuscata.* Moluccan Swiftlet. 3ss. 12. Sulawesi, Moluccas.
9. *Collocalia hirundinacea.* Mountain Swiftlet. 3ss. 12. New Guinea & Is.
10. *Collocalia spodiopygius.* White rumped Swiftlet. 7ss. 10. New Guinea, Pacific Is.
11. *Collocalia terraereginae.* Australian Swiftlet. 10. Queensland.
12. *Collocalia brevirostris.* Himalayan Swiftlet. 2ss. 14. Himalayas to SE Asia..
13. *Collocalia innominata.* Hume's Swiftlet. 13. China to Malaysia. (ss. of 12?)
14. *Collocalia vulcanorum.* Volcano Swiftlet. 14. Java. (ss. of 22?)
15. *Collocalia rogersi.* Indo-Chinese Swiftlet. 14. Laos, Thailand. (ss. of 12?)
16. *Collocalia whiteheadi.* Whitehead's Swiftlet. 4ss. 14. Philippines.
17. *Collocalia nuditarsus.* Bare legged Swiftlet. 14. New Guinea.
18. *Collocalia orientalis.* Mayr's Swiftlet. 13. Guadalcanal.
19. *Collocalia salangana.* Mossy-nest Swiftlet. 2ss. 12. Gr. Sundas, Sulawesi.
20. *Collocalia palawensis.* Palawan Swiftlet. 13. Palawan. (ss. of 23?)
21. *Collocalia lowi.* Low's Swiftlet. 13. Sumatra, Borneo.(ss. of 22?)
22. *Collocalia maxima.* Blacknest Swiftlet. 2ss. 14. India, SE Asia, Gr. Sundas.
23. *Collocalia vanikorensis.* Uniform Swiftlet. 11ss. 12. Moluccas, New Guinea, Solomon Is.
24. *Collocalia mearnsi.* Philippine Swiftlet. 11. Philippines.
25. *Collocalia palewensis.* Palau Swiftlet. 11. Palau (Caroline Is).
26. *Collocalia bartschi.* Mariana Swiftlet. 12. Guam.
27. *Collocalia inquieta.* Caroline Swiftlet. 3ss. 12. Yap, Truk, Ponape, Kusaie.
28. *Collocalia sawtelli.* Atiu Swiftlet. 13. Cook Is.
29. *Collocalia leucophaea.* Tahiti Swiftlet. 11. Society Is.
30. *Collocalia ocista.* Marquesan Swiftlet. 11. Marquesas Is.(ss. of 29?)
31. *Collocalia fuciphaga.* Thunberg's Swiftlet. 12. SE Asia, Lesser Sundas, Java.
32. *Collocalia inexpectata.* Edible nest Swiftlet. 12. Andaman Is., Nicobar Is. (ss. of 31?)
33. *Collocalia vestita.* Brown rumped Swiftlet. 12. SE Asia, Indonesia. (ss. of 31?)
34. *Collocalia germani.* German's Swiftlet 12. SE Asia, Philippines.
35. *Collocalia amelis.* Grey Swiftlet. 12. Philippines, Borneo.(ss. of 23?)
36. *Collocalia papuensis.* Papuan Swiftlet. 13. New Guinea.
37. *Hydrocuous gigas.* Waterfall / Giant Swiftlet. 17. Malaysia to Java.
38. *Hirundapus caudactucus.* White throated Needletail. 4ss. 20. Himalayas, SE Asia, Winters to Australia.
39. *Hirundapus cochinensis.* Silver backed / White vented Needletail. 2ss. 20. Nepal, SE Asia. Winters Sumatra, Java.
40. *Hirundapus giganteus.* Brown backed Needletail. 4ss. 23. India, SE Asia.
41. *Hirundapus celebensis.* Purple Needletail. 17. Sulawesi, Philippines, Asia.
42. *Zoonavena (Hirundapus) sylvatica.* White rumped Spinetail. 11. India, Nepal, Indo-China, SE Asia. Winters Sumatra, Java.

HEMIPROCNIDAE
1
2
3
4
APODIDAE
1
2
3
4
5
6
7
8
9
10
11
12
13
14
15
16
17
18
19
20
21
22
23
24
25
26
27
28
29
30
31
32
33
34
35
36
37
38
39
42
40
41

APODIDAE (2) Swifts

43. *Streptoprocne biscutata.* Bisculate Swift. 20. E Brazil.
44. *Cypseloides cherriei.* Spot fronted Swift. 14. Colombia, Venezuela.
45. *Cypseloides cryptus.* White chinned Swift. 15. Guyana, Peru, Winters C America.
45a. *Cypseloides storeri.* White fronted Swift. 15. Mexico.
46. *Cypseloides fumigatus.* Sooty Swift. 17. Brazil, Argentina.
47. *Cypseloides lemosi.* White chested Swift. 15. Colombia.
48. *Cypseloides major/rothschildi.* Rothschild's Swift. 15. Bolivia, Argentina.
49. *Cypseloides niger.* Black Swift. 3ss. 16. Alaska to Honduras. Winters West Indies.
50. *Cypseloides phelpsi.* Tepui Swift. 17. Venezuela, Guyana, N Brazil.
51. *Cypseloides rutilus.* Chestnut collared Swift. 3ss. 14. Mexico to Bolivia.
52. *Streptoprocne semicollaris.* White naped Swift. 28. Mexico.
53. *Cypseloides senex.* Great dusky Swift. 19. Brazil, Paraguay, Argentina.
54. *Streptoprocne zonaris.* White collared Swift. 5ss. 21. Greater Antilles. Mexico to Brazil & Argentina.
55. *Chaetura andrei.* Ashy tailed Swift. 2ss. 15. Venezuela, Colombia, Brazil.
56. *Neafrapus boehmi.* Batlike Spinetail. 8. Angola to Mozambique, Tanzania.
57. *Chaetura brachyura.* Short tailed Swift. 12. W Indies, Panama to Brazil.
58. *Neafrapus cassini.* Cassin's Spinetail. 15. Cameroon to Zaire.
59. *Chaetura chapmani.* Chapman's Swift. 2ss. 14. Trinidad, Panama to Brazil.
60. *Chaetura cinereiventris.* Grey rumped Swift. 7ss. 11. Nicaragua to Brazil, Trinidad.
61. *Chaetura egregia.* Pale rumped Swift. 13. Ecuador, Peru, Bolivia, Brazil.
62. *Zoonavena grandidieri.* Madagascar Spinetail. 12. Malagasy.
63. *Rhaphidura leucopygialis.* Silver rumped Spinetail. 11. Thailand, Malaya, Greater Sundas.
64. *Chaetura martinica.* Lesser Antillean Swift. 11. Lesser Antilles.
65. *Telacanthura melanopygia.* Black Spinetail. 16. Local, Liberia to Zaire.
66. *Mearnsia novaeguineae.* Papuan Needletail. 2ss. 12. New Guinea.
67. *Chaetura pelagica.* Chimney Swift. 14. N America, Winters Peru, Brazil.
68. *Mearnsia picina.* Philippine Spinetail. 13. Philippines.
69. *Raphidura sabini.* Sabine's Spinetail. 12. Sierra Leone to Uganda, Kenya.
70. *Chaetura spinicauda.* Band rumped Swift. 5ss. 12. Costa Rica to Brazil.
71. *Zoonavena thomensis.* Sao Theme Spinetail. 10. Sao Thome Is.
72. *Telacanthura ussheri.* Mottle throated Spinetail. 6ss. 14. Sub-saharan Africa to Angola.
73. *Chaetura vauxi.* Vaux's Swift. 6ss. 10. Canada, W USA to Mexico, Venezuela.

43
44
45
46
47
48
45A
49
50
51
52
53
54
55
56
57
58
57
59
60
61
62
63
64
65
66
67
68
69
70
71
72
73

APODIDAE (3)
Swifts

74. *Tachymarptis melba*. Alpine Swift. 8ss. 22. Eurasia, Africa, Malagasy.
75. *Tachymarptis aequatorialis*. Mottled Swift. 5ss. 22. E W & SW Africa.
76. *Apus reichenowi*. Reichenow's Swift. 22. Kenya.
77. *Apus bradfieldi*. Bradfield's Swift. 16. Namibia, Angola.
78. *Apus affinis*. Little Swift. 8ss. 13. India, Pakistan, Africa.
79. *Apus nipalensis*. House Swift. 13. Nepal, Assam.
80. *Apus apus*. Common Swift. 3ss. 17. Eurasia. Winters Africa & India.
81. *Apus barbatus*. African black Swift. 6ss. 18. Kenya to South Africa.
82. *Apus alexandri*. Alexander's Swift. 13. Cape Verde Is.
83. *Apus batesi*. Bates' Swift. 13. Cameroon, Zaire.
84. *Apus sladenii*. Fernando Po Swift. 16. Fernando Po & Cameroon.
85. *Apus caffer*. African white rumped Swift. 3ss. 15. Mediterranean, Africa South of Sahara.
86. *Apus horus*. Horus Swift. 14. E & S Africa.
87. *Apus acuticaudus*. Dark backed Swift. 17. Nepal, Assam, Andamans.
88. *Schoutedenapus myoptilus*. Scarce Swift. 3ss. 13. East Africa to Malawi.
89. *Schoutedenapus schoutedeni*. Schouteden's Swift. 15. Zaire.
90. *Apus niansae*. Nyanza Swift. 2ss. 15. Ethiopia, Somalia to Tanzania.
91. *Apus pacificus*. Fork tailed Swift. 4ss. 18. E Asia. Winters to Australia.
92. *Apus pallidus*. Pallid Swift. 3ss. 17. Mediterranean to Pakistan.
93. *Apus balstoni*. Madagascar Swift. 17. Malagasy, Comoro Is.
94. *Apus berliozi*. Forbes-Watson's Swift. 2ss. 17. Socotra Is.
95. *Apus toulsoni*. Loanda Swift. 15. Angola, Cabinda.
96. *Apus unicolor*. Plain Swift. 2ss. 13. Atlantic islands. Winters N Africa.
97. *Aeronautes andicola*. Andean Swift. 3ss. 15. Peru, Chile, Bolivia, Argentina.
98. *Aeronautes montivagus*. White tipped Swift. 2ss. 13. Venezuela to Bolivia.
99. *Aeronautes saxatalis*. White throated Swift. 2ss. 16. Canada to Honduras.
100. *Panyptila cayannensis*. Lesser swallow tailed Swift. 2ss. 12. Mexico to Bolivia & Brazil.
101. *Panyptila sanctihieronymi*. Great swallow tailed Swift. 18. Mexico, Costa Rica.
102. *Tachornis furcata*. Pygmy Swift. 2ss. 10. Venezuela, Colombia.
103. *Tachornis phoenicobia*. Antillean Palm Swift. 2ss. 11. Cuba, Jamaica, Hispaniola.
104. *Tachornis squamata*. Fork tailed Palm Swift. 2ss. 14. Trinidad, Venezuela to Amazonia.
105. *Cypsiurus parvus*. African Palm Swift. 4ss. 15. Arabia, Africa S of Sahara.
106. *Cypsiurus balasiensis*. Asian Palm Swift. 3ss. 15. India to SE Asia, Philippines.

-75-
-78-
80
81
87
79
82
77
76
83
89
85
86
-74-
90
91
92
95
96
93
84
94
88
101
97
98
99
100
103
104
105
102
106

TROCHILIDAE (1) Hummingbirds

1. *Tilmatura dupontii*. Sparkling tailed Hummingbird. 9. Mexico to Nicaragua.
2. *Androdon aequatorialis*. Tooth billed Hummingbird. 14. Colombia, Ecuador.
3. *Ramphodon dohrni*. Hook billed Hermit. 12. SE Brazil.
4. *Ramphodon naevius*. Saw billed Hermit. 17. Brazil.
5. *Glaucis aenea*. Bronzy Hermit. 11. Nicaragua to Colombia, Ecuador.
6. *Glaucis hirsuta*. Rufous breasted Hermit. 3ss. 13. Panama to Bolivia, Brazil, Grenada.
7. *Threnetes cristinae*. Christine's Barbthroat. 13. Brazil.
8. *Threnetes leucurus*. Pale tailed Barbthroat. 4ss. 13. Amazonia.
9. *Threnetes loehkeni*. Bronze tailed Barbthroat. 13. Brazil.
10. *Threnetes niger*. Sooty Barbthroat. 12. French Guyana, Brazil.
11. *Threnetes grzimeki*. Black Barbthroat, 12. Brazil.
12. *Threnetes ruckeri*. Band tailed Barbthroat. 4ss. 11. Nicaragua to Ecuador.
13. *Phaethornis anthophilus*. Pale bellied Hermit. 3ss. 16. Panama, Venezuela, Colombia.
14. *Phaethornis augusti*. Sooty capped Hermit. 3ss. 15. Guyana, Venezuela, Colombia.
15 .*Phaethornis bourcieri*. Straight billed Hermit. 2ss. 14. Amazonia.
16. *Phaethornis eurynome*. Scale throated Hermit. 16 Brazil, Paraguay, Argentina.
17. *Phaethornis gounellei*. Broad tipped Hermit. 12. E Brazil.
18. *Phaethornis griseogularis*. Grey chinned Hermit. 3ss. 10. Venezuela, Colombia, Peru, Brazil.
19. *Phaethornis guy*. Green Hermit. 4ss. 15. Costa Rica to Venezuela & Peru.
20. *Phaedornis hispidus*. White bearded Hermit. 15. Venezuela, to Bolivia & Brazil.
21. *Phaethornis idaliae*. Minute Hermit. 10. S.E. Brazil.
22. *Phaethornis longuemareus*. Little Hermit. 10ss. 11. Mexico to Peru & Brazil.
23. *Phaethornis malaris*. Great billed Hermit. 3ss. 16. French Guyana, Brazil.
24. *Phaethornis margarettae*. Margaretta's Hermit. 17. Brazil.
25. *Phaethornis maranhaoensis*. Maranhao Hermit. 12. Brazil.
26. *Phaethornis nattereri*. Cinnamon throated Hermit. 12. Brazil, Bolivia.
27. *Phaethornis philippi*. Needle billed Hermit. 15. Peru, Brazil.
28. *Phaethornis pretrei*. Planalto Hermit. 15. Brazil, Bolivia, Argentina.
29. *Phaethornis ruber*. Reddish Hermit. 4ss. 10. Guyanas, Venezuela, Bolivia, Brazil.
30. *Phaethornis nigrirostris*. Black billed Hermit. 15. Brazil.
31. *Phaethornis squalidus*. Dusky throated Hermit. 3ss. 12. Colombia to Brazil.
32. *Phaethornis koepckeae*. Koepc's Hermit. 14. Peru.
33. *Phaethornis siuarti*. White browed Hermit. 11. Peru, Bolivia.
34. *Phaethornis subochraceus*. Buff bellied Hermit. 13. Bolivia, Brazil.
35. *Phaethornis superciliosus*. Long tailed Hermit. 14ss. 16. Mexico to Amazonia.
36. *Phaethornis smyrmatophorus*. Tawny bellied Hermit. 3ss. 16. Colombia to Peru.
37. *Phaethornis yaruqui*. White whiskered Hermit. 2ss. 17. Colombia, Ecuador.
38. *Eutoxeres aquila*. White tipped Sicklebill. 2ss. 13. Costa Rica to Peru.
39. *Eutoxeres Condamini*. Buff tailed Sicklebill. 2ss. 13. Colombia, Peru.
40. *Doryfera johannae*. Blue fronted Lancebill. 2ss. 11. Amazonia.
41. *Doryfera ludoviciae*. Green fronted Lancebill. 4ss. 13. Costa Rica to Bolivia.
42. *Phaeochroa cuvierii*. Scaly breasted Hummingbird. 5ss. 13. Belize to Colombia.

1
2
3
4
5
6
7
8
9
10
11
12
13
14
15
16
17
18
19
20
21
22
23
24
25
26
27
28
29
30
31
32
33
34
35
36
37
38
39
40
41
42

TROCHILIDAE (2) Hummingbirds

43. *Campylopterus curvipennis*. Wedge tailed Sabrewing. 4ss. 13. Mexico, C America.
44. *Campylopterus excellens*. Long tailed Sabrewing. 15. Mexico.
45. *Campylopterus duidae*. Buff breasted Sabrewing. 2ss. 12. Venezuela, Brazil.
46. *Campylopterus ensipennis*. White tailed Sabrewing. 15. Venezuela.
47. *Campylopterus falcatus*. Lazuline Sabrewing. 12. Venezuela, Colombia, Ecuador.
48. *Campylopterus hemileucurus*. Violet Sabrewing. 2ss. 14. Mexico to Panama.
49. *Campylopterus hyperythrus*. Rufous breasted Sabrewing. 12. Venezuela, Brazil.
50. *Campylopterus largipennis*. Grey breasted Sabrewing. 3ss. 14. Amazonia.
51. *Campylopterus phainopeplus*. Santa Marta Sabrewing. 15. Colombia.
52. *Campylopterus rufus*. Rufous Sabrewing. 13. Mexico, Guatemala, Salvador.
53. *Campylopterus villaviscensis*. Napo Sabrewing. 14. Ecuador.
54. *Eupetomena macroura*. Swallow tailed Hummingbird. 4ss. 16. Guyanas, Brazil, Paraguay, Bolivia.
55. *Florisuga mellivora*. White necked Jacobin. 2ss. 12. Trinidad, Mexico to Brazil, Bolivia.
56. *Melanotrochilus fuscus*. Black Jacobin. 12. Brazil.
57. *Colibri coruscans*. Sparkling Violetear. 3ss. 12. Venezuela to Argentina.
58. *Colibri delphinae*. Brown Violetear. 12. Guatemala to Bolivia & Brazil.
59. *Colibri serrirostris*. White vented Violetear. 13. Bolivia, Brazil, Argentina.
60. *Colibri thalassinus*. Green Violetear. 5ss. 11. Mexico to Argentina.
61. *Anthracothorax dominicus*. Antillean Mango. 2ss. 12. Hispaniola, Puerto Rico.
62. *Anthracothorax mango*. Jamaican Mango. 12. Jamaica.
63. *Anthracothorax nigricollis*. Black throated Mango. 2ss. 12. Panama to Argentina.
64. *Anthracothorax prevostii*. Green breasted Mango. 5ss. 12. Mexico to Peru.
65. *Anthracothorax veraguensis*. Veraguan Mango. 11. Panama.(ss. of 64 ?).
66. *Anthracothorax viridigula*. Green throated Mango. 12. Venezuela, Guyanas, Brazil.
67. *Anthracothorax viridis*. Green Mango. 12. Puerto Rico.
68. *Avocettula recurvirostris*. Fiery tailed Awlbill. 9. Amazonia.
69. *Eulampis jugularis*. Purple throated Carib. 12. Lesser Antilles.
70. *Eulampis holosericeus*. Green throated Carib. 2ss. 12. Lesser Antilles, Puerto Rico.
71. *Chrysolampis mosquitus*. Ruby topaz Hummingbird. 9. Trinidad, Venezuela.
72. *Orthorhynchus cristatus*. Antillean crested Hummingbird. 4ss. 9. Puerto Rico, Lesser Antilles.
73. *Klais guimeti*. Violet headed Hummingbird. 2ss. 10. Honduras to Brazil, Bolivia.
74. *Abeilla abeilla*. Emerald chinned Hummingbird. 2ss. 8. Mexico to Nicaragua.
75. *Stephanoxis lalandi*. Black breasted Plovercrest. 2ss. 10. Brazil, Paraguay, Argentina.

43
44
46
47
48
49
50
45
51
52
53
54
55
56
57
58
59
60
61
62
63
64
65
66
67
68
69
70
71
72
73
74
75

TROCHILIDAE (3) Hummingbirds

76. *Lophornis chalybeus.* Festive Coquette. 3ss. 10. Brazil, Bolivia, Venezuela, Colombia.
77. *Lophornis delattrei.* Rufous crested Coquette. 3ss. 8. Colombia, Peru, Bolivia.
78. *Lophornis brachylopha.* Short crested Coquette. 8. Mexico.
79. *Lophornis magnificus.* Frilled Coquette. 8. E C Brazil.
80. *Lophornis ornatus.* Tufted Coquette. 8. Trinidad, Venezuela, Guyanas, Brazil.
81. *Lophornis melaniae.* Dusky Coquette. 8. Colombia. (unique).
82. *Lophornis pavoninus.* Peacock Coquette. 3ss. 11. Guyana, Venezuela.
83. *Lophornis stictolophus.* Spangled Coquette. 8. Venezuela to Peru.
84. *Lophornis insignibarbis.* Bearded Coquette. 9. Colombia. (unique).
85. *Lophornis/Paphosia adorabilis.* White crested Coquette. 8. Costa Rica, Panama.
86. *Lophornis/P. helenae.* Black crested Coquette. 7. Mexico to Costa Rica.
87. *Popelairia conversii.* Green Thorntail. 11/7. Costa Rica to Ecuador.
88. *Popelairia langsdorffii.* Black bellied Thorntail. 14/9. Amazonia.
89. *Popelairia letitiae.* Coppery Thorntail. 11/8. Bolivia.
90. *Popelairia popelairia.* Wire crested Thorntail. 12/10. Colombia, Ecuador, Peru.
91. *Discosura longicauda.* Racket tailed Coquette. 11/7. Venezuela, Guyanas, Brazil
92. *Chlorestes notatus.* Blue chinned Sapphire. 3ss. 10. Trinidad, N of S America.
93. *Chlorostilbon alice.* Green tailed Emerald. 9. Venezuela.
94. *Chlorostilbon aureoventris.* Glittering bellied Emerald. 3ss. 10. Brazil, Bolivia, Paraguay, Uruguay, Argentina.
95. *Chlorostilbon canivetti.* Fork tailed Emerald. 9ss. 8. Mexico to Costa Rica.

95a. *Chlorostilbon assimilis.* Garden Emerald. 8. Costa Rica, Panama.

96. *Chlorostilbon gibsoni.* Red billed Emerald. 4ss. 9. Venezuela, Colombia.
97. *Chlorostilbon mangaeus.* Puerto Rican Emerald. 9. Puerto Rico.
98. *Chlorostilbon vitticeps.* Simon's Emerald. 9. Ecuador.
99. *Chlorostilbon mellisugus.* Blue tailed Emerald. 5ss. 8. Costa Rica to Peru, Brazil
100. *Chlorostilbon poortmanni.* Short tailed Emerald. 2ss. 11. Venezuela, Colombia.
101. *Chlorostilbon inexpectatus.* Berlepsch's Emerald. 8. Colombia. (unique)
102. *Chlorostilbon ricordii.* Cuban Emerald. 2ss. 11. Bahamas, Cuba, Florida.

102a. *Chlorostilbon bracei.* Brace's Emerald. 10. Bahamas. (Extinct)

103. *Chlorostilbon auratus.* Cabini's Emerald. 11. Peru.(unique)
104. *Chlorostilbon russatus.* Coppery Emerald. 8. Colombia, Venezuela.
105. *Chlorostilbon stenura.* Narrow tailed Emerald. 2ss. 9. Colombia, Venezuela.
106. *Chlorostilbon swainsonii.* Hispaniolan Emerald. 11. Hispaniola.
107. *Cynanthus latirostris.* Broad billed Hummingbird. 7ss. 9. S USA, Mexico.
108. *Cynanthus sordidus.* Dusky Hummingbird. 9. Mexico.
109. *Cynophaia bicolor.* Blue headed Hummingbird. 11. Dominica, Martinique.
110. *Thalurania colombica.* Blue crowned Woodnymph. 10/9. Mexico to Panama.
111. *Thalurania fannyi.* Green crowned Woodnymph. 10/9. Panama to Ecuador.
112. *Thalurania furcata.* Fork tailed Woodnymph. 16ss. 13:10. Most of S America.
113. *Thalurania glaucopis.* Violet capped Woodnymph. 12. Brazil. Paraguay, Argentina.
114. *Thalurania watertonii.* Long tailed Woodnymph. 13. Brazil.
115. *Thalurania hypochlora.* Emerald bellied Woodnymph. 10. Ecuador.
116. *Thalurania lerchi.* Lerch's Woodnymph. 10. Colombia. (unique).
117. *Thalurania ridgwayi.* Mexican Woodnymph. 13. Mexico.
118. *Thalurania townsendi.* Honduras Woodnymph: 13. Honduras, Guatemala.

76
77
78
79
77A
84
81
80
82
83
85
86
87
88
89
90
91
92
93
95 A
94
95
96
97
101
103
98
102
104
99
100
102 A
107
106
105
108
115
116
111
110
112
109
114
117
113
118

TROCHILIDAE (4) Hummingbirds

119. *Panterpe insignis*. Fiery throated Hummingbird. 11. Costa Rica, Panama.
120. *Neolesbia nehrkorni*. Nehrkorn's Sylph. 11. Colombia.
121. *Damophila julie*. Violet bellied Hummingbird. 3ss. 8. Panama to Ecuador.
122. *Augasma cyaneoberylina*. Berlioz' Woodnymph. 9. Brazil
123. *Augasma maragdinia*. Emerald Woodnymph. 9. Brazil.
124. *Lepidopyga caeruleogularis*. Sapphire throated Hummingbird. 3ss. 9. Panama to Colombia.
125. *Lepidopyga goudoti*. Shining green Hummingbird. 4ss. 11. Venezuela, Colombia.
126. *Lepidopyga lilliae*. Sapphire bellied Hummingbird. 9. Colombia.
127. *Hylocharis chrysura*. Gilded Sapphire. 12. Brazil, Bolivia, Uruguay, Argentina.
128. *Hylocharis cyanus*. White chinned Sapphire. 4ss. 11. Venezuela, Colombia.
129. *Hylocharis eliciae*. Blue throated Goldentail. 9. Mexico to Panama.
130. *Hylocharis grayi*. Blue headed Sapphire. 2ss. 10. Panama to Ecuador.
131. *Hylocharis leucotis*. White eared Hummingbird. 3ss. 9. Arizona to Nicaragua.
132. *Hylocharis sapphirina*. Rufous throated Sapphire. 11.Most of S America.
133. *Hylocharis xantusii*. Xanthus' Black fronted Hummingbird. 9. Mexico.
134. *Hylocharis pyropygia*. Flame rumped Sapphire. 9. Brazil.
135. *Chrysuronia oenone*. Golden tailed Sapphire. 5ss. 11. Trinidad, Venezuela to Bolivia, Brazil.
136. *Goldmania violiceps*. Violet capped Hummingbird. 9. Panama, Colombia.
137. *Goethalsia bella*. Rufous cheeked Hummingbird. 9. Panama, Colombia.
138. *Trochilus polytmus*. Streamertail. 25:11. Jamaica.
139. *Leucochloris albicollis*. White throated Hummingbird. 12:10. Brazil, Paraguay, Argentina.
140. *Polytmus guainumba*. White tailed Goldenthroat. 3ss. 11. Most of S America.
141. *Polytmus milleri*. Tepui Goldenthroat. 12. Venezuela.
142. *Polytmus theresiae*. Green tailed Goldenthroat. 2ss. 11. Amazonia.
143. *Leucippus baeri*. Tumbes Hummingbird. 11. Peru.
144. *Leucippus chlorocercus*. Olive spotted Hummingbird. 11. Ecuador, Peru, Brazil.
145. *Leucippus fallax*. Buffy Hummingbird. 3ss. 11. Venezuela, Colombia.
146. *Leucippus taczanowskii*. Spot throated Hummingbird. 2ss. 12. Peru.
147. *Taphrospilus hypostictus*. Many-spotted Hummingbird. 2ss. 14. Ecuador, Peru, Bolivia, Brazil, Argentina.
148. *Amazilia amabilis*. Blue chested Hummingbird. 2ss. 10. Colombia, Ecuador.
149. *Amazilia decora*. Charming Hummingbird. 10. Costa Rica, Panama.
150. *Amazilia amazilia*. Amazilia Hummingbird. 5ss. 11. Ecuador, Peru.
151. *Amazilia beryllina*. Berylline Hummingbird. 4ss. 10. Mexico to Salvador.
152. *Amazilia boucardi*. Mangrove Hummingbird. 10. Costa Rica.
153. *Amazilia candida*. White bellied Emerald. 3ss. 10. Mexico to Costa Rica.
154. *Amazilia castaneiventris*. Chestnut bellied Hummingbird. 10. Colombia.
155. *Amazilia chionogaster*. White bellied Hummingbird. 2ss. 11. Peru, Brazil, Argentina.
156. *Amazilia chionopectus*. White chested Emerald. 3ss. 9. Trinidad, Guyanas, Venezuela.
157. *Amazilia cyanifrons*. Indigo capped Hummingbird. 2ss. 10. Costa Rica to Colombia.

119
121
124
125
122
123
120
126
127
128
129
130
131
132
133
135
136
137
138
134
139
140
141
142
143
144
147
148
145
146
149
151
150
152
153
154
155
156
157

TROCHILIDAE (5) Hummingbirds

158. *Amazilia cyanocephala.* Azure crowned Hummingbird. 2ss. 10. Mexico, Nicaragua
159. *Amazilia cyanura.* Blue tailed Hummingbird. 2ss. 9. Mexico to Costa Rica.
160. *Amazilia distans.* Tachira Emerald. 10. Venezuela.
161. *Amazilia edward.* Snowy breasted Hummingbird. 4ss. 10. Panama.
162. *Amazilia fimbriata.* Glittering throated Emerald. 10ss. 10. Colombia, Bolivia
163. *Amazilia franciae.* Andean Emerald. 4ss. 11. Colombia, Ecuador, Peru.
164. *Amazilia lactea.* Sapphire spangled Emerald. 3ss. 11. Venezuela, Peru, Brazil.
165. *Amazilia leucogaster.* Plain bellied Emerald. 2ss. 12. Guyanas, Venezuela, Brazil
166. *Amazilia luciae.* Honduran Emerald. 9. Honduras.
167. *Amazilia cyaneotincta.* Blue spotted Hummingbird. 9. Colombia.
168. *Amazilia microrhyncha.* Small billed Azurecrown. 8. Honduras. (unique.)
169. *Amazilia handleyi.* Escudo Hummingbird. 12. Panama.
170. *Amazilia rosenbergi.* Purple chested Hummingbird. 10. Colombia, Ecuador.
171. *Amazilia rutila.* Cinnamon Hummingbird. 4ss. 10. Mexico to Costa Rica.
172. *Amazilia saucerottei.* Steely vented Hummingbird. 5ss. 11. Costa Rica to Colombia.
173. *Amazilia tobaci.* Copper rumped Hummingbird. 7ss. 10. Trinidad, Tobago, Venezuela.
174. *Amazilia tzacatl.* Rufous tailed Hummingbird. 11. Mexico to Ecuador.
175. *Amazilia versicolor.* Versicoloured Emerald. 4ss. 9. Colombia to Argentina.
176. *Amazilia violiceps.* Violet crowned Hummingbird. 2ss. 10. Arizona, Mexico.
177. *Amazilia viridicauda.* Green & white Hummingbird. 11. Peru.
178. *Amazilia viridifrons.* Green fronted Hummingbird. 10. Mexico.
179. *Amazilia viridigaster.* Green bellied Hummingbird. 3ss. 11. Amazonia.
180. *Amazilia yucatanensis.* Buff bellied Hummingbird. 3ss. 11. Texas to Guatemala.
181. *Eupherusa poliocerca.* White tailed Hummingbird. 8. Mexico.
182. *Eupherusa eximia.* Stripe tailed Hummingbird. 5ss. 9. Mexico to Panama.
183. *Eupherusa cyanophrys.* Blue capped Hummingbird. 8.leteer. 3ss. 14. Panama to Ecuador.
191. *Aphantochroa cirrochloris.* Sombre Hummingbird. 12. Brazil.
192. *Adelomyia melanogenys.* Speckled Hummingbird. 7ss. 10. Venezuela to Argentina.
193. *Anthocephala floriceps.* Blossomcrown. 2ss. 10. Colombia.
194. *Urosticte benjamini.* Purple bibbed Whitetip. 4ss. 8. Colombia, Ecuador.
195. *Urosticte ruficrissa.* Rufous vented Whitetip. 9. Colombia, Ecuador, Peru.
196. *Phlogophilus harterti.* Peruvian Piedtail. 9. Peru.
197. *Phlogophilus hemileucurus.* Ecuadorian Piedtail. 9. Ecuador.
198. *Clytolaema rubricauda.* Brazilian Ruby. 11. Brazil.
199. *Polyplancta/Heliodoxa* aurescens. Gould's Jewelfront. 14. Amazonia.
200. *Lampornis amethystinus.* Amethyst throated Hummingbird. 5ss. 11. C America.
201. *Lampornis calolaema.* Purple throated Mountain Gem. 11. Nicaragua to Panama.
202. *Lampornis castaneoventris.* White throated/Variable Mountain Gem. 11. Nicaragua to Panama.
203. *Lampornis cinereicauda.* Grey tailed Mountain Gem. 11. Costa Rica.
204. *Lampornis clemenciae.* Blue throated Hummingbird. 2ss. 13. USA Mexico Border
205. *Lampornis hemileucus.* White bellied Mountain Gem. 11. Panama.
206. *Lampornis viridipallens.* Green throated Mountain Gem. 5ss. 11. Mexico to Nicaragua.
207. *Lampornis sybillae.* Green breasted Mountain Gem. 11. Honduras to Nicaragua.

158
159
160
161
162
163
164
165
166
167
168
169
170
171
172
173
174
175
176
177
181
183
178
179
180
182
-184-
185
186
187
188
189
190
191
192
193
194
196
197
198
195
199
200
201
202
207
203
204
205
206

TROCHILIDAE (6) Hummingbirds

208. *Lamprolaima rhami*. Garnet throated Hummingbird. 2ss. 12. Mexico to Honduras.
209. *Heliodoxa branickii*. Rufous webbed Brilliant. 13. Peru, Bolivia.
210. *Heliodoxa gularis*. Pink throated Brilliant. 13. Ecuador, Peru, Colombia.
211. *Heliodoxa imperatrix*. Empress Brilliant. 16. Colombia, Ecuador.
212. *Heliodoxa jacula*. Green crowned Brilliant. 3ss. 14. Costa Rica to Ecuador.
213. *Heliodoxa leadbeateri*. Violet fronted Brilliant. 3ss. 15 :13. Colombia & Venezuela to Bolivia.
214. *Heliodoxa rubinoides*. Fawn breasted Brilliant. 3ss. 13. Colombia, Ecuador, Peru.
215. *Heliodoxa schreibersii*. Black throated Brilliant. 2ss. 11. Ecuador, Brazil, Peru.
216. *Heliodoxa xanthogonys*. Velvet browed Brilliant. 12. Venezuela.
217. *Eugenes fulgens*. Magnificent Hummingbird. 3ss. 14. SW USA to Panama.
218. *Hylonympha macrocerca*. Scissor tailed Hummingbird. 21:14. Venezuela.
219. *Sternoclyta cyanopectus*. Violet chested Hummingbird. 14. Venezuela.
220. *Topaza pella*. Crimson Topaz. 4ss. 20. N W Amazonia.
221. *Topaza pyra*. Fiery Topaz. 20. Venezuela, Colombia, Peru, N W Brazil.
222. *Oreotrochilus adela*. Wedge tailed Hillstar. 14. Bolivia.
223. *Oreotrochilus estella*. Andean Hillstar. 5ss. 14. Ecuador to Chile, Argentina.
224. *Oreotrochilus chimborazo*. Ecuadorian Hillstar. 14. Ecuador.
225. *Oreotrochilus leucopleurus*. White sided Hillstar. 14. Bolivia, Chile, Argentina.
226. *Oreotrochilus melanogaster*. Black breasted Hillstar. 11. Peru.
227. *Urochroa bougueri*. White tailed Hillstar. 3ss. 15. Colombia, Ecuador.
228. *Patagona gigas*. Giant Hummingbird. 2ss. 21. Ecuador to Chile, Argentina.
229. *Aglaeactis aliciae*. Purple backed Sunbeam. 12. Peru.
230. *Aglaeactis castelnaudi*. White tufted Sunbeam. 12. Peru.
231. *Aglaeactis cupripennis*. Shining Sunbeam. 4ss. 12. Colombia, Ecuador, Peru.
232. *Aglaeactis pamela*. Black hooded Sunbeam. 12. Bolivia.
233. *Lafresnaya lafresnaya*. Mountain Velvetbreast. 5ss. 13. Venezuela, Colombia, Peru.
234. *Pterophanes cyanopterus*. Great Sapphirewing. 3ss. 19. Colombia to Bolivia.

208
209
210
211
212
213
214
215
216
217
218
219
220
221
222
-223-
224
225
226
227
228
229
230
231
232
233
234

TROCHILIDAE (7) Hummingbirds

235. *Coeligena bonapartei*. Golden bellied Starfrontlet. 3ss. 14. Colombia, Venezuela.
236. *Coeligena coeligena*. Bronzy Inca. 6ss. 13. Venezuela, Colombia to Bolivia.
237. *Coeligena helianthea*. Blue throated Starfrontlet. 2ss. 14. Colombia, Venezuela.
238. *Coeligena iris*. Rainbow Starfrontlet. 7ss. 14. Ecuador, Peru.
239. *Coeligena lutetiae*. Buff winged Starfrontlet. 16. Colombia to Ecuador.
240. *Coeligena orina*. Dusky Starfrontlet. 15. Colombia.
241. *Coeligena phalerata*. White tailed Starfrontlet. 14. Colombia.
242. *Coeligena prunellei*. Black Inca. 14. Colombia.
243. *Coeligena torquata*. Collared Inca. 7ss. 13. Venezuela, Colombia to Bolivia.
244. *Coeligena conradii*. Conrad's Inca. 13. Venezuela, Colombia.
245. *Coeligena violifer*. Violet fronted Starfrontlet. 3ss. 16. Peru, Bolivia.
246. *Coeligena wilsoni*. Brown Inca. 15. Colombia, Ecuador.
247. *Ensifera ensifera*. Sword billed Hummingbird. 23. Venezuela, Colombia to Bolivia.
248. *Sephanoides fernandensis*. Fernandez Firecrown. 2ss. 11. Juan Fernandez Is.
249. *Sephanoides sephanoides*. Green backed Firecrown. 11. Argentina, Chile.
250. *Boissonneaua flavescens*. Buff tailed Coronet. 2ss. 13. Venezuela to Ecuador.
251. *Boissonneaua jardini*. Velvet-purple Coronet. 12. Colombia, Ecuador.
252. *Boissonneaua matthewsii*. Chestnut breasted Coronet. 12. Colombia to Peru.
253. *Heliangelus clarissae*. Longuemare's Sunangel. 11. Colombia, Venezuela.
254. *Heliangelus amethysticollis*. Amethyst throated Sunangel. 5ss. 11. Venezuela, Colombia, Ecuador, Peru.
255. *Heliangelus regalis*. Royal Sunangel. 11. Peru.
256. *Heliangelus exortis*. Tourmaline Sunangel. 11. Ecuador, Peru.
257. *Heliangelus luminosus*. Glistening Sunangel. 11. Colombia.
258. *Heliangelus mavors*. Orange throated Sunangel. 11. Colombia, Venezuela.
259. *Heliangelus micraster*. Little Sunangel. 9. Ecuador, Peru.
260. *Heliangelus spencei*. Merida Sunangel. 11. Venezuela.
261. *Heliangelus rothschildi*. Rothschild's Sunangel. 11. Colombia.
262. *Heliangelus strophianus*. Gorgeted Sunangel. 11. Colombia, Ecuador.
263. *Heliangelus squamigularis*. Olive throated Sunangel. 9. Colombia.
264. *Heliangelus viola*. Purple throated Sunangel. 13. Ecuador, Peru.
265. *Heliangelus speciosa*. Green throated Sunangel. 12. Colombia.
266. *Eriocnemis alinae*. Emerald bellied Puffleg. 10. Colombia, Ecuador, Peru.
267. *Eriocnemis cupreoventris*. Coppery bellied Puffleg. 12. Colombia, Venezuela.
268. *Eriocnemis derbyi*. Black thighed Puffleg. 2ss. 11. Colombia, Ecuador.
269. *Eriocnemis glaucopoides*. Blue capped Puffleg. 10. Bolivia, Argentina.
270. *Eriocnemis godini*. Turquoise throated Puffleg. 12. Colombia, Ecuador.
271. *Eriocnemis luciani*. Sapphire vented Puffleg. 3ss. 14. Colombia, Ecuador, Peru.
272. *Eriocnemis mirabilis*. Colourful Puffleg. 10. Colombia.
273. *Eriocnemis mosquera*. Golden breasted Puffleg. 14. Colombia, Ecuador.
274. *Eriocnemis soderstromi*. Soderstrom's Puffleg. 12. Ecuador.
275. *Eriocnemis nigrivestis*. Black breasted Puffleg. 10. Ecuador, Peru.
276. *Eriocnemis isaacsonii*. Isaacson's Puffleg. 11. Colombia.
277. *Eriocnemis vestitus*. Glowing Puffleg. 3ss. 11. Venezuela, Colombia, Ecuador.
278. *Haplophaedia aureliae*. Greenish Puffleg. 5ss. 11. Panama to Colombia, Ecuador, Peru & Bolivia.
279. *Haplophaedia lugens*. Hoary Puffleg. 11.Colombia, Ecuador.

235
236
237
238
239
240
241
242
243
244
245
246
247
248
249
250
251
252
253
254
255
256
257
258
259
260
261
262
263
264
265
266
267
268
269
270
271
272
273
274
275
276
277
278
279

TROCHILIDAE (8) Hummingbirds

280. *Ocreatus underwoodii.* Booted Racket tail. 8ss. 13:9. Venezuela, Colombia, Bolivia.
281. *Lesbia nana.* Green tailed Trainbearer. 6ss. 16:12. Venezuela, Colombia, Bolivia.
282. *Lesbia victoriae.* Black tailed Trainbearer. 5ss. 25:15. Colombia to Peru.
283. *Sappho sparganura.* Red tailed Comet. 2ss. 17:14. Bolivia, Chile, Argentina.
284. *Polyonymus caroli.* Bronze tailed Comet. 14:12. Peru.
285. *Ramphomicron dorsale.* Black backed Thornbill. 11. Colombia.
286. *Ramphomicron microrhynchum.* Purple backed Thornbill.3ss. 9. Venezuela, Colombia, Peru, Ecuador.
287. *Metallura aeneocauda.* Scaled Metaltail. 2ss. 12. Peru, Bolivia.
288. *Metallura odomae.* Neblina Metaltail. 12. Peru.
289. *Metallura baroni.* Violet throated Metaltail. 13. Ecuador.
290. *Metallura eupogon.* Fire throated Metaltail. 11. Peru.
291. *Metallura iracunda.* Perija Metaltail. 12. Colombia to Ecuador.
292. *Metallura phoebe.* Black Metaltail. 14. Peru, Bolivia.
293. *Metallura theresiae.* Coppery Metaltail. 11. Peru.
294. *Metallura tyrianthina.* Tyrian Metaltail. 8ss. 9. Venezuela, Colombia, Bolivia.
295. *Metallura purpureicauda.* Purple tailed Thornbill. 11. Ecuador.(hybrid?)
296. *Metallura williami.* Viridian Metaltail. 3ss. 10. Colombia, Ecuador.
297. *Chalcostigma herrani.* Rainbow bearded Thornbill. 2ss. 11. Colombia, Ecuador.
298. *Chalcostigma heteropogon.* Bronze tailed Thornbill. 14:11. Colombia, Venezuela.
299. *Chalcostigma olivaceum.* Olivaceous Thornbill. 2ss. 15. Peru to Bolivia.
300. *Chalcostigma ruficeps.* Rufous capped Thornbill. 2ss. 10. Ecuador, Bolivia.
301. *Chalcostigma stanleyi.* Blue mantled Thornbill. 3ss. 13. Ecuador, Peru, Bolivia
302. *Oxypogon guerinii.* Bearded Helmetcrest. 4ss. 12. Colombia, Venezuela
303. *Opisthoprora euryptera.* Mountain Avocetbill. 12. Colombia, Ecuador.
304. *Tephrolesbia griseiventris.* Grey bellied Comet. 16. Peru.
305. *Aglaiocercus coelestis.* Violet tailed Sylph. 3ss. 17:11. Colombia, Ecuador.
306. *Aglaiocercus kingi.* Long tailed Sylph. 7ss. 19:11. Venezuela, Colombia, Ecuador, Peru, Bolivia.

Zodata glyceris (unique) is syn. for 295.

280
281
282
283
284
285
286
287
289
290
295
291
292
293
294
288
296
297
298
299
300
301
302
303
304
305
306

TROCHILIDAE (9)
Hummingbirds

307. *Oreonympha nobilis.* Bearded Mountaineer. 2ss. 14. Peru.
308. *Augastes lumachellus.* Hooded Visorbearer. 11. Brazil.
309. *Augastes scutatus.* Hyacinth Visorbearer. 9. Brazil.
310. *Augastes schistes geoffroyi.* Wedge billed Hummingbird. 2ss. 10. Venezuela & Colombia to Bolivia.
311. *Heliothryx aurita.* Black eared Fairy. 4ss. 13:11. Colombia to Brazil, Bolivia.
312. *Heliothryx barroti.* Purple crowned Fairy. 13:10. Colombia to Ecuador.
313. *Heliactin cornuta.* Horned Sungem. 10. Surinam, Brazil, Bolivia.
314. *Loddigesia mirabilis.* Marvellous Spatuletail. 14 + tail.11. Peru.
315. *Heliomaster constantii.* Plain capped Starthroat. 12. Mexico to Costa Rica.
316. *Heliomaster furcifer.* Blue tufted Starthroat. 13. Bolivia, Brazil, Argentina.
317. *Heliomaster longirostris.* Long billed Starthroat. 4ss. 14. Mexico to Brazil & Bolivia.
318. *Heliomaster squamosus.* Stripe breasted Starthroat. 13. Brazil.
319. *Rhodopis vesper.* Oasis Hummingbird. 4ss. 14. Peru, Chile.
320. *Thaumastura cora.* Peruvian Sheartail. 13:10. Peru.
321. *Philodice bryantae.* Magenta throated Woodstar. 9. Costa Rica, Panama.
322. *Philodice mitchelli.* Purple throated Woodstar. 10. Colombia to Ecuador.
323. *Doricha Eliza.* Mexican Sheartail. 9. Mexico.
324. *Doricha enicura.* Slender Sheartail. 11. Mexico to Honduras.
325. *Microstilbon burmeisteri.* Slender tailed Woodstar. 8:7. Bolivia, Argentina.
326. *Calothorax lucifer.* Lucifer Hummingbird. 10. Texas, Mexico.
327. *Calothorax pulcher.* Beautiful Hummingbird. 10. Mexico.
328. *Archilochus alexandri.* Black chinned Hummingbird. 9. Br. Columbia to Texas. Winters Mexico.
329. *Archilochus colubris.* Ruby throated Hummingbird. 9. Canada to SE USA. Winters to Panama.

307
308
309
310
311
312
313
314
315
316
317
318
319
320
321
322
323
324
325
326
327
328
329

TROCHILIDAE (10) Hummingbirds

330. *Calliphlox amethystina.* Amethyst Woodstar. 8:7. Colombia to Bolivia & Argentina.
331. *Philodice/Calliphlox evelynae.* Bahama Woodstar. 9. Bahamas.
332. *Mellisuga helenae.* Bee Hummingbird. 6:7. Cuba, Isle of Pines.
333. *Mellisuga minima.* Vervain Hummingbird. 2ss. 7. Greater Antilles.
334. *Calypte anna.* Anna's Hummingbird. 10. California to Mexico.
335. *Calypte costae.* Costa's Hummingbird. 8. California to Mexico.
336. *Stellula calliope.* Calliope Hummingbird. 2ss. 8. Br. Columbia to California. Winters Mexico.
337. *Atthis ellioti.* Wine throated Hummingbird. 2ss. 7. Mexico.
338. *Atthis heloisa.* Bumblebee Hummingbird. 2ss. 7. Mexico.
339. *Myrtis fanny.* Purple collared Woodstar. 10. Peru, Ecuador.
340. *Eulidia yarrellii.* Chilean Woodstar. 9. N Chile.
341. *Myrmia micrura.* Short tailed Woodstar. 7. Peru, Ecuador.
342. *Acestrura berlepschi.* Esmeralda's Woodstar. 8. Ecuador.
343. *Acestrura decorata.* Gould's Woodstar. 9. Colombia.
344. *Acestrura bombus.* Little Woodstar. 7. Peru, Ecuador.
345. *Acestrura astreans.* Santa Marta Woodstar. 8. Colombia.
346. *Acestrura heliodor.* Gorgeted Woodstar. 8. Panama to Venezuela & Ecuador.
347. *Acestrura harterti.* Hartert's Woodstar. 8. Colombia.
348. *Acestrura mulsanti.* White bellied Woodstar. 9. Colombia to Ecuador.
349. *Chaetocercus jourdanii.* Rufous shafted Woodstar. 3ss. 8. Trinidad, Venezuela, Colombia.
350. *Selasphorus ardens.* Glow throated Hummingbird. 7. Panama.
351. *Selasphorus flammula.* Volcano Hummingbird. 7. Costa Rica, Panama.
352. *Selasphorus platycercus.* Broad tailed Hummingbird. 2ss. 11. Alaska, W USA to Guatemala.
353. *Selasphorus rufus.* Rufous Hummingbird. 9. Alaska, NW USA, Winters Mexico.
354. *Selasphorus sasin.* Allen's Hummingbird. 2ss. 9. California to Mexico.
355. *Selasphorus scintilla.* Scintillant Hummingbird. 7. Costa Rica, Panama.
356. *Selasphorus simoni.* Cerise throated Hummingbird. 7. Costa Rica.
357. *Selasphorus torridus.* Heliotrope throated Hummingbird. 7. Costa Rica, Panama.

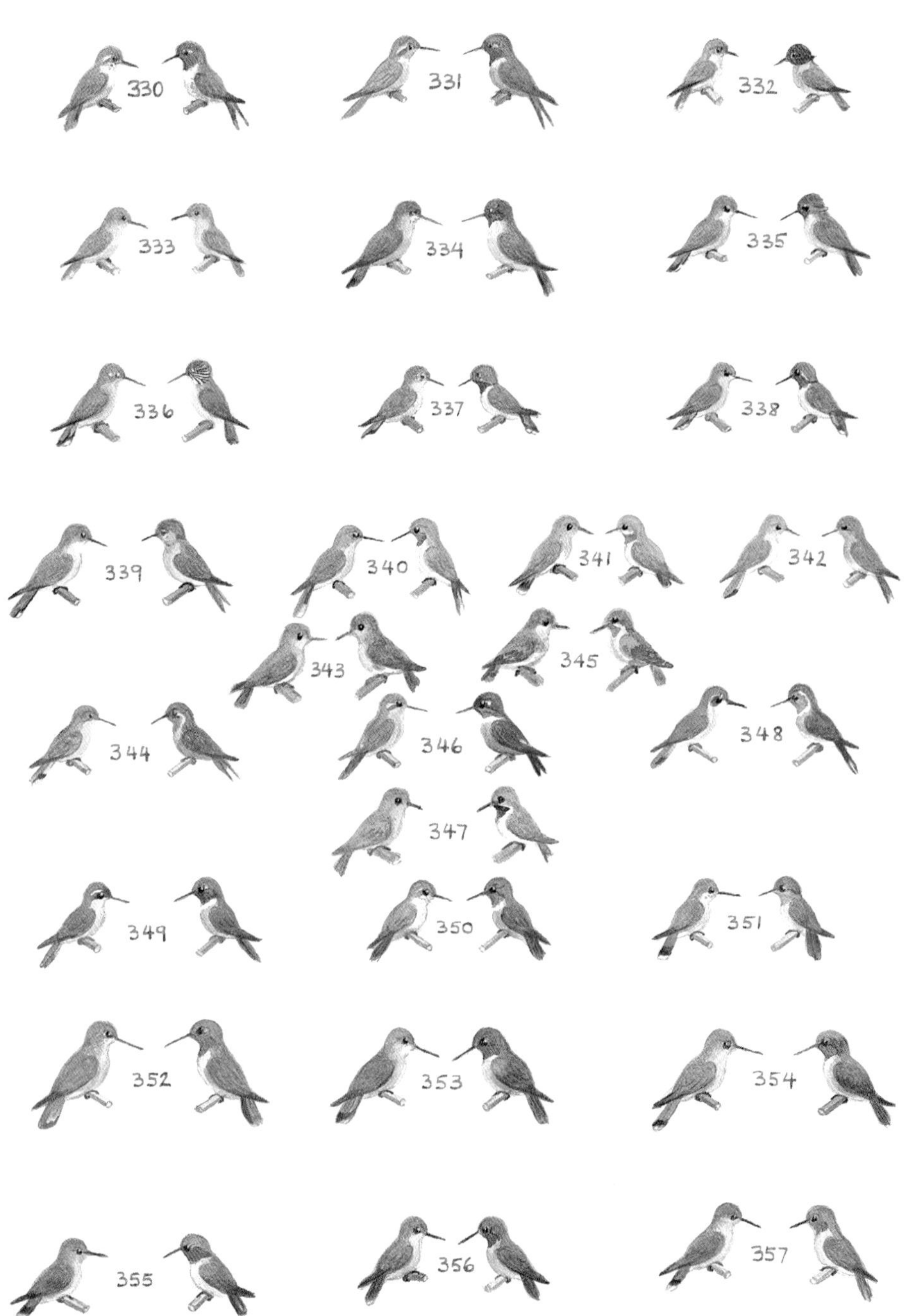

330
331
332
333
334
335
336
337
338
339
340
341
342
343
345
344
346
348
347
349
350
351
352
353
354
355
356
357

COLIIDAE, TROGONIDAE
Mousebirds, Trogons

1. *Colius castanotus*. Red backed Mousebird. 35. Congo, Angola.
2. *Colius colius*. White backed Mousebird. 35. Namibia, Botswana, RSA.
3. *Colius indicus*. Red faced Mousebird. 6ss. 35. Tanzania, Zaire, Angola to Cape.
4. *Colius leucocephalus*. White headed Mousebird. 2ss. 35. Somalia, Kenya, Tanzania.
5. *Colius macrourus*. Blue naped Mousebird. 4ss. 35. W C E & S Africa.
6. *Colius striatus*. Speckled Mousebird. 18ss. 35. C & S Africa.

Family 84. TROGONIDAE (1). Trogons.

1. *Pharomacrus antisianus*. Crested Quetzal. 34. Venezuela to Bolivia.
2. *Pharomacrus fulgidus*. White tipped Quetzal. 2ss. 34. Venezuela, Colombia.
3. *Pharomacrus mocinno*. Resplendent Quetza1. 2ss. 36.(+60 male). Mexico to Panama.
4. *Pharomacrus pavoninus*. Pavonine Quetzal. 4ss. 34. Venezuela to Brazil, Bolivia.
5. *Pharomacrus auriceps*. Golden headed Quetzal. 35. Panama to Bolivia.
6. *Euptilotis neoxenus*. Eared Trogon. 34. Mexico.
7. *Trogon aurantiiventris*. Orange bellied Trogon. 3ss. 35. Costa Rica, Panama.
8. *Trogon citreolus*. Citreoline Trogon. 3ss. 26. Mexico.
9. *Trogon melanocephalus*. Black headed Trogon. 26. Mexico to Costa Rica.
10. *Trogon clathratus*. Lattice tailed Trogon. 29. Costa Rica, Panama.
11. *Trogon collaris*. Collared Trogon. 7ss. 26. Mexico to Bolivia & Brazil.

C 1
2
3
4
5
6
TROGONIDAE
1
2
3
-4-
-5-
-6-
7
-8
9
-10-
-11-

TROGONIDAE (2)
Trogons

12. *Trogon comptus.* White eyed Trogon. 28. Colombia.
13. *Trogon curucui.* Blue crowned Trogon. 4ss. 24. Colombia to Brazil, Argentina.
14. *Trogon elegans.* Elegant Trogon. 5ss. 29. Arizona to Costa Rica.
15. *Trogon massena.* Slaty tailed Trogon. 3ss. 32. Mexico to Ecuador.
16. *Trogon melanurus.* Black tailed Trogon. 5ss. 28/33. Panama to Brazil, Bolivia.
17. *Trogon mexicanus.* Mountain Trogon. 3ss. 30. Mexico to Honduras.
18. *Trogon personatus.* Masked Trogon. 8ss. 25. Guyana,Venezuela to Bolivia.
19. *Trogon rufus.* Black throated Trogon. 6ss. 26. Honduras to Paraguay, Argentina.
20. *Trogon surrucura.* Surucua Trogon. 2ss. 27. Brazil, Paraguay, Argentina.
21. *Trogon violaceus.* Violaceous Trogon. 6ss. 23. Trinidad, Mexico to Brazil & Bolivia.
22. *Trogon viridis.* White tailed Trogon. 3ss. 29. Panama to Brazil & Bolivia.
23. *Trogon bairdii.* Baird's Trogon. 29. Costa Rica, Panama.
24. *Trogon / Priotelus temnurus.* Cuban Trogon. 2ss. 26. Cuba, Isle of Pines.
25. *Trogon / Priotelus roseigaster.* Hispaniolan Trogon. 28. Hispaniola.

12
13
14
15
16
17
18
19
20
21
22
23
24
25

TROGONIDAE
Trogons

26. *Apaloderma aequatoriale.* Bare cheeked Trogon. 32. Cameroon, Gabon, Zaire.
27. *Apaloderma narina.* Narina's Trogon. 4ss. 30. Africa S of Sahara.
28. *Apaloderma vittatum.* Bar tailed Trogon. 25. Central & SE Africa.
29. *Harpactes ardens.* Philippine Trogon. 2ss. 30. Philippines.
30. *Harpactes diardii.* Diard's Trogon. 2ss. 30. Malaya, Sumatra, Borneo.
31. *Harpactes duvaucelii.* Scarlet rumped Trogon. 24. Malaya, Sumatra, Borneo.
32. *Harpactes erythrocephalus.* Red headed Trogon. 10ss. 34. Himalayas, China, Hainan, SE Asia, Indonesia.
33. *Harpactes fasciatus.* Malabar Trogon. 3ss. 28. India, Sri Lanka.
34. *Harpactes kasumba.* Red naped Trogon. 2ss. 31. Malaya, Sumatra, Borneo.
35. *Harpactes oreskios.* Orange breasted Trogon. 5ss. 30. China, SE Asia, Greater Sundas.
36. *Harpactes orrophaeus.* Cinnamon rumped Trogon. 2ss. 25. Malaya, Sumatra, Borneo.
37. *Harpactes reinwardti.* Reinwardt's Blue tailed Trogon. 2ss. 34. Sumatra, Java.
38. *Harpactes wardi.* Ward's Trogon. 35. Burma, Tonkin.
39. *Harpactes whiteheadi.* Whitehead's Trogon. 30. North Borneo.

26
27
28
29
30
31
32
33
34
35
36
37
38
39

ALCEDINIDAE (1)
Kingfishers

1. *Megaceryle alcyon*. Belted Kingfisher. 2ss. 30. Alaska to S USA. Winters S America.
2. *Megaceryle lugubris*. Crested Kingfisher. 3ss. 42. Kashmir to Japan, SE Asia.
3. *Megaceryle maxima*. Giant Kingfisher. 2ss. 46. Africa S of Sahara.
4. *Ceryle rudis*. Pied Kingfisher. 4ss. 26. Africa, Middle East to SE Asia.
5. *Megaceryle torquata*. Ringed Kingfisher. 3ss. 40. Mexico to Tierra del Fuego, Lesser Antilles, Trinidad.
6. *Chloroceryle aenea*. American pygmy Kingfisher. 2ss. 14. Mexico to Bolivia & Brazil.
7. *Chloroceryle amazona*. Amazon Kingfisher. 2ss. 29. Mexico to Argentina.
8. *Chloroceryle americana*. Green Kingfisher. 9ss. 19. Southern USA to N Chile & N Argentina.
9. *Chloroceryle inda*. Green & rufous Kingfisher. 2ss. 22. Nicaragua to Bolivia & Brazil.

1
2
3
4
5
6
7
8
9

ALCEDINIDAE (2) Kingfishers

10. *Alcedo atthis*. Common Kingfisher. 8ss. 16. Palearctic, S Asia to Indonesia.
11. *Alcedo coerulescens*. Small blue Kingfisher. 14. Java to Sumbawa.
12. *Alcedo cristata*. Malachite Kingfisher. 4ss. 13. Africa S of Sahara.
13. *Alcedo vintsioides*. Madagascar malachite Kingfisher. 2ss. 13. Malagasy.
14. *Alcedo euryzona*. Blue banded Kingfisher. 2ss. 18. Burma, Malaya, Gr. Sundas.
15. *Alcedo thomensis*. Sao Thome Kingfisher. 13. Sao Thome.
16. *Alcedo azurea*. Azure Kingfisher. 8ss. 19. Australia, New Guinea, Pacific Islands.
17. incl. *A. a. ochrogaster*. Ochre breasted Azure Kingfisher. 19. New Guinea.
18. *Alcedo leucogaster*. White bellied Kingfisher. 5ss. 13. Fernando Po, W & C Africa.
19. incl. *A. l. nais*. Principe Kingfisher. 13. Principe Is.
20. *Alcedo meninting*. Blue eared / Malaysian Kingfisher. 10ss. 17. S & SE Asia, Malaysia, Indian Ocean Is.
21. *Alcedo semitorquata*. Half collared Kingfisher. 19. East to Southern Africa.
22. *Alcedo quadribrachys*. Shining Blue Kingfisher. 2ss. 16. Africa S of Sahara.
23. *Alcedo Hercules*. Blyth's Kingfisher. 23. Sikkim to China, Burma, Laos.
24. *Ceyx argentatus*. Silvery Kingfisher. 2ss. 14. Philippines.
25. *Ceyx cyanopectus*. Dwarf river / 2ss. 13. Philippines. Philippine pectoral Kingfisher.
26. *Ceyx erithacus*. Black backed / 5ss. 14. India, China, SE Asia, Philippines,Oriental dwarf Kingfisher. Indian Ocean Is. (consp. with 36.?)
27. *Ceyx fallax*. Celebes pygmy Kingfisher. 2ss. 11. Sulawesi.
28. *Ceyx lecontei*. African dwarf Kingfisher. 10. Guinea, Sierra Leone to Gabon.
29. *Ceyx lepidus*. Variable dwarf Kingfisher. 16ss. 14. Philippines to Solomon Islands.
30. incl. *C. l. pallidus*. Pale dwarf Kingfisher. 14. Solomon Islands.
31. *Ceyx goodfellowi*. Goodfellow's Kingfisher. 2ss. 14. Philippines.
32. *Ceyx madagascariensis*. Madagascar Pygmy Kingfisher. 12. Malagasy.
33. *Ceyx melanurus*. Philippine forest Kingfisher. 3ss. 13. Philippines.
34. *Ceyx picta*. African pygmy Kingfisher. 3ss. 12. Africa S of Sahara.
35. *Alcedo pusilla*. Little / Mangrove Kingfisher. 8ss. 12. New Guinea, Australia, Solomon Islands.
36. *Ceyx rufidorsum*. Rufous backed Kingfisher. 2ss. 14. Malaysia, Thailand, Philippines, Indonesia. (consp 26.?)
37. *Ceyx websteri*. Bismarck Kingfisher. 22. New Britain, New Ireland.
38. *Pelargopsis amauroptera*. Brown winged Kingfisher. 35. Coasts of Bangladesh to Malaysia.
39. *Pelargopsis capensis*. Stork billed Kingfisher. 15ss. 36. India, Sri Lanka, SE Asia, Philippines, Indonesia.
40. *Pelargopsis melanorhyncha*. Great / Black billed Kingfisher. 3ss. 36. Sulawesi & adjacent islands.
41. *Lacedo pulchella*. Banded Kingfisher. 4ss. 20. SE Asia & greater Sundas.

13
15
11
12
14
10
16
20
21
18
23
19
17
25
22
24
27
30
31
28
29
26
32
36
35
34
37
33
39
41
40
38

ALCEDINIDAE (3) Kingfishers

42. *Dacelo gaudichaud.* Rufous bellied Kookaburra. 28. New Guinea, Aru, Papuan Islands. \ par
43. *Dacelo leachii.* Blue winged Kookaburra. 6ss. 40. New Guinea, W N & NE Australia. \ par
44. *Dacelo novaeguineae.* Laughing Kookaburra. 2ss. 45. Australia incl. Tasmania. \par
45. *Dacelo tyro.* Spangled Kookaburra. 2ss. 33. Aru Is, New Guinea. \par
46. *Clytoceyx rex.* Shovel billed Kingfisher. 2ss. 31. New Guinea.
47. *Melidora macrorhina.* Hook billed Kingfisher. 3ss. 26. New Guinea & Islands.
48. *Cittura cyanotis.* Blue eared / Lilac cheeked Kingfisher. 3ss. 27. Sulawesi.
49. *Halcyon albiventris.* Brown hooded Kingfisher. 4ss. 23. Africa S of Sahara.
50. *Halcyon albonotata.* White backed Kingfisher. 16. New Britain.

42
43
44
45
46
47
50
-49-
48

ALCEDINIDAE (4)
Kingfishers

51. *Halcyon australasia.* Cinnamon backed Kingfisher 5ss. 22. Timor, Lesser Sunda Islands.
52. *Halcyon badia.* Chocolate backed Kingfisher. 3ss. 21. Liberia to Uganda.
53. *Actenoides bougainvillei.* Moustached Kingfisher. 2ss. 30. Solomon Islands.
54. *Halcyon chelicuti.* Striped Kingfisher. 3ss. 18. Africa S of Sahara.
55. *Halcyon chloris.* (White) Collared Kingfisher. 48ss. 24. NE Africa to India, SE Asia, Australasia & Pacific Is.
56. incl. *H. c. enigma.* Obscure Kingfisher. 21. Talaut Is.
57. *H. c. albicilla.* White headed Mangrove Kingfisher. 24. Mariana Is.
58. *Halcyon cinnamomina.* Micronesian Kingfisher. 3ss. 24. Guam.
59. incl. *H. c. reichenbachii.* Ponape Kingfisher. 24. Ponape.
60. *H. c. pelewensis.* Palau Kingfisher. 20. Palau.
61. *Actenoides concretus.* Rufous collared Kingfisher. 3ss. 23. Thailand, Malaya, Sumatra, Borneo.
62. *Halcyon coromanda.* Ruddy Kingfisher. 8ss. 25. S & E Asia to Indonesia.
63. *Halcyon sengalensis.* Woodland Kingfisher. 3ss. 23. WC & E Africa.
64. *Halcyon cyanoventris.* Javan Kingfisher. 26. Java, Bali.
65. *Halcyon diops.* Blue & white Kingfisher. 19. N Moluccas.
66. *Halcyon lazuli.* Lazuli Kingfisher. 22. S Moluccas.
67. *Caridonax/Halcyon fulgidus.* Glittering / Blue & white Kingfisher.2ss. 30. Flores, Lesser Sundas.
68. *Halcyon funebris.* Sombre Kingfisher. 30. Halmahera & N Moluccas.
69. *Halcyon gambieri.* Tuamotu Kingfisher. 2ss. 22. Mangareva I.
70. incl. *H. g. gertrudae.* Niau Kingfisher. 22. Niau Is.(Tuamotu archipelago.)
71. *Halcyon godeffroyi.* Marquesas Kingfisher. 22. Marquesas Is.
72. *Actenoides hombroni.* Blue capped Kingfisher. 27. Mindanao.
73. *Halcyon leucocephala.* Grey headed Kingfisher. 6ss. 22. Cape Verde Is, Africa S of Sahara, SW Arabia.
74. *Halcyon leucopygia.* Ultramarine Kingfisher. 20. Solomon Islands.
75. *Actenoides lindsayi.* Spotted (Wood) Kingfisher. 3ss. 25. Philippines.

51
52
53
54
55
56
57
62
61
58
65
63
66
59
64
71
69
70
68
67
60
72
73
74
75

ALCEDINIDAE (5)
Kingfishers

76. *Halcyon/Todiramphus macleayi*. Forest Kingfisher. 4ss. 20. New Guinea, N E Australia.
77. *Halcyon malimbica*. Blue breasted Kingfisher. 6ss. 26. W & Central Africa.
78. *Halcyon megarhyncha*. Mountain yellow billed Kingfisher. 3ss. 24. New Guinea & Islands.
79. *Halcyon farquhari*. Chestnut bellied Kingfisher 20. Vanuatu.
80. *Halcyon nigrocyanea*. Blue black Kingfisher. 3ss. 23. Irian Jaya, W New Guinea.
81. incl. *H. n. quadricolor*. Northern form. 23. N New Guinea, Japen.
82. *H. n. stictolaema*. Southern form. 23. S New Guinea.
83. *Halcyon pileata*. Black capped Kingfisher. 30. India, China, Malaysia, Indonesia.
84. *Halcyon pyrrhopygia*. Red backed Kingfisher. 22. Australia.
85. *Halcyon recurvirostris*. Flat billed Kingfisher. 22. Samoa.
86. *Halcyon ruficollaris*. Mangaia Kingfisher. 22. Mangaia, Cook Island. (ss. of 93?)
87. *Halcyon sancta*. Sacred Kingfisher. 6ss. 22. Philippines to New Zealand.
88. *Halcyon saurophaga*. Beach Kingfisher. 3ss. 30. N. Moluccas, New Guinea, Bismarck archipelago.
89. *Halcyon senegaloides*. Mangrove Kingfisher. 2ss. 22. E & SE African coasts.
90. *Halcyon smyrnensis*. White breasted Kingfisher. 6ss. 28. Asia Minor, India, China, S E Asia,
91. incl. *H. s. gularis*. White throated Kingfisher. 28. Philippines.
92. *Halcyon / Syma torotoro*. Lesser yellow billed Kingfisher. 7ss. 20. New Guinea to N E Australia.

Note. 89 is very similar to 63,

76
77
78
80
79
83
81
82
86
87
88
91
85
84
89
90
92

ALCEDINIDAE (6)
Kingfishers

93. *Halcyon/Todiramphus tuta*. Chattering Kingfisher. 3ss. 22. Cook Is, Borabora.
94. *Halcyon / T. venerata*. Tahiti Kingfisher. 2ss. 21. Tahiti, Society Is.
95. incl. *H. v. youngi*. Society Islands Kingfisher. 21. Moorea I.
96. *Halcyon / T. winchelli*. Rufous lored Kingfisher. 2ss. 26. Negros, S Philippines.
97. *Actenoides/Halcyon monacha*. Lonely / Celebes green Kingfisher. 2ss. 31. Sulawesi.
98. *Actenoides p. princeps*. Scaly / Princely Kingfisher. 3ss. 24. Sulawesi.
99. incl. *A. p. erythroramphus*. Bar headed Kingfisher. 24. Hills, Sulawesi.
100. *Halcyon miyakoensis*. Miyako Kingfisher. 24. Ryukyu Is. (extinct).
101. *Tanysiptera carolinae*. Numfor Paradise Kingfisher. 26. Numfor Is. (New Guinea).
102. *Tanysiptera danae*. Brown headed Paradise Kingfisher. 23. NE New Guinea.
103. *Tanysiptera ellioti*. Kofiau Paradise Kingfisher. 22. Kofiau I. (Papua).
104. *Tanysiptera galatea*. Common Paradise Kingfisher. 12ss. 22. New Guinea, Moluccas.
105. *Tanysiptera hydrocharis*. Aru / Little Paradise Kingfisher. 19. Aru I. (New Guinea).
106. *Tanysiptera nympha*. Red breasted Paradise Kingfisher. 23. New Guinea.
107. *Tanysiptera riedelii*. Biak Paradise Kingfisher. 22. Biak I. (New Guinea).
108. *Tanysiptera sylvia*. Buff breasted Paradise Kingfisher. 4ss. 23. New Guinea, Bismarck Archipelago, N E Australia.

93
94
95
96
97
98
99
101
100
102
103
104
juv
106
105
107
108

TODIDAE, MOTMOTIDAE
Todies, Motmots

Family 86. TODIDAE. Todies

1. *Todus angustirostris*. Narrow billed Tody. 11. Hispaniola.
2. *Todus mexicanus*. Puerto Rican Tody. 11. Puerto Rico.
3. *Todus multicolor*. Cuban Tody. 11. Cuba, Isle of Pines.
4. *Todus subulatus*. Broad billed Tody. 12. Hispaniola & Gonave.
5. *Todus todus*. Jamaican Tody. 11. Jamaica.

Family 87. MOTMOTIDAE. Motmots.

1. *Hylomanes momotula*. Tody Motmot. 3ss. 17. Mexico, C America, Colombia.
2. *Aspatha gularis*. Blue throated Motmot. 27. Mexico to Honduras.
3. *Electron carinatum*. Keel billed Motmot. 35. Mexico to Costa Rica.
4. *Electron platyrhynchum*. Broad billed Motmot. 6ss. 35. Honduras to Brazil, Bolivia.
5. *Eumomota superciliosa*. Turquoise browed Motmot. 7ss. 33. Mexico, C America.
6. *Baryphthengus ruficapillus*. Rufous capped Motmot. 45. Brazil, Paraguay, Argentina.
7. *Baryphthengus martii*. Rufous Motmot. 3ss. 45. Nicaragua to Upper Amazonia.
8. *Momotus mexicanus*. Russet crowned Motmot. 4ss. 30. Mexico, Guatemala.
9. *Momotus momota*. Blue crowned Motmot. 22ss. 39. Trinidad, Mexico to Argentina & Brazil.
10. incl. *M. m. aequatorialis*. Highland Motmot. 39. Colombia, Ecuador.

1
2
3
4
5
MOTMOTIDAE
1
2
3
4
7
5
8
6
9
10

MEROPIDAE (1)
Bee Eaters

1. *Nyctiornis amictus*. Red bearded Bee Eater. 33. Malaya, Sumatra, Borneo.
2. *Nyctiornis athertoni*. Blue bearded Bee Eater. 2ss. 35. India, China, S E Asia.
3. *Meropogon forsteni*. Purple bearded Bee Eater. 31. Sulawesi.
4. *Merops albicollis*. White throated Bee Eater. 30. Senegal to Ethiopia, Arabia, Tanzania.
5. *Merops apiaster*. European Bee Eater. 27. Europe, C Asia. Winters S Asia, Africa.
6. *Merops boehmi*. Boehm's Bee Eater. 23. Tanzania, Zambia, Malawi.
7. *Merops breweri*. Black headed Bee Eater. 25. Cameroon, Gabon, Zaire.
8. *Merops bulocki*. Red throated Bee Eater. 2ss. 21. Senegal to Zaire, Sudan, Uganda.
9. *Merops bullockoides*. White fronted Bee Eater. 23. Gabon to Angola, Kenya, Tanzania, Natal.
10. *Merops gularis*. Black Bee Eater. 2ss. 19. Sierra Leone to Cameroon, Angola, Uganda.
11. *Merops hirundeus*. Swallow tailed Bee Eater. 3ss. 22. Senegal, Ghana, Zaire, Uganda, Kenya, Tanzania, Angola, Natal.
12. *Merops oreobates*. Cinnamon chested Bee Eater. 21. Sudan to Tanzania, Zaire.
13. *Merops leschenaulti*. Chestnut headed Bee Eater. 3ss. 21. India, S W China, S E Asia, Andaman Is, Java, Bali.

1
2
3
4
5
6
7
10
8
9
11
12
13

MEROPIDAE (2), LEPSOMATIDAE
Bee Eaters, Courols

Family 88. MEROPIDAE (2). Bee Eaters.

14. *Merops malimbicus*. Rosy Bee Eater. 32. Ghana to Zaire.
15. *Merops muelleri*. Blue headed Bee Eater. 2ss. 19. Sierra Leone to Cameroon, Zaire & Kenya.
16. *Merops nubicus*. (Northern) Carmine Bee Eater. 32. Senegal to Eritrea, Tanzania.
17. *Merops nubicoides*. Southern Carmine Bee Eater. 33. Angola to Natal. Winters Zaire, Tanzania.
18. *Merops orientalis*. (Little) Green Bee Eater. 9ss. 20. W to E Africa, Middle East to SE Asia.
19. *Merops ornatus*. Rainbow Bee Eater. 19. Australia, West Papuan & Solomon Is.
20. *Merops philippinus*. Blue tailed Bee Eater. 2ss. 30. India, China, SE Asia, New Guinea, Indonesia.
21. *Merops pusillus*. Little Bee Eater. 5ss. 16. Africa S. of Sahara.
22. *Merops revoilii*. Somali Bee Eater. 16. Somalia, Eritrea, Kenya.
23. *Merops superciliosus*. Madagascar Bee Eater. 4ss. 30. Malagasy & (Mainly) East Africa.
24. *Merops persicus*. Blue cheeked Bee Eater. 30. N. Egypt, SW Asia. Winters to S Africa.
25. *Merops variegatus*. Blue breasted Bee Eater. 3ss. 19 .Equatorial Africa.
26. *Merops viridis*, Blue throated Bee Eater. 2ss. 28. China, SE Asia, Philippines, Greater Sundas.

Family 89. LEPTOSOMATIDAE, Courols.

1. *Leptosomus discolor*. Cuckoo-Roller. 3ss. 42. Malagasy, Comoro Is.

14
15
16
17
18
19
20
21
22
23
24
25
26
1
LEPTOSOMATIDAE

BRACHYPTERACIIDAE, CORACIIDAE
Ground Rollers, Rollers

Family 90. BRACHYPTERACIIDAE. Ground Rollers.

1. *Atelornis crossleyi*. Rufous headed Ground Roller. 30. Malagasy.
2. *Atelornis pittoides*. Pitta-like Ground Roller. 30. Malagasy.
3. *Brachypteracias leptosomus*. Short legged Ground Roller. 30. Malagasy. Comoro Is.
4. *Brachypteracias squamigera*. Scaly Ground Roller. 30. Malagasy.
5. *Uratelornis chimaera*. Long tailed Ground Roller. 42. Malagasy.

Family 91. CORACIIDAE. Rollers.

1. *Coracias abyssinica*. Abyssinian Roller. 45. Senegal to Kenya, S W Arabia.
2. *Coracias benghalensis*. Indian Roller. 3ss. 33. Arabia to India, Sri Lanka, China, SE Asia.
3. *Coracias caudata*. Lilac breasted Roller. 2ss. 31. Ethiopia to South Africa.
4. *Coracias cyanogaster*. Blue bellied Roller. 35. Senegal to Sudan & Zaire.
5. *Coracias garrulus*. European Roller. 2ss. 30. Europe to C Asia. Winters to S Africa.
6. *Coracias naevia*. Rufous crowned Roller. 2ss. 37. Africa S of Sahara.
7. *Coracias spatulata*. Racquet tailed Roller. 37. Angola to Tanzania & Mozambique.
8. *Coracias temminckii*. Purple winged Roller. 36. Sulawesi.
9. *Eurystomus glaucurus*. Broad billed Roller. 4ss. 25. Africa S of Sahara, Malagasy.
10. *Eurystomus gularis*. Blue throated Roller. 2ss. 25. Senegal to Zaire, Angola.
11. *Eurystomus orientalis*. Dollarbird. 10ss. 30. India, China, Asia, Malaysia, Indonesia, Australasia.
12. *Eurystomus azureus*. Purple / Azure Roller. 32. N Moluccas.

BRACHYPTERACIDAE
B 1
2
4
CORACIIDAE
C 1
3
B 5
2
5
4
3
6
9
7
8
12
10
- 11 -

UPUPIDAE, PHOENICULIDAE
Hoopoes, Wodd Hoopoes

Family 92. UPUPIDAE. Hoopoes.

1. *Upupa epops.* (Eurasian) Hoopoe. 9ss. 28. Palearctic & S Asia.Winters tropical Africa. (Male only illustrated.)
2. *Upupa africana.* African Hoopoe. 28.Africa S of Sahara, Malagasy. (Female only illustrated.)

Family 93. PHOENICULIDAE. Wood Hoopoes.

1. *Rhinopomastus aterrimus.* Black Woodhoopoe / Scimitar-Bill. 4ss. 23. Senegal to Zaire, Ethiopia, Angola.

2 incl. *R. a. notatus.* Sudan Woodhoopoe. 23. Sudan. (unique male.)

3. *Phoeniculus bollei.* White headed Woodhoopoe. 3ss. 32. Ghana, Cameroon, Zaire, Kenya.
4. *Phoeniculus castaneiceps.* Forest Woodhoopoe. 2ss. 28. Ghana, Nigeria, Cameroon, Zaire, Uganda.
5. *Rhinopomastus cyanomelas.* Scimitar-bill. 2ss. 28. Kenya to Zaire, Angola, South Africa.
6. *Phoeniculus damarensis.* Violet Woodhoopoe. 37. NE Africa to Angola, Namibia.
7. *Phoeniculus somaliensis.* Black billed Woodhoopoe. 38. Ethiopia, Somalia, Kenya.
8. *Phoeniculus granti.* Grant's Woodhoopoe. 35. Ethiopia, W Kenya. (ss of 6.?)
9. *Rhinopomastus minor.* Abyssinian Scimitar-bill. 4ss. 23. Ethiopia to Tanzania.
10. *Phoeniculus purpureus.* Green Woodhoopoe. 6ss. 45. Most of Africa S of Sahara.

UPUPIDAE
PHOENICULIDAE
2
1
1
4
3
2
5
6
10
8
7
9

BUCEROTIDAE (1)
Hornbills

1. *Tockus alboterminatus.* African Crowned Hornbill. 49. Ethiopia to S Africa.
2. *Tockus / Ocyceros birostris.* Indian grey Hornbill. 61. N & C India.
3. *Tockus bradfieldi.* Bradfield's Hornbill. 60. Zimbabwe, S W Africa.
4. *Tockus camurus.* Red billed dwarf Hornbill. 37. Liberia to Zaire.
5. *Tockus deckeni.* Van der Decken's Hornbill. 44. Ethiopia to Tanzania.
6. *Tockus jacksoni.* Jackson's Hornbill. 42. Sudan, Ethiopia, Kenya.
7. *Tockus erythrorhynchus.* Red billed Hornbill. 3ss. 42. Senegal to Somalia Tanzania, Malawi, Transvaal, Namibia.
8. *Tockus fasciatus.* African Pied Hornbill. 2ss. 52. Cameroon, Equatorial Africa, Sudan, Congo, Angola.
9. incl. *T. f. semifasciatus.* Allied Hornbill. 52. Senegal to Ghana.
10. *Tockus leucomelas.* Southern yellow billed Hornbill. 47. Angola, Mozambique to Natal.
11. *Tockus flavirostris.* Eastern yellow billed Hornbill. 44. East Africa.
12. *Tockus / Ocyceros griseus.* Malabar grey Hornbill. 59. S W India.
13. *Tockus / Ocyceros gingalensis.* Ceylon grey Hornbill. 59. Sri Lanka.
14. *Tockus hartlaubi.* Black dwarf Hornbill. 2ss. 37. Guinea to Zaire.
15. *Tockus hemprichii.* Hemprich's Hornbill. 55. Eritrea, Somalia, Ethiopia, Kenya.
16. *Tockus monteiri.* Monteiro's Hornbill. 55. Angola, Namibia.
17. *Tockus nasutus.* African grey Hornbill. 4ss. 45. Africa S of Sahara, S W Arabia.
18. *Tockus pallidirostris.* Pale billed Hornbill. 2ss. 48. Kenya, Tanzania, Malawi, Angola.

1
2
3
4
5
6
7
8
9
10
11
12
13
14
15
16
17
18

BUCEROTIDAE (2)
Hornbills

19. *Tockus/Berenicornis albocristatus.* Long tailed / White crested Hornbill. 3ss. 65. Sierra Leone to Gabon & Uganda.
20. *Aceros/Berenicornis comatus.* Asian White crowned Hornbill. 98. SE Asia, Sumatra, Borneo.
21. *Anorrhinus/Ptilolaemus tickelli.* Brown Hornbill. 3ss. 72. Assam, Burma, Indo-China.
22. *Anorrhinus galerita.* Bushy crested Hornbill. 3ss. 82. Malaya, Sumatra, Borneo.
23. *Penelopides exarhatus.* Temminck's /Sulawesi Hornbill. 2ss. 50. Sulawesi.
24. *Penelopides panini.* Visayan / Tarictic Hornbill. 3ss. 60. C Philippines.
25. *Penelopides manillae.* Luzon Hornbill. 60. Luzon, N Philippines.
26. *Penelopides mindorensis.* Mindoro Hornbill. 60. Mindoro, C Philippines.
27. *Penelopides affinis.* Mindanao Hornbill. 60. Mindanao, S Philippines.
28. *Penelopides samarensis.* Samar Hornbill. 60. Samar, Leyte. S Philippines.
29. *Aceros cassidix.* Knobbed (Sulawesi wrinkled) Hornbill. 70. Sulawesi & Islands.
30. *Aceros everetti.* Sumba Wreathed Hornbill. 70. Sumba, Lesser Sundas.
31. *Aceros leucocephalus.* White headed / Writhed Hornbill. 80. S E Philippines.
32. *Aceros waldeni.* Writhe billed Hornbill. 80. Negros, C Philippines.
33. *Aceros corrugatus.* Wrinkled Hornbill. 80. Malaya, Sumatra, Borneo.

Females of 24, 27, 28 are similar to 25.

19
20
21
22
23
24
25
26
27
28
29
30
31
32
- 33 -

Plate 151 Family 94.

BUCEROTIDAE (3)
Hornbills

34. *Aceros nipalensis*. Rufous necked Hornbill. 122. Himalayas, S W China, N SE Asia.
35. *Aceros plicatus*. Blyth's / Papuan wreathed Hornbill. 6ss. 88. SE Asia, Indonesia, New Guinea.
36. *Aceros subruficollis*. Plain pouched Hornbill. 85. Burma, Thailand, Malaysia, Sumatra, Borneo.
37. *Aceros undulatus*. Wreathed/ Bar pouched Hornbill. 2ss. 114:98. Assam, China, Malaysia, Indonesia.
38. *Aceros narcondami*. Narcondam Hornbill. 66. Andaman Is.
39. *Anthracoceros coronatus*. Malabar / Indian Pied Hornbill. 110. India, Sri Lanka.
40. *Anthracoceros albirostris*. Oriental / Northern Pied Hornbill. 2ss. 90. NE India, SE Asia to Indonesia. Incl. *A. a. convexus*. Sunda Pied Hornbill. Similar but larger. Not illustrated.
41. *Anthracoceros malayanus*. Black Hornbill. 75. Malaysia, Sumatra, Borneo.
42. *Anthracoceros marchei*. Palawan Hornbill. 80. Palawan & adjacent Islands.
43. *Anthracoceros montani*. Sulu Hornbill. 80. Sulu Archipelago, SW Philippines.

34
35
36
-37-
38
39
40
41
42
43

BUCEROTIDAE (4) Hornbills

44. *Ceratogymna/Bycanistes brevis.* Silvery cheeked Hornbill. 70. Ethiopia to Malawi, Mozambique.
45. *Ceratogymna bucinator.* Trumpeter Hornbill. 62. Kenya to Angola & Cape.
46. *Ceratogymna sharpii.* White tailed / Laughing Hornbill. 60. Nigeria to Zaire & Angola.
47. *Ceratogymna cylindricus.* Brown cheeked Hornbill. 75. Sierra Leone to Benin.
48. *Ceratogymna albotibialis.* White thighed Hornbill. 72. Nigeria to Congo.
49. *Ceratogymna fistulator.* Piping Hornbill.50. Senegal to Angola & Uganda.
50. *Ceratogymna subcylindricus.*Black & white casqued / Grey cheeked Hornbill. 2ss. 75. Ghana to E Africa, Angola.
51. *Ceratogymna atrata.* Black casqued Hornbill. 90. Liberia to Sudan, Angola.
52. *Ceratogymna elata.* Yellow casqued Hornbill. 90. Guinea to Cameroon.

Measurements are for male Hornbills. Females normally smaller.

44
45
46
47
48
49
-50-
-51-
-52-

BUCEROTIDAE (5)
Hornbills

53. *Buceros bicornis*. Great (Pied) Hornbill. 2ss. 130. India, SW China, SE Asia to Sumatra.
54. *Buceros hydrocorax*. Rufous Hornbill. 4ss. 110. Philippines.
55. *Buceros rhinoceros*. Rhinoceros Hornbill. 4ss. 120. Malaysia, Sumatra, Java, Borneo.
56. *Rhinoplax vigil*. Helmeted Hornbill. 125 + 40. Malaysia, Sumatra, Borneo.
57. *Bucorvus abyssinicus*. Abyssinian Ground Hornbill. 107. Gambia to Kenya & Ethiopia.
58. *Bucorvus leadbeateri / cafer.* Southern Ground Hornbill. 105. Kenya & Tanzania to Angola, Cape.

53
54
55
56
57
58

Plate 154 Family 95, 96

GALBULIDAE, BUCCONIDAE
Jacamars, Puffbirds

Family 95. GALBULIDAE. Jacamars

1. *Galbalcyrhynchus leucotis*. Chestnut Jacamar. 20. Upper Amazonia.
2. *Galbalcyrhynchus perusianus*. White eared Jacamar. 20. Peru, Brazil, Bolivia.
3. *Brachygalba albogularis*. White throated Jacamar. 16. Peru, Brazil.
4. *Brachygalba goeringi*. Pale headed Jacamar. 18. Colombia, Venezuela.
5. *Brachygalba lugubris*. Brown Jacamar. 7ss. 17. Amazon & Orinoco basins.
6. *Brachygalba salmoni*. Dusky backed Jacamar. 17. Panama, Colombia.
7. *Jacamaralcyon tridactyla*. Three toed Jacamar. 16. SE Brazil.
8. *Galbula albirostris*. Yellow billed Jacamar. 19. Amazon & Orinoco basins.
9. *Galbula cyanicollis*. Blue necked Jacamar. 19. Brazil.
10. *Galbula cyanescens*. Bluish fronted Jacamar. 24. Brazil, Bolivia, Peru.
11. *Galbula dea*. Paradise Jacamar. 4ss. 31. Upper Amazon basin.
12. *Galbula galbula*. Green tailed Jacamar. 19. Colombia, Venezuela, Guyanas, Brazil.
13. *Galbula leucogastra*. Bronzy Jacamar. 2ss. 22. Guyanas, Venezuela, Brazil.
14. *Galbula pastazae*. Coppery chested Jacamar. 28. Ecuador, Colombia, Brazil.
15. *Galbula ruficauda*. Rufous tailed Jacamar. 5ss. 23. Mexico to Brazil & Argentina.
16. *Galbula melanogenia*. Black chinned Jacamar. 23. Mexico to Ecuador.
17. *Galbula tombacea*. White chinned Jacamar. 2ss. 22. Colombia, Peru, Brazil.
18. *Galbula chalcothorax*. Purplish Jacamar. 22. Brazil, Ecuador, Peru.
19. *Jacamerops aurea*. Great Jacamar. 4ss. 30. Panama, Costa Rica to Bolivia & Brazil.

Family 96. BUCCONIDAE (1) Puffbirds.

1. *Notharcus macrorhynchos*. White necked Puffbird. 5ss. 25. Mexico to Argentina.
2. *Notharcus ordii*. Brown banded Puffbird. 20. Venezuela, Brazil.
3. *Notharcus pectoralis*. Black breasted Puffbird . 20. Panama, Colombia, Ecuador.
4. *Notharcus tectus*. Pied Puffbird. 3ss. 15. Costa Rica to Brazil & Bolivia.
5. *Bucco capensis*. Collared Puffbird. 2ss. 19. Amazon & Orinoco basins.
6. *Bucco macrodactylus*. Chestnut capped Puffbird. 2ss. 14. Venezuela to Brazil & Bolivia.
7. *Bucco noanamae*. Sooty capped Puffbird. 18. Colombia.
8. *Bucco tamatia*. Spotted Puffbird. 6ss. 18. Venezuela, Guyanas, Brazil

BUCCONIDAE

BUCCONIDAE (2)
Puffbirds

9. *Nystalus chacuru*. White eared Puffbird. 2ss. 21. Brazil, Peru, Paraguay, Argentina.
10. *Nystalus maculatus*. Spot backed Puffbird. 4ss. 20. Brazil, Bolivia, Paraguay, Argentina.
11. *Nystalus radiatus*. Barred Puffbird. 21. Panama to Ecuador.
12. *Nystalus striolatus*. Striolated Puffbird. 2ss. 21. Ecuador, Bolivia, Brazil.
13. *Hypnelus ruficollis*. Russet throated Puffbird. 6ss. 23. Colombia, Venezuela.
14. *Malacoptila fulvogularis*. Black streaked Puffbird. 3ss. 23. Colombia to Bolivia
15. *Malacoptila fusca*. White chested Puffbird. 2ss. 18. Venezuela, Amazonia.
16. *Malacoptila mystacalis*. Moustached Puffbird. 23. Venezuela, Colombia.
17. *Malacoptila panamensis*. White whiskered Puffbird. 5ss. 20. Mexico to Ecuador.
18. *Malacoptila rufa*. Rufous necked Puffbird. 2ss. 20. Ecuador, Peru, Brazil.
19. *Malacoptila semicincta*. Semi-collared Puffbird. 18. Peru, Brazil, Bolivia.
20. *Malacoptila striata*. Crescent chested Puffbird. 2ss. 21. Brazil.
21. *Micromonacha lanceolata*. Lanceolated Monklet. 2ss. 14. Costa Rica to Brazil.
22. *Nonnula amaurocephala*. Chestnut headed Nunlet. 15. W Brazil.
23. *Nonnula brunnea*. Brown Nunlet. 15. Colombia, Ecuador, Peru.
24. *Nonnula rubecula*. Rusty breasted Nunlet. 5ss. 17. Venezuela to Brazil, Paraguay, Argentina.
25. *Nonnula ruficapilla*. Rufous capped Nunlet. 4ss. 15. Peru, Bolivia, Brazil.
26. *Nonnula frontalis*. Grey cheeked Nunlet. 15. Panama to Colombia.
27. *Nonnula sclateri*. Fulvous chinned Nunlet. 15. Brazil.
28. *Hapaloptila castanea*. White faced Nunbird. 25. Colombia, Ecuador.
29. *Monasa atra*. Black Nunbird. 26. Venezuela, Guyanas, Brazil.
30. *Monasa flavirostris*. Yellow billed Nunbird. 26. Colombia to Peru, Brazil.
31. *Monasa morphoeus*. White fronted Nunbird. 7ss. 29. Nicaragua to Brazil.
32. *Monasa nigrifrons*. Black fronted Nunbird. 2ss. 29. Colombia, Bolivia, Brazil.
33. *Chelidoptera tenebrosa*. Swallow-wing Puffbird. 3ss. 16. Venezuela to Bolivia & Brazil.

9
10
11
12
13
14
15
16
17
18
19
20
21
22
23
24
25
26
27
28
29
30
31
32
33

CAPITONIDAE (1) Barbets

Family 97. CAPITONIDAE. Barbets

1. *Capito aurovirens*. Scarlet crowned Barbet. 18. Colombia, Peru, Brazil.
2. *Capito dayi*. Black girdled Barbet. 18. Brazil.
3. *Capito hypoleucus*. White mantled Barbet. 3ss. 18. Colombia.
4. *Capito maculicoronatus*. Spot crowned Barbet. 4ss. 18. Panama to Colombia.
5. *Capito niger*. Black spotted Barbet. 15ss. 19. Amazon & Orinoco basins.
6. *Capito brunneipectus*. Brown chested Barbet. 19. Brazil.
7. *Capito quinticolor*. Five-coloured Barbet. 18. Colombia.
8. *Capito squamatus*. Orange fronted Barbet. 18. Colombia, Ecuador.
9. *Eubucco bourcierii*. Red headed Barbet. 6ss. 16. Costa Rica to Peru.
10. *Eubucco richardsoni*. Lemon throated Barbet. 4ss. 15. Upper Amazon.
11. *Eubucco tucinkae*. Scarlet hooded Barbet. 17. Peru.
12. *Eubucco versicolor.* Versicoloured Barbet. 3ss. 17. Peru, Bolivia.
13. *Semnornis frantzii*. Prong billed Barbet. 17. Costa Rica, Panama.
14. *Semnornis ramphastinus*. Toucan Barbet. 2ss. 20. Colombia, Ecuador.
15. *Psilopogon pyrolophus*. Fire tufted Barbet. 27. Malaysia, Sumatra.
16. *Megalaima armillaris*. Blue crowned Barbet. 2ss. 20. Java, Bali.
17. *Megalaima asiatica*. Blue throated Barbet. 4ss. 23. N India to SE Asia.
18. *Megalaima australis*. Blue eared Barbet. 7ss. 18. Himalayas to China S E Asia & Gr. Sundas.

1
2
3
4
5
6
7
8
9
10
11
12
13
14
15
16
17
18

CAPITONIDAE (2)
Barbets

19. *Megalaima chrysopogon*. Gold whiskered Barbet. 3ss. 30. Thailand, Malaysia, Sumatra, Borneo.
20. *Megalaima corvina*. Brown throated Barbet. 26. Java.
21. *Megalaima eximia*. Black throated / Bornean Barbet. 2ss. 15. Borneo.
22. *Megalaima faiostricta*. Green eared Barbet. 2ss. 24. China, Indo-China, Thailand.
23. *Megalaima flavifrons*. Yellow fronted Barbet. 21. Sri Lanka.
24. *Megalaima franklinii*. Golden throated Barbet. 5ss. 23. India, China, SE Asia.
25. *Megalaima haemacephala*. Coppersmith Barbet. 5ss. 16. India, Sri Lanka, Philippines, SE Asia, Indonesia.
26. *Megalaima henrici*. Yellow crowned Barbet. 2ss. 21. Thailand, Malaysia, Borneo, Sumatra.
27. *Megalaima incognita*. Moustached Barbet. 3ss. 23. Burma, Thailand, Indo-China.
28. *Megalaima javensis*. Black banded Barbet. 26. Java.
29. *Megalaima lagrandieri*. Red vented Barbet. 2ss. 30. Laos, Vietnam.
30. *Megalaima lineata*. Lineated Barbet. 2ss. 29. Himalayas to Malaysia, Indo-China, Java, Bali.
31. *Megalaima monticola*. Mountain Barbet. 23. North Borneo.
32. *Megalaima mystacophanos*. Red throated Barbet. 3ss. 24. Malaya, Sumatra, Borneo
33. *Megalaima oorti*. Black browed Barbet. 5ss. 20. SE Asia, Hainan, Taiwan, China, Sumatra.
34. *Megalaima pulcherrima*. Golden naped Barbet. 20. North Borneo.
35. *Megalaima rafflesi*. Red crowned/ Many coloured Barbet. 4ss. 25. Malaya, Sumatra, Borneo,
36. *Megalaima rubricapilla*. Crimson fronted Barbet / Small Coppersmith. 2ss. 17. S India, Sri Lanka.
37. *Megalaima virens*. Great Barbet. 4ss. 33. Himalayas, Tibet, China, N SE Asia.
38. *Megalaima viridis*. Little green / White cheeked Barbet. 23. S India.
39. *Megalaima zeylanica*. Brown headed / Oriental green Barbet. 4ss. 27. India, Sri Lanka.
40. *Caloramphus fuliginosus*. Brown Barbet. 3ss. 17. Burma, Malaysia, Borneo, Sumatra.

19
20
21
32
♀
22
23
24
25
26
27
28
29
30
31
32
♂
33
34
35
36
37
38
39
40

CAPITONIDAE (3) Barbets

41. *Gymnobucco bonapartei*. Grey throated Barbet. 17. Cameroon, Zaire, Sudan.
42. *Gymnobucco calvus*. Naked faced Barbet. 3ss. 20. Sierra Leone to Zaire, Angola.
43. *Gymnobucco peli*. Bristle nosed Barbet. 19. Ghana to Gabon.
44. *Gymnobucco sladeni*. Sladen's Barbet. 20. Zaire.
45. *Stactolaema achietae*. Anchieta's Barbet. 3ss. 20. Zaire, Zambia, Angola.
46. *Buccanodon duchaillui*. Yellow spotted Barbet. 15. Sierra Leone, Gabon to Uganda.
47. *Stactolaema/Smilorhis leucotis*. White eared Barbet. 3ss. 18. Kenya to Natal.
48. *Stactolaema/Cryptilybia olivacea*. Green Barbet. 5ss. 15. Kenya to Mozambique.
49. *Stactolaema whytii*. Whyte's Barbet. 6ss. 18. Tanzania, Malawi to Zimbabwe.
50. *Pogoniulus atroflavus*. Red rumped Tinkerbird. 12. W & C Africa.
51. *Pogoniulus biolineatus*. Yellow rumped Tinkerbird. 3ss. 10. Kenya to Natal.
52. *Pogoniulus chrysoconus*. Yellow fronted Tinkerbird. 3ss. 10. Africa S of Sahara.
53. *Pogoniulus coryphaeus*. Western green Tinkerbird. 3ss. 9. Cameroon to Uganda.
54. *Pogoniulus leucomystax*. Moustached green Tinkerbird. 9. Kenya to Malawi.
55. *Pogoniulus leucolaima*. Lemon rumped Tinkerbird. 3ss. 10. W & C Africa.
56. *Pogoniulus makawai*. White chested Tinkerbird. 10. Zambia. (unique).
57. *Pogoniulus pusillus*. Red fronted Tinkerbird. 3ss. 10. Ethiopia to Swaziland.
58. *Pogoniulus acolopaceus*. Speckled Tinkerbird. 3ss. 11. Sierra Leone, Fernando Po to Kenya & Angola.
59. *Pogoniulus simplex*. Green Tinkerbird. 10. Kenya, Tanzania, Malawi.
60. *Pogoniulus subsulphureus*. Yellow throated Tinkerbird. 3ss. 10. W & C Africa.
61. *Lybius bidentatus*. Double toothed Barbet. 2ss. 23. Guinea to Angola, Zaire, Kenya, Tanzania, Ethiopia.
62. *Tricholaema diademata*. Red fronted Barbet. 2ss. 13. Sudan to Tanzania.
63. *Tricholaema frontata*. Miombo Pied Barbet. 12. Angola to Malawi.
64. *Lybius dubius*. Bearded Barbet. 25. Senegambia to Chad.
65. *Lybius guifsobalito*. Black billed Barbet. 15. Ethiopia to Zaire.
66. *Lybius/Tricholaema hirsuta*. Hairy breasted Barbet. 3ss. 15. Sierra Leone to Uganda, Angola.
67. incl. *T. h. flavipunctata*. Spot headed Barbet. 15. W & C Africa.
68. *Tricholaema lacrymosa*. Spot flanked Barbet. 2ss. 12. Kenya, Uganda, Tanzania.
69. *Lybius leucocephalus*. White headed Barbet. 6ss. 15. Sub-saharan Africa.
70. *Lybius chaplini*. Chaplin's Barbet. 15. S Zambia.
71. *Tricholaema leucomelas*. Pied Barbet. 3ss. 16. Zimbabwe, Botswana, S Africa.
72. *Tricholaema melanocephala*. Black throated Barbet. 4ss. 12. East Africa.
73. incl. *T. m flavibuccalis*. Yellow cheeked Barbet. 12. Tanzania.

41
42
43
44
45
46
47
48
49
50
51
52
53
54
55
56
57
58
59
60
61
63
62
64
65
66
67
68
69
70
71
72
73

CAPITONIDAE (4), INDICATORAE
Barbets, Honeyguides

74. *Lybius melanopterus.* Brown breasted Barbet. 16. Somalia to Mozambique.
75. *Lybius minor.* Black backed Barbet. 2ss. 15. Zaire, Angola.
76. incl. *L. m. maccalounii.* Macclounie's Barbet. 15. Zaire, Zambia, Malawi.
77. *Lybius rolleti.* Black breasted Barbet. 28. Central Africa.
78. *Lybius rubrifacies.* Red faced Barbet. 15. Uganda, Rwanda, Tanzania.
79. *Lybius torquatus.* Black collared Barbet. 7ss. 18. Angola to Kenya, S Africa.
80. incl. *L. t. zombae.* Zomba Barbet. 18. Malawi, Tanzania.
81. *Lybius undatus.* Banded Barbet. 4ss. 13. Ethiopia.
82. *Lybius vieilloti.* Viellot's Barbet. 3ss. 15. Senegal to Ethiopia, Zaire.
83. *Trachyphonus darnaudii.* D'Arnaud's Barbet. 3ss. 15. Sudan to Tanzania.
84. *Trachyphonus erythrocephalus.* Red & yellow Barbet. 23. Ethiopia to Tanzania.
85. *Trachyphonus margaritatus.* Yellow breasted Barbet. 2ss. 21. Niger to Sudan, Ethiopia, Somalia.
86. *Trachyphonus purpuratus.* Yellow billed Barbet. 4ss. 22. W & C Africa.
87. *Trachyphonus vaillanti.* Crested Barbet. 2ss. 23. Tanzania & Southern Africa.
88. *Trachyphonus usambiro.* Usambiro Barbet. 18. Kenya, Tanzania.

Family 98. INDICATORIDAE. Honeyguides.

1. *Prodotiscus insignis.* Cassin's Honeyguide. 2ss. 12. W & C Africa.
2. *Prodotiscus zambesiae.* Green backed Honeyguide. 13. Ethiopia to Angola.
3. *Prodotiscus regulus.* Wahlberg's Honeyguide. 2ss. 12. Africa S of Sahara.
4. *Melignomon zenkeri.* Zenker's Honeyguide. 12. Cameron to Uganda.
5. *Melignomon aisentrauti.* Yellow footed Honeyguide. 12. Liberia, Cameroon.
6. *Indicator archipelagus.* Malaysian Honeyguide. 17. Malaya, Sumatra, Borneo.
7. *Indicator exilis.* Least Honeyguide. 3ss. 12. Equatorial Africa.
8. *Indicator indicator.* Greater Honeyguide. 20. Africa S of Sahara.
9. *Indicator maculatus.* Spotted Honeyguide. 2ss. 19. Gambia to Ghana, Congo.
10. *Indicator meliphilus.* Pallid Honeyguide. 12. Kenya to Malawi, Zimbabwe.
11. *Indicator minor.* Lesser Honeyguide. 6ss. 14. Africa S of Sahara.
12. *Indicator conirostris.* Thick billed Honeyguide. 2ss. 15. Ghana, Nigeria to Uganda.
13. *Indicator pumilio.* Dwarf Honeyguide. 11. Zaire, Rwanda.
14. Indicator variegatus. Scaly throated Honeyguide. 18. Ethiopia to Cape.
15. *Indicator wilcocksii.* Willcocks' Honeyguide. 3ss. 12. Cameroon, Nigeria, Guinea.
16. *Indicator xanthonotus.* Yellow rumped Honeyguide. 2ss. 15. W Himalayas to Assam.
17. *Melichneutes robustus.* Lyre tailed Honeyguide. 16. Cameroon to Zaire.

74
75
77
78
79
81
76
82
83
80
84
85
86
87
INDICATORIDAE
1
3
4
6
16
88
2
5
9
7
10
15
8
13
JUV
11
12
14
17

RAMPHASTIDAE (1) Toucans

Family 99. RAMPHASTIDAE. Toucans

1. *Aulacorhynchus calorhynchus*. Yellow billed Toucanet. 36. Colombia, Venezuela.
2. *Aulacorhynchus coeruleicinctus*. Blue banded Toucanet. 42. Peru, Bolivia.
3. *Aulacorhynchus derbianus*. Chestnut tipped Toucanet. 5ss. 41. Venezuela, Guyana to Bolivia.
4. *Aulacorhynchus haematopygus*. Crimson rumped Toucanet. 2ss. 47. Venezuela to Ecuador.
5. *Aulacorhynchus huallagae*. Yellow browed Toucanet. 45. Peru.
6. *Aulacorhynchus prasinus*. Emerald Toucanet. 14ss. 37. Mexico to Bolivia.
7. *Aulacorhynchus caeruleogularis*. Blue throated Toucanet. 37. Costa Rica to Panama.
8. *Aulacorhynchus sulcatus*. Groove billed Toucanet. 2ss. 35. Venezuela.
9. *Pteroglossus aracari*. Black necked Aracari. 4ss. 40. Guyanas, Venezuela, Brazil.
10. *Pteroglossus beauharnaesii*. Curl crested Aracari. 47. Peru, Bolivia, Brazil.
11. *Pteroglossus bitorquatus*. Red necked Aracari. 3ss. 35. Brazil.
12. *Pteroglossus castanotis*. Chestnut eared Aracari. 2ss. 49. Colombia to Argentina.
13. *Pteroglossus erythropygius*. Pale mandibled Aracari. 51. Ecuador.
14. *Pteroglossus flavirostris*. Ivory billed Aracari. 38. Colombia, Venezuela, Ecuador, Brazil.
15. *Pteroglossus azara*. Azara Aracari. 38. Brazil. (probably Consp. with 14).
16. *Pteroglossus mariae*. Brown mandibled Aracari. 38. Peru, Bolivia, Brazil.
17. *Pteroglossus pluricinctus*. Many banded Aracari. 45. Venezuela, Brazil & Peru.
18. *Pteroglossus sanguineus*. Stripe billed Aracari. 51. Colombia, Ecuador.

1
2
3
4
5
6
8
9
7
10
11
12
13
14
15
17
16
18

RAMPHASTIDAE (2)
Toucans

19. *Pteroglossus torquatus*. Collared Aracari. 4ss. 42. Mexico to Colombia &Venezuela.
20. *Pteroglossus frantzii*. Fiery billed Aracari. 39. Costa Rica, Panama.
21. *Pteroglossus viridis*. Green Aracari. 3ss. 36. Venezuela, Guyanas, N Brazil.
22. *Pteroglossus inscriptus*. Lettered Aracari. 35. E & S Brazil.
23. *Selenidera culik*. Guianan Toucanet. 32. Guyanas, N Brazil.
24. *Selenidera maculirostris*. Spot-billed Toucanet. 34. Brazil, Argentina.
25. *Selenidera gouldii*. Gould's Toucanet. 34. Brazil, Bolivia.
26. *Selenidera natteri*. Tawny tufted Toucanet. 34. Guyanas, Venezuela, Brazil.
27. *Selenidera reinwardtii*. Golden collared Toucanet. 2ss. 33. Colombia to Peru & Brazil.
28. *Selenidera spectabilis*. Yellow eared Toucanet. 37. Honduras to Ecuador.
29. *Baillonius bailloni*. Saffron Toucanet. 40. Brazil, Paraguay, Argentina.
30. *Andigena cucullata*. Hooded mountain Toucan. 51. Peru, Bolivia.
31. *Andigena hypoglauca*. Grey breasted mountain Toucan. 2ss.50. Colombia, Ecuador, Peru.
32. *Andigena Laminirostris*. Plate billed mountain Toucan. 49. Ecuador, Colombia.
33. *Andigena nigrirostris*. Black billed mountain Toucan. 3ss. 55. Venezuela to Ecuador.

19
20
21
♂
♀
22
23
24
25
26
27
28
29
30
31
32
33

RAMPHASTIDAE (3)
Toucans

34. *Ramphastos ambiguus*. Black mandibled Toucan. 2ss. 60. Venezuela to Peru.
35. *Ramphastos brevis*. Choco Toucan. 47. Colombia, Ecuador.
36. *Ramphastos aurantiirostris*. Orange billed Toucan. 60. Venezuela, Guyanas. (phase of 45 ?)
37. *Ramphastos citreolaemus*. Citron-throated Toucan. 58. Colombia, Venezuela.
38. *Ramphastos culminatus*. Yellow-ridged Toucan. 49. Colombia, Venezuela, Brazil, Bolivia.
39. *Ramphastos cuvieri*. Cuvier's Toucan. 59. N Amazonia.
40. *Ramphastos inca*. Inca Toucan. 60. Bolivia. (form of 39 ?)
41. *Ramphastos dicolorus*. Red breasted Toucan. 45. Brazil, Paraguay, Argentina.
42. *Ramphastos sulfuratus*. Keel-billed Toucan. 2ss. 48. Mexico to Venezuela & Colombia.
43. *Ramphastos swainsonii*. Chestnut mandibled Toucan. 55. Honduras to Ecuador.
44. *Ramphastos toco*. Toco Toucan. 2ss. 61. Guyanas, Brazil, Paraguay, Argentina.
45. *Ramphastos vitellinus*. Channel billed Toucan. 4ss. 49. Guyanas, Venezuela, Brazil.
46. *Ramphastos tucanus*. Red billed Toucan. 2ss. 58. Guyanas, Venezuela, Brazil.

34
35
36
37
38
39
40
41
42
43
44
45
46

PICIDAE (1)
Wrynecks, Piculets

Family 100. PICIDAE. Piculets

1. *Jynx ruficollis*. Rufous necked Wryneck. 4ss. 17. Africa S of Sahara.
2. *Jynx torquilla*. (Northern) Wryneck. 4ss. 16. Eurasia. Winters Africa, India, SE Asia.
3. *Picumnus innominatus*. Speckled Piculet. 3ss. 10. India, China, SE Asia, Sundas.
4. *Picumnus aurifrons*. Gold fronted Piculet. 6ss. 8. Amazonia.
5. *Picumnus borbae*. Bar breasted Piculet. 9. Peru, Brazil.
6. *Picumnus lafresnayei*. Lafresnaye's Piculet. 4ss. 9. Colombia to Peru, Brazil.
7. *Picumnus pumilus*. Orinoco Piculet. 10. Colombia, NW Brazil.
8. *Picumnus exilis*. Golden spangled Piculet. 7ss. 9. Venezuela, Guyanas, Brazil.
9. *Picumnus nigropunctatus*. Black dotted Piculet. 9. Venezuela.
10. *Picumnus sclateri*. Ecuadorian Piculet. 3ss. 9. Ecuador, Peru.
11. *Picumnus squamulatus*. Scaled Piculet. 5ss. 9. Colombia, Venezuela.
12. *Picumnus spilogaster*. White bellied Piculet. 2ss. 9. Venezuela, Guyanas, Brazil.
13. *Picumnus leucogaster*. Northern White bellied Piculet. 9. Venezuela, Brazil.
14. *Picumnus pallidus*. Pale Piculet. 9. NE Brazil. (13 & 14 probable ss. of 12)
15. *Picumnus minutissimus*. Guianian Piculet. 8. The Guyanas.
16. *Picumnus pygmaeus*. Spotted Piculet. 9. E Brazil.
17. *Picumnus steindachneri*. Speckle chested Piculet. 9. NE Peru.
18. *Picumnus varzeae*. Varzea Piculet. 9. Brazil.
19. *Picumnus cirratus*. White barred Piculet. 7ss. 9. Guyana to Argentina.
20. *Picumnus dorbygnianus*. Ocellated Piculet. 8. Bolivia.
21. *Picumnus temminckii*. Ochre collared Piculet. 9. Brazil, Paraguay, Argentina.
22. *Picumnus albosquamatus*. White wedged Piculet. 2ss. 9. Bolivia, Brazil.
23. incl. *P. a. guttifer*. Arrowhead Piculet. 9. Brazil.
24. *P. a. asterias*. Blackish Piculet. 9. Brazil.
25. *Picumnus fuscus*. Rusty necked Piculet. 10. Bolivia, Brazil.
26. *Picumnus rufiventris*. Rufous breasted Piculet. 3ss. 10. Colombia to Bolivia.
27. *Picumnus fulvescens*. Tawny Piculet. 9. NE Brazil.

(male unknown presumed to be as shown.)

28. *Picumnus limae*. Ochraceous Piculet. 9. E Brazil.
29. *Picumnus nebulosus*. Mottled Piculet. 9. Brazil, Uruguay, Argentina.
30. *Picumnus castelnau*. Plain breasted Piculet. 9. Ecuador, Peru.
31. *Picumnus subtilis*. Fine barred Piculet. 9. S E Peru.
32. *Picumnus olivaceus*. Olivaceous Piculet. 6ss. 9. Guatemala to Ecuador.
33. *Picumnus granadensis*. Greyish Piculet. 2ss. 9. Colombia.
34. *Picumnus cinnamomeus*. Chestnut Piculet. 4ss. 10. Colombia, Venezuela.
35. *Nesoctites micromegas*. Antillean Piculet. 2ss. 11. Hispaniola, Gonave I.
36. *Sasia africana*. African Piculet. 8. Nigeria to Zaire.
37. *Sasia abnormis*. Rufous Piculet. 2ss. 8. Malay Peninsula, Greater Sundas.
38. *Sasia ochracea*. White browed Piculet. 8. Himalayas, China, Burma, Thailand, Vietnam.

14
1
2
27
6
22
23
24
4
5
30
34
19
20
8
33
3
28
15
29
9
32
7
16
26
10
12
11
17
21
18
35
25
36
37
38
31
13

PICIDAE (2)
Woodpeckers

39. *Geocolaptes olivaceus*. Ground Woodpecker. 2ss. 27. South Africa.
40. *Colaptes auratus auratus*. Common (Yellow shafted) Flicker. 13ss. 30. SE USA.
41. incl. *C. a. cafer*. Red shafted Flicker. 32. W USA.
42. *C. a. chrysoides*. Gilded / Mearns' Flicker. 28. California.

Other ss. from Alaska, Canada to Nicaragua, Cuba, Cayman Is.

43. *Colaptes campestris*. Campo Flicker. 30. Bolivia, Brazil.
44. incl. *C. c. campestroides*. Field Flicker. 33. Brazil, Paraguay, Uruguay, Argentina.
45. *Colaptes fernandinae*. Fernandina's Flicker. 30. Cuba.
46. *Colaptes pitius*. Chilean Flicker. 33. Chile & Argentina.
47. *Colaptes rupicola*. Andean Flicker. 3ss. 35. Peru, Bolivia, N Chile.
48. *Colaptes atricollis*. Black necked Woodpecker. 2ss. 27. Peru.
49. *Colaptes melanochloros*. Green barred Woodpecker. 4ss. 28. Bolivia, Brazil, Paraguay, Uruguay, Argentina.
50. *Colaptes melanolaimus*. Golden breasted Woodpecker. 28. Bolivia, Argentina.
51. *Colaptes punctigula*. Spot breasted Woodpecker. 6ss. 21. Panama, Colombia, Venezuela, Guyanas, Brazil.

39
40
41
42
43
44
45
46
47
48
49
50
51

PICIDAE (3)
Woodpeckers

52. *Piculus aeriginosus*. Bronze winged Woodpecker. 22. NE Mexico. (consp 60.)
53. *Piculus auricularis*. Grey crowned Woodpecker. 21. W Mexico.
54. *Piculus aurulentus*. Yellow browed Woodpecker. 22. Brazil, Paraguay, Argentina.
55. *Piculus chrysochloros*. Golden-green Woodpecker. 9ss. 23. Panama to Argentina.
56. *Piculus flavigula*. Yellow throated Woodpecker. 3ss. 20. Amazon & Orinoco basins.
57. Pi*culus leucolaemus*. White throated Woodpecker. 20. Ecuador, Bolivia, Brazil.
58. *Piculus litae*. Lita Woodpecker. 18. Colombia, Ecuador.
59. *Piculus rivolii*. Crimson mantled Woodpecker. 5ss. 27. Venezuela to Bolivia.
60. *Piculus rubiginosus*. Golden-olive Woodpecker. 18ss. 22. Mexico to Bolivia.
61. *Piculus simplex*. Rufous winged Woodpecker. 18. Honduras to Panama.
62. *Piculus callopterus*. Stripe cheeked Woodpecker. 18. Panama.
63. *Campethera abingoni*. Golden tailed Woodpecker. 6ss. 20. Africa S of Sahara.
64. *Campethera mombassica*. Mombassa Woodpecker. 17. Coast Somalia, Kenya, Tanzania.
65. *Campethera bennetti*. Bennett's Woodpecker. 2ss. 20. Southern Africa.
66. *Campethera scriptoricauda*. Reichenow's Woodpecker. 20. Angola, Mozambique.
67. *Campethera cailliautii*. Little spotted Woodpecker. 3ss. 16. E Africa, S to Mozambique.
68. *Campethera caroli*. Brown eared Woodpecker. 2ss. 18. Sierra Leone to Kenya & Angola.
69. *Campethera maculosa*. Little green Woodpecker. 18. Guinea to Ghana.
70. *Campethera nivosa*. Buff spotted Woodpecker. 3ss. 14. W & C Africa.
71. *Campethera notata*. Knysna Woodpecker. 20. Natal, Cape Province.
72. *Campethera nubica*. Nubian Woodpecker. 2ss. 17. Sudan to Mozambique.
73. *Campethera permista*. Green backed Woodpecker. 17. Cameroon to Mozambique & Angola.
74. *Campethera punctuligera*. Fine spotted Woodpecker. 2ss. 20. W & N C Africa.
75. *Campethera tullbergi*. Tullberg's Woodpecker. 2ss. 19. WC & EC Africa.
76. incl. *C. t. taeniolaema*. Fine banded Woodpecker. 19. Kenya, Uganda, Zaire.

52
53
54
57
55
56
58
59
61
60
62
65
66
64
63
68
67
69
73
72
71
70
76
74
75

PICIDAE (4)
Woodpeckers

77. *Celeus castaneus*. Chestnut coloured Woodpecker. 22. Mexico to Panama.
78. *Celeus immaculatus*. Immaculate Woodpecker. 25. Panama. (Unique?)
79. *Celeus elegans*. Chestnut Woodpecker. 5ss. 27. Amazon & Orinoco basins.
80. incl. *C. e. jumana*. Chestnut crested Woodpecker. 27. Colombia, Venezuela, Brazil.
81. *Celeus flavescens*. Blond crested Woodpecker. 3ss. 22. Brazil to Argentina.
82. *Celeus flavus*. Cream coloured Woodpecker. 4ss. 26. Amazon, Orinoco basins.
83. *Celeus grammicus*. Scaly breasted Woodpecker. 4ss. 22. Amazonia.
84. *Celeus loricatus*. Cinnamon Woodpecker. 4ss. 22. Nicaragua to Ecuador.
85. *Celeus lugubris*. Pale crested Woodpecker. 2ss. 22. Bolivia, Ecuador, Brazil.
86. *Celeus spectabilis*. Rufous headed Woodpecker. 3ss. 27. Ecuador, Bolivia.
87. *Celeus torquatus*. Ringed Woodpecker. 3ss. 25. Amazon & Orinoco basins.
88. *Celeus undatus*. Waved Woodpecker. 3ss. 22. Venezuela, Guyanas, Brazil.
89. *Celeus brachyurus*. Rufous Woodpecker. 9ss. 25. India, China, Hainan, SE Asia, Greater Sundas.
90. *Picus awokera*. Japanese Woodpecker. 2ss. 29. Japan & Islands.
91. *Picus canus*. Grey headed Woodpecker. 11ss. 32. Eurasia, Sumatra.
92. *Picus chlorolophus*. Lesser Yellownape. 9ss. 26. India, China, SE Asia, Sumatra.
93. incl. P. c. chlorigaster. South Indian Lesser Yellownape. 25. S India.
94. *Picus erythropygius*. Black headed Woodpecker. 2ss. 31. Burma, Thailand, Vietnam, Cambodia.
95. *Picus flavinucha*. Greater Yellownape. 6ss. 34. India, China, SE Asia, Sumatra.

77
80
81
82
78
79
83
84
85
86
87
88
89
90
91
92
95
93
- 94 -

PICIDAE (5) Woodpeckers

96. *Picus mentalis*. Checker-throated Woodpecker. 3ss. 28. Malaya to Borneo, Java.
97. *Picus mineaceus*. Banded Woodpecker. 5ss. 25. Malaysia, Indonesia.
98. *Picus xanthopygaeus*. Streak throated Woodpecker. 29. India, SE Asia, China.
99. *Picus puniceus*. Crimson winged Woodpecker. 4ss. 25. Malaya, Greater Sundas.
100. *Picus rabieri*. Red collared Woodpecker. 30.Tonkin, Laos, Annam.
101. *Picus squamatus*. Scaly bellied Woodpecker. 2ss. 35. Iran to N India.
102. *Picus vaillantii*. Levaillant's Woodpecker. 30. Morocco to Tunis.
103. *Picus viridanus*. Streak breasted Woodpecker. 30. Burma, Thailand, Malaya.
104. *Picus viridis*. Green Woodpecker. 11ss. 31. Europe to Iran, Baluchistan.
105. *Picus vittatus*. Laced Woodpecker. 6ss. 30. SE Asia, Sumatra, Java, Bali.

96
97
98
99
100
101
102
103
104
105

PICIDAE (6)
Woodpeckers

106. *Dinopium benghalense.* Black rumped Flameback. 6ss. 29. India, Pakistan.
107. incl. *D. b. erithronoton.* Ceylon Red backed Woodpecker. 29. Sri Lanka.
108. *Dinopium javanense.* Common Flameback. 6ss. 30. India, China, SE Asia to Philippines, Greater Sundas.
109. *Dinopium rafflesii.* Olive backed Woodpecker. 3ss. 27. Malaya, Sumatra, Borneo.
110. *Dinopium shorii.* Himalayan Flameback. 30. India, Nepal to Burma.
111. *Gecinulus viridis.* Bamboo Woodpecker. 2ss. 27. Thailand, Burma, Malaysia.
112. *Gecinulus grantia.* Pale headed Woodpecker. 4ss. 24. Nepal, Indo-China, China, Burma, Thailand.
113. *Meiglyptes jugularis.* Black & buff Woodpecker. 19. Burma, Thailand, Indo-China.
114. *Meiglyptes tristis.* Buff rumped Woodpecker. 4ss. 18. Malaya, Greater Sundas.
115. *Meiglyptes tukki.* Buff necked Woodpecker. 7ss. 21. Malaya, Sumatra, Borneo.
116. *Mulleripicus funebris.* Sooty Woodpecker. 2ss. 35. Philippines.
117. *Mulleripicus pulverulentus.* Great Slaty Woodpecker. 2ss. 50. India, China, SE Asia, Sumatra, Java, Borneo, Palawan.
118. *Mulleripicus fulvus.* Ashy Woodpecker. 2ss. 40. Sulawesi.

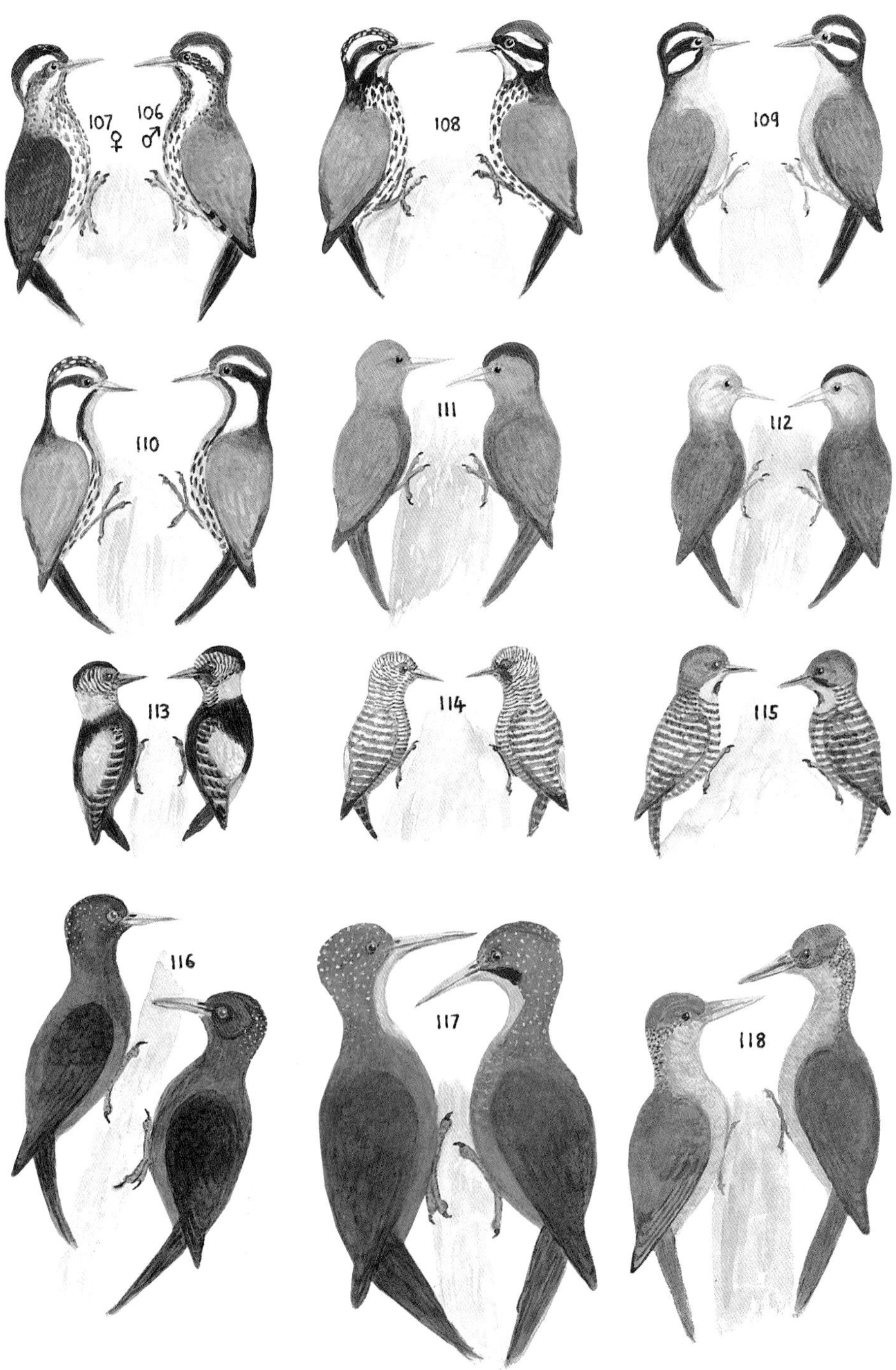
107 ♀
106 ♂
108
109
110
111
112
113
114
115
116
117
118

PICIDAE (7) Woodpeckers

119. *Dryocopus galeatus*. Helmeted Woodpecker. 30. Brazil, Paraguay, Argentina.
120. *Dryocopus javensis*. White bellied Woodpecker. 14ss. 43. India, China, Korea to SE Asia, Philippines, Java, Bali.
121. *Dryocopus hodgei*. Andaman Woodpecker. 38. Andaman Is.
122. *Dryocopus lineatus*. Lineated Woodpecker. 5ss. 30. Mexico to Argentina.
123. *Dryocopus martius*. Black Woodpecker. 2ss. 45. C Europe to China, Japan.
124. *Dryocopus pileatus*. Pileated Woodpecker. 2ss. 45. Canada, USA.
125. *Dryocopus schulzi*. Black bodied Woodpecker. 30. N Argentina.
126. *Campephilus gayaquilensis*. Guayaquil Woodpecker. 35. Ecuador, Peru.
127. *Campephilus guatemalensis*. Pale billed Woodpecker. 3ss. 34. Mexico to Panama.
128. *Campephilus haematogaster*. Crimson bellied Woodpecker. 2ss. 36. Panama to Peru.

119
120
122
121
123
124
125
126
127
128

PICIDAE (8)
Woodpeckers

129. *Campephilus leucopogon*. Cream backed Woodpecker. 32. Bolivia, Brazil, Argentina.
130. *Campephilus melanoleucos*. Crimson crested Woodpecker. 3ss. 35. Panamato Argentina.
131. *Campephilus pollens*. Powerful Woodpecker. 2ss. 35. Colombia, Ecuador, Peru.
132. *Campephilus robustus*. Robust Woodpecker. 35. Brazil, Paraguay, Argentina.
133. *Campephilus rubricollis*. Red necked Woodpecker. 3ss. 34. Amazonia.
134. *Melanerpes candidus*. White Woodpecker. 27. Brazil to Argentina.
135. *Melanerpes aurifrons*. Golden fronted Woodpecker. 9ss. 23. Texas to Nicaragua.
136. *Melanerpes hoffmanni*. Hoffmann's Woodpecker. 17. Honduras to Costa Rica.
137. *Melanerpes uropygialis*. Gila Woodpecker. 21. SW USA to Baja, California.
138. *Melanerpes carolinus*. Red bellied Woodpecker. 3ss. 23. Canada to Texas.
139. *Melanerpes chrysauchen*. Golden naped Woodpecker. 2ss. 19. Costa Rica, Panama, Colombia.
140. *Melanerpes chrysogenys*. Golden cheeked Woodpecker. 3ss. 21. Mexico.
141. *Melanerpes cruentatus*. Yellow tufted Woodpecker. 2ss. 20. Tropical South America east of Andes.
142. *Melanerpes formicivorus*. Acorn Woodpecker. 8ss. 24. American Pacific coast from Oregon to Colombia.

129
130
131
132
133
134
135
136
137
138
139
140
141
142

PICIDAE (10)
Woodpeckers

143. *Melanerpes flavifrons.* Yellow fronted Woodpecker. 2ss. 18. Brazil, Paraguay, Argentina.
144. *Melanerpes erythrocephalus.* Red headed Woodpecker. 2ss. 23. Canada, E USA.
145. *Melanerpes herminieri.* Guadeloupe Woodpecker. 27. Guadeloupe.
146. *Melanerpes hypopolius.* Grey breasted / Balsas Woodpecker.7ss. 21. Mexico.
147. *Melanerpes lewis.* Lewis' Woodpecker. 27. Western N America, winters N Mexico.
148. *Melanerpes portoricensis.* Puerto Rican Woodpecker. 25. Puerto Rico.
149. *Melanerpes pucherani.* Black cheeked Woodpecker. 2ss. 19. Mexico to Ecuador.
150. *Melanerpes radiolatus.* Jamaican Woodpecker. 27. Jamaica.
151. *Melanerpes rubricapillus.* Red crowned Woodpecker. 3ss. 17. Trinidad, Tobago, Costa Rica to Colombia, Surinam.
152. *Melanerpes pygmaeus.* Yucatan Woodpecker. 3ss. 15. Cozumel Is.
153. incl. *M. p. rubricomus.* Red vented Woodpecker. 16. Yucatan.
154. *Melanerpes rubrifrons.* Red fronted Woodpecker. 20. Venezuela, Guyanas, Brazil.

Now considered colour phase of 141.

155. *Melanerpes striatus.* Hispaniolan Woodpecker. 23. Hispaniola.
156. *Melanerpes superciliaris.* West Indian Woodpecker. 7ss. 28. Bahamas, West Indies
157. *Sphyrapicus nuchalis.* Red naped Sapsucker. 20. Western N America, Mexico.
158. *Sphyrapicus ruber.* Red breasted Sapsucker. 2ss. 20. Alaska, Oregon to California.
159. *Sphyrapicus thyroideus.* Williamson's Sapsucker. 2ss. 24. Br. Columbia, USA. winters to N Mexico.
160. *Sphyrapicus varius.* Yellow bellied Sapsucker. 20. N America. Winters Panama, West Indies.
161. *Trichopicus/Melanerpes cactorum.* White fronted Woodpecker. 17. Peru to C Argentina.

143
144
145
146
147
148
149
150
151
152
153
154
155
156
157
158
159
160
161

PICIDAE (10)
Woodpeckers

162. *Veniliornis affinis*. ed stained Woodpecker. 5ss. 17. Amazon, Orinoco.
163. *Veniliornis chocoensis*. Choco Woodpecker. 15. Colombia, Ecuador.
164. *Veniliornis callonotus*. Scarlet backed Woodpecker. 2ss. 14. Colombia - Peru.
165. *Veniliornis cassini*. Golden collared Woodpecker. 2ss. 15. Venezuela, Brazil.
166. *Veniliornis dignus*. Yellow vented Woodpecker. 4ss. 18. Venezuela to Peru.
167. *Veniolornis frontalis*. Dot-fronted Woodpecker. 17. NW Argentina.
168. *Veniolornis fumigatus*. Smoky brown Woodpecker. 7ss. 16. Mexico to Argentina.
169. *Veniolornis kirkii*. ed rumped Woodpecker. 5ss. 17. Costa Rica to Ecuador, Trinidad, Tobago.
170. *Veniolornis maculifrons*. Yellow eared Woodpecker. 16. SE Brazil.
171. *Veniolornis nigriceps*. Bar bellied Woodpecker. 3ss. 20. Colombia to Bolivia.
172. *Veniliornis passerinus*. Little Woodpecker. 11ss. 15. Venezuela & Guyanas to Brazil & Argentina.
173. *Veniolornis sanguineus*. Blood coloured Woodpecker. 14. Guyanas.
174. *Veniolornis spilogaster*. White spotted Woodpecker. 17. SE South America.
175. *Dendropicos abyssinicus*. Abyssinian Woodpecker. 15. Ethiopia.
176. *Dendropicos elachus*. Little grey Woodpecker. 11. Senegal to Sudan.
177. *Dendropicos fuscescens*. Cardinal Woodpecker. 9ss. 13. Africa S of Sahara.
178. *Dendropicos gabonensis*. Gabon Woodpecker. 3ss. 12. Cameroon to Zaire.
179. incl. D. g. lugubris. Melancholy Woodpecker. 12. Guinea to Ghana.
180. *Dendropicos poecilolaemus*. Speckle breasted Woodpecker. 15. Cameroon to Uganda, Kenya.
181. *Dendropicos stierlingi*. Stierling's Woodpecker. 16. Tanzania, Malawi, Mozambique.
182. *Picoides albolarvatus*. White headed Woodpecker. 2ss. 19. W of N America.
183. *Picoides arcticus*. Black backed Woodpecker. 20. Alaska, Canada, N USA.
184. Dendrocopos assimilis. Sind Woodpecker. 22. Iran, Pakistan.
185. *Dendrocopos atratus*. Stripe breasted Woodpecker. 2ss. 21. Burma, Thailand, Laos ,Vietnam.
186. *Dendrocopos auriceps*. Brown fronted Woodpecker. 20. Afghanistan to Nepal, India, China.

162
164
163
165
166
167
168
169
170
171
172
173
174
175
176
177
178
179
180
181
182
183
184
185
186

PICIDAE (11) Woodpeckers

187. *Picoides borealis*. Red cockaded Woodpecker. 2ss. 21. Southern USA.
188. *Dendrocopos canicapillus*. Grey capped Woodpecker. 15ss. 14. S & E Asia.
189. *Dendrocopos wattersi*. Formosan Woodpecker. 14. Taiwan.
(now considered to be Juvenile of 188.)
190. *Dendrocopos cathpharius*. Crimson breasted Woodpecker. 5ss. 18. Nepal, Laos to West China.
191. *Dendrocopos darjellensis*. Darjeeling Woodpecker. 2ss. 24. India, Nepal to SW China & N SE Asia.
192. *Dendrocopos dorae*. Arabian Woodpecker. 20. W Arabia.
193. *Dendrocopos hardwickei*. Pygmy pied Woodpecker. 14. E India.
(now considered conspecific 208.)
194. *Dendrocopos himalayensis*. Himalayan Woodpecker. 2ss. 25. Afghanistan to Nepal.
195. *Dendrocopos hyperythrus*. Rufous bellied Woodpecker. 4ss. 23. India to China, SE Asia.
196. *Dendrocopos kizuki*. (Japanese) Pygmy Woodpecker. 13ss. 15. E Asia & Islands.
197. *Dendrocopos leucopterus*. White winged Woodpecker. 16ss. 25. Central Asia.
198. *Dendrocopos leucotos*. White backed Woodpecker. 16ss. 25. Eurasia.
199. *Dendrocopos lignarius*. Striped Woodpecker. 16. Bolivia, Chile, Argentina.
200. *Dendrocopos macei*. Fulvous breasted Woodpecker. 6ss. 19. India, Sri Lanka, Burma.
201. *Dendrocopos maculatus*. Philippine Woodpecker. 8ss. 14. Philippines, Sulu.
202. *Dendrocopos mahrattensis*. Yellow crowned Woodpecker. 5ss. 19. India, Burma, Sri Lanka.
203. *Dendrocopos major*. Great spotted Woodpecker. 14ss. 22. Palearctic & Oriental regions.
204. *Dendrocopos medius*. Middle spotted Woodpecker. 7ss. 21. C Europe to Iran.
205. *Dendrocopos minor*. Lesser spotted Woodpecker. 10ss. 14. Europe to NE Asia.
206. *Picoides mixtus*. Checkered woodpecker. 4ss. 16. SE South America.
207. *Dendrocopos moluccensis*. Sunda Woodpecker. 2ss. 13. Malaya, Sunda Is.
208. *Dendropicos nanus*. Brown capped Woodpecker. 3ss. 13. Indian sub-continent.

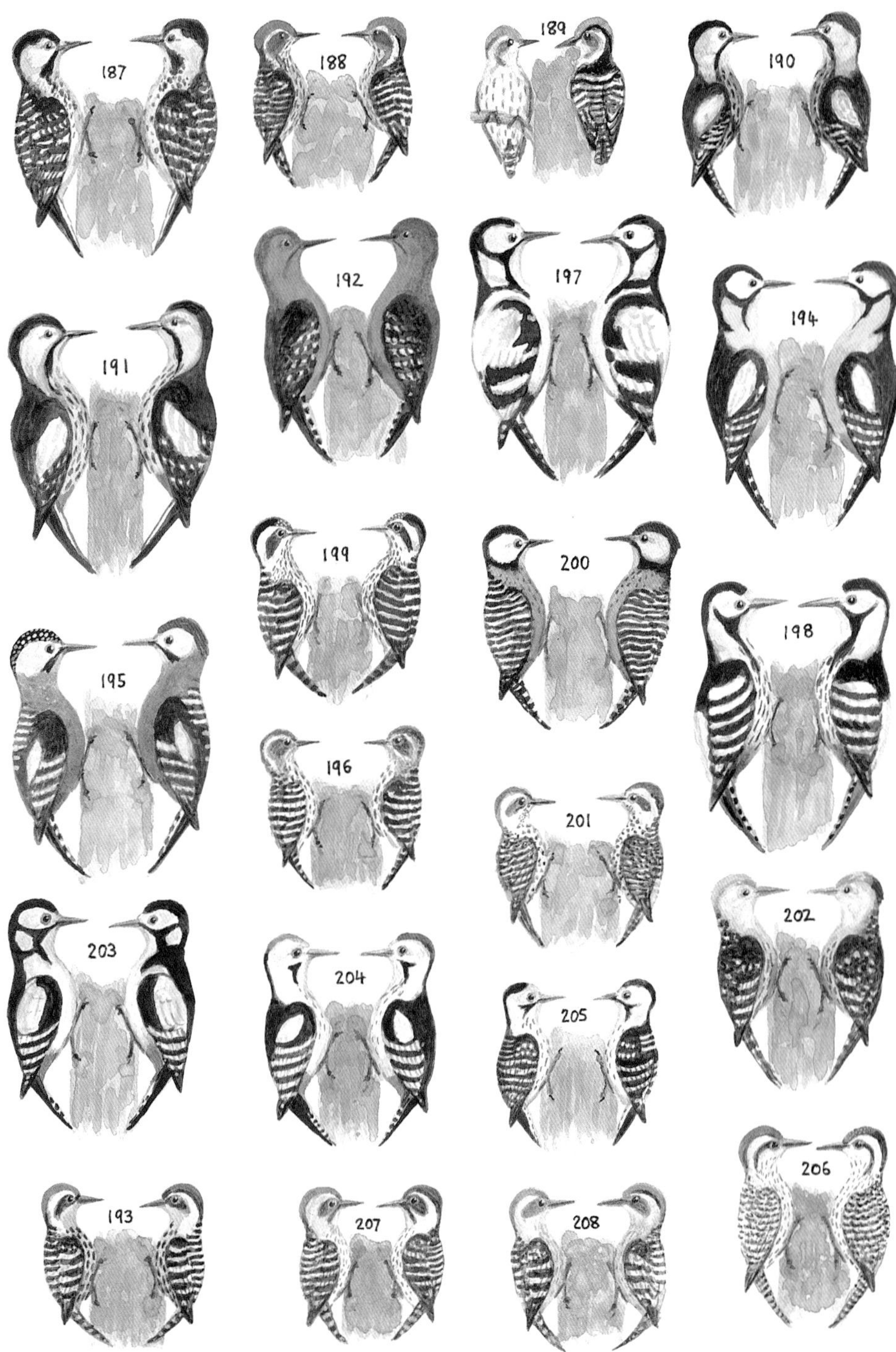
187
188
189
190
192
197
194
191
199
200
198
195
196
201
202
203
204
205
206
193
207
208

PICIDAE (12)
Woodpeckers

209. *Picoides nuttallii.* Nuttall's Woodpecker. 17. California, Baja.
210. *Dendropicos obsoletus.* Brown backed Woodpecker. 5ss. 13. E, C & W Africa.
211. *Picoides pubescens.* Downy Woodpecker. 8ss. 14. North America.
212. *Picoides scalaris.* Ladder backed Woodpecker. 14ss. 17. SE USA to Belize.
213. *Picoides stricklandi* . Strickland's / Brown barred Woodpecker. 4ss. 18. Mexico.
214. incl. *P. s. arizonae.* Arizona Woodpecker. 19.Mexico, New Mexico, Arizona.
215. *Dendrocopus syriacus.* Syrian Woodpecker. 4ss. 22. Balkans, Levant to Iran.
216. *Dendrocopus temmincki.* Sulawesi (Pygmy) Woodpecker. 11. Sulawesi & adjacent Islands.
217. *Picoides tridactylus.* Three toed Woodpecker. 11ss. 23. Eurasia, N America.
218. *Picoides villosus.* Hairy Woodpecker. 21ss. 22. North & Central America.
219. *Sapheopipo noguchii.* Okinawa Woodpecker. 25. Okinawa.
220. *Xiphidiopicus percussus.* Cuban (Green) Woodpecker. 2ss. 23. Cuba, Isle of Pines.
221. *Dendropicos elliotii.* Elliot's Woodpecker. 6ss. 18. Cameroon to Uganda.
222. *Dendropicos goertae.* Grey Woodpecker. 4ss. 20. Equatorial Africa.
222a. *Dendropicos spodocephalus.* Grey headed Woodpecker. 20. E Africa.
223. *Dendropicos griseocephalus.* Olive Woodpecker. 4ss. 19. Tanzania to Cape.
224. *Dendropicos pyrrhogaster.* Fire bellied Woodpecker. 22. West Africa.
225. *Dendropicos xantholophus.* Golden crowned Woodpecker. 21. Cameroon to Uganda, Angola.
226. *Dendropicos namaquus.* Bearded Woodpecker. 5ss. 23. E, C & S Africa.
227. *Hemicircus canente.* Heart-spotted Woodpecker. 2ss. 15. India, Burma, Thailand.
228. *Hemicircus concretus.* Grey & buff Woodpecker. 3ss. 12. Malaysia, Indonesia.

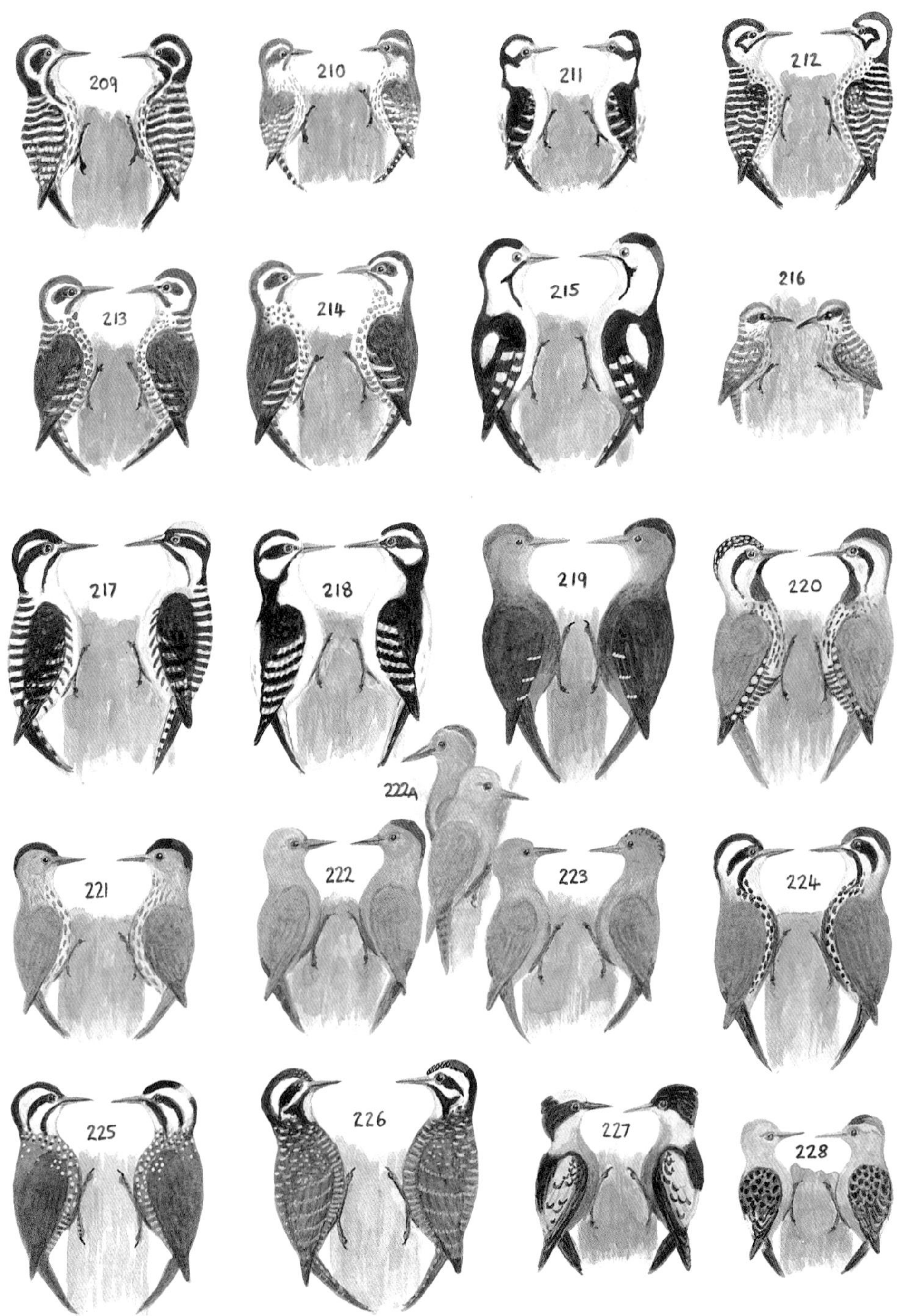
209
210
211
212
213
214
215
216
217
218
219
220
222A
221
222
223
224
225
226
227
228

PICIDAE (13)
Woodpeckers

229. *Blythipicus pyrrhotis.* Bay Woodpecker. 5ss. 30. Himalayas, China, Hainan, SE Asia.
230. *Blythipicus rubiginosus.* Maroon Woodpecker. 2ss. 23. Malaya, Sumatra, Borneo.
231. *Chrysocolaptes festivus.* White naped Woodpecker. 2ss. 29. India, Sri Lanka.
232. *Chrysocolaptes lucidus.* Greater Flameback. 14ss. 33. Indian sub-continent, China, SE Asia, Gr. Sundas, Philippines.
233. *Reinwardtipicus validus.* Orange backed Woodpecker. 2ss. 30. Malaysia, Sumatra, Borneo, Java.
234. *Campephilus imperialis.* Imperial Woodpecker. 51. Mexico. Last seen 1957.
235. *Campephilus magellanicus.* Megellanic Woodpecker. 39. Chile, Argentina.
236. *Campephilus principalis.* Ivory billed Woodpecker. 2ss. 47. Possibly still survives in Cuba. Formerly USA.

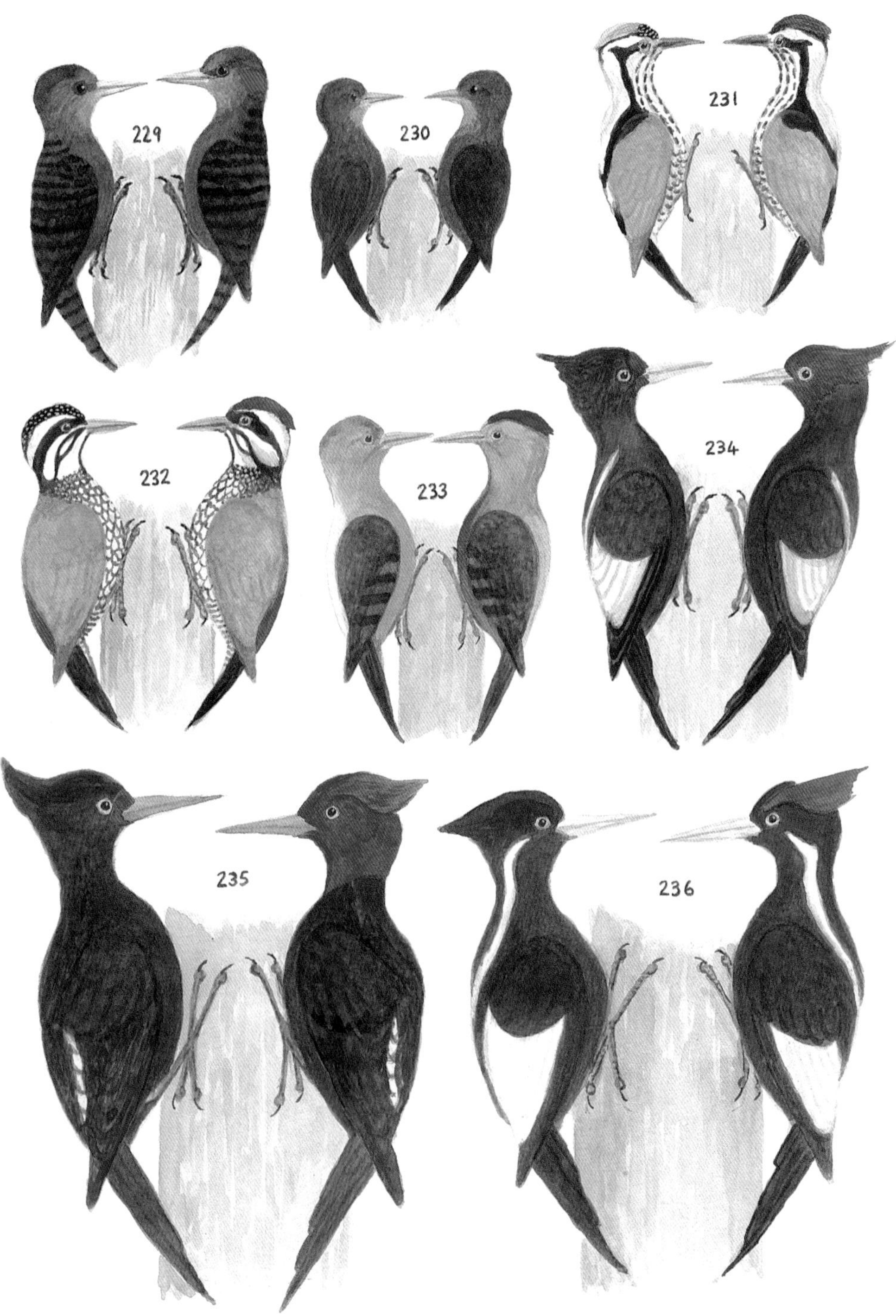
229
230
231
232
233
234
235
236

EURYLAIMIDAE (0)
Broadbills

Family 101. EURYLAIMIDAE. Broadbills.

1. *Smithornis capensis*. African Broadbill. 7ss. 13. Liberia to Kenya, Angola & Natal.
2. *Smithornis rufolateralis*. Rufous sided Broadbill. 2ss. 11. Liberia to Uganda, Zaire, Cameroon.
3. *Smithornis sharpei*. Grey headed Broadbill. 3ss. 15. Cameroon, Zaire, Fernando Po.
4. *Pseudocalyptomena graueri*. Green / Grauer's Broadbill. 12. Zaire, Uganda.
5. *Corydon sumatranus*. Dusky Broadbill. 7ss. 27. SE Asia, Sumatra, Borneo.
6. *Cymbirhynchus macrorhynchos*. Black & red Broadbill. 6ss. 25. SE Asia, Sumatra, Borneo.
7. *Eurylaimus javanicus*. Banded Broadbill. 5ss. 22. SE Asia, Greater Sundas.
8. *Eurylaimus ochromalus*. Black & Yellow Broadbill. 3ss. 16. SE Asia, Borneo, Sumatra.
9. *Eurylaimus steerii*. Wattled Broadbill. 3ss. 20. S Philippines.
10. *Serilophus lunatus*. Silver breasted Broadbill. 10ss. 17. SE Asia, Sumatra.
11. incl. *S. l. rubropygius*. Collared / Hodgson's Broadbill. 17. Himalayas, Yunnan, Hainan, SE Asia.
12. *Psarisomus dalhousiae*. Long tailed Broadbill. 5ss. 27. Himalayas, SE Asia, Borneo, Sumatra.
13. *Calyptomena hosii*. Hose's / Magnificent green Broadbill. 20. North Borneo.
14. *Calyptomena viridis*. (Lesser) Green Broadbill. 3ss. 18. Malaya, Sumatra, Borneo & Is.
15. *Calyptomena whiteheadi*. Whitehead's / Black throated Broadbill. 26. Borneo.

Family 102. DENDROCOLAPTIDAE (1). Woodcreepers.

1. *Dendrocincla anabatina*. Tawny winged Woodcreeper. 2ss. 17. Mexico to Costa Rica.
2. *Dendrocincla fuliginosa*. Plain brown Woodcreeper. 13ss. 20. Honduras to Amazonia, Trinidad, Tobago.
3. *Dendrocincla homochroa*. Ruddy Woodcreeper. 4ss. 19. Mexico to Venezuela.
4. *Dendrocincla merula*. White chinned Woodcreeper. 7ss. 18. Guyanas, Amazonia.
5. *Dendrocincla tyrannina*. Tyrannine Woodcreeper. 25. Venezuela to Peru.
6. *Dendrocincla macrorhyncha*. Large Tyrannine Woodcreeper. 27. E Ecuador.
7. *Dendrocincla turdina*. Thrushlike Woodcreeper. 20. Brazil, Paraguay, Argentina.
8. *Deconychura longicauda*. Long tailed Woodcreeper. 7ss. 21. Panama to Amazonia.

EURYLAIMIDAE
1
2
3
4
5
6
7
8
9
10
11
12
13
14
15
DENDROCOLAPTIDAE
1
2
3
4
5
8
7
6

DENDROCOLAPTIDAE (2) Woodcreepers

9. *Deconychura stictolaema*. Spot throated Woodcreeper. 3ss. 19. Amazon basin.
10. *Sittasomus griseicapillus*. Olivaceous Woodcreeper. 19ss. 16. Mexico to Argentina, Tobago.
11. *Glyphorhynchus spirurus*. Wedge billed Woodcreeper. 14ss. 14. Mexico to Amazon basin.
12. *Drymornis bridgesii*. Scimitar billed Woodcreeper. 30. Paraguay, Uruguay, Argentina.
13. *Nasica longirostris*. Long billed Woodcreeper. 35. Amazon, Orinoco basins.
14. *Dendexetastes rufigula*. Cinnamon throated Woodcreeper. 4ss. 24. Amazonia.
15. *Hylexetastes perrotii*. Red billed Woodcreeper. 2ss. 30. Guyanas to Brazil.
15a. incl. *H. p. uniformis*. Uniform Woodcreeper. 27. C Brazil.
15b. *Hylexetastes brigidai*. Brigida's Woodcreeper. 28. E Brazil.
16. *Hylexetastes stresemanni*. Bar bellied Woodcreeper. 27. Brazil, Peru.
17. *Xiphocolaptes albicollis*. White throated Woodcreeper. 2ss. 29. SW S America.
18. *Xiphocolaptes villanovae*. Vila nova Woodcreeper. 27. E Brazil.
19. *Xiphocolaptes falcirostris*. Moustached Woodcreeper. 27. E Brazil.
20. *Xiphocolaptes franciscanus*. Snethlage's Woodcreeper. 27. Brazil.(local)
21. *Xiphocolaptes major*. Great rufous Woodcreeper. 3ss. 32. Brazil, Bolivia, Paraguay, Argentina.
22. *Xiphocolaptes promeropirhynchus*. Strong billed Woodcreeper. 23ss. 29. Mexico to Brazil, Bolivia, Peru.
23. *Dendrocolaptes certhia*. Barred Woodcreeper. 13ss. 27. Mexico to Bolivia.
24. *Dendrocolaptes concolor*. Concolor Woodcreeper. 27. N Brazil. (Race of 23?)
25. *Dendrocolaptes hoffmanni*. Hoffmann's Woodcreeper. 28. Brazil.
26. *Dendrocolaptes picumnus*. Black banded Woodcreeper. 12ss. 26. Guatemala to Argentina.
27. *Dendrocolaptes platyrostris*. Planalto Woodcreeper. 2ss. 25. Brazil to Paraguay, Argentina.
28. *Xiphorhynchus elegans*. Elegant Woodcreeper. 2ss. 21. Colombia, Ecuador, Peru, Brazil.
29. *Xiphorhynchus erythropygius*. Spotted Woodcreeper. 5ss. 22. Mexico to Ecuador.
30. *Xiphorhynchus eytoni*. Dusky billed Woodcreeper. 27. Brazil.
31. *Xiphorhynchus flavigaster*. Ivory billed Woodcreeper. 8ss. 23. Mexico to Costa Rica.

9
10
11
12
13
14
15A
15
16
17
18
15B
19
22
23
24
21
20
29
28
30
25
26
27
31

DENDROCOLAPTIDAE (3) Woodcreepers

32. *Xiphorhynchus guttatus*. Buff throated Woodcreeper. 15ss. 21. Guatemala to Bolivia, Brazil.
33. *Xiphorhynchus lachrymosus*. Black striped Woodcreeper. 2ss. 23. Nicaragua to Colombia, Ecuador.
34. *Xiphorhynchus necopinus*. Zimmer's Woodcreeper. 21. Brazil.
35. *Xiphorhynchus obsoletus*. Striped Woodcreeper. 4ss. 19. Amazon, Orinoco basins.
36. *Xiphorhynchus ocellatus*. Ocellated Woodcreeper. 6ss. 21. Amazon basin.
37. *Xiphorhynchus pardalotus*. Chestnut rumped Woodcreeper. 2ss.21. Venezuela, Guyanas, Brazil.
38. *Xiphorhynchus picus*. Straight billed Woodcreeper. 17ss. 22. Panama to Brazil.
39. *Xiphorhynchus spixii*. Spix's Woodcreeper. 4ss. 21. Upper Amazon basin.
40. *Xiphorhynchus striatigularis*. Stripe throated Woodcreeper. 23. Mexico. (Unique.)
41. *Xiphorhynchus triangularis*. Olive backed Woodcreeper. 4ss. 22. Venezuela to Bolivia.
42. *Lepidocolaptes affinis*. Spot crowned Woodcreeper. 12ss. 19. Mexico to Bolivia.
43. *Lepidocolaptes albolineatus*. Lineated Woodcreeper. 5ss. 19. Amazonia.
44. *Lepidocolaptes angustirostris*. Narrow billed Woodcreeper. 9ss. 21. Brazil to Bolivia, Argentina.
45. *Lepidocolaptes fuscus*. Lesser Woodcreeper. 4ss. 18. Brazil, Paraguay, Argentina.
46. *Lepidocolaptes leucogaster*. White striped Woodcreeper. 2ss. 22. Mexico.
47. *Lepidocolaptes souleyettii*. Streak headed Woodcreeper. 8ss. 19. Mexico to Amazon basin.
48. *Lepidocolaptes squamatus*. Scaled Woodcreeper. 3ss. 20. SW South America.
49. *Campyloramphus falcularius*. Black billed Scythebill. 27. SW South America.
50. *Campyloramphus procurvoides*. Curve billed Scythebill. 4ss. 22. Amazonia.
51. *Campyloramphus pucherani*. Greater Scythebill. 29. Colombia, Ecuador, Peru.
52. *Campyloramphus pusillus*. Brown billed Scythebill. 4ss. 23. Costa Rica to Colombia.
53. *Campyloramphus trochilirostris*. Red billed Scythebill. 13ss. 20. Panama to Argentina.

32
33
34
35
36
37
38
39
40
41
42
43
44
45
46
47
48
49
50
51
52
53

FURNARIIDAE (1)
Ovenbirds

Family 103. FURNARIIDAE. Ovenbirds.

1. *Geobates poeciloptera*. Campo Miner. 11. C Brazil.
2. *Geositta antarctica*. Short billed Miner. 15. Chile, Argentina, Islands.
3. *Geositta crassirostris*. Thick billed Miner. 16. W Peru.
4. *Geositta cunicularia*. Common Miner. 8ss. 16. Peru, Brazil to Tierra del Fuego.
5. *Geositta isabellina*. Creamy rumped Miner. 17. C Chile, W Argentina.
6. *Geositta maritima*. Greyish Miner. 13. Peru, N Chile.
7. *Geositta peruviana*. Coastal Miner. 13. Peru coast.
8. *Geositta punensis*. Puna Miner. 15. Peru to N Argentina & Chile.
9. *Geositta rufipennis*. Rufous banded Miner. 4ss. 17. Bolivia, Chile, Argentina.
10. *Geositta saxicolina*. Dark winged Miner. 16. Peru.
11. *Geositta tenuirostris*. Slender billed Miner. 18. Ecuador, Peru to Argentina.
12. *Upucerthia andaecola*. Rock Earthcreeper. 18. Argentina, Bolivia, Chile.
13. *Upucerthia certhioides*. Chaco Earthcreeper. 4ss. 17. Paraguay, Argentina.
14. *Upucerthia dumetaria*. Scale throated Earthcreeper. 22. Peru to Tierra del Fuego.
15. incl. *U. d. saturatior*. Chilean Earthcreeper. 22. C Chile.
16. *Upucerthia harterti*. Bolivian Earthcreeper. 16. Bolivia.
17. *Upucerthia jelskii*. Plain breasted Earthcreeper. 18. Bolivia, Peru, Chile.
18. *Upucerthia ruficauda*. Straight billed Earthcreeper. 2ss. 18. Peru, Bolivia to Chile, Argentina.
19. *Upucerthia serrana*. Striated Earthcreeper. 2ss. 20. Peru.
20. *Upucerthia validirostris*. Buff breasted Earthcreeper. 3ss. 21. Argentina.
21. *Upucerthia albigula*. White throated Earthcreeper. 20. Peru, Chile.
22. *Eremobius phoenicurus*. Band tailed Earthcreeper. 17. SW Argentina.
23. *Chilia melanura*. Crag Chilia. 2ss. 20. N & C Chile.
24. *Cinclodes antarcticus*. Blackish Cinclodes . 2ss. 18. Cape Horn, Falkland Is.
25. *Cinclodes olrogi*. Olrog's Cinclodes . 16. N Argentina.
26. *Cinclodes atacamensis*. White winged Cinclodes . 2ss. 19. Peru, Chile, Argentina.
27. *Cinclodes excelsior*. Stout billed Cinclodes. 3ss. 21. Colombia, Ecuador.
28. *Cinclodes fuscus*. Bar winged Cinclodes . 8ss. 18. Venezuela to Argentina.
29. *Cinclodes comechingonus*. Cordoba /Chestnut winged Cinclodes . 16. Argentina.
30. *Cinclodes nigrofumosus*. Seaside Cinclodes. 22. N Chile & Islands.
31. *Cinclodes taczanowskii*. Surf Cinclodes. 22. Peru.
32. *Cinclodes oustaleti*. Grey flanked Cinclodes . 3ss. 17. Chile & Islands.
33. *Cinclodes pabsti*. Long tailed Cinclodes. 21. SE Brazil.
34. *Cinclodes palliatus*. White bellied Cinclodes. 20. Peru.
35. *Cinclodes patagonicus*. Dark bellied Cinclodes. 2ss. 20. Chile, Argentina.
36. Clibanornis dendrocolaptoides. Canebreak Groundcreeper. 20. SE Brazil, Paraguay, Argentina.

1
2
3
4
5
6
7
8
9
10
11
12
13
14
15
16
17
18
19
20
21
22
23
24
25
26
27
28
29
30
31
32
33
34
35
36

FURNARIIDAE (2)
Ovenbirds

37. *Furnarius cristatus*. Crested Hornero . 5. Paraguay, Bolivia, Argentina.
38. *Furnarius figulus*. White / Wing banded Hornero. 2ss. 20. Brazil.
39. *Furnarius leucopus*. Pale legged Hornero . 6ss. 16. Guyana to Brazil, Ecuador.
40. *Furnarius minor*. Lesser Hornero . 5. Colombia, Peru, Brazil.
41. *Furnarius rufus*. Rufous Hornero . 5ss. 19. Brazil, Bolivia to Argentina.
42. *Furnarius torridus*. Pale billed / Bay Hornero . 16. Peru, Brazil.
43. *Limnornis curvirostris*. Curve billed Reedhaunter . 17. Brazil, Uruguay, Argentina.
44. *Sylviorthorhynchus desmursii*. Des Murs' Wiretail. 24. Chile, Argentina.
45. *Aphrastura masafuerae*. Mas Afuera Rayadito . 12. Juan Fernandez Is. (extinct.)
46. *Aphrastura spinicauda*. Thorn tailed Rayadito . 10. Chile, Argentina & Islands.
47. *Leptasthenura aegithaloides*. Plain mantled Tit Spinetail . 15. SW S America.
48. *Leptasthenura andicola*. Andean Tit Spinetail . 5ss. 16. Venezuela to Bolivia.
49. *Leptasthenura fuliginiceps*. Brown capped Tit Spinetail . 2ss. 15. Bolivia, Argentina.
50. *Leptasthenura pileata*. Rusty crowned Tit Spinetail . 4ss. 16. Peru,
51. *Leptasthenura platensis*. Tufted Tit Spinetail . 15. S Brazil, Uruguay.
52. *Leptasthenura setaria*. Araucaria Tit Spinetail . 17. SE Brazil, NE Argentina.
53. *Leptasthenura striata*. Streaked Tit Spinetail . 3ss. 16. Peru, N Chile.
54. *Leptasthenura striolata*. Striolated Tit Spinetail . 15. SE Brazil.
55. *Leptasthenura xenothorax*. White browed Tit Spinetail . 16. Peru.
56. *Leptasthenura yanacensis*. Tawny Tit Spinetail . 16. Peru, Bolivia.
57. *Phleocryptes melanops*. Wren-like Rushbird . 5ss. 14. Peru, Brazil to Argentina.
58. *Spartonoica maluroides*. Bay capped Wren Spinetail . 13. Brazil, Uruguay, Argentina.
59. *Schizoeaca coryi*. Ochre browed Thistletail . 17. Venezuela.
60. *Schizoeaca fuliginosa*. While chinned Thistletail . 11ss. 18. Venezuela to Peru.
61. *Schizoeaca perijana*. Perija Thistletail. 21. Colombia, Venezuela.
62. *Schizoeaca griseomurina*. Mouse coloured Thistletail . 18. Ecuador, Peru.
63. *Schizoeaca vilcabambae*. Vilcabamba Thistletail . 18. Peru.
64. *Schizoeaca harterti*. Black throated Thistletail . 17. Bolivia.
65. *Schizoeaca helleri*. Puna Thistletail . 7. SE Peru.
66. *Schizoeaca palpebralis*. Eye ringed Thistletail . 18. C Peru.
67. *Schoeniophylax phryganophila*. Chotoy Spinetail. 2ss. 23. S South America.
68. *Oreophylax/Schizoeaca moreirae*. Itatiata Spinetail. 18. Brazil.
69. *Synallaxis albescens*. Pale breasted Spinetail . 17. Costa Rica to Argentina.
70. *Synallaxis albigularis*. Dark breasted Spinetail . 16. W Amazonia.
71. *Synallaxis azarae*. Azara's Spinetail . 7ss. 17. Venezuela to NW Argentina.
72. *Synallaxis brachyura*. Slaty Spinetail . 5ss. 16. Honduras to Peru.
73. *Synallaxis cabanisi*. Cabinis' Spinetail . 4ss. 16. Peru to Bolivia.
74. *Synallaxis cherriei*. Chestnut throated Spinetail . 2ss. 13. Brazil, Peru, Ecuador.
75. *Synallaxis cinerascens*. Grey bellied Spinetail . 13. Brazil, Paraguay, Uruguay, Argentina.
76. *Synallaxis cinnamomea*. Stripe breasted Spinetail . 7ss. 16. Trinidad, Tobago, Venezuela, Colombia.
77. *Synallaxis courseni*. Apurimac Spinetail . 19. Peru.

37
38
39
40
41
42
43
44
45
46
47
48
49
50
51
52
53
54
55
56
57
58
59
60
61
64
62
63
65
66
67
68
69
70
71
72
73
74
75
76
77

FURNARIIDAE (3)
Ovenbirds

78. *Synallaxis erythrothorax*. Rufous breasted Spinetail . 3ss. 13. C America.
79. *Synallaxis frontalis*. Sooty fronted Spinetail . 2ss. 15. SE, SC S America.
80. *Synallaxis fuscorufa*. Rusty headed Spinetail . 17. Colombia.
81. *Synallaxis gujanensis*. Plain crowned Spinetail . 7ss. 16. Amazon, Orinoco.
82. *Synallaxis maranonica*. Maranon Spinetail . 16. N Peru.
83. *Synallaxis albilora*. White lored / Ochre breasted Spinetail . 15. Brazil, Paraguay.
84. *Synallaxis gularis*. White browed Spinetail . 4ss. 14. Venezuela to Peru.
85. *Synallaxis hypospodia*. Cinnereous breasted Spinetail . 15. Peru, Brazil, Bolivia.
86. *Synallaxis moesta*. Dusky Spinetail . 3ss. 16. Colombia to Peru.
87. *Synallaxis poliophrys*. Grey browed Spinetail . 14. French Guyana. (ss.86?)
88. *Synallaxis propinqua*. White bellied Spinetail. Amazonia. French Guyana.
89. *Synallaxis ruficapilla*. Rufous capped Spinetail . 15. Brazil, Paraguay, Argentina.
90. *Synallaxis rutilans*. Ruddy Spinetail . 7ss. 14. Amazon, Orinoco, Guyanas.
91. *Synallaxis spixi*. Chicli Spinetail . 15. Brazil, Paraguay, Uruguay, Argentina.
92. *Synallaxis stictothorax*. Necklaced Spinetail. 3ss. 12. Ecuador, Peru.
93. *Synallaxis subpudica*. Silvery throated Spinetail . 17. Colombia.
94. *Synallaxis superciliosa*. Buff browed Spinetail . 2ss. 17. Bolivia, Argentina.
95. *Synallaxis tithys*. Black faced Spinetail . 15. Ecuador, Peru.
96. *Synallaxis unirufa*. Rufous Spinetail . 4ss. 17. N & W South America.
97. *Synallaxis zimmeri*. Russet bellied Spinetail . 16. Peru.
98. *Synallaxis castanea*. Black throated Spinetail . 17. Venezuela.
99. *Synallaxis infuscata*. Pinto's / Plain Spinetail . 15. E Brazil.
100. *Synallaxis macconnelli*. MacConnell's Spinetail . 14. Venezuela & adjacent areas.
101. *Synallaxis hellmayri*. Red shouldered Spinetail . 16. NE Brazil.
102. *Certhiaxis cinnamomea*. Yellow chinned Spinetail . 8ss. 15. Most S America.
103. *Certhiaxis mustelina*. Red & White Spinetail . 13. Peru, Amazonia.
104. *Limnoctites / Limnornis rectirostris*. Straight billed Reedhaunter . 17. Brazil, Uruguay, Argentina.
105. *Synallaxis candei*. White whiskered Spinetail . 3ss. 15. Colombia, Venezuela.
106. *Synallaxis kollari*. Hoary throated Spinetail . 15. N Brazil.
107. *Synallaxis scutata*. Ochre cheeked Spinetail . 2ss. 15. Bolivia, Argentina.
108. *Cranioleuca albicapilla*. Creamy crested Spinetail . 2ss. 17. Peru.
109. *Cranioleuca albiceps*. Light crowned Spinetail . 2ss. 15. Peru, Bolivia.
110. *Cranioleuca antisiensis*. Line cheeked Spinetail . 3ss. 15. Ecuador, Peru.
111. *Cranioleuca baroni*. Baron's Spinetail. 20. NC Peru.
112. *Cranioleuca/Synallaxis elegantior*. Elegant Spinetail . 19. Colombia, Venezuela.
113. *Cranioleuca curtata*. Ash browed Spinetail . 3ss. 14. Colombia to Peru.
114. *Cranioleuca furcata*. Fork tailed Spinetail . 17. Peru. (immature 113.?)
115. *Cranioleuca demissa*. Tepui Spinetail . 15. Venezuela, Guyana, Brazil.
116. *Cranioleuca erythrops*. Red faced Spinetail . 3ss. 14. Costa Rica to Ecuador.
117. *Cranioleuca gutturata*. Speckled Spinetail . 3ss. 13. Guyanas, Amazonia.
118. *Cranioleuca hellmayri*. Streak capped Spinetail . 14. Colombia.
119. *Cranioleuca marcapatae*. Marcapata Spinetail . 16. Peru.
120. *Cranioleuca muelleri*. Scaled Spinetail . 15. N Brazil.
121. *Cranioleuca obsoleta*. Olive Spinetail . 13. Brazil, Paraguay, Argentina.
122. *Cranioleuca pallida*. Pallid Spinetail . 13. SE Brazil.

122a. *Cranioleuca henricae*. Bolivian Spinetail . 15. Bolivia (Inquisivi).

78
79
80
81
82
83
84
85
86
87
88
89
90
91
92
93
94
95
96
97
98
99
100
101
102
103
104
105
106
107
108
109
110
111
112
113
114
115
116
117
122A
118
119
120
121
122

FURNARIIDAE (4)
Ovenbirds

123. *Cranioleuca pyrrhophia*. Stripe crowned Spinetail. 3ss. 14. S South America.
124. *Cranioleuca semicineria*. Grey headed Spinetail. 2ss. 14. SE Brazil.
125. *Cranioleuca subcristata*. Crested Spinetail. 2ss. 15. Colombia, Venezuela.
126. *Cranioleuca sulphurifera*. Sulphur bearded Spinetail. 15. SE South America.
127. *Cranioleuca vulpina*. Rusty Backed Spinetail. 6ss. 15. Amazon & Orinoco.
127a. *Cranioleuca dissita*. Coiba Spinetail. 15. Coiba I.(Panama.).
128. *Siptornopsis hypochondriacus*. Great Spinetail. 19. N Peru.
129. *Asthenes anthoides*. Austral Canastero. 16. Chile to Tierra del Fuego.
130. *Asthenes baeri*. Short billed Canastero. 2ss. 15. Brazil to Argentina.
131. *Asthenes berlepschi*. Berlepsch's Canastero. 17. Bolivia.
132. *Asthenes cactorum*. Cactus Canastero. 14. Peru.
133. *Asthenes dorbignyi*. Creamy breasted Canastero. 5ss. 16. Peru to Chile, Argentina.
134. *Asthenes flammulata*. Many striped Canastero. 5ss. 16. Colombia to Peru.
135. *Asthenes hudsoni*. Hudson's Canastero. 16. Uruguay, Argentina.
136. *Asthenes humicola*. Dusky tailed Canastero. 2ss. 16. Chile, Argentina.
137. *Asthenes humilis*. Streak throated Canastero. 3ss. 16. Peru, Bolivia.
138. *Asthenes maculicauda*. Scribble tailed Canastero. 17. Peru, Bolivia, Argentina.
139. *Asthenes modesta*. Cordilleran Canastero. 7ss. 15. Peru to Chile, Argentina.
139a. *Asthenes luizae*. Cipo Canastero. 15. SE Brazil.
140. *Asthenes ottonis*. Rusty fronted Canastero. 16. SE Peru.
141. *Asthenes patagonica*. Patagonian Canastero. 15. Argentinean Patagonia.
142. *Asthenes pudibunda*. Canyon Canastero. 2ss. 16. Peru.
143. *Asthenes heterura*. Iquico Canastero. 15. Bolivia.
144. *Asthenes pyrrholeuca*. Lesser Canastero. 4ss. 15. Argentina, Chile. Winters N to Paraguay, Uruguay, Bolivia.
145. *Asthenes sclateri*. Cordoba Canastero. 16. N Argentina.
146. *Asthenes steinbachi*. Chestnut Canastero. 16. W Argentina.
147. *Asthenes urubambensis*. Line fronted Canastero. 2ss. 19. Peru, Bolivia.
148. *Asthenes virgata*. Junin Canastero. 17. SC Peru.
149. *Asthenes wyatti*. Streak backed Canastero. 9ss. 15. Venezuela to Peru.
150. *Asthenes punensis*. Puna Canastero. 17. Peru, Bolivia, Argentina.
151. *Thripophaga berlepschi*. Russet mantled Softtail. 17. Peru.
152. *Thripophaga cherriei*. Orinoco Softtail. 16 Venezuela.
153. *Thripophaga fusciceps*. Plain Softtail. 3ss. 17. Brazil, Bolivia, Peru, Ecuador.
154. *Thripophaga macroura*. Striated Softtail. 17. E Brazil
155. *Thripophaga/Asthenes usheri*. White tailed Canastero. 17. SW Peru.
156. *Phacellodomus dorsalis*. Chestnut backed Thornbird. 20. N Peru.
157. *Phacellodomus erythrophthalmus*. Red eyed Thornbird. 2ss. 18. E Brazil.
158. *Phacellodomus ruber*. Greater Thornbird. 20. Brazil, Bolivia, Paraguay, Argentina.
159. *Phacellodomus rufifrons*. Common/Rufous fronted Thornbird. 6ss. 16. Most of South America.
160. *Phacellodomus sibilatrix*. Little Thornbird. 12. Paraguay, Uruguay, Argentina.
161. *Phacellodomus striaticeps*. Streak fronted Thornbird. 2ss. 16. Peru to Argentina.
162. *Phacellodomus striaticollis*. Freckle breasted Thornbird. 2ss. 17. Brazil, Bolivia, Uruguay, Paraguay, Argentina.

123
124
125
126
127
128
129
130
131
132
127 A
133
134
135
136
137
139 A
138
139
140
141
142
143
144
145
146
147
148
149
150
151
152
153
154
155
156
157
158
159
160
161
162

FURNARIIDAE (5)
Ovenbirds

163. *Coryphistera alaudina*. Larklike Brushrunner. 2ss. 15. Bolivia to N Argentina.
164. *Septornis striaticollis*. Spectacled Prickletail. 11. Colombia to Peru.
165. *Xenerpestes minlosi*. Double banded Graytail. 2ss. 11. Panama, Colombia.
166. *Xenerpestes singularis*. Equatoria1 Graytail. 13. Ecuador.
167. *Metopothrix aurantiacus*. Orange fronted Plushcrown. 1l. Amazon basin.
168. *Roraima adusta*. Roraiman Barbtail. 3ss. 15. Venezuela, Guyana, Brazil.
169. *Margarornis bellulus*. Beautiful Treerunner. 15. Panama. (Darien).
170. *Margarornis rubiginosus*. Ruddy Treerunner. 2ss. 15. Costa Rica, Panama.
171. *Margarornis squamiger*. Pearled Treerunner. 3ss. 16. Venezuela to Bolivia.
172. *Margarornis stellatus*. Fulvous Treerunner. 15. Colombia, Ecuador.
173. *Anumbius annumbi*. Firewood gatherer. 21. Brazil, Paraguay, Uruguay, Argentina.
174. *Premnornis guttuligera*. Rusty winged Barbtail. 2ss. 15. Venezuela to Peru.
175. *Premnoplex brunnescens*. Spotted Barbtail. 8ss. 15. Costa Rica to Ecuador.
176. *Premnoplex tatei*. White throated Barbtail. 2ss. 15. Venezuela.
177. *Pseudocolaptes boissonneautii*. Streaked Tuftedcheek. 10ss. 20. Venezuela to Bolivia.
178. *Pseudocolaptes lawrencii*. Buffy Tuftedcheek. 3ss. 20. Costa Rica to Ecuador.
179. *Berlepschia rikeri*. Point tailed Palmcreeper. 20. Venezuela to Brazil.
180. *Pseudoseisura cristata*. Rufous Cacholote. 2ss. 22. Brazil, Bolivia, Paraguay.
181. *Pseudoseisura gutturalis*. White throated Cacholote. 25. Argentina.
182. *Pseudoseisura lophotes*. Brown Cacholote. Brazil, Bolivia to Argentina.
183. *Hyloctistes subulatus*. Striped Woodhaunter. 6ss. 16. Nicaragua to Bolivia.
184. *Ancistrops strigilatus*. Chestnut winged Hookbill. 2ss. 17. Upper Amazon.
185. *Anabazenops fuscus*. White collared Foliage gleaner. 19. SE Brazil.
186. *Syndactyla guttulata*. Guttulated Foliage gleaner. 3ss. 18. Venezuela.
187. *Syndactyla rufosuperciliata*. Buff browed Foliage gleaner. 5ss. 17. Bolivia, Brazil, Paraguay, Uruguay, Argentina.
188. *Syndactyla subularis*. Lineated Foliage gleaner. 7ss. 17. Costa Rica to Peru.
189. *Simoxenops striatus*. Bolivian Recurvebill. 18. Bolivia.
190. *Simoxenops ucayalae*. Peruvian Recurvebill. 21. Peru, Brazil.
191. *Philydor amaurotis*. White browed Foliage gleaner. 17. Brazil, Argentina.
192. *Anabacerthia striaticollis*. Montane Foliage gleaner. 6ss. 16. Venezuela to Bolivia.
193. *Anabacerthia variegaticeps*. Scaly throated Foliage gleaner. 2ss. 16 Mexico to Ecuador.
194. *Philydor atricapillus*. Black capped Foliage gleaner. 16.Brazil to Argentina.
195. *Philydor dimidiatus*. Russet mantled Foliage gleaner. 2ss. 17. Brazil.
196. incl. *P. d. baeri*. Baer's Foliage gleaner. 17. Brazil, Paraguay.
197. *Philydor erythrocercus*. Rufous rumped Foliage gleaner. 6ss. 16. N South America.
198. *Philydor erythropterus*. Chestnut winged Foliage gleaner. 2ss.17. Amazonia.
199. *Philydor hylobius*. Neblina Foliage gleaner. 17. Brazil. (Now considered Juv. 206.)
200. *Philydor lichtensteini*. Ochre breasted Foliage gleaner. 17. Brazil to Argentina.
201. *Philydor pyrrhodes*. Cinnamon rumped Foliage gleaner. 17. Brazil, Paraguay.
202. *Philydor ruficaudatus*. Rufous tailed Foliage gleaner. 2ss. 17. Upper Amazon.
203. *Philydor rufus*. Buff fronted Foliage gleaner. 7ss. 18. Costa Rica to Argentina.
204. *Philydor fuscipennis*. Slaty winged Foliage gleaner. 16. Panama to Ecuador.
205. *Philydor ochrogaster*. Ochre breasted Foliage gleaner. 16. Peru, Bolivia.
206. *Philydor novaesi*. Alagoas Foliage gleaner. 18. NE Brazil.
207. *Philydor erythronotus*. Rufous backed Foliage gleaner. 16. Panama to Ecuador.

163
164
165
166
167
168
169
170
171
172
173
174
175
176
177
178
179
180
181
182
183
184
185
186
187
188
189
190
191
192
193
194
195
196
197
198
204
205
206
199
200
201
202
207
203

FURNARIIDAE (6)
Ovenbirds

208. *Automolus dorsalis*. Crested Foliage gleaner. 18. Colombia to Peru.
209. *Automolus infuscatus*. Olive backed Foliage gleaner. 5ss. 18. Amazonia.
210. *Automolus leucophthalmus*. White eyed Foliage gleaner. 3ss. 18. Argentina, Paraguay, Brazil.
211. *Automolus melanopezus*. Brown rumped Foliage gleaner. 18. Colombia to Peru.
212. *Automolus ochrolaemus*. Buff throated Foliage gleaner. 8ss. 18. Mexico to Bolivia & Brazil.
213. *Automolus roraimae*. White throated Foliage gleaner. 4ss.18. Venezuela.
214. *Automolus rubiginosus*. Ruddy Foliage gleaner. 16ss. 18. Mexico to Bolivia.
215. *Syndactyla ruficollis*. Rufous necked Foliage gleaner. 2ss.18. Peru, Ecuador.
216. *Automolus rufipileatus*. Chestnut crowned Foliage gleaner. 2ss. 18. Amazon & Orinoco basins.
217. *Hylocryptus erythrocephalus*. Henna-hooded Foliage gleaner. 2ss. 21. Peru, Ecuador.
218. *Hylocryptus rectirostris*. Chestnut capped Foliage gleaner. 21. Brazil.
219. *Cichlocolaptes leucophrus*. Pale browed Treehunter. 21. Brazil.
220. *Heliobletus contaminatus*. Sharp billed Treehunter. 11. SE South America.
221. *Thripadectes flammulatus*. Flammulated Treehunter. 2ss. 23. Venezuela to Peru.
222. *Thripadectes holostictus*. Striped Treehunter. 3ss. 20. Venezuela to Bolivia.223. Thripadectes ignobilis. Uniform Treehunter. 19. Colombia, Ecuador.
224. *Thripadectes melanorhynchus*. Black billed Treehunter. 2ss. 20. Colombia, Ecuador, Peru.
225. *Thripadectes rufobrunneus*. Streak breasted Treehunter. 21. Costa Rica, Panama.
226. *Thripadectes scrutator*. Buff throated Treehunter. 25. Peru, Bolivia.
227. *Thripadectes virgaticeps*. Streak capped Treehunter. 6ss. 22. Venezuela to Ecuador.
228. *Xenops milleri*. Rufous tailed Xenops. 10. Guyanas, Amazon basin.
229. *Xenops minutus*. Plain Xenops. 10ss. 10. Mexico to Brazil, NE Argentina.
230. *Xenops rutilans*. Streaked Xenops. 11ss. 12. Costa Rica to Argentina, Trinidad.
231. *Xenops tenuirostris*. Slender billed Xenops. 3ss. 11. Guyanas, Amazonia.
232. *Megaxenops parnaguae*. Great Xenops. 16. NE Brazil.
233. *Pygarrhichas albogularis*. White throated Treerunner. 14. Chile, Argentina.
234. *Sclerurus albigularis*. Grey throated Leaftosser. 6ss. 18. Trinidad, Tobago, Costa Rica to Bolivia.
235. *Sclerurus caudacutus*. Black tailed Leaftosser. 6ss. 17. Amazon basin.
236. *Sclerurus guatemalensis*. Scaly throated Leaftosser. 3ss. 17. Mexico to Colombia, Ecuador.
237. *Sclerurus mexicanus*. Tawny throated Leaftosser. 7ss. 16. Mexico to Brazil.
238. *Sclerurus rufigularis*. Short billed Leaftosser. 4ss. 15. Amazonia.
239. *Sclerurus scansor*. Rufous breasted Leaftosser. 2ss. 18. Brazil, Paraguay, Argentina.
240. *Lochmias nematura*. Sharp tailed Streamcreeper. 6ss. 15. Panama to Argentina.
241 *Acrobatornis fonsecai* Acrobatic Ovenbird. 17. Bahia (Brazil)

208
209
210
211
212
213
214
215
216
217
218
219
220
221
222
223
224
225
226
227
228
229
230
231
232
233
234
235
236
237
238
239
240
241

FORMICARIDAE (1) Antshrikes

Family 104. FORMICARIDAE. Antshrikes.

1. *Cymbilaimus lineatus*. Fasciated Antshrike. 3ss. 17. Nicaragua, Amazonia.
2. *Cymbilaimus sanctaemarae*. Bamboo Antshrike. 17. Bolivia, Peru, Brazil.
3. *Hypoedalius guttatus*. Spot-backed Antshrike. 2ss. 20. Brazil, Paraguay, Argentina.
4. *Batara cinerea*. Giant Antshrike. 3ss. 25. Brazil, Bolivia, Paraguay.
5. *Mackenziaena leachi*. Large tailed Antshrike. 26. Brazil, Paraguay, Argentina.
6. *Mackenziaena severa*. Tufted Antshrike. 23. Brazil, Argentina, Paraguay.
7. *Frederickena unduligera*. Undulated Antshrike. 4ss. 22. Upper Amazon basin.
8. *Frederickena viridis*. Black throated Antshrike. 7ss. 22. Venezuela, Guyanas, Brazil.
9. *Taraba major*. Great Antshrike. 10ss. 20. Mexico to Brazil, Uruguay, Argentina.
10. *Sakesphorus bernardi*. Collared Antshrike. 4ss. 18. Ecuador, Peru.
11. *Sakesphorus canadensis*. Black crested Antshrike. 7ss. 16. N of S America.
12. *Sakesphorus cristatus*. Silvery cheeked Antshrike. 16. E Brazil.
13. *Sakesphorus luctuosus*. Glossy Antshrike. 2ss. 17. Lower Amazon Basin.
14. *Sakesphorus melanonotus*. Black backed Antshrike. 15. Venezuela, Colombia.
15. *Sakesphorus melanothorax*. Band tailed Antshrike. 17. Guyanas, Brazil.
16. *Biatas nigropectus*. White bearded Antshrike. 17. Brazil, Argentina.

1
2
3
4
5
6
7
8
9
10
11
12
13
14
15
16

FORMICARIIDAE (2)
Antshrikes

17. *Thamnophilus aethiops*. White shouldered Antshrike. 9ss. 15. Orinoco, Amazon.
18. *Thamnophilus amazonicus*. Amazonian Antshrike. 5ss. 15. Amazonia.
19. *Thamnophilus aroyae*. Upland Antshrike. 14. Peru, Bolivia.
20. *Thamnophilus bridgesi*. Black hooded Antshrike. 16. Costa Rica, Panama.
21. *Thamnophilus caerulescens*. Variable Antshrike. 12ss. 15. Peru to Argentina. Uruguay, Paraguay, Bolivia, Brazil.
22. *Thamnophilus cryptoleucus*. Castelnau's Antshrike. 17. Peru, Brazil, Ecuador.
23. *Thamnophilus doliatus*. Barred Antshrike. 18ss. 16. Mexico to Argentina.
24. *Thamnophilus insignis*. Streak backed Antshrike. 2ss. 15. Venezuela.
25. *Thamnophilus multistriatus*. Bar crested Antshrike. 4ss. 16. Colombia, Venezuela.
26. *Thamnophilus murinus*. Mouse coloured Antshrike. 3ss. 13. Guyanas, Amazonia.
27. *Thamnophilus nigriceps*. Black Antshrike. 2ss. 14. Panama, Colombia.
28. *Thamnophilus nigrocinerius*. Blackish Grey Antshrike. 6ss. 16. Amazonia.
29. *Thamnophilus palliatus*. Lined / Chestnut backed Antshrike. 6ss. 16. Amazonia.

T. p. tenuepunctatus. Similar appearance, but may be distinct species.

30. *Thamnophilus praecox*. Cocha Antshrike. 16. Border of Ecuador & Peru.
31. *Thamnophilus punctatus*. Slaty Antshrike. 12ss. 14. Belize to Brazil, Ecuador.
32. *Thamnophilus ruficapillus*. Rufous capped Antshrike. 5ss. 17. S of South America.
33. *Thamnophilus schistaceus*. Plain winged Antshrike. 5ss. 13. Upper Amazon.
34. *Thamnophilus torquatus*. Rufous winged Antshrike. 13. CS Brazil.
35. *Thamnophilus unicolor*. Uniform Antshrike. 3ss. 15. Colombia, Ecuador, Peru.
36. *Pygiptila stellaris. Spot winged Antshrike.* 4ss. 13. Guyanas, Amazonia.
37. *Megastictus margaritatus*. Pearly Antshrike. 13. Upper Amazon.

17
18
19
20
21
22
23
24
25
26
27
28
29
30
?
31
32
33
34
35
36
37

FORMICARIIDAE (3)
Antbirds

38. *Neoctantes niger*. Black Bushbird. 15. Amazon headwaters.
39. *Clytoctantes alixii*. Recurve-billed Bushbird. 16. Venezuela, Colombia.

39a. *Clytoctantes atrogularis*. Rondonia Bushbird. 16. SW Brazil.

40. *Xenornis setifrons*. Speckled Antshrike. 16. Panama, Colombia.
41. *Thamnistes anabatinus*. Russet Antshrike. 7ss. 14. Mexico to Bolivia.
42. *Dysithamnus mentalis*. Plain Antvireo. 18ss. 12. Mexico to Argentina.
43. *Dysithamnus puncticeps*. Spot crowned Antvireo. 3ss. 11. Costa Rica to Ecuador.
44. *Dysithamnus stictothorax*. Spot breasted Antvireo. 14. SE Brazil.
45. *Dysithamnus striaticeps*. Streak crowned Antvireo. 12. Honduras to Costa Rica.
46. *Dysithamnus xanthopterus*. Rufous backed Antvireo. 14. SE Brazil.
47. *Thamnomanes ardesiacus*. Dusky throated Antshrike. 2ss. 13. Amazonia.
48. *Thamnomanes caesius*. Cinereous Antshrike. 5ss. 15. Amazonia.
49. *Thamnomanes occidentalis*. Western Antshrike. 2ss. 16. Colombia, Ecuador.
50. *Thamnomanes /Dysithamnus leucostictus*. White streaked Antvireo. 3ss. 13. Venezuela, Colombia, Ecuador.
51. *Thamnomanes / D. plumbeus*. Plumbeous Antvireo. 13. Brazil.
52. *Thamnomanes saturninus*. Saturnine Antshrike. 2ss. 13. Peru, Bolivia, Brazil.
53. *Thamnomanes schistogynus*. Bluish slate Antshrike. 15. Peru, Bolivia, Brazil.
54. *Myrmotherula ambigua*. Yellow throated Antwren. 8. Colombia, Venezuela, Brazil.
55. *Myrmotherula assimilis*. Leaden Antwren. 11. Upper Amazon basin.
56. *Myrmotherula axillaris*. White flanked Antwren. 6ss. 10. Salvador to Brazil.
57. *Myrmotherula fluminensis*. Rio de Janeiro Antwren. 10. SE Brazil.
58. *Myrmotherula behni*. Plain winged Antwren. 4ss. 11. NW South America.
59. *Myrmotherula brachyura*. Pygmy Antwren. 2ss. 8. Panama to Brazil & Bolivia.
60. *Myrmotherula cherriei*. Cherrie's Antwren. 11. Colombia, Venezuela, Brazil.
61. *Myrmotherula spodionota*. Foothill Antwren. 10. Ecuador, Peru.

38
39A
-39-
39A
40
41
42
43
44
45
46
47
48
49
50
52
53
54
51
-55-
57
♀?
56
61
58
59
60

FORMICARIIDAE (4) Antbirds

62. *Myrmotherula / Formicivora erythronotos*. Black hooded Antwren. 11. SE Brazil
63. *Myrmotherula erythrura*. Rufous tailed Antwren. 2ss. 11. Colombia, Peru, Brazil.
64. *Myrmotherula fulviventris*. Checker-throated Antwren. 3ss. 11. Honduras to Ecuador.
65. *Myrmotherula grisea*. Ashy Antwren. 11. Bolivia.
66. *Myrmotherula gularis*. Star throated Antwren. 10. SE Brazil.
67. *Myrmotherula guttata*. Rufous bellied Antwren. 9. Guyanas, Venezuela, Brazil.
68. *Myrmotherula gutturalis*. Brown bellied Antwren. 11. Guyanas, Venezuela, Brazil.
69. *Myrmotherula haematonota*. Stipple throated Antwren. 5ss. 11. Venezuela, Colombia to Bolivia & Brazil.
70. *Myrmotherula hauxwelli*. Plain throated Antwren. 4ss. 9. Colombia, Bolivia, Brazil.
71. *Myrmotherula iheringi*. Ihering's Antwren. 2ss. 9. Brazil.
72. *Myrmotherula klagesi*. Klages's Antwren. 8. Brazil.
73. *Myrmotherula leucophthalma*. White eyed Antwren. 4ss. 12. Peru, Bolivia, Brazil.
74. *Myrmotherula longicauda*. Stripe Chested Antwren. 4ss. 11. Colombia to Bolivia.
75. *Myrmotherula longipennis*. Long winged Antwren. 6ss. 10. N of S America.
76. *Myrmotherula menetriesii*. Grey Antwren. 5ss. 10. Guyanas, Venezuela, Amazonia.
77. *Myrmotherula minor*. Salvadori's Antwren. 9. Brazil.
78. *Myrmotherula obscura*. Short billed Antwren. 8. Colombia, Peru, Brazil.
79. *Myrmotherula ornata*. Ornate Antwren. 5ss. 10. Colombia, Bolivia, Brazil.
80. *Myrmotherula schisticolor*. Slaty Antwren. 3ss. 10. Mexico to Peru.
81. *Myrmotherula sclateri*. Sclater's Antwren. 8. Brazil, Bolivia, Peru.
82. *Myrmotherula sunensis*. Rio Suno Antwren. 2ss. 9. Colombia, Peru, Brazil.
83. *Myrmotherula surinamensis*. Streaked Antwren. 3ss. 9. Panama to Brazil.
84. *Myrmotherula unicolor*. Unicolored Antwren. 10. SE Brazil.
85. *Myrmotherula urosticta*. Band tailed Antwren. 10. SE Brazil.
86. *Dichrozona cincta*. Banded Antbird. 3ss. 12. Amazonia.
87. *Myrmochilus strigilatus*. Stripe backed Antbird. 2ss. 16. Bolivia, Brazil, Paraguay, Argentina.
88. *Microhopias quixensis*. Dot winged Antwren. 10ss. 12. Mexico to Brazil.

88a. *Stymphalornis acitirostris*. Parana Antbird. 14. Bahia. (Brazil)

62
63
64
65
66
67
68
69
70
71
72
73
74
75
76
77
78
79
80
81
82
83
84
85
88
A
86
87
88

FORMICARIIDAE (5) Antbirds

89. *Herpsilochmus axillaris*. Yellow breasted Antwren. 4ss. 12. Colombia, Peru, Ecuador.
90. *Herpsilochmus dorsimaculatus*. Spot backed Antwren. 12. Venezuela, Colombia, Brazil.
91. *Herpsilochmus longirostris*. Large billed Antwren. 14. S Brazil, Bolivia.
92. *Herpsilochmus pectoralis*. Pectoral Antwren. 12. E Brazil.
93. *Herpsilochmus parkeri*. Ash throated Antwren. 13. Peru.
94. *Herpsilochmus pileatus*. Pileated / Bahia Antwren. 3ss. 13. Brazil.
95. *Herpsilochmus motacilloides*. Creamy bellied Antwren. 13. Peru.
96. *Herpsilochmus roraimae*. Roraiman Antwren. 13. Venezuela, Brazil, Guyanas.
97. *Herpsilochmus rufimarginatus*. Rufous winged Antwren. 4ss. 11. Panama to Brazil & Argentina.
98. *Herpsilochmus stictocephalus*. Todd's Antwren. 12. Guyanas, Venezuela.
99. *Herpsilochmus sticturus*. Spot tailed Antwren. 10. Guyanas, Venezuela, Brazil.
100. *Herpsilochmus dugandi*. Dugand's / Velvety Antwren. 10. Colombia, Ecuador, Peru.
101. *Herpsilochmus atricapillus*. Black capped Antwren. 12. Brazil to Argentina.
102. *Formicivora grisea*. White fringed Antwren. 9ss. 12. Tobago & N S America.
103. *Formicivora iheringi*. Narrow billed Antwren. 11. E Brazil.
104. *Formicivora melanogaster*. Black bellied Antwren. 2ss. 13. Brazil, Bolivia.
105. *Formicivora rufa*. Rusty backed Antwren. 3ss. 13. Brazil, Peru, Paraguay.
106. *Formicivora serrana*. Serra Antwren. 13. SE Brazil.
107. *Drymophila caudata*. Long tailed Antbird. 3ss. 15. Venezuela to Bolivia.
108. *Drymophila devillei*. Striated Antbird. 2ss. 13. Ecuador, Bolivia, Brazil.
109. *Drymophila ferruginea*. Ferruginous Antbird. 13. Brazil.
110. *Drymophila genei*. Rufous tailed Antbird. 13. Brazil.
111. *Drymophila malura*. Dusky tailed Antbird. 13. Brazil, Argentina, Paraguay.
112. *Drymophila ochropyga*. Ochre rumped Antbird 12. SE Brazil.
113. *Drymophila squamata*. Scaled Antbird. 12. Brazil.
114. *Terenura callinota*. Rufous rumped Antwren. 3ss. 11. Costa Rica to Peru.
115. *Terenura humeralis*. Chestnut shouldered Antwren. 2ss. 11. Brazil, Peru, Ecuador.
116. *Terenura maculata*. Streak capped Antwren. 10. Brazil, Paraguay, Argentina.
117. *Terenura sharpei*. Yellow rumped Antwren. 11. Bolivia, Peru.
118. *Terenura spodioptila*. Ash winged Antwren. 4ss. 10. Venezuela, Guyanas, Brazil.
119. *Terenura sicki*. Alagoas / Orange bellied Antwren. 11. Guyanas, Brazil.

89
90
91
92
93
94
95
96
97
98
99
100
♂
?
101
102
103
104
105
106
107
108
109
110
111
112
113
114
115
119
116
117
118

FORMICARIIDAE (6)
Antbirds

120. *Cercomacra brasiliana.* Rio de Janeiro Antbird. 16. SE Brazil.
121. *Cercomacra carbonaria.* Rio branco Antbird. 15. Brazil.
122. *Cercomacra cinerascens.* Grey Antbird. 4ss. 16. Amazonia, Guyanas.
123. *Cercomacra ferdinandi.* Bananal Antbird. 16. Is. de Bananal.(Brazil).
124. *Cercomacra melanaria.* Mato Grosso Antbird. 18. Bolivia & Mato Grosso. (Brazil)
124a. *Cercomacra manu.* Manu Antbird. 17. Peru, Bolivia, Brazil.
125. *Cercomacra nigrescens.* Blackish Antbird. 6ss. 15. Guyanas, Brazil, Bolivia.
126. *Cercomacra nigricans.* Jet Antbird. 2ss. 15. Panama to Ecuador.
127. *Cercomacra serva.* Black Antbird. 2ss. 15. Colombia, Bolivia, Brazil.
128. *Cercomacra tyrannina.* Dusky Antbird. 7ss. 15. Mexico to Ecuador.
128a. *Cercomacra laeta.* Belem Antbird. 13. Brazil.
129. *Myrmeciza berlepschi.* Stub tailed Antbird. 12. Colombia, Ecuador.
130. *Myrmeciza nigricauda.* Esmeralda's Antbird. 13. Colombia, Ecuador.
131. *Pyriglena atra.* Fringe backed Fire-eye. 17. E Brazil.
132. *Pyriglena leuconota.* White backed Fire-eye. 10ss. 17. Colombia to Paraguay.
133. *Pyriglena leucoptera.* White shouldered Fire-eye. 17. Brazil, Paraguay.
134. *Rhopornis ardesiaca.* Slender Antbird. 17. E Brazil.
135. *Myrmoborus leucophrys.* White browed Antbird. 4ss. 13. Amazon & Orinoco basins.
136. *Myrmoborus lugubris.* Ash breasted Antbird. 4ss. 15. Amazonia.
137. *Myrmoborus melanurus.* Black tailed Antbird. 12. NE Peru.
138. *Myrmoborus myotherinus.* Black faced Antbird. 8ss. 12. Amazonia.
139. *Hypocnemis cantator.* Warbling Antbird. 11ss. 11. Guyanas, Amazonia.
140. *Hypocnemis hypoxantha.* Yellow browed Antbird. 2ss. 11. Colombia, Peru, Brazil.
141. *Hypocnemoides maculicauda.* Band tailed Antbird. 2ss. 13. Peru, Bolivia, Brazil.
142. *Hypocnemoides melanopogon.* Black chinned Antbird. 3ss. 12. Amazonia.
143. *Myrmochanes hemileucus.* Black & white Antbird. 12. Ecuador, Brazil, Bolivia.

120
121
122
123
124
125
124A
126
-127-
128A
128
129
130
131
132
133
134
135
136
137
138
139
140
141
142
143

FORMICARIIDAE (7) Antbirds

144. *Gymnocichla nudiceps*. Bare crowned Antbird. 4ss. 16. C America, Colombia.
145. *Sclateria naevia*. Silvered Antbird. 4ss. 15. N of S America, Trinidad.
146. *Percnostola caurensis*. Caura Antbird. 2ss. 17. Venezuela, Brazil.
147. *Percnostola leucostigma*. Spot winged Antbird. 9ss. 15. Guyanas, Amazonia.
148. *Percnostola lophotes*. Rufous crested Antbird. 16. Peru.
149. *Percnostola macrolopha*. White lined Antbird. 15. Peru. (unique male).
150. *Percnostola rufifrons*. Black headed Antbird. 3ss. 15. Guyanas, Amazonia.
151. *Percnostola schistacea*. Slate coloured Antbird. 15. Colombia, Peru, Brazil.
152. *Myrmeciza atrothorax*. Black throated Antbird. 7ss. 13. Amazonia, Guyanas.
153. *Myrmeciza disjuncta*. Yapacana Antbird. 12. Venezuela.
154. *Myrmeciza exsul*. Chestnut backed Antbird. 5ss. 14. Nicaragua to Ecuador.
155. *Myrmeciza ferruginea*. Ferruginous backed Antbird. 2ss. 13. Guyanas, Amazon.
156. *Myrmeciza fortis*. Sooty Antbird. 2ss. 16. Colombia, Peru, Brazil.
157. *Myrmeciza goeldii*. Goeldi's Antbird. 19. Peru, Bolivia, Brazil.
158. *Myrmeciza griseiceps*. Grey headed Antbird. 13. Ecuador, Peru.
159. *Myrmeciza hemimelaena*. Chestnut tailed Antbird. 2ss. 12. Colombia, Bolivia, Brazil.
160. *Myrmeciza hyperythra*. Plumbeous Antbird. 17. Colombia, Bolivia, Brazil.
161. *Myrmeciza immaculata*. Immaculate Antbird. 4ss. 18. Costa Rica to Ecuador.
162. *Myrmeciza laemosticta*. Dull mantled Antbird. 5ss. 13. Costa Rica to Venezuela.
163 *Myrmeciza longipes*. White bellied Antbird. 4ss. 13. Panama to Guyanas, Brazil.
164. *Myrmeciza loricata*. White bibbed Antbird. 15. SE Brazil.

144
145
146
147
148
♀
149
150
151
152
153
154
155
156
157
158
159
160
161
162
163
164

FORMICARIIDAE (8)
Antbirds

165. *Myrmeciza melanoceps*. White shouldered Antbird. 18. Colombia, Peru, Brazil.
166. *Myrmeciza pelzelni*. Grey bellied Antbird. 12. Colombia, Venezuela, Brazil.
167. *Myrmeciza ruficauda*. Scalloped Antbird. 2ss. 15. E Brazil.
168. *Myrmeciza squamosa*. Squamate Antbird. 15. SE Brazil.
169. *Myrmeciza stictothorax*. Spot breasted Antbird. 13. Brazil.
170. *Formicarius analis*. Black faced Antthrush. 14ss. 18. Mexico to Amazonia, Trinidad.
171. *Formicarius colma*. Rufous capped Antthrush. 4ss. 17. N of South America.
172. *Formicarius nigricapillus*. Black headed Antthrush. 2ss. 16. Costa Rica to Ecuador.
173. *Formicarius rufifrons*. Rufous fronted Antthrush. 18. SE Peru.
174. Formicarius rufipectus. Rufous breasted Antthrush. 4ss. 17. Costa Rica to Peru.
175. *Chamaeza campanisoma*. Short tailed Antthrush. 11ss. 20. Most of S America.
176. *Chamaeza mollissima*. Barred Antthrush. 2ss. 20. Colombia to Bolivia.
177. *Chamaeza nobilis*. Striated Antthrush. 3ss. 23. Colombia, Bolivia, Brazil.
178. *Chamaeza ruficauda*. Rufous tailed Antthrush. 3ss. 21. Colombia, Venezuela, Brazil.

178a. *Chamaeza turdina*. Schwartz's Antthrush. 20. Colombia, Venezuela.

178b. Chamaeza meruloides. Such's Antthrush. 21. SE Brazil.

179 *Pithys albifrons*. White plumed Antbird. 3ss. 11. Colombia, Venezuela, Brazil.

180. *Pithys castanea*. White masked Antbird. 15. Ecuador.(Unique)
181. *Gymnopithys leucaspis*. White cheeked Antbird. 9ss. 13. Colombia, Ecuador, Brazil.
182. *Gymnopithys bicolor*. Bicoloured Antbird. 13. Honduras to NW South America.
183. *Gymnopithys lunulata*. Lunulated Antbird. 15. Ecuador, Peru.
184. *Gymnopithys rufigula*. Rufous throated Antbird. 3ss. 15. Guyanas, Venezuela, Brazil.
185. *Gymnopithys salvini*. White throated Antbird. 2ss. 15. Peru, Bolivia, Brazil.
186. *Rhegmatorhina berlepschi*. Harlequin Antbird. 15. Brazil.
187. *Rhegmatorhina cristata*. Chestnut crested Antbird. 15. NW Brazil.
188. *Rhegmatorhina gymnops*. Santarem / Bare-eyed Antbird. 15. N Brazil.
189. *Rhegmatorhina hoffmannsi*. White breasted Antbird. 15. W Brazil.
190. *Rhegmatorhina melanosticta*. Hairy crested Antbird. 4ss. 16. Colombia, Brazil, Bolivia.

165
166
167
168
169
170
171
172
173
♂
♀
174
175
176
177
178
179
180
181
182
183
184
185
186
187
188
189
178 A
178 B
190

FORMICARIIDAE (9)
Antbirds

191. *Hylopezus berlepschi.* Amazonian Antpitta. 2ss. 13. Brazil, Bolivia, Peru.
192. *Hylopezus fulviventris.* White lored Antpitta. 5ss. 15. Nicaragua to Ecuador.
192a. *Hylopezus dives.* Fulvous bellied Antpitta. 15. Honduras to Colombia.
193. *Hylopezus macularius.* Spotted Antpitta. 4ss. 15. Orinoco & Amazon basins.
194. *Hylopezus ochroleucus.* White browed Antpitta. 2ss. 13. Brazil.
195. *Hylopezus perspicillatus.* Spectacled/Streak chested Antpitta. 5ss. 13. Nicaragua to Ecuador.
196. *Hylopezus nattereri.* Speckle breasted Antpitta. 13. Brazil, Paraguay, Argentina.
197. *Hylophylax naevia.* Spot backed Antbird. 6ss. 11. Orinoco & Amazon basins.
198. *Hylophylax naevoides.* Spotted Antbird. 3ss. 11. Honduras to Ecuador.
199. *Hylophylax poecilonota.* Scale backed Antbird. 7ss. 12. Guyanas, Orinoco. Amazonia.
200. *Hylophylax punctulata.* Dot backed Antbird. 2ss. 10. Venezuela to Brazil, Bolivia.
201. *Skutchia borbae.* Pale faced Antbird. 18. Brazil.
202. *Phlegopsis barringeri.* Argus Bare-eye. 18. Colombia. (Unique).
203. *Phlegopsis erythroptera.* Reddish winged Bare-eye. 2ss. 17. Amazonia.
204. *Phlegopsis nigromaculata.* Black spotted Bare-eye. 4ss. 17. Colombia to Bolivia & Brazil.
205. *Phaenostictus mcleannani.* Occelated Antbird. 4ss. 19. Nicaragua to Ecuador.
206. *Myrmornis torquata.* Wing banded Antbird. 2ss. 15. Nicaragua to Brazil.
207. *Pittasoma michleri.* Black crowned Antpitta. 2ss. 18. Costa Rica to Colombia.
208. *Pittasoma rufopileatum.* Rufous crowned Antpitta. 3ss. 16. Colombia, Ecuador.
209. *Grallaricula cocullata.* Hooded Antpitta. 2ss. 11. Colombia, Venezuela.
210. *Grallaricula ferrugineipectus.* Rusty breasted Antpitta. 3ss. 12. Venezuela to Bolivia.
211. *Grallaricula flavirostris.* Ochre breasted Antpitta. 8ss. 11. Costa Rica to Bolivia.
212. *Grallaricula lineifrons.* Crescent faced Antpitta. 12. Ecuador, Colombia.
213. *Grallaricula loricata.* Scallop breasted Antpitta. 10. Venezuela.
214. *Grallaricula nana.* Slate crowned Antpitta. 6ss. 10. Venezuela to Peru.
215. *Grallaricula peruviana.* Peruvian Antpitta. 10. N Peru, Ecuador.
216. *Grallaricula ochraceifrons.* Ochre fronted Antpitta. 11. N Peru.
217. *Myrmothera campanisoma.* Thrushlike Antpitta. 6ss. 14. Amazon basin, Guyanas.
218. *Myrmothera simplex.* Tepui /Brown breasted Antpitta. 3ss. 14. Venezuela, Brazil.
219. *Grallaria albigula.* White throated Antpitta. 20. Peru to Argentina.
220. *Grallaria alleni.* Moustached Antpitta. 20. Colombia.(2 specimens).
221. *Grallaria andicola.* Stripe headed Antpitta. 17. Peru, Bolivia.
222. *Grallaria punensis. Puno Antpitta. 17.* SE Peru, Bolivia.
223. *Grallaria bangsi.* Santa Marta Antpitta. 17. Colombia.
223a. *Grallaria kaestneri.* Cundimarca Antpitta. 17. Colombia.
224. *Grallaria chthonia.* Tachira Antpitta. 17. Venezuela.
225. *Grallaria flavotincta.* Yellow breasted Antpitta. 18. Colombia, Ecuador.

191
192
193
194
195
192A
196
197
198
199
200
201
216
202
203
204
205
206
207
208
209
210
213
211
212
219
214
215
217
218
223A
225
220
221
222
223
224

FORMICARIIDAE (10), CONOPHAGIDAE Antbirds, Gnateaters

226. *Grallaria dignissima.* Ochre striped Antpitta. 17. Colombia, Ecuador, Peru.
227. *Grallaria eludens.* Elusive Antpitta. 17. Peru.
228. *Grallaria erythrotis.* Rufous faced Antpitta. 18. Bolivia.
229. *Grallaria excelsa.* Great Antpitta. 2ss. 26. Venezuela.
230. *Grallaria gigantea.* Giant Antpitta. 3ss. 26. Colombia, Ecuador.
231. *Grallaria griseonucha.* Grey naped Antpitta. 2ss. 15. Venezuela.
232. *Grallaria guatimalensis.* Scaled Antpitta. 8ss. 17. Trinidad, Mexico to Bolivia.
233. *Grallaria haplonota.* Plain backed Antpitta. 3ss. 18. Venezuela, Ecuador.
234. *Grallaria hypoleuca.* White bellied Antpitta. 3ss. 17. Colombia to Peru.
235. *Grallaria prewalskii.* Rusty tinged Antpitta. 17. N Peru.
236. *Grallaria erythroleuca.* Red & White Antpitta. 18. E Peru.
237. *Grallaria capitalis.* Bay Antpitta. 20. E Peru.
238. *Grallaria milleri.* Brown banded Antpitta. 13. Colombia. (Last recorded 1911.)
239. *Grallaria nuchalis.* Chestnut naped Antpitta. 3ss. 20. Colombia to Peru.
240. *Grallaria carrikeri.* Pale billed Antpitta. 20. N Peru.
241. *Grallaria quitensis.* Tawny Antpitta. 3ss. 16. Colombia, Ecuador, Peru.
242. *Grallaria ruficapilla.* Chestnut crowned Antpitta. 7ss. 20. Venezuela, Peru.
243. *Grallaria watkinsi.* Scrub Antpitta. 20. Ecuador, Peru.
244. *Grallaria rufocinerea.* Bicoloured Antpitta. 17. Colombia.
245. *Grallaria rufula.* Rufous Antpitta. 14. Venezuela to Bolivia.
246. *Grallaria squamigera.* Undulated Antpitta. 2ss. 22. Venezuela to Bolivia.
247. *Grallaria Varia.* Variegated Antpitta. 5ss. 18. Venezuela to Argentina.
248. *Grallaria blakei.* Chestnut Antpitta. 14. Peru.

Family 105. CONOPHAGIDAE. Gnateaters.

1. *Conopophaga ardesiaca.* Slaty Gnateater. 2ss 13. Peru, Bolivia.
2. *Conopophaga aurita.* Chestnut belted Gnateater. 13. Amazonia, N to Guyanas.
3. *Conopophaga castaneiceps.* Chestnut crowned Gnateater. 4ss. 13. Colombia to Peru.
4. *Conopophaga lineata.* Rufous Gnateater. 2ss. 11. Brazil, Paraguay, Argentina.
5. *Conopophaga cearae.* Caatinga Gnateater. 11. NE Brazil.(consp. 4.)
6. *Conopophaga melanogaster.* Black bellied Gnateater. 14. Brazil, Bolivia.
7. *Conopophaga melanops.* Black cheeked Gnateater. 2ss. 13. E Brazil.
8. *Conopophaga peruviana.* Ash throated Gnateater. 13. Peru & SW Amazonia.
9. *Conopophaga roberti.* Hooded Gnateater. 13. NE Brazil.

226
227
228
229
230
231
232
233
234
235
236
237
240
239
241
242
243
244
245
246
247
238
248
CONOPOPHAGIDAE
-1-
-2-
-3-
-4-
-5-
-6-
-7-
-8-
-9-

RHINOCRYPTIDAE
Tapaculos

Family 106. RHINOCRYPTIDAE. Tapculos.

1. *Pteroptochos castaneus*. Chestnut throated Huet-huet. 25. C Chile.
2. *Pteroptochos megapodius*. Moustached Turca. 2ss. 22. N & C Chile.
3. *Pteroptochos tarnii*. Black throated Huet-huet. 25. S Chile, W Argentina.
4. *Scelorchilus albicollis*. White throated Tapaculo. 2ss. 20. Chile.
5. *Scelorchilus rubecula*. Chucao Tapaculo. 2ss. 17. S Chile, W Argentina.
6. *Rhinocrypta lanceolata*. Crested Gallito. 2ss. 22. Paraguay, Argentina, Bolivia.
7. *Teledromus fuscus*. Sandy Gallito. 17. W Argentina.
8. *Liosceles thoracicus*. Rusty bellied Tapaculo. 3ss. 20. Colombia to Peru, Brazil.
9. *Merulaxis ater*. Slaty Bristlefront. 19. SE Brazil.
10. *Merulaxis stresemanni*. Stresemann's Bristlefront. 22. E Brazil.
11. *Melanopareia elegans*. Elegant Crescent-chest. 2ss. 14. Ecuador, Peru.
12. *Melanopareia maranonica*. Maranon Crescent-chest. 16. NC Peru.
13. *Melanopareia maximiliani*. Olive crowned Crescent-chest. 2ss. 15. Bolivia, Paraguay, Argentina.
14. *Melanopareia torquata*. Collared Crescent-chest. 2ss. 12. EC Brazil, Bolivia.
15. *Scytalopus argentifrons*. Silvery fronted Tapaculo. 11. Costa Rica, Panama.
16. *Scytalopus chiriquensis*. Chiriqui Tapaculo. 11. Panama.
17. *Scytalopus femoralis*. Rufous vented Tapaculo. 7ss. 12. Venezuela to Peru.
18. *Scytalopus indigoticus*. White breasted Tapaculo. 12. SE Brazil.

18a. *Scytalopus psychopompus*. Chestnut sided Tapaculo. 12. SE Brazil.

19. *Scytalopus latebricola*. Brown rumped Tapaculo. 4ss. 12. Venezuela, Colombia.
20. *Scytalopus macropus*. Large footed Tapaculo. 15. Peru.
21. *Scytalopus magellanicus*. Andean Tapaculo. 12ss. 12. Venezuela to Tierra del Fuego, Falkland Is.

21a. *Scytalopus schulenbergi*. Diademed Tapaculo. 12. Bolivia to Peru.

22. *Scytalopus novacapitalis*. Brasilia Tapaculo. 12. C Brazil.
23. *Scytalopus panamensis*. Tacarcuna Tapaculo. 12. E Panama.
24. *Scytalopus vicinior*. Narino Tapaculo. 12. E Panama, W Colombia.
25. *Scytalopus speluncae*. Mouse coloured Tapaculo. 12. Brazil, Argentina.
26. *Scytalopus superciliaris*. White browed Tapaculo. 12. Bolivia, Argentina.
27. *Scytalopus unicolor*. Unicoloured Tapaculo. 5ss. 15. Venezuela to Bolivia.
28. *Myornis senilis*. Ash coloured Tapaculo. 13. Colombia to Peru.
29. *Psilorhamphus guttatus*. Spotted Bamboowren. 13. Brazil, Argentina.
30. *Eugralla paradoxa*. Ochre flanked Tapaculo. 12. Chile, Argentina.
31. *Acropternis orthonyx*. Ocellated Tapaculo. 2ss. 22. Venezuela to Peru.

1
2
3
4
5
6
7
8
9
10
11
12
13
14
15
16
18A
17
18
19
20
21
22
23
24
21A
25
26
27
28
29
30
31

TYRANNIDAE (1)
Shrike, Ground & Bush Tyrants

Family 107. TYRANNIDAE. Shrike, Ground & Bush Tyrants.

1. *Agriornis albicauda*. White tailed Shrike-Tyrant. 25. Ecuador, Chile, Argentina.
2. *Agriornis livida*. Great Shrike Tyrant. 2ss. 27. Chile, S Argentina.
3. *Agriornis microptera*. Grey bellied Shrike Tyrant. 2ss. 25. Peru, Chile, Argentina.
4. *Agriornis montana*. Black billed Shrike Tyrant. 6ss. 22. Colombia to Argentina.
5. *Neoxolmis rufiventris*. Chocolate vented Tyrant. 22. Chile, Argentina. Winters Uruguay.
6. *Xolmis cinerea*. Grey Monjita. 2ss. 22. Surinam, Brazil to Argentina.
7. *Xolmis coronata*. Black crowned Monjita. 21. Argentina. Winters to Bolivia, Brazil.
8. *Heteroxolmis dominicana*. Black & white Monjita. 20. Brazil to Argentina.
9. *Xolmis irupero*. White Monjita. 2ss. 18. Brazil, Bolivia, Paraguay, Uruguay.
10. *Agriornis murina*. Mouse brown Monjita /Lesser Shrike Tyrant. 18. Argentina, Winters Paraguay, Bolivia.
11. *Xolmis rubetra*. Rusty backed Monjita. 18. Argentina.

11a. *Xolmis salinarum*. Salinas Monjita. 16. N Argentina.

12. *Polioxolmis rufipennis*. Rufous webbed Tyrant. 21. Peru, Bolivia, Argentina.
13. *Xolmis velata*. White rumped Monjita. 20. Brazil, Bolivia, Paraguay.
14. *Xolmis pyrope*. Fire eyed Diucon. 22. Chile, Argentina.
15. *Muscisaxicola albifrons*. White fronted Ground Tyrant. 23. Andes, Peru, Chile.
16. *Muscisaxicola albilora*. White browed Ground Tyrant. 17. Chile, Argentina. Winters Ecuador.
17. *Muscisaxicola alpina*. Plain capped Ground Tyrant. 6ss. 17. Colombia, Bolivia.
18. *Muscisaxicola capistrata*. Cinnamon bellied Ground Tyrant. 17. S Argentina & S Chile. Winters Peru.
19. *Muscisaxicola flavinucha*. Ochre naped Ground Tyrant. 2ss. 20. Argentina, Chile. Winters to Peru.
20. *Muscisaxicola fluviatilis*. Little Ground Tyrant. 13. Upper Amazon basin.
21. *Muscisaxicola frontalis*. Black fronted Ground Tyrant. 18. Chile, Argentina. Winters to Peru.
22. *Muscisaxicola juninensis*. Puna Ground Tyrant. 16. Peru to Chile, Argentina.
23. *Muscisaxicola macloviana*. Dark faced Ground Tyrant. 2ss. 15. Tierra del Fuego, Falkland Is. to Peru.
24. *Muscisaxicola maculirostris*. Spot billed Ground Tyrant. 3ss. 14. Colombia to Argentina & Chile.
25. *Muscisaxicola rufivertex*. Rufous naped Ground Tyrant. 3ss. 17. Peru to Chile & Argentina.
26. *Muscisaxicola cinerea*. Cinereous Ground Tyrant. 14. Bolivia, Chile, Argentina.
27. *Muscigralla brevicauda*. Short tailed Field Tyrant. 11. Ecuador, Peru.
28. *Lessonia rufa*. Patagonian/Rufous backed Negrito. 2ss. 12. Chile, Argentina. Winters SE Brazil.
29. *Lessonia oreas*. Andean / Salvin's Negrito. 13. Peru, N Chile & Argentina.
30. *Cnemarchus/Myiotheretes erythropygius*. Red rumped Bush Tyrant. 2ss. 22. Colombia to Bolivia.
31. *Myiotheretes fumigatus*. Smoky Bush Tyrant. 4ss. 20. Venezuela to Peru.
32. *Myiotheretes fuscorufus*. Rufous bellied Bush Tyrant. 19. Peru, Bolivia.
33. *Myiotheretes pernix*. Santa Marta Bush Tyrant. 19. Colombia.
34. Myiotheretes striaticollis. Streak throated Bush Tyrant. 2ss. 22. Venezuela to Argentina.
35. Silvicultrix jelskii. Jelski's Chat Tyrant. 14. Peru, Ecuador.

1
2
3
4
5
6
7
8
9
10
11
12
13
14
15
16
17
18
19
20
21
22
23
24
25
26
27
11A
28
29
30
31
32
33
35
34

TYRANNIDAE (2)
Tyrants

36. *Ochthoeca cinnamomeiventris.* Slaty backed Chat Tyrant. 4ss. 12. Venezuela to Bolivia.
37. incl. *c. nigrita.* Blackish Chat Tyrant. 12. Venezuela.
38. *Silvicultrix diadema.* Yellow bellied Chat Tyrant. 6ss. 12. Venezuela to Peru.
39. *Silvicultrix frontalis.* Crowned Chat Tyrant. 5ss. 12. Colombia to Peru.
40. *Ochthoeca fumicolor.* Brown backed Chat Tyrant. 5ss. 17. Venezuela to Bolivia.
41. *Ochthoeca leucophrys.* White browed Chat Tyrant. 6ss. 14. Peru, Chile, Argentina.
42. *Ochthoeca oenanthoides.* D'Orbigny's Chat Tyrant. 2ss. 16. Peru, Chile, Argentina.
43. *Ochthoeca piurae.* Piura Chat Tyrant. 12. Peru.
44. *Silvicultrix pulchella.* Golden browed Chat Tyrant. 3ss. 12. Ecuador, Peru, Bolivia.
45. *Ochthoeca rufipectoralis.* Rufous breasted Chat Tyrant. 7ss. 13. Venezuela to Bolivia.
46. *Sayornis nigricans.* Black Phoebe. 8ss. 15. SW USA to Argentina.
47. *Sayornis phoebe.* Eastern Phoebe. 15. S Canada & USA. Winters Mexico, Cuba.
48. *Sayornis saya.* Say's Phoebe. 3ss. 17. W N America, Alaska to Mexico.
49. *Colonia colonus.* Long tailed Tyrant. 5ss. 25. Honduras to Brazil, Argentina.
50. *Gubernetes yetapa.* Streamer tailed Tyrant. 42. Bolivia, Brazil, Paraguay, Argentina.
51. *Alectrurus tricolor.* Cock tailed Tyrant. 20:13. Bolivia, Brazil, Paraguay, Argentina.
52. *Alectrurus risora.* Strange tailed Tyrant. 35. Brazil, Paraguay, Uruguay, Argentina.
53. *Knipolegus aterrimus.* White winged Black Tyrant. 4ss. 17. Peru, Brazil to Argentina.
54. *Knipolegus signatus.* Andean Tyrant. 2ss. 16. Peru.
55. incl. *K. s. cabanisi.* Plumbeous Andean Tyrant. 16. Peru, Bolivia, Argentina,
56. *Knipolegus cyanirostris.* Blue billed Black Tyrant. 15. Brazil, Uruguay, Argentina.
57. *Knipolegus lophotes.* Crested Black Tyrant. 20. Brazil, Uruguay, Paraguay.
58. *Knipolegus nigerrimus.* Velvety-black Tyrant. 18. SE Brazil.
59. *Knipolegus orenocensis.* Riverside Tyrant. 3ss. 15. Orinoco & Amazon basins.
60. *Knipolegus subflammulatus.* Berlioz Tyrant. 15. Bolivia (same as 55?)
61. *Knipolegus poecilurus.* Rufous tailed Tyrant. 5ss. 15. Venezuela, Brazil, Bolivia, Trinidad & Tobago.
62. *Knipolegus hudsoni.* Hudson's Black Tyrant. 15. Argentina. Winters Bolivia, Brazil.
63. *Knipolegus poecilocercus.* Amazonian Black Tyrant. 13. Amazonia, Guyana.
64. *Knipolegus striaticeps.* Cinereous Tyrant. 11. Argentina, Paraguay, Bolivia, Brazil.
65. *Hymenops perspicillatus.* Spectacled Tyrant . 2ss. 13. Argentina ,Brazil, Bolivia Paraguay.
66. *Muscipipra vetula.* Shear-tailed Grey-Tyrant. 23. Brazil, Paraguay, Argentina.
67. *Fluvicola nengeta.* Masked Water Tyrant. 2ss. 13. Ecuador, Peru, Brazil.

37
36
38
39
40
41
42
43
44
45
46
47
48
49
50
51
52
53
55
54
60
56
57
58
57
61
62
63
64
65
66
67

TYRANNIDAE (3)
Tyrant Flycatchers

68. *Fluvicola pica.* Pied Water Tyrant. 12. Trinidad & N of South America.
69. *Fluvicola albiventer.* Black backed Water Tyrant. 12. Brazil to Argentina.
70. *Arundicola leucocephala.* White headed Marsh Tyrant. 12. Trinidad, Most of South America.
71. *Pyrocephalus rubinus.* Vermillion Flycatcher. 13ss. 15. SW USA to Argentina, Chile, Galapagos Islands.
71a. Melanistic phase of 71. 15. W Peru.
72. incl. *P. r. nanus.* Dwarf Peruvian Form. 14. Peru.
73. *P. r. dubius.* Galapagos Flycatcher. 15. Galapagos Islands.
74. *Ochthornis littoralis.* Drab Water Tyrant. 14. Guyana, Venezuela, Brazil, Bolivia.
75. *Ochthoeca salvini.* Tumbes Tyrant. 14. Peru.
76. *Satrapa icterophrys.* Yellow browed Tyrant. 16. Brazil, Bolivia, Argentina, Winters Venezuela.
77. *Machirornis rixosus.* Cattle Tyrant. 3ss. 20. Venezuela to Brazil, Argentina.
78. *Sirystes sibilator.* Sirystes. 5ss. 17. Panama to Argentina.
79. *Tyrannus sanana.* Fork tailed Flycatcher. 4ss. 40. Mexico to Argentina.
80. *Tyrannus albogularis.* White throated Kingbird. 5ss. 17. Venezuela, Guyanas, Brazil, Bolivia.
81. *Tyrannus apolites.* Heine's Kingbird. 20. Brazil. (may be hybrid.)
82. *Tyrannus caudifasciatus.* Loggerhead Kingbird. 7ss. 23. Bahamas, N West Indies.
83. *Tyrannus couchii.* Couch's Kingbird. 21. Texas, Mexico.
84. *Tyrannus crassirostris.* Thick billed Kingbird. 3ss. 22. Mexico.
85. *Tyrannus cubensis.* Giant Kingbird. 26. Cuba, Caicos Is.
86. *Tyrannus dominicensis.* Grey Kingbird. 5ss. 21. S USA, West Indies, N S America.
87. *Tyrannus forficatus.* Scissor tailed Flycatcher. 26-36. SE USA to Panama.
88. *Tyrannus melancholicus.* Tropical Kingbird. 4ss. 23. Arizona to Argentina.
89. *Tyrannus niveigularis.* Snowy throated Kingbird. 19. Colombia, Ecuador, Peru.
90. *Tyrannus tyrannus.* Eastern Kingbird. 19. E N America. Winters S America.
91. *Tyrannus verticalis.* Western Kingbird. 19. SW Canada, W USA. Winters C America.
92. *Tyrannus vociferans.* Cassin's Kingbird. 2ss. 17. SW USA to Guatemala.
93. *Myiozetetes luteiventris.* Dusky chested Flycatcher. 2ss. 15. Surinam, Amazonia.
94. *Tyrannopsis sulphurea.* Sulphury Flycatcher. 18. Trinidad, NC South America.
95. *Griseotyrannus aurantioatrocristatus.* Crowned Slaty Flycatcher. 17. Brazil, Argentina. Winters to Venezuela.
96. *Empidonomus varius.* Variegated Flycatcher. 18. South America E of Andes.
97. *Legatus leucophais.* Piratic Flycatcher. 15. Mexico to most of S America, Trinidad.
98. *Conopias cinchoneti.* Lemon browed Flycatcher. 16. Venezuela to Peru.
99. *Conopias parva.* Yellow throated / White ringed Flycatcher. 2ss. 15. Costa Rica to Ecuador, Brazil.
100. *Conopias trivirgata.* Three striped Flycatcher. 15. Amazonia to Argentina.

68
69
70
71 ♀
72
73
71 ♂
71(a)
74
75
76
77
78
79
80
81
82
83
84
85
86
87
88
89
90
91
92
93
94
95
96
97
98
99
100

TYRANNIDAE (4)
Tyrant Flycatchers

101. *Megarhynchus pitangua*. Boat billed Flycatcher. 6ss. 24. Mexico to Argentina, Trinidad.
102. *Myiodynastes bairdii*. Baird's Flycatcher. 23. Ecuador, Peru.
103. *Myiodynastes solitarius*. Solitary Flycatcher. 21. Peru, Uruguay, Argentina.
104. *Myiodynastes chrysocephalus*. Golden crowned Flycatcher. 4ss. 21. Panama to Peru.
105. *Myiodynastes hemichrysus*. Golden bellied Flycatcher. 20. Costa Rica, Panama.
106. *Myiodynastes luteiventris*. Sulphur bellied Flycatcher. 2ss. 21. Arizona to Costa Rica. Winters Peru, Bolivia.
107. *Myiodynastes maculatus*. Streaked Flycatcher. 21. Mexico to Uruguay.
108. *Conopias albovittata*. White ringed Flycatcher. 15. Honduras to Ecuador.
109. *Myiozetetes cayanensis*. Rusty margined Flycatcher. 5ss. 17. Panama to Brazil.
110. *Myiozetetes granadensis*. Grey capped Flycatcher. 3ss. 17. Nicaragua to Brazil.
111. *Myiozetetes/Phelpsia inornata*. White bearded Flycatcher. 15. Venezuela.
112. *Myiozetetes similis*. Social Flycatcher. 17. Mexico to Argentina.
113. *Xenopsaris albinucha*. White naped Xenopsaris. 12. Venezuela to Argentina.
114. *Attila bolivianus*. Dull capped Attila. 21. Upper Amazon basin.
115. *Attila cinnamomeus*. Cinnamon Attila. 17. Guyanas, Venezuela to Bolivia, Brazil.
116. *Attila citriniventris*. Citron-bellied Attila. 17. Venezuela to Peru, Brazil.
117. *Attila rufus*. Grey hooded Attila. 23. SE Brazil.
118. *Attila spadiceus*. Bright rumped Attila. 11ss. 19. Mexico to Brazil.
119. *Attila torridus*. Ochraceous Attila. 20. Ecuador.
120. *Casiornis fusca*. Ash throated Casiornis. 17. E Brazil.
121. *Casiornis rufa*. Rufous Casiornis. 17. Brazil, Peru, Argentina.
122. *Laniocera hypopyrrha*. Cinereous Mourner. 22. Amazon basin & Guyanas.
123. *Laniocera rufescens*. Speckled Mourner. 3ss. 20. Guatemala to Ecuador.
124. *Pitangus lictor*. Lesser Kiskadee. 2ss. 17. Panama to Brazil, Bolivia.
125. *Pitangus sulphuratus*. Great Kiskadee. 12ss. 23. Trinidad, Texas to Argentina.
126. *Pseudattila/Attila phoenicurus*. Rufous tailed Attila. 17. Brazil, Argentina.
127. *Rhytipterna holerythra*. Rufous Mourner. 2ss. 20. Mexico to Ecuador.
128. *Rhytipterna immunda*. Pale bellied Mourner. 21. Colombia, Guyanas, Brazil.
129. *Rhytipterna simplex*. Greyish Mourner. 23. Venezuela, Guyanas to Brazil & Bolivia.

101
102
103
104
105
106
107
108
109
110
111
113
112
114
115
116
117
118
119
120
121
122
123
124
125
126
127
128
129

TYRANNIDAE (5) Flycatchers, Pewees

130. *Myiarchus apicalis*. Apical Flycatcher. 20. Colombia.
131. *Myiarchus barbirostris*. Sad Flycatcher. 16. Jamaica.
132. *Myiarchus cephalotes*. Pale edged Flycatcher. 3ss. 19. Venezuela to Bolivia.
133. *Myiarchus cinerascens*. Ash throated Flycatcher. 2ss. 18. W USA to Costa Rica.
134. *Myiarchus crinitus*. Great crested Flycatcher. 21. E N America, Winters N South America.
135. *Myiarchus ferox. Short crested* Flycatcher. 3ss. 20. Costa Rica to Argentina.
136. *Myiarchus venezuelensis*. Venezuelan Flycatcher. 20. Colombia, Venezuela, Tobago.
137. *Myiarchus panamensis*. Panama Flycatcher. 20. Costa Rica, Panama, Venezuela, Colombia.
138. *Myiarchus oberi*. Lesser Antillean Flycatcher. 3ss. 20. West Indies.
139. *Myiarchus sagrae*. La Sagra's Flycatcher. 2ss. 20. Cuba, Bahamas, Cayman Is.
140. *Myiarchus nugator*. Grenada Flycatcher. 20. Grenada, Southern Lesser Antilles.
141. *Myiarchus magnirostris*. Large billed Flycatcher. 15. Galapagos Is.
142. *Myiarchus nuttingi*. Nutting's Flycatcher. 3ss. 17. Mexico to Costa Rica.
143. *Myiarchus phaeocephalus*. Sooty crowned Flycatcher. 2ss. 20. Ecuador, Peru.
144. *Myiarchus semirufus*. Rufous Flycatcher. 17. Peruvian coast.
145. *Myiarchus stolidus*. Stolid Flycatcher. 2ss. 20. Hispaniola, Jamaica.
146. *Myiarchus antillarum*. Puerto Rican Flycatcher. 20. Puerto Rico.
147. *Myiarchus sclateri*. Sclater's Flycatcher. 20. Martinique.
148. *Myiarchus swainsoni*. Swainson's Flycatcher. 5ss. 20. Venezuela to Argentina, Brazil.
149. *Myiarchus tuberculifer*. Dusky capped Flycatcher. 15ss. 16. S USA to Argentina.
150. *Myiarchus tyrannulus*. Brown crested Flycatcher. 7ss. 20. S USA to Argentina.
151. *Myiarchus validus*. Rufous tailed Flycatcher. 23. Jamaica.
152. *Myiarchus yucatanensis*. Yucatan Flycatcher. 17. Yucatan, Cozumel Is.
153. *Nesotriccus ridgwayi*. Cocos Island Flycatcher. 13. Cocos Is. (off Costa Rica).
154. *Deltarhynchus flammulatus*. Flammulated Flycatcher. 15. S Mexico.
155. *Contopus albogularis*. White throated Pewee. 12. Guyanas.
156. *Contopus borealis*. Olive sided Flycatcher. 17. Alaska, N America. Winters Bolivia.
157. *Contopus caribaeus*. Greater Antillean Pewee. 7ss. 16. Bahamas to Hispaniola.
158. *Contopus cinereus*. Tropical Pewee. 8ss. 13. Mexico to Argentina.
159. *Contopus fumigatus*. Smoke coloured Pewee. 7ss. 17. Venezuela to Argentina.
160. *Contopus lugubris*. Dark Pewee. 17. Costa Rica, Panama.
161. *Contopus latirostris*. Lesser Antillean Pewee. 3ss. 16. Lesser Antilles.
162. *Contopus nigrescens*. Blackish Pewee. 12. Guyana, Brazil, Ecuador, Peru.
163. *Contopus ochraceus*. Ochraceous Pewee. 16. Costa Rica, Panama.
164. *Contopus pertinax*. Greater Pewee / Cone's Flycatcher. 3ss. 15. S USA to Nicaragua.
165. *Contopus sordidulus*. Western wood Pewee. 7ss. 13. Alaska to C America, Winters Peru.
166. *Contopus virens*. Eastern wood Pewee. 13. E N America. Winters to Argentina.
167. Contopus richardsoni. Richardson's wood Pewee. 13. Now considered synonymous with 166.

130
131
132
133
134
135
136
137
138
139
140
141
142
143
144
145
146
147
148
149
150
151
152
153
154
155
156
157
158
159
160
161
162
163
164
165
166
167

TYRANNIDAE (6)
Tyrant Flycatchers, Spadebills

168. *Empidonax affinis*. Pine Flycatcher. 5ss. 13. Mexico.
169. *Empidonax albigularis*. White throated Flycatcher. 3ss. 12. Mexico to Panama.
170. *Empidonax alnorum*. Alder Flycatcher. 13. Alaska to SW USA. Winters to N S America.
171. *Empidonax atriceps*. Black capped Flycatcher. 11. Costa Rica, Panama.
172. *Empidonax difficilis*. Western Flycatcher. 5ss. 12. Western N America to Mexico.
172a. *Empidonax occidentalis*. Cordilleran Flycatcher. 12. Western USA to Mexico.
173. *Empidonax / lathotriccus euleri*. Euler's Flycatcher. 3ss. 13. SC South America.
174. incl. *E. / l. lawrencei*. Lawrence's Flycatcher. 2ss. 12. West Indies, Venezuela, Amazonia.
175. *Empidonax flavescens*. Yellowish Flycatcher. 4ss. 12. Mexico to Panama.
176. *Empidonax flaviventris*. Yellow bellied Flycatcher. 12. N America. Winters Panama.
177. *Empidonax fulvifrons*. Buff breasted Flycatcher. 6ss. 10. SW USA to Honduras.
178. *Empidonax griseipectus*. Grey breasted Flycatcher. 12. Ecuador, Peru.
179. *Empidonax hammondii*. Hammond's Flycatcher. 11. W N America. Winters to Nicaragua.
180. *Empidonax minimus*. Least Flycatcher. 11. Canada, USA. Winters Mexico to Panama.
181. *Empidonax oberholseri*. Dusky Flycatcher. 12. Western N America. Winters Guatemala.
182. *Empidonax trailli*. Willow Flycatcher. 13. Canada, USA. Winters Panama to Bolivia.
183. *Empidonax virescens*. Acadian Flycatcher. 13. Eastern N America. Winters W S America.
184. *Empidonax wrightii*. Grey Flycatcher. 12. California, Arizona. Winters Mexico.
185. *Xenotriccus mexicanus*. Pileated Flycatcher. 13. Mexico.
186. *Xenotriccus callizonus*. Belted Flycatcher. 12. Mexico, Guatemala, Salvador.
187. *Cnemotriccus fuscatus*. Fuscous Flycatcher. 7ss. 15. S America, S to Argentina.
188. *Mitrephanes phaeocercus*. Tufted Flycatcher. 10ss. 13. Mexico to Ecuador.
188a. *Mitrephanes olivaceus*. Olive Flycatcher. 13. Peru to Bolivia.
189. *Myiobius erythrurus*. Ruddy tailed Flycatcher. 7ss. 10. Mexico to Amazonia.
190. *Aphanotriccus audax*. Black billed Flycatcher. 12. Panama, Colombia.
191. *Aphanotriccus capitalis*. Tawny-chested Flycatcher. 11. Costa Rica, Nicaragua.
192. *Myiobius atricaudus*. Black tailed Flycatcher. 7ss. 12. Costa Rica to Brazil.
193. *Myiobius barbatus*. Bearded Flycatcher. 7ss. 12. Honduras to Brazil & Peru.
194. incl. *M. b. sulphureipygius*. Sulphur rumped Flycatcher. 12. Mexico to Honduras.
195. *Myiobius villosus*. Tawny breasted Flycatcher. 4ss. 13. Panama to Bolivia.
196. *Myiotriccus ornatus*. Ornate Flycatcher. 4ss. 11. Colombia to Peru.
197. *Pyrrhomyias cinnamomea*. *Cinnamon* Flycatcher. 6ss. 12. Venezuela, Colombia to Argentina.
198. *Myiophobus cryptoxanthus*. Olive chested Flycatcher. 12. Ecuador, Peru.
199. *Myiophobus fasciatus*. Bran coloured Flycatcher. 7ss. 11. Costa Rica to Argentina.
200. *Myiophobus flavicans*. Flavescent Flycatcher. 5ss. 12. Venezuela to Peru.
201. *Myiophobus inornatus*. Unadorned Flycatcher. 12. Peru, Bolivia.
202. *Myiophobus lintoni*. Orange banded Flycatcher. 12. Ecuador, Peru.
203. *Myiophobus ochraceiventris*. Ochraceous breasted Flycatcher. 2ss. 12. Peru, Bolivia.
204. *Myiophobus phoenicomitra*. Orange crested Flycatcher. 2ss. 12. Colombia, Ecuador.
205. *Myiophobus pulcher*. Handsome Flycatcher. 3ss. 11. Colombia, Ecuador, Peru.
206. *Myiophobus roraimae*. Roraiman Flycatcher. 3ss. 10. Guyana, Amazonia to Peru.
207. incl. *M. r. rufipennis*. Puno Flycatcher. 10. Peru.
208. *Hirundinea ferruginea*. Cliff Flycatcher. 3ss. 17. NW South America.
208a. *Hirundinea bellicose*. Swallow Flycatcher. 17. SE South America.
209. *Onychorhynchus coronatus*. (Amazonian) Royal Flycatcher. 4ss. 17. Amazonia.
210. incl. *O. c. mexicanus*. Northern Royal Flycatcher. 17. Mexico to Colombia, Venezuela.
211. *Platyrinchus coronatus*. Golden crowned Spadebill. 3ss. 10. Honduras to Brazil.
212. *Platyrinchus flavigularis*. Yellow throated Spadebill. 2ss. 10. NW S America.
213. *Platyrinchus leucoryphus*. Russet winged Spadebill. 12. SE S America.
214. *Platyrinchus mystaceus*. White throated Spadebill. 14ss. 10. Costa Rica to Argentina.
215. *Platyrinchus cancrominus*. Stub tailed Spadebill. 10. Mexico to Costa Rica.
216. *Platyrinchus platyrhynchos*. White crested Spadebill. 4ss. 11. Guyana, Amazonia
217. *Platyrinchus saturatus*. Cinnamon crested Spadebill. 2ss. 10. Amazonia.
218. *Cnipodectes subbrunneus*. Brownish Flycatcher. 3ss. 17. Panama to Brazil.
219. *Tolmomyias assimilis*. Yellow margined Flycatcher. 8ss. 14. Costa Rica to Amazonia
220. *Tolmomyias flaviventris*. Yellow breasted Flycatcher. 8ss. 12. NC S America.
221. *Tolmomyias poliocephalus*. Grey crowned Flycatcher. 3ss. 12. Amazonia.
222. *Tolmomyias sulphurescens*. Yellow olive Flycatcher. 15ss. 15. Mexico to Argentina.

168
169
170
171
172
172 A
173
174
175
176
177
178
179
180
181
188A
182
183
184
185
186
187
188
189
190
191
192
193
194
195
196
197
198
199
200
201
202
203
204
205
206
207
208
208 A
209
210
211
212
213
215
217
214
216
218
219
220
221
222

TYRANNIDAE (7)
Flatbills, Tody & Pygmy Tyrants

223. *Rhynchocyclus brevirostris*. Eye-ringed Flatbill. 4ss. 16. Mexico to NW South America.
224. *Rhynchocyclus fulvipectus*. Fulvous breasted Flatbill. 17. Colombia to Bolivia.
225. *Rhynchocyclus olivaceus*. Olivaceous Flatbill. 8ss. 16. Panama to Brazil.
226. *Ramphotrigon fuscicauda*. Dusky tailed Flatbill. 8ss. 12. Colombia to Peru.
227. *Ramphotrigon megacephala*. Large headed Flatbill. 3ss. 12. Local, South America.
228. *Ramphotrigon ruficauda*. Rufous tailed Flatbill. 15ss. 15. Guyanas, Amazonia.
229. *Poecilotriccus albifacies*. White cheeked Tody Flycatcher. 10. Peru. (Unique).
230. *Todirostrum calopterum*. Golden winged Tody Flycatcher. 2ss. 9. Colombia to Peru.
231. *Todirostrum pulchellum*. Black backed Tody Flycatcher. 9. Peru.
232. *Poecilotriccus capitale*. Black & white Tody Flycatcher. 2ss. 10. NW South America
233. *Todirostrum chrysocrotaphum*. Yellow browed Tody Flycatcher. 5ss. 9. Amazonia.
234. *Todirostrum pictum*. Painted Tody Flycatcher. 9. Guyanas, Brazil, Venezuela.
235. *Todirostrum cinereum*. Common Tody Flycatcher. 9ss. 10. Mexico to Brazil.
236. *Todirostrum viridianum*. Short tailed Tody Flycatcher. 8. Trinidad, Venezuela.
237. *Todirostrum fumifrons*. Smoky fronted Tody Flycatcher. 2ss. 9. Guyanas, Brazil.
238. *Todirostrum senex*. Buff cheeked Tody Flycatcher. 10. Brazil.(1 spec. 1829).
239. *Todirostrum latirostre*. Rusty fronted Tody Flycatcher. 7ss. 10. Amazonia.
240. *Todirostrum maculatum*. Spotted Tody Flycatcher. 5ss. 10. Amazon, Orinoco basins
241. *Todirostrum nigriceps*. Black headed Tody Flycatcher. 10. Costa Rica to Ecuador.
242. *Todirostrum plumbeiceps*. Ochre faced Tody Flycatcher 4ss. 10. Peru, Brazil, Argentina.
243. *Todirostrum poliocephalum*. Yellow lored Tody Flycatcher. 10. Brazil.
244. *Todirostrum russatum*. Ruddy Tody Flycatcher. 10. Venezuela, Brazil.
245. *Todirostrum sylvia*. Slate headed Tody Flycatcher. 5ss. 11. Mexico to Brazil.
246. *Todirostrum hypospodium*. Berlepsch's Tody Flycatcher. 11. Colombia. (Unique).
247. *Hemitriccus furcatus. Fork tailed Pygmy* Tyrant. 10. Brazil.
248. *Oncostoma cinereigulare*. Northern Bentbill. 9. Mexico to Panama.
249. *Oncostoma olivaceum*. Southern Bentbill. 9. Panama, Colombia.
250. *Hemitriccus aenigma*. Zimmer's Tody Tyrant. 10. Amazonian Brazil.
251. *Hemitriccus inornatus*. Pelzeln's Tody Flycatcher. 10. NW Brazil.
252. *Hemitriccus granadensis*. Black Throated Tody Tyrant. 7ss. 10. Venezuela to Peru.
253. *Hemitriccus margaritaceiventer*. Pearly vented Tody Tyrant. 7ss. 10. Most of S. America.
254. *Hemitriccus mirandae*. Buff breasted Tody Tyrant. 2ss. 10. E Brazil.
255. *Hemitriccus kaempferi*. Kaempfer's Tody Tyrant. 10. SE Brazil.(l spec 1929).
256. *Hemitriccus nidipendulus*. Hangnest Tody Tyrant. 2ss. 10. E Brazil.
257. *Hemitriccus orbitatus*. Eye-ringed Tody Tyrant. 11. SE Brazil.
258. *Hemitriccus rufigularis*. Buff throated Tody Tyrant. 12. Peru, Bolivia.
259. *Hemitriccus spodiops*. Yungas Tody Tyrant. 10. Bolivia.
260. *Hemitriccus striaticollis*. Stripe-necked Tody Tyrant. 3ss. 11. Peru, Brazil.
261. *Hemitriccus iohannis*. Johannes' Tody Tyrant. 4ss. 10. Colombia to Brazil, Bolivia.
262. *Hemitriccus zosterops*. White eyed Tody Tyrant. 4ss. 10. Guyanas, Amazonia.
263. *Hemitriccus josephinae*. Boat billed Tody Tyrant. 12. Guyana, Surinam, Brazil.
264. *Hemitriccus minor*. Snethlage's Tody Tyrant. 3ss. 9. Surinam, Amazonian Brazil.
265. *Poecilotriccus ruficeps*. Rufous headed Tody Tyrant. 4ss. 10. Venezuela to Peru.
266. *Taeniotriccus andrei*. Black chested Tyrant. 2ss. 11. Venezuela, Brazil.
267. *Lophotriccus eulophotes*. Long crested Pygmy Tyrant. 10. Brazil, Peru.
268. *Lophotriccus pileatus*. Scale crested Pygmy Tyrant. 6ss. *10. Costa* Rica, Brazil.
269. *Lophotriccus vitiosus*. Double banded Pygmy Tyrant. 4ss. 10. Amazonia.
270. *Lophotriccus galeatus*. Helmeted Pygmy Tyrant. 10. Guyana, Amazon basin.
271. *Atalotriccus pilaris*. Pale eyed Pygmy Tyrant. 4ss. 9. Panama to Venezuela, Guyana.
272. *Myiornis auricularis*. Eared Pygmy Tyrant. 9. Brazil, Paraguay, Argentina.
273. *Myiornis ecaudatus*. Short tailed Pygmy Tyrant. 3ss. 7. Panama to Guyanas.
274. *Myiornis atricapillus*. Black capped Pygmy Tyrant. 7. Costa Rica to Ecuador.
275. *Myiornis albiventris*. White bellied Pygmy Tyrant. 7. C Peru.
276. *Pseudotriccus pelzelni*. Bronze-olive Pygmy Tyrant. 4ss. 11. Panama to Peru.
277. *Pseudotriccus ruficeps*. Rufous headed Pygmy Tyrant. 11. Colombia to Bolivia.
278. *Pseudotriccus simplex*. Hazel-fronted Pygmy Tyrant. 11. Peru, Bolivia.
279. *Hemitriccus diops*. Drab breasted Bamboo Tyrant. 12. SE Brazil, Paraguay.
280. *Hemitriccus flammulatus*. Flammulated Bamboo Tyrant. 2ss. 12. Peru, Bolivia.
281. *Hemitriccus cinnamomeipectus*. Cinnamon breasted Tody Flycatcher. 12. Peru.
282. *Hemitriccus obsoletus*. Brown breasted Bamboo Tyrant. 2ss. 12. SE Brazil.

223
224
225
226
227
228
229
♀
♂
230
232
231
233
236
235
237
238
239
234
240
241
242
243
244
245
246
247
248
249
250
251
252
253
254
256
255
257
258
259
260
262
261
263
264
265
266
267
268
269
270
271
272
273
274
275
276
277
278
279
280
281
282

TYRANNIDAE (8)
Tyrant Flycatchers

283. *Phylloscartes eximius*. Southern Bristle Tyrant. 11. Brazil, Paraguay, Argentina.
284. *Phylloscartes flaviventris*. Rufous lored Tyrannulet. 12. Peru, Venezuela.
285. *Phylloscartes gualaquizae*. Ecuadorian Tyrannulet. 11. Ecuador, Peru.
286. *Phylloscartes ophthalmicus*. Marble faced Bristle Tyrant. 3ss. 12. Venezuela, Bolivia.
287. *Phylloscartes orbitalis*. Spectacled Bristle Tyrant. 10. Ecuador, Peru, Bolivia.
288. *Phylloscartes poecilotis*. Variegated Bristle Tyrant. 2ss. 11. Peru,Venezuela.
289.*Phylloscartes venezuelanus*. Venezuelan Bristle Tyrant. 10. Venezuela.
290. *Phylloscartes sylviolus*. Bay ringed Tyrannulet. 11. Brazil, Paraguay, Argentina.
291. *Phylloscartes chapmani*. Chapman's Tyrannulet. 2ss. 11. Venezuela.
292. *Phylloscartes ceciliae*. Alagoas Tyrannulet. 13. Brazil.
292a. *Phylloscartes beckeri*. Bahia Tyrannulet. 13. Brazil.
293. *Phylloscartes difficilis*. Serra do Mar Tyrannulet. 12. SE Brazil.
294. *Phylloscartes lanyoni*. Antioquia Bristle Tyrant. 12. Colombia.
295. *Phylloscartes flavovirens*. Yellow-green Tyrannulet. 11. Panama.
296. *Phylloscartes nigrifrons*. Black fronted Tyrannulet. 13. Venezuela.
297. *Phylloscartes oustaleti*. Oustalet's Tyrannulet. 12. Brazil.
298. *Phylloscartes paulistus*. Sao Paulo Tyrannulet. 11. Brazil, Paraguay.
299. *Phylloscartes roquetti*. Minas Gerais Tyrannulet. 10. E Brazil.
300. *Phylloscartes superciliaris*. Rufous browed Tyrannulet. 3ss. 12, Costa Rica, Panama.
301. *Phylloscartes ventralis*. Mottle-cheeked Tyrannulet. 3ss. 12. SC South America.
302. *Phylloscartes virescens*. Olive-green Tyrannulet. 12. Guyanas.
303. *Capsiempsis flaveola*. Yellow Tyrannulet. 6ss. 11. Nicaragua to Argentina.
304. *Euscarthmus melorhyphus*. Tawny crowned Pygmy Tyrant. 3ss.11. Tropical S America.
305. *Euscarthmus rufomarginatus*. Rufous sided Pygmy Tyrant. 2ss. 12. Surinam, Brazil.
306. *Pseudocolopteryx acutipennis*. Subtropical Doradito. 11. Colombia to Argentina.
307. *Pseudocolopteryx dinellianus*. Dinelli's Doradito. 9. NW Argentina.
308. *Pseudocolopteryx flaviventris*. Warbling Doradito. 12. Brazil to Argentina, Chile.
309. *Pseudocolopteryx sclateri*. Crested Doradito. 10. Brazil, Paraguay, Argentina.
310. *Polystictus pectoralis*. Bearded Tachuri. 3ss. 10. Local, S America.
311. *Polystictus superciliaris*. Grey backed Tachuri. 10. E Brazil.
312. *Culicivora caudacuta*. Sharp tailed Grass Tyrant. 12. Bolivia, Brazil, Argentina.
313. *Tachuris rubrigastra*. Many-coloured Rush Tyrant. 4ss. 12. Peru, Argentina, Chile.
314. *Anairetes alpinus*. Ash-breasted Tit-Tyrant. 13. Peru, Bolivia.
315. *Anairetes flavirostris*. Yellow billed Tit-Tyrant. 4ss. 11. Peru, Chile, Argentina.
316. *Anairetes parulus*. Tufted Tit-Tyrant. 4ss. 11. Colombia to Tierra del Fuego.
317. *Anairetes reguloides*. Pied-Crested Tit-Tyrant. 3ss. 13. Peru to N Chile.
318. *Anairetes nigrocristatus*. Maranon Tit-Tyrant. 10. N Peru.
319. *Anairetes fernandezianus*. Juan Fernandez Tit Tyrant. 10. Juan Fernandez Is. (Chile).
320. *Anairetes agilis*. Agile Tit-Tyrant. 12. Colombia to Ecuador.
321. *Anairetes agraphia*. Unstreaked Tit-Tyrant. 2ss. 12. SE Peru.
322. *Stigmatura budytoides*. Greater Wagtail-Tyrant. 4ss. 14. Brazil to Argentina.
323. *Stigmatura napensis*. Lesser Wagtail-Tyrant. 2ss. 13. Brazil, Amazon basin.
324. *Serpophaga araguayae*. Bananal Tyrannulet. 11. Goias (Brazil, Unique.)
325. *Serpophaga cinerea*. Torrent Tyrannulet. 3ss. 11. Costa Pica to Bolivia.
326. *Serpophaga griseiceps*. Grey crowned Tyrannulet. 10. Bolivia.(4 specimens)
327. *Serpophaga hypoleuca*. River Tyrannulet. 3ss. 11. Venezuela to Bolivia, Brazil.
328. *Serpophaga munda*. White bellied Tyrannulet. 11. CS South America.
329. *Serpophaga nigricans*. Sooty Tyrannulet. 12. Brazil, Bolivia to Argentina.
330. *Serpophaga subcristata*. White crested Tyrannulet. 2ss. 11. SC & S South America. *Serpophaga berliozi*. Berlioz Tyrannulet is the same as Myiopagis gaimardii (362).q.v.
331. *Inezia inornata*. Plain Tyrannulet. 11. S of South America.
332. *Inezia subflava*. Pale-tipped Tyrannulet. 5ss. 12. Guyanas, Brazil, Venezuela.
333. *Inezia tenuirostris*. Slender billed Tyrannulet. 9. Colombia, Venezuela.
334. *Mecocerculus calopterus*. Rufous winged Tyrannulet. 12. Ecuador, Peru.
335. *Mecocerculus hellmayri*. Buff banded Tyrannulet. 11. Peru, Bolivia, Argentina.
336. *Mecocerculus leucophrys*. White throated Tyrannulet. 12ss. 13. Andes, S America
337. *Mecocerculus minor*. Sulphur bellied Tyrannulet. 11.Venezuela to Peru.
338. *Mecocerculus poecilocercus*. White tailed Tyrannulet. 11. Colombia to Peru.
339. *Mecocerculus stictopterus*. White banded Tyrannulet. 3ss. 12. Venezuela to Bolivia.
340. *Coloramphus parvirostris*. Patagonian Tyrant. 13. Chile, Argentina.

283
284
292
285
292A
286
294
287
288
289
290
291
293
295
296
297
298
299
300
301
302
303
304
305
306
307
308
309
310
311
312
313
314
315
316
317
318
319
320
321
322
323
324
325
326
327
328
329
330
331
332
333
334
335
336
337
338
339
340

TYRANNIDAE (9)
Elaenias, Tyrannulets

341. *Elaenia albiceps*. White crested Elaenia. 6ss. 15. Colombia to Tierra del Fuego.
342. *Elaenia chiriquensis*. Lesser Elaenia. 3ss. 13. Costa Rica to Argentina.
343. *Elaenia cristata*. Plain crested Elaenia. 2ss. 13. NC South America.
344. *Elaenia dayi*. Great Elaenia. 3ss. 20. Venezuela.
345. *Elaenia fallax*. Greater Antillean Elaenia. 2ss. 15. Jamaica, Hispaniola.
346. *Elaenia flavogaster*. Yellow bellied Elaenia. 4ss. 15. Mexico to Argentina.
347. *Elaenia frantzii*. Mountain Elaenia. 4ss. 13. Guatemala to Venezuela.
348. *Elaenia gigas*. Mottle-backed Elaenia. 19. Colombia to Bolivia.
349. *Elaenia martinica*. Caribbean Elaenia. 7ss. 15. S West Indies.
350. *Elaenia mesoleuca*. Olivaceous Elaenia. 15. SE Brazil, Paraguay, Argentina.
351. *Elaenia obscura*. Highland Elaenia. 2ss. 19. Ecuador, Paraguay, Brazil, Argentina.
352. *Elaenia pallatangae*. Sierran Elaenia. 4ss. 15. Venezuela to Bolivia.
353. *Elaenia parvirostris*. Small-billed Elaenia. 15. SC South America. Winters to Guyanas.
354. *Elaenia pelzelni*. Brownish Elaenia. 20. Amazonian Brazil, Peru.
355. *Elaenia ruficeps*. Rufous crowned Elaenia. 15. Guyanas, Venezuela, Brazil.
356. *Elaenia spectabilis*. Large Elaenia. 2ss. 17. Colombia to Brazil, Argentina.
357. *Elaenia strepera*. Slaty Elaenia. 15. Bolivia, Argentina. Winters Colombia, Venezuela
358. *Elaenia ridleyana*. Noronha Elaenia. 16. Fernando de Noronha Is. (Brazil).
359. *Myiopagis caniceps*. Grey Elaenia. 4ss. 12. Panama to Brazil, Argentina.
360. *Myiopagis cotta*. Jamaican Elaenia. 15. Jamaica.
361. *Myiopagis flavivertex*. Yellow-crowned Elaenia. 12. Guyanas, Amazon basin.
362. *Myiopagis gaimardii*. Forest Elaenia. 6ss. 12. Trinidad, Panama to Amazonia.
363. *Myiopagis subplacens*. Pacific Elaenia. 15. Ecuador, Peru.
364. *Myiopagis viridicata*. Greenish Elaenia. 10ss. 13. Mexico to N Argentina.
365. *Suiriri suiriri*. Suiriri Flycatcher. 3ss. 13. Lower Amazonia to Argentina.
366. *Suiriri affinis*. Campo Suiriri. 14. Surinam, Brazil, Bolivia.
367. *Sublegatus modestus*. Southern Scrub-Flycatcher. 3ss. 14. Brazil, Argentina.
368. *Sublegatus obscurior*. Dusky Scrub-Flycatcher. 5ss. 14. Amazonia.
369. *Sublegatus arenarum*. (Northern) Scrub-Flycatcher. 15. Costa Rica to Brazil.
370. *Pseudelaenia leucospodia*. Grey & White Tyrannulet. 2ss. 12. Ecuador, Peru.
371. *Phaeomyias murina*. Mouse coloured Tyrannulet. 8ss. 12. Trinidad, S America.
372. *Camptostoma imberbe*. Northern bearded Tyrannulet. 9. S USA to Costa Rica.
373. *Camptostoma obsoletum*. Southern bearded Tyrannulet. 15ss. 11. Costa Rica to Argentina.
374. *Phyllomyias reiseri*. Reiser's Tyrannulet. 14. Brazil, Paraguay.
375. *Phyllomyias sclateri*. Sclater's Tyrannulet. 2ss. 12. Peru to Argentina.
376. *Phyllomyias virescens*. Greenish Tyrannulet. 2ss. 14. Venezuela to Argentina.
377. *Phyllomyias fasciatus*. Planalto Tyrannulet. 4ss. 11. Brazil, Paraguay, Argentina.
378. *Phyllomyias griseiceps*. Sooty headed Tyrannulet. 4ss. 10. Panama to Amazonia.
379. *Phyllomyias australis*. Olrog's Tyrannulet. 11. NW Argentina.
380. *Zimmerius bolivianus*. Bolivian Tyrannulet. 2ss. 12. Peru, Bolivia.
381. *Zimmerius cinereicapillus*. Red billed Tyrannulet. 12. Ecuador, Peru.
382. *Phyllomyias cinereiceps*. Ashy headed Tyrannulet. 11. Colombia, Ecuador, Peru.
383. *Zimmerius gracilipes*. Slender footed Tyrannulet. 3ss. 11. Guyanas, Amazonia.
384. *Phyllomyias nigrocapillus*. Black-capped Tyrannulet. 3ss. 11. Venezuela to Peru.
385. *Phyllomyias uropygialis*. Tawny rumped Tyrannulet. 12. Venezuela to Peru.
386. *Zimmerius vilissimus*. Paltry Tyrannulet. 5ss. 12. Mexico to Colombia.
387. *Zimmerius chrysopsannulet*. 12. Peru to Colombia.. Golden-faced Tyrannulet. 11. Colombia to Peru.
388. *Zimmerius viridiflavus*. Peruvian Tyrannulet. 6ss. 12. Venezuela to Peru.
389. *Zimmerius improbus*. Venezuelan Tyrannulet. 12. Venezuela, Colombia.
390. *Phyllomyias griseocapilla*. Grey capped Tyrannulet. 11. SE Brazil.
391. *Phyllomyias plumbeiceps*. Plumbeous-crowned Tyr

341
342
343
344
345
346
347
348
349
350
351
352
353
358
354
355
356
357
366
350
361
362
363
359
364
365
367
369
368
371
370
372
373
374
375
376
378
377
379
380
381
382
383
389
384
385
386
387
388
390
391

TYRANNIDAE, OXYRUNCIDAE, PHYTOTOMIDAE (10)
Tyrant Flycatchers, Sharpbill, Plantcutters

392. *Tyrannulus elatus*. Yellow crowned Tyrannulet. 2ss. 10. Costa Rica to Bolivia, Brazil.
393. *Phyllomyias burmeisteri*. Rough legged Tyrannulet. 5ss. 11. Venezuela to Argentina.
394. *Phyllomyias zeledoni*. White-fronted Tyrannulet. 11. Costa Rica, Panama.
395. *Ornithion brunneicapillum*. Brown-capped Tyrannulet. 2ss. 8. Costa Rica to Ecuador.
396. *Ornithion inerme*. White lored Tyrannulet. 9. NE of S America.
397. *Ornithion semiflavum*. Yellow bellied Tyrannulet. 9. Mexico, C America.
398. *Leptopogon amaurocephalus*. Sepia-capped Flycatcher. 8ss. 13. Mexico to Argentina.
399. *Leptopogon rufipectus*. Rufous breasted Flycatcher. 2ss. 13. Venezuela to Peru.
400. *Leptopogon superciliaris*. Slaty capped Flycatcher. 7ss. 13. Costa Rica to Bolivia.
401. *Leptopogon taczanowskii*. Inca Flycatcher. 19. E Peru.
402. *Mionectes olivacens*. Olive striped Flycatcher. 7ss. 15. Costa Rica to Peru.
403. *Mionectes striaticollis*. Streak necked Flycatcher. 6ss. 15. Colombia to Bolivia.
404. *Mionectes macconnelli*. McConnell's Flycatcher. 4ss. 12. N of S America.
405. *Mionectes oleagineus*. Ochre bellied Flycatcher. 15ss. 12. Mexico to Brazil, Trinidad.
406. *Mionectes rufiventris*. Grey hooded Flycatcher. 13. Brazil, Paraguay, Argentina.
407. *Corythopis delalandei*. Southern Antpipit. 14. Bolivia, Brazil, Paraguay, Argentina.
408. *Corythopis torquata*. Ringed Antpipit. 4ss. 14. S America, S to Brazil, Bolivia.

Nos. 407, 408. are now commonly placed in *Conopophagidae*: Gnateaters. (Family 105, Plate 194.)

Family 108. OXYRUNCIDAE. Sharpbill.

1. *Oxyruncus cristatus*. Sharpbill . 5ss. 17. Scattered from Costa Rica to Paraguay.

Family 109. PHYTOTOMIDAE. Plantcutters.

1. *Phytotoma raimondii*. Peruvian Plantcutter. 17. Peru.
2. *Phytotoma rara*. Rufous tailed Plantcutter. 19. Chile, Argentina, Falkland Is.
3. *Phytotoma rutila*. White tipped Plantcutter. 18. Bolivia, Argentina, Uruguay.

392
393
394
395
396
397
398
399
400
401
402
403
404
405
406
407
408
OXYRUNCIDAE
1
PHYTOTOMIDAE
1
2
3

PIPRIDAE (1)
Manakins

Family 110. PIPRIDAE. Manakins.

1. *Pipra aureola*. Crimson hooded Manakin. 4ss. 10. Guyanas, Venezuela, Brazil.
2. *Pipra caeruleocapilla*. Cerulean-capped Manakin. 9. Peru.
3. *Pipra chloromeros*. Round tailed Manakin. 11. Peru, Bolivia.
4. *Pipra cornuta*. Scarlet-horned Manakin. 12. Venezuela, Guyana, Brazil.
5. *Pipra coronata*. Blue crowned Manakin. 7ss. 9. Costa Rica to Bolivia, Brazil.
6. incl. *P. c. exquisita*. Exquisite Manakin. 9. Peru, Brazil.
7. Pipra *erythrocephala*. Golden-headed Manakin. 3ss. 9. Panama to Brazil, Peru.
8. *Pipra fasciicauda*. Band tailed Manakin. 5ss. 10. Amazon basin to Argentina.
9. *Pipra iris*. Opal-crowned Manakin. 2ss. 9. SE Brazil.
10. *Pipra isidorei*. Blue rumped Manakin. 2ss. 8. Colombia to N Peru.
11. *Pipra mentalis*. Red capped Manakin. 3ss. 10. Mexico to Ecuador.
12. *Pipra nattereri*. Snow-capped Manakin. 9. Brazil, Bolivia.
13. *Pipra pipra*. White crowned Manakin. 13ss. 10. Costa Rica to Brazil & Peru.
14. *Pipra rubrocapilla*. Red headed Manakin. 10. Peru, Brazil, Bolivia.
15. *Pipra serena*. White fronted Manakin. 9. Guyanas, Venezuela, Brazil.

15a. *Pipra suavissima*. Tepui Manakin. 9. Guyana, Venezuela.

16. *Pipra vilaboasi*. Golden crowned Manakin. 9. Brazil.
17. *Pipra obscura*. Sick's Manakin. 8. Brazil.2specimens. Perhaps female 16.
18. *Pipra filicauda*. Wire tailed Manakin. 11. Venezuela to Peru, Brazil.
19. *Antilophia galeata*. Helmeted Manakin. 15. Brazil, Paraguay.
20. *Chiroxiphia caudata*. Swallow tailed / Blue Manakin. 15. Brazil, Paraguay, Argentina.
21. *Chiroxiphia lanceolata*. Lance tailed Manakin. 13. Costa Rica to Venezuela.
22. *Chiroxiphia linearis*. Long tailed Manakin. 10+12. Mexico to Costa Rica.
23. *Chiroxiphia pareola*. Blue backed Manakin. 5ss. 12. NE S America, Tobago.
24. *Chiroxiphia boliviana*. Yungas Manakin. 12. Bolivia, Peru.
25. *Masius chrysopterus*. Golden-winged Manakin. 5ss. 11. Venezuela to Peru.
26. *Ilicura militaris*. Fin-tailed Manakin. 12. SE Brazil.
27. *Corapipo gutturalis*. White-throated Manakin. 9. Guyanas, Venezuela, Brazil.

1
2
3
4
5
6
7
8
9
10
11
12
13
14
15
15A
16
♀?
17
♂?
18
19
20
21
22
23
24
25
26
27

PIPRIDAE (2)
Manakins

28. *Corapipo leucorhoa*. White bibbed Manakin. 2ss. 9. Colombia,Venezuela.
29. *Corapipo altera*. White ruffed Manakin. 10. Honduras to Colombia.
30. *Manacus corritus*. Almirante Manakin. 10. Panama.
31. *Manacus manacus*. White bearded Manakin. 11ss. 10. Trinidad & N of S America.
32. *Manacus candei*. White collared Manakin 11. Mexico to Costa Rica.
33. *Manacus vitellinus*. Golden collared Manakin. 3ss. 10. Panama, Colombia.
34. *Manacus aurantiacus*. Orange collared Manakin. 10. Costa Rica, Panama.

Manacus coronatus. (Not Illustrated) Boucard 's Manakin. Colombia . Single Species. Considered Hybrid

35. *Machaeropterus deliciosus*. Club winged Manakin. 10. Colombia, Ecuador.
36. *Machaeropterus pyracephalus*. Fiery capped Manakin. 2ss. 9. Amazon basin.
37. *Machaeropterus regulus*. Striped Manakin. 6ss. 9. Venezuela to Peru & Brazil.
38. *Xenopipo atronitens*. Black Manakin. 13. N & NW Amazonia.
39. *Chloropipo flavicapilla*. Yellow headed Manakin. 12. Colombia, Ecuador.
40. *Chloropipo holochlora*. Green Manakin. 4ss. 12. Panama to Peru.
41. *Chloropipo unicolor*. Jet Manakin. 12. Ecuador, Peru.
42. *Chloropipo uniformis*. Olive Manakin. 2ss. 13. Venezuela, Guyanas, Brazil.
43. *Neopipo cinnamomea*. Cinnamon Tyrant-Manakin. 2ss. 9. Guyanas, Upper Amazon.
44. *Heterocercus aurantiivertex*. Orange crested Manakin. 14. Ecuador, Peru.
45. *Heterocercus flavivertex*. Yellow crested Manakin. 14. Colombia, Venezuela, Brazil.
46. *Heterocercus linteatus*. Flame crested Manakin. 14. Brazil, Peru, Bolivia.
47. *Heterocercus luteocephalus*. Golden crested Manakin. 14. Unique (hybrid?)
48. *Neopelma aurifrons*. Wied's Tyrant-Manakin. 12. E Brazil.
49. incl. *N. c. chrysolophum*. Pinto's Manakin. 2ss. 12. S Brazil.
50. *Neopelma chrysocephalum*. Saffron crested Manakin. 12. N of S America.
51. *Neopelma pallescens*. Pale bellied Tyrant-Manakin. 13. NE & C Brazil.
52. *Neopelma sulphureiventer*. Sulphur bellied Tyrant-Manakin. 12. W Amazonia.
53. *Tyranneutes stolzmanni*. Dwarf Tyrant-Manakin. 9. Venezuela, Bolivia, Brazil.
54. *Tyranneutes virescens*. Tiny Tyrant-Manakin. 8. S America, N of Amazon.
55. *Piprites chloris*. Wing barred Manakin. 7ss. 12. S America S to N Argentina.
56. *Piprites griseiceps*. Grey headed Manakin. 10. Guatemala to Costa Rica.
57. *Piprites pileatus*. Black capped Manakin. 12. S Brazil, N Argentina.
58. *Sapayoa aenigma*. Broad billed Manakin. 15. Panama to Ecuador.
59. *Schiffornis major*. Greater Schiffornis / Manakin. 15. Amazon basin.
60. *Schiffornis turdinus*. Thrushlike Schiffornis / Manakin. 13ss. 16. Mexico to Brazil.
61. *Schiffornis virescens*. Greenish Schiffornis / Manakin. 15. Brazil, Paraguay, Argentina.

Nos. 59-61 now thought to belong to Family 107.(*Tyrranidae*)

28
29
30
31
32
33
34
35
36
37
38
39
42
43
40
41
44
45
46
47
53
51
52
48
49
50
54
55
56
57
58
59
60
61

COTINGIDAE (1)
Cotingas

Family 111. COTINGIDAE. Cotingas.

1. *Rupicola peruviana.* Andean Cock of the rock. 4ss. 27. Venezuela to Bolivia, Peru.
2. *Rupicola rupicola.* Guianan Cock of the rock. 27. N Amazonia.
3. *Laniisoma elegans.* Shrike like Cotinga. 4ss. 17. Venezuela to Bolivia, Brazil.
4. *Phibaluza flavirostris.* Swallow tailed Cotinga. 22. Brazil, Paraguay, Argentina.
5. *Tijuca atra.* Black & gold Cotinga. 27. SE Brazil.
6. *Tijuca condita.* Grey winged Cotinga. 21. SE Brazil. (male unknown)
7. *Carpornis cucullatus.* Hooded Berryeater. 22. SE Brazil.
8. *Carpornis melanocephalus.* Black headed Berryeater. 20. SE Brazil.
9. *Porphyrolaema porphyrolaema.* Purple throated Cotinga. 16. Colombia, Peru, Brazil
10. *Cotinga amabilis.* Lovely Cotinga. 18. Mexico to Costa Rica.
11. *Cotinga cayana.* Spangled Cotinga. 21. Guyanas, Amazon & Orinoco basins.
12. *Cotinga cotinga.* Purple breasted Cotinga. 18. Guyanas, Venezuela, Brazil.
13. *Cotinga maculata.* Banded Cotinga. 20. Brazil.
14. *Cotinga maynana.* Plum throated Cotinga. 18. Upper Amazon basin.
15. *Cotinga nattereri.* Blue Cotinga. 18. Panama to Venezuela, Ecuador.
16. *Cotinga ridgwayi.* Turquoise Cotinga. 18. Costa Rica, Panama.
17. *Xipholina atropurpurea.* White winged Cotinga. 20. Brazil coast.
18. *Xipholina lamellipennis.* White tailed Cotinga. 20. Brazil S of Amazon.
19. *Xipholina punicea.* Pompadour Cotinga. 20. North of S America.

1
2
3
4
5
-7-
8
- 9 -
6
10
11
12
13
14
15
16
17
18
19

COTINGIDAE (2)
Cotingas, Fruiteaters

20. *Carpodectes antoniae*. Yellow billed Cotinga. 20. Costa Rica, Panama.
21. *Carpodectes hopkei*. Black tipped Cotinga. 23. Panama to Ecuador.
22. *Carpodectes nitidus*. Snowy Cotinga. 20. Honduras to Panama.
23. *Conioptilon mcilhennyi*. Black faced Cotinga. 20. SE Peru.
24. *Ampelion rubrocristata*. Red crested Cotinga. 20. Venezuela to Bolivia.
25. *Ampelion rufaxilla*. Chestnut crested Cotinga. 2ss. 22. Colombia to Bolivia.
26. *Doliornis sclateri*. Bay vented Cotinga. 20. Peru.
27. *Zaratornis stresemanni*. White cheeked Cotinga. 20. Peru.
28. *Pipreola arcuata*. Barred Fruiteater. 2ss. 22. Andes, Venezuela to Bolivia.
29. *Pipreola aureopectus*. Golden breasted Fruiteater. 2ss. 16. Colombia, Venezuela.
30. *Pipreola lubomirskii*. Black chested Fruiteater. 16. Colombia, Ecuador.
31. *Pipreola jucunda*. Orange breasted Fruiteater. 17. Colombia, Ecuador.
32. *Pipreola pulchra*. Masked Fruiteater. 17. Peru.
33. *Pipreola chlorolepidota*. Fiery throated Fruiteater. 12. Ecuador, Peru, Colombia.
34. *Pipreola formosa*. Handsome Fruiteater. 3ss. 16. Venezuela.
35. *Pipreola frontalis*. Scarlet breasted Fruiteater. 2ss. 16. Ecuador to Bolivia.
36. *Pipreola intermedia*. Band tailed Fruiteater. 2ss. 21. Peru, Bolivia.
37. *Pipreola riefferii*. Green & black Fruiteater. 5ss. 20. Venezuela to Peru.
38. *Pipreola whiteleyi*. Red banded Fruiteater. 2ss. 17. Guyana, Venezuela.
39. *Ampelioides tschudii*. Scaled Fruiteater. 20. Andes, Venezuela to Peru.
40. *Iodopleura fusca*. Dusky Purpletuft. 10. Guyanas, Venezuela.
41. *Iodopleura isabellae*. White browed Purpletuft. 11. Amazon basin.
42. *Iodopleura pipra*. Buff throated Purpletuft. 9. SE Brazil.
43. *Calyptura cristata*. Kinglet Calyptura. 8. SE Brazil.

20
21
22
23
24
25
26
27
28
29
30
31
32
33
34
35
36
37
38
39
40
41
42
43

COTINGIDAE (3)
Pihas, Becards, Tityras

44. *Lipaugus Cryptolophus*. Olivaceous Piha. 2ss. 22. Andes, Colombia to Peru.
45. *Lipaugus fuscocinereus*. Dusky Piha. 32. Colombia, Ecuador.
46. *Lipaugus lanioides*. Cinnamon vented Piha.. 26. SE Brazil.
47. *Lipaugus streptophorus*. Rose collared Piha. 21. Guyana, Venezuela, Brazil.
48. *Lipaugus unirufus*. Rufous Piha. 2ss. 22. Mexico to Colombia, Ecuador.
49. *Lipaugus vociferans*. Screaming Piha. 26. Guyanas & Amazon basin.
50. *Chirccylla uropygialis*. Scimitar winged Piha. 26. N Bolivia.

The following Nos. 52-72 are now commonly listed under *TYRANNIDAE*.

52. *Pachyramphus aglaiae*. Rose throated Becard. 12ss. 16. Texas to Costa Rica.
53. *Pachyramphus albogriseus*. Black & White Becard. 5ss. 14. Nicaragua to Peru.
54. *Pachyramphus castaneus*. Chestnut crowned Becard. 5ss. 14. Tropical S America.
55. *Pachyramphus cinnamomeus*. Cinnamon Becard. 4ss. 14. Mexico to Ecuador.
56. *Pachyramphus major*. Gray collared Becard. 3ss. 15. Mexico to Nicaragua.
57. *Pachyramphus marginatus*. Black capped Becard. 2ss. 14. S America, S to Brazil.
58. *Pachyramphus minor*. Pink throated Becard. 17. Guyanas & Amazon basin.
59. *Pachyramphus niger*. Jamaican Becard. 20. Jamaica.
60. *Pachyramphus polychopterus*. White winged Becard. 8ss. 15. Guatemala to Argentina.
61. *Pachyramphus homocrous*. One coloured Becard. 16. Colombia, Ecuador.
62. *Pachyramphus validus*. Crested Becard. 19. Peru, Bolivia, Brazil, Argentina,
63. *Pachyramphus rufus*. Cinereous Becard. 2ss. 13. Panama to Peru & Brazil.
64. *Pachyramphus spodiurus*. Slaty Becard. 14. Peru, Ecuador.
65. *Pachyramphus surinamus*. Glossy backed Becard. 14. Surinam, Cayenne, Brazil.
66. *Pachyramphus xanthogenys*. Yellow cheeked Becard. 2ss. 14. Ecuador, Peru.
67. *Pachyramphus versicolor*. Barred Becard. 3ss. 12. Costa Rica to Bolivia.
68. *Pachyramphus viridis*. Green backed Becard. 4ss. 15. Venezuela to Argentina.
69. *Tityra cayana*. Black tailed Tityra. 3ss. 20. E S America, Guyanas to Paraguay.
70. *Tityra inquisitor*. Black crowned Tityra. 6ss. 18. Mexico to Argentina.
71. *Tityra semifasciata*. Masked Tityra. 9ss. 20. Centra1 & much of South America.
72. *Tityra brasiliensis*. Brazilian Tityra. 19. Brazil. (= *T. leucura*. conspf. 69?)

* Note. 58, 61,& 62 sometimes regarded as separate genus '*PLATYPSARIS*', but now generally included in *Pachyramphus*.

62 *P. validus* was formerly known as *Platytpsaris rufus*.

44
45
46
47
48
49
50
51
54
52
53
55
56
57
58
59
60
61
62
63
64
65
66
67
68
69
70
71
72

COTINGIDAE (4)
Fruit Crows, Cotingas, etc.

73. *Haematoderus militaris*. Crimson Fruitcrow. 37. Guyanas, Lower Amazon.
74. *Querula Purpurata*. Purple throated Fruitcrow. 30. Costa Rica to Brazil & Bolivia.
75. *Pyroderus scutatus*. Red ruffed Fruitcrow. 5ss. 42. S America S to Argentina.
76. *Cephalopterus glabricollis*. Bare necked Umbrellabird. 45:37. Costa Rica, Panama.
77. *Cephalopterus ornatus*. Amazonian Umbrellabird. 47. Guyanas, Amazon basin.
78. *Cephalopterus penduliger*. Long-wattled Umbrellabird. 45. Colombia, Ecuador.
79. *Perissocephalus tricolor*. Capuchinbird. 35. Guyanas, Venezuela, Brazil.
80. *Gymnoderus foetidus*. Bare necked Fruitcrow. 37. Guyanas & Amazon basin.
81. *Procnias alba*. White Bellbird. 26. Venezuela, Guyanas, Brazil.
82. *Procnias averano*. Bearded Bellbird. 2ss. 25. Guyana, Venezuela, Colombia.
83. *Procnias nudicollis*. Bare throated Bellbird. 26. Brazil, Paraguay, Argentina.
84. *Procnias tricarunculata*. Three wattled Bellbird. 36:27. Honduras to Panama.
85. *Phoenicircus carnifex*. Guianan Red Cotinga. 21. Guyanas, Venezuela, Brazil.
86. *Phoenicircus nigricollis*. Black necked Red Cotinga. 23. Amazon basin.

73
74
75
76
77
78
79
80
81
82
83
84
85
86

PITTIDAE
Pittas

Family 112. PITTIDAE. Pittas.

1. *Pitta anerythra*. Black faced Pitta. 3ss. 15. Solomon Is.
2. *Pitta angolensis*. African Pitta. 3ss. 18. Tropical Africa.
3. *Pitta arcuata*. Blue banded Pitta. 15. Borneo, Palawan.
4. *Pitta baudii*. Blue headed Pitta. 20:17. Borneo.
5. *Pitta brachyura*. Indian Pitta. 2ss. 20. Indian sub-continent.
6. *Pitta megarhyncha*. Mangrove Pitta. 23. S E Asia.
7. *Pitta caerulea*. Giant Pitta. 2ss. 29. Malaya, Sumatra, Borneo.
8. *Pitta cyanea*. Blue Pitta. 23. NE India to SE Asia.
9. *Pitta elliotii*. Bar bellied Pitta. 23. Indo-China.
10. *Pitta erythrogaster*. Red bellied Pitta. 23ss. 17. Philippines, Sulawesi to New Guinea & Queensland.
11. *Pitta dohertyi*. Sula Pitta. 17. Sula Is. (off E Sulawesi).
12. *Pitta macklotii*. Blue breasted Pitta. 16. New Guinea, Queensland.
13. *Pitta granatina*. Garnet Pitta. 3ss. 16. Malaya, Sumatra, Borneo.
14. *Pitta guajana*. Banded Pitta. 6ss. 23. Malaya, Greater Sundas.
15. *Pitta gurneyi*. Gurney's Pitta. 22. Thailand, Burma.
16. *Pitta kochi*. Whiskered Pitta. 26. Luzon. (Philippines).
17. *Pitta iris*. Rainbow Pitta. 16. N & NW Australia.
18. *Pitta maxima*. Ivory breasted Pitta. 28. Halmahera, Batjan, N Moluccas.
19. *Pitta moluccensis*. Blue winged Pitta. 18. China, SE Asia, Borneo. Winters Gr. Sundas.
20. *Pitta nympha*. Fairy Pitta. 19. Japan, Korea, China. Winters SE Asia, Borneo.

1
2
3
4
5
6
19
20
13
7
8
9
10
12
11
14
15
16
17
18

PITTIDAE (2), PHILEPITTIDAE
Pittas, Asities, False Sunbirds

21. *Pitta nipalensis*. Blue naped Pitta. 2ss. 25. Himalayas, SE Asia.
22. *Pitta oatesi*. Rusty naped Pitta. 4ss. 25. Burma, Thailand, Indo-China.
23. *Pitta phayrei*. Eared Pitta. 2ss. 23. SW China, Burma, Thailand, Indo-China.
24. *Pitta reichenowi*. Green breasted Pitta. 17. Cameroon to Zaire & Uganda.
25. *Pitta schneideri*. Schneider's Pitta. 22. Sumatra. (Possibly extinct.)
26. *Pitta sordida*. Hooded Pitta. 13ss. 19. Himalayas, SE Asia, Philippines, New Guinea.
27. *Pitta soror*. Blue rumped Pitta. 4ss. 25. China, Thailand, Indo-China, Hainan.
28. *Pitta steeri*. Azure breasted Pitta. 2ss. 25. Philippines.
29. *Pitta venusta*. Black crowned Pitta. 17. Sumatra.
30. *Pitta superba*. Superb Pitta. 22. Manus Is.(Admiralty Islands.)
31. *Pitta elegans*. Elegant Pitta. 5ss. 17. Moluccas & Lesser Sundas.

Family 113. PHILEPITTIDAE. Asities, False Sunbirds.

1. *Philepitta castanea*. Velvet Asity. 15. Malagasy.
2. *Philepitta schlegeli*. Schlegel's Asity. 15. Malagasy.
3. *Neodrepanis coruscans*. Wattled false Sunbird. 9. Malagasy.
4. *Neodrepanis hypoxantha*. Small billed false Sunbird. 9. Malagasy.

21
22
23
24
25
26
27
28
29
30
32
31
PHILEPITTIDAE
1
2
3
4

ACANTHISITIDAE, MENURIDAE, ATRICHOR NITHIDAE

New Zealand Wrens, Lyrebirds, Scrub Birds

Family 114. ACANTHISITIDAE. New Zealand Wrens.

1. *Xenicus gilviventris*. Rock Wren. 10. South Island.
2. *Xenicus longipes*. Bush Wren. 3ss. 10. New Zealand. (perhaps extinct.)
3. *Acanthisitta chloris*. Rifleman. 3ss. 8. New Zealand.
4. *Traversia/Xenicus lyelli*. Stephen Island Wren. 10. Stephen I. (extinct.)

Family 115. MENURIDAE. Lyrebirds.

1. *Menura alberti*. Prince Albert's Lyrebird. 89:76. S E Queensland.
2. *Menura novaehollandiae*. Superb Lyrebird. 100:86. New South Wales, Victoria, Tasmania.

Family 116. ATRICHORNITHIDAE. Scrub Birds.

1. *Atrichornis clamosus*. Noisy / Western Scrubbird. 23:20. SW Australia.
2. *Atrichornis rufescens*. Rufous Scrubbird. 19:16. New South Wales, SE Queensland.

ACANTHISITTIDAE
1
2
3
4
1
MENURIDAE
2
ATRICHORNITHIDAE
1
2

ALAUDIDAE (1) Larks

Family 117. ALAUDIDAE. Larks.

1. *Mirafra africana.* Rufous naped Lark. 25ss. 15:18. Africa south of Sahara.
2. *Mirafra tropicalis.* East African Bushlark. 16. East & Central Africa.
3. *Mirafra africanoides.* Fawn coloured Lark. 10ss. 14. NE & S Africa.
4. *Mirafra alopex.* Abyssinian Lark. 14. Ethiopia, Somalia.
5. Certhilauda albescens. Karoo Lark. 7ss. 17. Namibia & South Africa.
6. *Certhilauda erythrochlamys.* Dune Lark. 17. Namibia.
7. *Mirafra albicauda.* White tailed Lark. 2ss. 13. Chad, Sudan to East Africa.
8. *Mirafra angolensis.* Angolan Lark. 5ss. 16. Angola, Zambia, Zaire.
9. *Mirafra apiata.* Clapper Lark. 6ss. 15. Namibia, Botswana, South Africa.
10. *Mirafra damarensis.* Damara Clapper Lark. 15. Namibia.
11. *Mirafra assamica.* Rufous winged Bushlark. 5ss. 15. India, SE Asia.
12. *Certhilauda burra.* Ferruginous Lark. 19. Namibia.
13. *Mirafra cantillans.* Singing Bushlark. 4ss. 15. N Africa & Arabia to India.
14. *Mirafra cheniana.* Latakoo Lark. 14. Zimbabwe, Botswana, South Africa.
15. *Certhilauda chuana.* Short clawed Lark. 19. Transvaal, Botswana.
16. *Mirafra collaris.* Collared Lark. 13. Kenya, Somalia.
17. *Certhilauda curvirostris.* Long billed Lark. 9ss. 20. Angola to South Africa.
18. *Mirafra cordofanica.* Kordofan Lark. 16. Africa S of Sahara.
19. *Mirafra erythroptera.* Indian (Red winged) Bushlark. 4ss. 14. India, Pakistan.
20. *Mirafra gilletti.* Gillett's Lark. 14. Ethiopia, Somalia, Kenya.
21. *Mirafra degodiensis.* Degodi Lark. 12. S Ethiopia.
22. *Mirafra hova.* Madagascar Lark. 13. Malagasy.
23. *Mirafra hypermetra.* Red winged Lark. 4ss. 23. NE Africa.
24. *Mirafra javanica.* Australasian Lark. 20ss. 15. SE Asia to S Australia.
25. *Mirafra candida.* Nyiro Lark. 15. Kenya.
26. Pinarocorys nigricans. Dusky Lark. 19. C & S Africa.
27. *Pinarocorys erythropygia.* Rufous rumped Lark. 17. Gambia to Uganda & Sudan.
28. *Mirafra passerina.* Monotonous Lark. 14. Namibia, Botswana, Zimbabwe.
29. *Mirafra poecilosterna.* Pink breasted Lark. 3ss. 15. Somalia to Tanzania.
30. *Mirafra pulpa.* Friedmann's Lark. 13. Ethiopia. (3 Specimens, extinct?)
31. *Heteromirafra ruddi.* Rudd's Lark. 2ss. 14. Transvaal, Orange Free State.
32. *Heteromirafra sidamoensis.* Sidamo Lark. 16. S Ethiopia. (2 specimens.)
33. *Heteromirafra archeri.* Archer's Lark. 15. Somalia. (last record 1955.)
34. *Mirafra rufa.* Rusty Lark. 3ss. 14. Mali, Sudan.
35. *Mirafra rufocinnamomea.* Flappet Lark. 12ss. 13. Africa south of Sahara.
36. *Mirafra sabota.* Sabota Lark. 6ss. 15. Botswana, Zimbabwe, RSA.
37. *Mirafra naevia.* Bradfield's Lark. 15. Angola to W South Africa.
38. *Mirafra sharpii.* (Red) Somali Lark. 16. N Somalia.
39. *Mirafra somalica.* Somali long billed Lark. 16. N Somalia.
40. *Mirafra ashi.* Ash's Lark. 16. Coastal Somalia. (only female known.)
41. *Mirafra williamsi.* Williams' Lark. 13. Marsabit, Kenya.
42. *Chersomanes albofasciata.* Spike heeled Lark. 18ss. 15. Tanzania to Cape.
43. *Eremopterix australis.* Black eared Finch / Sparrow-Lark. 13. Southern Africa.
44. *Eremopterix grisea.* Ashy crowned Finch-Lark. 13. India, Pakistan, Sri Lanka.
45. *Eremopterix leucopareia.* Fischer's Finch-Lark. 11. Kenya, Uganda, Malawi.
46. *Eremopterix leucotis.* Chestnut backed Finch-Lark. 4ss. 13. Africa S of Sahara.
47. *Eremopterix nigriceps.* Black crowned Finch-Lark. 4ss. 11. Atlantic Is., N Africa to Arabia, India.
48. *Eremopterix signata.* Chestnut headed Finch-Lark. 2ss. 11. Sudan to Kenya.
49. *Eremopterix verticalis.* Grey backed Finch-Lark. 3ss. 13. Angola, Zambia to South Africa.

1
2
3
5
6
4
7
8
9
10
11
12
13
14
15
16
18
17
19
20
22
27
21
23
24
25
26
28
29
30
31
37
32
33
40
34
35
36
38
39
41
42
43
44
45
46
47
48
49

ALAUDIDAE (2)
Larks

50. *Ammomanes cincturus.* Bar-tailed Lark. 4ss. 13/16. Sahara, Arabia, Afghanistan.
51. *Ammomanes deserti.* Desert Lark. 25ss. 15. Deserts N Africa to NW India.
52. *Ammomanes grayi.* Gray's Lark. 2ss. 14. SW Angola, Namibia.
53. *Ammomanes phoenicurus.* Rufous tailed Lark. 2ss. 16. India.
54. *Alaemon alaudipes.* Greater Hoopoe-Lark. 4ss. 23. Cape Verde Is., N Africa to NW India.
55. *Alaemon hamertoni.* Lesser Hoopoe-Lark. 3ss. 20. Somalia.
56. *Ramphocoris clotbey.* Thick billed Lark. 17. Morocco, N Africa to NW Arabia.
57. *Melanocorypha bimaculata.* Bimaculated Lark. 3ss. 16. S Eurasia. Winters NE Africa.
58. *Melanocorypha calandra.* Calandra Lark. 3ss. 19. Mediterranean, Middle East.
59. *Melanocorypha leucoptera.* White winged Lark. 17. Turkey, S Russia, C Asia.
60. *Melanocorypha maxima.* Long billed / Tibetan Lark. 2ss. 21. Tibet, India, China.
61. *Melanocorypha mongolica.* Mongolian Lark. 18. Mongolia, Manchuria.
62. *Melanocorypha yeltoniensis.* Black Lark. 19. Russia, Siberia. Winters Black Sea.
63. *Calandrella acutirostris.* Hume's Lark. 2ss. 15. SW Asia to Tibet.
64. *Calandrella cinerea.* Red capped Lark. 10ss. 15. E & S Africa.
65. *Calandrella erlangeri.* Erlanger's Lark. 15. Ethiopia.
66. *Calandrella brachydactyla.* Greater Short toed Lark. 15. Mediterranean to India.
67. *Calandrella cheleensis.* Asian short toed Lark. 14. China, Manchuria.
68. *Spizocorys conirostris.* Pink billed Lark. 5ss. 13. S Africa, Namibia.
69. *Eremalauda dunni.* Dunn's Lark. 2ss. 14. Sahara, W Arabia.
70. *Spizocorys fringillaris.* Botha's Lark. 12. Orange Free State.
71. *Spizocorys obbiensis.* Obbia Lark. 11. Somalia.
72. *Spizocorys personata.* Masked Lark. 4ss. 14. Ethiopia, Kenya.
73. *Calandrella raytal.* Indian Sandlark. 3ss. 13. Iran to India, Assam & Burma.
74. *Alauda razae.* Razo Skylark. 15. Razo I. (Cape Verde Is).
75. *Calandrella rufescens.* Lesser Short toed / Rufous Lark. 9ss. 13. S Palearctic.
76. *Calandrella athensis.* Athi Short toed Lark. 13. Kenya, Tanzania.
77. *Spizicorys sclateri.* Sclater's Lark. 3ss. 14. Namibia & W South Africa.
78. *Calandrella blanfordi.* Blanford's Lark. 14. Ethiopia, Somalia, Arabia.
79. *Calandrella somalica.* Rufous short toed Lark. 3ss. 13. Somalia.
80. *Eremalauda starki.* Stark's Lark. 13. Angola to Transvaal.
81. *Chersophilus duponti.* Dupont's Lark. 2ss. 16. S Spain, E Morocco to Egypt.
82. *Galerida cristata.* Crested Lark. 28ss. 16:18. Palearctic & sub-Saharan regions.
83. *Galerida deva.* Sykes' / Tawny Lark. 13. India.
84. *Pseudalaemon fremantlii.* Short tailed Lark. 3ss. 14. Ethiopia to Tanzania.
85. *Galerida magnirostris.* Large billed Lark. 3ss. 18. South Africa.
86. *Galerida malabarica.* Malabar Lark. 15. Pakistan, W India.
87. *Galerida modesta.* Sun Lark. 5ss. 14. Africa South of Sahara.
88. *Galerida thecklae.* Theckla Lark. 12ss. 16. Iberia, N & NE Africa.
89. *Lullula arborea.* Wood Lark. 2ss. 15. Europe, N Africa, Middle East.
90. *Alauda arvensis.* Skylark. 9ss. 18. Palearctic region.
91. *Alauda japonica.* Japanese Skylark. 18. Japan, China.
92. *Alauda gulgula.* Oriental Skylark. 12ss. 16. Oriental region incl. islands.
93. *Eremophila alpestris.* Horned / Shore Lark. 41ss. 18. Palearctic & Nearctic.
94. *Eremophila bilopha.* Temminck's Lark. 14. Sahara to Iraq.

50
51
52
53
54
55
56
57
58
59
60
61
62
63
64
65
66
67
68
69
70
71
72
73
74
75
76
77
78
79
80
81
82
83
84
85
86
87
88
89
90
91
92
93
94

HIRUNDINIDAE (1) Swallows & Martins

Family 118. HIRUNDINIDAE. Swallows & Martins.

1. *Pseudochelidon eurystomina*. African River Martin. 14. Zaire. Winters Gabon.
2. *Pseudochelidon sirintarae*. White eyed River Martin. 15+9. Thailand. (extinct?)
3. *Tachycineta albilinea*. Mangrove Swallow. 3ss. 12. Mexico to Panama, Peru.
4. *Tachycineta albiventer*. White winged Swallow. 14. S America south to Brazil.
5. *Tachycineta bicolor*. Tree Swallow. 13. Canada, N USA. Winters Caribbean, C America.
6. *Tachycineta meyeni*. Chilean Swallow. 13. Chile, Argentina. Winters Bolivia, Brazil.
7. *Tachycineta leucohorrhoa*. White rumped Swallow. 13. Brazil, Paraguay, Argentina. Winters Peru.
8. *Tachycineta thalassina*. Violet green Swallow. 3ss. 13. Alaska to Mexico. Winters to Panama.
9. *Tachycineta cyaneoviridis*. Bahama Swallow. 15. Bahamas. Some winter Cuba.
10. *Tachycineta euchrysea*. Golden Swallow. 2ss. 13. Jamaica, Hispaniola.
11. *Progne chalybea*. Grey breasted Martin. 2ss. 18. Mexico to Uruguay.
12. *Progne sinaloae*. Sinaloa Martin. 16. Mexico.
13. *Progne dominicensis*. Caribbean Martin. 3ss. 18. West Indies, Central America.
14. *Progne cryptoleuca*. Cuban Martin. 17. Cuba. Winters S America.
15. *Progne modesta*. Southern Martin. 3ss. 15. Galapagos, Peru, Brazil to Argentina.
16. *Progne subis*. Purple Martin. 3ss. 19. N & C America. Winters Venezuela, Brazil.
17. *Phaeoprogne tapera*. Brown chested Martin. 2ss. 18. S America S to Uruguay. Winters to Panama.
18. *Notiochelidon cyanoleuca*. Blue & white Swallow. 3ss. 13. C & S America.
19. *Notiochelidon flavipes*. Pale footed Swallow. 12. Venezuela, Ecuador, Peru.
20. *Notiochelidon murina*. Brown bellied Swallow. 3ss. 14. Venezuela to Bolivia.
21. *Notiochelidon pileata*. Black capped Swallow. 13. Mexico, Guatemala, Honduras.
22. *Atticora fasciata*. White banded Swallow. 15. South America S to Bolivia.
23. *Atticora melanoleuca*. Black collared Swallow. 14. Guyanas, Venezuela, Brazil.
24. *Neochelidon tibialis*. White thighed Swallow. 3ss. 12. Panama to Bolivia, Brazil.
25. *Alopochelidon fucata*. Tawny headed Swallow. 13. Venezuela to N. Argentina.
26. *Stelgidopteryx ruficollis*. Southern rough-wing Swallow. 4ss. 14. Panama to Argentina.
27. *Stelgidopteryx serripennis*. Northern rough-wing Swallow. 5ss. 14. USA, C America.
28. *Stelgidopteryx ridgwayi*. Ridgway's rough-wing Swallow. 1S. Mexico, Guatemala.
29. *Cheramoeca leucosternus*. White backed Swallow. 15. Internal Australia.
30. *Riparia cincta*. Banded Martin. 5ss. 16. Africa S of Sahara.
31. *Riparia congica*. Congo Sand Martin. 11. Middle & lower Congo river basin.
32. *Riparia paludicola*. Plain Martin. 8ss. 12. Africa, Malagasy, S Asia.
33. *Riparia riparia*. Sand Martin. 7ss. 10. Holarctic region. Winters tropics.
34. *Phedina borbonica*. Mascarene Martin. 2ss. 15. Malagasy, Mauritius, Reunion, Occasional E Africa.
35. *Phedina brazzae*. Brazza's Martin. 12. Zaire, Angola.
36. *Hirundo abyssinica*. Lesser striped Swallow. 6ss. 16. Africa S of Sahara.
37. *Hirundo aethiopica*. Ethiopian Swallow. 2ss. 14. Africa S of Sahara.
38. *Hirundo albigularis*. White throated Swallow. 2ss. 16. Africa S of Zambesi.
39. *Hirundo andrewsi*. Andrew's Swallow. 17. Kenya, Lake Naivasha. (ss. of 50?)
40. *Hirundo angolensis*. Angola Swallow. 2ss. 15. Central & EC Africa.

1
2
3
4
5
6
7
8
9
10
11
12
13
14
15
16
17
18
19
20
21
22
23
24
25
26
27
28
29
30
31
32
33
34
35
36
37
38
39
40

HIRUNDINIDAE (1)
Swallows & Martins

41. *Hirundo atrocaerula*. Blue Swallow. 20. Tanzania to Natal.
42. *Hirundo concolor*. Dusky Crag Martin. 2ss. 14. India, SE Asia.
43. *Hirundo cucullata*. Greater striped Swallow. 18. S Africa. Winters N to Tanzania.
44. *Hirundo daurica*. Red rumped Swallow. 12ss. 19. S Eurasia. Winters E Africa.
45. *Hirundo domicella*. West African Swallow. 17. Africa, South of Sahara.
46. *Hirundo dimidiata*. Pearl breasted Swallow. 2ss. 14. Tanzania to S Africa.
47. *Hirundo fluvicola*. Streak throated / Indian Cliff Swallow. 12. Kabul, India, Pakistan.
48. *Hirundo fuliginosa*. Forest Swallow. 12. Cameroon, Gabon.
49. *Hirundo fuligula*. African Rock Martin. 8ss. 13. Africa, South of Sahara.
50. *Hirundo griseopyga*. Grey rumped Swallow. 4ss. 17. Africa, South of Sahara.
51. *Hirundo leucosoma*. Pied winged Swallow. 13. Senegal to Nigeria.
52. *Hirundo lucida*. Red chested Swallow. 4ss. 18. Equatorial Africa.
53. *Hirundo megaensis*. White tailed Swallow. 12. Ethiopia.
54. *Hirundo neoxena*. Welcome Swallow. 15. SE & SW Australia, New Zealand.
55. *Hirundo nigricans*. Tree Martin. 3ss. 13. Australia to New Guinea, Solomon Is.
56. *Hirundo nigrita*. White throated Blue Swallow. 12. W & C Africa.
57. *Hirundo nigrorufa*. Black & Rufous Swallow. 13. Angola to Zambia.
58. *Hirundo obsoleta*. Pale Crag Martin. 7ss. 13. N Africa, Arabia to SW India.
59. *Hirundo preussi*. Preuss's Swallow. 12. West Africa to Congo.
60. *Hirundo rupestris*. Eurasian Crag Martin. 2ss. 15. Atlas Mountains to C Asia.
61. *Hirundo rustica*. (Barn) Swallow. 8ss. 19. N Hemisphere. Winters S Hemisphere
62. *Hirundo semirufa*. Rufous chested Swallow. 2ss. 24. Sub-Saharan Africa.
63. *Hirundo senegalensis*. Mosque Swallow. 3ss. 23. Africa S of Sahara.
64. *Hirundo smithii*. Wire tailed Swallow. 2ss. 20. Tropical Africa to SE Asia.
65. *Hirundo spilodera*. South African Cliff Swallow. 14. S Africa. Winters Congo basin.
66. *Hirundo perdita*. Red Sea Swallow. 14. Red Sea, Ethiopia.
67. *Hirundo striolata*. Striated Swallow. 5ss. 19. Assam, SE Asia, Indonesia.
68. *Hirundo tahitica*. Pacific Swallow. 10ss. 14. SE Asia to Oceania.
69. *Hirundo domicola*. Hill Swallow. 14. S India, Sri Lanka.
70. *Hirundo javanica*. House Swallow. 14. SE Asia, Philippines, Indonesia, New Guinea.
71. *Hirundo andecola*. Andean Swallow. 12ss. 14. Peru to N Chile.
72. *Hirundo ariel*. Fairy Martin. 11. Australia, Tasmania.
73. *Hirundo fulva*. Cave Swallow. 4ss. 13. SW USA, Mexico, Gr. Antilles to Ecuador.

73a. *Hirundo rufocollaris*. Chestnut collared Swallow. 13. Ecuador, Peru.

74. *Hirundo pyrrhonota*. Cliff Swallow. 4ss. 14. Alaska to Mexico. Winters Brazil, Argentina
75. *Hirundo rufigula*. Red throated Swallow. 13. Angola, Zambia, Zaire.
76. *Delichon dasypus*. Asian House Martin. 3ss. 13. India to Indonesia.
77. *Delichon nipalensis*. Nepal House Martin. Himalayas to Burma, Vietnam.
78. *Delichon urbica*. House Martin. 3ss. 14. Palearctic region. Winters Africa, S Asia.
79. *Psalidoprocne albiceps*. White headed Saw-wing. 2ss. 18. NE & C Africa.
80. *Psalidoprocne fuliginosa*. Mountain Saw-wing. 15. Cameroon, Fernando Po.
81. *Psalidoprocne nitens*. Square tailed Saw-wing. 2ss. 12. W & C Africa.
82. *Psalidoprocne obscura*. Fanti Saw-wing. 18. W Africa.
83. *Psalidoprocne pristoptera*. Blue Saw-wing. 3ss. 15. Ethiopia, Eritrea.
84. *Psalidoprocne mangbettorum*. Mangbettu Saw-wing. 19. NE Zaire, SW Sudan.
85. *Psalidoprocne orientalis*. Eastern Saw-wing. 18. WC Africa.
86. *Psalidoprocne oleaginea*. Ethiopian Saw-wing. 15. Ethiopia.
87. *Psalidoprocne antinorii*. Brown Saw-wing. 2ss. 18. Ethiopia.
88. *Psalidoprocne petiti*. Petit's Saw-wing. 16. Cameroon to Zaire.
89. *Psalidoprocne chalybea*. Shari Saw-wing. 15. Nigeria, Cameroon, Zaire.
90. *Psalidoprocne holomelas*. Black Saw-wing. 19. Ethiopia to S Africa.

41
42
43
44
45
46
47
48
49
50
51
52
53
54
55
56
57
58
59
60
61
62
63
64
65
67
68
70
71
66
73A
69
72
73
74
75
76
77
78
79
80
81
82
83
84
85
86
87
88
89
90

MOTACILLIDAE (1)
Wagtails & Pipits

Family 119. MOTACILLIDAE. Wagtails & Pipits.

1. *Dendronanthus indicus*. Forest Wagtail. 17. E Asia. Winters India to Java.
2. *Motacilla aguimp*. African Pied Wagtail. 2ss. 20. Africa S of Sahara.
3. *Motacilla alba*. White Wagtail. 11ss. 18. Eurasia, N Africa.
4. *Motacilla yarrelli*. Pied Wagtail. 18. British Isles, Iberia.
5. *Motacilla lugens*. Black backed Wagtail. 18. China, E Asia. (ss of 3?)
6. *Motacilla capensis*. Cape Wagtail. 5ss. 15. Kenya, Angola to Cape.
7. *Motacilla cineria*. Grey Wagtail. 5ss. 18. Palearctic. Winters Africa, SE Asia.
8. *Motacilla citreola*. Citrine Wagtail. 3ss. 17. C Eurasia. Winters S Asia.
9. *Motacilla clara*. Mountain Wagtail. 3ss. 18. Africa S of Sahara.
10. *Motacilla flava*. (Blue headed) Yellow Wagtail. 18ss.17. Eurasia, Alaska. Winters Africa, Australia.
11. incl. *M. f. flavissima*. (Yellow crowned) Yellow Wagtail. 17. NW Europe. Winters Africa.
12. *M. f. cinereocapilla*. Ashy headed Wagtail. 17. Mediterranean, Arabia.
13. *M. f. thunbergi*. Grey headed Wagtail. 17. Scandinavia, Russia. Winters Africa.
14. *M. f. beema*. Sykes' Wagtail. Russia, C Asia, India, N Africa.
15. *M. f. feldegg*. Black headed Wagtail. 17. Balkans, Middle East, E Africa.
16. *M. f. leucocephala*. White headed Wagtail. 17. Mongolia, C Asia, India.
17. *Motacilla flaviventris*. Madagascar Wagtail. 19. Malagasy.
18. *Motacilla grandis*. Japanese Wagtail. 21. Japan, Korea, E China, Taiwan.
19. *Motacilla madaraspatensis*. Large Pied / White browed Wagtail.21. India, Pakistan.
20. *Tmetothylacus tenellus*. Golden Pipit. 15. Somalia to Tanzania.
21. *Macronyx ameliae*. Rosy throated Longclaw. 19. Kenya to Natal & Angola.
22. *Macronyx aurantiigula*. Pangani Longclaw. 19. Somalia to Tanzania.
23. *Macronyx capensis*. Cape Longclaw. 3ss. 20. S E Africa.
24. *Macronyx croceus*. Yellow throated Longclaw. 20. Senegal to Sudan, S to Angola & Natal.
25. *Macronyx flavicollis*. Abyssinian Longclaw. 18. Ethiopia.
26. *Macronyx fullebornii*. Fuelleborn's Longclaw. 2ss. 20. Tanzania, Zambia, Angola.
27. *Macronyx grimwoodi*. Grimwood's Longclaw. 2ss. 22. Angola, Zambia, Zaire.
28. *Anthus sharpei*. Sharpe's Pipit. 17. Kenya.

28a. *Anthus longicaudatus*. Long tailed Pipit. 18. Kimberley, RSA

29. *Anthus antarcticus*. South Georgia Pipit. 17. South Georgia.
30. *Anthus bertheloti*. Canarian Pipit. 14. Canary Is, Madeira.
31. *Anthus bogotensis*. Paramo Pipit. 4ss. 15. Venezuela to Argentina.
32. *Anthus brachyurus*. Short tailed Pipit. 2ss. 12. E, C & S Africa.
33. *Anthus caffer*. Bush Pipit. 4ss. 14. Ethiopia to Natal & Angola.

1
2
3
5
4
NBr
6
Br
- 7 -
8
9
11
10
- 12 -
13
14
15
16
17
18
19
- 20 -
22
23
24
- 21 -
25
26
28A
28
29
27
30
31
32
33

MOTACILLIDAE (2)
Pipits

34. *Anthus campestris*. Tawny Pipit. 3ss. 16. Eurasia, N Africa. Winters South.
35. *Anthus cervinus*. Red throated Pipit. 15ss. 15. N Palearctic. Winters S Asia, Africa.
36. *Anthus chacoensis*. Chaco Pipit. 13. Paraguay, Argentina.
37. *Anthus chloris*. Yellow breasted Pipit. 17. Cape to Transvaal.
38. *Anthus correndera*. Correndera Pipit. 15. S South America, Falkland Is.
39. *Anthus crenatus*. Yellow tufted Pipit. 18. South Africa.
40. *Anthus furcatus*. Short billed Pipit. 2ss. 15. Brazil, Peru to Patagonia.
41. *Anthus godlewskii*. Blyth's Pipit. 20. E & C Asia. Winters India, Sri Lanka.
42. *Anthus gustavi*. Pechora Pipit. 3ss. 15. Russia, NE Asia. Winters Philippines, Indonesia.
43. *Anthus gutturalis*. Alpine Pipit. 3ss. 18. New Guinea.
44. *Anthus hellmayri*. Hellmayr's Pipit. 3ss. 14. Brazil, Peru, Chile, Argentina.
45. *Anthus hodgsoni*. Olive backed Pipit. 2ss. 15. Russia, Himalayas. Winters S Asia, Indonesia.
46. *Anthus leucophrys*. Plain backed Pipit. 7ss. 17. Africa S of Sahara.
47. *Anthus latistriatus* . Jackson's Pipit. 19. E Africa.
48. *Anthus lineiventris*. Striped Pipit. 18.Tanzania & Angola to South Africa.
49. *Anthus nyassae*. Woodland Pipit. 18. Central Africa.
50. *Anthus lutescens*. Yellowish Pipit. 3ss. 12. Panama to C Argentina.
51. *Anthus melindae*. Malindi Pipit. 15. Kenya & Somalia.
52. *Anthus nattereri*. Ochre breasted Pipit. 15. Brazil, Paraguay, N Argentina.
53. *Anthus nilghiriensis*. Nilgiri Pipit. 17. Madras, SW India.
54. *Anthus novaeseelandiae*. Australasian Pipit. 11ss. 19. Australia, New Zealand, New Guinea.
55. *Anthus cinnamomeus*. African Pipit. 15. SW Arabia, E & S Africa.
56. *Anthus cameroonensis*. Cameroon Pipit. 15. Cameroon.
57. *Anthus rufulus*. Paddyfield / Oriental Pipit. 15. Philippines, India, Indonesia, SE Asia.
58. *Anthus richardi*. Richard's Pipit. 17. E Palearctic. Winters India, China, SE Asia.
59. *Anthus hoeschi*. Mountain Pipit. 16. Angola, Namibia, Botswana.
60. *Anthus pallidiventris*. Long legged Pipit. 18. Angola, Gabon, Congo.
61. *Anthus pratensis*. Meadow Pipit. 2ss. 14. Western Palearctic region.
62. *Anthus roseatus*. Rosy Pipit. 16. India to Tibet, Burma, Hainan. Winters SE Asia.
63. *Anthus similis*. Long billed Pipit. 22ss. 19. Africa & Arabia to India.
64. *Anthus bannermanni*. Bannerman's Pipit. 15. W Africa.
65. *Anthus sokokensis*. Sokoke Pipit. 14. Sokoke forest, Kenya to Tanzania.
66. *Anthus spinoletta*. Water Pipit. 9ss. 17. Holarctic region.
67. *Anthus rubescens*. Buff bellied Pipit. 16. N America, Siberia. Winters C America, S Asia.
68. *Anthus petrosus*. Rock Pipit. 17. British Isles, W Europe.
69. *Anthus spragueii*. Sprague's Pipit. 17. W North America. Winters Mexico.
70. *Anthus sylvanus*. Upland Pipit. 18. Himalayas, Afghanistan to China.
71. *Anthus trivialis*. Tree Pipit. 2ss. 15. Palearctic. Winters Africa to India.
72. *Anthus vaalensis*. Buffy Pipit. 6ss. 19. Ethiopia, Central To South Africa.

34
Br
-35-
NB
36
37
38
39
40
41
42
43
44
45
46
47
48
49
50
51
52
53
54
55
56
57
58
59
60
61
62
63
64
65
66
67
68
69
70
71
72

CAMPEPHAGIDAE (1)
Cuckoo Shrikes

Family 120. CAMPHAGIDAE. Cuckoo Shrikes.

1. Pteropodocys / Coracina maxima. Ground Cuckoo Shrike. 2ss. 34. Internal Australia.
2. Coracina abbotti. Pygmy Cuckoo Shrike. 19. Sulawesi.
3. Coracina analis. New Caledonian Greybird. 28. New Caledonia.
4. Coracina atriceps. Moluccan Cuckoo Shrike. 27. Halmahera, Ceram, Moluccan Is.
5. Coracina azurea. Blue Cuckoo Shrike. 22. W, WC Africa.
6. Coracina bicolor. Pied Cuckoo Shrike / Muna Greybird. 25. Sulawesi.
7. Coracina boyeri. Boyer's Cuckoo Shrike. 2ss. 22. New Guinea, Misool, Yapen.
8. Coracina caeruleogrisea. Stout billed Cuckoo Shrike.3ss. 33. New Guinea, Yapen.
9. Coracina caerulescens. Blackish Cuckoo Shrike. 2ss. 23. Luzon.
10. Coracina caesia. Grey Cuckoo Shrike. 3ss. 22. Local in E, W & S Africa.
11. Coracina caledonica. Melanesian Cuckoo Shrike. 8ss. 32. New Caledonia, Vanuatu, Loyalty & Solomon Is.
12. Coracina cineria. Madagascar Cuckoo Shrike. 3ss. 24. Malagasy, Comoro Is.
13. Coracina fimbriata. Lesser Cuckoo Shrike. 5ss. 20. Malaysia, Greater Sundas.
14. Coracina fortis. Buru Cuckoo Shrike. 26. Buru, S Moluccas.
15. Coracina graueri. Grauer's Cuckoo Shrike. 25. E Zaire.
16. Coracina papuensis. White bellied Cuckoo Shrike. 14ss. 25. E Australia, New Guinea, Moluccas, Solomon Islands.
17. incl. C. p. robusta. Little Cuckoo Shrike. 27. E Australia.
18. Coracina macei. Large Cuckoo Shrike. 28. Indian sub-continent, N SE Asia, China.

1
2
3
4
5
6
7
8
9
10
11
12
13
14
15
16
17
18

CAMPEPHAGIDAE (2)
Cuckoo Shrikes

19. Coracina holopolia. Solomons /Black bellied Cuckoo Shrike. 3ss. 23. Solomon Islands.
20. Coracina larvata. Sunda Cuckoo Shrike / Black faced Greybird. 3ss. 23. Borneo, Sumatra, Java.
21. Coracina leucopygia. White rumped Cuckoo Shrike. 25. Sulawesi.
22. Coracina lineata. Yellow eyed Cuckoo Shrike. 10ss. 23. Papua, Solomon Is, NE Australia.
23. Coracina mcgregori. McGregor's Cuckoo Shrike / Sharp tailed Greybird. 21. S Philippines.
24. Coracina Longicauda. Hooded Cuckoo Shrike. 2ss. 33. New Guinea.
25. Coracina melanoptera. Black headed Cuckoo Shrike. 2ss. 20. India, Sri Lanka.
26. Coracina melaschistos. Black winged Cuckoo Shrike. 2ss. 24. N SE Asia, Himalayas.
27. Coracina montana. Black bellied Cuckoo Shrike. 2ss. 24. New Guinea.
28. Coracina panayensis. White winged Greybird. 26. Philippines.
29. Coracina newtoni. Reunion Cuckoo Shrike. 17. Reunion.
30. Coracina typica. Mauritius Cuckoo Shrike. 18. Mauritius.
31. Coracina novaehollandiae. Black faced Cuckoo Shrike. 19ss. 33. Australia, incl. Tasmania. Winters Wallacea, New Guinea.
32. Coracina javensis. Javan Cuckoo Shrike. 28. Java, Bali.
33. Coracina personata. Wallacean Cuckoo Shrike. 6ss. 28. Timor, Wetar, Lesser Sundas.
34. incl. C. p. pollens. Kai Cuckoo Shrike. 28. Kai Is. & Tanimbar.

19
20
21
22
23
24
25
26
27
29
28
30
31
33
34

CAMPEPHAGIDAE (3)
Cuckoo Shrikes

35. Coracina parvula. Halmahera Greybird. 24. Halmahera, N Moluccas.
36. Coracina pectoralis. White breasted Cuckoo Shrike. 26. Most of Africa.
37. Coracina polioptera. Indochinese Cuckoo Shrike. 3ss. 23. Vietnam, Laos, Burma, Thailand.
38. Coracina schistacea. Slaty Cuckoo Shrike. 2ss. 27. Wallacea.(Sula, Pelin Is.)
39. Coracina Schisticeps. Grey-headed Cuckoo Shrike. 4ss. 22. New Guinea & Islands.
40. Coracina melas. New Guinea / Black Cuckoo Shrike. 6ss. 23. New Guinea & Islands.
41. Coracina striata. Bar-bellied Cuckoo Shrike. 15ss. 27. Malaya, Andaman Is., Sumatra, Borneo Philippines.
42. Coracina ostenta. White winged Cuckoo Shrike. 25. Negros, Panay Is.
43. Coracina temminckii. Cerulean Cuckoo Shrike. 3ss. 25. Sulawesi.
44. Coracina dohertyi. Sumba Cicadabird. 22. Lesser Sumbas.
45. Coracina tenuirostris. (Slender billed) Cicadabird. 34ss. 23. Australia, New Guinea, Pacific Is. Female plumage very variable.
46. Coracina dispar. Kai Cicadabird. 23. Kai Is.
47. Coracina morio. Sulawesi Cicadabird. 12ss. 22. Sulawesi & adjacent Islands.
48. Coracina incerta. Sharpe's / Black shouldered Cicadabird.21. W Papuan Is, New Guinea.
49. Coracina mindanensis. Black bibbed Cicadabird. 24. Mindanao, Basilan.
50. Coracina sula. Sula Cicadabird. 23. Sula Island off Sulawesi.
51. Coracina ceramensis. Pale grey Cicadabird. 23. Ceram.
52. Campochaera sloetii. Golden Cuckoo Shrike. 2ss. 20. New Guinea.

Females 42, 48, 49 have paler head & underparts than male.

Female 49 has white undertail coverts.

35
36
37
38
39
40
41
42
43
44
48
49
45
46
47
50
45
JUV
51
52

CAMPEPHAGIDAE (4)
Trillers

53. Chlamydochaera jefferyi. Fruit Hunter. 23. North Borneo.
54. Lalage atrovirens. Black browed Triller. 3ss. 18. New Guinea & adjacent Islands.
55. Lalage moesta. White browed Triller. 18. Tanimbar.(Sundas).
56. Lalage aurea. Rufous bellied Triller. 18. Northern Moluccas.
57. Lalage leucomela. Varied Triller. 15ss. 18. E Australia. New Guinea & Is.
58. Lalage leucopyga. Long tailed Triller / Caterpillar eater. 6ss. 16. Solomon Is, Norfolk I, New Caledonia, New Hebrides
59. Lalage maculosa. Polynesian Spotted Triller. 16ss. 15. Fiji, Samoa & Islands. (a, b, c, d.)
60. Lalage melanoleuca. Black & white Triller. 2ss. 21. Philippines.
61. Lalage nigra. Pied Triller. 4ss. 17. Nicobar Is., Sundas, Philippines.

62 Lalage leucopygialis. White rumped Triller. 17. Sulawesi & Is.
63. Lalage sharpei. Samoan Triller. 2ss. 14. Samoa.
64. Lalage sueurii. White shouldered Triller. 17. Java, Bali, Sulawesi, Lesser Sundas .
65. Lalage tricolor. White winged Triller. 17. Australia. Winters New Guinea.
66. Campephaga flava. Black Cuckoo shrike. 20. NE, C & S Africa.
67. Campephaga lobata. Ghana / Wattled Cuckoo shrike. 2ss.19. Ghana & Liberia.
68. Campephaga oriolina. Oriole Cuckoo shrike. 19. Cameroon, Gabon, Zaire.
69. Campephaga petiti. Petit's Cuckoo shrike. 20. Equatorial Africa.
70. Campephaga phoenicea. Red shouldered Cuckoo shrike. 20. Africa S of Sahara.
71. Campephaga quiscalina. Purple throated Cuckoo shrike. 3ss. 20. W & C Africa.

53
54
56
55
(a)
57
58
(b)
59
(c)
60
64
Br
NB
(d)
62
62
-61-
66
65
67
68
69
63
70
71

CAMPEPHAGIDAE (5)
Minivets, Wood Shrikes

72. Pericrocotus brevirostris. Short billed Minivet. 4ss. 18. Himalayas, SE Asia, China.
73. Pericrocotus Cinnamomeus. Small Minivet. 11ss 16. SE Asia, Andamans, Sundas.
74. Pericrocotus igneus. Fiery Minivet. 15. Malaysia, Indonesia.
75. Pericrocotus divaricatus. Ashy Minivet. 2ss. 20. NE Asia, Winters SE Asia, Borneo.
76. Pericrocotus erythropygius. White bellied Minivet. 2ss. 15. S India, C Burma.
77. Pericrocotus ethologos. Long tailed Minivet. 7ss. 20. India, China, SE Asia.
78. Pericrocotus flammeus. Scarlet Minivet. 20ss. 22. India, SE Asia, Philippines.
79. Pericrocotus miniatus. Sunda Minivet. 19. Sumatra, Java.
80. Pericrocotus roseus. Rosy Minivet. 3ss. 20. Himalayas to China, India, SE Asia.
81. Pericrocotus cantonensis. Brown rumped Minivet. 18. China. Winters SE Asia.
82. Pericrocotus solaris. Grey chinned Minivet. 8ss. 18. Himalayas, China, SE Asia, Sumatra, Borneo.
83. Pericrocotus lansbergi. Flores Minivet. 18. Sumbawa & Flores.
84. Pericrocotus tegimae. Ryukyu Minivet. 19. Ryukyu Is.
85. Hemipus hirundinaceus. Black winged Flycatcher shrike. 4ss. 15. Malaysia, SE Asia, Sumatra, Borneo.
86. Hemipus picatus. Bar winged Flycatcher shrike. 4ss. 15. India, Sri Lanka, China, S E Asia, Sumatra, Borneo.
87. Tephrodornis gularis. Large Wood shrike. 11ss. 23. India, China, SE Asia, Sundas.
88. Tephrodornis Pondicerianus. Common Wood shrike. 4ss. 16. Indian subcontinent, S E Asia.

87 / 88 commonly placed with Wattle-eyes or Vangas.

72
73
74
75
76
77
78
79
80
81
82
83
84
85
86
87
88

PYCNONOTIDAE (1) Bulbuls

1. Spizixos canifrons. Crested Finchbill. 2ss. 21. Assam, China, Burma, Thailand.
2. Spizixos semitorques. Collared Finchbill. 2ss. 23. China, Tonkin, Taiwan.
3. Andropadus ansorgei. Ansorge's Greenbul. 3ss. 15. Sierra Leone to Zaire, Kenya.
4. Andropadus curvirostris. Plain Greenbul. 2ss. 18. Sierra Leone to Kenya, Angola.
5. Andropadus gracilirostris. Slender billed Greenbul. 4ss. 17. W Central Africa.
6. Andropadus gracilis. Little grey Greenbul. 3ss. 14. Sierra Leone, Uganda, Angola.
7. Andropadus hallae. Mrs Hall's Greenbul. 16. Zaire.(l specimen)
8. Andropadus importunus. Sombre Greenbul. 8ss. 18. E Africa, Somalia to Cape.
9. Andropadus somaliensis. Somali Greenbul. 18. Somalia, Ethiopia.
10. Andropadus latirostris. Yellow whiskered Greenbul. 4ss. 18. W & C Africa.
11. Andropadus masukuensis. Shelley's Greenbul. 3ss. 15. Kenya, Tanzania, Malawi.
12. Andropadus kakamegae. Kakamega Greenbul. 14. E Africa, Zaire.
13. Andropadus milanjensis. Stripe cheeked Greenbul. 4ss. 18. Kenya to Mozambique.
14. Andropadus oliveaceps. Olive headed Greenbul. 18. E Africa.
15. Andropadus montanus. Cameroun mountain Greenbul. 18. Cameroon.
16. Andropadus tephrolaemus. Grey throated Greenbul. 9ss. 18. WC & E Africa.
16a. Andropadus nigriceps. Mountain Greenbul. 18. Kenya to Mozambique.
17. Andropadus chlorigula. Green throated Greenbul. 18. Tanzania.
18. Andropadus virens. Little Greenbul. 6ss. 16. Africa, Fernando Po to Zanzibar.
19. Pycnonotus atriceps. Black headed Bulbul. 5ss. 18. India, SE Asia & Islands. (a. & b.). 2 phases.
20. Pycnonotus aurigaster. Sooty headed Bulbul. 9ss. 20. China, SE Asia, Java, Bali.
21. Pycnonotus barbatus. Common / Yellow vented Bulbul.18ss. 18. NE tropical Africa.
22. Pycnonotus dodsoni. Dodson's Bulbul. 18. Kenya, Somalia, Ethiopia.
23. Pycnonotus xanthopygos. White spectacled Bulbul. 18. Turkey, Arabia.
24. Pycnonotus tricolor. Dark capped Bulbul. 18. Namibia to Uganda, Tanzania.
25. Pycnonotus bimaculatus. Orange spotted Bulbul. 3ss. 20. Sumatra, Java, Bali.
26. Pycnonotus blanfordi. Streak eared Bulbul. 3ss. 20. SE Asia.
27. Pycnonotus brunneus. Red eyed Bulbul. 2ss. 18. Malaya, Sumatra, Borneo.
28. Pycnonotus cafer. Red vented Bulbul. 9ss. 22. India to Burma, China.
29. Pycnonotus capensis. Cape Bulbul. 20. SW South Africa.
30. Pycnonotus cyaniventris. Grey bellied Bulbul. 2ss. 16. Malaya, Sumatra, Borneo.
31. Pycnonotus erythrophthalmus. Spectacled Bulbul. 2ss. 17. Malaya, Sumatra, Borneo.
32. Pycnonotus eutilotus. Puffbacked Bulbul. 23. Malaya, Sumatra, Borneo.
33. Pycnonotus finlaysoni. Stripe throated Bulbul. 3ss. 19. China, SE Asia.
34. Pycnonotus flavescens. Flavescent Bulbu1. 4ss. 20. India to Vietnam, Thailand, Borneo.
35. Pycnonotus goiaver. Yellow vented Bulbul. 6ss. 20. SE Asia, Malay archipelago.
36. Pycnonotus jocosus. Red whiskered Bulbul. 9ss. 20. S, SE Asia & Is.
37. Pycnonotus leucogenys. Himalayan / White cheeked Bulbul. 5ss. 20. Arabia to Himalayas.
38. Pycnonotus leucotis. White eared Bulbul. 18. Iran to NW India.
39. Pycnonotus luteolus. White browed Bulbul. 2ss. 20. India, Sri Lanka.
40. Pycnonotus melanicterus. Black crested Bulbul. 12ss. 15. India, SE Asia, Sundas.
41. Pycnonotus melanoleucos. Black & white Bulbul. 17.Thailand, Malaya, Sumatra, Borneo.
42. Pycnonotus nieuwenhuisi. Blue wattled Bulbul. 2ss. 20. Sumatra, Borneo.

1
2
3
4
5
6
7
12
14
8
10
11
13
15
17
16A
20
16
18
19 (a)
19 (b)
21
22
23
24
25
26
27
28
29
9
30
31
32
33
34
35
36
37
38
39
40
41
42

PYCNONOTIDAE (2) Bulbuls

43. Pycnonotus nigricans. Black fronted Bulbul. 3ss. 20. S W Africa.
44. Pycnonotus pencillatus. Yellow eared Bulbul. 20. Sri Lanka.
45. Pycnonotus plumosus. Olive winged Bulbul. 2ss. 20. SE Asia, Indonesia.
46. Pycnonotus priocephalus. Grey headed Bulbul. 19. SW India.
47. Pycnonotus simplex. Cream vented Bulbul. 5ss. 17. Thailand, Malaysia, Indonesia.
48. Pycnonotus sinensis. Light vented Bulbul. 5ss. 18. China, Taiwan, Ryukyu Is, Vietnam.
49. Pycnonotus squamatus. Scaly breasted Bulbul. 3ss. 14. Malaysia, Indonesia.
50. Pycnonotus striatus. Striated Bulbul. 3ss. 23. Nepal, China, Burma, Indo-China.
51. Pycnonotus leucogrammicus. Cream striped Bulbul. 17. Sumatra.
52. Pycnonotus taivanus. Styan's Bulbul. 20. Taiwan.
53. Pycnonotus tympanistrigus. Spot necked Bulbul. 16. W Sumatra.
54. Pycnonotus urostictus. Yellow wattled Bulbul. 5ss. 19. Philippines.
55. Pycnonotus xantholaemus. Yellow throated Bulbul. 20. S India.
56. Pycnonotus xanthorrhous. Brown breasted Bulbul. 2ss. 20. China to Indo-China.
57. Pycnonotus zeylanicus. Straw headed Bulbul. 28. Malaya, Sumatra, Java, Borneo.
58. Calyptocichla serina. Golden Greenbul. 18. W Africa.
59. Baeopogon clamans. Sjostedt's / White tailed Greenbul. 20. Gabon to Zaire.
60. Baeopogon indicator. Honeyguide Greenbul. 4ss. 20. W & C Africa.
61. Ixonotus guttatus. Spotted Greenbul. 2ss. 16. Liberia to Ghana, Zaire, Uganda.
62. Chlorocichla falkensteini. Yellow necked Greenbul. 2ss. 18. W & C Africa.
63. Chlorocichla flavicollis. Yellow throated Greenbul. 6ss. 18/25. W & C Africa.
64. Chlorocichla flaviventris. Yellow bellied Greenbul. 3ss. 22. Kenya to Natal, Angola, Namibia.
65. Chlorocichla laetissima. Joyful Greenbul. 2ss. 22. E C Africa.
66. Chlorocichla prigoginei. Prigogine's Greenbul. 18. Zaire.
67. Chlorocichla simplex. Simple Greenbul. 22. Guinea to Zaire, Angola.
68. Thescelocichla leucopleura. Swamp Greenbul. 22. Senegal to Gabon, Uganda.
69. Phyllastrephus albigularis. White throated Greenbul. 2ss. 18. WC Africa.
70. Phyllastrephus zosterops. Spectacled Greenbul. 15/16. Malagasy.
71. incl. P. z. fulvescens. Northern short billed Tetraka. 15/16. Malagasy.
72. Phyllastrephus baumanni. Baumann's olive Greenbul. 20. Sierra Leone to Zaire.
73. Phyllastrephus hypochloris. Toro olive Greenbul. 16. Sudan, Kenya, Uganda, Zaire.
74. Phyllastrephus cerviniventris. Grey-olive Greenbul. 2ss. 18. Kenya to Mozambique.
75. Phyllastrephus cinereiceps. Grey crowned Greenbul. 14. Malagasy.
76. Phyllastrephus debilis . Tiny / Slender Greenbul. 3ss. 13. Kenya to Mozambique.
77. Phyllastrephus fischeri. Fischer's Greenbul. 4ss. 17. E African coast.
78. Phyllastrephus cabanisi. Cabani's Greenbul. 17. Angola, Zaire, Tanzania.
79. Phyllastrephus placidus. Shelley's Greenbul. 17. Kenya to Malawi, Mozambique.
80. Phyllastrephus leucolepis. Liberian Greenbul. 15. Liberia.

43
44
45
46
47
48
49
50
51
52
53
54
55
56
57
58
59
60
62
63
64
65
66
67
68
69
70
71
72
73
80
74
75
76
77
78
79

PYCNONOTIDAE (3)
Bulbuls

81. Phyllastrephus alfredi. Sharpe's Greenbul. 18. Tanzania, Malawi, Zambia.
82. Phyllastrephus flavostriatus. Yellow streaked Greenbul. 7ss. 19. E Africa, Tanzania to Cape.
83. Phyllastrephus fulviventris. Pale Olive Greenbul. 20. Central African Republic to Angola.
84. Phyllastrephus icterinus. Icterine Greenbul. 2ss. 15. Sierra Leone to Zaire.
85. Phyllastrephus lorenzi. Sassi's Greenbul. 19. E Zaire.
86. Phyllastrephus madagascariensis. Long billed Greenbul / Tetraka. 2ss. 18/20. Malagasy.
87. Arcanator orostruthus. Dapplethroat. 2ss. 20. Tanzania.
88. Phyllastrephus poensis. Cameroon Olive Bulbul. 17. Cameroon, Nigeria.
89. Phyllastrephus poliocephalus. Grey headed Bulbul. 23. Nigeria, Cameroon.
90. Phyllastrephus scandens. Leaflove. 4ss. 21. Senegal to Tanzania.
91. Phyllastrephus strepitans. Northern Brownbul. 17. Sudan to Tanzania.
92. Phyllastrephus tenebrosus. Dusky Greenbul / Tetraka. 19/21. Malagasy.
93. Phyllastrephus terrestris. Terrestrial Brownbul. 5ss. 18. Kenya to Angola, Cape.
94. Phyllastrephus / Oxylabes xanthophrys. Yellow browed Oxylabes. 17. Malagasy.
95. Phyllastrephus xavieri. Xavier's Greenbul. 3ss. 17. Cameroon, Zaire, Uganda.
96. Phyllastrephus apperti. Appert's Greenbul. 16. Malagasy.
97. Bleda canicapilla. Grey headed Bristlebill. 20. Sierra Leone to Nigeria.
98. Bleda eximia. Green tailed Bristlebill. 3ss. 19. C & W Africa.
99. Bleda syndactyla. Common Bristlebill. 3ss. 22. Senegal to Kenya, Zambia.
100. Nicator chloris. Yellow spotted Nicator. 22. Senegal to Uganda, Zaire.
101. Nicator gularis. Eastern Nicator. 22. Kenya to Natal.
102. Nicator vireo. Yellow throated Nicator. 14. Cameroon to Uganda, Angola.
103. Criniger barbatus. Western bearded Bulbul. 4ss. 21. Sierra Leone to Nigeria.

103a. Criniger chloronotus. Eastern bearded Bulbul. 21. Cameroon, Zaire.

104. Alophoixus bres. Grey cheeked Bulbul. 5ss. 21. Malaya, Philippines, Gr. Sundas.
105. Criniger calurus. Red tailed Greenbul. 3ss. 17. W & C Africa.
106. Alophoixus finschii. Finsch's Bulbul. 16. Thailand, Malaya, Sumatra, Borneo.
107. Alophoixus flaveolus. White throated Bulbul. 2ss. 21. Nepal to China, Burma, Thailand.
108. Alophoixus ndussumensis. White bearded Greenbul. 18. Zaire.
109. Alophoixus ochraceus. Ochraceous Bulbul. 8ss. 23. Indo-China, Malaysia, Sumatra.
110. Criniger olivaceus. Yellow bearded Greenbul. 17. Senegal, Guinea, Ghana.
111. Alophoixus pallidus. Puff throated Bulbul. 7ss. 24. Yunnan, Hainan, SE Asia.
112. Alophoixus phaeocephalus. Yellow bellied Bulbul. 4ss. 20. Malaya, Sumatra, Borneo.

Nos. 75 & 94 should perhaps be placed in Family 136 Timaliidae (Babblers). No 87 in either 136 or 141 (Warblers). Nos. 100,101,& 102 in Family 124(Shrikes).

81
82
83
84
85
86
87
88
89
90
91
92
93
94
95
96
97
98
99
100
101
102
103
104
105
106
107
108
109
110
111
103A
112

PYCNONOTIDAE (4)
Bulbuls

113. Setornis criniger. Hook billed Bulbul. 19. Sumatra, Borneo.
114. Alophoixus affinis. Golden Bulbul. 9ss. 21. Sulawesi, Moluccas.
115. Ixos amaurotis. Brown eared Bulbul. 14ss. 25. Japan, Philippines. Winters China, Korea.
116. Hypsipetes borbonicus. Olivaceous Bulbul. 2ss. 24. Reunion, Mauritius.
117. Iola olivacea. Buff vented Bulbul. 3ss. 20. Malaya, Sumatra, Borneo.
118. Hypsipetes crassirostris. Seychelles Bulbul. 26. Mahe, Praslin, Felicite Is.
119. Tricholestes criniger. Hairy backed Bulbul. 3ss. 16. Malaya, Sumatra, Borneo.
120. Ixos everetti. Yellowish Bulbul. 4ss. 25. Philippines.
121. Hemixos flavala. Ashy Bulbul. 9ss. 20. Himalayas, China, SE Asia, Indonesia.
122. Hemixos castanotus. Chestnut Bulbul. 21. S China, Tonkin, Hainan.
123. Iole indica. Yellow browed Bulbul. 3ss. 20. S India, Sri Lanka.
124. Hypsipetes madagascarensis. Black Bulbul. 16ss. 25. Malagasy, Indian Ocean Is.
125. Hypsipetes parvirostris. Comoro Bulbul. 2ss. 26. Comoro Is.
126. Hypsipetes leucocephalus. White headed Black Bulbul. 24. S SE Asia.
127. Ixos malaccensis. Streaked / Green backed Bulbul. 22. Malaya, Sumatra, Borneo.
128. Hypsipetes mcClellandii. Mountain Bulbul. 9ss. 24. Himalayas, China, SE Asia.
129. Hypsipetes nicobariensis. Nicobar Bulbul. 20. Nicobar Is.
130. Ixos palawanensis. Sulphur bellied Bulbul. 20. Palawan.
131. Ixos philippinus. Philippine Bulbul. 5ss. 24. Philippines.
132. Ixos rufigularis. Zamboanga Bulbul. 26. Mindanao, Basilan.
133. Iole propinqua. Grey eyed Bulbul. 6ss. 18. China to Burma, Thailand, Indo-China,
134. Ixos siquijorensis. Streak breasted Bulbul. 3ss. 25. C Philippine Is.
135. Hypsipetes thompsoni. White headed Bulbul. 20. Burma, Thailand.
136. Hypsipetes virescens. Sunda Bulbul. 2ss. 20. Java, Sumatra.
137. Iole virescens = Hypsipetes viridescens. Olive Bulbul. 18. Burma, Thailand.
138. Neolestes torquatus. Black collared Bulbul. 15. Gabon, Angola, Zaire.
139. Tylas eduardi. Kinkimayo. 2ss. 24. Malagasy.(perhaps belongs to Family 125.)

113
114
115
116
117
118
119
120
121
122
123
124
127
128
129
130
131
132
133
134
135
136
125
126
137
138
139

IRENIDAE
Leafbirds, Ioras

1. Aegithina lafresnayei. Great Iora. 3ss. 17. SW China, Thailand, Burma, Indo-China.
2. Aegithina nigrolutea. Marshall's / White tailed Iora. 14. N & C India.
3. Aegithina tiphia. Common Iora. 4ss. 15. Indian sub continent, SE Asia, Indonesia.
4. Aegithina viridissima. Green Iora. 2ss. 13. Malaya, Thailand, Sumatra, Borneo.
5. Chloropsis aurifrons. Golden fronted Leafbird. 7ss. 18. India, Sri Lanka, SE Asia, Indonesia.
6. Chloropsis cochinchinensis. Blue winged Leafbird. 10ss. 17. India, China, SE Asia, Borneo, Java.
7. Chloropsis cyanopogon. Lesser green Leafbird. 2ss. 17. Thailand, Malaysia, Indonesia.
8. Chloropsis flavipennis. Yellow quilled / Philippine Leafbird. 23. Cebu, Mindanao.
9. Chloropsis hardwickii. Orange bellied Leafbird. 4ss. 18. Himalayas, SE Asia.
10. Chloropsis palawanensis. Yellow throated Leafbird. 22. Palawan.
11. Chloropsis sonnerati. Greater green Leafbird. 20. Malaysia, Greater Sundas.
12. Chloropsis venusta. Blue masked Leafbird. 14. Sumatra.
13. Irena cyanogaster. Philippine Fairy-Bluebird. 4ss. 28. Philippines.
14. Irena puella. Asian Fairy-Bluebird. 6ss. 27. India, SE Asia, Indonesia.

1
2
3
4
5
6
7
8
9
10
11
12
13
14

PRIONOPIDAE, LANIIDAE
Helmet Shrikes, Puffback & Chagrin Shrikes

Family 123. PRIONOPIDAE. Helmet Shrikes.

1. Eurocephalus anguitimens. White crowned Shrike. 2ss. 23. Zimbabwe, Botswana.
2. Eurocephalus ruppelli. White rumped Shrike. 23. Sudan to Tanzania.
3. Prionops alberti. Yellow crested Helmet Shrike. 25. Tanzania, Zaire.
4. Prionops caniceps. Red billed /Chestnut bellied Helmet Shrike. 18. W Africa, Sierra Leone, Liberia to Nigeria.
5. Prionops rufiventris. Gabon / Chestnut breasted Helmet Shrike. 18. C Africa, Cameroon, Gabon, Zaire, Uganda,
6. Prionops gabela. Angola Red billed Helmet Shrike. 18. Angola.
7. Prionops plumatus. White / Straight crested Helmet Shrike. 8ss. 20. W Africa.
8. incl. P. p. cristatus. Curly crested Helmet Shrike. 20. Sudan to Kenya.
9. Prionops poliolophus. Grey crested Helmet Shrike. 25. Kenya, Tanzania.
10. Prionops retzii. Retz's Red billed Helmet Shrike. 6ss. 20. C Africa.
11. Prionops scopifrons. Chestnut fronted Helmet Shrike. 3ss. 18. Somalia to Southern Africa.

Family 124. LANIIDAE (1). Puffback & Chagrin Shrikes.

1. Lanioturdus torquatus. White tailed Chat-shrike. 2ss. 15. Angola, Namibia.
2. Nilaus afer. (Northern) Brubru. 10ss. 14. Most of Africa south of Sahara.
3. incl. N. a. nigritemporalis. Black browed Brubru. 14. Zaire, Tanzania to Natal.
4. Dryoscopus angolensis. Pink footed Puffback. 4ss. 15. Cameroon to Tanzania.
5. Dryoscopus cubla. Black backed Puffback. 6ss. 18. E & S Africa.
6. incl. D. c. affiniss. Zanzibar Puffback. 15. E Kenya, Zanzibar.
7. Dryoscopus gambensis. (Northern)Puffback. 5ss. 18. Senegal to Sudan & Tanzania.
8. Dryoscopus pringlii. Pringle's Puffback. 13. Ethiopia, Somalia to Tanzania.
9. Dryoscopus sabini. Large billed Puffback. 2ss. 16. Sierra Leone to Gabon, Zaire.
10. Dryoscopus senegalensis. Red eyed Puffback. 16. Nigeria to Uganda.
11. Tchagra australis. Brown crowned Tchagra. 11ss. 19. Africa south of Sahara.
12. Rhodophoneus cruentus. Rosy patched Bush shrike. 3ss. 23. NE, CE Africa.
13. Tchagra jamesi. Three streaked Bush shrike. 2ss. 17. Somalia, Kenya, Uganda.
14. Tchagra minuta. Marsh Tchagra. 4ss. 15. Equatorial Africa to Ethiopia.
15. Tchagra anchietae. Anchieta's Tchagra. 15. Angola to Tanzania, Malawi.
16. Tchagra senegala. Black crowned Tchagra. 13ss. 20. S Arabia & most of Africa.
17. Tchagra tchagra. Southern Tchagra / Levaillant's Bush shrike. 3ss. 22. RSA.

PRIONOPIDAE
1
2
3
4
5
6
7
8
9
10
11
LANIIDAE
1
2
3
4
5
6
7
8
9
11
10
14
12
13
16
15
17

LANIIDAE (2)
Shrikes

18. Laniarius aethiopicus. Tropical Boubou. 6ss. 23. Africa South of Sahara.
18a. Laniarius liberatus. Bulo Burti Boubou. 22. C Somaliland. (1 specimen.)
19. Laniarius atrococcineus. Crimson breasted Gonolek. Zimbabwe to Orange River & Angola.
20. Laniarius atroflavus. Yellow breasted Boubou. 2ss. 18. Cameroon, Nigeria.
21. Laniarius barbarus. (Common) Gonolek. 2ss. 22. Senegal to Ethiopia & Congo.
22. Laniarius bicolor. Gabon Boubou. 3ss. 24. Cameroon to Botswana, Angola.
23. Laniarius erythrogaster. Black headed Gonolek. 20. Cameroon to Tanzania.
24. Laniarius ferrugineus. Southern Boubou. 8ss. 23. Mozambique, Zimbabwe to Cape.
25. Laniarius fuelleborni. Fuelleborne's Boubou. 6ss. 19. Tanzania, Zambia, Malawi.
26. Laniarius funebris. Slaty Boubou. 2ss. 18. Sudan, Ethiopia, Kenya, Tanzania.
27. Laniarius leucorhynchus. Sooty Boubou. 20. Sierra Leone to Sudan, W Kenya.
28. Laniarius luhderi. Luhder's Bush Shrike. 4ss. 18. Cameroon to Uganda, Angola.
28a. Laniarius brauni. Orange breasted Bush Shrike. 18. Angola.
28b. Laniarius amboinensis. Gabela Bush Shrike. 18. Angola.
29. Laniarius mufumbiri. Papyrus Gonolek. 20. Uganda & EC Africa.
30. Laniarius poensis. Mountain Boubou. 16. Nigeria, Cameroon.
31. Laniarius turatii. Turati's Boubou. 18. Senegal to Sierra Leone.
32. Laniarius ruficeps. Red naped Bush Shrike. 3ss. 17. Ethiopia, Somalia, Kenya.
33. Malaconotus alius. Uluguru Bush Shrike. 23.Tanzania.
34. Malaconotus blanchoti. Grey headed Bush Shrike. 3ss. 15. Africa S of Sahara.
35. Telophorus bocagei. Grey-green Bush Shrike. 3ss. 15. Cameroon to Kenya, Angola.
36. Malaconotus cruentus. Fiery breasted Bush Shrike.3ss. 25. W & C Africa.
37. Telophorus dohertyi. Doherty's Bush Shrike. 18. Kenya, Uganda, Zaire.
38. Malaconotus gladiator. Green breasted Bush Shrike. 25. Cameroon, Nigeria.
39. Telophorus kupeensis. Serle's Bush Shrike. 20. Mt Kupe, Cameroon.
40. Malaconotus lagdeni. Lagden's Bush Shrike. 2ss. 22. Liberia to Ghana, Zaire.
41. Malaconotus monteiri. Monteiro's Bush Shrike. 25. Cameroon, Zaire, Angola.
42. Telophorus multicolor. Many coloured Bush Shrike. 3ss. 18. Sierra Leone to Tanzania & Angola.
    4 colour phases A, B, C, D. shown.
43. Telophorus nigrifrons. Black fronted Bush shrike. 3ss. 18. Kenya to Transvaal.
    4 colour phases A, B, C, D. shown.

18
19
20
21
22
18A
25
23
24
26
27
28
28A
28B
32
29
30
31
33
34
35
36
37
38
39
40
41
43
(a)
(b)
(c)
(d)
42
(a)
(b)
(c)
(d)

LANIIDAE (3)
Shrikes

44. Telophorus olivaceus. Olive Bush Shrike. 5ss. 19. Malawi to Cape.
45. Telophorus bertrandi. Rufous breasted Bush Shrike. 19. Malawi.

Now considered to be a colour phase of 44.

46. Telophorus quadricolor. Four coloured Bush Shrike. 2ss. 18. Somalia to Natal.
47. Telophorus sulfureopectus. Sulphur breasted Bush Shrike. 2ss. 18. Africa South of Sahara.
48. Telophorus viridis. Perrin's Bush Shrike. 18. Angola to Zambia & Zaire.
49. Telophorus zeylonus. Bokmakierie. 3ss. 23. Southern Africa.
50. Corvinella corvina. Yellow billed Shrike. 4ss. 30. Africa South of Sahara.
51. Corvinella melanoleuca. Magpie Shrike. 2ss. 37. Kenya to Natal & Angola.
52. Lanius bucephalus. Bull-headed Shrike. 2ss. 20. NE Asia. Winters China, Ryukyu Is.
53. Lanius cabinisi. Long tailed Fiscal. 30. Somalia to Tanzania.
54. Lanius collaris. Fiscal Shrike. 7ss. 23. Africa South of Sahara.
55. Lanius newtoni. Newton's Fiscal. 25. Sao Thome Is. (last recorded 1928.)
56. Lanius elegans. Grey Shrike. 22. Sahara, S Egypt. (ss. of 65.)
57. Lanius marwitzi. Uhehe Fiscal. 20. Tanzania.
58. Lanius jebelmarrae. Jebel Marra Grey Shrike. 20. W Sudan.
59. Lanius collurio. Red backed Shrike. 6ss. 18. Palearctic. Winters ES Africa.
60. Lanius phoenicuroides/isabellinus. Red tailed Shrike. 2ss. 18. SC Eurasia. Winters E Africa, S Asia.
61. Lanius bogdanowi. Bogdanow's Shrike. 18. Caspian Sea to China. (Hybrid 59x60?)
62. Lanius cristatus. Brown Shrike. 19. C to E Asia. Winters NE Africa, SE Asia.

44
45
47
46
48
49
50
51
52
53
54
55
56
57
58
59
60
61
62

LANIIDAE (4)
Shrikes

63. Lanius collurioides. Burmese Shrike. 2ss. 20. Assam, China, Burma, Vietnam.
64. Lanius dorsalis. Taita Fiscal. 20. Ethiopia to Tanzania.
65. Lanius excubitor. Great Grey / Northern Shrike. 20ss. 25. Holarctic, India. Winters to C Africa.
66. Lanius excubitoroides. Grey backed Fiscal. 3ss. 25. NE & C Africa.
67. Lanius gubernator. Emin's Shrike. 15. Ghana to Sudan, Uganda, Zaire.
68. Lanius ludovicianus. Loggerhead Shrike. 11ss. 18. Canada, USA, Mexico.
69. Lanius mackinnoni. Mackinnon's Shrike. 23. Kenya to Cameroon, Angola.
70. Lanius minor. Lesser Grey Shrike. 2ss. 20. S E Europe, WC Asia. Winters Africa.
71. Lanius nubicus. Masked Shrike. 17. SE Europe, Middle East. Winters to NE Africa.
72(a). Lanius schach. Black headed / Long tailed Shrike. 12ss. 25. Iran to India, China, SE Asia,
(b). Melanistic form. Philippines, Sundas, New Guinea.
73. Lanius senator. Woodchat Shrike. 3ss. 18. Western Palearctic. Winters Africa.
74. Lanius somalicus. Somali Fiscal. 20. Sudan, Ethiopia, Somalia, Kenya.
75. Lanius souzae. Souza's Shrike. 3ss. 17. Centra1 Africa.
76. Lanius sphenocercus. Chinese Grey Shrike. 2ss. 28. E Asia, Mongolia to S China.
77. Lanius tephronotus. Grey backed Shrike. 25. Himalayas, Tibet to China. Winters SE Asia.
78. Lanius tigrinus. Tiger Shrike. 18. NE Asia. Winters SE Asia, Philippines, Sundas.
79. Lanius validirostris. Strong billed / Mountain Shrike. 4ss.18. Philippines.
80. Lanius vittatus. Bay backed Shrike. 2ss. 18. S Russia, Iran to Pakistan, India.
81. Pityriasis gymnocephala. Bornean Bristlehead. 25. Borneo.

63
65
66
64
67
69
70
68
71
72
(a)
(b)
73
74
75
76
77
78
79
80
81

VANGIDAE, HYPOSITTADAE, BOMBYCILLI DAE, PTILOGONATIDAE, DULIDAE
Vanga Shrikes, Coral billed Nuthatch, Waxwings, Silky Flycatchers, Palmchat

Family 125. VANGIDAE. Vanga Shrikes.

1. Calicalius / Cyanolanius madagascariensis. Red tailed Vanga. 13. Malagasy.
1a. Calicalius rufocarpalis. Red shouldered Vanga. 14. Malagasy. (Male unknown.)
2. Schetba rufa. Rufous Vanga. 2ss. 22. Malagasy.
3. Vanga curvirostris. Hook billed Vanga. 2ss. 25. Malagasy.
4. Xenopirostris damii. Von Dam's Vanga. 29. Malagasy
5. Xenopirostris polleni. Pollen's Vanga. 23. Malagasy.
6. Xenopirostris xenopirostris. Lafresnaye's Vanga. 25. Malagasy.
7. Falculea palliata. Sickle billed Vanga. 32. Malagasy.
8. Leptopterus chabert. Chabert's Vanga. 2ss. 15. Malagasy.
9. Cyanolanius madagascariensis. Blue Vanga. 2ss. 17. Malagasy.
10. Artamella viridis. White headed Vanga. 2ss. 19. Malagasy.
11. Oriolia bernieri. Bernier's Vanga. 2ss. 21. Malagasy.
12. Euryceros prevosti. Helmet Vanga. 27. Malagasy.

Family 126. HYPOSITTADAE. Coral billed Nuthatch.

1. Hypositta corallirostris. Coral billed Nuthatch. 13. Malagasy.

Family 127. BOMBYCILLIDAE. Waxwings.

1. Bombycilla cedrorum. Cedar Waxwing. 15. Alaska to Georgia. Winters Mexico, Caribbean.
2. Bombycilla garrulus. (Bohemian) Waxwing. 3ss. 19. NW Eurasia, N America. Winters South.
3. Bombycilla japonica. Japanese Waxwing. 19. Siberia to Japan.

Family 128. PTILOGONATIDAE. Silky Flycatchers.

1. Ptilogonys caudatus. Long tailed silky Flycatcher. 23. Costa Rica, Panama.
2. Ptilogonys cinereus. Grey silky Flycatcher. 5ss. 20. Mexico, Guatemala.
3. Phainopepla nitens. Phainopepla. 2ss. 18. SW USA, Mexico.
4. Phainoptila melanoxantha. Black & yellow silky Flycatcher. 20. Costa Rica, Panama.
5. Hypocolius ampelinus. Hypocolius. 23. Arabia & Iraq to India.

Family 129. DULIDAE. Palmchat.

1. Dulus dominicus. Palm Chat. 17. Hispaniola.

VANGIDAE
1
2
3
4
5
1A
6
7
8
9
10
11
12
1
HYPOSITTADAE
BOMBYCILLIDAE
1
2
3
PTILOGONATIDAE
1
2
3
4
5
DULIDAE
1

CINCLIDAE, TROGLODYTIDAE (1) Dippers, Wrens

Family 130. CINCLIDAE. Dippers.

1. Cinclus cinclus. Dipper. 11ss. 18. Palearctic & Himalayas.
2. Cinclus leucocephalus. White capped Dipper. 3ss. 15. Venezuela to Bolivia.
3. Cinclus mexicanus. American Dipper. 5ss. 16. N America to Panama.
4. Cinclus pallasii. Brown / Pallas' Dipper. 4ss. 21. Asia.
5. Cinclus schultzi. Rufous throated Dipper. 15. NW Argentina.

Family 131. TROGLODYTIDAE. Wrens (1).

1. Campylorhynchus brunneicapillus. Cactus Wren. 7ss. 17. Mexico & SW USA.
2. Campylorhynchus fasciatus. Fasciated Wren. 2ss. 19. Peru, Ecuador.
3. Campylorhynchus griseus. Bicolored Wren. 5ss. 18. N of S America.
4. Campylorhynchus chiapensis. Giant Wren. 20+. S Mexico.
5. Campylorhynchus gularis. Spotted Wren. 17. WC Mexico.
6. Campylorhynchus jocosus. Boucard's Wren. 16. SC Mexico.
7. Campylorhynchus megalopterus. Grey barred Wren. 2ss. 18. E Mexico.
8. Campylorhynchus nuchalis. Stripe backed Wren. 3ss. 18. Colombia, Venezuela.
9. Campylorhynchus rufinucha. Rufous naped Wren. 5ss. 15. Mexico to Costa Rica.
10. incl. C. r. capistratus. Rufous backed Wren. 15. Salvador to Costa Rica.
11. Campylorhynchus turdinus. Thrush-like Wren. 6ss. 20. Colombia & Amazon basin.
12. Campylorhynchus albobrunneus. White headed Wren. 19. Panama, W Colombia.
13. Campylorhynchus yucatanicus. Yucatan Wren. 18. Coastal Yucatan.
14. Campylorhynchus zonatus. Band backed Wren. 7ss. 18. Mexico to Ecuador.
15. Odontorchilus branickii. Grey mantled Wren. 2ss. 12. Colombia to Bolivia.
16. Odontorchilus cinereus. Tooth billed Wren. 12. Brazil.
17. Catherpes mexicanus. Canyon Wren. 5ss. 12. W North America, Canada to Mexico.
18. Salpinctes obsoletus. Rock Wren. 6ss. 12. America, Canada to Costa Rica.
19. Hylorchilus/Catherpes sumichrasti. Slender billed Wren. 2ss. 14. SE Mexico.
20. Cinnycerthia peruana. Sepia-brown Wren. 4ss. 14. Colombia to Bolivia.
21. Cinnycerthia unirufa. Rufous Wren. 3ss. 18. Venezuela to Peru.
22. Cistothorus apolinari. Apolinar's / Marsh Wren. 13. Colombia
23. Cistothorus meridae. Paramo Wren. 10. Venezuela.
24. Cistothorus palustris. Long billed Marsh Wren. 11ss. 11. N America. Winters Mexico.
25. Cistothorus platensis. Sedge / Grass / Short billed Marsh Wren. 21ss. 10. N & S America.
26. Thryomanes bewickii. Bewick's Wren. 18ss. 12. Canada to S Mexico.
27. Thryomanes sissonii. Socorro Wren. 13. Socorro I.
28. Ferminia cerverai. Zapata Wren. 16. SW Cuba.

CINCLIDAE
1
2
3
4
5
TROGLODYTIDAE
1
2
3
4
5
6
7
8
9
10
11
12
13
14
15
16
17
18
19
20
21
22
23
24
25
26
27
28

TROGLODYTIDAE (2)
Wrens

29. Thryothorus atrogularis. Black throated Wren. 2ss. 14. Nicaragua to Panama.
30. Thryothorus spadix. Sooty headed Wren. 15. Panama, Colombia,
31.Thryothorus albinucha. White browed Wren. 13. Mexico, Guatemala.(ss. of 42?)
32. Thryothorus coraya. Coraya Wren. 9ss. 16. North of S America.
33. Thryothorus euophrys. Plain tailed Wren. 3ss. 17. Ecuador, Peru.
34. Thryothorus fasciatoventris. Black bellied Wren. 3ss. 15. Costa Rica to Colombia.
35. Thryothorus felix. Happy Wren. 6ss. 13. Mexico.
36. Thryothorus genibarbis. Moustached Wren. 12ss. 17. Venezuela to Ecuador.
37. Thryothorus mysticalis. Whiskered Wren. 16. Ecuador.
38. Thryothorus griseus. Grey Wren. 13. Brazil.
39. Thryothorus guarayanus. Fawn breasted Wren. 14. Bolivia, SW Brazil.
40. Thryothorus leucotis. Buff breasted Wren. 11ss. 14. Panama to Peru.
41. Thryothorus longirostris. Long billed Wren. 2ss. 16. NE & C Brazil.
42. Thryothorus ludovicianus. Carolina Wren. 9ss. 12. E & S USA, Mexico.
43. Thryothorus maculipectus. Spot Breasted Wren. 4ss. 14. Mexico to Salvador.
44. Thryothorus sclateri. Speckle breasted Wren. 14. Peru.
45. Thryothorus modestus. Plain Wren. 3ss. 13. Mexico to Panama.
46. incl. T. m. zeledoni. Canebreak Wren. 13. Nicaragua, Costa Rica, Panama.
47. Thryothorus nicefori. Nicefori's Wren. 16. Andes of Colombia.
48. Thryothorus nigricapillus. Black capped Wren. 5ss. 14. Nicaragua to Ecuador.
49. Thryothorus castaneus. Bay Wren. 14. Panama.
50. Thryothorus semibadius. Riverside Wren. 14. Costa Rica, Panama.
51. Thryothorus pleurostictus. Banded Wren. 7ss. 13. Mexico, Costa Rica.
52. Thryothorus rufalbus. Rufous & white Wren. 5ss. 15. Mexico to Northern S America.
53. Thryothorus rutilus. Rufous breasted Wren. 14. Costa Rica, Tobago, Northern S America.
54. Thryothorus sinaloa. Bar vented Wren. 3ss. 13. Mexico.
55. Thryothorus superciliaris. Superciliated Wren. 2ss. 15. Ecuador, Peru.
56. Thryothorus thoracicus. Stripe breasted Wren. 3ss. 12. Nicaragua to Panama.
57. Thryothorus leucopogon. Stripe throated Wren. 12. Panama to Ecuador.
58. Thryothorus eisenmanni. Inca Wren. 16. Andes of Peru.
59. Troglodytes aedon. (Northern) House Wren. 29ss. 12. S Canada to Falkland Is.
60. incl. T. a. musculus. Southern House Wren. 12. Brazil to Argentina.
61. Troglodytes tanneri. Clarion Wren. 13. Clarion Is.
62. Troglodytes brunneicollis. Brown throated Wren. 10. CS Mexico.
63. Troglodytes beani. Cozumel Wren. 12. Cozumel Is.
64. Thryorchilus browni. Timberline Wren. 3ss. 10. Costa Rica, Panama.
65. Troglodytes rufulus. Tepui Wren. 5ss. 11. Mountains of Venezuela.
66. Troglodytes solstitialis. Mountain Wren. 13ss. 11. Mexico to Argentina.

66a. Troglodytes monticola. Santa Marta / Paramo Wren. 12. NE Colombia.

67. Troglodytes rufociliatus. Rufous browed Wren. 10. Mexico to Nicaragua.
68. Troglodytes ochraceus. Ochraceous Wren. 10. Costa Rica.
69. Troglodytes troglodytes. (Winter) Wren. 37ss. 10. Holarctic, S to Himalayas.
70. Uropsila leucogastra. White bellied Wren. 4ss. 10. Mexico, Belize, Guatemala.
71. Henicorhina leucophrys. Grey breasted Wood Wren. 17ss. 11. Mexico to Bolivia.
72. Henicorhina leucosticta. White breasted Wood Wren. 11ss. 10. Mexico to Peru.
73. Henicorhina leucoptera. Bar winged Wood Wren. 11. Peru.
74. Microcerculus bambla. Wing banded Wren. 3ss. 11. Guyanas, Venezuela to Brazil, Peru.
75. Microcerculus marginatus. Southern Nightingale Wren. 11. Costa Rica to Brazil.

M. m. luscinia (Whistling Wren) & M. m. taeniatus (Scaly breasted Wren) may be Species.

76. Microcerculus philomela. Northern Nightingale Wren. 10. Central America.
77. Microcerculus ustulatus. Flutist Wren. 4ss. 10. Venezuela, Guyana, N Brazil.
78. Cyphorhinus aradus. Organ / quadrille Wren. 14ss. 13. Nicaragua to Colombia.
79. Cyphorhinus phaeocephalus. Song Wren. 12. Colombia, Ecuador.
80. Cyphorhinus modulator. Musician Wren. 13. Peru, W Brazil.
81. Cyphorhinus thoracicus. Chestnut breasted Wren. 2ss. 15. Colombia to Peru.

29
30
31
32
33
34
35
36
38
39
37
44
40
41
42
43
45
46
47
48
49
50
51
52
53
54
55
56
57
59
60
61
62
66A
63
64
65
66
67
68
73
69
70
71
72
58
75
74
76
77
78
79
80
81

MIMIDAE
Thrashers, Mockingbirds

1. *Dumetella carolinensis*. Grey Catbird. 20. N America. Winters C America, West Indies.
2. *Melanoptila glabrirostris*. Black Catbird. 20. Yucatan, Belize, Guatemala.
3. *Melanotis caerulescens*. Blue Mockingbird. 2ss. 25. Mexico.
4. *Melanotis hypoleucus*. Blue & white Mockingbird. 27. Mexico to Salvador.
5. *Mimus dorsalis*. Brown backed Mockingbird. 27. Bolivia, NW Argentina.
6. *Mimus gundlachii*. Bahama Mockingbird. 2ss. 27. Bahamas, Jamaica.
7. *Mimus longicaudatus*. Long tailed Mockingbird. 4ss. 28. Ecuador, NW Peru.
8. *Mimus patagonicus*. Patagonian Mockingbird. 23. WS Argentina, S Chile.
9. *Mimus polyglottos*. Mockingbird. 10ss. 23. USA. Bahamas, Cayman Is., Gr. Antilles.
10. *Mimus gilvus*. Tropical Mockingbird. 10ss. 23. West Indies, Mexico to Brazil.
11. incl. *M. g. magnirostris*. St Andrew Mockingbird. 27. St. Andrews Is.
12. *Mimus saturninus*. Chalk browed Mockingbird. 4ss. 25. Amazonia, SE S America.
13. *Mimus thenca*. Chilean Mockingbird. 28. Chile.
14. *Mimus triurus*. White banded Mockingbird. 23. Bolivia to Argentina.
15. *Nesomimus trifasciatus*. Charles Mockingbird. 25. Gardner Is., Champion Is., Galapagos Is.
16. *Nesomimus parvulus*. Galapagos Is. Mockingbird. 25. Galapagos.
17. *Nesomimus macdonaldi*. Hood Mockingbird. 27. Hood Is., Galapagos Is.
18. *Nesomimus melanotis*. Chatham Mockingbird. 25. Chatham Is., Galapagos Is.
19. *Mimodes graysoni*. Socorro Thrasher. 23. Socorro Is.
20. *Toxostoma bendirei*. Bendire Thrasher. 3ss. 21. SW USA, Mexico.
21. *Toxostoma cinereum*. Grey Thrasher. 2ss. 22. Baja, California.
22. *Toxostoma curvirostra*. Curve billed Thrasher. 7ss. 25. SW USA, Mexico.
23. *Toxostoma crissale*. Crissal Thrasher. 4ss. 26. SW USA, Mexico.
24. *Toxostoma guttatum*. Cozumel Thrasher. 22. Cozumel Is.
25. *Toxostoma lecontei*. Le Conte Thrasher. 3ss. 23. SW USA, Mexico.
26. *Toxostoma longirostre*. Long billed Thrasher. 2ss. 25. Texas, Mexico.
27. *Oreoscoptes montanus*. Sage Thrasher. 19. British Columbia to Mexico.

1
2
3
4
5
7
8
9
10
11
12
13
14
15
16
17
18
19
20
21
22
23
24
25
26
27

MIMIDAE (2)
Mockingbirds, Thrashers, Accentors

Family 132. MIMIDAE (2). Mockingbirds, Thrashers.

28. *Toxostoma ocellatum.* Ocellated Thrasher. 27. Mexico.
29. *Toxostoma redivivum.* California Thrasher. 2ss. 25. California, Baja, California.
30. *Toxostoma rufum.* Brown Thrasher. 2ss. 25. East of North America.
31. *Ramphocinclus brachyurus.* White breasted Thrasher / Trembler. 2ss.23. St Lucia, Martinique.
32. *Cinclocerthia ruficauda.* Brown Trembler. 6ss. 24. Lesser Antilles.
33. *Cinclocerthia gutturalis.* Grey Trembler. 25. Lesser Antilles.
34. *Donacobius atricapillus.* Black capped Mocking Thrush. 4ss. 23. Panama to Bolivia & Argentina.
35. *Margarops fuscatus.* Pearly eyed Thrasher. 3ss. 27. West Indies, Venezuela.
36. *Margarops/Allenia fuscus.* Scaly Breasted Thrasher. 23. Lesser Antilles.

No. 34 is now generally included in Family 131.

Family 133. PRUNELLIDAE. Accentors.

1. *Prunella atrogularis.* Black throated Accentor. 2ss. 14. Ural Mountains to W China.
2. *Prunella collaris.* Alpine Accentor. 9ss. 18. S Europe, C Asia to Japan.
3. *Prunella fagani.* Yemeni Accentor. 15. SW Arabia.
4. *Prunella fulvescens.* Brown Accentor. 6ss. 14. Mountains of C Asia.
5. *Prunella himalayana.* Rufous streaked / Altai Accentor. 15. Himalayas, C Asia.
6. *Prunella immaculata.* Maroon backed Accentor. 16. Nepal, Sikkim, Szechwan, Burma.
7. *Prunella koslowi.* Mongolian Accentor. 16. Mountains of Mongolia.
8. *Prunella modularis.* Hedge Accentor / Sparrow or Dunnock. 6ss. 15. W Palearctic.
9. *Prunella montanella.* Siberian Accentor. 15. Siberia. Winters China , Korea.
10. *Prunella ocularis.* Radde's Accentor. 2ss. 15. Armenia, Iran to Turkey.
11. *Prunella rubeculoides.* Robin Accentor. 2ss. 16. Pakistan to Tibet & W China.
12. *Prunella rubida.* Japanese Accentor. 2ss. 14. Japan & Kuriles.
13. *Prunella strophiata.* Rufous breasted Accentor. 2ss. 13. Afghanistan to Tibet, SW China & Burma.

28
29
30
31
32
34
35
36
33
PRUNELLIDAE
1
2
3
4
5
6
7
8
9
10
11
12
13

MUSCICAPIDAE, TURDINAE (1). Shortwings, Robins

1. *Heinrichia calligyna*. Great Shortwing. 3ss. 15. Sulawesi.
2. *Brachypteryx hyperythra*. Rusty bellied Shortwing. 13. Nepal to Assam.
3. *Brachypteryx leucophrys*. Lesser Shortwing. 5ss. 11. S Asia & W Indonesia.
4. *Brachypteryx major*. Rufous bellied Shortwing. 2ss. 15. SW India.
5. incl. *B. m. albiventris*. White bellied Shortwing. 15. Kerala, Madras.
6. *Brachypteryx Montana*. White browed Shortwing. 13ss. 13. S, SE Asia, Philippines, Sundas.
7. *Brachypteryx stellata*. Gould's Shortwing. 2ss. 13. Nepal, Tibet, Burma, Tonkin.
8. *Drymodes brunneopygia* . Southern Scrub Robin. 2ss. 21. SE, S & W Australia.
9. *Drymodes superciliaris*. Northern Scrub Robin. 5ss. 21. N Australia, New Guinea.
10. *Erithacus rubecula*. (European) Robin / Redbreast. 8ss. 14. Palearctic, N Africa.
11. *Erithacus akahige*. Japanese Robin. 3ss. 14. Japan, E Asia.
12. *Luscinia (Erithacus) brunnea*. Indian Blue Robin. 2ss. 15. Himalayas. Winters to Sri Lanka.
13. incl. *L. b. wickhami*. Chin Hills Blue Robin. 15. Chin Hills, Burma.
14. *Luscinia/(Erithacus) calliope*. Siberian Rubythroat. 15. Siberia. Winters S Asia, Philippines.
15. *Tarsiger/(Erithacus) chrysaeus*. Golden Bush Robin. 2ss. 14. Himalayas. Winters China, Burma.
16. *Luscinia/(Erithacus) cyane*. Siberian Blue Robin. 2ss. 15. E Asia. Winters to Philippines, Sundas.
17. *Tarsiger/(Erithacus) cyanurus*. Orange flanked Bush Robin. 3ss. 14. N Palearctic. Winters SE Asia, Gr. Sundas.
18. *Tarsiger/(Erithacus) hyperythrus*. Rufous breasted Bush Robin. 13. Himalayas. Winters to Burma.
19. *Tarsiger/(Erithacus) indicus*. White browed Bush Robin. 3ss. 15. Himalayas Winters Burma, Tonkin.
20. *Tarsiger/(Erithacus) johnstoniae*. Collared Bush Robin. 15. Mountains of Taiwan.
21. *Erithacus komadori*. Ryukyu Robin. 3ss. 14. Ryukyu Is.
22. *Luscinia luscinia*. Thrush Nightingale / Sprosser. 16.N Eurasia. Winters SE Africa.
23. *Luscinia megarhynchos*. Nightingale. 3ss. 16. Palearctic. Winters tropical Africa.
24. *Luscinia/ (Erithacus) obscura*. Black throated Blue Robin. 15. China.
25. *Luscinia/ (Erithacus)* pectardens. Firethroat. 15. Tibet, Yunnan.
26. *Luscinia/ (Erithacus) pectoralis*. White tailed Rubythroat. 3ss. 15. Himalayas. Winters India.
27. *Luscinia/ (Erithacus) ruficeps*. Rufous headed Robin. 15. China.
28. *Luscinia/ (Erithacus) sibilans*. Rufous tailed Robin. 16. Siberia, Kamchatka. Winters SE Asia.
29. *Luscinia svecicus*. (Red spotted) Bluethroat. 7ss. 15. N Eurasia. Winters S Asia.
30. incl. *L. s. cyanecula*. White spotted Bluethroat. 15. C Europe. Winters N Africa.

1
2
3
4
5
6
7
-10-
8
9
11
14
12
13
15
16
18
17
19
21
20
24
26
22
23
25
27
28
30
8r
29
8r
NB

MUSCICAPIDAE, TURDINAE (2). Akalats, Robin Chats

31. Namibornis herero. Herero Chat. 17. Namibia.
32. *Cercotrichas barbata*. Bearded / Miombo Scrub Robin. 2ss. 17. Angola, Malawi, Zambia.
33. *Cercotrichas coryphaeus*. Karoo Scrub Robin. 3ss. 16. S Africa, Namibia.
34. *Cercotrichas galactotes*. Rufous Scrub Robin. 5ss. 18. S Eurasia to Kenya.
35. *Cercotrichas hartlaubi*. Brown backed Scrub Robin. 2ss. 15. Central Africa.
36. *Cercotrichas leucophrys*. White browed Scrub Robin. 10ss. 15. CS Africa.
37. incl. *C. l. zambezianus*. Red backed Scrub Robin. 15. ES Africa.
38. *Cercotrichas leucosticta*. Western bearded / Forest Scrub Robin. 3ss.17. WC Africa.
39. *Cercotrichas paena*. Kalahari Scrub Robin. 4ss. 16. Southern Africa.
40. *Cercotrichas podobe*. Black Scrub Robin. 2ss. 22. Senegal, N Africa to SW Arabia.
41. *Cercotrichas quadrivirgata*. Eastern bearded Scrub Robin. 6ss. 17. Somalia to Natal.
42. *Cercotrichas signata*. Brown Scrub Robin. 4ss. 18. Transvaal to Cape.
43. *Pinarornis plumosus*. Boulder Chat. 25. Zimbabwe, Botswana.
44. *Chaetops frenatus*. Rufous Rockjumper. 22. SW South Africa.
45. *Chaetops aurantius*. Orange breasted Rockjumper. 22.Natal & E South Africa.
46. *Stiphrornis erythrothorax*. Forest Robin. 4ss. 12. Sierra Leone to Sudan, Uganda.
47. *Pogonocichla stallata*. White starred Bush Robin. 11ss. 16. Sudan to Cape.
48. *Swynnertonia swynnertoni*. Swynnerton's Robin. 2ss. 14. Zimbabwe, Tanzania, Mozambique.
49. *Sheppardia aequatorialis*. Equatorial Akalat. 13. Zaire to Sudan, Kenya.
50. *Sheppardia cyornithopsis*. Lowland Akalat. 4ss. 13. WC Africa.
51. *Sheppardia gabela*. Gabela Akalat. 13. Angola.
52. *Sheppardia gunningi*. East coast Akalat. 3ss. 13. Kenya to Mozambique.
53. *Cossypha/Sheppardia roberti*. White bellied Robin Chat. 2ss. 13. Cameroon to Uganda.
54. *Sheppardia sharpei*. Sharpe's Akalat. 2ss. 13. Tanzania, Malawi.
55. *Cossypha albicapilla*. White crowned Robin Chat. 3ss. 22. Senegal to Ethiopia.
56. *Xenocopsychus/Sheppardia ansorgei*. Angola Cave Chat. 19. W Angola.
57. *Cossypha aecheri*. Archer's Robin Chat. 3ss. 15. Zaire, Uganda.
58. *Sheppardia bocagei*. Bocage's / Rufous cheeked Akalat. 8ss.15. Angola, Zaire, Zambia.
59. *Sheppardia poensis/insulana*. Alexander's Akalat. 15. Fernando Po, W Africa.
60. *Cossypha caffra*. Cape Robin Chat. 6ss. 17. E & S Africa.
61 *Cossypha cyanocamptor*. Blue shouldered Robin Chat. 2ss. 17. Sierra Leone to Gabon, Sudan, Kenya.
62. *Cossypha dichroa*. Chorister Robin Chat. 20. Transvaal to Cape.
63. *Cossypha heinrichi*. White headed Robin Chat. 21. Angola to Zaire.
64. *Cossypha heuglini*. White browed Robin Chat. 5ss. 20. Africa S of Sahara.
65. *Cossypha humeralis*. White throated Robin Chat. 2ss. 16. Zimbabwe to Natal.
66. *Cossypha isabellae*. Mountain Robin Chat. 2ss. 15. Nigeria, Cameroon.
67. *Cossypha natalensis*. Red capped Robin Chat. 7ss. 18. Africa S of Sahara.
68. *Cossypha niveicapilla*. Snowy crowned Robin Chat. 2ss. 20. WC Africa.
69. *Cossypha/Sheppardia polioptera*. Grey winged Robin Chat. 4ss. 15. WC Africa.
70. *Cossypha semirufa*. Ruepell's / Black tailed Robin Chat. 3ss.18. Sudan, Ethiopia, Kenya, Tanzania.

31
32
33
34
35
36
37
38
39
40
41
42
43
44
45
46
47
48
49
50
51
52
53
54
55
56
57
58
59
60
61
62
63
64
65
66
67
68
69
70

MUSCICAPIDAE, TURDINAE (3). Alethes, Shamas, Redstarts

71. *Modulatrix stictigula.* Spot throat. 2ss. 14. Tanzania, Malawi.
72. *Cichladusa arquata.* Morning Warbler /Collared Palm Thrush. 20. Kenya to Mozambique.
73. *Cichladusa guttata.* Spotted Morning Warbler / Thrush. 2ss.17. Sudan, E Africa.
74. *Cichladusa ruficauda.* Rufous tailed Palm Thrush. 17. Gabon to Namibia.
75. *Cossypha/Alethe anomala.* Olive flanked Robin Chat (Alethe). 5ss.15. Tanzania to Mozambique.
76. *Alethe castanea.* Fire crested Alethe. 2ss. 18. Central Africa.
77. *Alethe choloensis.* Cholo Alethe. 2ss. 18. Malawi, Mozambique.
78. *Alethe diademata.* White tailed Alethe. 19. Gambia, Togo.
79. *Alethe fuelleborni.* White chested Alethe. 3ss. 22. Tanzania, Malawi, Mozambique.
80. *Sheppardia/Alethe/lowei.* Iringa Akalat / Alethe. 13. Tanzania, Malawi.
81. *Sheppardia/Alethe montana.* Usambara Akalat / Alethe. 13. NE Tanzania.
82. *Alethe poliocephala.* Brown chested Alethe. 7ss. 15. W & C Africa.
83. *Alethe poliophrys.* Red throated Alethe. 2ss. 17. Zaire, Uganda.
84. *Copsychus albospecularis.* Madagascar Magpie Robin. 18. Malagasy.
85. *Copsychus luzoniensis.* White browed Shama. 3ss. 17. Philippines.
86. *Copsychus malabaricus.* White rumped Shama. 18ss. 27/23. Indian region, SE Asia, Indonesia.
87. *Copsychus niger.* White vented Shama. 2ss. 20. Balabac, Calamianes, Palawan.
88. *Copsychus cebuensis.* Black Shama. 20. Cebu, SC Philippines.
89. *Trichixos/Copsychus pyrropygus.* Rufous tailed Shama. 20. Malaysia, Indonesia.
90. *Copsychus saularis.* Dyal / Magpie Robin. 18ss. 20. Oriental Region & Islands.
91. *Copsychus sechellarum.* Seychelles Magpie Robin. 25. Frigate Is.(Seychelles)
92. *Copsychus stricklandii.* White crowned Shama. 2ss. 27. Borneo.
93. *Irania gutturalis.* White throated Robin. 17. Turkey, Iraq, Iran. Winters Arabia.
94. *Phoenicurus alaschanicus.* Ala Shan Redstart. 15. W China.
95. *Phoenicurus auroreus.* Daurian Redstart. 2ss. 15. Siberia, Tibet. Winters to SE Asia.
96. *Phoenicurus caeruleocephalus.* Blue capped Redstart. 14. Himalayas, C Asia.

Note. No. 71 may really be a Bulbul but is included here. Arcanator orostruthus (Dappled Spot Throat) is now definitely considered to be a Bulbul & is shown on Plate 228. No 87.

71
72
73
74
75
76
77
78
81
79
80
82
83
84
85
86
87
88
89
90
91
92
93
94
95
96

MUSCICAPIDAE, TURDINAE (4). Redstarts, Forktails

97. *Phoenicurus erythrogaster.* Guldenstadt's/White winged Redstart. 2ss. 17. Mountains S Asia.
98. *Phoenicurus erythronotus.* Eversmann's / Rufous backed Redstart. 15. C Asia.
99. *Phoenicurus frontalis.* Blue fronted Redstart. 16. Himalayas. Winters SE Asia.
100. *Phoenicurus hodgsoni.* Hodgson's Redstart. 15. WC China. Winters India, Burma.
101. *Phoenicurus moussieri.* Moussier's Redstart. 12. Atlas Mountains, NW Africa.
102. *Phoenicurus ochrurus.* Black Redstart. 5ss. 14. Mediterranean to N China. Winters India, E Africa.
103. *Phoenicurus phoenicurus.* Redstart. 3ss. 14. Eurasia. Winters India, E Africa.
104. *Phoenicurus schisticeps.* White throated Redstart. 15. Tibet, China. Winters Burma.
105. *Rhyacornis bicolor.* Luzon water Redstart. 15. Luzon.
106. *Rhyacornis fuliginosus.* Plumbeous water Redstart. 2ss. 13. Himalayas, S Asia.
107. *Chaimarriornis leucocephalus.* White capped water Redstart / River Chat. 19. Himalayas, China, Indo-China.
108. *Hodgsonius phoenicuroides.* White bellied Redstart. 2ss. 19. Himalayas, Indo-China.
109. *Cinclidium diana.* Sunda Blue Robin. 2ss. 15. Sumatra, Java.
110. *Cinclidium frontale.* Blue fronted Robin. 2ss. 19. Nepal, Sikkim, Tonkin, Laos.
111. *Cinclidium leucurum.* White tailed Robin. 2ss. 17. Mountains of S Asia.
112. *Grandala coelicolor.* Grandala. 23. Kashmir to Tibet & C China.
113. *Enicurus immaculatus.* Black backed Forktail. 25. N India to Burma, Thailand.
114. *Enicurus leschenaulti.* White crowned Forktail. 6ss. 28. S & SE Asia.
115. *Enicurus maculatus.* Spotted Forktail. 4ss. 27. Himalayas, S China, SE Asia.
116. *Enicurus ruficapillus.* Chestnut naped Forktail. 20. Malaysia, Sumatra, Borneo.
117. *Enicurus schistaceus.* Slaty backed Forktail. 25. N India, S China, SE Asia.
118. *Enicurus scouleri.* Little Forktail. 2ss. 12. Mountains S Asia.
119. *Enicurus velatus.* Sunda / Lesser Forktail. 16. Sumatra, Java.

97
98
99
100
101
102
103
104
105
106
107
108
109
110
111
112
113
114
116
115
117
118
119

MUSCICAPIDAE, TURDINAE (5). Cochoas, Bluebirds, Solitaires, Ant Thrushes

120. *Cochoa azurea*. Blue / Javan Cochoa. 2ss. 23. Java, Sumatra.
121. *Cochoa purpurea*. Purple Cochoa. 28. India, China, Burma, Indo-China.
122. *Cochoa beccarii*. Sumatran Cochoa. 28. Sumatran Cochoa.
123. *Cochoa viridis*. Green Cochoa. 28. Himalayas, N SE Asia.
124. *Sialia currucoides*. Mountain Bluebird. 15. W N America, Alaska to Mexico.
125. *Sialia mexicana*. Western Bluebird. 6ss. 14. W of N America, Mexico.
126. *Sialia sialis*. Eastern Bluebird. 6ss. 14. E of N America, Mexico, Nicaragua.
127. *Myadestes myadestinus*. Kamao / Large Kauai Thrush. 20. Kauai (Hawaii).
128. *Myadestes lanaiensis*. Olomano / Lanai Thrush. 18. Molokai (Hawaii).
129. *Myadestes elisabeth*. Cuban Solitaire. 2ss. 19. Cuba, Isle of Pines.
130. *Myadestes genibarbis*. Rufous throated Solitaire. 6ss. 19. West Indies.
131. *Myadestes leucogenys*. Rufous-brown Solitaire. 4ss. 23. N & C South America.
132. *Myadestes occidentalis*. Brown-backed Solitaire. 6ss. 20. Mexico & C America.
133. *Myadestes ralloides*. Andean Solitaire. 6ss. 17. Costa Rica to Venezuela & Bolivia.
134. *Myadestes melanops*. Black faced Solitaire. 17. Costa Rica & Panama.
135. *Myadestes coloratus*. Varied Solitaire. 17. E Panama.
136. *Myadestes townsendi*. Townsend's Solitaire. 2ss. 16. Alaska To NW Mexico.
137. *Myadestes unicolor*. Slate coloured Solitaire. 2ss. 18. Mexico to Nicaragua.
138. *Entomodestes coracinus*. Black Solitaire. 23. Colombia & Ecuador.
139. *Entomodestes leucotis*. White cared Solitaire. 24. Peru, Bolivia.
140. *Neocossyphus finschii*. Finsch's Flycatcher-Thrush. 20. Sierra Leone to Nigeria.
141. *Neocossyphus fraseri*. Rufous Flycatcher-Thrush.3ss. 19. C Africa.
142. *Neocossyphus poensis*. White tailed Ant-Thrush. 3ss. 20. Sierra Leone to Uganda & Angola.
143. *Neocossyphus rufus*. Red tailed Ant-Thrush. 2ss. 20. Cameroon to Congo, Kenya & Tanzania.

120
121
122
123
124
125
126
127
128
129
130
131
132
133
134
135
136
137
138
139
140
141
142
143

MUSCICAPIDAE, TURDINAE (6). Chats

144. *Cercomela dubia*. Sombre Rock Chat. 15. C Ethiopia.
145. *Cercomela familiaris*. Familiar Chat. 11ss. 15. C & S Africa.
146. *Cercomela fusca*. Indian/Brown Rock Chat. 17. Pakistan, NE India.
147. *Cercomela melanura*. Blackstart. 6ss. 14. African deserts, Sinai, Arabia.
148. *Cercomela schlegelii*. Karoo Chat. 5ss. 15. SW Africa.
149. *Cercomela scotocerca*. Brown tailed Chat. 5ss. 13. Ethiopia, Sudan, Somalia.
150. *Cercomela sinuata*. Sicklewing Chat. 3ss. 15. South Africa.
151. *Cercomela sordida*. Hill / Moorland Chat. 5ss. 16. Ethiopia, Kenya, Tanzania.
152. *Cercomela tractrac*. Tractrac Chat. 5ss. 14. Namibia.
153. *Saxicola caprata*. Pied Bushchat. 16ss. 13. India to Malaya & New Guinea.
154. *Saxicola dacotiae*. Canary Islands Chat. 2ss. 13. Fuerteventura. (Canary Is).
155. *Saxicola ferrea*. Grey Bushchat. 15. Pakistan, Tibet, China, Burma, Indo-China.
156. *Saxicola gutturalis*. Timor / White bellied Bushchat. 15. Timor, Semau.
157. *Saxicola insignis*. Hodgson's White throated Bushchat. 17. C Asia. Winters India.
158. *Saxicola jerdoni*. Jerdon's Bushchat. 15. E India, Burma, Thailand, Indo-China.
159. *Saxicola leucura*. White tailed Stonechat. 13. Pakistan, N India.
160. *Saxicola macrorhyncha*. White browed Bushchat. 15. Afghanistan to NW India.
161. *Saxicola rubetra*. Whinchat. 13. W Palearctic. Winters Africa.
162. *Saxicola torquata* hibernans. Stonechat. 14. British Isles form.
163. *Saxicola torquata*. Stonechat. 25ss. 14. South African form.

163a. *Saxicola t. tectes*. Reunion Stonechat. 14. W Mascarene Is.

164. *Myrmecocichla aethiops*. Northern Anteater-Chat. 3ss. 20. Subsaharan Africa.
165. *Myrmecocichla albifrons*. White fronted Black-Chat. 5ss. 13. Senegambia to Ethiopia.
166. *Myrmecocichla arnotti*. White headed Black-Chat. 3ss. 18. S C Africa.
167. *Thamnolaea cinnamomeiventris*. Mocking / Cliff-Chat. 20. Africa S of Sahara
168. *Thamnolaea coronata*. White crowned Cliff-Chat. 2ss. 20. Nigeria to Sudan.
169. *Myrmecocichla formicivora*. Southern Anteater-Chat. 2ss. 18. Zimbabwe, RSA.
170. *Myrmecocichla melaena*. Rueppell's Black-Chat. 14. Ethiopia.
171. *Myrmecocichla nigra*. Sooty Chat. 16. W & C Africa.
172. *Thamnolaea semirufa*. White winged Cliff-Chat. 20. Eritrea, Ethiopia.
173. *Myrmecocichla tholloni*. Congo Moor-Chat. 18. Gabon to Angola & Zaire.

144
145
146
147
148
149
150
151
152
153
154
155
156
157
158
159
160
161
162
163
163A
164
165
166
167
168
169
170
171
172
173

MUSCICAPIDAE, TURDINAE (7). Wheatears

174. *Oenanthe alboniger*. Hume's Wheatear. 17. Local, Hills of S C Eurasia.
175. *Oenanthe bifasciata*. Buff streaked Wheatear / Chat. 18. RSA.
176. *Oenanthe bottae*. Botta's / Red breasted Wheatear. 3ss. 20. Ethiopia, SW Arabia.
177. *Oenanthe heuglini*. Heuglin's Wheatear. 14. Sudan, Ethiopia, Kenya.
178. *Oenanthe deserti*. Desert Wheatear. 3ss. 15. Deserts, Sahara, Asia to Mongolia.
179. *Oenanthe finschii*. Finsch's Wheatear. 2ss. 14. Egypt to Middle East, C Asia.
180. *Oenanthe hispanica*. Black eared Wheatear. 2ss. 15. S Europe, N Africa. Winters W Africa.
181. incl. *O. h. melanoleuca*. Black throated Wheatear. 15. Europe, Mediterranean. Winters N Africa.
182. *Oenanthe isabellina*. Isabelline Wheatear. 15. SC Eurasia. Winters E Africa, India.
183. *Oenanthe leucopyga*. White crowned Black / White tailed Wheatear. 3ss. 17. N Africa, Arabia, Iraq.
184. *Oenanthe leucura*. Black Wheatear. 2ss. 17. Mediterranean area.
185. *Oenanthe lugens*. Mourning Wheatear. 6ss. 14. Morocco to Middle East, Pakistan.
185a. *Oenanthe lugentoides*. Arabian Wheatear. 14. Saudi Arabia, Yemen.
186. *Oenanthe lugubris*. Abyssinian Black Wheatear. 15. Ethiopia.
187. *Oenanthe schalowi*. Schalow's Wheatear. 15. Kenya, Tanzania.
188. *Oenanthe moesta*. Red rumped Wheatear. 2ss. 17. N Africa, Egypt, Jordan, Iraq.
189. *Oenanthe monacha*. Hooded Wheatear. 17. Egypt through Arabia & Iran to Pakistan.
190. *Oenanthe monticola*. Mountain Chat / Wheatear. 5ss. 18. RSA. (very variable).
191. *Oenanthe oenanthe*. (Northern) Wheatear. 5ss. 15. Palearctic & N North America. Winters Africa, Arabia, India.
192. *Oenanthe seebohmi*. Seebohm's / Black throated Wheatear. 15. Morocco, Algeria, Tunisia.
193. *Oenanthe phillipsi*. Somali Wheatear. 14. Somalia.
194. *Oenanthe picata*. Variable or Eastern Pied Wheatear. 16. CS Asia. Winters India.
194a. *O. p. picata*.
194b. *O. p. capistrata*.
194c. *O. p. opistholeuca*.
195. *Oenanthe pileata*. Capped Wheatear. 3ss. 17. Africa south of Equator.
196. *Oenanthe pleschanka*. Pied Wheatear. 14. E Europe to W China. Winters E Africa.
197. *Oenanthe cyprica*. Cyprus Wheatear. 13. Cyprus. Winters NE Africa.
198. *Oenanthe xanthoprymna*. Rufous tailed Wheatear.4923ss. 14. Asia minor. Winters Africa.
199. incl. *O. x. chrysopygia*. Afghan Wheatear. 14. Afghanistan, SW Asia. Winters India.
200. *Saxicoloides fulicata*. Indian Robin. 5ss. 16 India, Pakistan, Nepal, Sri Lanka.
201. *Monticola/Pseudocossyphus imerinus*. Littoral Rock Thrush. 4ss. 16. Malagasy.

174
175
176
177
178
179
182
JUV
185A
183
181
180
185A
-185-
186
184
187
189
190
188
193
191
195
196
192
194
(a)
(b)
(c)
-197-
198
199
200
201

MUSCICAPIDAE, TURDINAE (8).
Rock & Whistling Thrushes

202. *Monticola angolensis.* Miombo Rock Thrush. 2ss. 17. Central Africa.
203. *Monticola/Pseudocossyphus bensoni.* Benson's Rock Thrush. 16. Malagasy.
204. *Monticola brevipes.* Short toed Rock Thrush. 3ss. 18. Souyh Africa to Angola.
204a. *Monticola pretoriae.* Transvaal Rock Thrush. 18. Transvaal, Botswana.
205. *Monticola cinclorhynchus.* Blue capped Rock Thrush. 17. Afghanistan, N India. Winters S India.
206. *Monticola gularis.* White throated Rock Thrush. 18-16. China, N SE Asia,
207. *Monticola explorator.* Sentinel Rock Thrush. 2ss. 18. South Africa to Mozambique.
208. *Monticola rufiventris.* Chestnut bellied Rock Thrush. 24. Pakistan to Tibet, China. Winters SE Asia.
209. *Monticola rufocinereus.* Little Rock Thrush. 2ss. 15. NE Africa, SW Arabia.
210. *Monticola rupestris.* Cape Rock Thrush. 22. RSA.
211. *Monticola saxatalis.* Rufous tailed Rock Thrush. 2ss. 19. S Palearctic. Winters E Africa.
212. *Monticola/Pseudocossyphus sharpei.* Forest Rock Thrush. 16. Malagasy.
213. *Monticola solitarius.* Blue Rock Thrush. 5ss. 20. S Palearctic to Indonesia. Winters N Africa.
214. *Myiophoneus blighi.* Ceylon Whistling Thrush. 20. Sri Lanka.
215. *Myiophoneus caeruleus.* Blue Whistling Thrush. 6ss. 31. Oriental region.
216. *Myiophoneus glaucinus.* Sunda Whistling Thrush. 3ss. 23. Greater Sundas.
217. *Myiophoneus horsfieldii.* Malabar Whistling Thrush. 25. W & C India.
218. *Myiophoneus insularis.* Formosan Whistling Thrush. 28. Tai Wan.
219. *Myiophoneus melanurus.* Shiny Whistling Thrush. 23. Sumatra.
220. *Myiophoneus robinsoni.* Malayan Whistling Thrush. 25. C Malaya.
221. *Geomalia heinrichi.* Geomalia / Celebes mountain Thrush. 28.Sulawesi.

202
203
204
205
206
207
208
209
210
211
212
213
214
215
216
204A
217
218
219
220
221

MUSCICAPIDAE, TURDINAE (9). Zoothera Thrushes

222. *Zoothera andromedae*. Sunda Ground Thrush. 21. Indonesia & Philippines.
223. *Zoothera cinerea*. Ashy Ground Thrush. 20. Luzon, Mindoro.
224. *Zoothera citrina*. Orange headed Thrush. 12ss. 21. India, China, SE Asia, Borneo, Sumatra.
225. *Zoothera dauma*. White's / Scaly Thrush. 16ss. 26. Irregular Asia to Australia, vagrant Europe.
226. *Zoothera major*. Amami Thrush. 29. Ryukyu Is.
227. *Zoothera dixoni*. Long tailed Thrush. 26. Tibet, Yunnan, Burma.
228. *Zoothera heinei*. Russet tailed Thrush. 25. E Australia.
229. *Zoothera dohertyi*. Chestnut backed Thrush. 20. Lombok, Timor & other Lesser Sunda Is.
230. *Zoothera machiki*. Fawn breasted Thrush. 26. Tanimbar, E Lesser Sunda Is.
231. *Zoothera horsfieldi*. Horsfield's Thrush. 27. Sumatra, Java, Lombok.
232. *Zoothera lunulata*. Olive tailed Thrush. 26. New Guinea, Queensland,
233. *Zoothera dumasi*. Moluccan Thrush. 16. Buru & Ceram. S Moluccas.
234. *Zoothera erythronota*. Red backed Thrush. 3ss. 20. Sulawesi, Peleng Is.
235. *Zoothera everetti*. Everett's Ground Thrush. 20. Sabah, Sarawak.
236. *Zoothera interpres*. Chestnut capped Thrush. 2ss. 16-20. Malaysia, Indonesia.
237. *Zoothera margaretae*. San Cristobal Ground Thrush. 2ss. 20. Solomon Is.
238. *Zoothera marginata*. Dark sided Thrush. 23. Nepal, China, Burma, Thailand, Indo-China.
239. *Zoothera mollissima*. Plain backed Thrush. 26. Himalayas. Winters SE Asia.
240. *Zoothera monticola*. (Great) Long billed Thrush. 2ss. 30. N India, Burma, Tonkin.
241. *Zoothera naevia*. Varied Thrush. 2ss. 20. Alaska to Oregon. Winters to SW USA.
242. *Zoothera peronii*. Orange banded Thrush. 2ss. 18. Timor, Wetar, adjacent Sundas.
243. *Zoothera pinicola*. Aztec Thrush. 21. Mexico.
244. *Zoothera schistacea*. Slaty backed / White eared Thrush. 16.Tanimbar.
245. *Zoothera sibirica*. Siberian Thrush. 2ss. 22. NE Asia. Winters SE Asia.
246. *Zoothera spiloptera*. Spot winged Thrush. 21. Sri Lanka.
247. *Zoothera talaseae*. New Britain Thrush. 23. Bismarck Archipelago & Solomon Is.
248. *Zoothera terrestris*. Bonin Thrush. 20. Bonin Is. (extinct).
249. *Zoothera wardii*. Pied Thrush. 22. N India. Winters Sri Lanka.

222
223
224
225
227
228
229
230
226
231
232
233
234
235
236
237
238
239
240
242
243
241
244
246
247
248
245
249

MUSCICAPIDAE, TURDINAE (10).
African Zoothera, Old World Thrushes

Note. African Zootherae are often described as Turdus.

250. *Zoothera piaggiae*. Abyssinian Ground Thrush. 4ss. 19. Sudan to Tanzania.
251. *Zoothera gurneyi*. Orange Thrush. 5ss. 19-23. E Africa, Kenya to Cape.
252. *Zoothera tanganjicae*. Kivu Ground Thrush. 19. Uganda & Zaire.
253. *Zoothera oberlaenderi*. Oberlaender's / Forest Ground Thrush. 19. Congo, Uganda
254. *Zoothera cameronensis*. Black eared Ground Thrush. 2ss. 18. C Africa.
255. *Zoothera princei*. Grey Ground Thrush. 3ss. 20. Sierra Leone to Zaire.
256. *Zoothera kibalensis*. Kibale / Prigogine's Ground Thrush. 20. Uganda.
257. *Zoothera crossleyi*. Crossley's Ground Thrush. 21. Nigeria, Cameroon, Congo.
258. *Zoothera guttata/fischeri*. Spotted Ground Thrush. 20-23. Kenya to Cape.
259. *Turdus olivaceus*. Olive Thrush. 16ss. 24. Africa S of Sahara.
260. *Turdus pelios*. African Thrush. 23. Sudan, Ethiopia.
261. *Turdus abyssinicus*. Abyssinian / Mountain Thrush. 8ss. 23. East Africa.
262. *Turdus helleri*. Taita Thrush. 24. S E Kenya.
263. *Turdus menachensis*. Yemen Thrush. 24. Yemen & Saudi Arabia.
264. *Turdus ludoviciae*. Somali Blackbird / Thrush. 24. Somalia.
265. *Turdus bewsheri*. Comoro Thrush. 3ss. 22. Comoro Is.
266. *Turdus libonayanus*. Kurrichane Thrush. 22. Tanzania, Congo to S Africa.
267. *Turdus litsipsirupa*. Groundscraper Thrush. 22. Ethiopia to Angola & Cape.
268. *Turdus olivaceofuscus*. Olivaceous Thrush. 2ss. 25. Sao Thome, Principe Is.
269. *Turdus poliocephalus*. Island Thrush. 49ss. 22. Islands from Indian Ocean to S Pacific.
270. incl. T. *p. 1ayardi*.22.Fiji. Subspecies are very Variable. All have yellow bills.
271. *Turdus tephronotus*. African Bare eyed Thrush. 22. E Africa S from Tanzania.
272. *Nesocichla eremita*. Starchy / Tristan Thrush. 3ss. 25. Tristan da Cunha.
273. *Turdus cardis*. Grey / Japanese Thrush. 21. E Asia. Winters SE Asia.
274. *Turdus celaenops*. Izu Thrush. 23. Yakushima & other Japanese Is.
275. *Turdus chrysolaus*. Brown headed Thrush. 2ss. 22. E Asia. Winters Philippines.
276. *Turdus dissimilis*. Black breasted Thrush. 2ss. 22. Bangladesh, Assam, SE Asia.
277. *Turdus hortulorum*. Grey backed Thrush. 23. Siberia, N Korea. Winters SE Asia.
278. *Turdus feae*. Grey sided Thrush. 23. N China. Winters SE Asia.
279. *Turdus pallidus*. Pale Thrush. 23. Siberia, Manchuria. Winters to SE Asia, Sumatra.

250
251
252
253
254
255
257
258
259
260
261
262
263
264
266
267
268
269
271
272
256
270
273
265
274
275
276
277
278
279

TURDINAE (11)
Old World Thrushes

280. *Turdus merula*. Blackbird. 16ss. 25. Eurasia, N Africa. Introduced New Zealand.
281. *Turdus ileacus*. Redwing. 2ss. 21. N Eurasia. Winters to S Eurasia, N Africa.
282. *Turdus pilaris*. Fieldfare. 25.Greenland, N Eurasia. Winters S to Mediterranean.
283. *Turdus torquatus*. Ring Ousel. 3ss. 24. Europe, SW Asia. Winters to Mediterranean.
284. *Turdus viscivorus*. Mistle Thrush. 2ss. 26. Eurasia.
285. *Turdus philomelos*. Song Thrush. 4ss. 22. Eurasia. Winters N Africa & Middle East.
286. *Turdus albocinctus*. White collared Blackbird. 27. Himalayas, Tibet, China, Burma.
287. *Turdus boulboul*. Grey winged Blackbird. 30. Himalayas, Pakistan to SE Asia.
288. *Turdus kessleri*. White backed Thrush. 27. Tibet, W China.
289. *Turdus mupinensis*. Chinese / Laubmann's Thrush. 25. China.
290. *Turdus naumanni*. Nauman's Thrush. 23. Manchuria, Mongolia, Korea, Yunnan.
291. *Turdus eunomus*. Dusky Thrush. 23. Manchuria, Siberia. Winters S Asia, Japan.
292. *Turdus obscurus*. Eyebrowed Thrush. 23. Siberia, Mongolia. Winters Himalayas, Indonesia.
293. *Turdus rubrocanus*. Chestnut Thrush. 2ss. 24. Himalayas, Tibet, W China.
294. *Turdus ruficollis*. Red throated Thrush. 2ss. 23. N & C Asia. Winters China to Iran
295. incl. *T. r. atrogularis*. Black throated Thrush. 23. N & C Asia. Winters China to Iran.
296. *Turdus unicolor*. Tickell's / Indian Grey Thrush. 21. Himalayas, India & Pakistan. Winters S India.
297. *Amalocichla incerta*. Lesser Ground Robin. 3ss. 15. New Guinea.
298. *Amalocichla sclateriana*. Greater Ground Robin. 2ss. 20. New Guinea.
299. *Cataponera turdoides*. Sulawesi Thrush. 5ss. 23. Sulawesi.
300. *Turdus relictensis/ulietensis*. Bay Thrush. 20. Society Is. (Extinct.)

280
281
282
283
284
285
286
287
288
292
290
289
293
291
294
295
296
297
298
299
300

MUSCICAPIDAE, TURDINAE (12)
New World Thrushes

301. *Cichlherminia lherminieri*. Forest Thrush. 4ss. 27. West Indies.
302. *Phaeornis/Myadestes obscurus*. Omao / Hawaiian Thrush. 4ss. 18. Hawaii.
303. *Phaeornis/Myadestes palmeri*. Puaiohi / Small Kauai Thrush. 17. Rauai Is.
304. *Catharus aurantiirostris*. Orange billed Nightingale Thrush. 12ss.17. Mexico to Venezuela.
305. *Catharus dryas*. Spotted Nightingale Thrush. 6ss. 15. Mexico to Bolivia.
306. *Catharus fuscater*. Slaty backed Nightingale Thrush. 7ss.18. Costa Rica to Bolivia.
307. *Catharus frantzii*. Ruddy capped Nightingale Thrush. 7ss.16. Costa Rica, Nicaragua, Panama.
308. *Catharus gracilirostris*. Black billed Nightingale Thrush. 2ss.15. Costa Rica, Panama.
309. *Catharus fuscescens*. Veery. 4ss. 17. Eastern N & C America. Winters to Brazil, Bolivia.
310. *Catharus guttatus*. Hermit Thrush. 8ss. 15. N America. Winters Bahamas to Salvador.
311. *Catharus mexicanus*. Black headed Nightingale Thrush. 3ss. 15. Mexico to Panama.
312. *Catharus minimus*. Grey cheeked Thrush. 2ss. 18. NE Siberia, Canada, USA. Winters Hispaniola, N S America.
313. *Catharus occidentalis*. Russet Nightingale Thrush. 5ss. 16. Mexico to Honduras, Salvador.
314. *Catharus ustulatus*. Swainson's Thrush. 4ss. 18. N America. Winters S to Argentina.
315. *Catharus mustelinus*. Wood Thrush. 20. E N America. Winters C America.
316. *Platycichla flavipes*. Yellow legged Thrush. 5ss. 22. N of S America.
317. *Platycichla leucops*. Pale eyed Thrush. 22. Scattered in Mountains of S America.
318. *Turdus albicollis*. White necked Thrush. 21ss. 24. Central & much of S America.
319. *Turdus assimilis*. White throated Thrush. 24. Mexico.
320. *Turdus amaurochalinus*. Creamy bellied Thrush. 24. Brazil, Peru to Argentina.
321. *Turdus aurantius*. White chinned Thrush. 26. Jamaica.
322. *Turdus chiguanco*. Chiguanco Thrush. 3ss. 28. Ecuador to Chile, Argentina.
323. *Turdus falcklandii*. Austral Thrush. 3ss. 25. Chile, Argentina, Falkland Is.
324. *Turdus fulviventris*. Chestnut bellied Thrush. 25. Venezuela to Peru.
325. *Turdus fumigatus*. Cocoa Thrush. 7ss. 23. N of S America, Lesser Antilles.
326. *Turdus hauxwelli*. Hauxwell's Thrush. 23. Venezuela to Bolivia & W Brazil.
327. *Turdus obsoletus*. Pale vented Thrush. 23. Costa Rica, Panama, NW Colombia.
328. *Turdus personus*. Lesser Antillean Thrush. 2ss. 23. Grenada, St Vincent.

For Myadestes see Plate 244.

301
302
303
304
305
306
307
308
309
310
311
312
313
314
315
316
317
321
318
319
323
320
324
327
322
325
326
328

MUSCICAPIDAE, TURDINAE (13)
New World Thrushes

329. *Turdus fuscater*. Great Thrush. 8ss. 32. Andes, Venezuela to Bolivia.
330. *Turdus grayi*. Clay coloured Robin / Thrush. 7ss. 24. Mexico to Colombia.
331. *Turdus haplochrous*. Unicoloured Thrush. 24. Bolivia.
332. *Turdus ignobilis*. Black billed Robin / Thrush. 5ss. 24. Venezuela to Bolivia.
333. *Turdus maculirostris*. Ecuadorian Thrush. 24. Ecuador, Peru.
334. *Turdus plebejus*. Mountain Robin / Thrush. 3ss. 25. Mexico to Panama.
335. *Turdus jamaicensis*. White eyed Thrush. 23. Jamaica.
336. *Turdus lawrencii*. Lawrence's Thrush. 23. Upper Amazon basin.
337. *Turdus leucomelas*. Pale breasted Thrush. 24. North of S America.
338. *Turdus maranonicus*. Maranon Thrush. 21. N Peru.
339. *Turdus migratorius*. American Robin. 8ss. 21. North America, Mexico.
340. *Turdus nigrescens*. Sooty Robin. 25. Costa Rica, Panama.
341. *Turdus nigriceps*. Andean Slaty Thrush / Black Robin.2ss. 23. Ecuador to Argentina
342. *Turdus subalaris*. Eastern Slaty Thrush. 23. Brazil, Paraguay, N Argentina.
343. *Turdus nudigenis*. Bare eyed Thrush. 3ss. 23. W Indies & N of South America.
344. *Turdus olivater*. Black hooded Thrush. 8ss. 23. Colombia, Venezuela.
345. *Turdus plumbeus*. Red legged Thrush. 6ss. 26. West Indies.
346. *Turdus ravidus*. Grand Cayman Thrush. 28. Cayman Is. (extinct?)
347. *Turdus reevei*. Plumbeous Backed Thrush. 24. Ecuador, Peru.
348. *Turdus rufitorques*. Rufous collared Robin. 24. Mexico, Guatemala, Salvador.
349. T*urdus rufiventris*. Rufous bellied Thrush. 2ss. 25. Brazil to Argentina.
350. *Turdus rufopalliatus*. Rufous backed Thrush / Robin. 3ss. 23. Mexico.
351. *Turdus graysoni*. Grayson's Thrush. 23. Tres Marias Is.
352. *Turdus serranus*. Glossy black Thrush. 5ss. 25. Venezuela to NW Argentina.
353. *Turdus infuscatus*. Black Thrush / Robin. 22. Mexico & Central America.
354. *Turdus swalesi*. La Selle Thrush. 27. Haiti.

329
330
331
332
333
334
335
336
337
338
339
Juv
340
343
344
341
345
342
346
348
349
351
347
350
352
354
353

MUSCICAPIDAE, ORTHONYCHINAE
Logrunners

1. *Orthonyx spaldingi*. Chowchilla / Northern Logrunner. 28. N Queensland.
2. *Orthonyx temmincki*. Southern Logrunner. 4ss. 21. E Australia, New Guinea.
3. *Androphobus viridis*. Green backed Babbler / Papuan Whipbird. 17. W New Guinea.
4. *Psophodes nigrogularis*. Western Whipbird. 3ss. 23. S Australia.
5. *Psophodes olivaceus*. Eastern Whipbird. 3ss. 27. Queensland to Victoria.
6. *Psophodes(Sphenostoma)cristatus*. Chirruping Wedgebill. 20. Internal SE Australia.
7. *Psophodes(Sphenostoma)occidentalis*. Chiming Wedgebill. 20. Internal W Australia.
8. *Cinclosoma ajax*. Painted / Ajax Quail-Thrush. 4ss. 23. New Guinea.
9. *Cinclosoma alisteri*. Nullarbor Quail-Thrush. 18. SW Australia.
10. *Cinclosoma castanotus*. Chestnut Quail-Thrush. 3ss. 24. SW & S Australia.
11. *Cinclosoma cinnamomeum*. Cinnamon Quail-Thrush. 4ss. 21. All Australia.
12. *Cinclosoma castaneothorax*. Chestnut breasted Quail-Thrush. 21. E Australia.
13. *Cinclosoma punctatum*. Spotted Quail-Thrush. 2ss. 27. New South Wales, Tasmania.
14. *Ptilorrhoa caerulescens*. Blue Jewel / Lowland Rail Babbler. 4ss. 22. New Guinea.
15. *Ptilorrhoa castanonota*. Chestnut backed Jewel / Mid mountain Rail Babbler. 7ss. 23. New Guinea.
16. *Ptilorrhoa leucosticta*. Spotted Jewel / High mountain Rail Babbler. 7ss. 20. New Guinea.
17. *Eupetes macrocerus*. Malaysian Rail Babbler. 25. Thailand, Malaya, Sumatra, Borneo.
18. *Melampitta gigantea*. Greater Melampitta. 29. W New Guinea.
19. Melampitta lugubris. Lesser Melampitta. 18. Mountains New Guinea.
20. Ifrita kowaldi. Ifrit / Blue capped Babbler. 2ss. 17. Mountains New Guinea.

6 & 7 are virtually indistinguishable in appearance but differ vocally.

Sexes are alike in most forms of 14, but in ss. geislerorum female is chestnut as shown.
Female of 16 shown is ss. loriae. Sexes are alike in all other forms.

For *Crateroscelis*, Mountain babblers & Fern Wren see Plate 271.

1
2
3
4
5
6
7
8
9
10
11
12
13
14
15
16
17
18
19
20

TIMALIINAE (1) Babblers

1. *Pellorneum albiventre.* Spot throated Babbler. 5ss. 13. Assam, Indo-China, Burma.
2. *Pellorneum capistratum.* Black capped Babbler. 5ss. 16. Malaysia, Indonesia.
3. *Pellorneum fuscocapillum.* Brown capped Babbler. 3ss. 16. Sri Lanka.
4. *Pellorneum palustre.* Marsh Babbler. 15. Assam.
5. *Pellorneum ruficeps.* Puff throated Babbler. 26ss. 16. S & W India.
6. *Malacocincla abbotti.* Abbott's Babbler. 9ss. 16. Nepal, SE Asia, Borneo, Sumatra.
7. *Illadopsis albipectus.* Scaly breasted Illadopsis. 2ss. 14. C Africa.
8. *Trichastoma bicolor.* Ferruginous Babbler. 16. Malaysia, *Sum*atra, Borneo.
9. *Trichastoma celebense.* Sulawesi Babbler. 6ss. 14. Sulawesi.
10. *Malacocincla cinereiceps.* Ashy headed Babbler. 13. Palawan & Balabec.
11. *Illadopsis cleaveri.* Blackcap Illadopsis. 5ss. 14. West Africa.
12. *Illadopsis fulvescens.* Brown Illadopsis. 6ss. 15. Sierra Leone to Angola.
13. *Illadopsis moloneyanum.* Nigerian Illadopsis. 15. W & C Africa.
14. *Malacocincla malaccensis.* Short tailed Babbler. 4ss. 13. Borneo, Sumatra.
15. *Malacocincla feriatum.* Ochraceous throated Babbler. 13. Sarawak.
16. *Malacocincla perspicillata.* Black browed Babbler. 15. Borneo. (Unique).
17. *Kakamega poliothorax.* Grey chested Illadopsis. 16. Cameroon to Kenya.
18. *Illadopsis puveli.* Puvel's Illadopsis. 2ss. 17. W & C Africa.
19. *Illadopsis Pyrrhoptera.* Mountain Illadopsis. 2ss. 14. E Africa to Zaire, Malawi.
20. *Pellorneum pyrrogenys.* Temminck's Babbler. 6ss. 14. Sumatra, Java, Borneo.
21. *Trichastoma rostratum.* White chested Babbler. 2ss. 15. Malaysia, Sumatra, Borneo.
22. *Illadopsis rufescens.* Rufous winged Illadopsis. 14. Sierra Leone to Ghana.
23. *Illadopsis rufipennis.* Pale breasted Illadopsis. 4ss. 14. W & C Africa.
24. Malacocincla sepiaria. Horsfield's Babbler. 7ss. 15. Malaysia, Indonesia.
25. *Pellorneum tickelli.* Buff breasted Babbler. 7ss. 15. Assam, China, SE Asia.
26. *Malacocincla vanderbilti.* Vanderbilt's Babbler. 15. Sumatra. (Unique).
27. *Leonardina/Trichastoma woodi.* Bagobo Babbler. 17. Mindanao.
28. *Ptyrticus turdinus.* Thrush Babbler. 3ss. 20. Central Africa.
29. *Malacopteron affine.* Sooty capped Babbler. 3ss. 17. Malaysia, Sumatra, Borneo.
30. *Malacopteron albogulare.* Grey breasted Babbler. 2ss. 15. Malaya, Sumatra, Borneo.
31. *Malacopteron cinereum.* Scaly crowned Babbler. 5ss. 16. SE Asia, Indonesia.
32. *Malacopteron magnirostre.* Moustached Babbler. 3ss. 17. SE Asia, Indonesia.
33. *Malacopteron magnum.* (Greater) Rufous crowned Babbler. 2ss. 18. SE Asia, Borneo.
34. *Malacopteron palawanense.* Melodious / Palawan Babbler. 17. Palawan.
35. *Pomatorhinus erythrocnemis.* Spot breasted Scimitar Babbler. 22. Himalayas to Taiwan.
36. *Pomatorhinus erythrogenys.* Rusty cheeked Scimitar Babbler. 15ss. 24. China, SE Asia.
37. *Pomatorhinus ferruginosus.* Coral billed Scimitar Babbler. 5ss. 22. Himalayas to Indo-China.
38. *Pomatorhinus horsfieldii.* Indian Scimitar Babbler. 5ss. 22. India, Sri Lanka.
39. *Pomatorhinus hypoleucos.* Large Scimitar Babbler. 5ss. 27. Assam, Hainan, SE Asia.
40. *Pomatorhinus montanus.* Chestnut backed Scimitar Babbler. 4ss. 20. Malaya, Indonesia.
41. *Pomatorhinus ochraceiceps.* Red billed Scimitar Babbler. 4ss. 24. Himalayas, SE Asia.
42. *Pomatorhinus ruficollis.* Streak breasted Scimitar Babbler. 14ss. 20. S E Asia, Himalayas.
43. *Pomatorhinus schisticeps.* White browed Scimitar Babbler. 13ss. 23. Himalayas, S E Asia.
44. *Garrilornis/Pomatostomus isidorei.* New Guinea rufous Babbler. 2ss. 28. New Guinea.
45. *Pomatostomus halli.* Hall's White throated Babbler. 23. Queensland.
46. *Pomatostomus ruficeps.* Chestnut crowned Babbler. 22. S E Australia.
47. *Pomatostomus superciliosus.* White browed Babbler. 4ss. 22. SC Australia.
48. *Pomatostomus temporaries.* Grey crowned Babbler. 11ss. 29. Australia, New Guinea.
49. *Pomatostomus rubeculus.* Red breasted Babbler. 29. NW Australia.
50. *Xiphirhynchus superciliaris.* Slender billed Scimitar Babbler. 4ss. 20. Nepal to Burma.
51. *Jabouilleia danjoui.* Short tailed Scimitar Babbler. 3ss. 20. Annam.

For *'Illadopsis' abyssinica & atriceps,* see *'Alcippe'.* Plate 259. Nos 227 and 228.

1
2
3
4
5
6
7
8
9
10
11
12
14
15
16
17
18
13
20
21
22
23
19
24
25
26
27
28
29
30
31
32
33
34
35
36
37
38
39
40
41
42
43
44
45
46
47
48
49
50
51

MUSCICAPIDAE, TIMALIINAE (2) Babblers

52. *Rimator malacoptilus*. Long billed Wren Babbler. 3ss. 13. Sikkim, Burma, Sumatra.
53. *Ptilocichla falcata*. Falcated Wren-Babbler. 18. Palawan, Balabac.
54. *Ptilocichla leucogrammica*. Bornean Wren-Babbler. 15. Borneo.
55. *Ptilocichla mindanensis*. Striated Wren-Babbler. 4ss. 17. Malaya, Sumatra, Borneo.
56. incl. *P. m. basilanica*. Basilan Wren-Babbler. 17. Basilan Is.
57. *Kenopia striata*. Striped Wren-Babbler. 14. Malaya, Thailand, Sumatra, Borneo.
58. *Napothera atrigularis*. Black throated Wren-Babbler. 17. Borneo.
59. *Napothera brevicaudata*. Streaked Wren-Babbler. 8ss. 15. China, N SE Asia.
60. *Napothera crassa*. Mountain Wren-Babbler. 13. Sabah, Borneo.
61. *Napothera crispifrons*. Limestone Wren-Babbler. 3ss. 14. Thailand, Indo-China.
62. incl. *N. c. calcicola*. Rufous Limestone Wren-Babbler. 14. NE Thailand.
63. *Napothera epilepitota*. Eyebrowed Wren-Babbler. 14ss. 11. Assam, SE Asia, Sundas.
64. *Napothera macrodactyla*. Large Wren-Babbler. 3ss. 18. Malaya, Sumatra, Java.
65. *Napothera rufipectus*. Rusty breasted Wren-Babbler. 18. W Sumatra.
66. *Napothera marmorata*. Marbled Wren-Babbler. 2ss. 22. Malaya, Sumatra.
67. *Napothera rabori*. Rabor's / Luzon Wren-Babbler. 3ss. 21. Luzon.
68. *Pnoepyga albiventer*. Scaly breasted Wren-Babbler. 2ss. 10. Burma, Yunnan. (a.) & (b.)

68a. *Pnoepyga Immaculata*. Nepal Wren-Babbler. 10. Nepal.

69. *Pnoepyga pusilla*. Pygmy Wren-Babbler. 8ss. 9. S SE Asia, Sundas. (a.) & (b.)
70. *Spelaeornis caudatus*. Rufous throated Wren-Babbler. 9. Sikkim, Nepal, Bhutan.
71. *Spelaeornis badeigularis*. Rusty throated / Mishmi Babbler. 9. NE India.
72. *Spelaeornis chocolatinus*. Long tailed Wren-Babbler. 4ss. 11. Himalayas to Tonkin.
73. *Spelaeornis formosus*. Spotted Wren-Babbler. 10. Sikkim to China, Burma.
74. *Spelaeornis longicaudatus*. Tawny breasted Wren-Babbler. 11. Assam, Manipur.
75. *Spelaeornis troglodytoides*. Bar winged Wren-Babbler. 5ss. s. 15. W & C Africa.
14. *Malacocincla malaccensis*. Short tailed Babbler. 4ss. 13. Borneo, Sumatra.
15. *Malacocincla feriatum*. Ochraceous throated Babbler. 13. Sarawak.
16. *Malacocincla perspicillata*. Black browed Babbler. 15. Borneo. (Unique).
17. *Kakamega poliothorax*. Grey chested Illadopsis. 16. Cameroon to Kenya.
18. *Illadopsis puveli*. Puvel's Illadopsis. 2ss. 17. W & C Africa.
19. *Illadopsis Pyrrhoptera*. Mountain Illadopsis. 2ss. 14. E Africa to Zaire, Malawi.
20. *Pellorneum pyrrogen* Philippines.
83. *Stachyris nigrocapitata*. Black crowned Babbler. 12. Philippines.
84. *Stachyris dennistouni*. Golden crowned Babbler. 15. Luzon.
85. *Stachyris chrysaea*. Golden Babbler. *6ss. 13.* Nepal to China, SE Asia, Sumatra.
86. *Stachyris erythroptera*. Chestnut winged Babbler. 6ss. 15. Malaya, Borneo, Sumatra.
87. *Stachyris grammiceps*. White breasted Babbler. 15. Java.
88. *Stachyris herberti*. Sooty Babbler. 17. Laos.
89. *Stachyris hypogrammica*. Palawan striped Babbler. 18. Palawan.
90. *Stachyris leucotis*. White necked Babbler. 3ss. 15. SE Asia, Sumatra, Borneo.
91. *Stachyris maculata*. Chestnut rumped Babbler. 4ss. 17. Malaya, Sumatra, Borneo.
92. *Stachyris melanothorax*. Crescent chested Babbler. 5ss. 13. Java, Bali.
93. *Stachyris nigriceps*. Grey throated Babbler. 13ss. 13. Himalayas to Sumatra, Borneo.
94. *Stachyris nigricollis*. Black throated Babbler. 2ss. 15. Thailand to Borneo.
95. *Stachyris nigrorum*. Negros striped / Black crowned Babbler. 17. Negros.
96. *Stachyris oglei*. Snowy throated Babbler. 13. Assam.
97. *Stachyris plateni*. Pygmy Babbler. 2ss. 12. Samar, Leyte, Mindanao.
98. *Stachyris poliocephala*. Grey headed Babbler. 2ss. 15. Malaya, Sumatra, Borneo.
99. *Stachyris pyrrhops*. Black chinned Babbler. 13. Himalayas, Pakistan to Nepal.
100. *Stachyris rodolphei*. Deignan's Babbler. 13. Thailand.
101. *Stachyris ruficeps*. Rufous capped Babbler. 7ss. 13. Sikkim to China, SE Asia.

68 and 68a have two colour phases (a.) & (b.)

52
53
54
55
56
57
58
59
60
61
62
63
68
A
64
65
66
67
(a)
68
(b)
(a)
69
(b)
70
72
73
74
75
76
71
77
79
78
80
81
82
83
84
85
86
87
88
89
90
91
92
93
94
95
96
97
98
99
100
101

MUSCICAPIDAE, TIMALIINAE (3)
Babblers

102. *Stachyris rufifrons.* Rufous fronted Babbler. 5ss. 13. Burma, SE Asia to Borneo, Sumatra.
103. *Stachyris speciosa.* Flame templed Babbler. 16. Negros, Panay.
104. *Stachyris striata.* Striped Tree Babbler. 13. Luzon.
104a. *Stachyris latistriata.* Panay striped Babbler. 13. C Philippines.
105. *Stachyris striolata.* Spot necked Babbler. 7ss. 17. China, SE Asia, Sumatra.
106. *Stachyris thoracica.* White bibbed Babbler. 2ss. 18. Java.
107. *Stachyris whiteheadi.* Chestnut faced Babbler. 15. Luzon.
108. *Dumetia phillipsi.* Rufous / Tawny bellied Babbler. 13. Sri Lanka.
109. *Dumetia hyperythra.* Tawny bellied / White throated Babbler. 3ss.13. India.
110. *Rhopocichla atriceps.* Dark fronted Babbler. 4ss. 13. SW India, Sri Lanka.
111. *Macronous flavicollis.* Grey cheeked Tit-Babbler. 14. Java & Is.
112. *Macronous gularis.* Striped Tit-Babbler. 25ss. 13. Oriental Region including Islands.
113. *Macronous kelleyi.* Grey faced Tit-Babbler. 14. Laos, Annam, Cochin-China.
114. *Macronous ptilosus.* Fluffy backed Tit-Babbler. 4ss. 16. Malaya to Sumatra, Borneo.
115. *Macronous striaticeps.* Brown Tit-Babbler. 4ss. 14. Philippines, Sula Archipelago.
116. *Micromacronous leytensis.* Miniature Tit-Babbler. 2ss. 8. Leyte.
117. *Timalia pileata.* Chestnut capped Babbler. 6ss. 16. Nepal, SE Asia, Java.
118. *Chrysomma sinense.* Yellow eyed Babbler. 3ss. 18. Pakistan to S China.
119. *Chrysomma(Moupinia)altirostre.* Jerdon's Babbler. 3ss. 17. Pakistan to Burma.
120. *Chrysomma(Moupinia)poecilotis.* Rufous tailed Babbler. 15. W China.
121. *Turdoides affinis.* Yellow billed Babbler. 2ss. 23. S India, Sri Lanka.
122. *Turdoides altirostris.* Iraq Babbler. 21. Iraq, Iran.
123. *Turdoides aylmeri.* Scaly Chatterer. 5ss. 18. Ethiopia to Tanzania.
124. *Turdoides bicolor.* Southern Pied Babbler. 26. Namibia, Transvaal, Botswana.
125. *Turdoides caudatus.* Common Babbler. 4ss. 23. Iraq to India.
126. *Turdoides earlei.* Striated Babbler. 2ss. 24. Pakistan to Burma.
127. *Turdoides fulvus.* Fulvous Chatterer. 4ss. 25. Morocco to Red Sea.
128. *Turdoides gularis.* White throated Babbler. 25. Burma.
129. *Turdoides gymnogenys.* Bare cheeked Babbler. 2ss. 24. Angola, Namibia.
130. *Turdoides hindei.* Hinde's Pied Babbler. 20. E Kenya.
131. *Turdoides hypoleucus.* Northern Pied Babbler. 2ss. 24. Kenya to Tanzania.
132. *Turdoides jardineii.* Arrow marked Babbler. 7ss. 23. E C & SE Africa.
133. *Turdoides leucocephalus.* White headed / Cretschmar's Babbler. 26. NE Africa.
134. *Turdoides leucopygius.* White rumped Babbler. 6ss. 26. NE Africa.
135. *Turdoides hartlaubi.* Angola Babbler. 2ss. 26. SC Africa.
136. *Turdoides longirostris.* Slender billed Babbler. 23. Nepal to Assam, Arakan.
137. *Turdoides malcolmi.* Large grey Babbler. 28. Interior Indian peninsula.
138. *Turdoides melanops.* Black lored Babbler. 3ss. 23. SW Africa.
139. *Turdoides nipalensis.* Spiny Babbler. 25. W & C Nepal.
140. *Turdoides plebejus.* (African) Brown Babbler. 5ss. 23. Sub-saharan Africa.
141. *Turdoides reinwardtii.* Blackcap Babbler. 3ss. 25. Senegal to C Africa.
142. *Turdoides rubiginosus.* Rufous Chatterer. 4ss. 19. Ethiopia to Tanzania.
143. *Turdoides sharpei.* Sharpe's Pied / Black faced Babbler. 23. Kenya, Tanzania.

102
103
104
104 A
105
106
107
108
110
111
112
113
114
115
109
117
118
119
120
121
122
116
123
124
125
126
127
128
129
130
131
132
134
138
133
135
136
137
139
140
141
142
143

Plate 257 Family 136.

MUSCICAPIDAE, TIMALIINAE (4)
Babblers

144. *Turdoides squamiceps*. Arabian Babbler. 3ss. 28. Arabia.
145. *Turdoides squamulatus*. Scaly Babbler. 2ss. 21. Coast of Somalia, Kenya.
146. *Turdoides striatus*. Jungle Babbler. 5ss. 25. Indian Sub-continent.
147. *Turdoides rufescens*. Orange billed / Ceylon Jungle Babbler. 25. Sri Lanka.
148. *Turdoides subrufus*. Rufous Babbler. 2ss. 25. SW India.
149. *Turdoides tenebrosus*. Dusky Babbler . 21. Zaire, Sudan, Ethiopia.
150. *Babax koslowi*. Tibetan Babax. 32. Tibet & China.
151. *Babax lanceolatus*. Chinese Babax. 3ss. 27. Tibet, China, Burma.
152. *Babax waddelli*. Giant Babax. 3ss. 31. Sikkim, Tibet, China.
153. *Garrulax affinis*. Black faced Laughing Thrush. 7ss. 25. Nepal, China, Tonkin.
154. *Garrulax morrisonianus* White whiskered Laughing Thrush. 26. Taiwan.
155. *Garrulax albogularis*. White throated Laughing Thrush. 4ss. 30. Kashmir to Tibet, China, Indo-China.
156. *Garrulax austeni*. Brown capped Laughing Thrush. 2ss. 25. Assam, Burma.
157. *Garrulax cachinnans*. Rufous breasted Laughing Thrush. 20. Nilgiri Highlands, India.
158. *Garrulax jerdoni*. Grey breasted Laughing Thrush. 3ss. 20. SW India.
159. *Garrulax caerulatus*. Grey sided Laughing Thrush. 7ss. 28. Nepal, China, Burma.
160. *Garrulax poecilorhynchus*. Rusty Laughing Thrush. 24. China, Taiwan.
161. *Garrulax canorus*. Hwamei / Melodious Laughing Thrush. 3ss. 25. S E Asia, Hawaii.
162. *Garrulax chinensis*. Black throated Laughing Thrush. 5ss. 28. N SE Asia.
163. *Garrulax nuchalis*. Chestnut backed Laughing Thrush. 26. Assam, Burma.
164. *Garrulax cineraceus*. Moustached Laughing Thrush. 3ss. 23. India, China, Burma.
165. *Garrulax cinereifrons*. Ashy headed Laughing Thrush. 23. Sri Lanka.
166. *Garrulax davidi*. Pere David's / Plain Laughing Thrush. 4ss. 29. NC China.
167. *Garrulax delesserti*. Wynaad Laughing Thrush. 2ss. 25. SE India.
168. *Garrulax gularis*. Rufous vented Laughing Thrush. 23. Bhutan to Burma, Laos.
169. *Garrulax elliotii*. Elliot's Laughing Thrush. 2ss. 25. Tibet to WC China.
170. *Garrulax erythrocephalus*. Chestnut crowned Laughing Thrush. 14ss. 26. Pakistan to Burma, Thailand, Malaya, Indo-China.
171. *Garrulax formosus*. Red winged Laughing Thrush. 2ss. 26. SW China to NW Tonkin.
172. *Garrulax galbanus*. Yellow throated Laughing Thrush. 2ss. 24. Assam, Burma.
173. incl. *G. g. courtoisi*. Yellow breasted Laughing Thrush. 23. Kiangsi, Wuynam.
174. *Garrulax henrici*. Prince Henri's Brown cheeked Laughing Thrush.27. Tibet.
175. *Garrulax leucolophus*. White crested Laughing Thrush. 5ss. 30. Yunnan, SE Asia, Sumatra.
176. *Garrulus lineatus*. Streaked Laughing Thrush. 5ss. 20. Afghanistan to Tibet.

144
145
146
147
148
149
150
151
152
153
154
156
157
158
155
159
161
164
162
163
160
166
165
169
167
168
170
175
171
172
176
173
174

MUSCICAPIDAE, TIMALIINAE (5) Babblers

177. *Garrulax lugubris.* Black Laughing Thrush. 26. Malaya, Sumatra.
178. *Garrulax calvus.* Bare headed Laughing Thrush. 25. Borneo.
179. *Garrulax lunulatus.* Barred Laughing Thrush. 25. C China.
180. *Garrulax bieti.* White speckled Laughing Thrush. 23. Sichuan, Yunnan.
181. *Garrulax maesi.* Grey Laughing Thrush. 4ss. 30. SW China, N SE Asia.
182. *Garrulax maximus.* Giant Laughing Thrush. 34. Tibet, W China.
183. *Garrulax merulinus.* Spot breasted Laughing Thrush. 3ss. 26. Himalayas.
184. *Garrulax milleti.* Black hooded Laughing Thrush. 30. Annam.
185. *Garrulax milnei.* Red tailed Laughing Thrush. 4ss. 26. Burma, Yunnan, Laos.
186. *Garrulax mitratus.* Chestnut capped Laughing Thrush. 5ss. 23. Malaya, Sumatra, Borneo.
187. *Garrulax monileger.* Lesser necklaced Laughing Thrush. 10ss. 30. Nepal, China, SE Asia.
188. *Garrulax ocellatus.* Spotted Laughing Thrush. 4ss. 31. India, Tibet, Burma, China.
189. *Garrulax palliatus.* Grey brown/Sunda Laughing Thrush. 2ss. 25. Borneo, Sumatra.
190. *Garrulax pectoralis.* Greater necklaced Laughing Thrush. 6ss. 32. Nepal, China to SE Asia.
191. *Garrulax perspicillatus.* Masked Laughing Thrush. 30. China to Indo-China.
192. *Garrulax ruficollis.* Rufous necked Laughing Thrush. 25. Nepal to Burma.
193. *Garrulax rufifrons.* Red fronted Laughing Thrush. 2ss. 27. Java.
194. *Garrulax rufogularis.* Rufous chinned Laughing Thrush. 7ss. 25. Pakistan to Burma & Tonkin.
195. *Garrulax sannio.* White browed Laughing Thrush. 4ss. 25. India, China, SE Asia.
196. *Garrulax squamatus.* Blue winged Laughing Thrush. 25. Nepal to Burma, Tonkin.
197. *Garrulax strepitans.* White necked Laughing Thrush. 2ss. 30. Burma, Thailand.
198. *Garrulax striatus.* Striated Laughing Thrush. 4ss. 32. Tibet, China, Burma.
199. *Garrulax subunicolor.* Scaly Laughing Thrush. 3ss. 24. Nepal, Yunnan, Tonkin.
200. *Garrulax sukatschewi.* Snowy cheeked Laughing Thrush. 21. S. Kansu.
201. *Garrulax variegatus.* Variegated Laughing Thrush. 2ss. 24. Pakistan & N India.
202. *Garrulax vassali.* White cheeked Laughing Thrush. 28. Annam, Laos.
203. *Garrulax virgatus.* Striped Laughing Thrush. 25. Assam, Burma.
204. *Garrulax yersini.* Collared Laughing Thrush. 27. Annam.

177
178
179
180
181
182
183
184
185
186
187
188
189
190
191
192
193
194
195
196
197
198
199
200
201
202
203
204

MUSCICAPIDAE, TIMALIINAE (6) Babblers

205. *Liocichla phoenicea.* Red faced / Crimson winged Liocichla. 4ss. 23. Himalayas.
206. *Liocichla ripponi.* Crimson headed Liocichla. 23. Burma, Thailand.
207. *Liocichla omeiensis.* Grey faced Liocichla. 19. Szechwan. (Mount Omei).
208. *Liocichla steerii.* Steere's Liocichla. 19. Taiwan.
209. *Leiothrix argentauris.* Silver eared Mesia. 8ss. 18. Yunnan, SE Asia, Sumatra.
210. *Leiothrix lutea.* Red billed Leiothrix / Peking Robin. 6ss. 15. China, SE Asia.
211. *Cutia nipalensis.* (Nepal) Cutia. 4ss. 19. Nepal to SE Asia.
212. *Pteruthius aenobarbus.* Chestnut fronted Shrike Babbler. 5ss. 11. S, SE Asia.
213. *Pteruthius flaviscapis.* White browed Shrike Babbler. 7ss. 14. S, SE Asia.
214. *Pteruthius melanotis.* Black eared Shrike Babbler. 2ss. 11. Himalayas, SE Asia.
215. *Pteruthius rufiventer.* Black headed Shrike Babbler. 2ss. 20. Himalayas, SE Asia.
216. *Pteruthius xanthochlorus.* Green Shrike Babbler. 4ss. 13. Himalayas, China, SE Asia.
217. *Gampsorhynchus rufulus.* White hooded Babbler. 3ss. 24. Nepal, China, SE Asia.
218. *Actinodura egertoni.* Rusty fronted Barwing. 4ss. 22. Nepal to Burma.
219. *Actinodura morrisoniana.* Formosan Barwing. 22. Taiwan.
220. *Actinodura nipalensis.* Hoary throated Barwing. 2ss. 20. Nepal, Sikkim, Tibet.
221. *Actinodura ramsayi.* Spectacled Barwing. 3ss. 24. China, Burma ,Thailand, Indo-China.
222. *Actinodura souliei.* Streaked Barwing. 2ss. 25. Yunnan, Tonkin.
223. *Actinodura waldeni.* Streak throated Barwing. 4ss. 20. Tibet, China, Burma.
224. *Minla cyanouroptera.* Blue winged Minla. 8ss. 16. Himalayas to Thailand, Malaya.
225. *Minla ignotincta.* Red tailed Minla. 4ss. 14. Himalayas, Burma, China, Tonkin.
226. *Minla strigula.* Chestnut tailed Minla. 6ss. 17. India,Tibet China, SE Asia.
227. *Alcippe/Illadopsis abyssinica.* Abyssinian Hill Babbler 7ss. 13. E WC Africa.
228. *Alcippe/Illadopsis atriceps.* Ruwenzori Hill Babbler. 13. Cameroon to Uganda.
229. *Alcippe brunnea.* Dusky Fulvetta. 8ss. 15. India, China, Burma, Indo-China.
230. *Alcippe brunneicauda.* Brown Fulvetta. 2ss. 15. Thailand, Malaya, Sumatra.
231. *Alcippe castaneceps.* Rufous winged Fulvetta. 4ss. 11. Himalayas to SE Asia.
232. *Alcippe chrysotis.* Golden breasted Fulvetta. 5ss. 11. Nepal, China, Tonkin.
233. *Alcippe cinerea.* Yellow throated Fulvetta. 11.Nepal, China, Burma, Laos.
234. *Alcippe cinereiceps.* Streak throated Fulvetta. 7ss. 11. Himalayas.

234a. *Alcippe ludlowi.* Ludlow's Fulvetta. 11. India, Tibet, Bhutan, China.

235. *Alcippe morrisonia.* Grey cheeked Fulvetta. 7ss. 15. China to Burma, Thailand.
236. *Alcippe nipalensis.* Nepal Fulvetta. 3ss. 15. Nepal to Burma.

205
206
207
208
209
210
211
212
213
214
215
216
217
218
219
220
221
222
223
224
225
226
227
228
229
230
231
232
233
234
235
236
234
A

MUSCICAPIDAE, TIMALIINAE (7) Babblers

237. *Alcippe peracensis.* Mountain Fulvetta. 4ss. 16. Annam, Laos, Thailand, Malaya.
238. *Alcippe poioicephala.* Brown cheeked Fulvetta. 8ss. 16. India, Assam, SE Asia.
239. *Alcippe pyrrhoptera.* Javan Fulvetta. 14. Java.
240. *Alcippe ruficapilla.* Spectacled Fulvetta. 3ss. 11. China, Yunnan, Laos.
241. *Alcippe rufogularis.* Rufous throated Tit Babbler. 6ss. 14. Bhutan, N SE Asia.
242. *Alcippe striaticollis.* Striped / Chinese Fulvetta. 11. NW China.
243. *Alcippe variegaticeps.* Gold fronted Fulvetta. 10. S China.
244. *Alcippe vinipectus.* White browed Tit Babbler. 8ss. 12. Himalayas.
245. *Alcippe dubia.* Rufous capped Fulvetta. 13. Burma, Assam, Yunnan.
246. *Kupeornis chapini.* Chapin's Flycatcher Babbler. 3ss. 18. E Zaire.
247. *Kupeornis gilberti.* White throated Mountain Babbler. 22. Cameroon, Nigeria.
248. *Lioptilus nigricapillus.* Bush Blackcap / Babbler. 17. Cape, Natal, Transvaal.
249. *Kupeornis rufocinctus.* Red collared Mountain Babbler. 19. Rwanda, Zaire.
250. *Parophasma galinieri.* Abyssinian Catbird. 18. Ethiopia.
251. *Phyllanthus atripennis.* Capuchin Babbler. 3ss. 23. Senegal to Zaire.
252. *Crocias albonotatus.* Spotted Sibia. 20. Java.
253. *Crocias langbianis.* Grey crowned Sibia. 23. Annam.
254. *Heterophasia annectans.* Chestnut backed Sibia. 4ss. 19. India, China, SE Asia.
255. *Heterophasia auricularis.* White eared Sibia. 22. Taiwan.
256. *Heterophasia capistrata.* Rufous Sibia. 3ss. 21. Himalayas, Pakistan to Assam.
257. *Heterophasia gracilis.* Grey Sibia. 23. Assam, Burma, Yunnan.
258. *Heterophasia melanoleuca.* Black headed Sibia. 6ss. 22. N SE Asia.
259. incl. *H. m. desgodinsi.* Black eared Sibia. 22. Burma, China.
260. *Heterophasia picaoides.* Long tailed Sibia. 4ss. 30. Nepal, SE Asia, Sumatra.
261. *Heterophasia pulchella.* Beautiful Sibia. 22. Tibet, Assam, Burma, Yunnan.
262. *Yuhina bakeri.* White naped Yuhina. 12. NE India, SW China, Burma.
263. *Yuhina brunneiceps.* Formosan Yuhina. 13. Taiwan.
264. *Yuhina castaniceps.* Striated Yuhina. 6ss. 13, Sikkim, S China, SE Asia.
265. *Yuhina everetti.* Chestnut crested Yuhina. 13. Borneo.
266. *Yuhina diademata.* White collared Yuhina. 17. S China, Burma, Tonkin.
267. *Yuhina flavicollis.* Whiskered Yuhina. 7ss. 13. N India, Tibet, China, SE Asia.
268. *Yuhina humilis.* Burmese Yuhina. 12. Burma, Thailand.
269. *Yuhina gularis.* Stripe throated Yuhina. 3ss. 15. Himalayas, Tibet to Indo-China.
270. *Yuhina nigrimenta.* Black chis crossleyi. Crossley's Babbler. 17. Malagasy.
271. *Yuhina occipitalis* Rufous vented / Slaty headed Yuhine 2ss 12 Himalayas Nepal to Burma Yunnan.
272. *Yuhine zantholeaca.* White bellied Yuhina 8ss 12 Himalayas to China, Malaysia, Sumatra, Borneo.
273. *Malia grata.* Celebis Melin / Babbler 22 Sulawesi.
274. *Myzornis pyrrhoura.* Five tailed Myzornis 12 nepal to Burma, Yunna.
275. *Horizorhinus dohrni.* Dohrn's Thrush Babbler 14 Principé I. may be a Flycatcher.
276. *Oxylabes madagascarensis.* Foditany / White throated Oxylabus 17 Malagasy
277. *Mystcornis Crossley.* Crossley's Babbler 16 Malagasy.

No. 273 Should Perhaps be Incl. Bulbuls P1.229)

237
238
239
240
241
242
243
244
245
246
247
248
249
250
251
252
253
254
255
256
257
258
259
260
261
262
263
264
265
266
267
268
269
270
271
272
274
275
276
273
277

MUSCICAPIDAE, PICATHARTIDAE PARADOX ORNITHINAE / PANURIDAE, CHAMAEIDAE Rockfowl / Rald Crow, White necked Rockfowl, Grey necked Rockfowl, Wren Tit

Subfamily 137. PICATHARTIDAE. Rockfowl / Rald Crows.

1. *Picathartes gymnocephalus.* White necked Rockfowl. 36. Guinea to Ghana.
2. *Picathartes oreas.* Grey necked Rockfowl. 35. Cameroon to Gabon.

SubfaFmily 138. PARADOXORNITHINAE / PANURIDAE. Parrotbills.

1. *Panurus biarmicus.* Bearded Tit / Reedling. 3ss. 16. Palearctic.
2. *Conostorna oemodiun.* Great Parrotbill. 30. Himalayas, Nepal, Tibet, China.
3. *Paradoxornis alphonsianus.* Ashy throated Parrotbill. 2ss. 13. China, Tonkin.
4. *Paradoxornis atrosuperciliaris.* B1ack browed Parrotbill. 2ss. 15. Himalayas.
5. *Paradoxornis conspicillatus.* Spectacled Parrotbill. 2ss. 12. WC China.
6. *Paradoxornis davidianus.* Short tailed Parrotbill. 3ss. 10. N SE Asia.
7. *Paradoxornis flavirostris.* Black breasted Parrotbill. 19. Nepal to Burma.
8. *Paradoxornis fulvifrons.* Fulvous Parrotbill. 4ss. 13. Tibet, Burma, China.
9. *Paradoxornis gularis.* Grey headed Parrotbill. 7ss. 17. India to China, SE Asia.
10. *Paradoxornis guttaticollis.* Spot breasted Parrotbill. 20. India to SE Asia.
11. *Paradoxornis heudei.* Reed Parrotbill. 2ss. 18. Siberia, Yangtse River.
12. *Paradoxornis nipalensis.* Black throated Parrotbill. 12ss. 10. India to Thailand.
13. *Paradoxornis poliotis.* Blyth's Parrotbill. 10. Nepal to Burma.
14. *Paradoxornis verreauxii.* Golden Parrotbill. 10. China, Tonkin, Laos, Taiwan.
15. *Paradoxornis paradoxus.* Three toed Parrotbill. 2ss. 21. SW China.
16. *Paradoxornis przewalskii.* Rusty throated Parrotbill. 12. China.
17. *Paradoxornis brunneus.* Brown winged / Yunnan Parrotbill. 11. Himalayas.
18. *Paradoxornis ruficeps.* Rufous headed Parrotbill. 3ss. 18. Nepal to Indo-China.
19. *Paradoxornis unicolor.* Brown Parrotbill. 21.Nepal, Tibet, China, Burma.
20. *Paradoxornis webbianus.* Vinous throated Parrotbill. 7ss. 12. Manchuria, China, SE Asia.
21. *Paradoxornis zappeyi.* Grey hooded Parrotbill. 12. SW China.

Subfamily 139. CHAMAEIDAE. Wren Tit.

1. *Chamaea fasciata.* Wren Tit. 6ss. 13. Western USA.

Subfamily 140. POLIOPTILINAE. Gnatwrens.

1. *Microbates cinereiventris.* Tawny faced Gnatwren. 4ss. 10. Nicaragua To Peru.
2. *Microbates collaris.* Collared Gnatwren. 3ss. 11. Colombia, Venezuela to Brazil.
3. *Ramphocaenus melanurus.* Black tailed Gnatwren. 14ss. 12. Brazil.
4. incl. *R. m. rufiventris.* Long billed Gnatwren. 12. Mexico to Peru.
5. *Polioptila albiloris.* White lored Gnatcatcher. 3ss. 10. Central America.
6. *Polioptila caerulea.* Blue grey Gnatcatcher. 8ss. 10. Canada to Mexico, Cuba.
7. *Polioptila dumicola.* Masked Gnatcatcher. 3ss. 12. Brazil, Bolivia, Argentina.
8. *Polioptila guianensis.* Guianan Gnatcatcher. 3ss. 10. Venezuela to Brazil.
9. *Polioptila lactea.* Creamy bellied Gnatcatcher. 11. Brazi1, Paraguay, Argentina.
10. *Polioptila lembeyi.* Cuban Gnatcatcher. 11. Cuba.
11. *Polioptila melanura.* Black tailed Gnatcatcher. 6ss. 10. California, Mexico.
12. *Polioptila californica.* California Gnatcatcher. 10. SW California.
13. *Polioptila nigriceps.* Black capped Gnatcatcher. 2ss. 10. Mexico.
14. *Polioptila plumbea.* Tropical Gnatcatcher. 12ss. 10. Mexico to Brazil & Peru.
15. incl. *P. p. bilineata.* White browed Gnatcatcher. 10. Colombia to Peru.
16. *Polioptila schistaceigula.* Slate throated Gnatcatcher. 10. Panama to Ecuador.

PICATHARTIDAE
1
2
PARADPOXORNITHINAE
1
2
3
4
5
6
7
8
9
10
11
12
13
14
15
16
17
18
19
20
21
CHAMAEIDAE
1
POLIOPTILINAE
1
2
3
4
5
NB
Br
5
6
7
8
9
10
11 Br
NB
12
NB
13 Br
14
15
16

Plate 262 Family 141.

MUSCICAPIDAE, SYLVIINAE (1)
Old World Warblers

1. *Tesia castaneocoronata*. Chestnut headed Tesia. 3ss. 8. Himalayas, China, SE Asia.
2. *Tesia cyaniventer*. Grey bellied Tesia. 9. Himalayas, Tibet, Yunnan, N SE Asia.
3. *Tesia everetti*. Russet capped Tesia. 9. Timor, Lesser Sunda Is.
4. *Tesia olivea*. Slaty bellied Tesia. 9. Sikkim, Yunnan, Burma, Vietnam.
5. *Tesia superciliaris*. Javan Ground Warbler/Tesia. 7. Java, Flores, Sumbawa.
6. *Cettia carolinae*. 13. Indonesia, Philippines.
14. *Cettia flavolivacea*. Aberrant Bush Warbler. 6ss. 11. Himalayas, China, N SE Asia.
15. *Cettia fortipes*. Strong footed Bush Warbler. 3ss. 11. Himalayas, China, SE Asia.
16. *Cettia montanus*. Brownish flanked Bush Warbler. 12. Indonesia, Borneo.
17. *Cettia major*. Large Bush Warbler. 2ss. 13. Nepal, China, Burma, Assam.
18. *Cettia pallidipes*. Pale footed Bush Warbler. 12. India, Burma, Andaman Is.
19. *Urosphena squamiceps*. Stub tailed Bush Warbler. 9. NE Asia. W 13. Indonesia, Philippines.
14. *Cettia flavolivacea*. Aberrant Bush Warbler. 6ss. 11. Himalayas, China, N SE Asia.
15. *Cettia fortipes*. Strong footed Bush Warbler. 3ss. 11. Himalayas, China, SE Asia.
16. *Cettia montanus*. Brownish flanked Bush Warbler. 12. Indonesia, Borneo.
17. *Cettia major*. Large Bush Warbler. 2ss. 13. Nepal, China, Burma, Assam.
18. *Cettia pallidipes*. Pale footed Bush Warbler. 12. India, Burma, Andaman Is.
19. *Urosphena squamiceps*. Stub tailed Bush Warbler. 9. NE Asia. Winters SE Asia.
20. *Urosphena subulata*. Timor Bush Warbler. 11.Timor.
21. *Urosphena whiteheadi*. Bornean Stubtail. 9. North Borneo.
22. *Bradypterus accentor*. Friendly Bush Warbler. 10. Borneo.
23. *Bradypterus alfredi*. Bamboo scrub Warbler. 3ss. 14. E & C Africa.
24. *Bradypterus baboecalus*. African swamp Warbler. 10ss. 12. Africa S of Sahara.
25. *Bradypterus barratti*. African scrub Warbler. 3ss. 16. Mozambique, S Africa.
26. *Bradypterus mariae*. Evergreen forest Warbler. 16. Kenya to Mozambique.
27. *Bradypterus lopezi*. Fernando Po Swamp Warbler. 13. Fernando Po.
28. *Bradypterus camerunensis*. Cameroon scrub Warbler. 13. Cameroon.
29. *Bradypterus carpalis*. White winged Warbler. 13. Uganda & E Congo.
30. *Bradypterus castaneus*. Chestnut backed Bush Warbler. 3ss.15. Buru, Ceran.
31. *Bradypterus caudatus*. Long tailed Bush Warbler. 3ss. 18. Luzon, Mindanao.
32. *Bradypterus cinnamomeus*. Cinnamon bracken Warbler. 8ss. 14. WC to E Africa.
33. *Bradypterus grandis*. Ja River scrub Warbler. 19. Cameroon, Gabon.
34. *Bradypterus graueri*. Grauer's Warbler. 13. Zaire, Rwanda.
35. *Bradypterus luteoventris*. Brown Bush Warbler. 2ss. 13. Himalayas, China, SE Asia.
36. *Bradypterus major*. Long billed Bush Warbler. 2ss. 14. W Himalayas, Mongolia.
37. *Bradypterus palliseri*. Ceylon Bush Warbler. 17. Sri Lanka.
38. *Bradypterus seebohmi*. Russet Bush Warbler. 5ss. 13. China, Luzon, Java, Timor.
39. *Bradypterus sylvaticus*. Knysna Scrub Warbler. 15. Natal to Cape.
40. *Bradypterus taczanovskius*. Chinese Bush Warbler. 2ss. 14. NE Asia. Winters Indo-China.
41. *Bradypterus thoracicus*. Spotted Bush Warbler. 5ss. 13. Himalayas.
42. *Bradypterus victorini*. Victorin's scrub Warbler. 10. Cape Province.
43. *Psamathia (Cettia) annae*. Palau Warbler. 15. Palau Is.
44. *Schoenicola platyura*. Broad tailed Grassbird. 3ss. 17. SW India, Sri Lanka.
45. *Schoenicola brevirostris*. Fan tailed Grassbird. 17. Africa S of Sahara.
46. *Megalurus albolimbatus*. Fly River Grassbird. 15. New Guinea.
47. *Megalurus gramineus*. Little Grassbird. 8ss. 14. Australia, Tasmania, New Guinea.
48. *Megalurus palustris*. Striated Grassbird. 3ss. 25. S SE Asia, Philippines, Java, Bali.
49. *Megalurus pryeri*. Marsh Grassbird. 2ss. 13. Honshu, NE China. Winters SE China.
50. *Megalurus timoriensis*. Tawny Grassbird. 18ss. 19. Philippines, Timor, New Guinea, Australia.
51. *Chaetornis striatus*. Bristled Grassbird. 20. Scattered Indian Sub-continent.
52. *Locustella certhiola*. Pallas' Grasshopper Warbler. 4ss. 13. Palearctic.
53. *Locustella fasciolata*. Gray's Grasshopper Warbler. 18. Siberia. Winters Indonesia.
54. *Locustella fluviatilis*. (Eurasian) River Warbler. 13. C E Europe. Winters E Africa.
55. *Locustella lanceolata*. Lanceolated Warbler. 13.Siberia. Winters Indonesia, New Guinea.
56. *Locustella luscinoides*. Savi's Warbler. 3ss. 14. Eurasia. Winters Africa.
57. *Locustella amnicola*. Sakhalin Warbler. 18. Sakhalin, Kurile Is. Winters Philippines.
58. *Locustella naevia*. Grasshopper Warbler. 4ss. 13. Europe, W Asia. Winters Africa.
59. *Locustella pleskei*. Pleske's Warbler. 13.Japan, Korea. Winters China.
60. *Locustella ochotensis*. Middendorf's Warbler. 16.Siberia to Japan. Winters Philippines.
61. *Acrocephalus aedon*. Thick billed Warbler. 2ss. 20. NC Asia. Winters SE Asia.
62. *Acrocephalus aequinoctialis*. Bokikokiko / Polynesian Reed Warbler. 2ss. 15. Christmas Is, Fanning Is.
63. *Acrocephalus agricola*. Paddyfield Warbler. 3ss. 12. C Eurasia. Winters S Asia.
64. incl. *A. a. tangorum*. Manchurian Reed Warbler. 12. Manchuria. Winters Thailand.
65. *Acrocephalus arundinaceus*. Great Reed Warbler. 3ss. 19. W Palearctic. Winters Africa .
66. *Acrocephalus atyphus*. Tuamotu Warbler. 6ss. 17. Tuamotu Is.
67. *Acrocephalus bistrigiceps*. Black browed Reed Warbler. 13.NE Asia. Winters SE Asia.

1
2
3
4
5
6
7
8
9
10
11
12
13
14
15
16
17
18
19
20
21
22
23
24
25
26
27
28
29
30
31
32
33
34
35
36
37
38
39
40
41
42
43
44
45
46
47
48
49
50
51
52
53
54
55
56
57
58
59
60
61
62
63
64
65
66
67

MUSCICAPIDAE, SYLVIINAE (2)
Old World Warblers

68. *Acrocephalus baeticatus*. South African Reed Warbler. 4ss. 12. Tropical Africa.
69. *Acrocephalus cinnamomeus*. Rufescent Reed Warbler. 3ss. 11. South Africa.
70. *Acrocephalus brevipennis*. Cape Verde swamp Warbler. 14. Cape Verde Is.
71. *Acrocephalus caffer*. Tahiti Long billed Warbler. 10ss. 18. Society Is.
72. *Acrocephalus concinens*. Blunt winged Paddyfield Warbler. 3ss. 13. EC, SE Asia.
73. *Acrocephalus dumetorum*. Blyth's Reed Warbler. 12. NW Eurasia. Winters SE Asia.
74. *Acrocephalus familiaris*. Millerbird. 12. Laysan. (extinct)
75. *Acrocephalus gracilirostris*. Lesser swamp Warbler. 9ss. 17. Chad, Sudan-Cape.
76. *Acrocephalus luscinia*. Nightingale Reed Warbler. 11. Mariana Is.
77. *Acrocephalus melanopogon*. Moustached Warbler. 3ss. 13. Mediterranean to India.
78. *Acrocephalus newtoni*. Madagascar swamp Warbler. 18. Malagasy.
79. *Acrocephalus orinus*. Large billed Reed Warbler. 13. N India.(Unique).
80. *Acrocephalus Paludicola*. Aquatic Warbler. 13. Europe, Middle East. Winters W Africa.
81. *Acrocephalus palustris*. Marsh Warbler. 13. Europe, Russia. Winters Africa.
82. *Acrocephalus rufescens*. Greater swamp Warbler. 5ss. 18. E, S & W Africa.
83. *Acrocephalus schoenobaenus*. Sedge Warbler. 13. Europe to Iran. Winters Africa.
84. *Acrocephalus sorghophilus*. Speckled Reed Warbler. 12. China, Philippines.
85. *Acrocephalus scirpaceus*. Reed Warbler. 2ss. 13. Europe, SW Asia. Winters Africa.
86. *Acrocephalus stentoreus*. Clamorous Reed Warbler. 12ss. 18. Palearctic, Australia.
87. *Acrocephalus vaughani*. Pitcairn Reed Warbler. 3ss. 17. Pitcairn Is.

87a. *Acrocephalus rimatorae*. Rimatara Reed Warbler. 17. Rimatara (Tubiai Is).

87b. *Acrocephalus taiti*. Henderson Island Reed Warbler. 17. Henderson Is. Pitcairn.

88. *Acrocephalus orientalis*. Eastern Reed Warbler. 17. Siberia, China. Winters SE Asia.
89. *Acrocephalus rehsei*. Nauru Warbler. 15. Nauru.
90. *Acrocephalus kingi*. Nihoa Millerbird. s. 18. Marquesas Is.
98. *Acrocephalus syrinx*. Caroline Warbler. 15.Caroline Is.
99. *Chloropeta gracilirostris*. Papyrus yellow Warbler. 2ss. 14. C Africa.
100. *Chloropeta natalensis*. African yellow Warbler. 4ss. 14. Africa S of Sahara.
101. *Chloropeta similis*. Mountain Warbler. 14. Sudan to Congo, Malawi.
102. *Sphenoeacus afer*. Cape Grass Warbler. 4ss. 21. Cape to Natal & Zimbabwe.
103. *Melocichla mentalis*. Moustached Grass Warbler. 6ss. 19. Sudan to Zimbabwe.
104. *Achaetops pycnopygius*. Dams. 18. Marquesas Is.

98. *Acrocephalus syrinx*. Caroline Warbler. 15.Caroline Is.
99. *Chloropeta gracilirostris*. Papyrus yellow Warbler. 2ss. 14. C Africa.
100. *Chloropeta natalensis*. African yellow Warbler. 4ss. 14. Africa S of Sahara.
101. *Chloropeta similis*. Mountain Warbler. 14. Sudan to Congo, Malawi.
102. *Sphenoeacus afer*. Cape Grass Warbler. 4ss. 21. Cape to Natal & Zimbabwe.
103. *Melocichla mentalis*. Moustached Grass Warbler. 6ss. 19. Sudan to Zimbabwe.

104. *Achaetops pycnopygius*. Damara Rockjumper. 2ss. 17. Damaraland.
105. *Hippolais caligata*. Booted Warbler. 3ss. 12. W Asia to Mongolia. Winters India.

105a. *Hippolais rama*. Sykes' Warbler. 12.Iran to Pakistan. Winters India.

106. *Hippolais icterina*. Icterine Warbler. 2ss. 14. Eurasia.Winters S Africa.
107. *Hippolais languida*. Upcher's Warbler. 14. SW Asia. Winters Arabia to Kenya.
108. *Hippolais olivetorum*. Olive tree Warbler. 15. Balkans, Asia minor. Winters Africa
109. *Hippolais pallida*. Olivaceous Warbler. 5ss. 14. Mediterranean to Iran. Winters E Africa.
110. *Hippolais polyglotta*. Melodious Warbler. 13. S Europe. Winters NW Africa.
111. *Sylvia althaea*. Hume's Whitethroat. 13. Iran, Afghanistan, Himalayas.
112. *Sylvia atricapilla*. Blackcap. 5ss. 14. Europe, Atlantic Is, Iran. Winters Africa.
113. *Sylvia borin*. Garden Warbler. 3ss. 14. Europe, SW Asia. Winters Africa.
114. *Sylvia cantillans*. Sub-alpine Warbler. 3ss. 12. S Europe, N Africa. Winters Africa.
115. *Sylvia communis*. Whitethroat. 3ss. 14. Europe, W Asia, N Africa. Winters Africa.
116. *Sylvia conspicillata*. Spectacled Whitethroat. 2ss. 13. SW Palearctic. Winters Africa.
117. *Sylvia curruca*. Lesser Whitethroat. 10ss. 13. Europe, W Asia. Winters Africa, India.
118. *Sylvia deserticola*. Tristram's Warbler. 2ss. 12. NW Africa.
119. *Sylvia hortensis*. Orphean Warbler. 4ss. 15. Europe, SW Asia. Winters Africa, India.
120. *Sylvia leucomelaena*. Blanford's / Red Sea Warbler. 15. Red Sea, Gulf of Aden.
121. *Sylvia melanocephala*. Sardinian Warbler. 7ss. 14. Mediterranean, Middle East.
122. *Sylvia ticehursti*. Meinertzhagan's Warbler. 12. Morocco.(Unique)
123. *Sylvia melanothorax*. Cyprus Warbler. 14. Cyprus. Winters Egypt.
124. *Sylvia minula*. Desert lesser Whitethroat. 13. Mongolia to NW India.
125. *Sylvia mystacea*. Menetrie's Warbler. 14. SC & W Asia. Winters NE Africa.
126. *Sylvia nana*. Desert Warbler. 3ss. 12. Deserts NW Africa to C Asia.
127. *Sylvia nisoria*. Barred Warbler. 2ss. 16. C Eurasia. Winters E Africa.
128. *Sylvia ruppelli*. Ruppell's Warbler. 14.Turkey, Mediterranean Is. Winters NE Africa.
129. *Sylvia sarda*. Marmora's Warbler. 2ss. 12. W Mediterranean S to Sahara.
130. *Sylvia undata*. Dartford Warbler. 5ss. 12. W & SW Europe, N Africa.

68
69
70
71
72
73
74
75
76
77
78
79
80
81
82
83
87A
85
86
90
87
88
89
87B
91
92
98
97
96
84
93
94
95
99
100
101
105
102
103
104
105A
106
107
111
108
109
110
112
113
118
114
115
116
119
117
120
121
123
125
122
124
126
127
128
129
130

MUSCICAPIDAE, SYLVIINAE (3)
Old World Warblers

131. *Phylloscopus affinis.* Tickell's Willow Warbler. 10. Himalayas, China. Winters India.
132. *Phylloscopus amoenus.* Kalambangra Warbler. 12. Solomon Is.
133. *Phylloscopus armandii.* Milne Edward's Warbler. 2ss. 12. China to N SE Asia.
134. *Phylloscopus bonelli.* Bonelli's Warbler. 2ss. 12. S Europe, Middle East. Winters Africa.
135. *Phylloscopus borealis.* Arctic Warbler. 7ss. 12. N Eurasia, Alaska. Winters S Asia.
136. *Phylloscopus budongoensis.* Uganda woodland Warbler. 12. Uganda, W Kenya.
137. *Phylloscopus cantator.* Yellow vented Warbler. 11. Himalayas, China to SE Asia.
138. *Phylloscopus ricketti.* Sulphur breasted Warbler. 2ss. 10. China, SE Asia.
139. *Phylloscopus collybita.* Chiffchaff. 8ss. 11. Palearctic. Winters N Africa, SE Asia.
140. *Phylloscopus sindianus.* Brown leaf Warbler. 11. C Asia.
140a. *Phylloscopus Lorenzii.* Caucasian Chiffchaff. 11. Caucasus.
141. *Phylloscopus coronatus.* Temminck's crowned Warbler. 12. E Asia. Winters SE Asia.
142. *Phylloscopus davisoni.* White tailed Leaf Warbler. 4ss. 10. China, N SE Asia.
143. *Phylloscopus hainanus.* Hainan leaf Warbler. 10. Hainan.
144. *Phylloscopus fuligiventer.* Smoky Warbler. 2ss. 10. Tibet & E Himalayas.
145. *Phylloscopus fuscatus.* Dusky Warbler. 2ss. 12. Siberia, China. Winters SE Asia.
146. *Phylloscopus griseolus.* Sulphur bellied Warbler. 12. SW C Asia. Winters India.
147. *Phylloscopus herberti.* Black capped woodland Warbler. 2ss. 9. W Africa.
148. *Phylloscopus ijimae.* Ijima's Leaf Warbler. 12. Ryukyu Is.
149. *Phylloscopus inornatus.* Yellow browed Warbler. 3ss. 11. Siberia. Winters S Asia.
150. *Phylloscopus laetus.* Red faced woodland Warbler. 2ss. 9. C Africa.
151. *Phylloscopus laurae.* Mrs Boulter's woodland Warbler. 2ss. 10. Zambia, Congo.
152. *Phylloscopus maculipennis.* Grey faced Warbler. 4ss. 9. Himalayas, Yunnan, Szechwan.
153. *Phylloscopus magnirostris.* Large billed Warbler. 12. Himalayas, China. Winters S Asia.
154. *Phylloscopus neglectus.* Plain Willow Warbler . 10. Iran to Pakistan. Winters Arabia.
155. *Phylloscopus nitidus.* Bright green Warbler. 10. WC Asia. Winters India.
156. *Phylloscopus occipitalis.* Western crowned Warbler. 12. Himalayas. Winters India.
157. *Phylloscopus olivaceus.* Philippine Leaf Warbler. 11. Philippines.
158. *Phylloscopus sarasinorun.* Sulawesi Leaf Warbler. 2ss. 11. Sulawesi.
159. *Phylloscopus presbytes.* Timor Leaf Warbler. 11. Timor.
160. *Phylloscopus cebuensis.* Lemon throated Leaf Warbler. 10. Philippines.
161. *Phylloscopus proregulus.* Pallas' Leaf Warbler. 10. Siberia, China. Winters SE Asia.
161a. *Phylloscopus chloronotos.* Pale rumped Warbler. 10. Himalayas. Winters SE Asia.
161b. *Phylloscopus emeiensis.* Emei Leaf Warbler. 10. S Sichuan.
162. *Phylloscopus sichuanensis.* Chinese Leaf Warbler. 10. Sichuan Province.
163. *Phylloscopus pulcher.* Orange barred Warbler. 2ss. 11. Himalayas,Tibet,China.
164. *Phylloscopus reguloides.* Blyth's crowned Warbler. 6ss. 11. Himalayas, S China, SE Asia. Winters SE Asia.
165. *Phylloscopus ruficapillus.* Yellow throated Woodland Warbler. 9. 6ss. Africa.
166. *Phylloscopus schwarzi.* Radde's Bush Warbler. 12. NE Asia, Winters SE Asia.
167. *Phylloscopus sibilatrix.* Wood Warbler. 12. Europe, W Asia. Winters Africa.
168. *Phylloscopus subaffinis.* Buff throated Warbler. 2ss. 11. China. Winters SE Asia.
169. *Phylloscopus arcanus.* Grant's Yellow bellied Warbler. 10. Nepal.
170. *Phylloscopus subviridis.* Brook'inian Warbler. 7ss. 14. Mediterranean, Middle East.
122. *Sylvia ticehursti.* Meinertzhagan's Warbler. 12. Morocco.(Unique)
123. *Sylvia melanothorax.* Cyprus Warbler. 14. Cyprus. Winters Egypt.
124. *Sylvia minula.* Desert lesser Whitethroat. 13. Mongolia to NW India.
125. *Sylvia mystacea.* Menetrie's Warbler. 14. SC & W Asia. Winters NE Africa.
126. *Sylvia nana.* Desert Warbler. 3ss. 12. Deserts NW Africa to C Asia.
127. *Sylvia nisoria.* Barred Warbler. 2ss. 16. C Eurasia. Winters E Africa. 11. WC Eurasia. Winters SE Asia.
176. *Phylloscopus* plumbeitarsus. Two barred Warbler. 11. E Asia. Winters SE Asia.
177. *Phylloscopus* trochilus. Willow Warbler. 3ss. 11. N Palearctic. Winters Africa, S Asia.
178. *Phylloscopus tytleri.* Tytler's Leaf Warbler. 20. Kashmir. Winters W India.
179. *Phylloscopus umbrovirens.* Brown Woodland Warbler. 7ss. 10. Arabia, E Africa.
180. *Seicercus affinis.* White spectacled Warbler. 2ss. 10. Himalayas to N SE Asia.
181. *Seicercus burkii.* Golden spectacled Warbler. 5ss. 10. Himalayas to S Asia.
182. *Seicercus castaniceps.* Chestnut crowned Warbler. 9ss. 10. SE Asia.
183. *Seicercus grammiceps.* Sunda flycatcher Warbler. 2ss. 10. Java, Bali, Sumatra.
184. *Seicercus montis.* Yellow breasted Warbler. 6ss. 10. Malaysia, Philippines.
185. *Seicercus poliogenys.* Grey cheeked Warbler. 10. Himalayas, Yunnan, N SE Asia.
186. *Seicercus xanthoschistos.* Grey hooded Warbler. 4ss. 10. Himalayas, Burma.
187. *Abroscopus albogularis.* Rufous faced Warbler. 3ss. 8. Himalayas, China, SE Asia.
188. *Tickellia hodgsoni.* Broad billed Warbler. 2ss. 10. Himalayas, Yunnan, SE Asia.
189. *Abroscopus schisticeps.* Black faced Warbler. 3ss. 9. Himalayas, Yunnan, SE Asia.
190. *Abroscopus superciliaris.* Yellow bellied Warbler. 8ss. 9. SE Asia.
191. *Nesillas aldabranus.* Aldabra Brush Warbler. 14. Aldabra.
192. *Nesillas mariae.* Moheli Brush Warbler. 14. Comoro Is.
193. *Bebrornis rodericanus.* Rodriguez Brush Warbler. 14. Rodriguez.
194. *Bebrornis sechellensis.* Seychelles Brush Warbler. 14. Cousin (Seychelles).
195. *Nesillas typica.* Tsikirity / Madagascar Brush Warbler. 5ss. 14. Malagasy.
195a. *Nesillas longicauda.* Anjouan Brush Warbler. 17. Anjouan.
195b. *Nesillas brevicauda.* Grand Comoro Brush Warbler. 14. Grand Comoro Is.
196. *Dromaeocercus brunneus.* Brown Emu-tail. 16. Malagasy.
197. *Amphilais seebohmi.* Grey Emu-tail. 16. Malagasy.

131
132
133
134
135
136
140A
137
138
141
142
144
145
143
146
147
148
149
150
151
162
152
153
154
155
156
157
158
161B
159
160
161
163
164
165
161A
140
171A
166
139
167
168
170
171
172
169
174
173
177
175
178
179
180
176
181
182
183
184
185
186
187
188
189
190
191
192
195A
195B
193
194
195
196
197

MUSCICAPIDAE, SYLVIINAE (4)
Old World Warblers

198. *Prinia atrogularis.* White browed Hill Prinia. 7ss. 17. Himalayas to SE Asia.
199. *Prinia bairdii.* Banded Prinia. 4ss. 12. Kenya to Cameroon, Angola.
200. *Prinia melanops.* Black faced Prinia. 12. Zaire, Kenya.
201. *Prinia buchanani.* Rufous fronted Prinia. 12. Pakistan, N &C India.
202. *Prinia burnesii.* Western long tailed Prinia. 17. Pakistan, India.
203. *Prinia cinerascans.* Eastern long tailed Prinia. 16. Bangladesh, Assam.
204. *Prinia cinereocapilla.* Grey crowned (Hodgson's) Prinia. 12. Nepal to Bhutan.
205. *Prinia/Spiloptila clamans.* Scaly Prinia / Cricket Warbler. 12. Mali to Ethiopia
206. *Prinia criniger.* Striated / Hill Prinia. 3ss. 16. Afghanistan to Himalayas & China.
207. *Prinia/Urolais epichlora.* Green Longtail. 3ss. 15. Cameroon, Fernando Po.
208. *Prinia/Heliolais erythroptera.* Red winged Warbler. 4ss. 14. W E & C Africa.
209. *Prinia familiaris.* Bar winged Prinia. 2ss. 13. Sumatra, Java, Bali.
210. *Prinia flavicans* . Black chested Prinia. 4ss. 14. S Africa.
211. *Prinia flaviventris.* Yellow bellied Prinia. 7ss. 13. India, SE Asia, Sumatra.
212. *Prinia gracilis.* Graceful Prinia. 10ss. 13. NE Africa, SW Asia, India.
213. *Prinia hodgsonii.* Franklin's/Grey breasted Prinia. 7ss. 12. India to SE Asia.
214. *Prinia leontica.* Sierra Leone Prinia. 15. Sierra Leone, Guinea to Ghana.
215. *Prinia leucopogon.* White chinned Prinia. 2ss. 15. Cameroon, C Africa.
216. *Prinia maculosa.* Karroo Prinia. 2ss. 14. Southern Africa.
217. *Prinia molleri.* Sao Thome long tailed Prinia. 15. Sao Thome.
218. *Prinia/Malcorus pectoralis.* Rufous eared Warbler. 3ss. 11. RSA & Namibia.
219. *Prinia polychroa.* Brown Hill Prinia. 4ss. 17. Yunnan, SE Asia, Java.
220. *Prinia/Phyllolais pulchella.* Buff bellied Warbler. 9. Chad, Ethiopia, Tanzania
221. *Prinia robertsi.* Forest Prinia / Briar Warbler. 14. Zimbabwe.
222. *Prinia rufescens.* Rufescent / Lesser Brown Prinia. 5ss.12. India, SE Asia.
223. *Prinia socialis.* Ashy / Long tailed Prinia. 4ss. 13. India, Burma.
224. *Prinia somalica.* Pale Prinia. 2ss. 12. Ethiopia, Somalia, Kenya.
225. *Prinia inornata.* Plain Prinia. 14. Pakistan to China, SE Asia, Java.
226. *Prinia subflava.* Tawny Prinia. 19ss. 11-14. Africa South of Sahara.
227. *Prinia fluviatilis.* River / Lake Chad Prinia. 12. Mali, Lake Chad area.
228. *Prinia/Phragmacia substriata.* White breasted / Namaqua Prinia. 14. S Africa.
229. *Prinia valida.* Ceylon Large Prinia. 13. Sri Lanka.
230. *Prinia sylvatica.* Jungle Prinia. 4ss. 15. Himalayas, India, Sri Lanka.
231. *Scotocerca inquieta.* Streaked Scrub Warbler. 9ss. 10. N Africa to Russia & India.
232. *Thamnornis chloropetoides.* Kiritika Warbler. 15. Malagasy.
233. *Drymocichla incana.* Red winged Grey Warbler. 11. Cameroon to Uganda.
234. *Randia pseudozosterops.* Rand's / Marvatsetra Warbler. 12. Malagasy .
235. *Amaurocichla bocagei.* Lazy / Bocage's Longbill. 13. Sao Thome.
236. *Rhopophilus pekinensis.* White browed Chinese Warbler. 3ss.18. N E Asia.
237. *Graminicola bengalensis.* Rufous rumped Grassbird. 3ss. 16. E & S Asia.
238. *Orthotomus atrogularis.* Dark necked Tailorbird. 8ss. 11. SE Asia.
239. *Orthotomus castaneiceps.* Philippine Tailorbird. 11. NE Philippines.
240. *Orthotomus frontalis.* Rufous fronted Tailorbird. 11. S Philippines.
241. *Orthotomus cinereiceps.* White eared Tailorbird. 2ss. 12. Basilan, Mindanao.
242. *Orthotomus cuculatus.* Mountain Tailorbird. 13ss. 12. Himalayas, SE Asia, Indonesia.
243. *Orthotomus heterolaemus.* Rufous headed Tailorbird. 12. S Philippines.
244. *Orthotomus derbianus.* Grey backed Tailorbird. 2ss. 12. Luzon, Palawan.
245. *Orthotomus nigriceps.* Black headed Tailorbird. 11. Mindanao.
246. *Orthotomus samarensis.* Yellow breasted Tailorbird. 11. Samar, Leyte Is.
247. *Orthotomus sepium.* Olive backed / Ashy Tailorbird. 2ss.12. Java, Lombok.
248. *Orthotomus sericeus.* Red tailed / Silky Tailorbird. 4ss. 12. SE Asia to Philippines.
249. *Orthotomus sutorius.* Common Tailorbird. 9ss. 13. India, SE Asia, China, Java.
250. *Orthotomus ruficeps.* Ashy grey Tailorbird. 8ss. 11. Burma to Indonesia, Philippines
251. *Orthotomus metopias.* African Tailorbird / Red capped Forest Warbler. 3ss. 10. Tanazania to Mozambique.

For *Orthotomus Moreaui*, Long billed Tailorbird, see Plate 267, No. 315 *Apalis moreaui*. Relationship Uncertain.

198
199
201
202
203
204
205
200
206
207
208
209
Br
210
NBr
211
212
213
214
215
216
227
217
218
219
220
221
Br
222
NB
229
223
Br
NB
224
225
226
228
230
231
232
233
234
235
236
237
-238-
240
242
243
239
241
244
245
246
247
248
249
250
251

MUSCICAPIDAE, SYLVIINAE (5)
Old World Warblers

252. *Cisticola erythiops.* Red faced Cisticola. 6ss. 13. Sub-saharan Africa.
253. incl. *C. e. lepe.* Lepe / (Angolan) Red faced Cisticola. 13. Angola.
254. *Cisticola cantans.* Singing Cisticola. 6ss. 14. W, E & SE Africa.
255. *Cisticola lateralis.* Whistling Cisticola. 3ss. 14. Gambia to Sudan, Angola.
256. *Cisticola anonyma.* Chattering Cisticola. 14. Ghana to Zaire & Angola.
257. *Cisticola woosnami.* Trilling Cisticola. 2ss. 13. Uganda, Tanzania, Congo.
258. *Cisticola bulliens.* Bubbling Cisticola. 14. Angola.
259. *Cisticola discolor.* Brown backed Cisticola. 4ss. 14. Cameroon.
260. *Cisticola chubbi.* Chubb's Cisticola. 14. E & WC Africa.
261. *Cisticola hunteri.* Hunter's Cisticola. 4ss. 14. Kenya, Tanzania.
262. *Cisticola nigriloris.* Black lored Cisticola. 15. Tanzania, Malawi, Zambia.
263. *Cisticola aberrans.* Lazy Cisticola. 9ss. 14. Kenya to Cape.
264. *Cisticola emini.* Rockloving Cisticola. 13. Zaire, Tanzania.
265. *Cisticola bodessa.* Boran Cisticola. 2ss. 13. Kenya, Sudan, Ethiopia.
266. *Cisticola chiniana.* Rattling Cisticola. 16ss. 13. C E & S Africa.
267. incl. *C. c. heterophrys.* Coastal form of Chiniana. 13. Kenya, Tanzania.
268. *Cisticola cinereola.* Ashy Cisticola. 14. Ethiopia to Tanzania.
269. *Cisticola ruficeps.* Red pate Cisticola. 4ss. 11. C Africa to Ethiopia.
269a. *Cisticola dorsti.* Dorst's Cisticola. 11. Nigeria, Cameroon, Chad.
270. *Cisticola mongalla.* Mongalla Cisticola. 2ss. 11. Sudan, Uganda.
271. *Cisticola rufilata.* Grey Cisticola. 4ss. 13. Zaire to Angola & Transvaal.
272. *Cisticola subruficapilla.* Red headed Cisticola. 7ss. 13. Angola to RSA.
273. *Cisticola namaqua.* Namaqua Cisticola. 13. Cape Province.
274. *Cisticola lais.* Wailing Cisticola. 14. Southern Africa.
275. *Cisticola distincta.* Lyne's Cisticola. 15. Kenya, Uganda.
276. *Cisticola restricta.* Tana River Cisticola. 14. Kenya.
277. *Cisticola njombe.* Churring Cisticola. 14. Zambia, Malawi, Tanzania.
278. *Cisticola galactotes.* Winding Cisticola. 13ss. 13. E &W Africa, S to Natal.
279. *Cisticola carruthersi.* Carruthers' Cisticola. 13. Zaire to Kenya.
280. *Cisticola pipiens.* Chirping Cisticola. 3ss. 14. Zaire to Botswana, Angola.
281. *Cisticola tinniens.* Tinkling / Levaillant's Cisticola. 5ss. 12. E SE Africa.
282. *Cisticola robusta.* Stout Cisticola. 7ss. 16. Ethiopia, Cameroon to Zambia.
283. *Cisticola angolensis.* Angola Cisticola. 16. Angola, Zambia.
284. *Cisticola aberdare.* Aberdare Mts. Cisticola. 16. Kenya.
285. *Cisticola natalensis.* Croaking / Striped Cisticola. 11ss. 14. Sub-saharan Africa
286. *Cisticola fulvicapilla.* Piping Cisticola. 9ss. 11. Southern Africa.
287. incl. *C. f. ruficapilla.* Neddicky. 11. Transvaal, Cape.
288. *Cisticola augusticauda.* Tabora Cisticola. 11. Kenya to Zambia.
289. *Cisticola brachyptera.* Siffling / Short winged Cisticola. 8ss.10. Africa.
290. *Cisticola rufa.* Rufous Cisticola. 11. Gambia to Cameroon.
291. *Cisticola troglodytes.* Foxy Cisticola. 2ss. 10. NC & NE Africa.
292. *Cisticola nana.* Tiny Cisticola. 9. Ethiopia, Kenya, Tanzania.
293. *Cisticola juncidis.* Zitting Cisticola. 18ss. 11. Eurasia, Africa, Australia.
294. *Cisticola haesitata.* Socotra Cisticola. 11. Socotra Is.
295. *Cisticola cherina. Madagascar Cisticola.* 12. Malagasy.
296. *Cisticola aridula.* Desert Cisticola. 9ss. 11. Africa South of Sahara.
297. *Cisticola textrix.* Tinktink / Cloud Cisticola. 5ss. 10. Angola, Zambia, RSA.
298. *Cisticola eximia.* Black backed Cisticola. 3ss. 11. W C & E Africa.
299. *Cisticola dambo.* Cloudscraper Cisticola. 2ss. 12. Zaire, Zambia, Angola.
300. *Cisticola brunnescens.* Pectoral patch / Pale crowned Cisticola. 9ss. 9. Africa.
301. *Cisticola ayresii.* Wing snapping Cisticola. 6ss. 8. C, S & SE Africa.
302. *Cisticola exilis.* Golden headed Cisticola. 13ss. 10. India, SE Asia, Australia.

Length of males shown. Females generally much smaller.

For '*C. melanura.*', see 328. Plate 267.
For '*C. incana.*', see 233. Plate 265.

Br
252
NB
JUV
253
Br
254
NB
Br
255
JUV
256
257
258
NB
Br
259
260
261
262
Br
263
NB
264
265
Br
266
NB
267
269A
Br
268
NB
Br
269
NB
Br
270
NB
Br
271
NB
Br
272
NB
273
Br
274
NB
275
276
277
Br
NB
278
279
Br
280
NB
281
282
Br
NB
Br
284
NB
Br
286
NB
283
285
288
289
Br
NB
Br
287
NB
290
291
292
JUV
293
Br
294
NB
295
296
Br
297
NB
298
299
300
301
Br
302
NB

Plate 267 Family 141.

MUSCICAPIDAE, SYLVIINAE (6)
Old World Warblers

303. *Apalis alticola*. Brown headed Apalis. 3ss. 13. Tanzania, Zaire, Malawi, Angola.
304. *Apalis argentea*. Kungwe Apalis. 2ss. 11. W Tanzania.
305. *Apalis binotata*. Masked Apalis. 3ss. 10. Cameroon to Congo & Uganda.
306. *Apalis chariessa*. White winged Apalis. 12. Kenya to Mozambique.
307. *Apalis chirindensis*. Chirinda Apalis. 14. Zimbabwe, Mozambique.
308. *Apalis cinerea*. Grey Apalis. 3ss. 13. Fernando Po, Cameroon to Sudan.
309. *Apalis flavida*. Black / Yellow breasted Apalis. 12ss. 12. Africa S of Sahara.
310. *Apalis caniceps*. Green tailed Apalis. 10. Kenya, Uganda, Tanzania.
311. *Apalis jacksoni*. Black throated Apalis. 3ss. 12. C & E Africa.
312. *Apalis karamojae*. Karamoja Apalis. 12. Uganda, Tanzania.
313. *Apalis personata*. Black faced / Masked Apalis. 10ss. 14. Uganda, Zaire.
314. *Apalis melanocephala*. Black headed Apalis. 10ss. 14. Kenya to Zimbabwe.
315. *Apalis/Orthotomus moreaui*. Long billed Apalis / Tailorbird. 2ss. 11. E Africa.
316. *Apalis nigriceps*. Black capped Apalis. 2ss. 10. Sierra Leone to Uganda, Congo.
317. *Apalis schoutadeni*. Schoutaden's Apalis. 10. Congo.(unique)
318. *Apalis eidos*. Peter's Apalis. 11. Zaire.
319. *Apalis rufifrons*. Red faced Apalis. 3ss. 11. Sudan, Ethiopia to Tanzania.
320. incl. *A. r. rufidorsalis*. Red backed Apalis. 11. SE Kenya.
321. *Apalis flavigularis*. Yellow throated Apalis. 12. Malawi.
322. *Apalis murinus*. Mouse Apalis. 12. Mozambique.
323. *Apalis griseiceps*. Grey capped Apalis. 12. Kenya, Tanzania.
324. *Apalis kaboboensis*. Prigogine's Apalis. 12. Mt Kabobo, Congo.
325. *Apalis goslingi*. Gosling's Apalis. 10. Cameroon to N Congo.
326. *Apalis porphyrolaema*. Chestnut throated Apalis. 2ss. 13. EC Africa.
327. *Apalis chapini*. Chapin's Apalis. 11.Tanzania.
328. *Apalis melanura*. Slender tailed Apalis. 11. Angola. (perhaps Cisticola 266)
329. *Apalis viridiceps*. Brown tailed Apalis. 12. Ethiopia, Somalia.
330. *Apalis pulchra*. Black collared Apalis. 2ss. 13. Cameroon to Sudan & Kenya.
331. *Apalis ruddi*. Rudd's Apalis. 2ss. 12. Mozambique.
332. *Apalis rufogularis*. Buff throated Apalis. 5ss. 12. Nigeria to Sudan, Angola.
333. *Apalis nigrescens*. Black backed Apalis. 12. Sudan to Zambia.
334. *Apalis ruwenzorii*. Collared Apalis. 2ss. 10. Ruwenzori Mts., Zaire.
335. *Apalis sharpii*. Sharpe's Apalis. 5ss. 11. W Africa to Tanzania & Zambia.
336. *Apalis bamendae*. Bamenda Apalis. 11. Tanzania.
337. *Apalis lynesi*. Namuli Apalis. 12. Mozambique.
338. *Apalis thoracica*. Bar throated Apalis. 20ss. 12. South Africa.
339. *Apalis arnoldi*. Zimbabwe Bar throated Apalis. 12. Zimbabwe.
340. *Apalis fuscigularis*. Teita Apalis. 12. Kenya.
341. *Scepomycter/Bathmocercus winifredi*. Mrs Moreau's Warbler. 15. Tanzania.
342. *Drymocichla incana*. Red winged grey Warbler. 13. Cameroon to Sudan, Congo.
343. *Hypergerus/Eminia lepidus*. Grey capped Warbler. 15. Kenya, Tanzania, Congo.
344. *Hypergerus atriceps*. Oriole Warbler. 20. Senegal to Cameroon & Congo.
345. *Bathmocercus cerviniventris*. Black headed Stream Warbler. 13. W Africa.
346. *Euryptila subcinnamomea*. Kopje Warbler. 14. Namibia to Cape.
347. *Bathmocercus rufus*. Black faced rufous Warbler. 2ss. 13. E, C & W Africa.
348. *Camaroptera brachyura*. Green backed Camaroptera. 6ss. 10. Eastern S Africa.
349. *Camaroptera brevicaudata*. Grey backed Camaroptera. 9ss. 10. E C & W Africa.
350. *Camaroptera harterti*. Hartert's Camaroptera. 10. Angola.
351. *Camaroptera chloronota*. Olive green Camaroptera. 4ss. 9. Congo to Kenya.
352. *Calamonastes fasciolatus*. Barred Wren Warbler. 3ss. 14. Tanzania to S Africa
353. *Poliolais lopesi*. White tailed Warbler. 3ss. 10. W C Africa.
354. *Calamonastes simplex*. Grey Wren Warbler. 5ss. 13. Africa.
355. *Calamonastes stierlingi*. Stierling's Wren Warbler. 5ss. 12. SE Africa.
356. *Camaroptera superciliaris*. Yellow browed Camaroptera. 5ss. 10. W C Africa.

Nos. 321, 322, 323, 337, 338, 339 & 340 are probably conspecific (*A. Thoracica.*)

303
304
305
306
313
307
309
310
311
329
308
312
314
315
316
337
340
317
318
319
320
321
322
323
324
325
326
328
330
331
332
333
338
339
335
336
334
342
343
344
341
346
345
347
348
Br
NB
349
354
351
352
355
350
Juv
353
356
327

SYLVIINAE (7) Old World Warblers

357. *Eremomela atricollis*. Black necked Eremomela. 2ss. 13. SC Africa.
358. *Eremomela badiceps*. Rufous / Brown crowned Eremomela. 2ss. 10. WC Africa.
359. *Eremomela canescans*. Green backed Eremomela. 4ss. 10. WC to E Africa.
360. *Eremomela flavicrissalis*. Yellow vented Eremomela. 11.Somalia Kenya.
361. *Eremomela gregalis*. Yellow rumped Eremomela. 2ss. 12. Namibia to Cape.
362. *Eremomela icteropygialis*. Yellow bellied Eremomela. 12ss. 9. Sub-Saharan Africa.
363. *Eremomela pusilla*. Senegal / Smaller G. B .Eremomela. 10. Senegal to Cameroon.
364. *Eremomela salvadorii*. Salvadori's Eremomela. 3ss. 9. WC Africa.
365. *Eremomela scotops*. Greencap Eremomela. 8ss. 11. EC Southern Africa.
366. *Eremomela turner*. Turner's Eremomela. 2ss. 10. EC Africa.
367. *Eremomela usticollis*. Burnt-neck Eremomela. 3ss. 12. Southern Africa.
368. *Sylvietta brachyura*. Northern Crombec. 3ss. 8. Senegal to Ethiopia, Tanzania.
369. *Sylvietta denti*. Lemon bellied Crombec. 2ss. 7. W Africa.
370. *Sylvietta isabellina*. Somali Long billed Crombec. 11. E Africa.
371. *Sylvietta leucophrys*. White browed Crombec. 4ss. 8. E Africa
372. *Sylvietta chapini*. Chapin's Crombec. 8. Zaire.
373. *Sylvietta philippae*. Somali short billed Crombec. 10. Somalia.
374. *Sylvietta rufescens*. Cape / Long billed Crombec. 8ss. 10. Southern Africa.
375. *Sylvietta ruficapilla*. Red capped Crombec. 6ss. 10. EC to SW Africa.
376. *Sylvietta virens*. Green Crombec. 5ss. 7. Sierra Leone to Angola & Uganda.
377. *Sylvietta whytii*. Red capped Crombec. 5ss. 10. Ethiopia to Zimbabwe.
378. *Hemitesia neumanni*. Neumann's Short tailed Warbler. 9. Zaire, Uganda.
379. *Macrosphenus concolor*. Grey Longbill. 2ss. 13. Sierra Leone to Uganda, Zaire.
380. *Macrosphenus flavicans*. Yellow Longbill. 2ss. 13. Nigeria to Angola, Sudan.
381. *Macrosphenus kempi*. Kemp's Longbill. 2ss. 13. Nigeria, Sierra Leone.
382. *Macrosphenus kretchneri*. Kretchmer's Longbill. 2ss. 15. Kenya to Mozambique.
383. *Macrosphenus leoninus*. Leonine Longbill. 13. W Africa. (unique, Juv.381?)
384. *Macrosphenus pulitzeri*. Pulitzer's Longbill. 13. Angola.
385. *Graueria vittata*. Grauer's Warbler. 16. Zaire.
386. *Parisoma/Sylvia boehni*. Banded Tit Warbler. 3ss. 12. Ethiopia to Tanzania.
387. *Parisoma /Sylvia buryi*. Yemen Tit Warbler. 15. Saudi Arabia.
388. *Parisoma/Sylvia layardi*. Layard's Tit Warbler. 4ss. 15. Southern Africa.
389. *Parisoma/Sylvia lugens*. Brown Tit Warbler. 4ss. 12. NE & EC Africa.
390. *Parisoma/Sylvia subcaeruleum*. Rufous vented Warbler. 4ss. 15. S.Africa.
391. *Hylia prasina*. Green Hylia. 2ss. 12. Fernando Po, Guinea to Angola, Tanzania.
392. *Hyliota flavigaster*. Yellow bellied Flycatcher. 3ss. 13. Africa S of Sahara.
393. *Hyliota australis*. Southern yellow bellied Flycatcher. 5ss. 13. SC Africa.
394. *Hyliota violacea*. Violet backed Flycatcher. 2ss. 13. Liberia to Ghana, Zaire.
395. *Pholidornis rushiae*. Titarens. Shade Warbler. 11. San Cristobal Is.
403. Megalurulus/Cichlornis grosvenori. Bismarck Thicketbird. 18. New Britain.
404. Megalurulus/Cichlornis whitneyi. Thicket Warbler. 18. Espiritu Santo Is.
405. Megalurulus/Cichlornis turipavae. Guadalcanal Thicketbird. 13. Guadalcanal.
406. Megalurulus/Cichlornis llaneae. Bougainville Thicketbird. 17. Bougainville.
407. Lamprolia victoriae. Silktail. 2ss. 13. Fiji.
408. Vitia/Cettia ruficapilla. Fiji Bush Warbler. 4ss. 12. Fiji.
409. Vitia/Cettia parens. Shade Warbler. 11. San Cristobal Is.
410. Ortygocichla/Trichocichla rufa. Long legged Warbler. 2ss. 17. Fiji.
411. Cryptosylvicola randrianasoloi. Cryptic Warbler. 10. E Madagascar.

No. 395 is often placed with Waxbills or Tits.

MUSCICAPIDAE. Subfamily 142. REGULIDAE. Kinglets, Tit Warblers.

1. *Regulus calendula*. Ruby crowned Kinglet. 3ss. 11. Canada to Mexico.
2. *Regulus regulus*. Goldcrest. 14ss. 9. Most of Eurasia.
3. *Regulus teneriffae*. Canary Islands Firecrest. 9. Canary Is.
4. *Regulus ignicapillus*. Firecrest. 4ss. 9. S Europe N Africa.
5. *Regulus goodfellowi*. Flamecrest. 10. Taiwan.
6. *Regulus satrapa*. Golden crowned Kinglet. 6ss. 10. W North America to Guatemala.
7. *Leptopoecile elegans*. Crested Tit Warbler. 2ss. 11. China, Tibet.
8. Leptopoecile sophiae. Severtzov's / White browed Tit Warbler. 4ss. 11. EC Asia.

Nos. 7 & 8 should perhaps be placed with

357
358
359
360
361
362
363
364
365
366
367
368
369
370
371
373
374
375
376
377
378
379
380
381
384
382
383
372
385
386
387
388
389
390
391
392
393
394
395
396
397
398
399
400
401
402
403
404
405
407
408
409
410
406
411
REGULIDAE
1
2
3
4
5
6
7
8

MUSCICAPIDAE, MALURINAE
Australian Fairy Wrens

1. *Malurus alboscapulatus.* Black & White Wren. 11ss. 11. New Guinea.
la. North western form. Female similar to male.
2. *Malurus amabilis.* Lovely Wren. 2ss. 14. N Queensland.
3. *Malurus assimilis.* Purple backed Wren. 14. Interior Australia. (ss of 9.)
4. *Malurus callainus.* Turquoise Wren. 12. C & S Australia. (ss of 15.)
5. *Malurus coronatus.* Lilac crowned Wren. 3ss. 15. N Australia.
6. *Malurus cyaneus.* Superb blue Wren. 5ss. 12. SE Australia, Tasmania.
7. *Malurus elegans.* Red winged Wren. 15. SW Australia.
8. *Malurus dulcis.* Lavender flanked Wren. 14. N Australia. (ss of 9.)
9. *Malurus lamberti.* Variegated Wren. 6ss. 14. SE Australia.
10. *Malurus leucopterus.* White winged Wren. 13. W Australia.
11. *Malurus leuconotus.* Blue & white / White backed Wren. 13. Internal Australia. (ss of 10.)
12. *Malurus melanocephalus.* Red backed Wren. 4ss. 12. N & E Australia.
13. *Malurus melanotus.* Black backed Wren. 12. EC Australia. (ss of 15.)
14. *Malurus pulcherrimus.* Blue breasted Wren. 8ss. 14. SW Australia.
15. *Malurus splendens.* Banded / Splendid Wren. 12. W Australia.
16. *Clytomyias insignis.* Orange crowned / Rufous Wren. 12. New Guinea.
17. *Malurus grayi.* Broad billed Wren Warbler. 12. New Guinea.
18. *Malurus campbelli.* Campbell's Fairy Wren. 13. New Guinea.
19. *Malurus cyanocephalus.* Emperor / Blue Wren Warbler. 4ss. 12. New Guinea & Is.
20. *Malurus/Sipodotus wallacei.* Wallace's Fairywren. 2ss. 11. New Guinea & Is.
21. *Stipiturus malachurus.* Southern Emu-Wren. 5ss. 19. Eastern South Australia, Tasmania.
22. *Stipiturus mallee.* Mallee Emu-Wren. 16. Victoria, New South Wales.
23. *Stipiturus ruficeps.* Rufous crowned Emu-Wren. 2ss. 14. Interior Australia.
24. *Amytornis barbatus.* Grey Grasswren. 19. New South Wales.
25. *Amytornis dorotheae.* Carpentarian Grasswren. 17. Northern territory.
26. *Amytornis goyderi.* Eyerean Grasswren. 14. South Australia.
27. *Amytornis housei.* Black Grasswren. 23. NW Australia.
28. *Amytornis purnelli.* Dusky Grasswren. 2ss. 17. Queensland, Northern Territory.
29. *Amytornis striatus.* Striated Grasswren. 4ss. 16. SE Australia.
30. *Amytornis textilis.* Thick billed Grasswren. 3ss. 17. New South Wales, South Australia.
31. *Amytornis modestus.* Western Grasswren. 17. Western Australia. (ss of 30.)
32. *Amytornis woodwardi.* White throated Grasswren. 21. N Australia.
33. *Amytornis whitei.* Rufous Grasswren. 16. NW & C Australia. (ss of 29.)

1A
(b)
1
2
3
4
5
6
7
8
9
10
11
12
13
14
15
16
17
18
19
20
21
22
23
24
25
26
27
28
29
30
31
32
33

MUSCICAPIDAE, ACANTHIZINAE
Australian Warblers

1. *Dasyornis brachypterus*. (Eastern) Bristlebird. 2ss 21. New South Wales.
2. incl. *D. b. longirostris*. Western Bristlebird. 18. SW Australia.
3. *Dasyornis broadbenti*. Rufous Bristlebird. 3ss. 25. Coast SE to SW Australia.
4. *Aphelocephala leucopsis*. Common Whiteface. 3ss. 11. Southern Australia.
5. incl. *A. l. castaneiventris*. Western Whiteface. 11. Western Australia.
6. *Aphelocephala nigricincta*. Banded Whiteface. 2ss. 12. Interior Australia.
7. *Aphelocephala pectoralis*. Chestnut breasted Whiteface. 10. South Australia.
8. *Smicrornis brevirostris*. Brown Weebill. 7ss. 9. Australia & Tasmania.
9. incl. *S. b. flavescens*. Yellow Weebill. 8. Northern Territory.
10. *Acanthiza chrysorrhoa*. Yellow tailed Thornbill. 7ss. 11. C & S Australia.
11. *Acanthiza apicalis*. Broad tailed Thornbill. 5ss. 11. Australia.
12. *Acanthiza ewingi*. Tasmanian Thornbill. 10. Tasmania & Is.
13. *Acanthiza inornata*. Western Thornbill. 2ss. 10. SW Australia.
14. *Acanthiza iredalei*. Slender billed Thornbill. 3ss. 9. Internal S Australia.
15. *Acanthiza katherina*. Mountain Thornbill. 10. Queensland.
16. *Acanthiza lineata*. Striated Thornbill. 4ss. 10. SE Australia.
17. *Acanthiza murina*. Papuan Thornbill / De Vis' Tree Warbler. 10. New Guinea.
18. *Acanthiza nana*. Little Thornbill. 6ss. 10. E Australia.
19. *Acanthiza pusilla*. Brown Thornbill. 5ss. 10. Tasmania,S Australia..
20. *Acanthiza reguloides*. Buff tailed Thornbill. 4ss. 11. E Australia.
21. *Acanthiza robustrirostris*. Slaty backed Thornbill. 2ss. 10. Internal Australia.
22. *Acanthiza uropygialis*. Chestnut tailed Thornbill. 2ss. 11. S Australia.
23. *Pyrrholaemus brunneus*. Redthroat. 12. W, C & S Australia.
24. *Finschia novaezelandiae*. New Zealand Creeper / Pipipi. 13. S Island, New Zealand.
25. *Mohoua ochrocephala*. Yellowhead. 15. S Island, New Zealand.
26. *Mohoua albicilla*. Whitehead. 15. N Island, New Zealand.
27. *Pycnoptilus floccosus*. Pilot Bird. 2ss. 17. SE Australia.
28. *Calamanthus fuliginosus*. Striated Field Wren. 14. SE Australia.
29. *Calamanthus campestris*. Rufous Field Wren. 7ss. 14. S Australia.
30. incl. *C. c. isabellinus*. Rusty Field Wren. 14. C. Australia.
31. *C. c. montanellus*. Rock Field Wren. 14. W Australia.
32. *Hylacola cautus*. Shy Heath / Ground Wren. 2ss. 13. SE & SW Australia.
33. *Hylacola pyrrhopygia*. Chestnut rumped Heath Wren. 2ss. 14. S Australia.
34. *Chthonicola sagittata*. Speckled Warbler. 2ss. 12. S & SE Australia.
35. *Gerygone albofrontata*. Chatham Is Gerygone. 12. Chatham I.
36. *Gerygone inornata*. Plain Gerygone / Flyeater. 4ss. 11. Timor & Sundas.
37. *Gerygone chloronotus*. Green backed Gerygone. 3ss. 10. New Guinea to NW Australia.
38. *Gerygone chrysogaster*. Yellow bellied Gerygone. 5ss. 11. New Guinea.
39. incl. *G. c. notata*. White bellied Gerygone. 11. Irian Jaya.
40. *Gerygone cinerea*. Mountain / Grey Gerygone. 9. New Guinea.
41. *Gerygone hypoxantha*. Biak Gerygone. 11. Biak.
42. *Gerygone flavolateralis*. Fan-tailed Gerygone. 4ss. 12. New Caledonia & Is.
43. *Gerygone fusca*. Western / White tailed Gerygone. 8ss. 10. Australia.
44. *Gerygone igata*. Riroriro / Grey Gerygone. 4ss. 11. New Zealand.
45. *Gerygone levigaster*. Buff breasted Gerygone. 4ss. 11. NE Australian coast.
46. incl. *G. l. cantator*. Mangrove Gerygone. 11. N & NE Australia.
47. *Gerygone magnirostris*. Large billed Gerygone. 11ss. 11. W Australia.
48. *Gerygone olivacea*. White throated Gerygone. 4ss. 11. NE Australia, New Guinea.
49. *Gerygone palpebrosa*. Black headed Gerygone. 6ss. 11. New Guinea.
50. incl. *G. p. flavida*. Fairy Gerygone. 4ss. 11. NE Australia, New Guinea.
51. *Gerygone richmondi*. Brown Gerygone. 11. NE Australia.
52. *Gerygone mouki*. Northern Gerygone. 10. Queensland.
53. *Gerygone ruficollis*. Treefern / Brown breasted Gerygone. 10. 2ss. New Guinea.
54. *Gerygone sulphurea*. Golden bellied Gerygone. 9. Malaysia to Sulawesi.
55. *Gerygone tenebrosa*. Dusky Gerygone. 12. NW Australia.
56. *Gerygone dorsalis*. Rufous sided Gerygone. 5ss. 13. Wallacea.
57. *Gerygone ruficauda*. Red tailed Gerygone. 12. Queensland.
58. *Gerygone personata*. Black throated Gerygone. 12. Queensland.
59. *Gerygone modesta*. Norfolk Island Gerygone. 12. Norfolk Island.
60. *Gerygone insularis*. Lord Howe Island Gerygone. 12. Lord Howe I.(extinct).
61. *Gerygone rubra*. Red backed Warbler / Garnet Robin. 2ss. 11. New Guinea.

1
2
3
4
5
6
7
8
9
10
11
12
13
14
15
16
17
18
19
20
21
22
23
24
26
25
27
28
29
30
31
32
57
56
33
34
35
36
37
38
41
42
43
44
40
39
59
45
46
47
48
49
50
51
52
53
54
55
58
61
61 JUV
60

MUSCICAPIDAE, ACANTHIZINAE
Australian Warblers

62. *Acanthornis / Sericornis magnus*. Scrub Tit. 12. Tasmania.
63. *Oreoscopus / Crateroscelis gutturalis*. Fern Wren. 13. Queensland.
64. *Sericornis arfakianus*. Grey green Scrub Wren. 2ss 10. New Guinea.
65. *Sericornis beccarii*. Beccari's / Tropical Scrub Wren. 7ss. 12. New Guinea, Queensland
66. incl. *S. b. minimus*. Little scrub Wren. 11. Cape York Peninsula.
67. *Sericornis virgatus*. Perplexing scrub Wren. 6ss. 12. New Guinea.
68. *Sericornis citreogularis*. Yellow throated scrub Wren. 2ss. 13. E Australia.
69. *Sericornis frontalis*. White browed scrub Wren. 15ss. 12. SE Australia & Is.
70. *Sericornis humilis*. Brown scrub Wren. 14. Tasmania & Is.
71. *Sericornis keri*. Atherton scrub Wren. 14. Queensland.
72. *Sericornis maculatus*. Spotted scrub Wren. 12. S & SW Australia.
73. *Sericornis magnirostris*. Large billed scrub Wren. 2ss. 13. E Australia.
74. *Sericornis nigroviridis*. Black & green scrub Wren. 10. New Guinea. (unique).
75. *Sericornis nouhuysi*. Large mountain scrub Wren. 4ss. 12. New Guinea.
76. *Sericornis papuensis*. Papuan scrub Wren. 3ss. 11. New Guinea.
77. *Sericornis perspicillatus*. Buff faced scrub Wren. 10. New Guinea.
78. *Sericornis rufescens*. Arfac / Vogelkop scrub Wren. 10. New Guinea.
79. *Sericornis spilodera*. Pale billed scrub Wren. 7ss. 12. New Guinea & Is.
80. *Origma solitaria*. Rock Warbler. 13. New South Wales.
81. *Cincloramphus cruralis*. Brown Songlark. 25/19. Australia.
82. *Cincloramphus mathewsi*. Rufous Songlark. 19/16. Australia.
83. *Crateroscelis murina*. Rusty / lowland Mouse Warbler. 2ss. 12. New Guinea.
84. *Crateroscelis nigrorufa*. Mid-mountain / Bicoloured Mouse Warbler. 6ss. 12. New Guinea.
85. *Crateroscelis robusta*. Mountain Mouse Warbler. 2ss. 12. New Guinea.

Nos. 81 & 82 are now often placed in Sylviidae.

MUSCICAPIDAE. Subfamily 145. EPHTHIANURIDAE. Australian Chats.

1. *Ephthianura albifrons*. White fronted Chat. 2ss. 11. Southern Australia.
2. *Ephthianura aurifrons*. Orange Chat. 11. Interior Australia.
3. *Ephthianura crocea*. Yellow Chat. 4ss. 11. Coastal N & E Australia.
4. *Ephthianura tricolor*. Crimson Chat. 11. C & E Australia.
5. *Ashbyia lovensis*. Desert Chat / Gibber Bird. 12. EC Australia.

EPHTHIANURIDAE

MUSCICAPIDAE, EOPSALTRIIDAE
Australian Robins etc

1. *Microeca f. tornenti.* Brown tailed Flyrobin. 13. NW & N Australia.
2. *Microeca f. flavigaster.* Lemon breasted Flyrobin. 4ss. 12. N & NW Australia.
3. *Microeca flavovirescens.* Olive Flyrobin. 2ss. 13. New Guinea & Is.
4. *Microeca griseoceps.* Yellow legged Flyrobin. 4ss. 12. Queensland, New Guinea.
5. *Microeca hemixantha.* Golden bellied Flyrobin. 13. Tanimber Is.
6. *Microeca leucophaea/fascinans.* Jacky Winter. 5ss. 14. Australia, New Guinea.
7. *Microeca papuana.* Canary Flyrobin. 2ss. 11. New Guinea.
8. *Eopsaltria australis.* Eastern Yellow Robin. 16ss. 16. SE Australia.
9. incl. *E. a. chrysorrhos.* Northern Yellow Robin. 16. Queensland to New South Wales.
10. *Eopsaltria griseogularis.* Western Yellow Robin. 2ss. 16. SW Australia.
11. *Eopsaltria flaviventris.* Yellow bellied Robin. 14. New Caledonia.
12. *Eopsaltria georgiana.* White breasted Robin. 16. SW Australia.
13. *Tregellasia capito.* Pale yellow Robin. 2ss. 15. New Guinea, E Australia.
14. *Tregellasia leucops.* White faced Robin. 10ss. 13. New Guinea, Cape York Peninsula.
15. *Petroica bivittata.* Forest / Alpine Robin. 11. New Guinea.
16. *Petroica australis.* South Island Robin. 3ss. 18. New Zealand, S Island.
17. incl. *P. a. longipes.* North Island Robin. 18. New Zealand, N Island.
18. *Petroica archboldi.* Snow mountain Robin. 2ss. 11. New Guinea.
19. *Petroica/Melanodryas cucullata.* Hooded Robin. 2ss. 16. Australia.
20. *Petroica goodenovii.* Red capped Robin. 12. Australia.
21. *Petroica macrocephala.* New Zealand Tom Tit. 5ss. 13. New Zealand & Is.
22. incl. *P. m. dannefaerdi.* Snares Island Tom Tit. 13. Snares Is.
23. *Petroica multicolor.* Scarlet Robin. 15ss. 13. Australia & Pacific Is.
24. *Petroica phoenicea.* Flame Robin. 15. SE Australia, Tasmania.
25. *Petroica rodinogaster.* Pink Robin. 12. Victoria, Tasmania.
26. *Petroica rosea.* Rose Robin. 11. SE Australia.
27. *Petroica traversi.* Chatham Island Robin. 15. Chatham I.
28. *Petroica/Melanodryas vittata.* Dusky Robin. 2ss. 16. Tasmania & other Is.
29. *Culicicapa ceylonensis.* Grey headed canary Flycatcher. 6ss. 13. S Asia, Indonesia.
30. *Culicicapa helianthea.* Citrine canary Flycatcher. 5ss. 12. Philippines, Sulawesi.
31. *Monachella mulleriana.* River / Torrent Flycatcher. 4ss. 15. New Britain, New Guinea.
32. *Poecilodryas albonotata.* Black throated Robin. 3ss. 18. New Guinea.
33. *Poecilodryas brachyura.* Black chinned White breasted Robin. 3ss. 15. New Guinea.
34. *Poecilodryas hypoleuca.* Black & white / White sided Robin. 3ss. 14. New Guinea.
35. *Poecilodryas placens.* Olive yellow Robin. 15. New Guinea.
36. *Peneoenanthe/Eopsaltria Pulverentula.* Mangrove Robin. 4ss. 16. N Australia, New Guinea.
37. *Poecilodryas superciliosa.* White browed Robin. 2ss. 14. NE Australia.
38. incl. *P. s. cerviniventris.* Buff sided Robin. 15. NW Australia.
39. *Peneothello bimaculatus.* White rumped Robin. 2ss. 13. NW New Guinea.
40. incl. *P. b. vicarius.* Smoky rumped Robin. 13. SE New Guinea.
41. *Peneothello cryptoleucus.* Smoky / Grey Robin. 2ss. 15. New Guinea.
42. *Peneothello cyanus.* Slaty / Blue grey Robin. 3ss. 15. New Guinea.
43. *Peneothello sigillatus.* White winged Robin. 4ss. 15. New Guinea.
44. *Heteromyias albispecularis.* Ground Thicket / Ashy Robin. 5ss. 17. New Guinea.
45. *Heteromyias cinereifrons.* Grey headed Robin. 17. N Queensland.
46. *Mayrornis lessoni.* Slaty Flycatcher. 13. Fiji.
47. *Mayrornis schistaceus.* Small slaty Flycatcher. 12. Vanikoro. (Santa Cruz)
48. *Mayrornis versicolor.* Ogea Flycatcher. 12. Fiji.
49. *Neolalage banksiana.* Buff bellied Flycatcher. 14. New Hebrides.

1
2
3
4
5
6
7
8
9
10
11
12
13
14
15
16
17
18
19
20
21
22
23
24
25
26
27
28
29
30
31
32
33
34
35
36
37
38
39
40
41
42
43
44
45
46
47
48
49

MUSCICAPIDAE, EOPSALTRIDAE, MUSCICAPINAE (1) Flycatcher-Robins, Old World Flycatchers

MUSCICAPIDAE. Subfamily 146. EOPSALTRIDAE (2). Flycatcher-Robins.

50. *Chasiempis sandwichensis.* Elepaio. 3ss. 14. Hawaii.
51. *Pomarea dimidiata.* Raratonga Flycatcher. 15. Raratonga.
52. *Pomarea mendozae.* Marquesan Flycatcher. 4ss. 16. Marquesas Is.
53. *Pomarea iphis.* Allied Flycatcher. 2ss. 15. Uahuka, Eiao. (Marquesas)
54. *Pomarea nigra.* Tahiti Flycatcher. 2ss. 15. Society Is.
55. *Pomarea whitneyi.* Large Fatuhiva Flycatcher. 20. Fatuhiva Is. (Marquesas.)
56. *Pachycephalopsis hattamensis.* Green thicket Flycatcher. 15. New Guinea.
57. *Pachycephalopsis poliosoma.* White throated Thicket Flycatcher. 16. New Guinea.

MUSCICAPINAE. Subfamily 147. MUSCICAPINAE (1). O1d World Flycatchers.

1. *Bradornis (Melaenornis) infuscatus.* Chat Flycatcher. 4ss. 20. Southern Africa.
2. *Bradornis(Melaenornis) mariquensis.* Mariqua Flycatcher. 2ss. 18. Southern Africa.
3. *Bradornis(Melaenornis) microrhynchus.* Large Grey Flycatcher. 4ss. 14. Sudan to Tanzania.
4. *Bradornis(Melaenornis) pumilus.* Little Grey Flycatcher. 12. Ethiopia, Somalia.
5. *Bradornis(Melaenornis) pallidus.* Pale Flycatcher. 11ss. 16. Africa South of Sahara.
6. *Empidornis(Melaenornis) semipartitus.* Silverbird. 3ss. 18. E Africa, Ethiopia to Tanzania.
7. *Melaenornis annamarulae.* Mrs Forbes Watson's black Flycatcher. 20. Liberia.
8. *Melaenornis ardesiaca.* Berlioz' yellow eyed black Flycatcher. 18. Zaire.
9. *Melaenornis chocolatinus.* Abyssinian slaty Flycatcher. 2ss. 15. Ethiopia.
10. *Dioptrornis(Melaenornis) fischeri.* White eyed slaty Flycatcher. 4ss. 15. E Africa.
11. *Dioptrornis(Melaenornis) brunneus.* Angolan slaty Flycatcher. 2ss. 14. Angola.
12. *Melaenornis edolioides.* Northern black Flycatcher. 3ss. 19. E & W Africa.
13. *Melaenornis pammelaina.* South African black Flycatcher. 2ss. 21. RSA to Kenya.
14. *Sigelus(Melaenornis) silens.* Fiscal Flycatcher. 19. Cape to Botswana, Mozambique.
15. *Fraseria(Melaenornis) cinerascens.* White browed Forest Flycatcher. 2ss. 19. W Africa.
16. *Fraseria(Melaenornis) ocreata.* African Forest Flycatcher. 3ss. 21. W & C Africa.
17. *Rhinomyias addita.* Streaky breasted Jungle Flycatcher. 16. Buru Is.
18. *Rhinomyias brunneata.* Brown chested / White gorgetted Jungle Flycatcher. 15. China.
19. *Rhinomyias colonus.* Henna tailed / Gleaming Jungle Flycatcher. 15. Sulawesi.
20. *Rhinomyias goodfellowi.* Slaty backed Jungle Flycatcher. 16. Mindanao.
21. *Rhinomyias gularis.* White browed Jungle Flycatcher. 4ss. 15. Philippines, Borneo.
22. *Rhinomyias albigularis.* White throated Jungle Flycatcher. 15.Philippines.
23. *Rhinomyias insignis.* Lepanto Jungle Flycatcher . 16. Luzon.
24. *Rhinomyias olivacea.* Olive backed / Fulvous chested Jungle Flycatcher. 3ss. 15. Malaysia, Indonesia.
25. *Rhinomyias oscillans.* Active / Russet backed Jungle Flycatcher. 15. Flores, Sumba.
26. *Rhinomyias ruficauda.* Rufous tailed Jungle Flycatcher. 7ss.14. Philippines, Borneo.
27. *Rhinomyias umbratilis.* White throated / Grey chested Jungle Flycatcher. 15. Sumatra, Borneo.

50
51
52
53
54
AD
55
JUV
56
57
MUSICAPIDAE
1
2
3
4
5
6
7
8
9
10
11
12
13
14
15
16
17
18
19
20
21
22
23
24
25
26
27

MUSCICAPIDAE, MUSCIAPINAE (2)
Old World Flycatchers

28. *Ficedula albicollis*. Collared Flycatcher. 13. E Europe, W Asia. Winters Tropical Africa.
29. *Ficedula basilanica*. Little slaty Flycatcher. 2ss. 12. Sulawesi to Philippines.
30. *Ficedula bonthaina*. Lisping / Lompobattang Flycatcher. 12. Sulawesi.
31. *Ficedula buruensis*. Cinnamon chested Flycatcher. 3ss. 13. Buru, Seram, Kai.
32. *Ficedula crypta*. Vaurie's / Russet Tailed Flycatcher. 2ss. 12. Mindanao.
33. *(Ficedula) Cyanoptila cyanomelana*. Blue & white Flycatcher. 3ss. 17. NE Asia. Winters Malaysia.
34. *Ficedula dumetoria*. Rufous breasted Flycatcher. 3ss. 12. Sumatra, Borneo, Java.
35. *Ficedula harterti*. Hartert's Flycatcher. 12. Sumba.
36. *Ficedula henrici*. Damar Flycatcher. 12. Damar.
37. *Ficedula hodgsonii*. Slaty backed Flycatcher. 13. Himalayas to SW China.
38. *Ficedula hyperythra*. Thicket / Snowy browed Flycatcher. 20ss. 13. India to SE Asia & Indonesia.
39. *Ficedula hypoleuca*. (European) Pied Flycatcher.5ss. 12. Eurasia. Winters Africa, SW Asia.
40. *Ficedula semitorquata*. Semi-collared Flycatcher. 13. SE Europe, SW Asia. Winters Africa.
41. *Ficedula monileger*. White gorgetted Flycatcher. 3ss. 13. India, SE Asia.
42. *Ficedula mugimaki*. Black & Orange Flycatcher. 13. NE Asia. Winters Philippines, SE Asia.
43. *Ficedula narcissina*. Black & yellow Flycatcher. 3ss. 13. Japan, E Asia. Winters Philippines, Borneo.
44. *Ficedula nigrorufa*. Black & rufous Flycatcher. 13. SW India.
45. *Ficedula parva*. Red breasted Flycatcher. 3ss. 13. Eurasia. Winters S Asia, Borneo.
46. *Ficedula subrubra*. Kashmir Flycatcher. 13. Himalayas. Winters Sri Lanka.
47. *Ficedula platenae*. Palawan Flycatcher. 12. Palawan.
48. *Ficedula rufigula*. Rufous throated / White vented Flycatcher. 12. Sulawesi.
49. *Ficedula sapphira*. Sapphire headed Flycatcher. 2ss. 11. S & SE Asia.
50. *Ficedula solitaris*. Rufous browed Flycatcher. 13. Vietnam, Malaya, Sumatra.
51. *Ficedula strophiata*. Orange gorgetted Flycatcher. 2ss. 13. S & SE Asia.
52. *Ficedula* White browed / Ultramarine Flycatcher. 2ss. 12. Himalayas. Winters SE Asia.
53. *Ficedula timorensis*. Black banded Flycatcher. 11. Timor.
54. *Ficedula tricolor*. Slaty blue Flycatcher. 4ss. 12. Himalayas, China, Burma.
55. *Ficedula westermanni*. Little Pied Flycatcher. 7ss. 11. Himalayas, SE Asia, Philippines.
56. *Ficedula zanthopygia*. Yellow rumped Flycatcher. 13. Korea. Winters SE Asia.

28
29
30
31
35
32
33
34
36
48
37
38
39
40
41
42
43
44
45
47
46
49
50
51
52
53
54
55
56

MUSCICAPIDAE, MUSCIAPINAE (3)
Old World Flycatchers, Niltavas

57. *(Niltava) Cyornis banyumas*. Hill blue Flycatcher. 8ss. 14. SE Asia, Indonesia.
58. *Cyornis lemprieri*. Palawan blue Flycatcher. 13. Palawan.
59. *Cyornis caerulata*. Large billed Flycatcher. 3ss. 14. Sumatra, Borneo.
60. *Cyornis concreta*. White tailed Flycatcher. 4ss. 18. SE Asia, Indonesia.
61. *Niltava davidi*. Fukien Flycatcher. 17. Fukien, Yunnan.
62. *Niltava grandis*. Large Niltava. 2ss. 21. Himalayas, SE Asia to Sumatra.
63. *Cyornis hainana*. Grant's Flycatcher. 15. Hainan & SE China.
64. *Cyornis herioti*. Blue breasted Flycatcher. 2ss. 13. Luzon.
65. *Niltava(Muscicapella) hodgsoni*. Pygmy blue Flycatcher. 2ss. 10. Himalayas, SE Asia, Indonesia.
66. *Cyornis hoevelli*. Blue fronted Flycatcher. 17. Sulawesi.
67. *Cyornis hyacinthinus*. Blue backed Flycatcher. 2ss. 19. Timor & Wetar.
68. *Niltava macgregoriae*. Small Niltava. 2ss. 13. Himalayas.
69. *Cyornis pallipes*. White bellied Flycatcher. 15. India.
70. *Cyornis poliogenys*. Brook's / Pale chinned Flycatcher. 3ss. 15. Nepal to Burma.
71. *Cyornis rubeculoides*. Blue throated Flycatcher. 5ss. 15. Himalayas, China. Winters S to Southern India, Malaysia.
72. *Cyornis ruecki*. Rueck's Flycatcher. 17. Malaysia.
73. *Cyornis rufigaster*. Mangrove blue Flycatcher. 13ss. 15. India, SE Asia, Philippines, Indonesia.
74. *Cyornis omissus*. Sulawesi Blue Flycatcher. 16. Sulawesi.
75. *Cyornis sanfordi*. Matinan Flycatcher. 17. Sulawesi.
76. *Niltava sumatrana*. Rufous vented Niltava. 15. Malaysia, Sumatra.
77. *Niltava sundara*. Rufous bellied Niltava. 3ss. 17. Himalayas, Yunnan, Laos, Burma.
78. *Cyornis superbus*. Bornean blue Flycatcher. 15. Borneo.
79. *Cyornis tickelliae*. Tickell's Blue Flycatcher. 4ss. 15. India, SE Asia, Philippines, Indonesia.
80. Cyornis; turcosus. Malaysian Blue Flycatcher. 2ss. 14. Malaysia, Borneo, Sumatra.
81. *Cyornis unicolor*. Pale blue Flycatcher. 3ss. 17. Himalayas, SE Asia, Indonesia.
82. *Niltava vivida*. Vivid Niltava. 2ss. 18. India, Tibet, China, Taiwan, S E Asia.

57
58
59
60
61
62
63
64
65
66
67
68
69
70
71
72
73
75
76
77
78
79
80
74
81
82

MUSCICAPIDAE, MUSCIAPINAE (4)
Old World Flycatchers

83. *Muscicapa(Eumyias) albicaudata.* Nilgiri Flycatcher. 15. SW India.
84. *Muscicapa ferruginea.* Ferruginous Flycatcher. 13. Himalayas. Winters to Indonesia.
85. *Muscicapa griseisticta.* Grey streaked Flycatcher. 13. NE Asia. Winters to Indonesia.
86. *Muscicapa(Eumyias) indigo.* Indigo Flycatcher. 3ss. 14. Sumatra, Java, Borneo.
87. *Muscicapa dauurica.* Asian brown Flycatcher. 4ss. 13. NE Asia. Winters to N Indonesia.
88. *Muscicapa randi.* Ashy breasted Flycatcher. 13. Philippines.
89. *Muscicapa williamsoni.* Brown streaked Flycatcher. 14. Burma, Malaysia, Borneo,
90. *Muscicapa muttui.* Brown breasted Flycatcher. 13. Sikkim to Burma, Sri Lanka.
91. *Muscicapa ruficauda.* Rusty tailed Flycatcher. 14. Turkestan to Bangladesh.
92. *(Muscicapa)Eumyias panayensis.* Island Flycatcher. 7ss. 14. Philippines, Moluccas, Sulawesi.
93. *Muscicapa segregata.* Sumba Flycatcher / Sumba brown Flycatcher. 13. Sumba.
94. *Muscicapa sibirica.* Siberian / Dark sided Flycatcher. 4ss.14. NE Asia. Winters SE Asia.
95. *Muscicapa(Eumyias) sordida.* Ceylon dusky blue Flycatcher. 14. Sri Lanka.
96. *Muscicapa(Eumyias) thalassina.* Verditer Flycatcher. 2ss. 16. India. Winters Indonesia.
97. *Muscicapa adusta.* Dusky Flycatcher. 15ss. 10. Ethiopia & Cameroon to Cape.
98. *Muscicapa aquatica.* Swamp Flycatcher. 5ss. 13. Senegal & Sudan to Zambia.
99. *Muscicapa caerulescens.* Ashy Flycatcher. 5ss. 13. Africa S of Sahara.
100. *Muscicapa cassini.* Cassin's grey Flycatcher. 13. Liberia to Uganda & Zambia.
101. *Muscicapa comitata.* Dusky Blue Flycatcher. 3ss. 12. W, E & C Africa.
102. *Muscicapa epulata.* Little grey Flycatcher. 9. Liberia to Gabon & Zaire.
103. *Muscicapa gambagae.* Gambaga Flycatcher. 12. Ghana to Somalia, Arabia.
104. *Muscicapa griseigularis.* Grey throated Flycatcher. 3ss. 10. Liberia to Nigeria, Uganda & Angola.
105. *Muscicapa infuscata.* Sooty Flycatcher. 3ss. 11. Nigeria to Uganda, Angola.
106. *Muscicapa lendu.* Chapin's Flycatcher. 13. Zaire to W Kenya.
107. *Muscicapa olivascens.* Olivaceous Flycatcher. 2ss. 14. Liberia to Zaire.
108. *Muscicapa itombwensis.* Prigogine's Flycatcher. 13. Itonbwe Mts., Zaire.
109. *Muscicapa sethsmithi.* (African) Rufous tailed / Yellow footed Flycatcher. 14. Cameroon to Gabon, Uganda.
110. *Muscicapa striata.* Spotted Flycatcher. 5ss. 14. Eurasia. Winters Africa.
111. *Muscicapa tessmanni.* Tessmann's Flycatcher. 14. Ivory Coast to Zaire.
112. *Muscicapa ussheri.* Ussher's dusky Flycatcher. 12. Sierra Leone to Nigeria.
113. *Muscicapa boehmi.* Boehm's Flycatcher. 2ss. 11. CS Africa.
114. *Muscicapa flavirostris.* Humblot's Flycatcher. 13. Comoro Is.
115. *Newtonia amphichroa.* Dark / Tulear Newtonia. 12. NE Malagasy.
116. *Newtonia archboldi.* Tabity / Archbold's Newtonia. 12. SW Malagasy.
117. *Newtonia brunneicauda.* Common Newtonia. 2ss. 12. Malagasy.
118. *Newtonia fanovanae.* Red tailed Newtonia. 12. E Malagasy.
119. *Myioparus plumbeus.* Grey Tit Flycatcher. 3ss. 14. Sub-saharan Africa.

83
84
85
86
87
88
89
90
91
92
93
94
95
96
97
98
99
100
101
102
103
104
105
106
107
108
109
110
111
112
114
115
116
117
118
113
119
110 JUV

MUSCICAPIDAE, RHIPIDURINAE
Fantail Flycatchers

1. *Rhipidura albicollis.* White throated Fantail. 9ss. 18. India, SE Asia, Indonesia.
2. incl. *R. a. albogularis.* Spot breasted Fantail. 17. India.
3. *Rhipidura albolimbata.* Friendly Fantail. 3ss. 15. New Guinea.
4. *Rhipidura atra.* Black Fantail. 2ss. 17. New Guinea & Is.
5. *Rhipidura aureola.* White browed Fantail. 3ss. 17. India to Vietnam.

6a. *Rhipidura brachyrhyncha.* Dimorphic / Rufous Fantail. 2ss. 16. New Guinea.

6b. *Rhipidura brachyrhyncha.* Dark phase.

7. *Rhipidura cockerelli.* White winged Fantail. 7ss. 16. Solomon Is.
8. *Rhipidura matthiae.* St Matthias rufous Fantail. 15. St Matthias Is.
9. *Rhipidura cyaniceps.* Blue headed Fantail. 4ss. 16. Philippines.
10. *Rhipidura dahli.* Bismarck Fantail. 2ss. 14. New Britain, New Ireland.
11. *Rhipidura diluta.* Brown capped Fantail. 17. Flores, Sumbawa.
12. *Rhipidura dedemi.* Streaky breasted fantail. 14. Ceram.
13. *Rhipidura drownei.* Mountain Fantail. 2ss. 14. Bougainville, Guadalcanal.
14. *Rhipidura euryura.* White bellied Fantail. 18. Java.
15. *Rhipidura fuliginosa.* Grey Fantail. 17ss. 16. N Guinea to Australia, N Zealand.
16. *Rhipidura phasiana.* Mangrove Fantail. 16. New Guinea.
17. *Rhipidura hyperythra.* Chestnut bellied Fantail. 4ss. 15. New Guinea, Aru.
18. *Rhipidura hypoxantha.* Yellow bellied Fantail. 13. S & SE Asia.
19. *Rhipidura javanica.* Pied Fantail. 3ss. 17. S E Asia, Philippines.
20. *Rhipidura lepida.* Palau Fantail. 18. Palau.
21. *Rhipidura leucophrys.* Willie Wagtail. 6ss. 21. Australia, New Guinea, Moluccas, Solomon Is.
22. *Rhipidura leucothorax.* White breasted Fantail. 2ss. 18. New Guinea.
23. *Rhipidura clamosa.* Karimui Fantail. 18. New Guinea.
24. *Rhipidura maculipectus.* Black thicket Fantail. 3ss. 19. New Guinea, Aru Is.
25. *Rhipidura malaitae.* Malaita Fantail. 15. Malaita Is.(Solomon Is.)
26. *Rhipidura nebulosa.* Samoan Fantail. 16. Western Samoa.
27. *Rhipidura nigrocinnamomea.* Black & Cinnamon Fantail. 2ss. 15. Mindanao.
28. *Rhipidura opistherythra.* Long tailed Fantail. 20. Tanimber Is.
29. *Rhipidura perlata.* Spotted Fantail. 17. Malaysia.
30. *Rhipidura personata.* Kandavu Fantail. 15. Kandavu.(Fiji).
31. *Rhipidura phoenicura.* Red tailed Fantail. 17. Java.
32. *Rhipidura rennelliana.* Rennell Fantail. 14. Solomon Is.
33. *Rhipidura rufidorsa.* Red backed / Grey breasted Fantail. 5ss. 13. W Papua, New Guinea.
34. *Rhipidura rufifrons.* Rufous Fantail. 32ss. 16. Australia & SW Pacific.
35. *Rhipidura squamata. Scaly breasted* Fantail. 15. Banda Is.
36. *Rhipidura rufiventris.* Northern Fantail. 26ss. 18. Timor & Papua to Australia.
37. *Rhipidura spilodera.* Streaked / Spotted Fantail. 6ss. 16. New Hebrides, New Caledonia, Fiji.
38. *Rhipidura superciliaris.* Blue Fantail. 3ss. 16. Philippines.
39. *Rhipidura superflua.* Tawny backed Fantail. 16. Buru.
40. *Rhipidura teysmanni.* Rusty bellied Fantail. 2ss. 18. Sulawesi.
41. *Rhipidura sulaensis.* Sula Fantail. 18. Sula Is.
42. *Rhipidura tenebrosa.* Dusky / Sombre Fantail. 16. Solomon Is.
43. *Rhipidura threnothorax.* Sooty Thicket Fantail. 4ss. 17. New Guinea & Is.
44. *Rhipidura kubaryi.* Pohnpei Fantail. 15. Pohnpei, Caroline Is.
45. *Rhipidura semirubra.* Manus Fantail. 15. Bismarck Archipelago.
46. *Rhipidura fuscorufa.* Cinnamon tailed Fantail. 18. Tanimbar.

1
2
3
4
5
6A
6B
7
10
8
9
11
12
13
14
15
16
17
18
19
20
21
22
24
25
23
26
27
28
29
30
35
31
32
33
34
36
37
39
38
41
40
42
43
44
45
46

MUSCICAPIDAE, PLATYSTEIRINAE
Puff back & Wattled Flycatchers

1. *Bias flammulatus*. African Shrike Flycatcher. 3ss. 17. E, W & C Africa.
2. *Pseudobias wardi*. Ward's Shrike Flycatcher. 15. Malagasy.
3. *Bias musicus*. Black & white Shrike Flycatcher. 5ss. 16. W, C & SE Africa.
4. *Batis capensis*. Cape Puffback. 5ss. 12. Mozambique, Zimbabwe, RSA.
5. *Batis diops*. Ruwenzori Puffback. 12. Zaire, Uganda.
6. *Batis fratrum*. Zululand Puffback. 12. Natal, Mozambique, Malawi.
7. *Batis margaritae*. Boulton's Puffback. 2ss. 10. Angola, Zambia.
8. *Batis dimorpha*. Malawi dimorphic Puffback. 2ss. 10. Malawi, Zambia, Mozambique.
9. *Batis minima*. Verreaux's Puffback. 2ss. 8. Gabon. (Only male known.)
10. *Batis minor*. Black headed Puffback. 4ss. 9. Cameroon to Angola, Somalia.
11. *Batis ituriensis*. Chapin's / Ituri Puffback. 8. Zaire.
12. *Batis minulla*. Angola Puffback. 9. Cameroon to Angola, Congo.
13. *Batis mixta*. Short tailed Puffback. 9. East Africa.
14. *Batis molitor*. Chinspot Puffback. 2ss. 12. E & S Africa.
15. *Batis occultus*. Lawson's Puffback. 8. Liberia, Ivory coast to Niger, Cameroon.
16. *Batis orientalis*. Grey headed Puffback. 3ss. 10. Nigeria, Chad to Eritrea.
17. *Batis perkeo*. Pygmy Puffback. 9. Ethiopia to Kenya.
18. *Batis poensis*. Fernando Po Puffback. 9. Fernando Po, Cameroon to Liberia.
19. *Batis pirit*. Pirit Puffback. 13. RSA, Namibia, Angola, Botswana.
20. *Batis senegalensis*. Senegal Puffback. 12. Senegal to Nigeria.
21. *Batis soror*. Pale Puffback. 10. E African coast, Kenya to Mozambique.
22. *Platysteira albifrons*. White fronted Wattle-eye. 10. SW Congo, N Angola.
23. *Platysteira blissetti*. Red cheeked Wattle-eye. 3ss. 9. Guinea to Cameroon.
24. *Platysteira jamesoni*. Jameson's Wattle-eye. 9. Zaire to Sudan & Kenya.
25. *Platysteira chalybea*. Reichenow's / Black necked Wattle-eye. 9. W Africa.
26. *Platysteira castanea*. Chestnut Wattle-eye. 2ss. 11. W Africa to Angola, Kenya.
27. *Platysteira concreta*. Yellow bellied Wattle-eye. 7ss. 11 W & C Africa.
28. *Platysteira cyanea*. Brown throated Wattle-eye. 3ss. 12. NE, C & W Africa.
29. *Platysteira peltata*. Black throated Wattle-eye. 3ss. 15. Coast Kenya to Natal.
30. *Platysteira tonsa*. White spotted Wattle-eye. 10. Fernando Po to Nigeria & Congo.
31. *Platysteira laticincta*. Bamenda / Banded Wattle-eye. 15. Cameroon.

1
2
3
4
5
6
7
10
15
11
12
8
13
-14-
9
16
17
18
19
20
21
22
23
24
25
26
27
30
31 ♀
28
29
31 ♂

MUSCICAPIDAE MONARCHINAE (1)
Monarch Flycatchers and Paradise Flycatchers

1. *Erythrocercus holochlorus*. Little yellow Flycatcher. 9. East Africa.
2. *Erythrocercus livingstonei*. Livingstone's Flycatcher. 3ss. 12. Tanzania to Mozambique.
3. *Erythrocercus mccallii*. Chestnut capped Flycatcher. 3ss. 10. West Africa.
4. *Elminia albicauda*. White tailed Blue Monarch. 17. Angola to Tanzania.
5. *Trochocercus albiventris*. White bellied crested Flycatcher. 2ss. 16. Uganda to Cameroon, Fernando Po.
6. *Trochocercus albonotatus*. White tailed crested Flycatcher. 3ss. 16. Kenya to Zimbabwe.
7. *Trochocercus cyanomelas*. Cape / African crested Flycatcher. 4ss. 18. Somalia to Natal.
8. *Elminia longicauda*. Blue Flycatcher. 3ss. 17. Sierra Leone to E & C Africa.
9. *Trochocercus nigromitratus*. Dusky crested Flycatcher. 15. Liberia to Uganda.
10. *Trochocercus nitens*. Blue headed crested Flycatcher. 2ss. 16. Nigeria to Angola, Uganda.
11. *Terpsiphone atrocaudata*. Japanese Paradise Flycatcher. 3ss. 44/17. Japan, China, Philippines.
12. *Terpsiphone atrochalybeia*. Sao Thome Farad Flycatcher. 26/17. Sao Thome.
13. *Terpsiphone batesi*. Bates' Farad Flycatcher. 20/17. Cameroon to Zaire.
14. *Terpsiphone bourbonniensis*. Mascarene Farad Flycatcher / Coq du bois. 25/17. Mauritius, Reunion.
15. *Terpsiphone cinnamomea*. Rufous Farad Flycatcher. 22/17. Philippines.
16. *Terpsiphone corvina*. Seychelles Farad Flycatcher. 35/18. La Digue Is.
17. *Terpsiphone cyanescens*. Blue Farad Flycatcher. 20/18. SW Philippines.
18. *Terpsiphone mutata*. Madagascar Farad Flycatcher, 6ss. 30/18. Malagasy. (also rufous phase.)
19. *Terpsiphone paradisi*. Asian Farad Flycatcher. 16ss. 36/18. S & SE Asia.
20. *Terpsiphone rufiventer*. Black headed Farad Flycatcher. 11ss. 34/18. W Africa.
21. *Terpsiphone rufocinerea*. Rufous vented Farad Flycatcher. 3ss. 27/18. W Africa.
22. *Terpsiphone bedfordi*. Bedford's Farad Flycatcher. 18. Zaire.
23. *Terpsiphone viridis*. African Farad Flycatcher. 11ss. 38/18. Sub-Saharan Africa.
24. *Terpsiphone unirufa*. Luzon Farad Flycatcher. 36/18. NC Philippines.
25. *Terpsiphone talautensis*. Talaud Farad Flycatcher. 25. Talaud Is.

Female Paradise Flycatchers are all slightly under 20 cm in length. Total length of males varies between approximately 20 & 40 cm. 19 & 23 (and perhaps some other) males have rufous & white phases.

1
2
3
4
5
6
7
8
9
10
23 –
12
20
13
21
18
14
25
17
-19-
(a)
(b)
11
16
24
15
22

MUSCICAPIDAE MONARCHINAE (2) Monarch Flycatchers

26. *Eutrichomyias rowleyi*. Cerulean Flycatcher. 20. Sangihe.
27. *Peltops blainvillii*. Lowland Peltops Flycatcher. 18. New Guinea.
28. *Peltops montanus*. Mountain Peltops Flycatcher. 20. New Guinea.
29. *Clytorhynchus hamlini*. Rennell Shrikebill. 20. Rennell Is., Solomons.
30. *Clytorhynchus nigrogularis*. Black throated Shrikebill. 2ss. 21. Fiji.
31. *Clytorhynchus pachycephaloides*. Southern Shrikebill. 2ss. 20. New Caledonia, New Hebrides.
32. *Clytorhynchus vitiensis*. Fiji / Uniform Shrikebill. 12ss. 19. Fiji, Tonga, Samoa.
33. *Metabolus rugiensis*. Truk Monarch. 20. Truk Is., Caroline Is.
34. *Myiagra albiventris*. White vented/Samoan Flycatcher. 13. Samoa.
35. *Myiagra atra*. Biak / Black Myiagra Flycatcher. 13. Numfor, Biak, New Guinea.
36. *Myiagra azureocapilla*. Blue headed Flycatcher. 3ss. 13. Fiji.
37. *Myiagra caledonica*. Melanesian Flycatcher. 6ss. 15. New Caledonia, Many Is.
38. *Myiagra cyanoleuca*. Satin Flycatcher. 4ss. 16. E Australia to New Guinea.
39. *Myiagra ferrocyanea*. Steel-blue Flycatcher. 6ss. 12. Solomon Is.
40. *Myiagra cervinicauda*. Ochre headed / Red tailed Flycatcher. 12. Solomon Is.
41. *Myiagra galeata*. Dark grey / Helmet Flycatcher. 4ss. 15. Moluccas, Kai Is.
42. *Myiagra inquieta*. Restless Flycatcher. 3ss. 21. Australia, New Guinea.
43. *Myiagra oceanica*. Micronesian Flycatcher. 4ss. 14. Truk.
44. *Myiagra erythrops*. Mangrove Flycatcher. 13. Palau.
45. *Myiagra freycineti*. Guam Flycatcher. 12. Guam.
46. *Myiagra pluto*. Pohnpei Flycatcher. 15. Ponape.
47. *Myiagra rubecula*. Leaden Flycatcher. 5ss. 16. NE Australia, New Guinea.
48. *Myiagra ruficollis*. Broad billed Flycatcher. 5ss. 16. Wallacea, New Guinea, N Australia.
49. *Myiagra vanikorensis*. Red bellied Flycatcher. 7ss. 13. Fiji, Santa Cruz.
50. *Myiagra alecto*. Shining Flycatcher. 11ss. 19. Australia, New Guinea, Moluccas.
51. *Myiagra hebetior*. Dull Flycatcher. 3ss. 16. St Matthias Is, Bismarck Archipelago.
52. *Hypothymis azurea*. Black naped Monarch. 24ss. 13. India, SE Asia, Wallacea, Philippines.
53. *Hypothymis puella*. Small blue / Pacific Monarch. 13. Sulawesi.
54. *Hypothymis coelestis*. Celestial blue Monarch. 2ss. 16. Philippines.
55. *Hypothymis helenae*. Short crested blue Monarch. 3ss. 14. Philippines.
56. *Philentoma pyrhoptera*. Chestnut winged Monarch. 2ss. 17. SE Asia.
57. *Philentoma velata*. Maroon breasted Monarch. 2ss. 20. Malaysia, Indonesia.
58. *Machaerirhynchus flaviventer*. Yellow breasted Boatbill Flycatcher. 6ss. 12. Queensland, New Guinea.
59. *Machaerirhynchus nigripectus*. Black breasted Flatbill Flycatcher. 3ss. 14. New Guinea.

Nos. 27 & 28 often placed in Cracticidae (Plate357.)

26
27
28
29
30
31
32
33
34
35
36
37
38
39
40
47
42
41
43
44
45
46
48
49
50
51
52
53
54
55
56
57
58
59

MUSCICAPIDAE MONARCHINAE (3)
Monarch Flycatchers

60. *Monarcha axillaris.* Black Monarch. 2ss. 16. New Guinea & Is.
61. *Monarcha barbatus.* Pied Monarch. 2ss. 15. Solomon Is.
62. *Monarcha browni.* Kulambangara Monarch. 4ss. 15. Solomon Is.
63. *Monarcha viduus.* San Cristobal / White collared Monarch. 2ss. 17. Solomon Is.
64. *Monarcha brehmii.* Biak Monarch. 17. Biak Is., NW New Guinea.
65. *Monarcha castaneiventris.* Chestnut bellied Monarch. 4ss. 17. Solomon Is.
66. *Monarcha erythrostictus.* Bougainville Monarch. 17. Solomon Is.
67. *Monarcha richardsii.* White capped Monarch. 17. Solomon Is
68. *Monarcha ugiensis.* Ugi Monarch. 17. Ugi, Solomon Is.
69. *Monarcha chrysomelas.* Black & yellow / Golden Monarch. 9ss. 13. New Guinea, Bismarck Archipelago.
70. *Monarcha cinerascans.* Island grey headed Monarch. 17ss. 18. Timor, New Guinea, Moluccas, Solomons.
71. *Monarcha frater.* Black winged Monarch. 4ss. 15. New Guinea, N Queensland.
72. *Monarcha godeffroyi.* Yap Monarch. 16. Yap Is. (Carolines).
73. *Monarcha guttatus.* Spot winged Monarch. 15. New Guinea, Aru.
74. *Monarcha infelix.* Manus Monarch. 2ss. 15. Admiralty Is, Bismarck Archipelago.
75. *Monarcha julianae.* Black backed Monarch. 16. Rofiau Is.
76. *Monarcha leucotis.* White eared Monarch. 4ss. 14. NE Australia.
77. *Monarcha pileatus.* Tufted / White naped Monarch. 14. Halmahera, N Moluccas.
78. *Monarcha castus.* Loetoe Monarch. 14. Tanimber Archipelago.
79. *Monarcha leucurus.* White tailed Monarch. 3ss. 15. Kai Is., Moluccas.
80. *Monarcha loricatus.* Black tipped Monarch. 15. Ruru, S Moluccas.
81. *Monarcha everetti.* White tipped Monarch. 15. Djampea Is., SW Wallacea.
82. *Monarcha manadensis.* Hooded / B1ack & white Monarch. 16. New Guinea.
83. *Monarcha melanopsis.* Black faced / Pearly winged Monarch. 17. NE Australia, W New Guinea.
84. *Monarcha menckei.* White breasted Monarch. 14. St Matthias Is, Bismarck.
85. *Monarcha mundus.* Black bibbed Monarch. 18. Tanimber Archipelago.
86. *Monarcha rubiensis.* Rufous Monarch. 18. New Guinea.
87. *Monarcha sacerdorum.* Mees' Monarch. 16. Flores, Lesser Sunda Is.
88. *Monarcha takatsukasae.* Tinian Monarch. 15. Tinian Is, Mariana Is.
89. *Monarcha trivirgatus.* Spectacled Monarch. 8ss. 16. Australia, New Guinea, Wallacea.
90. *Monarcha verticalis.* Black tailed / New Britain pied Monarch. 16. Bismarck Archipelago.
91. *Monarcha ateralbus.* Diaul Monarch. 16. Diaul Is.

91a. *Monarcha boanensis.* Black chinned Monarch. 15. Boano Is., S Moluccas.

92. *Arses kaupi.* Australian pied Flycatcher. 16. Queensland.
93. *Arses telescophthalmus.* Frilled Monarch. 2ss. 14. New Guinea, Queensland.
94. *Arses insularis.* Rufous collared Monarch. 6ss. 16. New Guinea, Japen.

60
61
62
63
64
65
66
67
68
69
70
72
71
73
74
75
76
77
78
79
-80-
81
82
83
84
85
86
87
88
90
91A
91
89
92
93
94

MUSCICAPIDAE, PACHYCEPHALINAE (1) Whistlers

1. *Eulacestoma nigropectus*. Wattled Ploughbill. 2ss. 13. New Guinea.
2. *Falcunculus frontatus*. Eastern crested Shrike Tit. 3ss. 19. E Australia.
3. incl. *F. f. leucogaster.* Western crested Shrike Tit. 18. W Australia.
4. *F. f. whitei.* Northern crested Shrike Tit. 16. N Australia.
5. *Oreoica gutturalis*. Crested Bellbird. 2ss. 23. Interior Australia.
6. *Pachycare flavogrisea*. Goldenface. 4ss. 13. New Guinea.
7. *Rhagologus leucostigma*. Mottled Whistler. 3ss. 16. New Guinea.
8. *Hylocitrea bonensis.* Buff throated / Olive flanked Thickhead / Whistler. 15. Sulawesi.
9. *Pachycephala aurea*. Yellow backed Whistler. 16. New Guinea.
10. *Pachycephala caledonica*. New Caledonian Whistler. 15. New Caledonia.
11. *Pachycephala grisola/cinerea*. Mangrove Whistler. 10ss. 16. S, SE Asia, Sundas.
12. *Pachycephala plateni.* Palawan Whistler. 16. SW Philippines.
13. *Pachycephala albiventris*. Green backed Whistler. 16. N, NC Philippines.
14. *Pachycephala homeyeri.* White vented Whistler. 16. C, S Philippines.
15. *Pachycephala flavifrons*. Yellow fronted Whistler. 17. Samoa.
16. *Pachycephala hyperythra*. Rusty / Rufous breasted Whistler. 4ss. 15. New Guinea.
17. *Pachycephala hypoxantha*. Bornean Whistler. 2ss. 16. Borneo.
18. *Pachycephala implicata*. Hooded mountain Whistler. 2ss. 16. Guadalcanal, Solomon Is.
19. *Pachycephala richardsi*. Bougainville Whistler. 16. Bougainville, Solomon Is.
20. *Pachycephala inornata*. Gilbert's Whistler. 2ss. 19. S Australia.
21. *Pachycephala lanioides*. White breasted Whistler. 4ss. 20. N Australia.
22. *Pachycephala lorentzi*. Lorentz's Whistler. 16. New Guinea.
23. *Pachycephala meyeri*. Vogelkop Whistler. 14. New Guinea.
24. *Pachycephala modesta*. Brown backed Whistler. 3ss. 14. New Guinea.
25. *Pachycephala schlegelii*. Regent Whistler. 3ss. 16. New Guinea & Is.
26. *Pachycephala olivacea*. Olive Whistler. 2ss. 20. SE Australia, Tasmania.
27. *Pachycephala griseonota*. Drab Whistler. 6ss. 15. Wallacea.
28. *Pachycephala arctitorquis*. Wallacean Whistler. 4ss. 14. Wallacea.

1
2
3
4
6
5
-7-
8
9
10
11
12
15
16
17
18
19
20
21
13
22
14
23
28
-27-
24
25
26

MUSCICAPIDAE, PACHYCEPHALINAE (2) Whistlers, Shrike Thrushes

29. *Pachycephala orpheus*. Fawn breasted Whistler. 2ss. 16. Timor,Wetar.
30. *Pachycephala pectoralis*. Golden Whistler. 67ss. 20. Java to Australia, Pacific Is.
31. *Pachycephala melanura*. Black tailed / Mangrove golden Whistler. 16. N Australia, New Guinea.
32. *Pachycephala melanops/jacquinoti*. Tongan Whistler. 22. Tonga.
33. *Pachycephala p. aurantiiventris*. Gold Whistler. 20. Fiji.
34. *Pachycephala p. teysmanni*. Saleyer Whistler. 22. Saleyer Is.
35. *Pachycephala p. torquata*. Ring necked Whistler. 16. Fiji.
36. *Pachycephala phaionota*. Island Whistler. 2ss. 16. Moluccas, Aru, New Guinea.
37. *Pachycephala philippinensis*. Yellow bellied Whistler. 7ss. 17. Philippines.
38. *Pachycephala / Coracornis raveni*. Maroon backed Whistler. 14. Sulawesi.
39. *Pachycephala / Aleadryas rufinucha*. Rufous naped Whistler. 5ss. 17. New Guinea.
40. *Pachycephala rufiventris*. Rufous Whistler. 8ss. 17. Australia, New Caledonia.
41. *Pachycephala leucogastra*. White bellied Whistler. 3ss. 15. New Guinea.
42. *Pachycephala monacha*. Black headed Whistler. 16. Aru Is., New Guinea.
43. *Pachycephala rufogularis*. Red lored Whistler. 20. SE Australia.
44. *Pachycephala tenebrosa*. = *Colluricincla umbrina*. Sooty Shrike Thrush / Whistler. 2ss. 18. New Guinea.
45. *Pachycephala simplex*. Brown Whistler. 11ss. 15. NE Australian coast.
46. incl. *P. s. griseiceps*. Grey Whistler. 15. New Guinea & Is.
47. *Pachycephala soror*. Sclater's Whistler. 4ss. 15. New Guinea.
48. *Pachycephala sulfuriventer*. Yellow bellied Whistler. 2ss. 17. Sulawesi.
49. *Pachycephala nudigula*. Bare throated Whistler. 2ss. 18. Sumbawa, Flores.

Females of 33, 34 & 36 resemble Female of 29.

29
30
31
33
36
34
37
32
35
38
39
40
43
47
42
45
46
44
41
48
49

MUSCICAPIDAE, PACHYCEPHALINAE (3)
Shrike Thrushes, Pitohuis

50. *Colluricincla boweri*. Bower's / Stripe breasted Shrike Thrush. 21. Queensland.
51. *Colluricincla brunnea*. Brown Shrike Thrush. 25. Northern Territory.
52. *Colluricincla harmonica*. Grey Shrike Thrush. 13ss. 25. Australia to New Guinea.
53. *Colluricincla megarhyncha*. Rufous Shrike Thrush. 30ss. 19. Sulawesi to Papua & Queensland.
54. incl. *C. m. Parvula*. Little Shrike Thrush. 19.NW Australian coasts.
55. *Colluricincla rufiventris*. Western Shrike Thrush. 24.WC Australia. (ss of 52).
56. *Colluricincla woodwardi*. Sandstone Shrike Thrush. 2ss. 26. N, NW Australia.
57. *Pitohui cristatus*. Crested Pitohui. 3ss. 25. New Guinea.
58. *Pitohui dichrous*. Black headed / Hooded Pitohui. 2ss. 23. New Guinea, Japen.
59. *Pitohui ferrugineus*. Rusty Pitohui. 6ss. 30. New Guinea & Is.
60. *Pitohui incertus*. Mottle / White bellied Pitohui. 22. New Guinea.

Pitohui Kirhocephalus. Variable Pitohui. 21 ss. Including below:

61. *P. k. kirhocephalus*. Grey hooded Pitohui. 19. NW New Guinea.
62. *P. k. cerviniventris*. Fawn breasted Pitohui. 20. Waigeu Is.
63. *P. k. uropygialis*. Rufous & Black Pitohui. 28. Salawoti, Misol Is.
64. *P. k. jobiensis*. Jobi Island Pitohui. 19.Kurudu, Japen Is.
65. *P. k. pallidus*. Buff hooded Pitohui. 19. Sagewin, Batanta Is.
66. *Pitohui nigrescens*. Black Pitohui. 6ss. 21. New Guinea.
67. *Pitohui/Colluricincla tenebrosus*. Morning Bird. 19. Palau Is.

Turnagra Capensis. New Zealand Thrush. 2ss. As below:

68. *T. c. turnagra*. North Island Piopio. 26. N.Island.NZ.
69. *T. c. capensis*. South Island Piopio. 26. S.Island.NZ.

50
51
52
53
54
55
56
57
58
59
60
62
63
64
65
61
66
67
68
69

AEGITHALIDAE
Long-tailed Tits, Pendline Tits,

1. *Aegithalos c. rosaceus*. Western Long tailed Tit. 14. British Isles.
2. *Aegithalos caudatus*. Northern Long tailed Tit. 19ss. 14. N.Palearctic.
3. *Aegithalos concinnus*. Black throated / Red headed Tit. 7ss. 10. E & SE Asia.
4. *Aegithalos fuliginosus*. Sooty / White necklaced Tit. 12. NW China.
5. *Aegithalos niveogularis*. White throated Tit. 10. Pakistan, Himalayas.
6. *Aegithalos iouschistos*. Blyth's / Black browed Tit. 4ss. 12. Himalayas, Burma, China.
7. *Aegithalos leucogenys*. White cheeked Tit. 10. Afghanistan to Baluchistan.
8. *Psaltria exilis*. Pygmy Tit. 8. Java.
9. *Psaltriparus minimus*. Common Bush Tit. 9ss. 9. W USA, Baja California.
10. *Psaltriparus melanotis*. Black eared Bush Tit. 4ss. 9. Texas to Guatemala.

Family 153. REMIZIDAE. Penduline Tits.

1. *Anthoscopus caroli*. African penduline Tit. 8ss. 8. E, C & S Africa.
2. *Anthoscopus sylviella*. Rungwe / Buff bellied penduline Tit 8. Kenya Tanzania.
3. *Anthoscopus flavifrons*. Yellow fronted / Forest Tit. 3ss. 9. W & C Africa.
4. *Anthoscopus minutus*. Southern Kapok / Cape Tit. 2ss. 8. Southern Africa.
5. *Anthoscopus musculus*. Mouse coloured Tit. 8. Ethiopia to Tanzania.
6. *Anthoscopus parvulus*. Yellow penduline Tit. 8. Senegal to Sudan.
7. *Anthoscopus punctifrons*. Sennar Kapok Tit. 8. Sahara to Eritrea.
8. *Remit pendulinus*. (Eurasian) penduline Tit. 6ss. 10. SE Europe to Siberia.
9. *Remit coronatus*. White crowned penduline Tit. 10. W & C Africa.
10. *Remit consobrinus*. Chinese penduline Tit. 10. Manchuria, N China, Korea.
11. *Auriparus flaviceps*. Verdin. 4ss. 9. SW USA, N Mexico.
12. *Cephalopyrus flammiceps*. Fire capped Tit. 2ss. 10. Kashmir to Szechwan.

Family 154. PARIDAE (1). Titmice, Chickadees.

1. *Parus afer*. Grey Tit. 5ss. 13. Ethiopia to Angola & Cape.
2. *Parus cinerascens*. Ashy Tit. 14. South Africa.
3. *Parus albiventris*. White bellied Tit. 14. Nigeria to Sudan & Tanzania.
4. *Parus amabilis*. Palawan Tit. 13. SW Philippines.
5. *Parus ater*. Coal Tit. 20ss. 11. Palearctic.
6. *Parus hyrcanus*. Iranian sombre Tit. 14. Iran, Azerbaijan.
7. *Parus guineensis*. White shouldered Black Tit. 12. W & C Africa.
8. *Parus pallidiventris*. Cinnamon breasted Tit. 14. SE Africa.
9. *Parus thruppi*. Somali Tit. 13. Somalia, E Africa.
10. *Parus atricapillus*. Black capped Chickadee. 7ss. 12. Canada, Eastern N USA.
11. *Parus bicolor*. Tufted Titmouse. 4ss. 14. E, C & SE USA.
12. *Parus atricristatus*. Black crested Tit. 12. Texas, Mexico.
13. *Parus bokharensis*. Turkestan Tit. 2ss. 15. Russia, Turkestan, Afghanistan.
14. *Parus caeruleus*. Blue Tit. 14ss. 11. Europe, SW Asia, N Africa, Canary Is.
15. *Parus carolinensis*. Carolina Chickadee. 5ss. 11. Southern USA.
16. *Parus carpi*. Carp's Black Tit. 14. Namibia, Angola.
17. *Parus cinctus*. Siberian Tit. 4ss. 14. N Europe, Siberia to Alaska, NW Canada.
18. *Parus cristatus*. Crested Tit. 6ss. 12. Pine forests Europe, Morocco, W Asia.
19. *Parus cyanus*. Azure Tit. 5ss. 13. Russia, Afghanistan, C Asia.
20. *Parus flavipectus*. Yellow breasted Tit. 2ss. 13. Iran to China.
21. Parus davidi. Rusty breasted / Pere David's Tit. 13. W China.
22. *Parus dichrous*. Grey / Brown crested Tit. 4ss. 12. Himalayas, Tibet, W China.
23. *Parus elegans*. Elegant Tit. 9ss. 12. Philippines.
24. *Parus fasciiventer*. Stripe breasted Tit. 3ss. 12. Rwanda, Zaire.
25. *Parus fringillinus*. Red throated Tit. 12. S Kenya, Tanzania.
26. *Parus funereus*. Dusky Tit. 2ss. 13. C Africa, Kenya to Cameroon & Angola.

AEGITHALIDAE
1
2
3
4
5
6
7
8
9
10
REMIZIDAE
1
2
3
4
5
6
10
8
7
11
9
12
PARIDAE
6
7
5
8
9
1
2
3
4
10
11
12
13
14
15
16
17
18
19
20
21
22
23
24
25
26

PARIDAE (2), SITTIDAE
Titmice, Chickadees, Nuthatches

27. *Parus gambeli.* Mountain Chickadee. 5ss. 11. West of N America.
28. *Parus griseiventris.* Northern Grey Tit. 13. Tanzania to Angola.
29. *Parus holsti.* (Formosan) Yellow Tit. 13. Taiwan.
30. *Parus hudsonicus.* Boreal Chickadee. 4ss. 11. Canada & N USA.
31. *Parus inornatus.* Plain Titmouse. 10ss. 13. SW USA, Baja California.
32. *Parus leucomelas.* (White winged) Black Tit. 4ss. 14. Africa S of Sahara.
33. *Parus leuconotus.* White backed Tit. 13. Eritrea, Ethiopia.
34. *Parus lugubris.* Sombre Tit. 7ss. 14. SE Europe to Iran.
35. *Parus major.* Great Tit. 31ss. 14. Europe, N Africa, Asia, Sunda Is.
36. *Parus melanolophus.* Spot winged Black crested Tit. 11. Afghanistan to Nepal.
37. *Parus montanus.* Willow Tit. 12. Palearctic.
38. *Parus monticolus.* Green backed Tit. 4ss. 13. Himalayas to China & Taiwan.
39. *Parus niger.* Southern Black Tit. 3ss. 15. S Africa to Zambia & Angola.
40. *Parus nuchalis.* White naped Tit. 13. WC & S India.
41. *Parus palustris.* Marsh Tit. 6ss. 12. Temperate Palearctic.
42. *Parus rubidiventris.* Red bellied Black crested Tit. 3ss. 12. W & C Asia.
43. *Parus rufescens.* Chestnut backed Chickadee. 3ss. 11. Alaska to California.
44. *Parus rufiventris.* Cinnamon breasted Tit. 3ss. 14. Tanzania to Zimbabwe, Congo.
45. *Parus rufonuchalis.* Rufous naped / Simla Black Tit. 13. N India, W & C Asia.
46. *Parus sclateri.* Mexican Chickadee. 3ss. 12. Mexico,SW USA.
47. *Parus semilarvatus.* White fronted Titmouse. 3ss. 14. Philippines.
48. *Parus superciliosus.* White browed Tit. 13. W China.
49. *Parus varius.* Varied Tit. 8ss. 13. Japan, Kurile Is., Korea, Manchuria.
50. *Parus castaneoventris.* Chestnut vented Tit. 11. Taiwan.
51. *Parus venustulus.* Yellow bellied Tit. 10. China.
52. *Parus wollweberi.* Bridled Titmouse. 3ss. 12. Mexico, SE USA.
53. *Parus xanthogenys.* Black lored yellow Tit. 3ss. 13. Himalayas, S China, N SE Asia.
54. *Parus spilonotus.* Chinese yellow cheeked Tit. 4ss. 14. Tibet, C & S China.
55. *Melanochlora sultanea.* Sultan Tit. 4ss. 20. Himalayas, China, SE Asia.
56. *Sylviparus modestus.* Yellow browed Tit. 3ss. 10. Himalayas, SE Asia.

Family 155. SITTIDAE. Nuthatches.

1. *Sitta azurea.* Azure / Blue Nuthatch. 3ss. 12. Malaysia, Sumatra, Java.
2. *Sitta canadensis.* Red breasted Nuthatch. 10. N America.
3. *Sitta carolinensis.* White breasted Nuthatch. 11ss. 12. N America, Mexico.
4. *Sitta castanea.* Chestnut breasted Nuthatch. 8ss. 13. Himalayas, India, SE Asia.
5. *Sitta europaea.* (Eurasian) Nuthatch. 20ss. 14. Palearctic.
6. *Sitta nagaensis.* Chestnut vented Nuthatch. 13. Scattered in Mountains of S Asia.
7. *Sitta cashmirensis.* Kashmir Nuthatch. 12. Kashmir to Baluchistan.
8. *Sitta formosa.* Beautiful Nuthatch. 17. Himalayas, N SE Asia.
9. *Sitta frontalis.* Velvet fronted Nuthatch. 10ss. 12. S SE Asia, Philippines, Sundas.
10. *Sitta solangiei.* Yellow billed / lilac Nuthatch. 2ss. 12. Vietnam.
11. *Sitta oenochlamys.* Sulphur billed Nuthatch. 12. Philippines.
12. *Sitta himalayensis.* White tailed Nuthatch. 2ss. 12. Himalayas, Yunnan, SE Asia.
13. *Sitta victoriae.* White browed Nuthatch. 12. Mt. Victoria, Burma.
14. *Sitta kruperi.* Krueper's Nuthatch. 12. Turkey to Caucasus.
15. *Sitta ledanti.* Algerian / Kabylie Nuthatch. 12. Algeria.
16. *Sitta. 1eucopsis.* White cheeked Nuthatch. 2ss. 11. Himalayas, W China.
17. *Sitta magna. Giant Nuthatch. 2ss. 20.* Yunnan, SE Asia.
18. *Sitta neumayer.* Western Rock Nuthatch. 5ss. 14. Greece, Turkey to Iran.
19. *Sitta pusilla.* Brown headed Nuthatch. 3ss. 9. SE USA, Bahamas.
20. *Sitta pygmaea.* Pygmy Nuthatch. 7ss. 9. W N America, Br. Colombia to Mexico.
21. *Sitta tephronota.* Eastern Rock Nuthatch. 3ss. 15. Iran to Kurdistan, Baluchistan.
22. *Sitta villosa.* Chinese / Snowy browed Nuthatch. 2ss. 10. China, Korea, Manchuria.
23. *Sitta whiteheadi.* Corsican Nuthatch. 12. Corsica.
24. *Sitta yunnanensis.* Yunnan Nuthatch. 11.Yunnan & E Sikang.

27
28
29
30
31
32
33
34
35
36
37
38
39
40
41
42
43
44
45
46
47
48
49
50
51
52
53
54
55
56
SITTIDAE
1
2
3
4
5
6
7
8
9
10
12
13
14
15
16
17
18
19
20
21
11
22
23
24

SITTIDAE, DAPHOENOSITTINAE, TICHADROMADINAE, CERTHIIDAE, RHABDORNITHIDAE, CLIMACTERIDAE Australian Nuthatches, Wall Creepers, Tree Creepers, Phillipaine Creepers, Australian Wall Creepers

Family SITTIDAE. Sub-family 156. DAPHOENOSITTINAE. Australian Nuthatches.

1. *Daphoenositta chrysoptera.* Varied Sitella. 10ss. 12. SE Australia.
2. incl. *D. c. striata.* Striated Sitella. 12. NE Australia.
3. *D. c. pileata.* Black capped Sitella. 12. S Australia.
4. *D. c. 1eucoptera.* White winged Sitella. 12. N Australia.
5. *D. c. 1eucocephala.* White headed Sitella. 12. E Australia.
6. *Daphoenositta papuensis.* Papuan Sitella. 6ss. 11. Papua New Guinea.
7. *Daphoenositta miranda.* Black Sitella/Pink faced Nuthatch. 3ss. 12. Papua NG.

Sub-family 157. TICHADROMADINAE. Wallcreeper.

1. *Tichodroma muraria.* Wallcreeper. 2ss. 16. CS Europe to S China, Mongolia.

Family 158. CERTHIIDAE. Tree Creepers.

1. *Certhia brachydactyla.* Short toed Tree Creeper. 13. CS Europe, N Africa, SW Asia.
2. *Certhia discolor.* Brown throated Tree Creeper. 5ss. 16. Himalayas to SE Asia.
3. *Certhia familiaris.* Common Tree Creeper. 25ss. 13. Eurasia, Britain to Japan.
4. *Certhia americana.* American Creeper. 16ss. 13. N.America S to Nicaragua.
5. *Certhia himalayana.* Bar tailed Tree Creeper. 6ss. 13. Afghanistan to China.
6. *Certhia nipalensis.* Rusty flanked Tree Creeper. 13. Nepal to Tibet & Burma.
7. *Salpornis spilonotus.* Spotted Creeper. 6ss. 15. EC Africa, NC India.

Family 159. RHABDORNITHIDAE. Philippine Creepers.

1. *Rhabdornis inornatus.* Plain headed / Stripe breasted Creeper. 6ss. 16. Philippines.
2. *Rhabdornis mysticalis.* Stripe headed / sided Creeper. 2ss. 14. Philippines.
3. *Rhabdornis grandis.* Long billed Creeper. 18. N Philippines.

Family 160. CLIMACTERIDAE. Australian Tree Creepers.

1. *Climacteris affinis.* White browed Tree Creeper. 2ss. 14. Australia.
2. *Climacteris erythrops.* Red browed Tree Creeper. 2ss. 14. E Australia.
3. *Climacteris leucophaea.* White throated Tree Creeper. 3ss. 17. E, SE Australia.
4. incl. *C. l. minor.* Little Tree Creeper. 14. Queensland.
5. *Climacteris placens.* Papuan Tree Creeper. 4ss. 14. New Guinea.
6. *Climacteris melanura.* Black tailed Tree Creeper. 2ss. 18. N, W Australia.
7. incl. *C. m. wellsi.* Allied / Southern black tailed Tree Creeper. 18. C, SW Australia.
8. *Climacteris picumnus.* Brown Tree Creeper. 2ss. 17. E, SE Australia.
9. incl. *C. p. melanota.* Black Tree Creeper. 16. NE Australia.
10. *Climacteris rufa.* Rufous Tree Creeper. 16. SW Australia.

1
2
3
4
5
6
7
TICHADROMADINAE
1
Br
NB
CERTHIIDAE
1
2
3
4
5
6
7
RHABDORNITHIDAE
3
1
2
CLIMACTERIDAE
1
2
3
4
5
6
7
8
9
10

DICAEIDAE (1)
Flowerpeckers

1. *Melanocharis striativentris*. Streaked Berrypecker. 4ss. 13. New Guinea.
2. *Melanocharis longicauda*. Lemon breasted Berrypecker. 5ss. 13. New Guinea.
3. *Melanocharis nigra*. Black Berrypecker. 4ss. 11. New Guinea & Is.
4. *Melanocharis arfakiana*. Obscure Berrypecker. 11. New Guinea.
5. *Melanocharis versteri*. Fan tailed Berrypecker. 4ss. 15. New Guinea.
6. *Ramphocharis(Melanocharis)crassirostris*. Spotted Berrypecker. 3ss. 11. N Guinea.
7. *Prionochilus maculatus*. Yellow breasted Flowerpecker. 4ss. 9. Burma, Malaya, Indonesia.
8. *Prionochilus olivaceus*. Olive backed Flowerpecker. 3ss. 9. Philippines.
9. *Prionochilus percussus*. Crimson breasted Flowerpecker. 3ss. 10. SE Asia, Indonesia.
10. *Prionochilus plateni (syn. P. johannae)*. Palawan yellow rumped Flowerpecker. 10. Palawan & adjacent Is.
11. *Prionochilus thoracicus*. Scarlet breasted Flowerpecker. 10. Malaya Borneo.
12. *Prionochilus xanthopygius*. Borneo yellow rumped Flowerpecker. 9. Borneo.
13. *Dicaeum aeruginosum*. Striped / Fairy Flowerpecker. 3ss. 10. Palawan.
14. *Dicaeum aeneum*. Midget Flowerpecker. 3ss. 8. Soloinon Is.
15. *Dicaeum erythrothorax*. Reddish / Flame breasted Flowerpecker. 2ss.9. Moluccas.
16. *Dicaeum eximium*. Red banded / Beautiful Flowerpecker.3ss. 9. New Ireland & Bismarck Archipelago.
17. *Dicaeum nehrkorni*. Crimson crowned Flowerpecker. 9. Sulawesi.
18. *Dicaeum pectorale*. Olive crowned Flowerpecker. 2ss. 9. New Guinea & Is.
19. *Dicaeum geelvinkianum*. Red capped Flowerpecker. 11ss. 9. Japen & New Guinea Is.
20. *Dicaeum nitidum*. Louisiade Flowerpecker. 2ss. 9. Louisiade Archipelago.
21. *Dicaeum vulneratum*. Ashy Flowerpecker. 9. Ceram & other Moluccan Is.
22. *Dicaeum agile*. Thick billed Flowerpecker. 9ss. 10. India, SE Asia, Indonesia.
23. *Dicaeum obsoletum*. Timor Flowerpecker. 9. Timor.
24. *Dicaeum annae*. Golden rumped Flowerpecker. 2ss. 9. Sumbawa, Flores.
25. *Dicaeum anthonyi*. Flame crowned Flowerpecker. 3ss. 9. Philippines.
26. *Dicaeum aureolimbatum*. Yellow sided Flowerpecker. 2ss. 9. Sulawesi.
27. *Dicaeum australe*. Red striped Flowerpecker. 2ss. 9. Philippines.
28. *Dicaeum bicolor*. Bicoloured Flowerpecker. 3ss. 9. Philippines.

1
2
3
4
5
6
7
8
11
10
9
12
13
14
15
16
17
18
19
20
21
22
23
24
25
26
27
28

DICAEIDAE (12)
Flowerpeckers, Pardalotes

29. *Dicaeum celebicum.* Black sided Flowerpecker. 5ss. 8. Sulawesi & Is.
30. *Dicaeum hirundinaceum.* Mistletoe Bird. 4ss. 10. Australia, Aru & other Is.
31. *Dicaeum ignipectus.* Fire breasted Flowerpecker. 12ss. 9. S, SE Asia. Philippines.
32. *Dicaeum monticolum.* Black sided Flowerpecker. 9. Borneo.
33. *Dicaeum sanguinolentum.* Blood breasted Flowerpecker. 7. Java, Flores, Timor.
34. incl. *D. s. wilhelminae.* Wilhelmina's Flowerpecker. 7. Sumba.
35. *Dicaeum chrysorrheum.* Yellow vented Flowerpecker. 2ss. 10. S, SE Asia.
36. *Dicaeum concolor.* Plain Flowerpecker. 7ss. 9. India, China, Andamans, Indonesia
37. *Dicaeum cruentatum.* Scarlet backed Flowerpecker. 8ss. 9. China, S, SE Asia.
38. *Dicaeum erythrorhynchos.* Tickell's / Pale billed Flowerpecker.2ss. 9. S Asia.
39. *Dicaeum everetti.* Brown backed Flowerpecker. 3ss. 10. Borneo, Malaya.
40. *Dicaeum hypoleucum.* White bellied Flowerpecker. 4ss. 9. Philippines.
41. *Dicaeum igniferum.* Black fronted Flowerpecker. 2ss. 9. Sumbawa, Flores & Is.
42. *Dicaeum maugei.* Blue cheeked / Red chested Flowerpecker. 5ss. 9. Timor, Is.
43. *Dicaeum melanoxanthum.* Yellow bellied Flowerpecker. 12. Nepal, S Asia.
44. *Dicaeum nigrilore.* Olive capped Flowerpecker. 9. Mindanao.
45. *Dicaeum proprium.* Whiskered / Grey breasted Flowerpecker. 9. Mindanao.
46. *Dicaeum pygmaeum.* Pygmy Flowerpecker. 4ss. 8. Philippines.
47. *Dicaeum quadricolor.* Four coloured Flowerpecker. 9. Cebu. (extinct).
48. *Dicaeum retrocinctum.* Scarlet collared Flowerpecker. 9. Mindoro.
49. *Dicaeum trigonostigma.* Orange bellied Flowerpecker. 16ss. 9. S SE Asia, Philippines.
50. *Dicaeum tristrami.* Mottled Flowerpecker. 9. San Cristobal.
51. *Dicaeum trochileum.* Scarlet headed Flowerpecker. 2ss. 8. Java, Borneo & Islands.
52. *Dicaeum vincens.* Legge's / White throated Flowerpecker. 9. Sri Lanka.
53. *Oreocharis arfaki.* Tit Berrypecker. 11. New Guinea.
54. *Paramythia montium.* Crested Berrypecker. 3ss. 20. New Guinea.
55. *Pardalotus melanocephalus.* Black headed Pardalote. 6ss. 11. Australia.
56. *Pardalotus ornatus.* Red tipped Pardalote. 11. SE Australia.
57. *Pardalotus punctatus.* Spotted Pardalote. 9. SE Australia, Tasmania.
58. *Pardalotus quadragintus.* Forty spotted Pardalote. 9. Tasmania, King Is.
59. *Pardalotus rubricatus.* Red browed Pardalote. 4ss. 12. Australia.
60. *Pardalotus striatus.* Yellow tipped Pardalote. 11. SE Australia, Tasmania.
61. *Pardalotus substriatus.* Striated Pardalote. 11. Non-tropical Australia..
62. *Pardalotus xanthopygus.* Yellow tailed Pardalote. 9. SE, S & SW Australia.

Nos. 53 & 54 are sometimes thought to belong to Family 121.(Bulbuls).

29
32
30
31
33
34
35
36
37
38
39
40
41
42
43
44
45
46
47
48
49
50
51
52
53
54
55
56
58
57
59
60
61
62

NECTARINIIDAE (1)
Sunbirds

1. *Anthreptes anchietae*. Anchieta's Sunbird. 10. C Africa, Tanzania to Angola.
2. *Anthreptes aurantium*. Violet tailed Sunbird. 12. Nigeria to Angola, Huru Forest.
3. *Anthreptes collaris*. Collared Sunbird. 13ss. 10. Most of Africa S of Sahara.
4. *Anthreptes fraseri*. Scarlet tufted Sunbird. 4ss. 13. W & WC Africa.
5. incl. *A. f. axillaris*. Grey headed Sunbird. 12. E Congo to Uganda.
6. *Anthreptes gabonicus*. Mouse brown Sunbird. 12. W Africa, Gambia to Congo.
7. *Anthreptes longuemarei*. Western Violet backed Sunbird. 4ss. 13. W, E & C Africa
8. *Anthreptes malacensis*. Plain / Brown throated Sunbird. 17ss. 14. SE Asia, Philippines, Wallacea.
9. *Anthreptes metallicus*. Nile Valley Sunbird. 18/9. SW Arabia, NE Africa.
10. *Anthreptes neglectus*. Uluguru violet backed Sunbird. 13. Kenya to Mozambique.
11. *Anthreptes orientalis*. Eastern violet backed Sunbird. 2ss. 12. Sudan, Somalia, Ethiopia, Tanzania.
12. *Anthreptes pallidigaster*. Amani Sunbird. 8. Kenya, Tanzania.
13. *Anthreptes platurus*. Pygmy Sunbird. 18/8. Senegal to NW Kenya.
14. *Anthreptes pujoli*. Berlioz' s Sunbird. 8. W Africa.(single male. valid spec.?)
15. *Anthreptes rectirostris*. Yellow chinned green Sunbird. 2ss. 11. W Africa.
16. incl. *A. r. tephrolaema*. Grey chinned green Sunbird. 11. W & WC Africa.
17. *Anthreptes reichenowi*. Plain backed Sunbird. 2ss. 10. Kenya to Mozambique, Zimbabwe.
18. *Anthreptes rhodolaema*. Shelley's / Red throated Sunbird. 12. Burma, SE Asia, Indonesia.
19. *Anthreptes rubritorques*. Banded green Sunbird. 9. NE Tanzania.
20. *Anthreptes simplex*. Plain Sunbird. 12. Burma, Malaysia, Indonesia & Is.
21. *Anthreptes singalensis*. Ruby cheeked Sunbird. 11ss. 11. S & SE Asia.
22. *Hypogramma hypogrammicum*. Blue / Purple naped Sunbird. 5ss. 15. SE Asia, Indonesia.
23. *Nectarinia adelberti*. Buff throated Sunbird. 2ss. 10. Sierra Leone to Nigeria.
24. *Nectarinia alinae*. Blue headed Sunbird. 2ss. 12. Uganda, Zaire.
25. *Nectarinia stuhlmanni*. Stuhlmann's double collared Sunbird. 7ss. 14. Uganda.
26. *Nectarinia prigoginei*. Prigogine's double collared Sunbird. 14. Zaire.
27. *Nectarinia amethystina*. Amethyst Sunbird. 6ss. 13. Somalia to Cape & Angola.
28. *Nectarinia asiatica*. Purple Sunbird. 3ss. 11. Oman, Iran to Thailand, Indo-China.
29. *Nectarinia ludovicensis*. Montane double collared Sunbird. 13. Angola.
30. *Nectarinia afra*. Greater double collared Sunbird. 6ss. 14. Uganda to S Africa.

Note. Relationship between the various double collared Sunbirds, i.e. nos. 25, 26, 29, 30, 41, 42, 67, 80 and 94, is rather obscure.

1
2
3
4
5
6
7
8
9
10
11
12
13
NB
13 Br
14
15
16
17
18
19
20
21
22
23
24
25
26
NB
27
28 Br
29
30
NB

NECTARINIIDAE (2)
Sunbirds

31. *Nectarinia balfouri*. Socotra Sunbird. 15. Socotra I.
32. *Nectarinia bannermani*. Bannerman's Sunbird. 14. Angola, Zambia, Congo.
33. *Nectarinia batesi*. Bates' olive Sunbird. 11. West Africa to Zambia.
34. *Nectarinia bifasciata*. (Little) Purple banded Sunbird. 3ss. 11. E, C & SE Africa.
35. *Nectarinia bocagii*. Bocage's Sunbird. 23/13. Angola, Congo.
36. *Nectarinia bouvieri*. Orange tufted Sunbird. 10. EC & WC Africa.
37. *Nectarinia buettikoferi*. Apricot breasted Sunbird. 12. Sumba.
38. Nectarinia solaris. Flame breasted Sunbird. 3ss. 13. Timor & Lesser Sundas.
39. *Nectarinia chalcomelas*. Violet breasted Sunbird. 12. Somali & Kenya coast.
40. *Nectarinia calcostetha*. Macklot's / Copper throated Sunbird. 13. Indo China, SE Asia, Indonesia, Philippines.
41. *Nectarinia chalybea*. Southern / Lesser double collared Sunbird. 6ss. 12. Southern Africa N to Congo, Tanzania.
42. *Nectarinia manoensis*. Miombo double collared Sunbird. 13. SE Africa.
43. *Nectarinia chloropygia*. Olive bellied Sunbird. 6ss. 13. E & W Africa.
44. *Nectarinia coccinigaster*. Splendid Sunbird. 15. E, C & W Africa.
45. *Nectarinia comorensis*. Anjouan Sunbird. 12. Anjouan forest, Comoro Is.
46. *Nectarinia congensis*. (Congo) Black bellied Sunbird. 24/14. Upper Congo.
47. *Nectarinia coquerelli*. (Mayotte) Yellow bellied Sunbird. 11. Mayotte, Comoros.
48. *Nectarinia cuprea*. Coppery Sunbird. 2ss. 11. W, C & E Africa.
49. *Nectarinia cyanolaema*. Blue throated brown Sunbird. 3ss. 13. W & C Africa.
50. *Nectarinia dussumieri*. Seychelles Sunbird. 15. Seychelles.
51. *Nectarinia erythrocerca*. Red chested Sunbird. 14/11. Sudan to Tanzania.
52. *Nectarinia famosa*. Malachite Sunbird. 3ss. 24/14. E Africa, Sudan to Cape.
53. *Nectarinia fuliginosa*. Carmelite Sunbird. 2ss. 15. W Africa, Liberia to Angola
54. *Nectarinia fusca*. Dusky Sunbird. 2ss. 12/10. Angola to Cape.
55. *Nectarinia habessinica*. Shining Sunbird. 5ss. 13. Arabia, East Africa.
56. *Nectarinia hartlaubi*. Principe Sunbird. 14/13. Principe.
57. *Nectarinia humbloti*. Humblot's Sunbird. 2ss. 11. Gr. Comoro, Mobeli.
58. *Nectarinia hunteri*. Hunter's Sunbird. 14. Somalia, Kenya, Tanzania.

31
32
33
34
NB
35
36
37
38
40
41
39
42
44
43
45
46
48
Br
NB
47
50
49
52
Br
51
NB
53
Br
NB
54
Br
NB
55
56
57
58

NECTARINIIDAE (3)
Sunbirds

59. *Nectarinia johannae.* Mme Johanna Verreaux's Sunbird. 2ss. 14. W Africa.
60. *Nectarinia johnstoni.* Red tufted malachite Sunbird. 3ss. 25/15. EC Africa.
61. *Nectarinia jugularis.* Olive backed Sunbird. 25ss. 11. S Asia to Solomon Is.
62. incl. *N. j. frenata.* Yellow breasted Sunbird. 11. New Guinea, Queensland & Islands.
63. *Nectarinia kilimensis.* Bronze Sunbird. 3ss. 21/14. E & C Africa.
64. *Nectarinia lotenia.* Long billed Sunbird. 2ss. 13. Indian peninsula, Sri Lanka.
65. *Nectarinia loveridgei.* Loveridge's Sunbird. 11. Mountains of Tanzania.
66. *Nectarinia mariquensis.* Mariqua Sunbird. 4ss. 14. Ethiopia to Namibia, Natal.
67. *Nectarinia mediocris.* Eastern double collared Sunbird. 4ss.10. East Africa from Kenya to Mozambique.
68. *Nectarinia minima.* Small Sunbird. 8. W India, Sri Lanka.
69. *Nectarinia minulla.* Tiny Sunbird. 2ss. 9. Fernando Po, West Africa.
70. *Nectarinia moreaui.* Moreau's Sunbird. 11. CE Tanzania.
71. *Nectarinia nectarinoides.* Smaller Black bellied Sunbird. 11/9. East Africa.
72. *Nectarinia neergardi.* Neergard's Sunbird. 10. Coast Mozambique, Zululand.
73. *Nectarinia newtonii.* Sao Thome Yellow breasted Sunbird. 12. Sao Thome.
74. *Nectarinia notata.* Long billed green Sunbird. 3ss. 15. Malagasy, Gr.Comoro.
75. *Nectarinia olivacea.* Olive Sunbird. 13ss. 14. Africa .
76. *Nectarinia oritis.* Cameroon Blue headed Sunbird. 3ss. 13. Fernando Po, Cameroon.
77. *Nectarinia osea.* Palestine Sunbird. 2ss. 10. Palestine to E Africa.
78. *Nectarinia oustaleti.* Oustalet's white bellied Sunbird. 12. Angola, Zambia.
79. *Nectarinia pembae.* Violet breasted Sunbird. 2ss. 12. Pemba Is, E Kenya.
80. *Nectarinia preussi.* Northern double collared Sunbird. 3ss. 9. W & E Africa.
81. *Nectarinia pulchella.* Beautiful Sunbird. 4ss. 15/12. Senegal to Ethiopia, Tanzania.
82. incl. *N. p. melanogastra.* Black bellied Sunbird. 15/12. Tanzania, SE Kenya.

59
-60- Br
NB
61
62
63
64
65
66
67
68
69
70
71
72
73
74
75
-76- Br
NB
-77-
Br
NB
Br
-78-
NB
81
82
Br
NB
79
80

NECTARINIIDAE (4) Sunbirds

83. *Nectarinia purpureiventris.* Purple breasted Sunbird. 24/15. Zaire, Uganda.
84. *Nectarinia regia.* Regal Sunbird. 3ss. 11. Mountains of C Africa.
85. *Nectarinia reichenbachii.* Reichenbach's Sunbird. 13/12. Ghana to Congo.
86. *Nectarinia reichenowi.* Golden winged Sunbird. 3ss. 22/15. Mountains E Africa, Congo.
87. *Nectarinia rockefelleri.* Rockefeller's Sunbird. 11. Zaire.
88. *Nectarinia rufipennis.* Rufous winged Sunbird. 11. Tanzania.
89. *Nectarinia rubescens.* Green throated Sunbird. 3ss. 13/12. E C & W Africa.
90. *Nectarinia seimundi.* Little green Sunbird. 3ss. 9. W Africa to Angola, Uganda.
91. *Nectarinia senegalensis.* Scarlet chested Sunbird. 7ss. 15. Africa S of Sahara.
92. *Nectarinia aspasia/sericea.* Black Sunbird. 24ss. 11. Wallacea, New Guinea, Bismarck Arch.
93. incl. *Nectarinia sangirensis.* Sangihe Black Sunbird. 11. Sangihe Is.
94. *Nectarinia shelleyi.* Shelley's (double collared) Sunbird. 2ss. 13. E SE Africa.
95. *Nectarinia sovimanga.* Souimanga Sunbird. 5ss. 11. Malagasy, Aldabra.
96. *Nectarinia sperata.* Van Hasselt's / Purple throated Sunbird. 12ss. 10. Bangladesh, SE Asia, Sundas, Philippines.
97. *Nectarinia superba.* Superb Sunbird 4ss. 14. W & C Africa.
98. *Nectarinia tacazze.* Tacazze Sunbird. 2ss. 23/14. Ethiopia to Kenya, Tanzania.
99. *Nectarinia talatala.* White bellied Sunbird. 11. Angola to Natal, Tanzania.
100. *Nectarinia thomensis.* Sao Thome Giant Sunbird. 21/18. Sao Thome.
101. *Nectarinia tsavoensis.* Tsavo purple banded Sunbird. 10. Kenya, Tanzania.
102. *Nectarinia ursulae.* Ursula's Sunbird. 10. Fernando Po, Cameroon.
103. *Nectarinia venusta falkensteini.* Variable (Yellow bellied) Sunbird. 10. E Africa.
104. *Nectarinia venusta igneiventris.* Variable (Orange bellied) Sunbird. 10. C Africa.
105. *Nectarinia venusta venusta.* Variable (White bellied) Sunbird. 6ss. 10. W Africa.
106. *Nectarinia veroxii.* Mouse coloured Sunbird. 3ss. 12. Natal, Cape.
107. incl. *N. v. fischeri.* Northern Grey Sunbird. 12. Somalia to Mozambique.
108. *Nectarinia verticalis.* Green headed Sunbird. 4ss. 14. W & C Africa.
109. *Nectarinia violacea.* Orange breasted Sunbird. 15/12. Cape province, RSA.

83
Br
NB
84
85
86
Br
86
NB
90
87
88
89
91
92
93
94
95
96
97
98 Br
NB
99
Br
NB
100
101
102
103
104
105
106
107
108
109
NB

NECTARINIIDAE (5)
Sunbirds

110. *Nectarinia zeylonica*. Purple rumped Sunbird. 3ss. 11. India, Bangladesh, Sri Lanka.
111. *Aethopyga boltoni*. Apo Sunbird. 2ss. 11. Mindanao.
112. *Aethopyga Christinae*. Fork tailed Sunbird. 2ss. 10. S China, Vietnam, Hainan.
113. *Aethopyga duyveenbodei*. Elegant / Yellow backed Sunbird. 11. Sangihe Is.
114. *Aethopyga eximia*. Kuhl's / White flanked Sunbird. 13. Java.
115. *Aethopyga flagrans*. Flaming Sunbird. 4ss. 10. Philippines.
116. *Aethopyga gouldiae*. Mrs Gould's Sunbird. 4ss. 11. W China, N SE Asia.
117. *Aethopyga ignicauda*. Fire tailed Sunbird. 11. Himalayas, Burma, Sikang, Yunnan.
118. *Aethopyga mysticalis*. Scarlet Sunbird. 2ss. 10. Malaya, Sumatra, Borneo, Java.
119. *Aethopyga nipalensis*. Green tailed Sunbird. 9ss. 11. Himalayas, Yunnan, N SE Asia.
120. *Aethopyga primigenius*. Hachisuka's / Grey hooded Sunbird. 11. Mindanao.
121. *Aethopyga pulcherrima*. Metallic winged / Mountain Sunbird. 3ss. 10. Philippines.
122. *Aethopyga saturata*. Black throated Sunbird. 11ss. 11. Himalayas, Yunnan, S E Asia.
123. *Aethopyga shelleyi*. Lovely / Palawan Sunbird. 6ss. 11. Sulu Archipelago, Philippines.
124. *Aethopyga siparaja*. Yellow backed / Crimson Sunbird. 16ss.11. Himalayas, India, SE Asia, Indonesia.
125. *Arachnothera affinis*. Grey breasted Spiderhunter. 5ss. 17. SE Asia.
126. *Arachnothera chrysogenys*. Yellow eared Spiderhunter. 2ss. 17. SE Asia.
127. *Arachnothera clarae*. Naked faced Spiderhunter. 4ss. 19. Philippines.
128. incl. *A. c. philippinensis*. Philippine Spiderhunter. 19. Samar, Leyte Is.
129. *Arachnothera crassirostris*. Thick billed Spiderhunter. 16. Malaysia, Borneo, Sumatra.
130. *Arachnothera everetti*. Everett's / Bornean Spiderhunter. 17. N & C Borneo.
131. *Arachnothera flavigaster*. Greater Yellow eared / Spectacled Spiderhunter. 21. Malaya, Sumatra, Borneo.
132. *Arachnothera juliae*. Whitehead's Spiderhunter. 18. North Borneo.
133. *Arachnothera longirostra*. Little Spiderhunter. 12ss. 16. Himalayas to SE Asia & Philippines.
134. *Arachnothera magna*. Streaked Spiderhunter. 5ss. 19. India, Yunnan, N SE Asia.
135. *Arachnothera robusta*. Long billed Spiderhunter. 2ss. 21. Malaya, Indonesia.

110
111
112
113
114
115
116
117
118
119
120
124
121
122
123
125
126
127
128
129
130
131
132
133
134
135

Plate 295 Family 163.

ZOSTEROPIDAE (1)
White eyes

1. *Zosterops erythropleurus.* Chestnut flanked White eye. 11. E & S Asia.
2. *Zosterops japonicas.* Japanese White eye. 9ss. 11. Japan, E Asia to Philippines.
3. *Zosterops meyeni.* Lowland White eye. 2ss. 11. Philippines.
4. *Zosterops palpebrosus.* Oriental White eye. 13ss. 11. China, Philippines, SE Asia.
5. *Zosterops siamensis.* Yellow bellied White eye. 11. Thailand, SE Asia.
6. *Zosterops ceylonensis.* Large Sri Lanka White eye. 11. Sri Lanka.
7. *Zosterops conspicillatus.* Bridled White eye. 7ss. 10. Mariana Is., Caroline Is.

7a. *Zosterops semperi.* Caroline Is. White eye. 10. Palau.

8. *Zosterops salvadorii.* Enggano White eye. 11. Enggano Is. (Sumatra)

8a. *Zosterops finschii.* Dusky White eye. 10. Palau.

9. *Zosterops atricapillus.* Black capped White eye. 2ss. 10. Sumatra, Borneo.
10. *Zosterops everetti.* Everett's White eye. 8ss. 11. Philippines, Malaysia.
11. incl. *Z. e. tahanensis/parvus.* Small White eye. 11. Thailand, Malaysia, Borneo.
12. *Zosterops nigrorum.* Philippine Yellow eye. 5ss. 10. Philippines.
13. *Zosterops montanus.* Mountain White eye. 8ss. 10. Various Is. From Philippines to Moluccas.

13a. *Zostcrops hypolais.* Plain White eye. 11. NW Caroline Is.

14. *Zosterops wallacei.* Yellow spectacled White eye. 11. Flores & other Is.
15. *Zosterops flavus.* Javan White eye. 10. Java, Borneo.
16. *Zosterops chloris.* Lemon bellied White eye. Moluccan Is.
17. *Zosterops albiventris.* White bellied White eye. 11. Moluccas to Torres Straits.
18. *Zosterops citrinellus.* Pale Silver eye. 11. Islands, Queensland to Indonesia.

18a. *Zosterops tephropleurus.* Lord Howe Island White eye. 10. Lord Howe Island.

19. *Zosterops consobrinorum.* Pale bellied White eye. 10. Sulawesi.
20. *Zosterops grayi.* Pearl bellied White eye. 12. Great Kei Island.
21. *Zosterops uropygialis.* Golden bellied White eye. 11. 1ittle Kei Island.
22. *Zosterops anomalus.* Lemon throated White eye. 11. Sulawesi.
23. *Zosterops atriceps.* Creamy throated White eye. 3ss. 11. Moluccas, New Guinea.
24. *Zosterops atrifrons.* Black crowned White eye. 5ss. 11. Sulawesi to New Guinea.
25. *Zosterops minor.* Black fronted White eye. 7ss. 10. New Guinea.
26. *Zosterops meeki.* White throated White eye. 4ss. 11. New Britain.
27. *Zosterops hypoxanthus.* Black headed White eye. 11. Bismarck Archipelago.
28. *Zosterops mysorensis.* Biak white eye. 11. Biak Is.
29. *Zosterops fuscicapillus.* Capped White eye. 2ss. 11. New Guinea.
30. *Zosterops buruensis.* Buru yellow White eye. 11. Buru.
31. *Zosterops kuehni.* Ambon yellow White eye. 11.Amboina, Ceram.
32. *Zosterops novaeguineae.* New Guinea mountain White eye. 7ss. 11. New Guinea.
33. *Zosterops metcalfii.* Yellow throated White eye. 11. Bougainville, Solomon Is.
34. *Zosterops natalis.* Christmas island White eye. 11. Christmas Is.
35. *Zosterops luteus.* Yellow Silver eye / Mangrove White eye. 2ss. 11. NW Australia.
36. *Zosterops griseotinctus.* Louisiades White eye. 5ss. 10. Nissan, Louisiades.
37. *Zosterops rennellianus.* Rennell White eye. 11. Rennell Is.
38. *Zosterops rendovae.* Grey throated White eye. 6ss. 11. Central Solomon Is.
39. *Zosterops Vellalavella.* Banded White eye. 11.Vellalavella Is. (Solomon Is.)
40. *Zosterops luteirostris.* Gizo yellow billed White eye. 11.Gizo. (Solomon Is.).
41. *Zosterops splendida.* Ganonga White eye. 11. Ganonga. (Solomon Is.).
42. *Zosterops kalambangrae.* Kalambangra White eye. 11. Kalambangra. (Solomon Is.).
43. *Zosterops tetiparia.* Tetipari White eye. 11. Tetipari I. (Solomon Is.).
44. *Zosterops murphyi.* Hermit / Mountain White eye. 12. Kalambangra. (Solomon Is.)
45. *Zosterops ugiensius.* Grey throated White eye. 3ss. 12. C Solomon Is.
46. *Zosterops stresemanni.* Malaita White eye. 13. Malaita Is. (Solomon Is.)
47. *Zosterops sanctaecrucis.* Santa Cruz White eye. 12. Santa Cruz Is.
48. *Zosterops samoensis.* Savaii / Samoan White eye. 10. Savaii Is. (Samoa).
49. *Zosterops explorator.* Layard's White eye. 11. Fiji.
50. *Zosterops flavifrons.* Yellow fronted White eye. 7ss. 11. New Hebrides.
51. *Zosterops minutus.* Small Lifu White eye. 11. Lifu, Loyalty Is.
52. *Zosterops inornatus.* Large Lifu White eye. 14. Lifu Is.

1
2
3
4
5
7A
8A
6
7
8
9
10
11
12
13
14
15
13A
18A
16
17
18
19
20
21
22
23
24
25
26
27
28
29
30
34
31
32
33
35
42
43
36
37
38
39
40
41
44
45
46
47
48
49
50
51
52

ZOSTEROPIDAE (2)
White eyes

53. *Zosterops laterals.* Silver eye. 14ss. 11. SE Australia, New Zealand, Fiji, New Hebrides.
54. *Zosterops gold.* Western Silver eye. 11. SW Australia.
55. *Zosterops strenua.* Robust White eye. 11. Lord Howe Is. (extinct).
56. *Zosterops tenuirostris.* Slender billed White eye. 14. Norfolk Is.
57. *Zosterops albogularis.* White chested White eye. 11. Norfolk Is.
58. *Zosterops xanthochrous.* Green backed White eye. 12. New Caledonia.
59. *Zosterops cinereus.* Grey brown White eye. 3ss. 11. Palau, Caroline Is.
60. *Zosterops abyssinicus.* White breasted White eye. 6ss. 12. Yemen, E Africa.
61 *Zosterops pallidus.* Pale / Cape White eye. 3ss. 12. RSA, Namibia.
62. *Zosterops senegalensis.* African yellow White eye. 21ss. 11. Africa.
63. incl. *Z. kikuyuensis.* Kikuyu White eye. 11. Kenya.
64. *Z. eurycricotus.* Broad ringed White eye. 11. Tanzania.
65. *Z. poliogaster.* Montane White eye. 11. Ethiopia.
66. *Z. silvanus.* Taita White eye. 11. SE Kenya.
67. *Z. virens.* Green White eye. 3ss. 12. SE Africa.
68. *Zosterops ficedulinus.* Principe White eye. 2ss. 12. Principe, Sao Thome.
69. *Zosterops griseovirescens.* Annobon White eye. 13. Annobon Is.
70. *Zosterops vaughani.* Pemba White eye. 10. Pemba Is.
71. *Zosterops borbonicus.* Bourbon / Mascarene grey White eye. 4ss. 11. Mauritius, Reunion.
72. *Zosterops olivaceus.* Mascarene olive White eye. 11. Mauritius.
73. *Zosterops chloronothos.* Reunion White eye. 12. Reunion.
74. *Zosterops madarespatanus.* Madagascar White eye. 6ss. 11. Malagasy, Aldabra.
75. incl. *Z. m. hovarum.* Hova grey backed White eye. 11. Malagasy.
76. *Zosterops mayottensis.* Chestnut sided White eye. 12. Mayotte.
77. *Zosterops semiflavus.* Chestnut flanked White eye. 12. Marianne, Seychelles. (extinct.)
78. *Zosterops modestus.* Seychelles White eye. 12. Mahe.
79. *Zosterops mouroniensis.* Comoro green White eye. 11. Gt. Comoro Is.
80. *Woodfordia superciliosa.* Woodford's White eye. 13. Rennell Is.
81. *Woodfordia lacertosa.* Sanford's White eye. 15. Santa Cruz Is.
82. *Rukia/Megazosterops palauensis.* Giant White eye. 14. Palau.
83. *Rukia oleaginea.* Large Yap White eye. 13. Yap Is.
84. *Rukia ruki.* Large Truk White eye. 14. Truk.
85. *Rukia longirostra.* Large Ponape White eye. 13. Ponape.
86. *Tephrozosterops stalkeri.* Bicoloured White eye. 14. Ceram.
87. *Madanga ruficollis.* Rufous throated White eye. 14. Buru.
88. *Lophozosterops pinaiae.* Grey hooded White eye. 17. Ceram.
89. *Lophozosterops goodfellowi.* Black masked White eye. 15. Mindanao.
90. *Lophozosterops squamiceps.* Streaky headed White eye. 11. Sulawesi.
91. *Lophozosterops javanica.* Javan grey throated White eye. 3ss. 13. Java, Bali.
92. *Lophozosterops superciliaris.* Yellow browed White eye. 2ss. 13. Flores, Sumbawa.
93. *Lophozosterops dohertyi.* Crested White eye. 2ss. 13. Lesser Sunda Is.
94. *Oculocincta squamifrons.* Pygmy White eye. 10. Borneo.
95. *Heleia crassirostris.* Thick billed White eye. 12. Lesser Sundas.
96. *Heleia muelleri.* Spot breasted White eye. 12. Timor.
97. *Chlorocharis emiliae.* Olive / Mountain Blackeye. 4ss. 11. Sarawak, N Borneo.
98. *Hypocryptadius cinnamomeus.* Cinnamon White eye / Ibon. 18. Mindanao.
99. *Speirops brunneus.* Fernando Po Speirops. 13. Fernando Po.
100. *Speirops leucophoeus.* Principe Speirops. 14. Principe.
101. *Speirops lugubris.* Black capped Speirops. 2ss. 13. Sao Thome.
102. *Speirops melanocephala.* Cameroon mountain Speirops. 12. Cameroon.

53
54
55
56
57
58
59
60
61
62
63
64
65
66
67
68
69
70
72
71
73
74
75
76
77
78
79
80
81
82
83
84
85
86
87
88
89
90
91
92
93
94
95
96
97
98
99
100
101
102

MELIPHAGIDAE (1) Honeyeaters

1. *Timeliopsis fulvigula*. Olive Straightbill / Mountain straight billed Honeyeater. 3ss. 15. New Guinea.
2. *Timeliopsis griseigula*. Tawny Straightbill / Lowland straight billed Honeyeater. 2ss. 17. New Guinea.
3. *Melilestes/Stresemannia bougainvillei*. Bougainville Honeyeater. 17. Solomon Is.
4. *Melilestes megarhynchus*. Long billed Honeyeater. 4ss. 23. New Guinea & Is.
5. *Toxoramphus novaeguineae*. Green crowned / Yellow bellied Longbill. 2ss.11. New Guinea, Japen, Aru.
6. *Toxoramphus poliopterus*. Slaty chinned / Grey winged Longbill. 2ss. 13. N Guinea.
7. *Oedistoma/Toxoramphus iliolophum*. Grey bellied / Plumed Longbill. 5ss. 10. New Guinea & Is.
8. *Oedistoma pygmaeum*. Pygmy Longbill. 5ss. 8. New Guinea & Is.
9. *Glycichaera fallax*. Green backed / White eyed Honeyeater. 5ss. 12. New Guinea & Is.
10. incl. *G. f. claudi*. Claudie River Honeyeater. 12. N Queensland, New Guinea.
11. *Lichmera alboauricularis*. White eared Honeyeater. 2ss. 15. New Guinea & Is.
12. *Lichmera argentauris*. Plain Olive Honeyeater. 3ss. 14. Halmahera & adjacent Is.
13. *Lichmera/Trichodera Cockerelli*. White streaked Honeyeater. 13. N Queensland.
14. *Lichmera deningeri*. Buru Honeyeater. 13. Buru, S Moluccas.
15. *Lichmera flavicans*. Yellow eared / Timor Honeyeater. 14. Timor.
16. *Lichmera incana*. Dark brown / Silver eared Honeyeater. 5ss. 13. New Caledonia, Loyalty Is, New Hebrides.
17. *Lichmera indistincta*. Brown Honeyeater. 5ss. 14. NW Australia, Lesser Sundas.

17a. *Lichmera limbata* . Indonesian Honeyeater. 14. Bali, Lombok, Timor, Sundas.

18. *Lichmera lombokia*. Lombok Honeyeater. 2ss. 14. Lombok, Flores, Sumbawa Is.
19. *Lichmera monticola*. Ceram Honeyeater. 15. Ceram.
20. *Lichmera notabilis*. Wetar Honeyeater. 14. Wetar.
21. *Lichmera squamata*. Scaled Honeyeater. 3ss. 15. Kai, Tanimber, S Banda, Sea Is.
22. *Myzomela adolphinae*. Red headed mountain Honeyeater. 9. New Guinea Mountains.
23. *Myzomela albigula*. White Chinned Honeyeater. 2ss. 13. Louisiade, Rossel Is.
24. *Myzomela blasii*. Drab Honeyeater. 13. Amboina, Ceram.
25. *Myzomela cardinalis*. Cardinal Honeyeater. 16ss. 11. SW Pacific Is.
26. *Myzomela rubatra*. Micronesian Honeyeater. 13. Mariana Is., Caroline Is.
27. *Myzomela chermesina*. Rotuma Honeyeater. 11. Rotuma Is.
28. *Myzomela cineracea*. Ashy / Bismarck Honeyeater. 2ss. 15 New Britain, Bismarck Arch.
29. *Myzomela cruentata*. Red Honeyeater. 6ss. 11. New Guinea, Bismarck Arch.
30. *Myzomela eichhorni*. Yellow vented Honeyeater. 3ss. 9. Solomon Is.
31. *Myzomela eques*. Red spot Honeyeater. 4ss. 14. New Guinea & Is.
32. *Myzomela erythrocephala*. Red headed Honeyeater. 2ss. 12. N Australia, New Guinea & Is.
33. *Myzomela dammermani*. Sumba Honeyeater. 12. Wetar, Sumbas.
34. *Myzomela erythromelas*. Black bellied Honeyeater. 10. New Britain.
35. *Myzomela jugularis*. Orange breasted Honeyeater. 10. Fiji.
36. *Myzomela kuehni*. Crimson hooded Honeyeater. 12. Wetar.
37. *Myzomela lafargei*. Scarlet naped / Small Bougainville Honeyeater. 10. Solomon Is.
38. *Myzomela malaitae*. Red bellied Honeyeater. 10. Malaite (Solomon Is.).
39. *Myzomela melanocephala*. Black headed Honeyeater. 11. Guadalcanal Is.
40. *Myzomela nigrita*. Black Honeyeater. 11ss. 10. New Guinea & Is.
41. *Myzomela pammelaena*. Ebony Honeyeater. 12. Admiralty Is., Bismarck Arch.
42. *Myzomela obscura*. Dusky Honeyeater. 9ss. 12. Queensland,New Guinea, Moluccas.
43. *Myzomela pulchella*. Beautiful / Olive-yellow Honeyeater. 11. New Ireland.
44. *Myzomela rosenbergii*. Red collared / Black & red Honeyeater. 3ss. 10. New Guinea, D'Entrecasteaux Archipelago.

1
2
3
4
5
6
7
8
9
10
11
12
13
14
15
16
17A
17
19
20
18
21
26
24
22
23
25
27
28
31
33
29
32
34
35
30
37
38
39
41
36
♂=♀
40
42
43
44

MELIPHAGIDAE (2) Honeyeaters

45. *Myzomela sanguinolenta.* Scarlet Honeyeater. 11ss. 10. Queensland, E Australia.
46. *Myzomela Chloroptera.* Sulawesi Honeyeater. 11. Sulawesi.
47. *Myzomela wakoloensis.* Wakolo Honeyeater. 11. Buru.
48. *Myzomela sclateri.* Scarlet bibbed Honeyeater. 12 New Guinea Is, New Britain.
49. *Myzomela boiei.* Banda Honeyeater. 11. Banda Is. (S Moluccas).
50. *Myzomela tristrami.* Tristram's / Sooty Honeyeater. 12. Solomon Is.
51. *Myzomela caledonica.* New Caledonian Honeyeater. 12. New Caledonia.
52. *Myzomela vulnerata.* Red rumped Honeyeater. 12. Timor.
53. *Certhionyx niger.* Black Honeyeater. 11. Interior Australia.
54. *Certhionyx variegatus.* Pied Honeyeater. 16. Interior Australia.
55. *Meliphaga albilineata.* White lined / Striped Honeyeater. 18. N Australia.
56. *Meliphaga albonotata.* White marked / Scrub Honeyeater. 19. New Guinea.
57. *Meliphaga analoga.* Mimic Honeyeater. 5ss. 17. New Guinea, Aru & Is.
58. *Meliphaga aruensis.* Puff backed Honeyeater. 2ss. 17. New Guinea.
59. *Meliphaga/Lichenostomus cassidix.* Helmeted Honeyeater. 21. Victoria.
60. *Meliphaga/Lichenostomus chrysops.* Yellow faced Honeyeater. 2ss. 17. E & SE Australia.
61. *Meliphaga/Lichenostomus cratitia.* Purple gaped Honeyeater. 2ss. 17. S Australia.
62. *Meliphaga/Lichenostomus fasciogularis.* Mangrove Honeyeater. 19. New South Wales, Queensland.
63. *Meliphaga/Lichenostomus flava.* Yellow Honeyeater. 18. Queensland.
64. *Meliphaga/Lichenostomus Flavescens.* Yellow tinted Honeyeater. 15. N Australia, S New Guinea.
65. *Meliphaga/Lichenostomus flavicollis.* Yellow throated Honeyeater. 20. Tasmania & Is.
66. *Meliphaga flavirictus.* Yellow gaped Honeyeater. 2ss. 15. New Guinea.
67. *Meliphaga/Xanthotis flaviventer.* Tawny breasted Honeyeater. 13ss. 19. New Guinea, Is. to Cape York.
68. *Meliphaga/Lichenostomus frenata.* Bridled Honeyeater. 20. Queensland.
69. *Meliphaga/Lichenostomus fusca.* Fuscous Honeyeater. 8ss. 15. SE New Guinea to N Australia.
70. *Meliphaga/Lichenostomus hindwoodi.* Eungella Honeyeater. 15. Queensland.
71. *Meliphaga gracilis.* Slender billed / Graceful Honeyeater. 4ss. 14. New Guinea to Queensland.
72. *Meliphaga/Guadalcanaria inexpectata.* Guadalcanal Honeyeater. 20. Solomon Is.
73. *Meliphaga/Lichenostomus keartlandi.* Grey headed Honeyeater. 16. Internal Australia.
74. *Meliphaga/Lichenostomus leucotis.* White eared Honeyeater. 2ss. 20. S Australia.
75. *Meliphaga lewinii.* (Greater) Lewin's Honeyeater. 2ss. 21. E Australia.
76. *Meliphaga/Xanthotis macleayana.* Yellow streaked / Macleay's Honeyeater. 19. Cairns area, Queensland.
77. *Meliphaga /Lichenostomus melanops.* Yellow tufted Honeyeater. 21. SE Australia.
78. *Meliphaga mimikae.* Mottle / Large spot breasted Honeyeater. 4ss. 17. New Guinea.
79. *Meliphaga montana.* Forest / White eared mountain Honeyeater. 7ss.17. New Guinea.
80. *Meliphaga auga.* Southern white eared mountain Honeyeater. 3ss. 18. New Guinea.

No. 80 is probably the same as M. albonotata. (56).

45
46
47
48
50
52
♂=♀
49
51
53
54
55
56
57
58
59
77
60
61
62
63
64
65
66
67
68
69
71
72
73
76
70
74
75
78
79
80

MELIPHAGIDAE (3)
Honeyeaters

81. *Meliphaga notata*. Yellow spotted / Lesser Lewin Honeyeater. 2ss. 17. Cape York Peninsula & Is.
82. *Meliphaga obscura*. Obscure / Lemon cheeked Honeyeater. 2ss. 19. New Guinea.
83. *Meliphaga orientalis*. Hill forest / Small spot breasted Honeyeater. 4ss. 15. New Guinea.
84. *Meliphaga/Lichenostomus ornata*. Mallee / Yellow plumed Honeyeater. 15. S Australia.
85. *Meliphaga/Lichenstomus penicillata*. White plumed Honeyeater. 8ss. 16. Interior Australia.
86. *Meliphaga/Lichenstomus plumula*. Yellow / Grey fronted Honeyeater. 3ss. 15. Australia.
87. *Meliphaga/Xanthotis polygramma*. Spotted Honeyeater. 6ss. 16. New Guinea.
88. *Meliphaga reticulata*. Reticulated / Streaky breasted Honeyeater. 16. Timor.
89. *Meliphaga/Lichenstomus subfrenata*. Black throated Honeyeater. 4ss. 20. New Guinea.
90. *Meliphaga/Lichenstomus unicolor*. White gaped Honeyeater. 20. N Australia.
91. *Meliphaga/Lichenstomus versicolor*. Varied Honeyeater. 4ss. 20. New Guinea & Is.
92. *Meliphaga vicina*. Tagula / Louisiades Honeyeater. 16. Tagula Is.
93. *Meliphaga/Lichenstomus virescens*. Singing Honeyeater. 5ss. 18. Australia.
94. *Oreornis Chrysogenys*. Orange cheeked Honeyeater. 25. New Guinea.
95. *Foulehaio carunculata*. Wattled Honeyeater. 3ss. 19. Samoa, Tonga, Fiji.
96. *Foulehaio/Xanthotis provocator*. Yellow faced / Kandava Honeyeater. 19. Fiji.
97. *Cleptornis marchei*. Golden Honeyeater. 14. Saipan Is. (Marianas) (Zosterops?)
98. *Apalopteron familiare*. Bonin / White-eyed Honeyeater. 2ss. 13. Bonin Is.
99. *Melithreptus affinis*. Black headed Honeyeater. 2ss. 13. Tasmania & Is.
100. *Melithreptus albogularis*. White throated Honeyeater. 2ss. 14. NE Australia, New Guinea.
101. *Melithreptus brevirostris*. Brown headed Honeyeater. 3ss. 14. S Australia.
102. *Melithreptus gularis*. Black chinned Honeyeater. 17. SE Australia.
103. *Melithreptus laetior*. Golden backed Honeyeater. 4ss. 16. N, W & C Australia.
104. *Melithreptus lunatus*. White naped Honeyeater. 2ss. 14. E Australia.
105. incl. *M. l. chloropsis*. Western white naped Honeyeater. 14. W Australia.
106. *Melithreptus validirostris*. Strong billed Honeyeater. 2ss. 16. Tasmania & Is.
107. *Entomyzon cyanotis*. Blue faced Honeyeater. 4ss. 31. N E S & C Australia, New Guinea.
108. *Notiomystis cincta*. Stitchbird. 17. Little Barrier Is., New Zealand.
109. *Pycnopygius cinerius*. Marbled / Grey fronted Honeyeater. 3ss. 22. New Guinea.
110. *Pycnopygius ixoides*. Plain / Olive brown Honeyeater. 6ss. 18. New Guinea.
111. *Pycnopygius stictocephalus*. Streak capped Honeyeater. 21. New Guinea, Aru.
112. *Philemon albitorques*. Manus / White naped Friar Bird. 35. Manus. (Admiralty Is.)
113. *Philemon argenticeps*. Silver crowned Friar Bird. 4ss. 29. N Australia.

81
82
83
84
85
86
87
88
89
90
91
92
93
94
95
96
97
98
99
100
101
102
103
106
104
105
108
Juv
107
109
110
111
112
113

MELIPHAGIDAE (4)
Honeyeaters

114. *Philemon brassi*. Brass's Friar Bird. 22. New Guinea.
115. *Philemon buceroides*. Timor helmeted Friar Bird. 5ss. 34. N Australian coast, L. Sunda Is.
116. *Philemon gordoni*. Melville Island Friar Bird. 31. Melville Is., N Australia.
117. *Philemon citreogularis*. Little / Yellow throated Friar Bird. 8ss. 25. E & NE Australia to New Guinea.
118. *Philemon kisserensis*. Grey Friar bird. 25. Lesser Sunda Is.
119. *Philemon cockerelli*. White streaked / New Britain Friar Bird. 2ss. 34. New Britain, Rook Is.
120. *Philemon corniculatus*. Bald / Noisy Friar Bird. 3ss. 33. E Australia.
121. *Philemon diemenensis*. New Caledonian Friar Bird. 34. New Caledonia, Loyalty.
122. *Philemon eichornii*. New Ireland helmeted Friar Bird. 34. New Ireland.
123. *Philemon fuscicapillus*. Dusky / Morotai Friar bird. 34. N Moluccas.
124. *Philemon/Melitograis gilolensis*. Striated / Gilolo Friar Bird. 23. Moluccas.
125. *Philemon inornatus*. Plain Friar Bird. 25. Timor.
126. *Philemon meyeri*. Meyer's Friar Bird. 22. New Guinea.
127. *Philemon moluccensis*. Black faced / Moluccas Friar bird. 3ss. 22. Buru Kai, Tanimber.
128. *Philemon novaeguineae*. New Guinea Friar Bird / Leatherhead. 9ss. 33. New Guinea to Queensland.
129. incl. *P. n. yorki*. Cape York Leatherhead. 35. N Queensland, Torres Strait.
130. *Philemon subcorniculatus*. Grey necked Friar bird. 30. Ceram, Moluccas.
131. *Ptiloprora erythropleura*. Rufous sided Friar Bird. 2ss. 17. New Guinea.
132. *Ptiloprora guisei*. Red backed Honeyeater. 4ss. 18. New Guinea.
133. *Ptiloprora mayri*. Mayr's streaked Honeyeater. 20. New Guinea.
134. *Ptiloprora meekiana*. Olive / Yellowish streaked Honeyeater. 2ss. 17. New Guinea.
135. *Ptiloprora perstriata*. Black backed streaked Honeyeater. 3ss. 20. New Guinea.
136. *Ptiloprora plumbea*. Leaden Honeyeater. 2ss. 16. New Guinea.

114
115
116
118
117
Juv
119
120
121
122
123
124
125
126
127
128
129
130
131
132
134
133
136
135

MELIPHAGIDAE (5)
Honeyeaters

137. *Melidectes belfordi*. Belford's Honeyeater. 5ss. 27. New Guinea.
138. *Melidectes foersteri*. Foerster's / Huon Honeyeater. 28. New Guinea.
139. *Melidectes rufocrissalia*. Reichenow's Honeyeater. 3ss. 26. New Guinea.
140. *Melidectes fuscus*. Sooty Honeyeater. 3ss. 23. New Guinea.
141. *Melidectes leucostephes*. White fronted Honeyeater. 26. New Guinea.
142. *Melidectes nouhuysi*. Short bearded Honeyeater. 27. New Guinea.
143. *Melidectes ochromelas*. Mid mountain Honeyeater. 3ss. 24. New Guinea.
144. *Melidectes princeps*. Long bearded Honeyeater. 27. New Guinea.
145. *Melidectes torquatus*. Cinnamon breasted Wattle Bird. 6ss. 23. New Guinea.
146. *Melidectes/Vosea whitemanensis*. Gilliard's / Bismarck / Mountain Honeyeater. 23. New Britain.
147. *Melipotes ater*. Spangled / Black / Huon Honeyeater. 31. Huon peninsula, New Guinea.
148. *Melipotes fumigatus*. Common / Smoky Honeyeater. 2ss. 22. New Guinea.
149. *Melipotes gymnops*. Arfak Honeyeater. 22. New Guinea.
150. *Myza celebensis*. Meyer's / Brown / Dark eared Honeysucker. 3ss. 23. Sulawesi.
151. *Myza sarasinorum*. Greater / Spot headed / White eared Honeysucker. 3ss. 25. Sulawesi.
152. *Meliarchus sclateri*. San Cristobal Honeyeater. 32. Solomon Is.
153. *Gymnomyza aubryana*. Red faced / Crow Honeyeater. 40. New Caledonia.
154. *Gymnomyza samoensis*. Mao / Black breasted Honeyeater. 28. Samoa.
155. *Gymnomyza viridis*. Giant / Green Honeyeater. 27. Fiji.
156. *Moho braccatus*. Kauai Oo. 20. Kauai.
157. *Moho bishopi*. Bishop's Oo. 29. Maui.
158. *Moho apicalis*. Oahu Oo. 30. Oahu. (extinct).
159. *Moho nobilis*. Hawaii Oo. 30. Hawaii. (extinct.
160. *Chaetoptila angustipluma*. Kioea. 32. Hawaii. (extinct).

Hybrids with 137 & 139 are common.

137
138
139
140
141
142
143
144
147
146
145
148
149
150
151
152
153
154
155
156
157
158
159
160

MELIPHAGIDAE (5), PROMEROPIPAE
Honeyeaters, Sugarbirds

161. *Phylidonyris albifrons.* White fronted Honeyeater. 18. Australia.
162. *Phylidonyris/Glyciphilus melanops.* Tawny crowned Honeyeater 3ss. 16. South Australia, Tasmania.
163. *Phylidonyris nigra* White cheeked Honeyeater 2ss. 17. E & SW Australia.
164. *Phylidonyris notabilis.* White bellied Honeyeater. 2ss. 18. New Hebrides.
165. *Phylidonyris novaehollandiae.* Yellow winged / New Holland Honeyeater. 5ss.18. SW, SE Australia, Tasmania.
166. *Phylidonyris pyrrhoptera.* Crescent Honeyeater. 5ss. 15. S Australia, Tasmania.
167. *Phylidonyris undulata.* Barred Honeyeater 18. New Caledonia.
168. *Ramsayornis fasciatus.* Bar breasted Honeyeater. 3ss. 12. N.Australia.
169. *Ramsayornis modestus.* Brown backed Honeyeater. 11. New Guinea, N Queensland.
170. *Plectorhyncha lanceolata.* Striped Honeyeater. 21. E Australia.
171. *Conopophila albogularis.* Rufous banded Honeyeater 2ss. 12. S New Guinea to N Australia.
172. *Conopophila(Grantiella) picta.* Painted Honeyeater 16. E Australia.
173. *Conopophila(Grantiella) rufogularis.* Rufous throated Honeyeater 2ss. 14. N Australia.
174. *Conopophila Whitei* (White's) Grey Honeyeater. 11. Mid to Western Australia.
175. *Xanthomyza phrygia* Regent Honeyeater. 21. E Australia.
176. *Cissomela(Certhionyx)pectoralis.* Band Honeyeater 13. N Australia.
177. *Acanthorhynchus superciliosus.* Western Spinebill 15. SW Australia.
178. *Acanthorhynchus tenuirostris.* Eastern Spinebill. 7ss. 16. E Australia, Tasmania.
179. *Manorina flavigula* Yellow throated / White rumped Miner. 6ss. 26. Australia.
180. *Manorina (Myzantha)melanocephala.* Noisy Miner 2ss. 26. E Australia, Tasmania.
181. *Manorina melanophrys.* Bell Miner 19. SE Australia.
182. *Manorina obscura* Dusky Miner 25. SE Australia.
183. *Manorina melanotis* Black eared Miner 25. SE Australia.
184. *Anthornis melanura* New Zealand Bellbird 4ss. 20. New Zealand.
185. *Anthochaera carunculata.* Red Wattle Bird. 2ss. 35. S Australia.
186. *Anthochaera chrysoptera.* Little Wattle Bird 4ss. 28. S E Australia, Tasmania.
187. *Anthochaera lunulata.* Western Wattle Bird. 28. SW Australia.
188. *Anthochaera paradoxa.* Yellow Wattle Bird. 41. Tasmania.
189. *Anthochaera(Acanthagenys)rufogularis.* Spiny cheeked Honeyeater. 24. Interior Australia.
190. *Prosthemadera novaeseelandiae.* Parson Bird or Tui 3ss. 29/31. New Zealand.

Family 165 PROMEROPIDAE Sugarbirds.

1. *Promerops cafer* Cape Sugarbird 40/27. Cape Province.
2. *Promerops gurneyi* Gurney's Sugarbird 2ss. 26. South Africa, Zimbabwe.

161
162
163
164
165
166
167
168
169
170
171
172
173
174
176
175
177
178
179
180
181
183
184
185
188
187
182
189
PROMEROPIDAE
1
2
186
190

EMBERIZIDAE (1) EMBERIZINAE
Buntings

1. *Melophus lathami.* Crested Bunting. 16. Himalayas, China, Northern SE Asia.
2. *Latoucheornis siemsseri.* Chinese Blue Bunting. 15. C China.
3. *Emberiza aureola.* Yellow breasted Bunting. 2ss. 14. N Eurasia. Winters EC, SE Asia.
4. *Emberiza bruniceps.* Red headed Bunting. 16. WC Asia. Winters India.
5. *Emberiza buchanani.* Grey necked Bunting. 3ss. 16. Turkey to Mongolia. Winters India.
6. *Emberiza cabanisi.* Cabinis' Bunting. 3ss. 15. Africa South of Sahara.
7. incl. *E. c. orientalis.* Three streaked Bunting. 15. SE Africa.
8. *Emberiza caesia.* Cretzschman's Bunting. 16. SE Europe, Crete, Cyprus, Palestine.
9. *Emberiza/Miliaria calandra.* Corn Bunting. 18. Europe, N Africa, Middle East.
10. *Emberiza capensis.* Cape / Southern Rock Bunting. 11ss.14. Cape, Angola, Malawi.
11. *Emberiza chrysophrys.* Yellow browed Bunting. 15. Siberia. Winters S China.
12. *Emberiza cia.* Rock Bunting. 11ss. 16. S Europe, N Africa to Mongolia, China.
13. incl. *E. c. godlewskii.* Godlewski's Bunting. 16. C Asia.
14. *Emberiza cineracea.* Cinereous / Ashy headed Bunting. 2ss.16. Turkey to Iran. Winters to E Africa.
15. *Emberiza cioides.* Siberian Meadow / Long tailed Bunting. 5ss. 17. C & E Asia.
16. *Emberiza cirlus.* Cirl Bunting. 2ss. 16. Europe, N Africa. Introduced New Zealand.
17. *Emberiza citrinella.* Yellow Hammer. 3ss. 17. Europe, N Africa to Mongolia. Introduced New Zealand.
18. *Emberiza elegans.* Yellow headed / throated Bunting. 3ss. 15. E Asia, S to Yunnan & N Burma.
19. *Emberiza flaviventris.* Golden breasted Bunting. 4ss. 16. Uganda, Angola, Cape.
20. *Emberiza affinis*(=forbesii). Brown rumped Bunting. 3ss. 15. Senegal, Cameroon to Ethiopia, Uganda.
21. *Emberiza fucata.* Grey hooded / Chestnut eared Bunting. 3ss. 16. Himalayas, China, Japan.
22. *Emberiza hortulana.* Ortolan Bunting. 16. Eurasia. Winters Arabia, C Africa.
23. *Emberiza impetuani.* Larklike Bunting. 2ss. 14. Cape to Transvaal, Angola.
24. *Emberiza janskowski.* Rufous backed / Jankowski's Bunting. 16. Manchuria, Korea
25. *Emberiza koslowi.* Koslov's / Tibetan Bunting. 16. E Tibet.
26. *Emberiza leucocephala.* Pine Bunting. 2ss. 17. Siberia, Tibet, China. Winters Iraq, S China, N India.

1
2
3
4
5
6
7
8
9
11
10
12
13
14
15
16
17
18
19
20
21
22
23
24
25
26

EMBERIZIDAE (2)
Buntings

27. *Emberiza melanocephala.* Black headed Bunting. 16. SE Europe, SW Asia. Winters India.
28. *Emberiza pallasi.* Pallas' Reed Bunting. 3ss. 14. Mongolia, NC Asia.
29. *Emberiza poliopleura.* Somali golden breasted Bunting. 14. Sudan to E Africa.
30. *Emberiza pusilla.* Little Bunting. 12. N Eurasia. Winters India, China, SE Asia.
31. *Emberiza rustica.* Rustic Bunting. 2ss. 15. N Eurasia. Winters China, Japan.
32. *Emberiza rutila.* Chestnut Bunting. 14. Siberia, Mongolia. Winters China, SE Asia.
33. *Emberiza scheeniclus.* Reed Bunting. 15ss. 17. Most of Palearctic.
34. *Emberiza socotrana.* Socotra mountain Bunting. 14. Socotra.
35. *Emberiza spodocephala.* Black faced / Masked Bunting. 3ss. 14. E Asia.
36. *Emberiza stewarti.* White capped / Chestnut breasted Bunting. 15. Asia. Winters India.
37. *Emberiza striolata.* House Bunting. 5ss. 14. N Africa, SW Asia to India.
38. *Emberiza sulphurata.* Japanese Yellow Bunting. 14. Japan. Winters Taiwan, Philippines.
39. *Emberiza tahapisi.* Cinnamon breasted rock Bunting. 5ss. 14. Arabia & Africa south of Sahara.
40. *Emberiza tristrami.* Tristram's Bunting. 14. NE Asia. Winters S China.
41. *Emberiza variabilis.* (Japanese) Grey Bunting. 16. E Asia.
42. *Emberiza yessoensis.* Ochre rumped / Swinhoe's / Japanese Reed Bunting. 2ss. 16. E.Asia.
43. *Calcarius lapponicus.* Lapland Bunting / Longspur. 3ss. 16. Holarctic Tundra. Winters South
44. *Calcarius mccownii.* McCown's Longspur. 15. Canada, USA. Winters to Mexico.
45. *Calcarius ornatus.* Chestnut collared Longspur. 15. Canada. Winters USA, Mexico.
46. *Calcarius pictus.* Smith's Longspur. 16. Canada. Winters USA.
47. *Plectrophenax nivalis.* Snow Bunting. 4ss. 17. N Holarctic. Winters S Europe, S USA.
48. *Plectrophenax hyperboreus.* McKay's Bunting. 17. Bering Sea Is. Winters Alaska.

27
28
29
30
31
32
33
34
35
36
37
38
39
40
41
42
-43-
Br
NB
NB
Br
-44-
NB
Br
-45-
46
- Br -
47
-NB-
Br
48
NB

EMBERIZIDAE (3)
American Sparrows

49. *Calamospiza melanocorys.* Lark Bunting. 18. N American Plains. Winters to Mexico.
50. *Zonotrichia albicollis.* White throated Sparrow. 17. Canada, N USA. Winters S USA.
51. *Zonotrichia atricapilla.* Golden crowned Sparrow. 18. Alaska, Canada. Winters S USA.
52. *Zonotrichia capensis.* Rufous collared Sparrow. 25ss. 15. C & S America.
53. *Melospiza georgiana.* Swamp Sparrow. 2ss. 15. Much of N America.
54. *Passerella iliaca.* Fox Sparrow. 18ss. 18. Much of N America.
55. incl. *P. i. fuliginosa.* Sooty Sparrow. 18. Pacific NW America.
56. *P. i. schistacea.* Small billed Sparrow. 18. N America.
57. *Zonotrichia leucophrys.* White crowned Sparrow. 5ss. 17. N America.
58. *Melospiza lincolni.* Lincoln Sparrow. 3ss. 15. N America. Winters to C America.
59. *Melospiza melodia.* Song Sparrow. 37ss. 15. N America, Mexico.
60. *Melospiza maxima.* Large song Sparrow. 18. Aleutian Is.
61. *Melospiza saltonis.* Desert song Sparrow. 14. Nevada, California.
62. *Zonotrichia querula.* Harris' Sparrow. 19. Canada, N USA. Winters S USA.
63. *Junco caniceps.* Grey headed Junco. 3ss. 14. CS USA. Winters to Mexico.
64. *Junco hyemalis.* Dark-eyed / Slate coloured Junco. 13ss. 13. Canada To Mexico.
65. *Junco aikeni.* White winged Junco. 15. WC USA. Winters S USA.
66. *Junco oreganus.* Oregon Junco. 13. Alaska, Canada. Winters California.
67. *Junco insularis.* Guadeloupe Junco. 14. Guadeloupe.
68. *Junco phaeonotus.* Yellow-eyed / Mexican Junco. 5ss. 15. CS Mexico.
69. *Junco bairdi.* Baird's Junco. 14. Baja, California.
70. *Junco alticola.* Guatemalan Junco. 15. S Mexico, Guatemala.
71. *Junco vulcani.* Volcano Junco. 15. Costa Rica, Panama.
72. *Myospiza/Ammodramus aurifrons.* Yellow browed Sparrow. 4ss. 13. Amazon basin.
73. *Myospiza/Ammodramus humeralis.* Grassland Sparrow. 4ss. 13. E South America.
74. *Xenospiza baileyi.* Sierra Madre Sparrow. 13. N & C Mexico.
75. *Ammodramus bairdii.* Baird's Sparrow. 14. Canada, W USA. Winters to Mexico.
76. *Ammodramus henslowii.* Henslow's Sparrow. 2ss. 13. E USA.
77. *Passerculus sandwichensis.* Savannah Sparrow. 21ss. 14. Aleutian Is. to Canada, USA, Mexico & C America.
78. *Passerculus princeps.* Ipswich Sparrow. 16. Nova Scotia. Winters to S USA.
79. *Passerculus rostratus.* Large billed Sparrow. 14. California, Mexico.
80. *Passerculus beldingi.* Belding's Sparrow. 14. California, Mexico.
81. *Ammodramus savannarum.* Grasshopper Sparrow. 11ss. 13. Canada to W Indies, C America & North of S America.
82. *Ammodramus caudacutus.* Sharp tailed Sparrow. 5ss. 13. Canada & USA.
83. incl. *A. c. subvirgatus.* Acadilan Sparrow. 13. NE Coast of Canada. Winters S USA.
84. *A. c. nelsoni.* Nelson's Sparrow. 13. WC Canada. Winters S USA.
85. *Ammodramus leconteii.* Le Conte's Sparrow. 13. S Canada, N USA. Winters SC USA.
86. *Ammodramus maritimus.* Seaside Sparrow. 8ss. 15. Coast E & S USA.
87. incl. *A. m. mirabilis.* Cape Sable Sparrow. 15. Florida coast.
88. *A. m. fisheri. Louisiana Sparrow.* 15. S & SW USA.
89. *A. m. nigrescens.* Dusky Sparrow. 15. Florida saltmarshes.

49
Br
NB
50
51
52
53
54
55
56
57
58
59
60
61
62
63
64
65
66
67
71
68
69
70
72
73
74
75
76
77
78
79
80
81
82
83
84
85
86
87
88
89

EMBERIZIDAE (4)
American Sparrows

90. *Spizella Arborea.* (American) Tree Sparrow. 2ss. 16. Canada, Alaska. Winters USA.
91. *Spizella atrogulari.s.* Black chinned Sparrow. 4ss. 15. Mexico, SW USA.
92. *Spizella breweri.* Brewer's Sparrow. 2ss. 14. W Canada, N USA. Winters S to Mexico.
93. incl. *S. b. taverni.* Timberline Sparrow. 15. Yukon, Br. Colombia. Winters S USA.
94. *Spizella pallida.* Clay coloured Sparrow. 14. Plains of N America.
95. *Spizella passerina.* Chipping Sparrow. 7ss. 14. N. America to Mexico, Salvador.
96. *Spizella pusilla.* Field Sparrow. 2ss. 15. Canada, EC USA. Winters S USA, Mexico.
97. *Spizella wortheni.* Worthen's Sparrow. 13. NE Mexico.
98. *Pooecetes gramineus.* Vesper Sparrow. 3ss. 16. Canada, USA. Winters to Mexico.
99. *Chondestes grammacus.* Lark Sparrow. 2ss. 17. Canada, USA. Winters to Mexico, Guatemala.
100. *Amphispiza belli.* Sage Sparrow. 5ss. 16. W USA, Mexico.
101. *Amphispiza bilineata.* Black throated Sparrow. 9ss. 14. Mexico, SW USA.
102. *Aimophila aestivalis.* Bachman's Sparrow. 3ss. 15. E USA.
103. *Aimophila botterii.* Botteri's Sparrow. 10ss. 15. Arizona, Texas to Costa Rica.
104. *Aimophila petenica.* Yellow carpalled/Peten Sparrow. 14. Mexico, C America.
105. *Aimophila carpalis.* Rufous winged Sparrow. 3ss. 13. Arizona, Mexico.
106. *Aimophila Cassinii.* Cassin's Sparrow. 15. SC USA, Mexico.
107. *Aimophila humeralis.* Black chested Sparrow. 15. Mexico.
108. *Aimophila mysticalis.* Bridled Sparrow. 15. Mexico.
109. *Aimophila notosticta.* Oaxaca Sparrow. 16. Mexico.
110. *Aimophila quinquestriata.* Five striped Sparrow. 2ss. 15. Mexico, Arizona.
111. *Aimophila rufescens.* Rusty Sparrow. 10ss. 18. Mexico to Costa Rica.
112. *Aimophila ruficauda.* Stripe headed Sparrow. 4ss. 16. Mexico to Costa Rica.
113. *Aimophila ruficeps.* Rufous crowned Sparrow. 14ss. 15. SW USA, Mexico.
114. *Aimophila(Rhynchospiza)stolzmanni.* Tumbes Sparrow. 15. Ecuador, Peru.
115. *Aimophila strigiceps.* Stripe capped Sparrow. 2ss. 16. Argentina.
116. *Aimophila sumichrasti.* Cinnamon tailed Sparrow. 16. Mexico.
117. *Torreornis inexpectata.* Zapata Sparrow. 2ss. 16. Cuba.
118. *Oriturus superciliosus.* Striped Sparrow. 2ss. 16. Mexico.
119. *Phrygilus alaudinus.* Band tailed Sierra Finch. 5ss. 17/13. Ecuador, Chile, Argentina.
120. *Phrygilus atriceps.* Black hooded Sierra Finch. 3ss. 17. Peru to Argentina.
121. *Phrygilus carbonarius.* Carbonated Sierra Finch. 14. Argentina.
122. *Phrygilus dorsalis.* Red backed Sierra Finch. 17. Argentina.
123. *Phrygilus erythronotus.* White throated Sierra Finch. 17. Peru, Bolivia, Chile.
124. *Phrygilus fruticeti.* Mourning Sierra Finch. 2ss. 17. Peru to Argentina.
125. *Phrygilus gayi.* Grey hooded Sierra finch. 3ss. 17. Chile, Argentina.
126. *Phrygilus punensis.* Peruvian Sierra Finch. 18. Peru, Bolivia.
127. *Phrygilus patagonicus.* Patagonian Sierra Finch. 15. Chile & Chilean Is.
128. *Phrygilus plebejus.* Ash breasted Sierra Finch. 2ss. 13. Ecuador to Argentina.
129. *Phrygilus unicolor.* Plumbeous Sierra Finch. 6ss. 15. Venezuela to Argentina.

90
91
92
93
94
95
96
97
98
99
100
101
102
103
104
105
106
107
108
109
110
111
112
113
114
115
116
117
118
119
120
121
122
123
124
128
125
126
127
129

EMBERIZIDAE (5) American Finches

130. *Melanodera melanodera.* Black throated Finch. 2ss. 14. Chile, Argentina, Falklands.
131. *Melanodera xanthogramma.* Yellow bridled Finch. 4ss. 17. Chile, Argentina.
132. *Haplospiza rustica.* Slaty Finch. 4ss. 13. Mexico to Bolivia.
133. *Haplospiza unicolor.* Uniform Finch. 13. SE Brazil to N Argentina.
134. *Acanthidops bairdii.* Peg billed Finch. 14. Costa Rica.
135. *Lophospingus griseocristatus.* Grey crested Finch. 15. Bolivia to Argentina.
136. *Lophospingus pusillus.* Black crested Finch. 13. Bolivia, Paraguay, Argentina.
137. *Donocospiza albifrons.* Long tailed Reed Finch. 17. Brazil to Argentina.
138. *Rowettia goughensis.* Gough Bunting. 14. Gough Is.
139. *Nesospiza acunhae.* Nightingale Finch. 11. Inaccessible Is. Tristan da Cunha, Nightingale Is.
140. *Nesospiza wilkinsi.* Wilkins Finch. 2ss. 14. Atlantic Is. (as in 139.)
141. *Diuca diuca.* Common Diuca Finch. 4ss. 16. Chile, Argentina.
142. *Diuca speculifera.* White winged Diuca Finch. 2ss. 17. Peru, Bolivia, N Chile.
143. *Idiopsar brachyurus.* Short tailed Finch. 18. Peru, Bolivia, W Chile.
144. *Piezorhina cinerea.* Cinereous Finch. 16. NW Peru.
145. *Xenospingus concolor.* Slender billed Finch. 16. Peru & Chile coast.
146. *Incaspiza laeta.* Buff bridled Inca Finch. 14. Peru.
147. *Incaspiza ortizi.* Grey winged Inca Finch. 16. Peru.
148. *Incaspiza personata.* Rufous backed Inca Finch. 16. Peru.
149. *Incaspiza pulchra.* Great Inca Finch. 16. Peru.
150. *Incaspiza watkinsi.* Little Inca Finch. 13. Peru.
151. *Poospiza alticola.* Plain tailed Warbling Finch. 16. N Peru.
152. *Poospiza/Compospiza baeri.* Tucuman Mountain Finch. 18. NW Argentina.
153. *Poospiza boliviana.* Bolivian Warbling Finch. 16. C Bolivia.
154. *Poospiza caesar.* Chestnut breasted Mountain Finch. 18. SE Peru.
155. *Poospiza cinerea.* Cinereous Warbling Finch. 14. C Brazil.
156. *Poospiza erythrophrys.* Rusty browed Warbling Finch. 2ss. 13. Bolivia, Argentina.
157. *Poospiza/Compospiza garleppi.* Cochabamba Mountain Finch. 18. Bolivia.

130
131
132
133
134
135
136
137
138
139
140
141
142
143
144
145
146
147
148
149
150
151
152
153
154
155
156
157

EMBERIZIDAE (6) American Finches

158. *Poospiza hispaniolensis.* Collared Warbling Finch. 13. Ecuador, Peru.
159. *Poospiza hypochondria.* Rufous sided Warbling Finch. 2ss. 16. Bolivia, N Argentina.
160. *Poospiza lateralis.* Red rumped Warbling Finch. 2ss. 14. South of S America.
161. *Poospiza melanoleuca.* Black capped Warbling Finch. 13. Bolivia, Brazil, Argentina.
162. *Poospiza nigrorufa.* Black & rufous Warbling Finch. 3ss. 14. Brazil, Bolivia, Argentina.

162a. *Poospiza whitii.* Black & Chestnut Warbling Finch. 14. Argentina, Bolivia.

163. *Poospiza ornata.* Cinnamon Warbling Finch. 14. NW Argentina.
164. *Poospiza rubecula.* Rufous breasted Warbling Finch. 16. N Peru.
165. *Poospiza thoracica.* Bay chested Warbling Finch. 13. SE Brazil.
166. *Poospiza torquata.* Ringed Warbling Finch. 2ss. 13. Bolivia, Paraguay, NC Argentina.
167. *Sicalis auriventris.* Greater Yellow Finch. 18. Chile, N Argentina.
168. *Sicalis citrina.* Stripe tailed Yellow Finch. 3ss. 12. Irregular in tropical S America.
169. *Sicalis columbiana.* Orange fronted yellow Finch. 3ss. 11. Amazon & Orinoco.
170. *Sicalis flaveola.* Saffron Finch. 4ss. 14. Tropical S America, Panama, Jamaica.
171. *Sicalis lebruni.* Patagonian Yellow Finch. 15. Argentina.
172. *Sicalis lutea.* Puna Yellow Finch. 14. Peru to N Argentina.
173. *Sicalis luteocephala.* Citron headed Yellow Finch. 15. Bolivia.
174. *Sicalis luteola.* Grassland Yellow Finch. 8ss. 11. W Antilles.
175. *Sicalis luteiventris.* Misto Yellow Finch. 13. South of S America.
176. *Sicalis olivascens.* Greenish Yellow Finch. 4ss. 14. Peru to Argentina.
177. *Sicalis raimondii.* Raimond's Yellow Finch. 11. Peru.
178. *Sicalis taczanovskii.* Sulphur breasted Finch. 13. SW Ecuador, N Peru.
179. *Sicalis uropygialis.* Bright rumped Yellow Finch. 3ss. 14. Peru, N Chile, Argentina.
180. *Emberizoides herbicola.* Wedge tailed Grass Finch. 6ss. 19. C & S America.
181. *Emberizoides duidae.* Mt Duida Grass Finch. 21. Venezuela.
182. *Emberizoides ypiranganas.* Grey cheeked / Lesser Grass Finch. 2ss. 17. Brazil, Argentina.
183. *Embernagra longicauda.* Buff throated Pampas Finch. 22. Brazil.(3 specimens).
184. *Embernagra platensis.* Great Pampa Finch. 2ss. 21. Brazil, Bolivia, Argentina.
185. *Volatina jacarina.* Blue black Grassquit. 3ss. 10. Mexico to N Chile, Argentina.
186. *Sporophila albogularis.* White throated Seedeater. 12. NE Brazil
187. *Sporophila americana.* Wing barred Seedeater. 4ss. 12. Tobago, Venezuela to Brazil.
188. *Sporophila aurita.* Variable / Hick's Seedeater. 3ss. 11. Mexico to W Colombia.
189. *Sporophila ardesiaca.* Dubois' Seedeater. 12. S Brazil.
190. *Sporophila bouvreuil.* Capped Seedeater. 4ss. 11. Brazil, Paraguay, Argentina.
191. *Sporophila caerulescens.* Double collared Seedeater. 3ss. 12. Brazil, Bolivia, Argentina.
192. *Sporophila cataneiventris.* Chestnut bellied Seedeater. 10. Amazon basin.

193 *Sporophila cinnamomea.* Chestnut Seedeater. 11. Brazil, Paraguay.

194. *Sporophila collaris.* Rusty collared Seedeater. 3ss. 11. SE Brazil to Argentina.
195. *Sporophila falcirostris.* Temminck's Seedeater. 12. SE Brazil.

158
159
160
161
162
162A
163
164
165
166
167
168
169
170
171
172
173
174
176
177
178
179
175
185
187
180
181
182
183
184
188
186
189
190
191
192
193
194
195

EMBERIZIDAE (7) Seedeaters

196. *Sporophila frontalis*. Buffy fronted Seedeater. 13. Brazil, NE Argentina.
197. *Sporophila hypochroma*. Rufous rumped Seedeater. 11. Bolivia, Argentina.
198. *Sporophila hypoxantha*. Tawny bellied Seedeater. 10. Brazil, Bolivia, Argentina.
199. *Sporophila insulata*. Tumaco Seedeater. 11. Tumaco Is. (Colombia).
200. *Sporophila intermedia*. Grey Seedeater. 4ss. 12. Trinidad, NE of S America.
201. *Sporophila leucoptera*. White bellied Seedeater. 4ss. 13. Brazil to Argentina.
202. *Sporophila lineola*. Lined Seedeater. 3ss. 11. Trinidad, Tobago, tropical S America.
202a. *Sporophila bouvronides*. Lesson's Seedeater. 11. Northern S America.
203. *Sporophila luctuosa*. Black & White Seedeater. 12. Venezuela to Bolivia.
204. *Sporophila melanogaster*. Black bellied Seedeater. 11. SE Brazil.
205. *Sporophila melanops*. Hooded Seedeater. 11. Brazil. (1 specimen. Hybrid?)
206. *Sporophila minuta*. Ruddy breasted Seedeater. 4ss. 10. Mexico to Brazil.
207. *Sporophila nigricollis*. Yellow bellied Seedeater. 3ss. 12. C & S America.
208. *Sporophila nigrorufa*. Black & Tawny Seedeater. 11. Brazil, Bolivia.
209. *Sporophila(Tiaris?)obscura*. Dull coloured Seedeater / Grassquit. 4ss.11. Venezuela & Peru to Argentina.
210. *Sporophila palustris*. Marsh Seedeater. 11. S of South America.
211. *Sporophila peruviana*. Parrot billed Seedeater. 2ss. 12. Peru & Ecuador.
212. *Sporophila plumbea*. Plumbeous Seedeater. 3ss. 11. Amazon basin.
213. *Sporophila ruficollis*. Dark throated Seedeater. 11. Brazil, Bolivia, Argentina.
214. *Sporophila schistacea*. Slate coloured Seedeater. 4ss. 12. Mexico to C S America.
215. *Sporophila simplex*. Drab Seedeater. 11. Peru.
216. *Sporophila zelichi*. Narosky's Seedeater. 10. NE Argentina.
217. *Sporophila telasco*. Chestnut throated Seedeater. 11. Ecuador to n Chile.
218. *Sporophila torqueola*. White collared Seedeater. 4ss. 11. Mexico to El Salvador.
219. *Oryzoborus angolensis*. Lesser Seed Finch. 3ss. 13. Much of S America.
220. *Oryzoborus nuttingi*. Nicaraguan Seed Finch. 14. Nicaragua to Panama.
221. *Oryzoborus funereus*. Thick billed Seed Finch. 14. Mexico to N South America.
222. *Oryzoborus crassirostris*. Large billed Seed Finch. 7ss. 14. C to S America.
223. *Oryzoborus atrirostris*. Black billed Seed Finch. 15. Peru, Bolivia.
224. *Oryzoborus Maximilliana*. Greater Large billed Seed Finch. 15. Brazil.
225. *Amaurospiza concolor*. Blue Seedeater. 3ss. 12. Mexico to Ecuador.
226. incl. *A. c. relicta*. Guerrero Seedeater. 13. Mexico.
227. *Amaurospiza moesta. Blackish blue* Seedeater. 13. Brazil, Argentina.
228. *Melopyrrha nigra*. Cuban Bullfinch. 2ss. 14. Cuba, Isle of Pines.
229. *Dolospingus fringilloides*. White naped Seedeater. 15. Venezuela, Brazil.
230. *Catamenia analis*. Band tailed Seedeater. 14. Colombia to Bolivia.
231. *Catamenia homochroa*. Paramo Seedeater. 2ss. 13. Venezuela to Bolivia.
232. *Catamenia oreophila*. Santa Marta Seedeater. 13. Colombia.(6 females only).
233. *Catamenia inornata*. Plaincoloured Seedeater. 3ss. 14. Andes, Venezuela to Argentina.
234. *Tiaris bicolor*. Black faced Grassquit. 8ss. 11. W Indies, Colombia, Venezuela.
235. *Tiaris canora*. Melodious / Cuban Grassquit. 12. Cuba, I of Pines.
236. *Tiaris fuliginosa*. Sooty Grassquit. 3ss. 12. Trinidad, Venezuela, Brazil.
237. *Tiaris olivacea*. Yellow faced Grassquit. 5ss. 12. Mexico to Venezuela, West Indies.

196
197
198
199
200
201
202
203
204
202
A
205♂
♀?
206
207
208
209
210
211
212
213
214
215
217
218
219
221
222
224
225
226
227
228
229
230
231
232♀
♂?
216
233
234
220
235
236
237
223

EMBERIZIDAE (8)
New World Finches, Towhees

238. *Loxipasser anoxanthus*. Yellow shouldered Grassquit. 13. Jamaica.
239. *Loxigilla noctis*. Lesser Antillean Bullfinch. 9ss. 13. Lesser Antilles.
240. *Loxigilla portoricensis*. Puerto Rican Bullfinch. 19. Puerto Rico.
241. *Loxigilla violacea*. Greater Antillean Bullfinch. 5ss. 16. Gr. Antilles.
242. *Melanospiza richardsoni*. St. Lucia Black Finch. 13. St. Lucia.
242a. *Geospiza conirostris*. Vegetarian / Large ground Finch. 3ss. 15. Galapagos.
243. *G. c. conirostris*. Hood Island form. 15. Hood Is. (Espanola).
244. *G. c. propinque*. Northern islands form. 15. Tower Is. (Genovesa).
245. *Geospiza difficilis*. Sharp billed Ground Finch. 3ss. 13. Galapagos.
246. *Geospiza fortis*. Medium Ground Finch. 13. Galapagos.
247. *Geospiza fuliginosa*. Small Ground Finch. 11. Galapagos.
248. *Geospiza magnirostris*. Large Ground Finch. 16. Galapagos.
249. *Geospiza scandens*. (Small) Cactus Ground Finch. 4ss. 14. Galapagos.
250. *Camarhynchus crassirostris*. Vegetarian Tree Finch. 17. Galapagos.
251. *Camarhynchus heliobates*. Mangrove Finch. 13. Galapagos,
252. *Camarhynchus pallidus*. Woodpecker Finch. 3ss. 15. Galapagos.
253. *Camarhynchus parvulus*. Small (insectivorous) Tree Finch. 2ss. 11. Galapagos.
254. *Camarhynchus pauper*. Medium Tree Finch. 13. Galapagos.
255. *Camarhynchus psittacula*. Large Tree Finch. 3ss. 15. Galapagos.
256. *Certhidea olivacea*. Warbler Finch. 8ss. 10. Galapagos.
257. *Pinaroloxias inornata*. Cocos Finch. 11. Cocos Is.
258. *Pipilo aberti*. Abert's Towhee. 3ss. 21. SW USA.
259. *Pipilo albicollis*. White throated Towhee. 2ss. 18. Mexico.
260. *Pipilo/Chlorurus chlorurus*. Green tailed Towhee. 17. SW USA.
261. *Pipilo erythrophthalmus*. Eastern / Rufous sided Towhee. 25ss. 20. E USA.
262. incl. *P. e. alleni*. White eyed Towhee. 20. Florida.
263. *P. e. macronyx*. Olive backed Towhee. 20. Mexico, Guatemala.
264. *P. e. maculatus*. Western / Spotted Towhee. 20. Mexico.
265. *Pipilo fuscus senicula*. Brown Towhee, Pacific race. 18ss. 23. California.
266. incl. *P. f. fuscus*. Brown Towhee, Rocky Mts. race (Canyon Towhee.) 23. Rocky Mountains.
266a. *P. f. crissalis*. California Towhee. 23. California & Baja.
267. *Pipilo ocai*. Collared Towhee. 5ss. 21. Mexico.
268. *Pipilo socorroensis*. Socorro Towhee. 18. Socorro Is. (consp. 266 ?)
269. *Melozone biarcuatum*. Prevost's Ground Sparrow. 2ss. 15. Chiapas, C America.
270. incl. *M. b. cabanisi*. Cabini's Ground Sparrow. 15. Costa Rica.
271. *Melozone kieneri*. Rusty crowned Ground Sparrow. 4ss. 15. Mexico.
272. *Melozone leucotis*. White eared Ground Sparrow. 3ss. 15. Mexico to Costa Rica.
273. incl. *M. l. occipitalis*. Salvin's Ground Sparrow. 15. Mexico, Guatemala, Salvador.

(Camarhyncus conjunctus, aureus & giffordi are probably hybrids.)

238
239
240
241
242
243
244
245
246
247
248
249
250
251
252
253
254
255
256
257
258
259
260
261
262
263
264
266A
268
270
272
266
267
265
269
271
273

EMBERIZIDAE (9)
Sparrows, Brush Finches

274. *Arremon abeilli.* Black capped Sparrow. 2ss. 15. Ecuador, Peru.
275. *Arremon aurantiirostris.* Orange billed Sparrow. 8ss. 15. Mexico to Peru.
276. *Arremon flavirostris.* Saffron billed Sparrow. 4ss. 17. Brazil, Bolivia, Argentina.
277. *Arremon schlegeli.* Golden winged Sparrow. 3ss. 16. Colombia, Venezuela.
278. *Arremon taciturnus.* Pectoral Sparrow. 4ss. 17. NE of S America.
279. *Arremonops conirostris.* Black striped Sparrow. 5ss. 18. Honduras to Peru.
280. *Arremonops chloronotus.* Green backed Sparrow. 2ss. 14. Mexico & C America.
281. *Arremonops rufivirgatus.* Olive Sparrow. 9ss. 14. Texas to Costa Rica.
282. *Arremonops tocuyensis.* Tocuyo Sparrow. 13. Colombia, Venezuela.
283. *Atlapetes albiceps.* White headed Brush Finch. 17. Ecuador, Peru.
284. *Atlapetes albinucha.* White naped Brush Finch. 17. Mexico to Colombia.
285. *Atlapetes albofrenatus.* Moustached Brush Finch. 2ss. 18. Colombia, Venezuela.
286. *Atlapetes brunneinucha.* Chestnut capped Brush Finch. 10ss. 19. Mexico to Venezuela & Ecuador.
287. *Atlapetes apertus.* Plain breasted Brush Finch. 18. Mexico.
288. *Atlapetes citrinellus.* Yellow striped Brush Finch. 17. Argentina.
289. *Atlapetes flaviceps.* Olive headed Brush Finch. 17. Colombia.
290. *Atlapetes fulviceps.* Fulvous headed Brush Finch. 17. Bolivia, Argentina.
291. *Atlapetes fusco-olivaceus.* Dusky headed Brush Finch. 17. Colombia.
292. *Atlapetes gutturalis.* Yellow throated Brush Finch. 7ss. 18. Mexico to Colombia.
293. *Atlapetes leucopsis.* White rimmed Brush Finch. 19. Colombia, Ecuador.
294. *Atlapetes leucopterus.* White winged Brush Finch. 2ss. 15. Ecuador, Peru.
295. *Atlapetes melanocephalus.* Santa Marta Brush Finch. 16. Colombia.
296. *Atlapetes nationi.* Rusty bellied Brush Finch. 3ss. 18. Ecuador, Peru.
297. *Atlapetes pallidiceps.* Pale headed Brush Finch. 17. Ecuador.
298. *Atlapetes pallidinucha.* Pale naped Brush Finch. 2ss. 18. Colombia, Venezuela, Ecuador.
299. *Atlapetes personatus.* Tepui Brush Finch. 12ss. 17. Venezuela.
300. *Atlapetes duidae.* Duida Brush Finch. 17. Venezuela.
301. *Atlapetes pileatus.* Rufous capped Brush Finch. 2ss. 13. Mexico.
302. *Atlapetes rufigenis.* Rufous eared Brush Finch. 2ss. 19. Peru.
303. *Atlapetes rufinucha.* Rufous naped Brush Finch. 12ss. 17. Venezuela to Bolivia.
304. *Atlapetes schistaceus.* Slaty Brush Finch. 6ss. 18. Venezuela to Peru.
305. *Atlapetes seebohmi.* Bay crowned Brush Finch. 2ss. 18. NW Peru.
306. *Atlapetes semirufus.* Ochre breasted Brush Finch. 6ss. 17. Venezuela, Colombia.
307. *Atlapetes torquatus.* Stripe headed Brush Finch. 14ss. 19. NW South America.
308. incl. *A. t. virenticeps.* Green striped Brush Finch. 18. C Mexico.
309. *A. t. assimilis.* Grey striped Brush Finch. 18. NW South America.
310. *Atlapetes atricapillus.* Black headed Brush Finch. 19. Panama, Colombia.
311. *Atlapetes tricolor.* Tricoloured Brush Finch. 2ss. 19. Colombia, Ecuador, Peru.
312. *Pezopetes capitalis.* Large footed Finch (Sparrow). 19. Costa Rica, Panama.
313. *Oreothraupis arremonops.* Tanager Finch. 20. Colombia, Ecuador.
314. *Pselliophorus luteoviridis.* Yellow-Green Finch. 18. Panama. (unique).
315. *Pselliophorus tibialis.* Yellow thighed Finch. 18. Costa Rica, Panama.
316. *Lysurus castaneiceps.* Olive Finch. 2ss. 15. Costa Rica to Colombia & Peru.
317. *Lysurus crassirostris.* Sooty faced Finch. 17. Costa Rica, Panama.
318. *Urothraupis stolzmanni.* Black backed Bush Tanager. 17. Colombia, Ecuador.

No. 318 should perhaps be placed in family 169.

274
275
276
277
278
279
280
281
282
283
284
285
286
287
288
289
290
291
292
293
294
295
296
301
297
298
299
300
302
303
304
305
306
307
308
309
310
311
312
313
314
315
316
317
318

EMBERIZIDAE (10), CATAMBLYRHYNCHINAE, CARDINALINAE
Finches, Cardinals, Plush capped Finch, Cardinal Grosbeaks

EMBERIZIDAE (10). Finches, Cardinals.

319. *Charitospiza eucosma.* Coal crested Finch. 12. Brazil, Argentina.
320. *Coryphaspiza melanotis.* Black masked Finch. 2ss. 13. SE of South America.
321. Saltatricula multicolor. Many coloured Chaco Finch. 16. S of South America.
322. *Gubernatrix cristata.* Yellow Cardinal. 19. Brazil, Uruguay, NE Argentina.
323. *Coryphospingus cucullatus.* Red crested Finch. 3ss. 14. Guyanas to Argentina.
324. *Coryphospingus pileatus.* Pileated Finch. 3ss. 13. Colombia, Venezuela, Brazil.
325. *Rhodospingus cruentus.* Crimson Finch. 11. Ecuador, Peru.
326. *Paroaria baeri.* Crimson fronted Cardinal. 2ss. 17. Brazil.
327. *Paroaria capitata.* Yellow billed Cardinal. 2ss. 17. Brazil, Bolivia, Argentina.
328. *Paroaria coronata.* Red crested Cardinal. 18. Brazil to Argentina.
329. *Paroaria dominicana.* Red cowled / Dominican Cardinal. 17. NE Brazil.
330. *Paroaria gularis.* Red capped Cardinal. 3ss. 17. S America E of Andes.

P. humberti (single specimen) is probably melanistic form of 329.

Family 167. CATAMBLYRHYNCHINAE. Plush capped Finch.

1. *Catamblyrhynchus diadema.* Plush capped Finch. 3ss. Andes, Venezuela to Argentina.

Family 168. CARDINALINAE. Cardinal Grosbeaks.

1. *Spiza americana.* Dickcissel. 16. E Canada, USA. Winters Mexico, S America.
2. *Pheucticus aureoventris.* Black backed Grosbeak. 5ss. 21. Venezuela to Argentina.
3. *Pheucticus chrysopeplus.* Yellow Grosbeak. 5ss. 20. Mexico to Venezuela.
4. *Pheucticus tibialis.* Black thighed Grosbeak. 20. Costa Rica, Panama.
5. *Pheucticus ludovicianus.* Rose breasted Grosbeak. 19. N America. Winters C & S America.
6. *Pheucticus chrysogaster.* Golden bellied Grosbeak. 20. Colombia, Ecuador, Peru.
7. *Pheucticus melanocephalus.* Black headed Grosbeak. 2ss. 21. N America, Mexico.
8. *Cardinalis cardinalis.* Cardinal. 18ss. 22. EC USA to Mexico, Guatemala.
9. *Cardinalis phoeniceus.* Vermilion Cardinal. 20. Venezuela, Colombia.
10. *Pyrrhuloxia sinuatus.* Pyrrhuloxia. 3ss. 22. Arizona, Texas.
11. *Caryothraustes canadensis.* Yellow green Grosbeak. 3ss. 17. Colombia, Venezuela, Guyanas, Brazil.
12. *Caryothraustes poliogaster.* Black faced Grosbeak. 17. Mexico to Panama.
13. *Caryothraustes humeralis.* Yellow shouldered Grosbeak. 16. Colombia, Ecuador, Brazil.
14. *Rhodothraupis celaeno.* Crimson collared Grosbeak. 19. Mexico.
15. *Periporphyrus erythromelas.* Red & Black Grosbeak. 21. Venezuela, Guyanas, Brazil.

319
320
322
323
324
321
325
326
327
328
329
330
1
CATAMBLYRHYNCHINAE
CARDINALINAE
1
2
3
4
5
6
7
8
9
10
11
12
13
14
15

EMBERIZIDAE (11)
Cardinalinae, Cardinal Grosbeaks etc.

16. *Pitylus grossus.* Slate coloured Grosbeak. 2ss. 19. Nicaragua to Argentina.
17. *Pitylus fuliginosus.* Black throated Grosbeak. 21. Brazil, Paraguay, Argentina
18. *Saltator albicollis.* Streaked Saltator. 12ss. 19. West Indies, C & N South America.
19. *Saltator atriceps.* Black headed Saltator. 6ss. 23. Mexico to Panama.
20. *Saltator atricollis.* Black throated Saltator. 21. Bolivia, Brazil, Paraguay.
21. *Saltator atripennis.* Black winged Saltator. 2ss. 21. Colombia, Ecuador.
22. *Saltator aurantiirostris.* Golden billed Saltator. 5ss. 19/21. Ecuador, N Argentina.
23. *Saltator nigriceps.* Black cowled Saltator. 22. Ecuador, Peru.
24. *Saltator cinctus.* Masked Saltator. 21. E Ecuador. (unique).
25. *Saltator coerulecens.* Greyish Saltator. 13ss. 21. Mexico to Argentina.
26. *Saltator maxillosus.* Thick billed Saltator. 20. Brazil, Paraguay, Argentina.
27. *Saltator maximus.* Buff throated Saltator. 5ss. 22. Mexico to Brazil.
28. *Saltator orenocensis.* Orinocan Saltator. 2ss. 18. Orinoco basin.
29. *Saltator rufiventris.* Rufous bellied Saltator. 22. Bolivia.
30. *Saltator similis.* Green winged Saltator. 2ss. 21. Brazil, Bolivia, Argentina.
31. *Passerina amoena.* Lazuli Bunting. 14. West of N America & Mexico.
32. *Cyanocompsa brissonii.* Ultramarine Grosbeak / Bunting. 5ss.17. S America, E of Andes, not extreme south.
33. *Guiraca caerulea.* Blue Grosbeak. 7ss. 17. S USA & Mexico to Costa Rica.
34. *Porphyrospiza caerulescens.* Blue Finch. 14. Brazil, Bolivia.
35. *Passerina ciris.* Painted Bunting. 2ss. 14. S USA & Mexico to Panama.
36. *Passerina cyanea.* Indigo Bunting. 14. E of N America. Winters Mexico, Caribbean.
37. *Cyanocompsa cyanoides.* Blue black Grosbeak. 4ss. 17. Mexico to Brazil.
38. *Cyanoloxia glaucocaerulea.* Indigo Grosbeak. 15. Brazil, N Argentina.
39. *Passerina leclancherii.* Orange breasted Bunting. 2ss. 13. Mexico.
40. *Cyanocompsa parellina.* Blue Bunting. 4ss. 14. Mexico to Nicaragua.
41. *Passerina rositae.* Rose bellied Bunting. 14. Mexico.
42. *Passerina versicolor.* Varied Bunting. 4ss. 14. SW USA to Guatemala.

16
17
18
19
20
21
22
23
24
25
26
27
28
29
30
31
32
33
34
35
36
37
38
39
40
41
42

THRAUPINAE
Tanagers (1)

1. *Orchesticus abeilli*. Brown Tanager. 18. SE Brazil.
2. *Schistoclamys.melanopsis*. Black faced Tanager. 5ss. 17. N of S America.
3. *Schistoclamys ruficapillus*. Cinnamon Tanager. 3ss. 16. E Brazil.
4. *Neothraupis fasciata*. White banded Tanager. 16. Brazil, Bolivia, Paraguay.
5. *Cypsnagra hirundinacea*. White rumped Tanager. 2ss. 15. Brazil, Bolivia, Paraguay.
6. *Conothraupis mesoleuca*. Cone Billed Tanager. 14. Mato Grosso (Brazil).
7. *Conothraupis speculigera*. Black & White Tanager. 17. Peru & Ecuador.
8. *Lamprospiza melanoleuca*. Red billed pied Tanager. 14. Guyanas, Amazonia.
9. *Cissopis leveriana*. Magpie Tanager. 2ss. 27. S America, E of Andes.
10. *Chlorornis riefferii*. Grass green Tanager. 5ss. 21. Colombia, Bolivia.
11. *Compsothraupis loricata*. Scarlet throated Tanager. 23. Brazil.
12. *Sericossopha albocristata*. White capped Tanager. 25. Venezuela to Peru.
13. *Nesospingus speculiferus*. Puerto Rican Tanager. 17. Puerto Rico.
14. *Chlorospingus canigularis*. Ashy throated Bush Tanager. 14. Costa Rica to Peru.
15. *Chlorospingus flavigularis*. Yellow throated Bush Tanager. 3ss. 16. N of South America.
16. *Chlorospingus tacarcunae*. Tacarcuna Bush Tanager. 13. Panama to Colombia.
17. *Chlorospingus flavovirens*. Yellow green Bush Tanager. 14. Ecuador.
18. *Chlorospingus inornatus*. Mount Pirre Bush Tanager. 12. Panama.
19. *Chlorospingus ophthalmicus*. Common Bush Tanager. 23ss. 14. Mexico to Argentina.
20. *Chlorospingus parvirostris*. Short billed / Yellow whiskered Bush Tanager 3ss. 15. Colombia to Bolivia.
21. *Chlorospingus pileatus*. Sooty capped Bush Tanager. 2ss. 13. Costa Rica, Panama.
22. incl. *C. p. punctulatus*. Dotted Bush Tanager. 13. Panama.
23. *Chlorospingus semifuscus*. Dusky Bush Tanager. 13. Colombia, Ecuador.
24. *Chlorospingus zeledoni*. Volcano Bush Tanager. 13. Costa Rica. (ss. of 21?).
25. *Cnemoscopus rubrirostris*. Grey hooded Bush Tanager. 2ss. 17. Peru, Venezuela.
26. *Hemispingus atropileus*. Black capped Hemispingus. 2ss. 17. Venezuela to Bolivia.
27. *Hemispingus calophrys*. Yunga's / Orange browed Hemispingus. 14. Bolivia.
28. *Hemispingus frontalis*. Oleaginous Hemispingus. 5ss. 15. Peru, Venezuela.
29. *Hemispingus goeringi*. Slaty backed Hemispingus. 15. Venezuela.
30. *Hemispingus melanotis*. Black eared Hemispingus. 6ss. 15. Venezuela to Bolivia.
31. *Hemispingus parodii*. Parodi's Tanager. 14. Peru.
32. *Hemispingus reyi*. Grey capped Hemispingus. 15. Venezuela.
33. *Hemispingus superciliaris*. Superciliarised Hemispingus. 7ss. 14. Venezuela to Bolivia.
34. *Hemispingus rufosuperciliaris*. Rufous browed Hemispingus. 15. Peru.
35. *Hemispingus trifasciatus*. Three striped Hemispingus. 14. Peru, Bolivia.
36. *Hemispingus verticalis*. Black headed Hemispingus. 14. Venezuela to Ecuador.
37. *Hemispingus xanthophthalmis*. Drab Hemispingus. 15. Peru.

1
2
3
4
5
6
7
8
9
10
11
12
13
14
15
16
17
18
19
20
21
22
23
24
25
26
27
28
29
30
31
32
33
34
35
36
37

THRAUPINAE
Tanagers (2)

38. *Pyrrhocoma ruficeps.* Chestnut headed Tanager. 13. Brazil, Paraguay, Argentina.
39. *Thlylpopsis fulviceps.* Fulvous headed Tanager. 4ss. 14. Colombia, Venezuela.
40. *Thlylopsis inornata.* Buff bellied Tanager. 14. Peru.
41. *Thlylopsis ornata.* Rufous chested Tanager. 3ss. 13. Colombia to Peru.
42. *Thlylopsis pectoralis.* Brown flanked Tanager. 13. Peru.
43. *Thlylopsis ruficeps.* Rust & Yellow Tanager. 13. Peru, Bolivia, Argentina.
44. *Thlylpopsis sordida.* Orange headed Tanager. 3ss. 17. E South America, S to Argentina.
45. *Hemithraupis flavicollis.* Yellow backed Tanager. 11ss. 14. Panama to Brazil.
46. *Hemithraupis guira.* Guira Tanager. 8ss. 13. E South America, S to Argentina.
47. *Hemithraupis ruficapilla.* Rufous headed Tanager. 2ss. 13. Brazil.
48. *Chrysothlypis chrysomelas.* Black & Yellow Tanager. 2ss. 13. Costa Rica, Panama.
49. *Chrysothlypis salmoni.* Scarlet & White Tanager. 13. Colombia, Ecuador.
50. *Nemosia Pileata.* Hooded Tanager. 6ss. 14. E S America, S to Argentina.
51. *Nemosia rourei.* Cherry throated Tanager. 14. Brazil (Rio).
52. *Phaenicophilus palmarum.* Black crowned Palm Tanager. 17. Hispaniola, Saona.
53. *Phaenicophilus poliocephalus.* Grey crowned Palm Tanager. 2ss. 17. Hispaniola.
54. *Calyptophilus frugivorus.* Chat Tanager. 3ss. 19. Hispaniola, Gonave.
55. *Nephelornis oneilli.* Pardusco. 13. C Peru.
56. *Rhodinocincla rosea* Rose breasted Thrush Tanager. 5ss. 20. Mexico to Colombia & Venezuela.
57. *Mitrospingus Cassinii.* Dusky faced Tanager. 2ss. 18. Costa Rica to Ecuador.
58. *Mitrospingus oleagineus.* Olive backed Tanager. 2ss. 19. Venezuela, Guyana, Brazil.
59. *Chlorothraupis carmioli.* Carmiol's / Olive Tanager. 4ss. 18. Nicaragua to Peru.
60. *Chlorothraupis olivacea.* Lemon spectacled Tanager. 17. Panama, Colombia, Ecuador.
61. *Chlorothraupis stolzmanni.* Ochre breasted Tanager. 2ss. 17. Colombia, Ecuador.
62. *Orthogonys chloricterus.* Olive green Tanager. 20. SE Brazi1.
63 *Eucometis penicillata.* Grey headed Tanager. 7ss. 17. Mexico to Paraguay.
64. *Lanio aurantius.* Black throated Shrike Tanager. 17. Mexico, C America.
65. *Lanio leucothorax.* White throated Shrike Tanager. 4ss. 18. Honduras, Panama.
66. *Lanio fulvus.* Fulvous Shrike Tanager. 2ss. 17. North of S America.
67. *Lanio versicolor.* White winged Shrike Tanager. 2ss. 17. Upper Amazon basin.
68. *Creurgops dentata.* Slaty Tanager. 15. Peru, Bolivia.
69. *Creurgops verticalis.* Rufous crested Tanager. 16. Venezuela to Peru.

No. 55 is sometimes placed in Family 173.

38
39
40
41
42
43
44
45
46
47
48
49
50
51
52
53
54
56
55
57
58
59
60
61
62
63
64
65
66
67
68
69

THRAUPINAE
Tanagers (3)

70. *Heterospingus rubrifrons.* Sulphur rumped Tanager. 16. Costa Rica to Ecuador.
71. *Heterospingus xanthopygius.* Scarlet browed Tanager. 3ss. 16. Nicaragua to Ecuador.
72. *Tachyphonus coronatus.* Ruby crowned Tanager. 17. Brazil, Paraguay, Argentina.
73. *Tachyphonus cristatus.* Flame crested Tanager. 10ss. 16. NE of South America.
74. *Tachyphonus delatrii.* Tawny crested Tanager. 14. Nicaragua to Ecuador.
75. *Tachyphonus luctuosus.* White shouldered Tanager. 5ss. 13. Honduras to Ecuador & Brazil.
76. *Tachyphonus nattereri.* Natterer's Tanager. 15. SW Brazil.
77. *Tachyphonus Phoenicius.* Red shouldered Tanager. 16. N of S America.
78. *Tachyphonus rufiventer.* Yellow crested Tanager. 15. Peru, Brazil, Bolivia.
79. *Tachyphonus rufus.* White lined Tanager. 17. Costa Rica to Argentina.
80. *Tachyphonus surinamus.* Fulvous crested Tanager. 4ss. 15. N of S America.
81. *Trichothraupis melanops.* Black goggled Tanager. 15. S of S America.
82. *Habia cristata.* Crested Ant Tanager. 18. W Colombia.
83. *Habia gutturalis.* Sooty Ant Tanager. 18. NW Colombia.
84. *Habia atrimaxillaris.* Black cheeked Ant Tanager. 17. Costa Rica.
85. *Habia fuscicauda.* Red throated Ant Tanager. 6ss. 17. Mexico to Colombia.
86. *Habia rubica.* Red crowned Ant Tanager. 17ss. 17. Mexico To Argentina.
87. *Piranga bidentata.* Flame coloured Tanager. 5ss. 17. Mexico to Panama.
88. *Piranga erythrocephala.* Red headed Tanager. 2ss. 14. Mexico.
89. *Piranga flava.* Hepatic Tanager. 16ss. 17. SW USA to Argentina.
90. *Piranga leucoptera.* White winged Tanager. 4ss. 14. Mexico to Bolivia.
91. *Piranga ludoviciana.* Western Tanager. 16. W N America. Winters Mexico to Panama.
92. *Piranga olivacea.* Scarlet Tanager. 17. E N America. Winters E S America.
93. *Piranga roseogularis.* Rose throated Tanager. 3ss. 14. Cozumel, Guatemala.
94. *Piranga rubra.* Summer Tanager. 3ss. 16. S USA to Mexico. Winters to Venezuela.
95. *Piranga rubriceps.* Red hooded Tanager. 18. Colombia, Ecuador, Peru.

No. 85 is very variable.
No 89. may include more than one species.

70
71
72
73
74
75
76
77
78
79
80
81
82
83
84
85
86
87
88
89
90
91
92
93
94
95

THRAUPINAE
Tanagers (4)

96. *Calochaetes coccineus.* Vermillion Tanager. 16. Colombia, Ecuador, Peru.
97. *Ramphocelus bresilius.* Brazilian Tanager. 2ss. 18. E Brazil.
98. *Ramphocelus carbo.* Silver beaked Tanager. 8ss. 17. E South America, S to Paraguay.
99. *Ramphocelus dimidiatus.* Crimson backed Tanager. 5ss. 17. Panama, Venezuela, Colombia.
100. *Ramphocelus flammigerus.* Flame rumped Tanager. 2ss. 20. W Colombia.
101. incl. *R. f. icteronotus.* Yellow rumped Tanager. 20. Panama to Ecuador.
102. *Ramphocelus melanogaster.* Huallaga / Black bellied Tanager. 2ss. 17. Peru.
103. *Ramphocelus nigrogularis.* Masked Crimson Tanager. 18. Upper Amazon basin.
104. *Ramphocelus passeirinii.* Scarlet rumped / Song Tanager. 2ss. 16. Mexico to Panama.
105. *Ramphocelus sanguinolentis.* Crimson collared Tanager. 2ss. 16. Mexico, Panama.
106. *Spindalis zena.* Stripe headed Tanager. 8ss. 17. Bahamas, Greater Antilles.
107. *Thraupis abbas.* Yellow winged Tanager. 16. Mexico to Nicaragua.
108. *Thraupis bonariensis.* Blue & Yellow Tanager. 4ss. 17. S of S America.
109. *Thraupis cyanocephala.* Blue capped Tanager. 8ss. 17. Trinidad, South America.
110. *Thraupis cyanoptera.* Azure shouldered Tanager. 19. Bolivia, Paraguay.
111. *Thraupis episcopus.* Blue Grey Tanager. 13ss. 17. Mexico to Bolivia.
112. *Thraupis ornata.* Golden chevronned Tanager. 18. SE Brazil.
113. *Thraupis palmarum.* Palm Tanager. 4ss. 17. Nicaragua to Paraguay & Bolivia.
114. *Thraupis sayaca.* Sayaca Tanager. 16ss. 17. Brazil to Uruguay, Argentina.
115. *Thraupis glaucolpa.* Glaucous Tanager. 17. Colombia, Venezuela.
116. *Cyanicterus cyanicterus.* Blue backed Tanager. 18. Venezuela, Guyanas.
117. *Buthraupis/Bangsia arcaei.* Blue & Gold Tanager. 2ss. 15. Costa Rica, Panama.
118. *Buthraupis/Bangsia aureocincta.* Gold ringed Tanager. 17. Colombia.
119. *Buthraupis/Bangsia edwardsi.* Mossbacked Tanager. 17. Colombia, Ecuador.
120. *Buthraupis eximia.* Black chested mountain Tanager. 4ss. 22. Venezuela, Ecuador.
121. *Buthraupis aureodorsalis.* Golden backed mountain Tanager. 23. Peru.
122. *Buthraupis/Bangsia melanochlamys.* Black & Gold Tanager. 17. W Colombia.
123. *Buthraupis montana.* Hooded mountain Tanager. 5ss. 22. Venezuela to Bolivia.
124. *Buthraupis/Bangsia rothschildi.* Golden crested Tanager. 17. Colombia, Ecuador.
125. *Buthraupis wetmorei.* Masked mountain Tanager. 22. Colombia, Ecuador.
126. *Wetmorethraupis sterrohopteron.* Orange throated / Wetmore's Tanager. 19. Peru.

96
97
98
99
100
101
102
103
104
105
106
107
108
109
110
111
112
113
114
115
116
117
118
119
120
121
122
123
124
125
126

THRAUPINAE
Tanagers (5)

127. *Anisognathus somptuosus.* Blue shouldered mountain Tanager. 9ss. 18. Venezuela to Bolivia.
128. *Anisognathus igniventris.* Scarlet belied mountain Tanager. 4ss. 19. Venezuela to Bolivia.
129. *Anisognathus lachrymosus.* Lacrimose mountain Tanager. 9ss. 18. Venezuela to Peru.
130. *Anisognathus melanogenys.* Santa Marta mountain Tanager. 19. Colombia.
131. *Anisognathus notabilis.* Black chinned mountain Tanager. 20. Colombia, Ecuador.
132. *Stephanophorus diadematus.* Diademed Tanager. 19. Brazil to Argentina.
133. *Iridosornis analis.* Yellow throated Tanager. 15. Ecuador, Peru.
134. *Iridosornis jelskii.* Golden collared Tanager. 2ss. 15. Peru, Bolivia.
135. *Iridosornis porphyrocephala.* Purplish mantled Tanager. 15. Colombia, Ecuador.
136. *Iridosornis rufivertex.* Golden crowned Tanager. 4ss. 17. Venezuela to Peru.
137. *Iridosornis reinhardti.* Yellow scarfed Tanager. 15. Peru.
138. *Dubusia taeniata.* Buff breasted mountain Tanager. 3ss. 18. Venezuela to Peru.
139. *Delothraupis castaneoventris.* Chestnut bellied mountain Tanager. 2ss. 16. Peru & Bolivia.
140. *Pipraeidea melanota.* Fawn breasted Tanager. 2ss. 15. Peru to Argentina.
141. *Euphonia affinis.* Scrub Euphonia. 2ss. 10. Mexico to Costa Rica.
142. incl. *E. a. godmani.* Pale vented Euphonia. 10. Mexico.
143. *Euphonia anneae.* Tawny capped Euphonia. 2ss. 12. Costa Rica to Colombia.
144. *Euphonia cayannensis.* Golden sided Euphonia. 11. Venezuela, Guyanas, Brazil.
145. *Euphonia chalybea.* Green throated Euphonia. 12. Brazil to Argentina.
146. *Euphonia chlorotica.* Purple throated Euphonia. 5ss. 11. E S America.
147. *Euphonia chrysopasta.* White lored / Golden bellied Euphonia. 2ss. 11. Amazon & Orinoco basins.
148. *Euphonia concinna.* Velvet fronted Euphonia. 10. Colombia.
149. *Euphonia cyanocephala.* Golden rumped Euphonia. 3ss. 11. Brazil to Argentina.
150. *Euphonia finschi.* Finsch's Euphonia. 10. Guyanas.
151. *Euphonia fulvicrissa.* Fulvous vented Euphonia. 3ss. 10. Panama to Ecuador.
152. *Euphonia gouldi.* Olive backed Euphonia. 3ss. 9. Mexico to Panama.
153. *Euphonia hirundinacea.* Yellow throated Euphonia. 5ss. 10. Mexico to Panama.
154. *Euphonia imitans.* Spot crowned Euphonia. 10. Costa Rica, Panama.
155. *Euphonia jamaica.* Jamaican Euphonia. 12. Jamaica.
156. *Euphonia laniirostris.* Thick billed Euphonia. 5ss. 10. Costa Rica to Peru.
157. *Euphonia luteicapilla.* Yellow crowned Euphonia. 9. Central America.
158. *Euphonia mesochrysa.* Bronze green Euphonia. 3ss. 10. Colombia to Bolivia.
159. *Euphonia minuta.* White vented Euphonia. 2ss. 10. Mexico to Brazil, Ecuador.
160. *Euphonia musica.* Antillean Euphonia. 9ss. 10. Lesser Antilles, S America.
161. *Euphonia elegantissima.* Blue hooded Euphonia. 10. Mexico to Honduras.
162. *Euphonia pectoralis.* Chestnut bellied Euphonia. 12. Brazil to Argentina.
163. *Euphonia plumbea.* Plumbeous Euphonia. 9. Venezuela to Brazil.
164. *Euphonia rufiventris.* Rufous bellied Euphonia. 11. Orinoco & Amazon basins.
165. *Euphonia saturata.* Orange crowned Euphonia. 11. Colombia, Ecuador, Peru.
166. *Euphonia trinitatis.* Trinidad Euphonia. 10. Trinidad, Tobago, N S America.
167. *Euphonia violacea.* Violaceous Euphonia. 3ss. 12. Trinidad, Most S America.
168. *Euphonia xanthogaster.* Orange bellied Euphonia. 9ss. 11. Panama, E S America.

127
128
129
130
131
132
133
134
135
136
137
138
139
140
141
142
143
144
145
146
147
148
149
150
151
152
153
154
155
156
157
158
159
160
161
162
163
164
165
166
167
168

THRAUPINAE
Tanagers (6)

169. *Chlorophonia cyanea*. Blue naped Chlorophonia. 7ss. 12. South America.
170. *Chlorophonia flavirostris*. Yellow collared Chlorophonia. 2ss. 10. NW S America.
171. *Chlorophonia occipitalis*. Blue crowned Chlorophonia. 2ss. 12. Mexico to Nicaragua.
172. *Chlorophonia callophrys*. Golden browed Tanager. 13. Costa Rica, Panama.
173. *Chlorophonia pyrrhophrys*. Chestnut breasted Chlorophonia. 12. NW South America.
174. *Chlorochrysa calliparaea*. Orange eared Tanager. 3ss. 13. Colombia to Bolivia.
175. *Chlorochrysa nitidissima*. Multicoloured Tanager. 12. Colombia.
176. *Chlorochrysa phoenicotis*. Glistening green Tanager. 13. Colombia, Ecuador.
177. *Tangara meyerdeschauenseei*. Green capped Tanager. 14. E Peru.
178. *Tangara argyrofenges*. Straw backed / Green throated Tanager. 2ss. 12. Peru, Bolivia.
179. *Tangara arthus*. Golden Tanager. 9ss. 15. Venezuela, Colombia.
180 incl. *T. a. aequatorialis*. Ecuadorian Golden Tanager. 15. Ecuador, Peru.
181. *Tangara cabanisi*. Azure rumped Tanager. 15. Mexico, Guatemala.
182. *Tangara callophrys*. Opal crowned Tanager. 15. Colombia, Ecuador, Brazil, Peru.
183. *Tangara cayana*. Burnished Buff Tanager. 7ss. 15. NE South America.
184. *Tangara chilensis*. Paradise Tanager. 14ss. 15. NE & C S America.
185. *Tangara chrysotis*. Golden eared Tanager. 15. Colombia to Bolivia.
186. *Tangara cucullata*. Hooded / Lesser Antillean Tanager. 2ss. 12. St. Vincent, Grenada.
187. *Tangara cyanicollis*. Blue necked Tanager. 7ss. 14. Colombia to Brazil.
188. *Tangara cyanocephala*. Red necked Tanager. 3ss. 14. Brazil, Paraguay, Argentina.
189. *Tangara cyanoptera*. Black headed Tanager. 2ss. 12. Colombia, Venezuela, Guyana, Brazil.
190. *Tangara cyanotis*. Blue browed Tanager. 2ss. 12. NW S America.
191. *Tangara cyanoventris*. Gilt edged Tanager. 15. SE Brazil.
192. *Tangara desmaresti*. Brassy breasted Tanager. 15. SE Brazil coast.
193. *Tangara dowii*. Spangle cheeked Tanager. 2ss. 13. Costa Rica, Panama.
194. *Tangara fucosa*. Green naped Tanager. 12. E Panama.
195. *Tangara fastuosa*. Superb / Seven coloured Tanager. 15. E Brazil.
196. *Tangara florida*. Emerald Tanager. 2ss. 15. Costa Rica, Panama, Colombia.
197. *Tangara guttata*. Speckled Tanager. 6ss. 14. Trinidad, Costa Rica, N South America.
198. incl. *T. g. chrysophrys*. Yellow fronted Tanager. 13. Venezuela to Brazil .
199. *Tangara gyrola*. Bay headed Tanager. 9ss. 13. Costa Rica to Bolivia, Ecuador.
200. *Tangara viridissima*. Bay & Green Tanager. 13 Trinidad ,Venezuela.
201. *Tangara heinei*. Black capped Tanager. 13. Venezuela, Colombia, Ecuador.
202. *Tangara philippsi*. Sira Tanager. 13. E Peru.
203. *Tangara icterocephala*. Silver throated Tanager. 3ss. 14. Costa Rica to Ecuador.
204. *Tangara inornata*. Plain coloured Tanager. 3ss. 13. Costa Rica, Panama, Colombia.
205. *Tangara johannae*. Blue whiskered Tanager. 15. Colombia, Ecuador.
206. *Tangara labradoroides*. Metallic green Tanager. 2ss. 13. NW South America.
207. *Tangara larvata*. Golden masked / hooded Tanager. 4ss. 13. Mexico to Colombia, Ecuador.
208. *Tangara lavinia*. Rufous winged Tanager. 4ss. 12. Guatemala to Ecuador.
209. *Tangara mexicana*. Turquoise Tanager. 5ss. 14. Trinidad, N of S America.
210. *Tangara nigrocincta*. Masked Tanager. 14. Amazonia.
211. *Tangara nigroviridis*. Beryl spangled Tanager. 4ss. 13. Venezuela to Bolivia
212. *Tangara palmeri*. Grey & Gold Tanager. 16. Panama, Colombia, Ecuador.
213. *Tangara parzudakii*. Flame faced Tanager. 3ss. 15. Venezuela to Peru.
214. *Tangara punctata*. Spotted Tanager. 5ss. 12. Upper Amazon basin.

Tangara arnaulti is a hybrid of 182 X 212.
Tangara gouldii is a hybrid of 191 X 190.

169
170
171
172
173
174
175
176
177
178
179
180
181
182
183
184
185
186
187
188
189
190
191
192
193
194
195
196
197
198
201
199
200
206
203
204
205
206
202
208
209
210
211
212
213
214

THRAUPINAE, COERIBIDAE
Tanagers (7), Honeycreepers, Flower Piercers, Conebills

215. *Tangara peruviana.* Black backed Tanager. 15. SE Brazil.
216. *Tangara preciosa.* Chestnut backed Tanager. 17. Brazil, Paraguay, Uruguay, Argentina.
217. *Tangara ruficervix.* Golden naped Tanager. 6ss. 14. Colombia to Bolivia.
218. *Tangara rufigenis.* Rufous cheeked Tanager. 15. Venezuela.
219. *Tangara rufigula.* Rufous throated Tanager. 13. Colombia, Ecuador.
220. *Tangara schrankii.* Green & Gold Tanager. 3ss. 15. Colombia, Amazon basin.
221. *Tangara seledon.* Green headed Tanager. 15. SE Brazil to Argentina.
222. *Tangara varia.* Dotted Tanager. 11. Venezuela, Guyanas, Brazil.
223. *Tangara vassorii.* Blue & Black Tanager. 3ss. 15. Venezuela, Colombia, Ecuador.
224. *Tangara velia.* Opal rumped Tanager. 4ss. 15. NE of S America.
225. *Tangara viridicollis.* Silvery Tanager. 2ss. 14. Peru, Ecuador.
226. *Tangara vitriolina.* Scrub Tanager. 15. Colombia, Ecuador.
227. *Tangara xanthocephala.* Saffron crowned Tanager. 3ss. 14. Venezuela to Bolivia.
228. *Tangara xanthrogastra.* Yellow bellied Tanager. 2ss. 12. North of S America.
229. *Tangara/Iridophanes pulcherrima.* Yellow / Golden collared Tanager / Honey-Creeper 2ss. 13. Colombia, Ecuador.

Family 170. COERIBIDAE. Honeycreepers, Flower Piercers, Conebills.

1. *Dacnis albiventris.* White bellied Dacnis. 12. Upper Amazon basin.
2. *Dacnis berlepschi.* Scarlet breasted Dacnis. 12. Colombia, Ecuador.
3. *Dacnis cayana.* Blue Dacnis. 8ss. 14. Nicaragua to Argentina.
4. *Dacnis flaviventer.* Yellow bellied Dacnis. 2ss. 12. North of S America.
5. *Pseudodacnis hartlaubi.* Turquoise Dacnis Tanager. 11. Colombia.
6. *Dacnis lineata.* Black faced Dacnis. 3ss. 12. North of S America.
7. *Dacnis nigripes.* Black legged Dacnis. 12. SE Brazil.
8. *Dacnis venusta.* Scarlet thighed Dacnis. 2ss. 13. Costa Rica to Ecuador.
9. *Dacnis viguieri.* Viridian Dacnis. 12. Panama, Colombia.
10. *Chlorophanes spiza.* Green Honeycreeper. 7ss. 14. Mexico to Brazil.
11. *Cyanerpes caeruleus.* Purple Honeycreeper. 5ss. 11. S America S to Brazil.
12. *Cyanerpes cyaneus.* Red legged Honeycreeper. 12ss. 14. W Indies, N of S America.
13. *Cyanerpes lucidus.* Shining Honeycreeper. 2ss. 11. Mexico, Panama, Colombia.
14. *Cyanerpes nitidus.* Short billed Honeycreeper. 2ss. 11. Colombia, Venezuela, Brazil.
15. *Xenodacnis parina.* Tit-like Dacnis. 3ss. 12. Peru.

215
216
217
218
219
220
221
222
223
224
225
226
227
228
229
COEREBIDAE
1
2
3
4
5
6
7
8
9
10
11
12
13
14
15

THRAUPINAE (8), COERIBIDAE, TERSINAE, ZELEDONIIDAE
Flower Piercers, Conebills, Swallow Tanager, Wren Thrush

16. *Diglossa albilatera.* White sided Flowerpiercer. 4ss. 13. Venezuela to Peru.
17. *Diglossa baritura.* Cinnamon bellied Flowerpiercer. 9ss. 13. Mexico to N S America
18. incl. *D. b. sittoides.* Rusty Flowerpiercer. 12. Bolivia, Argentina.
19. *D. b. plumbea.* Slaty Flowerpiercer. 13. Costa Rica, Panama.
20. *Diglossopis caerulescens.* Bluish Flowerpiercer. 6ss. 14. Venezuela to Brazil.
21. *Diglossa carbonaria.* Carbonated Flowerpiercer. 7ss. 13. Bolivia.
22. incl. *D. c. humeralis.* Black Flowerpiercer. 13. Colombia, Venezuela.
23. *D. c. brunneiventris.* Black throated Flowerpiercer. 13. Colombia, Chile.
24. *D. c. gloriosa.* Merida Flowerpiercer. 13. Venezuela.
25. *Diglossopis cyanea.* Masked Flowerpiercer. 5ss. 15. Venezuela to Bolivia.
26. *Diglossa duidae.* Scaled Flowerpiercer. 2ss. 15. Venezuela.
27. *Diglossopis glauca.* Deep blue Flowerpiercer. 2ss. 12. Colombia to Bolivia.
28. *Diglossopis indigotica.* Indigo Flowerpiercer. 12. Colombia, Ecuador.
29. *Diglossa lafresnayei.* Glossy Flowerpiercer. 6ss. 15. Venezuela to Bolivia.
30. incl. *D. l. gloriosissima.* Chestnut bellied Flowerpiercer. 14. N South America.
31. *D. l. mysticalis.* Moustached Flowerpiercer. 14. Bolivia, Peru.
32. *Diglossa major.* Greater Flowerpiercer. 4ss. 17. Venezuela, N Brazil.
33. *Diglossa venezuelensis.* Venezuelan Flowerpiercer. 15. Venezuela.
34. *Euneornis campestris.* Orangequit. 14. Jamaica.
35. *Oreomanes fraseri.* Giant Conebill. 3ss. 18. Colombia to Bolivia.

The following twelve species are commonly included in Family 123. Parulidae.

36. *Conirostrum albifrons.* Capped Conebill. 6ss. 14. Andes, NW South America.
37. *Conirostrum bicolor.* Bicoloured Conebill. 2ss. 10. Amazonia.
38. *Conirostrum cinereum.* Cinereous Conebill. 3ss. 13. Colombia to Bolivia.
39. *Conirostrum ferrugineiventris.* White browed Conebill. 13. Peru, Bolivia.
40. *Conirostrum leucogenys.* White eared Conebill. 3ss. 10. Panama, Venezuela, Colombia.
41. *Conirostrum margaritae.* Pearly breasted Conebill. 10. Brazil, Peru.
42. *Conirostrum rufum.* Rufous browed Conebill. 14. Colombia.
43. *Conirostrum sitticolor.* Blue backed Conebill. 3ss. 14. Venezuela to Bolivia.
44. *Conirostrum speciosum.* Chestnut vented Conebill. 3ss. 11. Local S America.
45. *Conirostrum tamarugensis.* Tamarugo Conebill. 13. Chile, Peru.
46. *Coereba flaveola.* Bananaquit. 41ss. 11. Caribbean, most of S America.
47. incl. *C. f. laurae.* Black Bananaquit. 11. Los Testigos Is.

Family 171. TERSINAE. Swallow Tanager.

1. *Tersina viridis.* Swallow Tanager. 3ss. 13. Panama to Argentina (E of Andes).

Family 172. ZELEDONIIDAE. Wren Thrush.

1. *Zeledonia coronata.* Wren Thrush. 12. Costa Rica, Panama.

16
17
19
20
24
22
25
26
27
28
29
30
31
32
33
34
35
36
37
38
39
40
41
42
43
44
45
46
47
18
23
21
TERSINAE
1
ZELEDONIIDAE
1

PARULIDAE (1) American Wood Warblers

1. *Mniotilta varia.* Black & White Warbler. 13. N America. Winters to N of S America.
2. *Vermivora bachmanni.* Bachman's Warbler. 12. SE USA. Winters Caribbean.
3. *Vermivora celata.* Orange crowned Warbler. 4ss. 13. N America. Winters Caribbean.
4. *Vermivora chrysoptera.* Golden winged Warbler. 12. N America. Winters to Venezuela.
5. *Vermivora crissalis.* Colima Warbler. 15. Texas, Mexico.
6. *Vermivora/Parula gutturalis.* Flame throated Warbler. 11. Costa Rica, Panama.
7. *Vermivora luciae.* Lucy's Warbler. 11. SW USA, W Mexico.
8. *Vermivora peregrina.* Tennessee Warbler. 12. Canada, USA. Winters to Venezuela.
9. *Vermivora pinus.* Blue winged Warbler. 12. EC USA. Winters Caribbean, Colombia.
10. *Vermivora ruficapilla.* Nashville Warbler. 2ss. 12. N America. Winters to Guatemala.
11. *Vermivora/Parula superciliosa.* Crescent-chested Warbler. 12. Mexico to Nicaragua.
12. *Vermivora virginiae.* Virginia's Warbler. 12. E USA. Winters Mexico.
13. (constant hybrids) *v. leucobronchialis.* Brewster's Warbler. 12. E USA.
14. (between 4 & 9.)*V. lawrencii.* Lawrence's Warbler. 12. E USA.
15. *Parula americana.* Northern Parula Warbler. 11. EC USA. Winters C America, West Indies.
16. *Parula pitiayumi.* Tropical Parula / Olive backed Warbler. 14ss. 11. C & S America to Argentina.
17. *Dendroica adelaidae.* Adelaide's Warbler. 3ss. 12. Puerto Rico, Barbuda, St. Lucia.
18. *Dendroica angelae.* Elfin Woods Warbler. 13. Puerto Rico.
19. *Dendroica caerulescens.* Black throated Blue Warbler. 2ss. 13. N America. Winters N of S America.
20. *Dendroica castanea.* Bay breasted Warbler. 14. E N America. Winters to Venezuela.
21. *Dendroica cerulea.* Cerulean Warbler. 12. N America. Winters S America.
22. *Dendroica chrysoparia.* Golden cheeked Warbler. 14. Texas. Winters to Nicaragua.
23. *Dendroica coronata.* Yellow rumped / Myrtle Warbler. 4ss. 14. N & C America.
24. incl. *D. c. auduboni.* Audubon's Warbler. 14. Canada to C America.
25. *Dendroica discolor.* Prairie Warbler. 2ss. 13. E USA. Winters West Indies.
26. *Dendroica dominica.* Yellow throated Warbler. 4ss. 14. SE USA. Winters Bahamas Cuba, Jamaica.
27. *Dendroica fusca.* Blackburnian Warbler. 13. N America. Winters Guatemala to Peru.
28. *Dendroica graciae.* Grace's Warbler. 4ss. 13. WC USA to Nicaragua.
29. *Dendroica kirtlandii.* Kirtland's Warbler. 15. Michigan. Winters Bahamas.
30. *Dendroica magnolia.* Magnolia Warbler. 13. N America. Winters Gr. Antilles, Panama.
31. *Dendroica nigrescens.* Black throated Grey Warbler. 2ss. 13. Br. Colombia to Mexico
32. *Dendroica occidentalis.* Hermit Warbler. 14. USA. Winters to Nicaragua.
33. *Dendroica palmarum.* Palm Warbler. 2ss. 14. N America. Winters to C & S America.

1
2
3
4
5
6
7
8
NB
9
10
11
12
- 13 -
14
15
16
17
18
19
20
21
22
23
24
25
26
27
28
29
30
31
32
33

PARULIDAE (2)
American Wood Warblers, Yellowthroats

34. *Dendroica pensylvanica*. Chestnut sided Warbler. 13. N America. Winters C & S America.
35. *Dendroica petechia*. Yellow Warbler. 37ss. 13. All Americas incl. Caribbean.
36. *Dendroica pharetra*. Arrow headed Warbler. 13. Jamaica.
37. *Dendroica pinus*. Pine Warbler. 4ss. 14. N America, Bahamas, Hispaniola.
38. *Dendroica pityophila*. Olive capped Warbler. 12. Cuba, Bahamas .
39. *Dendroica plumbea*. Plumbeous Warbler. 14. Dominica, Guadeloupe.
40. *Dendroica striata*. Blackpoll Warbler. 14. N America. Winters Panama to Chile.
41. *Dendroica tigrina*. Cape May Warbler. 13. Winters C America, W Indies.
42. *Dendroica townsendi*. Townsend's Warbler. 13. Alaska, N USA. Winters C America.
43. *Dendroica virens*. Black throated Green Warbler. 13. Canada, E USA. Winters Mexico.
44. *Dendroica vitellina*. Vitelline Warbler. 3ss. 13. Cayman & Swan Is.
45. *Catharopeza bishopi*. Whistling Warbler. 14. St Vincent.
46. *Seiurus aurocapillus*. Ovenbird. 3ss. 15. Canada, USA. Winters to Venezuela.
47. *Seiurus motacilla*. Louisiana Waterthrush. 15. CE USA. Winters Caribbean, Venezuela.
48. *Seiurus noveboracensis*. Northern Waterthrush. 3ss. 15. Canada, N USA. Winters to S USA & N of S America.
49. *Limnothlypis swainsoni*. Swainson's Warbler. 14. CE USA. Winters C America.
50. *Helmitheros vermivorus*. Worm eating Warbler. 13. E USA. Winters C America.
51. *Protonotaria citrea*. Prothonotary Warbler. 14. E USA. Winters to N of S America.
52. *Geothlypis aequinoctalis*. Masked Yellowthroat. 4ss. 13. Tropical S America.
53. *Geothlypis chiriquensis*. Chiriqui Yellowthroat. 12. Chiriqui.
54. *Geothlypis/oporornis agilis*. Connecticut Warbler. 15. N America. Winters S America.
55. *Geothlypis/oporornis formosa*. Kentucky Warbler. 13. E USA. Winters to S America.
56. *Geothlypis nelsoni*. Hooded Yellowthroat. 2ss. 12. Mexico.
57. *Geothlypis/Oporornis philadelphia*. Mourning Warbler. 13. N America. Winters N of S America.
58. *Geothlypis/Oporornis tolmiei*. McGillivray's Warbler. 13. N America. Winters to Panama.
59. *Geothlypis/Chamaethlypis poliocephala*. Grey crowned Yellowthroat. 7ss. 14. Texas, Mexico & C America.
60. *Geothlypis rostrata*. Bahama Yellowthroat. 3ss. 15. Bahamas.
61. *Geothlypis semiflava*. Olive crowned Yellowthroat. 2ss. 12. Honduras to Ecuador.
62. *Geothlypis speciosa*. Black-polled Yellowthroat. 2ss. 13. Mexico.
63. *Geothlypis trichas*. Common Yellowthroat. 15ss. 13. N America, Mexico. Winters Colombia, Venezuela.
64. incl. *G. t. chapalensis*. Chapala Yellowthroat. 13. Jalisco.
65. *Geothlypis beldingi*. Peninsular Yellowthroat. 2ss. 13. Baja, California.
66. *Geothlypis flavovelata*. Altamira / Yellow crowned Yellowthroat. 13. Mexico.

34
NB
35
36
37
38
39
40
41
42
43
44
45
46
47
48
49
50
51
52
53
54
55
56
57
58
59
60
61
62
63
64
65
66

PARULIDAE (3)
American Wood Warblers, Redstarts, Chats.

67. *Microligea palustris.* Green tailed Ground Warbler. 2ss. 14. Hispaniola.
68. *Teretistris fernandinae.* Yellow headed Warbler. 13. Cuba, Is. of Pines.
69. *Teretistris fornsi.* Oriente Warbler. 13. Cuba.
70. *Leucopeza semperi.* Semper's Warbler. 14. St Lucia.
71. *Wilsonia canadensis.* Canada Warbler. 13. Canada, USA. Winters C to S America.
72. *Wilsonia citrina.* Hooded Warbler. 13. Canada, USA. Winters Mexico to Panama.
73. *Wilsonia pusilla.* Wilson's Warbler. 3ss. 12. Canada, USA. Winters Mexico, Panama.
74. *Cardellina rubrifrons.* Red faced Warbler. 14. SW USA. Winters Mexico, C America.
75. *Ergaticus ruber.* Red Warbler. 3ss. 12. Mexico.
76. *Ergaticus versicolor.* Pink headed Warbler. 12. Mexico, Guatemala.
77. *Setophaga ruticilla.* American Redstart. 13. N America. Winters to Peru & Guyanas.
78. *Myioborus albifacies.* White faced Redstart. 14. S Venezuela.
79. *Myioborus albifrons.* White fronted Redstart. 13. W Venezuela.
80. *Myioborus brunniceps.* Brown capped Redstart. 4ss. 13. S America, E of Andes
81. *Myioborus castaneocapillus.* Tepui Redstart. 12. Venezuela to Brazil.
82. *Myioborus cardonai.* Saffron breasted Redstart. 12. Venezuela.
83. *Myioborus flavivertex.* Yellow crowned Redstart. 14. Colombia.
84. *Myioborus melanocephalus.* Spectacled Redstart. 5ss. 14. Colombia to Bolivia.
85. *Myioborus miniatus.* Slate throated Redstart. 12ss. 15. Mexico to Brazil.
86. *Myioborus ornatus.* Golden fronted Redstart. 2ss. 12. Colombia, Venezuela.
87. *Myioborus pariae.* Yellow faced Redstart. 13. Venezuela.
88. *Myioborus pictus.* Painted Redstart. 2ss. 15. Arizona to Nicaragua.
89. *Myioborus torquatus.* Collared Redstart. 12. Costa Rica, Panama.
90. *Euthlypis lachrymosa.* Fan tailed Warbler. 3ss. 14. Mexico to Nicaragua.
91. *Basileuterus basilicus.* Santa Marta Warbler. 15. Colombia.
92. *Basileuterus belli.* Golden browed Warbler. 5ss. 12. Mexico, C America.
93. *Basileuterus bivittatus.* Two banded Warbler. 3ss. 14. Much of South America.
94. *Basileuterus chrysogaster.* Golden bellied Warbler. 2ss. 12. Colombia, Ecuador, Peru.
95. *Basileuterus cinereicollis.* Grey throated Warbler. 2ss. 14. Colombia.
96. *Basileuterus conspicillatus.* White lored Warbler. 15. Colombia.
97. *Basileuterus coronatus.* Russet crowned Warbler. 7ss. 15. Colombia.
98. *Basileuterus culicivorus.* Golden crowned Warbler. 13ss. 13. Mexico to Uruguay.
99. *Basileuterus flaveolus.* Flavescent Warbler. 14. Colombia to Paraguay.
100. *Basileuterus fraseri.* Grey & Gold Warbler. 2ss. 15. Ecuador, Peru.
101. *Basileuterus griseiceps.* Grey headed Warbler. 14. Venezuela.
102. *Basileuterus hypoleucus.* White bellied Warbler. 12. Brazil, Paraguay.
103. *Basileuterus leucoblepharus.* White browed Warbler. 2ss. 15. SW of S America.
104. *Basileuterus leucophrys.* White striped Warbler. 16. SC Brazil.
105. *Basileuterus luteoviridis.* Citrine Warbler. 5ss. 14. NW of S America.
106. *Basileuterus melanogenys.* Black cheeked Warbler. 4ss. 13. C America.
107. *Basileuterus nigrocristatus.* Black crested Warbler. 14. Venezuela, Peru.
108. *Basileuterus rufifrons.* Rufous capped Warbler. 8ss. 13. Mexico to N South America.
109. *Basileuterus ignotus.* Pirre Warbler. 12. Panama.
110. *Basileuterus delattrii.* Delattre Warbler. 12. Guatemala to Costa Rica.
111. *Basileuterus signatus.* Pale legged Warbler. 2ss. 13. Peru to Argentina.
112. *Basileuterus trifasciatus.* Three banded Warbler. 2ss. 12. Ecuador, Peru.
113. *Basileuterus tristriatus.* Three striped Warbler. 12ss. 13. Panama to Bolivia.
114. *Basileuterus rivularis.* (Neotropic) River Warbler. 9ss. 12. S America.
115. *Basileuterus fulvicauda.* Buff rumped Warbler. 14. C & S America.
116. *Peucedramus taeniatus.* Olive Warbler. 6ss. 13. Arizona to Nicaragua.
117. *Xenoligea montana.* White winged Warbler. 14. Hispaniola.
118. *Granatellus pelzelni.* Rose breasted Chat. 2ss. 12. Amazonia.
119. *Granatellus sallaei.* Grey throated Chat. 2ss. 12. Mexico to Belize.
120. *Granatellus venustus.* Red breasted Chat. 3ss. 15. Mexico.
121. incl. *G. v. fracescae.* Tres Marias Chat. 15. Tres Marias Is.
122. *Icteria virens.* Yellow breasted Chat. 3ss. 19. Canada, USA. Winters C America.

71
72
73
67
68
69
70
74
75
76
77
78
79
80
82
83
84
85
86
87
88
89
90
91
92
93
94
95
96
97
98
99
100
101
102
103
104
105
106
107
108
110
111
112
113
114
115
109
116
118
81
117
119
120
121
122

DREPANIDIDAE
Hawaiian Honeycreepers

1. *Himatione sanguinea.* Apapane. 13. All Hawaiian Is.
2. *Himatione freethi.* Laysan Honeycreeper . 13. (extinct.)
3. *Palmeria dolci.* Akohekohe / Crested Honeycreeper. 17. Maui. (v scarce).
4. *Chiropody anna.* Ula A Hawane. 1l. Hawaii. (probably extinct)
5. *Vestiaria coccinea.* Iiwi. 14. Highlands of Main Is.
6. *Drepanis pacifica.* Mamo. 20. Hawaii. (extinct).
7. *Drepanis funerea.* Black Mamo. 20. Molokai. (extinct.)
8. *Viridonia/Chlorodrepanis/Loxops virens.* Amakihi. 4ss. 12. Oahu, Maui, Hawaii.
9. *Viridonia /C/L stejnegeri.* Kauai Amakihi. 12. Kauai.
10. *Viridonia/C/L parva.* Lesser Amakihi / Anianiau. 1l. Kauai. (extinct).
11. *Viridonia/C/L sagittirostris.* Large Amakihi / Green Solitaire. 18. Hawaii. (Probably extinct)
12. *Paroreomyza/Loxops maculata.* Oahu Creeper / Alauahio. 6ss. 1l. Oahu.
13. incl. *P. m. montana.* Maui Creeper. 12. Lanai. (extinct). Maui.
14. *P. m. flammea.* Molokai Creeper / Kakawahie. 13. Molokai.
15. *Paroreomyza/Oreomystis bairdi.* Kauai Creeper / Akikiki. 13. Kauai.
16. *Paroreomyza/Oreomystis mana.* Olive green / Hawaii Creeper. 1l. Hawaii.
17. *Loxos coccinea.* Hawaii Akepa. 4ss. 12. Hawaii.
18. incl. *L. c. rufa.* Oahu Akepa. 1l. Oahu.
19. *L. c. ochracea.* Maui Akepa. 1l. Maui.
20. *L. c. caeruleirostris.* Kauai Akepa/Akekee. 12. Kauai.
21. *Hemignathus obscurus.* Akialoa. 19. Hawaii.(extinct).
22. *Hemignathus procerus.*=Ellisianus. Kauai Akialoa. 19. Kauai.
23. *Hemignathus lucidus.* Nakupuu. 4ss. 14. Maui, Kauai.
24. *Hemignathus wilsoni.* Akiapolaau. 19. Hawaii.
25. *Pseudonestor xanthophrys.* Maui Parrotbill. 14. Maui.
26. *Psittirostra psittacea.* Ou. 16. Hawaii, Kauai.
27. *Dysmorodrepanis munroi.* Lanai Hookbill. 15. Lanai. (extinct).
28. *Telespiza(toxoides) ultima.* Nihoa Finch. 17. Nihoa.
29. *Loxoides(Telespiza)cantans.* Laysan Canary / Finchbill. 2ss. 17. Laysan, Nihoa.
30. *Loxoides(Rhodocanthis)palmeri.* Greater Koa Finch / Hopue. 22. Hawaii. (extinct)
31. *Loxoides(Psittarostra)flaviceps.* Lesser Koa Finch. 20. Hawaii. (extinct)
32. *Loxoides(Psittarostra)kona.* Kona / Grosbeak Finch. 18. Hawaii. (extinct)
33. *Loxoides(Psittarostra)bailleui.* Palila 14. Hawaii.
34. *Melamprosops Phoeosoma.* Pol 'o' Uli / Black faced Honeycreeper. 13. Maui.

JUV
1
3
JUV
5
7
2
6
4
9
8
10
22
20
17
21
23
11
18
19
13
24
14
25
26
15
12
16
27
30
31
29
28
33
32
34

VIREONIDAE
Peppershrikes, Vireos, Greenlets

1. *Cyclarhis gujanensis.* Rufous browed Peppershrike. 21ss. 15. Mexico to Argentina
2. *Cyclarhis nigrirostris.* Black billed Peppershrike. 2ss. 15. Colombia, Ecuador.
3. *Vireolanius melitophrys.* Chestnut sided Shrike-Vireo. 2ss. 20. Mexico, Guatemala.
4. *Vireolanius pulchellus.* Green Shrike-Vireo. 4ss. 14. Mexico, C America.
5. *Vireolanius eximius.* Yellow browed Shrike-Vireo. 14. Colombia, Venezuela.
6. *Vireolanius l. mikettae* Grey capped Shrike-Vireo. 14. Colombia, Ecuador.
7. *Vireolanius leucotis.* Slaty capped Shrike-Vireo. 4ss. 14. Amazonia.
8. *Vireo(Neochloe)brevipennis.* Slaty Vireo. 11. S Mexico.
9. *Vireo huttoni.* Hutton's Vireo. 8ss. 13. W America, Vancouver to Guatemala.
10. *Vireo atricapillus.* Black capped Vireo. 11. Kansas to Mexico.
11. *Vireo griseus.* White eyed Vireo. 6ss. 13. ES USA, Mexico, Bermuda.

12 incl. *V. g. perquisitor.* Veracruz Vireo. 11. EC Mexico.

13. *Vireo caribaeus.* St Andrew Vireo. 12. St Andrew Is.
14. *Vireo crassirostris.* Thick billed Vireo. 3ss. 12. Bahamas, West Indies.
15. *Vireo gundlachii.* Cuban Vireo. 3ss. 13. Cuba & Isle of Pines.
16. *Vireo modestus.* Jamaica Vireo. 12. Jamaica.
17. *Vireo pallens.* Mangrove / Pale Vireo. 4ss. 11. Coasts Mexico, Guatemala.
18. *Vireo bairdi.* Cozumel Vireo. 11. Cozumel Is.
19. *Vireo bellii.* Bell's Vireo. 5ss. 12. W USA, Mexico. Winters to Nicaragua.
20. *Vireo vicinior.* Grey Vireo. 14. SW USA. Winters Mexico.
21. *Vireo nelsoni.* Dwarf Vireo. 10. S Mexico.
22. *Vireo hypochryseus.* Golden Vireo. 3ss. 12. Mexico.
23. *Vireo nanus.* Flat billed Vireo. 12. Hispaniola, Gonave Is.
24. *Vireo latimeri.* Puerto Rican Vireo. 12. Puerto Rico.
25. *Vireo osburni.* Blue mountain Vireo. 15. Jamaica.
26. *Vireo carmioli.* Yellow winged Vireo. 11. Costa Rica, Panama.
27. *Vireo solitarius.* Blue headed Vireo. 9ss. 14. Canada, USA. Winters to Mexico.
28. incl. *V. s. cassinii.* Cassin's Vireo. 13. W USA. Winters to Guatemala.
29. *V. s. plumbeus.* Plumbeous Vireo. 15. WC USA. Winters Mexico.
30. *Vireo flavifrons.* Yellow throated Vireo. 14. Canada, E USA. Winters to N S America.
31. *Vireo philadelphicus.* Philadelphia Vireo. 13. Canada, USA. Winters Mexico, Colombia.
32. *Vireo olivaceus.* Red eyed Vireo. 15ss. 15. Canada to Argentina, West Indies.
33. *Vireo gracilirostris.* Noronha Vireo. 14. Fernando de Noronha.
34. *Vireo flavoviridis.* Yellow green Vireo. 15. Mexico to Amazon basin.
35. *Vireo chivi.* Chivi Vireo. 15. W & SW Amazonia.
36. *Vireo magister.* Yucatan Vireo. 2ss. 15. Yucatan, Belize & adjacent Is.
37. *Vireo altiloquus.* Black whiskered Vireo. 6ss. 16. Florida & Caribbean Is.
38. *Vireo gilvus.* Warbling Vireo. 16ss. 12. N America to Venezuela, Bolivia.
39. *Vireo swainsoni.* Western warbling Vireo. 11. Alaska, W USA. Winters to C America.
40. *Vireo leucophrys.* Brown capped Vireo. 12. Colombia, Ecuador, Peru.

40a. *Vireo chocoensis.* Choco Vireo. 12. Colombia.

41. *Hylophilus poicilotis.* Rufous crowned Greenlet. 2ss. 12. S of South America.

41a. *Hylophilus amaurocephalus.* Grey eyed Greenlet. 12. E Brazil.

42. *Hylophilus hypoxanthus.* Dusky capped Greenlet. 5ss. 12. NE of South America.
43. *Hylophilus semicinereus.* Grey chested Greenlet. 3ss. 11. Venezuela to Brazil.
44. *Hylophilus pectoralis.* Ashy headed Greenlet. 11. Guyanas to Brazil.
45. *Hylophilus sclateri.* Tepui Greenlet. 11. Venezuela to Brazil.
46. *Hylophilus muscicapinus.* Buff cheeked Greenlet. 2ss. 10. Venezuela, Guyana, Brazil.
47. *Hylophilus brunneiceps.* Brown headed Greenlet. 2ss. 11. Colombia to Brazil.
48. *Hylophilus semibrunneus.* Rufous naped Greenlet. 12. Colombia to Ecuador.
49. *Hylophilus aurantiifrons.* Golden fronted Greenlet. 3ss. 11. Panama, N South America.
50. *Hylophilus flavipes.* Scrub Greenlet. 8ss. 11. Tobago, Costa Rica to N South America.
51. *Hylophilus olivaceus.* Olivaceous Greenlet. 12. Ecuador, Peru.
52. *Hylophilus decurtatus.* Grey headed Greenlet. 3ss. 10. Mexico to Colombia.
53. *Hylophilus minor.* Lesser Greenlet. 10. Colombia, Ecuador.
54. *Hylophilus ochraceiceps.* Tawny crowned Greenlet. 9ss. 11. Mexico to Bolivia.
55. *Hylophilus thoracicus.* Lemon chested Greenlet 12. Venezuela to Bolivia.
56. *Hylophilus puellus.* Tafelberg Greenlet. 10. Surinam.

1
2
3
4
5
6
7
8
9
10
11
12
13
14
15
16
17
18
19
20
21
22
23
24
25
26
27
30
31
33
34
35
36
37
38
40
41
41A
42
43
44
45
46
47
48
49
50
51
52
53
28
29
54
55
32
39
56
40A

ICTERIDAE (1)
Oropendolae

1. *Psarocolius oseri.* Casqued Oropendola. 37. Ecuador, Peru.
2. *Psarocolius latirostris*, Band tailed Oropendola. 31. Ecuador, Peru, W Brazil.
3. *Psarocolius decumanus.* Crested Oropendola. 42. Panama to Bolivia, Argentina.
4. *Psarocolius viridis.* Green Oropendola. 42. Amazon basin.
5. *Psarocolius atrovirens.* Dusky Green Oropendola. 39. Peru, Bolivia.
6. *Psarocolius angustifrons.* Russet backed Oropendola. 42. Venezuela to Bolivia.
7. *Psarocolius wagleri.* Chestnut headed Oropendola. 2ss. 35. Mexico to Ecuador.
8. *Psarocolius montezuma.* Montezuma Oropendola. 50. Mexico to Panama.
9. *Psarocolius Cassini.* Chestnut mantled Oropendola. 40. NW Colombia.
10. *Psarocolius bifasciatus.* Para Oropendola. 45. N Brazil.
11. *Psarocolius guatemozinus.* Black Oropendola. 40. Panama, NW Colombia.
12. *Psarocolius yuracares.* Olive Oropendola. 2ss 50. Amazon basin.

Females are smaller than males but otherwise similar.

1
2
3
4
5
6
7
8
9
10
11
12

ICTERIDAE (2)
Caciques, New World Orioles.

13. *Cacicus cela.* Yellow rumped Cacique. 3ss. 28. Panama to Brazil, Bolivia.
14. *Cacicus chrysopterus.* Golden winged Cacique. 20. Bolivia, Brazil, Argentina.
15. *Cacicus haemorrhous.* Red rumped Cacique. 2ss. 25. Amazonia to Argentina.
16. *Cacicus/Amblycercus holosericeus.* Yellow billed Cacique. 3ss. 21. Mexico to Bolivia.
17. *Cacicus koepckeae.* Selva Cacique. 22. Peru.
18. *Cacicus leucoramphus.* Mountain Cacique. 3ss. 27. Venezuela to Peru, Bolivia.
19. incl. *C. l. chrysonotus.* Bolivian Cacique. 27. Peru, Bolivia.
20 *Cacicus(Cassiculus)melanicterus.* Yellow winged Cacique. 29. W Mexico.
21. *Cacicus sclateri.* Ecuadorian Cacique. 10. Ecuador, Peru.
22. *Cacicus solitarius.* Solitary Cacique. 26. Amazonia to Argentina.
23. *Cacicus uropygialis.* Scarlet rumped Cacique. 3ss. 27. Honduras to Peru.
24. *Icterus auratus.* Orange Oriole. 18. Mexico.
25. *Icterus auricapillus.* 18. Panama, Venezuela, Colombia.
26. *Icterus bonana.* Martinique Oriole. 20. Martinique.
27. *Icterus cayanensis.* Epaulet Oriole. 5ss. 20. S America except extreme South.
28. *Icterus chrysocephalus.* Moriche Oriole. 20. Peru to Surinam.
29. *Icterus chrysater.* Yellow backed Oriole. 4ss. 21. Mexico to N South America.
30. *Icterus cocullatus.* Hooded Oriole. 10ss. 20. SW USA, Mexico, Belize.
31. *Icterus dominicensis.* Black cowled Oriole. 6ss. 20. Most of N America, Mexico.
32. incl. *I. d. prosthemelas.* Strickland Oriole. 20. Mexico to Nicaragua.
33. *Icterus galbula.* Northern / Baltimore Oriole. 4ss. 22. E North America, Mexico. Winters Colombia.
34. incl. *I. g. bullockii.* Bullock's Oriole. 22. Canada, W USA. Winters Mexico, Nicaragua.
35. *I. g. abeilli.* Black backed Oriole. 22. Mexico.
36. *Icterus graceannae.* White edged Oriole. 20. Ecuador, Peru.
37. *Icterus graduacaudata.* Audubon's Oriole. 5ss. 24. Mexico.
38. *Icterus gularis.* Altamira / Lichtenstein's / Black throated Oriole. 6ss. 22. Mexico, Guatemala, Salvador.
39. *Icterus icterus.* Troupial. 6ss. 23. S America S to Paraguay.
40. incl. *I. i. croconotus.* Amazonian / Orange backed Troupial. 23. Amazonia.
41. *Icterus laudabilis.* St Lucia Oriole. 21. St Lucia.
42. *Icterus leucopteryx.* Jamaican Oriole. 3ss. 21. Jamaica, Gr. Cayman Is.
43. *Icterus maculialatus.* Bar winged Oriole. 18. Mexico, Guatemala, Salvador.

Length of males shown. Females are generally smaller.

13
14
15
16
17
18
19
21
-20-
22
23
24
25
26
27
28
29
30
31
32
33
34
36
37
35
39
40
41
38
42
43

ICTERIDAE (3)
New World Orioles & American Blackbirds.

44. *Icterus mesomelas.* Yellow tailed Oriole. 4ss. 23. Mexico to Peru.
45. *Icterus nigrogularis.* Yellow Oriole. 4ss. 21. N of South America.
46. *Icterus oberi.* Montserrat Oriole. 21. Montserrat.
47. *Icterus parisorum.* Scott's Oriole. 23. SW USA & Mexico.
48. *Icterus pectoralis.* Spot breasted Oriole. 2ss. 24. Mexico to Costa Rica.
49. *Icterus pustulatus* . Scarlet headed / Streak backed Oriole. 6ss. 20. Mexico to Costa Rica.
50. incl. *I. p. graysoni.* Tres Marias Oriole. 20. Tres Marias Is.
51. *I. p. sclateri.* Sclater's Oriole. 19. Salvador to Costa Rica.
52. *Icterus spurius.* Orchard Oriole. 3ss. 17. E North America, Mexico.
53. incl. *I. s. fuertesi.* Ochre Oriole. 17. E Mexico.
54. *Icterus wagleri.* Black vented Oriole. 20. Mexico to Nicaragua.
55. *Neopsar nigerrimus.* Jamaican Blackbird. 18. Jamaica.
56. *Gymnomystax mexicanus.* Oriole Blackbird. 26. Amazon & Orinoco basins.
57. *Xanthocephalus xanthocephalus.* Yellow headed Blackbird. 24. W of North America.
58. *Xanthopsar flavus.* Saffron cowled Blackbird. 20. S of South America.
59. *Agelaius cyanops.* Unicoloured Blackbird. 4ss. 23. Brazil to Argentina.
60. *Agelaius humeralis.* Tawny shouldered Blackbird. 2ss. 20. Cuba & Haiti.
61. *Agelaius icterocephalus.* Yellow hooded Blackbird. 2ss. 18. Colombia, Venezuela, Guyanas.
62. *Agelaius phoeniceus.* Red winged Blackbird. 26ss. 22. N & C America, Bahamas.
63. *Agelaius ruficapillus.* Chestnut capped Blackbird. 2ss. 17. Cayenne to Paraguay.
64. *Agelaius thilius.* Yellow winged Blackbird. 3ss. 18. Peru & Brazil southward.
65. *Agelaius tricolor.* Tricoloured Blackbird. 3ss. 21. SW USA.
66. *Agelaius xanthomus.* Yellow shouldered Blackbird. 22. Puerto Rico.
67. *Agelaius xanthophthalmus.* Pale/Yellow eyed Blackbird. 23. Peru.

Icterus xantholaemus, Yellow throated / Lletget's Blackbird, from Ecuador is now considered to be either juvenile or hybrid of 44.

44
45
46
47
48
49
50
51
52
53
54
55
56
57
58
59
60
61
62
63
64
65
66
67

ICTERIDAE (4) Blackbirds & Meadowlarks.

68. *Leistes militaris.* Red breasted Blackbird. 17. Panama to Brazil.
69. *Leistes superciliaris.* Bonaparte's / White browed Blackbird. 17. Argentina, Brazil.
70. *Pezites/Sturnella bellicosa.* Peru Meadowlark. 3ss. 20. Ecuador, Peru, Chile.
71. *Pezites/Sturnella defillipii.* Lesser Red breasted Meadowlark. 19. Brazil, Uruguay, Argentina.
72. *Sturnella loyca.* Long tailed Meadowlark. 2ss. 25. Argentina, Chile, Falkland Is.
73. *Sturnella magna.* Eastern Meadowlark. 15ss. 24. SE USA, Cuba to Brazil.
74. *Sturnella neglecta.* Western Meadowlark. 24. S Canada, USA.(except SE).

74a. *Sturnella lilianae.* Lilian's Meadowlark. 24. Arizona, Texas, Mexico.

75. *Pseudoleistes guirahuro.* Yellow rumped Marshbird. 23. Brazil, Paraguay, Uruguay, Argentina.
76. *Pseudoleistes virescens.* Brown & yellow Marshbird. 23. Brazil to Argentina
77. *Amblyramphus holosericeus.* Scarlet headed Blackbird. 23. S of South America.
78. *Hypopyrrhus pyrohypogaster.* Red bellied Grackle. 28. Colombia.
79. *Curaeus curaeus.* Austral Blackbird. 3ss. 26. S Chile, Argentina.
80. *Curaeus forbesi.* Forbes' Blackbird. 22. E Brazil.
81. *Gnorimopsar chopi.* Chopi Blackbird. 2ss. 23. Bolivia, Brazil, Argentina.
82. *Oreopsar bolivianus.* Bolivian Blackbird. 23. Bolivia.
83. *Lampropsar tanagrinus.* Velvet fronted Grackle. 5ss. 22. Amazon & Orinoco.
84. *Macroagelaius imthuri.* Golden tufted Grackle. 25. NE of S America.
85. *Macroagelaius subalaris.* Mountain Grackle. 28. Colombia.
86. *Dives atroviolacea.* Cuban Blackbird. 26. Cuba Isle of Pines.
87. *Dives dives.* Melodious Blackbird. 3ss. 23. Mexico to Nicaragua.
88. Incl. *D. d. warszewiczi.* Scrub Blackbird. 23. Ecuador, Peru.
89. *Quiscalus lugubris.* Carib Grackle. 8ss. 25. Lesser Antilles.
90. *Quiscalus niger.* Greater Antillean Grackle. 7ss. 28. Cuba, Jamaica, Hispaniola, Cayman Is, Puerto Rico.

68
69
70
71
72
73
74
74A
75
76
77
78
79
80
81
82
83
84
85
86
87
88
89
90

ICTERIDAE (5)
Gackles, Blackbirds, Cowbirds.

91. *Quiscalus major*. Boat tailed Grackle. 2ss. 37. Coasts of E & S USA.
92. *Quiscalus(Cassidix)mexicanus*. Great tailed Grackle. 8ss. 38. SW USA & Mexico to Peru & Venezuela.
93. *Quiscalus nicaraguensis*. Nicaraguan Grackle. 27. Nicaragua.
94. *Quiscalus quiscala*. Common / Purple / Bronzed Grackle. 3ss. 32. N America except extreme North
95. *Quiscalus palustris*. Slender billed Grackle. 32. Mexico. (Extinct.?)
96. *Euphagus carolinus*. Rusty Blackbird. 2ss. 22. Canada. Winters to E USA.
97. *Euphagus cyanocephalus*. Brewer's Blackbird. 23. Canada. Winters to Mexico.
98. *Molothrus(Tangavius)aeneus*. Bronzed / Brown Cowbird.4ss. 22. Mexico to Colombia.
99. incl. *M. a. armenti*. Bronze-Brown Cowbird. 21. Colombia.
100. *Molothrus ater*. Brown headed Cowbird. 21. Colombia.
101. *Molothrus badius*. Bay winged Cowbird. 3ss. 20. S of South America.
102. *Molothrus bonariensis*. Shiny Cowbird. 7ss. 22. Panama, West Indies, Most of S America.
103. *Molothrus rufoaxillaris*. Screaming Cowbird. 17. S of South America.
104. *Scaphidura oryzivora*. Giant Cowbird. 2ss. 35. Mexico to Argentina.
105. *Dolichinyx orizivorus*. Bobolink. 18. Canada, USA. Winters to Argentina.

91
92
95
93
94
96
Br
NB
98
99
97
102
100
104
103
101
105

FRINGILLIDAE, CARDUELINAE (1) Finches, Old World Seedeaters, Goldfinches, Canaries etc.

Sub-family 177. FRINGILLINAE. Chaffinches.

1. *Fringilla coelebs*. Chaffinch. 14ss. 15. Europe, W Asia, N Africa.
2. *Fringilla montifringilla*. Brambling. 14. N Europe to Japan. Winters Mediterranean, India.
3. *Fringilla teydea*. Blue Chaffinch. 2ss. 16. Tenerife & Gr. Canary I.

Subfamily 178. CARDUELINAE. Goldfinches, Canaries, etc.

1. *Serinus alario*. Blackhead Canary. 2ss. 13. South Africa, Namibia.
2. *Serinus leucolaema*. Damara Canary. 13. S Africa.
3. *Serinus albogularis*. White throated Seedeater. 5ss. 15. S Africa to Angola.
4. *Serinus atrogularis*. Yellow rumped Seedeater. 8ss. 11. E & S Africa.
5. *Serinus reichenowi*. Kenya yellow rumped Seedeater. 11. Sudan to Tanzania.
6. *Serinus rothschildi*. Olive rumped Serin. 11. SW Arabia.
7. *Serinus ankoberensis*. Ankober Serin. 12. C Ethiopia.

7a. *Serinus whytii*. Yellow browed / Streaky Seedeater. 15. E African Mtns.

8. *Serinus burtoni*. Thick billed / Grosbeak Seedeater. 5ss. 14. E C &W Africa.
9. *Serinus melanochrous*. Kipengere Seedeater. 14. Tanzania.
10. *Serinus canaria*. Canary. 13. Canary Is, Madeira, Azores.
11. *Serinus canicollis=flavivertex*. Yellow crowned / Cane Canary. 6ss. 13. E C S Africa.
12. *Serinus capistratus*. Blackfaced Canary. 2ss. 13. Gabon, Angola, EC Africa.
13. *Serinus citrinella*. Citril Finch. 2ss. 12. S Europe, Mediterranean Is.
14. *Serinus citrinelloides*. African Citril. 5ss. 11. Sudan, Ethiopia.
15. *Serinus hypostictus*. East African Citril. 11. Kenya to Mozambique.
16. *Serinus frontalis*. Yellow faced Citril. 11. E Africa, Zaire.
17. *Serinus citrinipectus*. Lemon breasted Canary. 10. Mozambique, Malawi.
18. *Serinus donaldsoni*. Abyssinian Grosbeak Canary. 14. Ethiopia.
19. *Serinus buchanani*. Kenya Grosbeak Canary. 14. E Africa.
20. *Serinus dorsostriatus*. White bellied Canary. 12. E Africa.
21. *Serinus/Carduelis estherae*. Malay Goldfinch. 4ss. 12. Philippines, Indonesia.
22. *Serinus flavigula*. Yellow throated Seedeater. 11. Ethiopia.

22a. *Serinus xanthopygius*. Abyssinian yellow rumped Seedeater. 11. Ethiopia.

23. *Serinus flaviventris*. Yellow Canary. 7ss. 13. Namibia, Botswana to Cape.
24. *Serinus gularis*. Streaky headed Seedeater. 11ss. 15. Africa S of Sahara.
25. *Serinus canicapillus*. West African Seedeater. 15. Senegal, Ghana to Zaire.
26. *Serinus koliensis*. Papyrus Canary. 11. Kenya, Uganda, Congo.
27. *Serinus leocopterus*. White winged Seedeater. 15. Cape Province.
28. *Serinus leucopygius*. White rumped Seedeater. 3ss. 12. Senegal to NE Africa.
29. *Serinus menachensis. Yemeni Seedeater.* 12. Arabia.
30. *Serinus mennelli*. Black eared Seedeater. 14. Angola, Zimbabwe, Malawi.
31. *Serinus mozambicus*. Yellow fronted Canary. 11ss. 12. Africa S of Sahara.
32. *Serinus nigriceps*. Black headed Siskin (Serin). 11. Ethiopia.
33. *Serinus pusillus*. Gold / Red fronted Serin. 12. Asia Minor to Kashmir.
34. *Serinus reichardi*. Reichard's Seedeater. 15. Local E & S Africa.
35. *Serinus rufobrunneus*. Principe Seedeater. 2ss. 14. W African Is.
36. *Serinus scotops*. Forest Canary. 3ss. 13. South Africa.
37. *Serinus serinus*. Serin. 11. Baltic to N Africa.
38. *Serinus striolatus*. Streaky Seedeater. 4ss. 15. E Africa.
39. *Serinus sulphuratus*. Brimstone Canary. 3ss. 15. Kenya to Cape.
40. *Serinus Symonsi*. Drakensberg Siskin. 12. Drakensberg Mtns., S Africa
41. *Serinus syriacus*. Syrian Siskin. 13. Syria, Lebanon. Winters Iraq, Egypt.
42. Serinus(Carduelis)Tibetans. Tibetan Siskin. 12. Tibet, Nepal. Winters SE Asia.
43. Serinus tottus. Cape Siskin. 12. Cape, Lethoso.
44. Serinus tristriatus. Brown rumped Seedeater. 13. Eritrea, Somalia, Ethiopia.

FRINGILLIDAE
1
2
Br
NB
3
CARDUELINAE
-1-
2
3
4
5
6
7
7A
8
9
10
11
12
13
14
15
16
17
18
19
20
21
22
22A
23
24
25
26
27
28
29
30
31
32
33
34
35
36
37
38
39
40
41
42
43
44

FRINGILLIDAE, (CARDUELINAE) (2) Finches.

45. *Neospiza concolor.* Sao Thome Grosbeak Canary. 20. Sao Thome. (extinct.?)
46. *Linurgus olivaceus.* Oriole Finch. 4ss. 15. C E Africa.
47. *Rhynchostruthus socotranus.* Golden winged Grosbeak. 3ss. 15. Socotra, Arabia, Somalia.
48. *Carduelis ambigua.* Black headed Greenfinch. 2ss. 13. Tibet, E & SE Asia.
49. *Carduelis carduelis.* (Eurasian) Goldfinch. 12ss. 12. Eurasia, N Africa.
50 incl. *C. c. caniceps.* Grey headed Goldfinch. 13. Pakistan, Nepal.
51. *Carduelis chloris.* Greenfinch. 4ss. 15. Europe, N Africa, SW Asia.
52. *Carduelis sinica.* Grey capped Greenfinch. 6ss. 14. E Asia, Kuriles.
53. *Carduelis spinoides.* Yellow breasted Greenfinch. 3ss. 13. Himalayas.
54. *Carduelis monguilloti.* Vietnamese Greenfinch. 13. S E Asia.
55. *Carduelis spinus.* (Eurasian) Siskin. 12. Eurasia, N Africa.
56. *Carduelis atrata.* Black Siskin. 12. Peru to Chile & Argentina.
57. *Carduelis atriceps.* Black capped Siskin. 11. Chiapas, Guatemala.
58. *Carduelis pinus.* Pine Siskin. 3ss. 13. N America, Mexico, Guatemala.
59. *Carduelis crassirostris.* Thick billed Siskin. 2ss. 14. Peru, Chile, Argentina
60. *Carduelis cucullata.* Red Siskin. 10. Colombia, Venezuela.
61. *Carduelis dominicensis.* Antillean Siskin. 11. Hispaniola.
62. *Carduelis barbata.* Black chinned Siskin. 13. Chile & Argentina.
63. *Carduelis magellanica.* Hooded Siskin. 11ss. 13. Most of S America.
64. incl. *C. m. sanctaecrucis.* Santa Cruz Siskin. 12. Bolivia.
65. *Carduelis notata.* Black headed Siskin. 3ss. 11. Mexico & C America.
66. *Carduelis olivacea.* Olivaceous Siskin. 11. Ecuador, Peru, Bolivia.
67. *Carduelis uropygialis.* Yellow rumped Siskin. 11. Peru to Chile, Argentina.
68. *Carduelis xanthogastra.* Yellow bellied Siskin. 2ss. 11. Costa Rica to Venezuela & Bolivia.
69. *Carduelis siemiradzkii.* Saffron Siskin. 10. SW Ecuador.
70. *Carduelis spinescens.* Andean Siskin. 3ss. 10. Venezuela, Colombia.
71. *Carduelis tristis.* American Goldfinch. 4ss. 13. S Canada, USA, Mexico.
72. *Carduelis lawrencei.* Lawrence's Goldfinch. 12. SW USA, Mexico.
73. *Carduelis psaltria.* Lesser Goldfinch. 5ss. 10. W USA to Mexico.
74. incl. *C. p. colombianus.* Dark backed Goldfinch. 10. Mexico to Venezuela, Peru.
75. *Carduelis yarrelli.* Yellow faced Siskin. 10. NE Venezuela, E Brazil.
76. *Acanthis/Carduelis cannabina.* Linnet. 13. Europe to NW India, N Africa & Is.
77. *Acanthis/Carduelis flavirostris.* Twite. 8ss. 13. N Europe to Kashmir, Tibet.
78. *Acanthis/Carduelis johannis.* Warsangli Linnet. 13. Somalia.(unique)

45
46
47
48
49
JUV
50
51
52
53
55
56
57
58
59
60
61
62
63
64
65
66
67
68
69
70
71
NB
72
74
54
73
75
76
77
78

FRINGILLIDAE, (CARDUELINAE) (3)
Finches & Redpolls.

79. *Acanthis/Carduelis F.* cabaret. Lesser Redpoll. 12. Britain, Switzerland.
80. *A/C F. flammea*. Common / Mealy Redpoll. 6ss. 13. Holarctic. Winters S Europe, China.
81. *A/C F. rostrata*. Greenland / Greater Redpoll. 14. NE Canada. Winters N USA, Europe.
82. *A/C F. islandica*. Iceland Redpoll. 13. Iceland.
83. *A/C F. hornemanni*. Arctic Redpoll. 14. Greenland, Canada. Winters Britain, S Canada.
84. *A/C F. exilipes*. Hoary / Coue's Redpoll. 13. N Eurasia, America. Winters C Europe.
85. *Acanthis yemenensis*. Yemeni Linnet. 13. SW Arabia.
86. *Leucosticta arctoa*. Rosy Finch. 4ss. 16. C Asia, Siberia, Alaska.
87. incl. *L. a. atrata*. Black rosy Finch. 15. SW & C USA.
88. *L. a. australis*. Brown capped rosy Finch. 16. SW USA.
89. *L. a. tephrocotis*. Grey crowned rosy Finch. 16. WC Canada & USA.
90. *Leucosticta brandti*. Brandt's rosy Finch. 5ss. 18. C Asia to Mongolia, China.
91. *Leucosticta nemoricola*. Hodgson's rosy Finch. 2ss. 15. Afghanistan to China.
92. *Callacanthis burtoni*. Red browed Finch. 17. Himalayas, Pakistan to Sikkim.
93. *Rhodopechys githaginea*. Trumpeter Finch. 4ss. 13. Canary Is, Sahara to Pakistan.
94. *Rhodopechys mongolica*. Mongolian Finch. 15. Transcaucasia to Mongolia.
95. *Rhodopechys obsoleta*. (Lichtenstein's) Desert Finch. 14. Asia minor, Pakistan.
96. *Rhodopechys sanguinea*. Crimson winged Finch. 2ss. 15. Morocco to SC Asia.
97. *Uragus sibiricus*. Long tailed Rosefinch. 5ss. 17. Siberia, E Asia, Kuriles.
98. incl. *U. s. henrici*. Sikang Rosefinch. 14. Hokkaido, Sikang.
99. *Urocynchramus pylzowi*. Prevalski's Rosefinch. 15. W China.
100. *Carpodacus cassinii*. Cassin's Finch. 16. British Colombia to Mexico.
101. *Carpodacus edwardsii*. Large / Dark rumped Rosefinch. 2ss. 17. Himalayas to W China, N Burma.
102. *Carpodacus eos*. Stresemann's / Pink rumped Rosefinch. 13. W China.
103. *Carpodacus erythrinus*. Common Rosefinch / Scarlet Grosbeak. 14. Finland, N Asia. Winters to N India.

79
80
81
82
83
84
85
86
87
88
90
89
91
92
93
94
95
96
99
97
98
100
101
102
103

Plate 335 Family 177,178.

FRINGILLIDAE (4)
Rosefinches.

104. *Carpodacus mexicanus.* House Finch. 11ss. 14. Western N America, Mexico.
105. *Carpodacus nipalensis.* Dark (breasted) Rosefinch. 3ss 15. Himalayas to N Burma & W China.
106. *Carpodacus pulcherrimus.* Beautiful Rosefinch. 4ss. 15. Tibet to Mongolia.
107. *Carpodacus puniceus.* Red fronted / breasted Rosefinch. 5ss. 20. W C Asia, Himalayas to China.
108. *Carpodacus purpureus.* Purple Finch. 2ss. 15. N America.
109. *Carpodacus rhodochlamys.* Red mantled Rosefinch. 3ss. 18. Himalayas.
110. *Carpodacus rhodochrous.* Pink browed Rosefinch. 15. Kashmir to Sikkim.
111. *Carpodacus rhodopeplus.* Spotted Rosefinch. 2ss. 15. Himalayas.
112. incl. *C. R. verreauixii.* Sharpe's Rosefinch. 13. China, N Burma.
113. *Carpodacus roborowskii.* Tibetan Rosefinch. 16. Himalayas, Tsinghai.
114. *Carpodacus roseus.* Pallas' Rosefinch. 15. Altai, Baikal, China.
115. *Carpodacus rubescens.* Blanford's / Crimson Rosefinch. 15. Himalayas.
116. *Carpodacus rubicilla.* Caucasian / Great Rosefinch. 4ss. 20. Caucasus to China.
117. *Carpodacus rubicilloides.* Streaked / Eastern Rosefinch. 2ss. 19. Himalayas, Tibet to W China.
118. *Carpodacus synoicus.* Siniai Rosefinch. 4ss. 14. Siniai to China.
119. *Carpodacus thura.* White browed Rosefinch. 5ss. 17. Afghanistan to China.
120. *Carpodacus trifasciatus.* Three banded Rosefinch. 17. W China.
121. *Carpodacus vinaceus.* Vinaceous Rosefinch. 2ss. 13. W China, Taiwan.
122. *Chaunoproctus ferreorostris.* Bonin Finch. 18. Bonin Is. (extinct).
123. *Pinicola enucleator.* Pine Grosbeak. 11ss. 23. N Holarctic.
124. *Pinicola subhimachala.* Crimson browed / Red headed Finch. 20. Himalayas.

104
105
106
107
108
109
110
111
112
113
114
115
116
117
118
119
120
121
122
123
124

FRINGILLIDAE (5) Bullfinches, Grosbeaks.

125. *Haematospiza sipati.* Scarlet Finch. 18. Himalayas to Yunnan & Burma.
126. *Loxia curvirostris.* (Red) Crossbill. 18ss. 16. Holarctic, S to Himalayas & Nicaragua.
127. *Loxia scotica.* Scottish Crossbill. 16. Scotland.
128. *Loxia leucoptera.* Two barred / White winged Crossbill. 3ss. 14. N Siberia, Canada & N USA.
129. *Loxia pytopsittacus.* Parrot Crossbill. 17. Scandinavia.
130. *Pyrrhula aurantiaca.* Orange Bullfinch. 14. NW Himalayas.
131. *Pyrrhula erythaca.* Beavan's / Grey headed Bullfinch. 3ss. 17. E Asia.
132. *Pyrrhula erythrocephala.* Red headed Bullfinch. 17. Himalayas, Tibet.
133. *Pyrrhula leucogenys.* Philippine Bullfinch. 4ss. 15. Luzon & Mindanao.
134. *Pyrrhula nipalensis.* Brown Bullfinch. 5ss. 17. Pakistan to E & SE Asia.
135. *Pyrrhula pyrrhula.* Bullfinch. 10ss. 15. Eurasia.
136. incl. *P. p. griseiventris.* Grey bellied Bullfinch. 15. Korea, Japan.
137. *Coccothraustes/Hesperiphona abeillei.* Hooded Grosbeak. 14ss. 16. Mexico & Guatemala.
138. *Coccothraustes/Mycerobas affinis* . Allied / Collared Grosbeak. 22. Himalayas, Burma, China.
139. *Coccothraustes/Mycerobas carnipes.* White winged Grosbeak. 2ss. 22. Iran.
140. *Coccothraustes coccothraustes.* Hawfinch. 5ss. 18. Palearctic. Winters S to Mongolia, E Asia.
141. *C/Mycerobas icterioides.* Black & Yellow Grosbeak. 22. Afghanistan, Himalayas.
142. *C/Mycerobas melanozanthos.* Spotted Wing Grosbeak. 22. Himalayas, E & SE Asia.
143. *C/euphona migratorius.* Yellow billed Grosbeak / Black tailed Hawfinch. 18. E Asia.
144. *C/euphona personatus.* Japanese Grosbeak / Masked Hawfinch. 2ss. 21. E Asia.
145. *C/Hesperiphona vespertina.* Evening Grosbeak. 3ss. 18. Canada, USA, Mexico.
146. *Pyrrhoplectes epauletta.* Gold headed / naped Finch. 15. Himalayas. Winters Burma.

125
126
127
128
129
130
131
132
133
134
135
136
137
138
139
140
141
142
143
144
145
146

ESTRILDIDAE (1)
Waxbills

1. *Parmoptila rubrifrons.* Red fronted Antpecker. 2ss. 11. Parts of W & C Africa.
2. *Parmoptila woodhousei.* Flowerpecker Weaver Finch. 2ss. 11. W & C Africa.
3. *Nigrita bicolor.* Chestnut headed Negro Finch. 2ss. 11. W & C Africa.
4. *Nigrita canicapilla.* Grey crowned Negro Finch. 7ss. 15. W & C Africa.
5. *Nigrita fusconota.* White breasted Negro Finch. 2ss. 10. W, C & E Africa.
6. *Nigrita luteifrons.* Pale fronted Negro Finch. 2ss. 12. W & C Africa.
7. *Nesocharis ansorgei.* White collared Olive-Back. 11. Ituri, Rwanda.
8. *Nesocharis capistrata.* Grey headed Olive-Back. 13. Gambia to Congo & Sudan.
9. *Nesocharis shelleyi.* Fernando Po / Little Olive-Back. 2ss. 9. Fernando Po, Cameroon.
10. *Pytilia afra.* Orange winged Pytilia. 11. Ethiopia to Mozambique, Angola.
11. *Pytilia hypogrammica.* Red faced / Yellow winged Pytilia. 11. WC Africa.
12. *Pytilia melba.* Green winged Pytilia. 8ss. 12. Africa S of Sahara.
13. *Pytilia phoenicoptera.* Crimson winged Pytilia / Aurora Finch. 3ss. 12. Gambia to Congo, Sudan, Uganda.
14. incl. *P. p. lineata.* Red billed Aurora Finch. 12. Ethiopia.
15. *Mandingoa nitidula.* Green backed Twin-spot. 4ss. 10. Africa S of Sahara.
16. *Cryptospiza jacksoni.* Dusky Crimson-wing. 12. Congo, Rwanda, Uganda.
17. *Cryptospiza reichenovii.* Red faced Crimson-wing. 3ss. 12. Mountains of EC Africa.
18. *Cryptospiza salvadorii.* Abyssinian Crimson-wing. 3ss. 12. Ethiopia, Tanzania.
19. *Cryptospiza shelleyi.* Shelley's Crimson-wing. 13. Zaire, Uganda.
20. *Pyrenestes minor.* Lesser Seedcracker. 13. Tanzania to Mozambique.
21. *Pyrenestes ostrinus.* Black bellied Seedcracker. 14. Ivory Coast to Angola, Uganda, Zambia.
22. *Pyrenestes sanguineus.* Crimson Seedcracker. 2ss. 14. Gambia to Ivory Coast.
23. *Spermophaga haematina.* Western / Red breasted Bluebill. 2ss. 15. WC Africa.
24. *Spermophaga poliogenys.* Grant's Bluebill. 15. Congo, Uganda.
25. *Spermophaga ruficapilla.* Red headed Bluebill. 2ss. 15. Angola to E Africa.
26. *Euschistospiza cinereovinacea.* Dusky Twin-spot. 2ss. 10. C Africa.
27. *Euschistospiza dybowskii.* Dybowski's Twin-spot. 11. W Africa to Sudan.
28. *Clytospiza monteiri.* Brown Twin-spot. 12. Sierra Leone to Sudan.
29. *Hypargos margaritatus.* Rosy / Pink throated Twin-spot. 11. Mozambique, Zululand.
30. *Hypargos niveoguttatus.* Peter's Twin-spot. 5ss. 13. EC & SE Africa.

1
2
3
4
5
6
7
8
9
10
11
12
13
14
15
16
17
18
19
20
21
22
23
24
25
26
27
28
29
30

ESTRILDIDAE (2)
Waxbills

31. *Lagonosticta landanae*. Pale billed Firefinch. 10. Angola.
32. *Lagonosticta larvata*. Masked / Black throated Firefinch. 4ss. 10. Ethiopia.
33. *Lagonosticta vinacea*. Vinaceous Firefinch. 2ss. 11. W Africa to Sudan.
34. incl. *L. v. nigricollis*. Black faced Firefinch. 11. C to E & NE Africa.
35. *Lagonosticta nitidula*. Brown Firefinch. 2ss. 11. SC Africa.
36. *Lagonosticta rara*. Black bellied Firefinch. 2ss. 10. W Africa to Kenya, Sudan.
37. *Lagonosticta rhodoparaia*. Jameson's Firefinch. 3ss. 10. E, C & S Africa.
37a. *Lagonosticta umbrinodorsalis*. Reichenow's Firefinch. 10. WC Africa.
38. *Lagonosticta rubricata*. African Firefinch. 6ss. 10. Africa S of Sahara.
39. *Lagonosticta virata*. Kulikoro Firefinch. 10. Mali.
40. *Lagonosticta rufopicta*. Bar breasted Firefinch. 2ss. 10. Gambia to Sudan.
41. *Lagonosticta senegala*. Red billed Firefinch. 9ss. 10. Africa S of Sahara.
42. *Uraeginthus angolensis*. Cordon Bleu. 4ss. 11. SE & S Africa.
43. *Uraeginthus bengalus*. Red cheeked Cordon Bleu. 5ss. 12. W, NC & E Africa.
44. *Uraeginthus cyanocephala*. Blue capped Cordon Bleu. 13. East Africa.
45. *Uraeginthus granatina*. Common Grenadier. 3ss. 14. Southern Africa.
46. *Uraeginthus ianthinogaster*. Purple Grenadier. 3ss. 14. East Africa.
47. *Estrilda astrild*. Waxbill. 17ss. 12. Most of Africa S of Sahara.
48. *Estrilda atricapilla*. Black headed Waxbill. 3ss. 11. C Africa.
48a. *Estrilda kandti*. Kandt's Waxbill. 11. Kenya, Uganda, Zaire.
49. *Estrilda caerulescens*. Lavender Waxbill. 10. Senegal to Chad & Cameroon.
50. *Estrilda erythronotos*. Black cheeked Waxbill. 3ss. 13. Kenya to Angola, Cape.
51. *Estrilda charmosyna*. Red rumped Waxbill. 3ss. 14. East Africa.
52. *Estrilda melpoda*. Orange cheeked Waxbill. 2ss. 10. W & C Africa.
53. *Estrilda nigriloris*. Black lored Waxbill. 12. Congo.
54. *Estrilda nonnula*. Black crowned Waxbill. 3ss. 11. W C & E Africa.
55. *Estrilda paludicola*. Fawn breasted Waxbill. 6ss. 10. W C & E Africa.
56. *Estrilda ochrogaster*. Abyssinian Waxbill. 10. Ethiopia, Sudan.
57. *Estrilda perreini*. Black tailed Waxbill. 4ss. 11. C to SE Africa.
58. *Estrilda poliopareia*. Anambra Waxbill. 10. Nigeria.
59. *Estrilda rhodopyga*. Crimson rumped Waxbill. 2ss. 11. E & SE Africa.
60. *Estrilda rufibarba*. Arabian Waxbill. 11. SW Arabia.
61. *Estrilda thomensis*. Cinderella Waxbill. 11. Sao Theme.
62. *Estrilda troglodytes*. Black rumped Waxbill. 10. Senegal to Sudan, Ethiopia.
63. *Estrilda melanotis*. Swee Waxbill. 10. South Africa.
64. *Estrilda kilimensis*. Yellow bellied Waxbill. 10. Zaire, Uganda to Zambia.
65. *Estrilda bocagei*. Green Waxbill. 10. Angola.
66. *Estrilda quartinia*. East African Swee. 10. Ethiopia to Zambia.

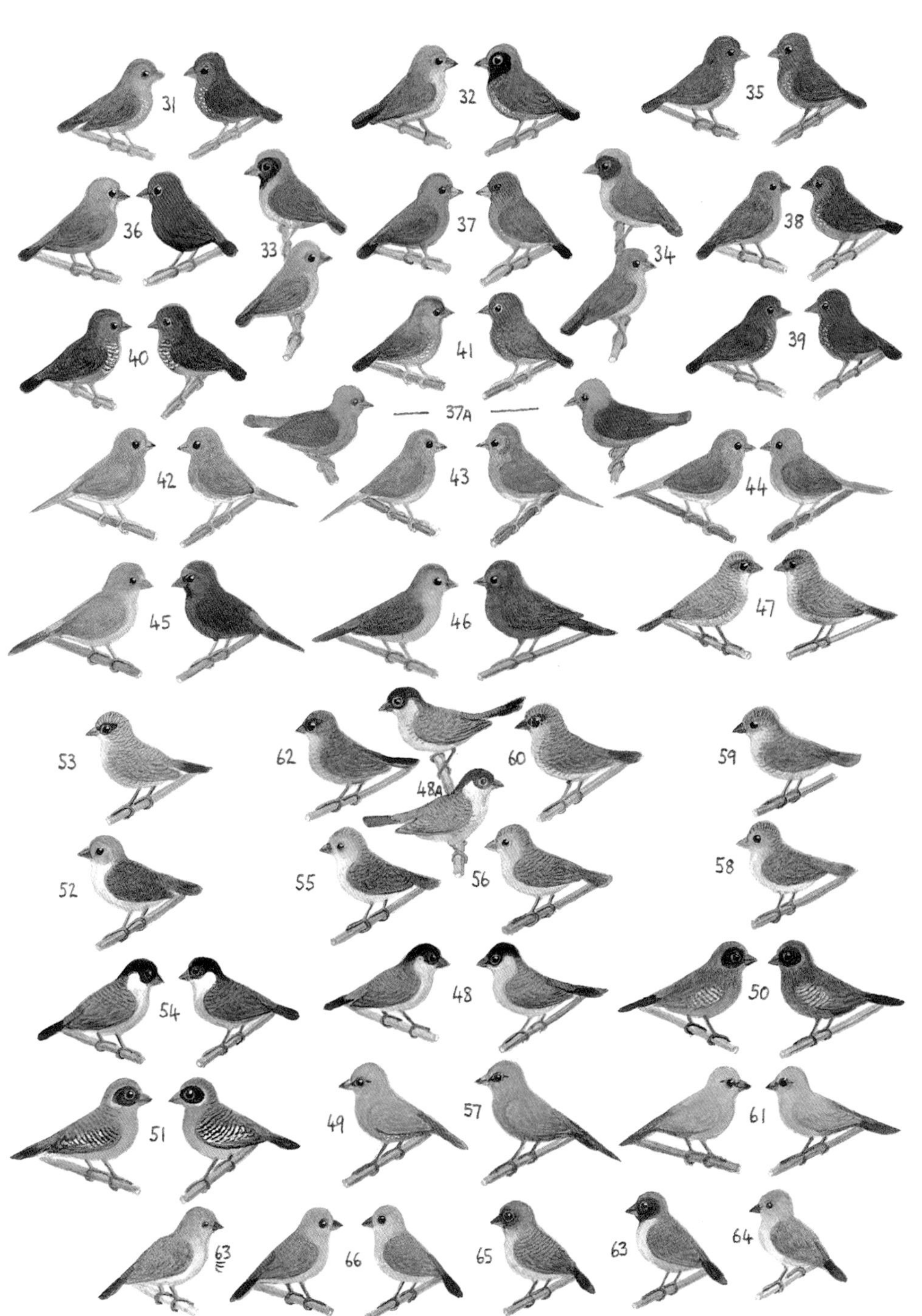
31
32
35
36
33
37
34
38
40
41
39
37A
42
43
44
45
46
47
53
62
60
59
48A
52
55
56
58
54
48
50
51
49
57
61
63
66
65
63
64

ESTRILDIDAE (3)
Avadavats, Quail Finches, Australasian Finches.

67. *Amandava amandava.* Red Munia / Strawberry Finch. 3ss. 10. India to Timor.
68. *Amandava formosa.* Green Munia / Avadavat. 10. C India.
69. *Amandava subflava.* Zebra Waxbill. 2ss. 9. Africa S of Sahara.
70. *Ortygospiza atricollis.* Common / African Quailfinch. 10ss. 10. Africa.
71. incl. *O. a. fuscocrissa.* Dark / Ethiopian Quailfinch. 10. Ethiopia.
72. *Ortygospiza gabonensis.* Red billed Quailfinch. 3ss. 10. E W & C Africa.
73. *Ortygospiza locustella.* Locustfinch. 13ss. 9. C & S Africa.
74. *Aeginthia/Neochmia temporalis.* Red browed Firetail. 3ss. 11. E Australia.
75. *Emblema/Stagonopleura bella.* Beautiful Firetail. 12. Tasmania & Is.
76. *Emblema/Stagonopleura guttata.* Diamond Firefinch. 12. S & E Australia.
77. *Emblema/Stagonopleura oculata.* Red eared Firetail. 12. SW Australia.
78. *Emblema picta.* Painted Finch. 11. Interior Australia.
79. *Oreostruthus fuliginosus.* Crimson sided Mountain Finch. 3ss. 13. New Guinea.
80. *Neochmia phaeton.* Crimson Finch. 2ss. 13. N Australia, New Guinea.
81. incl. *N. p. albiventer.* Pale Crimson Finch. 13. Cape York Peninsula.
82. *Neochmia ruficauda.* Star Finch. 2ss. 11. N & E Australia.
83. *Poephila acuticauda.* Long tailed Finch. 2ss. 16. N Queensland.
84. incl. *P. a. hecki.* Yellow billed Finch. 16. NW Australia.
85. *Poephila/Taeniopygia* bichenovii. Double barred Finch. 2ss. 11. NE Australia.
86. incl. *T. b. annulosa.* Black ringed Finch. 11. NW Australia.
87. *Poephila cincta.* Black throated Finch. 3ss. 10. E Australia.
88. incl. *P. c. atropygialis.* Black tailed / Parson Finch. 10. N Queensland.
89. *Poephila /Taeniopygia guttata.* Zebra Finch. 2ss. 10. Australia, Sunda Is.
90. *Poephila personata.* Masked Grass Finch. 2ss. 13. N Australia.
91. incl. *P. p. leucotis.* White eared Finch. 13. Cape York Peninsula.
92. *Erythrura psittacea.* Red throated Parrotfinch. 11. New Caledonia.
93. *Erythrura cyaneovirens.* Red headed Parrotfinch. 5ss. 11. W Samoa.
94. *Erythrura regia. Royal Parrotfinch. 11.* New Hebrides.
95. *Erythrura pealii.* Fiji Parrotfinch. 11. Fiji.
96. *Erythrura tricolor.* Three coloured Parrotfinch. 11. Timor, Wetar, Tanimbar.
97. *Erythrura kleinschmidtii.* Pink billed Parrotfinch. 11. Fiji.
98. *Erythrura papuana.* Papuan Parrotfinch. 15. New Guinea.
99. *Erythrura trichroa. Blue faced* Parrotfinch. 10ss. 12. Sulawesi to New Guinea, N Australia New Hebrides.

67
68
69
70
71
72
73
74
75
76
77
78
79
80
81
82
83
84
85
86
87
88
89
90
91
92
93
94
95
96
98
97
99

ESTRILDIDAE (4)
Parrot Finches & Mannikins

100. *Erythrura prasina.* Pin-tailed Parrotfinch. 2ss. 14/12. S E Asia.
101. *Erythrura coloria.* Mindanao Parrotfinch. 11. Mindanao.
102. *Erythrura viridifacies.* Green faced Parrotfinch. 11. Luzon.
103. *Erythrura hyperythra.* Bamboo Parrotfinch. 8ss. 10. SE Asia, Indonesia.
104. (a.), (b.) & (c.) *Chloebia gouldiae.* Gouldian Finch. 13. N Australia. (3 phases)
105. *Aidemosyne/Neochmia modesta.* Plum headed Finch. 11. Australia.
106. *Lonchura/Lepedopygia nana.* Bib-Finch / Madagascar Munia. 9. Malagasy.
107. *Lonchura malabarica.* Indian / White throated Silverbill. 2ss. 12. S Asia.
108. *Lonchura griseicapilla.* Grey headed Silverbill. 11. Ethiopia to Tanzania.
109. *Lonchura cantans.* African Silverbill. 12. Senegal to Sudan & E Africa.
110. *Lonchura cucullata.* Bronze Mannikin. 2ss. 10. Africa S of Sahara.
111. *Lonchura bicolor.* Black & White Mannikin. 6ss. 11. Africa S of Sahara.
112. *Lonchura nigriceps.* Rufous backed Mannikin. 11. E Africa to Natal.
113. *Lonchura fringilloides.* Magpie Mannikin. 13. Senegal to Sudan & Natal.
114. *Lonchura flaviprymna.* Yellow tailed Munia. 10. N Australia.
115. *Lonchura forbesi.* New Ireland Finch. 11. New Ireland.
116. *Lonchura fuscans.* Dusky Mannikin. 10. Borneo & adjacent Is.
117. *Lonchura grandis. Great billed* Mannikin. 4ss. 12. New Guinea.
118. *Lonchura hunsteini.* Mottled / White headed Finch. 3ss. 10. New Ireland & Is.
119. *Lonchura nigerrima.* Black breasted Weaver Finch. 9. New Hanover Is.
120. *Lonchura kelaarti.* Rufous bellied Hill Munia. 3ss. 10. India, Sri Lanka.
121. *Lonchura leucogastra.* White bellied Munia. 6ss. 10. SE Asia. Philippines.
122. *Lonchura leucogastroides.* Javanese Munia. 10. Sumatra, Java, Bali, Lombok.
123. *Lonchura leucosticta.* White spotted Mannikin. 10. New Guinea.
124. *Lonchura maja.* White headed Munia. 11. SE Asia, Indonesia.
125. *Lonchura malacca.* Black headed Munia. 9ss. 11. India, SE Asia, Indonesia.
126. incl. *L. m. atricapilla.* Rice Bird. 11. India, Burma.
127. *Lonchura ferruginosa.* White capped Munia. 11. Java.
128. *Lonchura melaena.* Bismarck / Thick billed Munia. 11. New Britain.
129. *Lonchura molucca.* Black faced Munia . 3ss. 10. Sulawesi, Molucccas, Lesser Sundas .
130. *Lonchura monticola.* Alpine Munia. 11. New Guinea.
131. *Lonchura montana.* Snow mountain Munia. 11. New Guinea.
132. *Lonchura nevermanni.* Grey crowned Munia. 11. New Guinea.
133. *Lonchura pallida.* Pallid Finch. 2ss. 11. Sulawesi, Lesser Sunda Is.
134. *Lonchura punctulata.* Nutmeg Finch. 11ss. 11. India, China, SE Asia, Philippines.
135. *Lonchura(Heteromunia)pectoralis.* Pictorella Finch. 11. N Australia.
136. *Lonchura castaneothorax.* Chestnut breasted Munia. 6ss. 10. New Guinea, NE Australia
137. *Lonchura spectabilis.* Hooded Munia. 4ss. 10. New Britain, New Guinea.
138. *Lonchura quinticolor.* Five coloured Finch. 11. Lombok, Flores & Is.
139. *Lonchura striata.* White rumped Munia. 6ss. 11. Indian sub continent.
140. incl. *L. s. acuticauda.* Bengal Munia. 11. India, Burma.
141. *Lonchura stygia.* Black Mannikin. 10. S New Guinea.
142. *Lonchura teerinki.* Black breasted Munia. 2ss. 10. New Guinea.
143. *Lonchura tristissima.* Streak headed Munia. 3ss. 10. New Guinea.
144. *Lonchura vana.* Arfac Mannikin. 10. New Guinea.
145. *Lonchura caniceps.* Grey headed Munia. 3ss. 10. New Guinea.
145a. *Lonchura pallidiventer.* Cream bellied Munia. 11. Kalimantan.
146. *Padda fuscata.* Timor Sparrow. 12. Timor.
147. *Padda oryzivora.* Java Sparrow. 15. Java, Bali.
148. *Amadina fasciata.* Cut-throat. 3ss. 12. Africa S of Sahara.
149. *Amadina erythrocephala.* Red headed Finch. 2ss. 13. Southern Africa.

100
101
102
103
104
(a)
JUV
(b)
(c)
105
106
107
108
109
110
111
112
113
114
115
116
117
118
119
120
121
122
123
124
125
126
127
128
129
130
131
132
133
134
135
136
137
138
139
140
141
142
143
144
145
146
147
145 A
148
149

PLOCEIDAE (1) VIDUINAE, BUBALORNITHINAE Indigo Birds, Whydahs, Buffalo Weavers.

There is great uncertainty as to how many true species of Indigobird exist. Some authorities consider there are twelve or more, others that there is only one species with several forms or phases. The general feeling seems to be that there are between three & seven species with numerous forms, not true subspecies as they have no constant Characteristics. Their main difference lies in their parasitic habits and these are imperfectly known. Seven supposed species are portrayed here.

1. *Vidua (Hypochera) Chalybeata.* Senegal / Village / Combassou. 11. W, E & C Africa. Incl. *aenea, ultramarina,* or Green / Purple / Steel blue *centralis, amauropteryx,* Indigobird. *neumanni, okavangoiensis.*
2. *Vidua (Hypochera) funerea.* Dusky / Black / Variable 11. SCW Africa. incl. *lusituensis* or White footed Indigobird.

2a. *Vidua codringtoni.* Twinspot Indigobird. 11. SC Africa. incl. *Nigerrima.*

3. *Vidua purpurascens.* Dusky / Purple Indigobird 11. ES Africa. incl. *incognita, lorenzi.* or Violet Widowfinch.
4. *Vidua (Hypochera) Wilsoni.* Wilson' s / Alexander' s 11 WE Africa. incl. *camerunensis, nigeriae.* or Baka Indigobird. Cameroon / Nigerian Combassou.
5. *Vidua larvaticola.* Baka Indigobird. 11. EWS Africa.
6. *Vidua raricola.* Jambandu Indigobird. 11 WC Africa.
7. *Vidua hypocherina.* Steel blue Whydah. 30/10. E Africa.
8. *Vidua fischeri.* Straw tailed Whydah. 28/10. E Africa.
9. *Vidua regia.* Shaft tailed Whydah. 34/14. S Africa.
10. *Vidua macroura.* Pin tailed Whydah. 44/12. Africa.
11. *Vidua paradisea.* Eastern Paradise Whydah. 38/15. Africa.
12. *Vidua orientalis.* Northern Broad tailed Whydah. 35/15. Africa.
13. *Vidua togoensis.* Togo Paradise Whydah. 45/13. W Africa.
14. *Vidua interjecta.* Nigerian Paradise Whydah. 41/14. W Africa.
15. *Vidua obtusa.* Chapin's Paradise Whydah. 33/13. SC Africa.

BUBALORNITHINAE Buffalo Weavers.

1. *Bubalornis albirostris.* White billed Buffalo Weaver. 3ss. 25. Africa South of Sahara.
2. *Bubalornis niger.* Red billed Buffalo Weaver. 2ss. 24. Southern Africa.
3. *Dinemellia dinemelli.* White headed Buffalo Weaver. 2ss. 26. E & EC Africa.

VIDUINAE
1
2
3
6
4
5
7
8
2A
9
14
13
15
10
11
12
PLOCEINAE
1
2
3

PLOCEIDAE (2), PASSERINAE (1)
Sparrows & Weavers

4. *Plocepasser donaldsoni.* Donaldson Smith's Sparrow Weaver. 15. N Kenya.
5. *Plocepasser mahali.* White browed Sparrow Weaver. 6ss. 17. E to S Africa.
6. *Plocepasser rufoscapulatus.* Chestnut backed Sparrow Weaver. 16. SC Africa.
7. *Plocepasser superciliosus.* Chestnut crowned Sparrow Weaver. 2ss. 15. E, W & C Africa.
8. *Histurgops ruficauda.* Rufous tailed Weaver. 22. Tanzania.
9. *Pseudonigrita arnaudi.* Grey headed Social Weaver. 3ss. 13. E Africa.
10. *Pseudonigrita cabanisi.* Black capped Social Weaver. 13. E Africa.
11. *Philetairus socius.* Sociable Weaver. 4ss. 14. SW & S Africa.
12. *Passer ammodendri.* Saxaul Sparrow. 4ss. 15. C Asia to China.
13. *Passer castanopterus.* Somali Sparrow. 2ss. 13. Somalia, Ethiopia, Kenya.
14. *Passer domesticus.* House Sparrow. 11ss. 14. World-wide.
15. incl. *P. D. italiae.* Italian Sparrow. 14. Italy.
16. *Passer/Sorella eminibey.* Chestnut Sparrow. 11. Sudan to Tanzania.
17. *Passer/Auripasser euchlorus.* Arabian Golden Sparrow. 11. Somalia, SW Arabia.
18. *Passer flaveolus.* Pegu / Plain backed Sparrow. 13. Indo-China, Thailand, Burma.
19. *Passer gongonensis.* Parrot billed Sparrow. 18. Ethiopia, Kenya.
20. *Passer griseus.* Grey headed Sparrow. 7ss. 15. Africa S of Sahara.

20a. *Passer diffusus.* Cape Sparrow. 14. Southern Africa.

21. *Passer hispaniolensis.* Spanish Sparrow. 2ss. 14. Iberia, Canary Is, N Africa to Afghanistan.
22. *Passer motitensis.* Great Sparrow. 6ss. 15. S Africa.
23. incl. *P. m. iagoensis.* Rufous backed Sparrow. 13. Cape Verde Is.
24. *Passer rufocinctus.* Kenya rufous Sparrow. 13. Kenya, N Tanzania.
25. *Passer insularis.* Socotra Sparrow. 13. Socotra I.
26. *Passer/Auripasser luteus.* Golden Sparrow. 12. Nigeria to Somalia.
27. *Passer melanurus.* Mossie. 2ss. 15. S Africa & Angola.
28. *Passer moabiticus.* Dead Sea Sparrow. 2ss. 12. Jordan to Iran.
29. *Passer montanus.* Tree Sparrow. 10ss. 14. Eurasia South to Indonesia.
30. *Passer' pyrrhonotus.* Sind / Jungle Sparrow. 12. Pakistan & SE Iran.
31. *Passer rutilans.* Cinnamon / Russet Sparrow. 3ss. 13. Afghanistan to E Asia.
32. *Passer simplex.* Desert Sparrow. 3ss. 13. Sahara to Iran.
33. *Passer/Carpospiza suahelicus.* Swaheli Sparrow. 15. E & EC Africa.
34. *Passer swainsonii.* Swainson's Sparrow. 14. Sudan, Ethiopia, Somalia.
35. *Petronia/Carpospiza brachydactyla.* Pale Rock Sparrow. 14. Middle East & E Africa.
36. *Petronia dentata.* Bush Petronia. 2ss. 13. Senegal to Sudan & SW Arabia.
37. *Petronia petronia.* Streaked Rock Sparrow. 6ss. 14. S Europe, N Africa to C Asia.
38. *Petronia pyrgita.* Yellow spotted Petronia. 14. E Africa.
39. *Petronia superciliaris.* Yellow throated Petronia. 14. Tanzania to S Africa.
40. *Petronia xanthocollis.* Chestnut shouldered Petronia. 13. Iraq to India.

4
5
6
7
8
9
10
11
12
13
14
15
16
18
19
20
20A
21
28
22
23
24
25
26
17
27
29
30
31
33
32
34
35
36
37
38
39
40

PLOCEIDAE (3), PASSERINAE (1), PLOCEINAE Snowfinches & Weavers

41. *Montifringilla adamsi*. Adams / Tibet Snow Finch. 2ss. 16. Tibet, Himalayas.
42. *Montifringilla Blanfordi*. Blanford's Snow Finch. 3ss. 15. Himalayas.
43. *Montifringilla davidiana*. Pere David's Snow Finch. 2ss. 15. Altai, Mongolia.
44. *Montifringilla nivalis*. Snow Finch. 4ss. 17. S Europe & Asia to China.
45. *Montifringilla ruficollis*. Red necked Snow Finch. 2ss. 15. Tibet.
46. *Montifringilla taczanowskii*. White rumped Snow Finch. 17. Tibet.
47. *Montifringilla theresae*. Afghan / Bar tailed Snow Finch. 14. Afghanistan. Winters Transcaspia.
48. *Sporopipes frontalis*. Speckle fronted Weaver. 3ss. 13. W & E Africa.
49. *Sporopipes squamifrons*. Scaly fronted Weaver. 2ss. 10. S Africa, Zimbabwe.

PLOCEINAE (1). Weavers.

50. *Amblyospiza albifrons*. Grosbeak Weaver. 10ss. 18. Africa S of Sahara.
51. *Ploceus albinucha*. Maxwell's Black Weaver. 3ss. 17. W Africa to Uganda.
52. *Ploceus alienus*. Strange Weaver. 14. Congo / Uganda border.
53. *Ploceus angolensis*. Bar winged Weaver. 15. Angola, Namibia, Congo.
54. *Ploceus aurantius*. Orange Weaver. 2ss. 13. Liberia to Congo, Uganda, Tanzania.
55. *Ploceus aureonucha*. Golden naped Weaver. 14. N E Congo.
56. *Ploceus badius*. Cinnamon Weaver. 2ss. 14. E & S Sudan.
57. *Ploceus baglafecht*. Baglafecht Weaver. 8ss. 15. E Africa to Malawi, Zambia.

58 incl. *P. b. reichenowi*. Reichenow's Weaver. 15. Kenya, Tanzania.

59. *P. b. emini*. Emin's Weaver. 15. Sudan, Uganda.
60. *P. b. stuhlmanni*. Stuhlmann's Weaver. 15. Uganda, Tanzania, Zaire.
61. *Ploceus Bannermani*. Bannerman's Weaver. 14. Cameroon.
62. *Ploceus batesi*. Bates' Weaver. 14. S Cameroon.
63. *Ploceus bertrandi*. Bertram's Weaver. 15. Tanzania, Malawi, Mozambique.
64. *Ploceus bicolor*. Dark backed / Forest Weaver. 8ss. 16. Fernando Po, Most of Africa.
65. *Ploceus bojeri*. Golden Palm Weaver. 15. Kenya, Somalia.
66. *Ploceus capensis*. Cape Weaver. 2ss. 17. S Africa.
67. *Ploceus castaneiceps*. Taveta Golden Weaver. 14. Kenya, Tanzania.
68. *Ploceus castanops*. Northern brown throated Weaver. 14. Rwanda, E Africa.
69. *Ploceus spilonotus*. Spotted backed Weaver. 7ss. 17. Southern Africa. (conspecific with 70.)
70. *Ploceus cucullatus*. Village / Black headed Weaver. 17. W Africa.
71. *Ploceus dicrocephalus*. Salvadori's Weaver. 15. Kenya, Somalia, Ethiopia .
72. *Ploceus dorsomaculatus*. Yellow capped Weaver. 15. Cameroon, Congo, Zaire.
73. *Ploceus galbula*. Ruppell's Weaver. 14. NE Africa, SW Arabia.

41
42
43
44
45
46
47
48
49
50
51
52
53
54
55
56
61
62
57-
NB
58
59
60
64
63
65
66
67
68
71
69
70
72
73

PLOCEIDAE (4), PLOCEINAE (2). Weavers

74. *Ploceus heuglini.* Heuglin's masked Weaver. 14. E W & C Africa.
75. *Ploceus golandi.* Clarke's Weaver. 13. Kenya coast. (unique).
76. *Ploceus(Hyphantornis)grandis.* Giant Weaver. 21. Sao Thome.
77. *Ploceus benghalensis.* Bengal / Black breasted Weaver. 15. N India to Assam.
78. *Ploceus hypoxanthus=Chrysalus.* Asiatic Golden Weaver. 2ss. 15. SE Asia.
79. *Ploceus manyar.* Streaked Weaver. 4ss. 15. India to Indonesia.
80. *Ploceus megarhynchus.* Yellow / Finn's Weaver. 2ss. 16. Himalayas, NE India.
81. *Ploceus phillipinus.* Baya Weaver. 5ss. 15. India, SE Asia, Sumatra.
82. *Ploceus insignis.* Brown capped Weaver. 2ss. 14. C Africa.
83. *Ploceus intermedius.* (Lesser) Masked Weaver. 2ss. 15. Ethiopia to S Africa.
84. *Ploceus reichardi.* Tanzania masked Weaver. 14. SW Tanzania.
85. *Ploceus jacksoni.* Jackson's / Golden backed Weaver. 15. E Africa.
86. *Ploceus luteolus.* Little (Masked) Weaver. 2ss. 11. W & E Africa.
87. *Ploceus melanocephalus.* Black headed Weaver. 4ss. 15. E W & C Africa.
88. *Ploceus capitalis.* Yellow collared Weaver. 14. Nigeria to Chad.
89. *Ploceus melanogaster.* Black billed Mountain Weaver. 2ss. 14. W, C & E Africa
90. *Ploceus nelicourvi.* Nelicourvi Weaver. 16. Malagasy.
91. *Ploceus nigerrimus.* Viellot's Weaver. 2ss. 18. Liberia to Angola & E Africa.
92. *Ploceus nigriceps.* Layard's Black headed Weaver. 16. E & SE Africa.
93. *Ploceus nigricollis.* Black necked Weaver. 3ss. 15. W & E Africa.
94. *Ploceus brachypterus.* Swainson's Weaver. 15. Senegal To Cameroons.
95. *Ploceus nigrimentum.* Black chinned Weaver. 17. Angola, Zaire.
96. *Ploceus ocularis.* Spectacled Weaver. 3ss. 15. Africa S of Sahara.
97. *Ploceus olivaceiceps.* Olive headed Golden Weaver. 14. Tanzania, Malawi, Mozambique.

74
75
76
77
78
79
80
81
82
83
84
85
86
NB
87
89
90
88
91
92
93
94
95
96
97

PLOCEIDAE (5), PLOCEINAE (3). Weavers

98. *Ploceus nicolli.* Usambara Weaver. 14. Tanzania.
99. *Ploceus pelzelni.* Slender billed Weaver. 3ss. 11. Ghana to Angola, Zambia & Kenya.
100. *Ploceus preussi.* Golden backed Weaver. 14. Sierra Leone, Cameroon, Congo.
101. *Ploceus burnieri.* Kilombero Weaver. 13. Tanzania.
102. *Ploceus princeps.* Principe Golden Weaver. 18. Principe.
103. *Ploceus rubiginosus.* Chestnut Weaver. 2ss. 16. NE & SW Africa.
104. *Ploceus (?Foudia) sakalava.* Sakalava Weaver. 2ss. 16. Malagasy.
105. *Ploceus ruweti.* Lufira masked Weaver. 13. Zaire.
106. *Ploceus spekei.* Speke's Weaver. 15. Ethiopia to Tanzania.
107. *Ploceus spekoides.* Fox's Weaver. 15. Uganda.
108. *Ploceus sanctithomae.* Sao Thome Weaver. 15. Sao Thome.
109. *Ploceus subaureus.* (African) Golden Weaver. 3ss. 15. E Africa, Kenya to Cape.
110. *Ploceus Subpersonatus.* Loanga Weaver. 13. Gabon to N Congo.
111. *Ploceus/Pachyphantes superciliosus.* Compact Weaver. 13. W E & C Africa.
112. *Ploceus taeniopterus.* Northern masked Weaver. 2ss. 14. Sudan to Congo.
113. *Ploceus temporalis.* Angolan / Bocage's Weaver. 16. Angola, Zambia.
114. *Ploceus tricolor.* Yellow mantled Weaver. 2ss. 15. W & C Africa.
115. *Ploceus velatus.* Southern masked Weaver. 9ss. 15. Southern Africa.
116. *Ploceus vitellinus.* Vitelline masked Weaver. 2ss. 14. Sudan, W Africa.
117. *Ploceus katangae.* Katanga masked Weaver. 13. Zaire, Zambia.
118. *Ploceus victoriae.* Lake Victoria Weaver. 14. Uganda.
119. *Ploceus weynsi.* Weyn's Weaver. 15. Congo, Uganda, Tanzania.
120. *Ploceus xanthops.* Holub's Golden Weaver. 18. Kenya & Congo to S Africa.
121. *Ploceus xanthopterus.* Southern Brown throated Weaver. 3ss. 15. Malawi, Zambia, Botswana, Natal.

98
99
100
101
102
103
105
104
106
107
108
109
110
111
NB
112
113
114
115
NB
NB
116
117
118
119
120
♀?
121
NB
NB

PLOCEIDAE (6), PLOCEINAE (4). Malimbes, Queleas, Fodies.

122. *Malimbus flavipes.* Yellow legged Malimbe. 15. Zaire.
123. *Malimbus cassini.* Black throated Malimbe. 18. Cameroon, Gabon, Congo.
124. *Malimbus ballmani.* Tai Malimbe. 16. Ivory Coast.
125. *Malimbus coronatus.* Red crowned Malimbe. 17. Cameroon, NE Congo.
126. *Malimbus erythrogaster.* Red bellied Malimbe. 18. Nigeria, Cameroon, Congo.
127. *Malimbus ibadanensis.* Ibadan Malimbe. 19. E Nigeria.
128. *Malimbus malimbicus.* Crested Malimbe. 2ss. 18. Sierra Leone to Uganda & Angola.
129. *Malimbus nitens.* Blue billed / Gray's Malimbe. 3ss. 16. W C Africa.
130. *Malimbus racheliae.* Rachel's Malimbe. 16. Nigeria to Cameroon, Gabon.
131. *Anaplectes melanotis/leuconotus.* Red winged Weaver. 3ss. 15. WCE Africa.
132. *Anaplectes rubriceps.* Red headed Weaver. 15. Tanzania to Angola & RSA.
133. *Malimbus rubricollis.* Red headed Malimbe. 5ss. 18. WC Africa.
134. *Malimbus scutatus.* Red vented Malimbe. 2ss. 17. Sierra Leone to Ghana.
135. *Brachycope anomala.* Bob tailed Weaver. 12. SE Cameroon, W Congo.
136. *Quelea cardionalis.* Cardinal Quelea. 2ss. 12. Sudan to Zambia.
137. *Quelea erythrops.* Red headed Quelea. 13. Senegal to Ethiopia, RSA.
138. *Quelea quelea.* Common / Red billed Quelea. 3ss. 13. Africa S of Sahara.
139. *Foudia eminentissima.* Mascarene Fody. 5ss. 14. Aldabra, Comoro Is.
140. *Foudia flavicans.* Rodriguez Fody. 14. Rodriguez.
141. *Foudia madagascariensis.* Cardinal / Madagascar Fody. 15. Malagasy, Mauritius, Reunion, Seychelles.
142. *Foudia omissa.* Red Forest Fody. 15. E Malagasy.
143. *Foudia rubra.* Mauritius Fody. 15. Mauritius.
144. *Foudia sechellarum.* Seychelles Fody / Toctoc. 15. Frigate Is, Cousin, Cousine.

Foudia bruante. Reunion Fody is extinct, if it ever existed, which is doubtful.

Some, but not all, male Fodies have non-breeding dress, resembling females.

122
123
124
125
126
127
128
129
130
131
133
134
132
137
136
138
135
139
140
146
142
143
144

PLOCEIDAE (7), PLOCEINAE (5). Bishops & Widow Birds.

145. *Euplectes afer.* Yellow crowned Bishop / Napoleon Weaver. 4ss. 12. Africa S of Sahara.
146. *Euplectes diadematus.* Fire fronted Bishop. 10. Juba River, Kenya, Tanzania.
147. *Euplectes gierowii.* Black Bishop. 3ss. 15. Sudan to Tanzania, Congo, Angola.
148. *Euplectes nigroventris.* Zanzibar Red / Black vented Bishop. 10. Kenya to Mozambique.
149. *Euplectes hordeacus.* Black winged / Red crowned Bishop. 2ss. 13. Senegal to Sudan, Angola, Zimbabwe.
150. *Euplectes orix.* Red Bishop. 4ss. 12. E to S Africa.
151. *Euplectes franciscanus.* West Nile / Orange Bishop. 10. Senegal to E Africa. (Intro. Puerto Rico.)
152. *Euplectes aureus.* Golden backed Bishop. 13. Sao Thome, Angola.
153. *Euplectes capensis.* Yellow rumped Bishop. 5ss. 15. E C & S Africa.
154. *Euplectes axillaris.* Fan tailed Widow Bird. 18/15. E C & S Africa.
155. *Euplectes albonotatus.* White winged Widow Bird. 4ss. 19/15. W, E & C Africa.
156. *Euplectes ardens.* Red Collared Widow Bird. 4ss. 28/15. Africa S of Sahara.
157. *Euplectes concolor.* Black Widow Bird. 28/15. W C Africa.
158. *Euplectes suaheliucus.* Red naped Widow Bird. 28/15. Kenya Tanzania.
159. *Euplectes jacksoni.* Jackson's Widow Bird. 33/14. Kenya Tanzania.
160. *Euplectes progne.* Long tailed Widow Bird/Sakabula. 4ss. 65/15. Kenya to Zambia, Angola & S Africa.
161. *Euplectes hartlaubi.* Marsh Widow Bird. 36/15. W E & C Africa.
162. *Euplectes psammocromius.* Mountain / Buff shouldered Widow Bird. 51/20. Tanzania to Malawi.
163. *Euplectes macrocercus.* Yellow shouldered Widow Bird. 30/14. E Africa.
164. *Euplectes macrourus.* Yellow mantled Widow Bird. 30/14. W C & E Africa.
165. *Anomalospiza imberbis.* Parasitic Weaver. 12. Sierra Leone to Ethiopia & Transvaal.

145
146
147
148
149
150
151
152
153
154
155
156
157
158
159
160
162
-161-
164
163
165

STURNIDAE (1)
Asians & Australasian Starlings

1. *Aplonis atrifusca.* Samoan Starling. 30. Samoa.
2. *Aplonis brunneicapilla.* White eyed Starling. 20. Solomon Is.
3. *Aplonis cantoroides.* Little / Singing Starling. 18. New Guinea to Solomon Is.
4. *Aplonis crassa.* Tanimbar Starling. 18. Tanimbar Is.
5. *Aplonis cinerascens.* Cook Islands Starling. 20. Raratonga.
6. *Aplonis corvina.* Kittlitz's / Kosrae Starling. 25. Caroline Is. (extinct?)
7. *Aplonis mavornata.* Mysterious Starling. 18. Raiata, Society Is. (extinct.)
8. *Aplonis feadensis.* Atoll Starling. 2ss. 20. Bismarck Archipelago, Solomon Is.
9. *Aplonis insularis.* Rennell Islands Starling. 17. Rennell Is.
10. *Aplonis fusca.* Norfolk Island Starling. 20. Norfolk & Lord Howe Is.
11. *Aplonis grandis.* Brown winged Starling. 3ss. 25. Solomon Is.
12. *Aplonis dichroa.* San Cristabel Starling. 18. San Cristabel & other Solomon Is.
13. *Aplonis magna* Long tailed Starling. 2ss . 28-41. New Guinea Is.
14. *Aplonis metallica.* Metallic / Shining / Colonial Starling. 5ss. 23. Queensland, New Guinea, Solomon Is, Moluccas.
15. *Aplonis minor.* Lesser glossy Starling. 3ss. 17. Philippines, Indonesia.
16. *Aplonis mysolensis.* Moluccan Starling. 4ss. 40. W Papuan Is. to Wallacea.
17. *Aplonis mystacea.* Grant's / Mimic / Yellow eyed Starling. 20. New Guinea.
18. *Aplonis opaca.* Micronesian Starling. 7ss. 21. Micronesia.
19. *Aplonis panayensis.* Asian glossy Starling / Glossy Starling. 13ss. 20. E India to SE Asia, Indonesia, Philippines.
20. *Aplonis pelzelni.* Ponape Starling. 18. Ponape.
21. *Aplonis santovestris.* Mountain Starling. 18. New Hebrides.
22. *Aplonis striata.* Striped Glossy Starling. 2ss. 18. New Caledonia, Loyalty Is.
23. *Aplonis tabuensis.* Striped/Polynesian Starling. 12ss. 18. S Polynesia.
24. *Aplonis zelandica.* New Hebrides / Rusty winged Starling. 3ss. 17. New Hebrides.

1
2
3
4
5
9
10
6
7
8
14
15
12
13
11
16
20
17
18
19
21
22
23
24

STURNIDAE ()
Starlings

25. *Poeoptera kenricki*. Kenrick's Starling. 2ss. 15. Kenya, Tanzania.
26. *Poeoptera lugubris*. Narrow tailed Starling. 2ss. 18. Sierra Leone to Uganda & S to Angola.
27. *Poeoptera stuhlmanni*. Stuhlmann's Starling. 15. Sudan to Uganda & Congo.
28. *Grafisia torquata*. White collared Starling. 21. Cameroon to N Congo.
29. *Onychognanthus albirostris*. White billed Starling. 25. Ethiopia.
30. *Onychognanthus blythii* . Somali Chestnut winged Starling. 28. Eritrea to Somalia & Socotra.
31. *Onychognanthus frater*. Socotra Chestnut winged Starling. 30. Socotra .
32. *Onychognanthus fulgidus*. Chestnut winged Starling. 2ss. 28. W Africa, Uganda.
33. *Onychognanthus morio*. Red winged Starling. 4ss. 28. Africa South of Sahara.
34. *Onychognanthus nabouroup*. Pale winged Starling. 2ss. 26. Southern Africa.
35. *Onychognanthus salvadorii*. Bristle crowned Starling. 40. Somalia to Kenya.
36. *Onychognanthus tenuirostris*. Slender billed chestnut winged Starling. 2ss. 25. E Africa, Ethiopia to Malawi.
37. *Onychognanthus tristramii*. Tristram's Starling (Grackle). 25. SW Arabia.
38. *Onychognanthus walleri*. Waller's chestnut winged Starling. 3ss. 20. Cameroon to Sudan & S to Malawi.

25
26
27
29
28
30
31
34
32
33
36
37
35
38

STURNIDAE (3)
Starlings

39. *Lamprotornis acuticaudus.* Sharp tailed glossy Starling. 20. S C Africa.
40. *Lamprotornis australis.* Burchell's / Greater glossy Starling. 2ss. 34. Transvaal, SW Africa.
41. *Lamprotornis caudatus.* Long tailed glossy Starling. 35. Senegal to Sudan.
42. *Lamprotornis chalcurus.* Bronze tailed glossy Starling. 2ss. 21. E & W Africa.
43. *Lamprotornis chalybaeus.* Blue eared glossy Starling. 4ss. 22. W to SE Africa.
44. *Lamprotornis chloropterus.* Swainson's / Lesser blue eared Starling. 3ss. 18. C Africa.
44a. *Lamprotornis elisabeth.* Southern blue eared glossy Starling. 19. E Africa.
(adult indistinguishable from 44 in Field.)
45. *Lamprotornis corruscus.* Black bellied glossy Starling. 2ss. 18. E African coast.
46. *Lamprotornis cupreocauda.* Copper tailed glossy Starling. 21. Sierra Leone, Liberia, Ghana.
47. *Lamprotornis iris.* Emerald Starling. 19. Fr. Guinea to Ivory coast.
48. *Lamprotornis mevesii.* Meve's Long tailed Starling. 4ss. 34. C & SW Africa.
49. *Lamprotornis nitens.* Cape / Red shouldered glossy Starling. 3ss. 24. S Africa.
50. *Lamprotornis ornatus.* Ornate / Principe glossy Starling. 30. Principe.
51. *Lamprotornis purpureiceps.* Velvet / Purple headed Starling. 18. W C Africa.
52. *Lamprotornis purpureus.* Purple glossy Starling. 2ss. 24. W C Africa.
53. *Lamprotornis purpuropterus.* Ruppell's glossy Starling. 2ss. 34. E Africa.
54. *Lamprotornis splendidus.* Splendid Starling. 4ss. 30. E W & C Africa.
55. *Cinnyricinclus femoralis.* Abbott's Starling. 16. Kenya, Tanzania.
56. *Cinnyricinclus leucogaster.* Amethyst / Violet backed Starling. 4ss. 18. Africa S of Sahara.
57. *Cinnyricinclus sharpii.* Sharpe's Starling. 16. E & C Africa.
58. *Speculipastor bicolor.* Magpie Starling. 19. E Africa.
59. *Neocichla gutturalis.* White winged babbling Starling. 2ss. 20. C Africa.
60. *Spreo albicapillus.* White crowned Starling. 23. Somalia, Ethiopia.
61. *Spreo bicolor.* Pied Starling. 26. South Africa.
63. *Spreo fischeri.* Fischer's Starling. 18. E Africa.
64. *Spreo hildebrandti.* Hildebrandt's Starling. 18. Kenya, Tanzania.
64. *Spreo pulcher.* Chestnut breasted Starling. 2ss. 17. E & W Africa.
66. *Spreo regius.* Regal / Golden breasted Starling. 2ss. 33. E Africa.
67. *Spreo superbus.* Superb Starling. 18. E Africa.
68. *Spreo (Cosmopsorus) unicolor.* Ashy Starling. 30. S Kenya, Tanzania.

39
40
41
42
43
44
44A
JUV
45
46
47
48
49
50
51
52
53
54
55
56
57
58
59
60
61
62
68
63
64
66
67
65

STURNIDAE (4)
Starlings

69. *Saraglossa aurata*. Madagascar Starling. 20. Malagasy.
70. *Saraglossa spiloptera*. Spotted winged Starling. 18. Himalayas, Burma, Thailand.
71. *Creatophora cinerea*. Wattled Starling. 21. Arabia, Sudan to Angola & Cape.
72. *Sturnus burmanicus*. Jerdon's / Vinous breasted Starling. ss. 25. Indo-China, Burma, Thailand.
73. *Sturnus cineraceus*. White cheeked / Grey Starling. 23. NE Asia. Winters S China.
74. *Sturnus contra*. Asian Pied Starling. 5ss. 24. India to Indo-China, Indonesia.
75. *Sturnus erythropygius* . White headed Starling . 3ss. 21. Andaman, Nicobar Islands.
76. *Sturnus malabaricus*. Chestnut tailed / Grey headed Starling. 3ss. 20. India & SE Asia.
77. *Sturnus melanopterus*. Black winged Starling. 3ss. 23. Java, Bali, Lombok.
78. *Sturnus nigricollis*. Black collared Starling. 27. S China, SE Asia.
79. *Sturnus pagodarum*. Brahminy Starling. 22. Afghanistan to India & Sri Lanka.
80. *Sturnus philippensis*. Violet backed / Red cheeked Starling. 19. E Asia. Winters Philippines, Borneo.
81. *Sturnus roseus*. Rose coloured Starling. 21. Europe to Turkestan. Winters India.
82. *Sturnus senex*. Ceylon White faced Starling. 22. Sri Lanka.
83. *Sturnus sericeus*. Silky / Red billed Starling. 24. CS China. Winters Indo-China.
84. *Sturnus sinensis*. White shouldered / Grey backed Starling. 20. China. Winters Indo-China.
85. *Sturnus sturninus* . Daurian / Purple backed Starling . 18 . E Asia. Winters SE Asia .
86. *Sturnus unicolor*. Spotless Starling. 21. S Europe, NW Africa.
87. *Sturnus vulgaris*. Common Starling. 11ss. 21. Eurasia. Intro. Africa, Australia, America.
88. *Leucopsar rothschildi*. Rothschild's Myna / Grackle. 25. Bali.
89. *Necropsar leguati*. Rodriguez Starling. 25. Rodriguez. (extinct).
90. *Fregilupus varius*. Bourbon crested Starling. 30. Reunion. (extinct).

69
70
71
NB
72
73
74
75
76
77
78
79
80
81
82
83
84
85
86
JUV
Br
87
NB
89
90
88

STURNIDAE (5)
Starlings

91. *Acridotheres albocinctus.* Collared Myna. 24. E India, Burma, Yunnan.
92. *Acridotheres Cristatellus.* Crested Myna. 3ss. 26. China, Indo-China. Introduced Philippines, Canada.
93. *Acridotheres fuscus.* Jungle Myna. 6ss. 24. India to Malaya to Sulawesi.
94. *Acridotheres javanicus.* Javan / White vent-ed Myna. 25. Java.
95. *Acridotheres ginginianus.* Bank Myna. 21. Plains of N India.
96. *Acridotheres grandis.* Great Myna. 26. Assam, Burma, Thailand, Indo-China.
97. *Acridotheres tristis.* Common / Indian Myna. 3ss. 24. S Asia, Indian Ocean Is.
98. *Mine anais.* Golden (breasted) Myna. 3ss. 24. New Guinea & Japen.
99. *Ampeliceps (Mino) coronatus.* Gold crested Myna. 21. E India to SE Asia.
100. *Mine dumontii.* Papuan / Yellow faced Myna. 3ss. 25. New Guinea to Solomon Is.
101. *Basilornis celebensis.* Celebes / King Starling. 23. Sulawesi.
102. *Basilornis corythaix.* Moluccan / Ceram Starling. 23. Ceram.
103. *Basilornis galeatus.* Sula / Crested Starling. 23. Banggai, Sula Is.
104. *Basilornis miranda.* Mount Apo Starling. 24. Mindanao.
105. *Streptocitta albertinae.* Bare eyed / Sula Magpie / Myna. 20. Sula Is.
106. *Streptocitta albicollis.* Sulawesi Magpie / Buton Starling. 20. Sulawesi.
107. *Streptocitta torquata.* White necked Myna. 20. N Sulawesi.
108. *Sarcops calvus.* Bald Starling / Coleto. 3ss. 24. Philippines, Sula Is.
109. *Gracula ptilogenys.* Ceylon Myna. 25. Sri Lanka.
110. *Gracula religiosa.* Hill Myna. 10ss. 30. India, SE Asia, Indonesia.
111. incl. *G. r. venerata.* Sumbara Myna. 30. Sumbara Is.
112. *Enodes erythrophris* . Fiery browed Myna. 3ss. 27. Sulawesi.
113. *Scissirostrum dubium.* Grosbeak / Finch billed Starling. 28. Sulawesi.
114. *Buphagus africanus.* Yellow billed Oxpecker. 2ss. 19. Africa S of Sahara.
115. *Buphagus erythrorhynchus.* Red billed Oxpecker. 4ss. 18. E & SE Africa.

91
92
93
94
95
96
97
98
99
100
101
102
103
104
105
106
107
108
109
111
110
112
113
114
115

ORIOLIDAE (1)
Old World Orioles

Family 182. ORIOLIDAE (I). Old World Orioles.

1. *Oriolus szalayi*. Brown Oriole.27. New Guinea & W Papuan Is.
2. *Oriolus pharochromus*. Dusky Brown / Ruddy Oriole. 26. Halmahera.
3. *Oriolus forsteni*. Grey collared Oriole. 27. Ceram.
4. *Oriolus bouroensis*. Black eared / Buru Oriole. 21. Buru & Tenimber Is.
5. *Oriolus melanotis/viridifuscus*. Olive brown / Dark Oriole. 2ss. 26. Timor, Wetar.
6. *Oriolus sagittatus*. Olive backed / White bellied Oriole. 3ss. 27. New Guinea, NE Australia.
7. *Oriolus flavicinctus*. Green / Yellow Oriole. 2ss. 27. N Australia, New Guinea & Is.
8. *Oriolus xanthonotus*. Dark throated Oriole. 9ss. 18. Malaysia to Philippines

8a. *Oriolus steeri*. Philippine Oriole. 18. Masbate, Negros.

9. *Oriolus albiloris*. White lored Oriole. 18. Luzon.
10. *Oriolus isabellae*. Isabella Oriole. 18. Luzon.
11. *Oriolus oriolus*. Golden Oriole. 2ss. 24. Europe, W Asia. Winters E & S Africa.
12. *Oriolus auratus*. African Golden Oriole. 2ss. 23. Africa S of Sahara.
13. *Oriolus chlorocephalus*. Green headed Oriole. 3ss. 22. Tanzania to Mozambique.
14. *Oriolus crassirostris*. Great billed Oriole. 25. Sao Thome.
15. *Oriolus brachyrhynchus*. Western Black headed Oriole. 2ss. 25. W C Africa.
16. *Oriolus monacha*. Black headed / Forest Oriole. 2ss. 23. Ethiopia, Eritrea.
17. *Oriolus larvatus*. Eastern Black headed Oriole. 23. Africa S of Sahara.
18. *Oriolus percivali*. Montane Oriole. 23. E Africa.
19. *Oriolus nigripennis*. Black winged Oriole. 2ss. 25. Fernando Po, Sierra Leone to Uganda & N Angola.
20. *Oriolus chinensius*. Black naped Oriole. 23ss. 26. Himalayas, SE Asia to Indonesia.
21. *Oriolus tenuirostris*. Slender billed Oriole. 26. Nepal, Burma, Thailand.
22. *Oriolus xanthornis*. Asian Black headed Oriole. 6ss. 25. India, Sri Lanka, SE Asia to Borneo.

1
2
3
4
5
6
7
8
8A
10
9
11
12
13
14
15
16
17
18
19
20
21
22

ORIOLIDAE, (2), ARTAMIDAE
Old World Orioles, Wood Swallows

23. *Oriolus hosii*. Black Oriole. 21. Borneo.
24. *Oriolus cruentus*. Black & crimson / Crimson breasted Oriole. 4ss. 27. Malaysia, Indonesia.
25. *Oriolus trailli*. Maroon Oriole. 4ss. 26. Himalayas, Yunnan, N SE Asia.
26. *Oriolus mellianus*. Streseman's Maroon / Silver Oriole. 27. China. Winters South.
27. *Sphecotheres flaviventris*. Northern / Yellow Figbird. 2ss. 28. NE Australia.
28. *Sphecotheres hypoleucus*. Wetar Figbird. 26. Wetar.
29. *Sphecotheres vieilloti*. Southern / Green Figbird. 2ss. 28. E Australia, S New Guinea.
30. Sphecotheres viridis. Timor Figbird. 28. Timor. (consp. with 28/29?)

Family 183. ARTAMIDAE. Wood Swallows.

1. *Artamus cinereus*. Black faced Wood Swallow. 5ss. 18. E Australia, Timor, S New Guinea.
2. *Artamus cyanopterus*. Dusky Wood Swallow. 2ss. 17. Tasmania, S E Australia.
3. *Artamus fuscus*. Ashy Wood Swallow. 17. S China, SE Asia, India, Sri Lanka.
4. *Artamus insignis*. Bismarck Wood Swallow. 18. New Britain, New Ireland.
5. *Artamus leucorhynchus*. White breasted Wood Swallow. 11ss. 17. Andamans, Indonesia, Australia.
6. *Artamus mentalis*. Fiji Wood Swallow. 16. N Fiji.
7. *Artamus maximus*. Greater / Black breasted Wood Swallow. 20. New Guinea.
8. *Artamus minor*. Little Wood Swallow. 13. NC Australia.
9. *Artamus monachus*. Hooded / White backed Wood Swallow. 2ss. 18. Sulawesi.
10. *Artamus personatus*. Masked Wood Swallow. 18. Australia.
11. *Artamus superciliosus*. White browed Wood Swallow. 20. E Australia.

23
24
25
26
27
28
29
30
ARTAMIDAE
1
2
3
4
5
7
6
8
9
10
11

DICRURIDAE
Drongos

Family 184. DICRURIDAE. Drongos.

1. *Chaetorhynchus papuensis*. Papuan / Mountain Drongo. 20. New Guinea & Is.
2 *Dicrurus megarhynchus*. Ribbon tailed Drongo. 31. New Ireland.
3. *Dicrurus adsimilis*. Fork tailed Drongo. 5ss. 24. Fernando Po, Africa S of Sahara.
4. *Dicrurus modestus*. Velvet mantled Drongo. 27. Princepe.
5. *Dicrurus atripennis*. Shining Drongo. 24. Guinea, Sierra Leone to Gabon.
6. *Dicrurus ludwigi*. Square tailed Drongo. 3ss. 18. Local, Africa S of Sahara.
7. *Dicrurus aldabranus*. Aldabra Drongo. 25. Aldabra.
8. *Dicrurus andamanensis*. Andaman Drongo. 2ss. 35. Andaman & Cocos Is.
9. *Dicrurus Annectens*. Crow billed Drongo. 27. Himalayas to SE Asia.
10. *Dicrurus aeneus*. Bronzed Drongo. 3ss. 24. India, S China to Indonesia.
11. *Dicrurus balicassius*. Ballicassino Drongo. 3ss. 29. Philippines.
12. *Dicrurus caerulescens*. White bellied Drongo. 3ss. 24. India, Sri Lanka.
13. *Dicrurus forficatus*. Crested Drongo. 2ss. 26. Malagasy, Comoro Is.
14. *Dicrurus fuscipennis*. Grand Comoro Drongo. 30. Grand Comoro Is.
15. *Dicrurus hottentottus*. Spangled / Hair curled Drongo. 3ss. 30. India, SE Asia, Indonesia to Solomon Is.
16. *Dicrurus bracteatus*. Spangled Drongo. 27. New Guinea, NE Australia.
17. *Dicrurus leucophaeus*. Ashy Drongo. 14ss. 29. Afghanistan to Indonesia.
18. *Dicrurus macrocercus*. Black Drongo. 7ss. 27. Iran & Asia to Indonesia.
19. *Dicrurus montanus*. (Celebes) Mountain Drongo. 25. Sulawesi.
20. *Dicrurus paradiseus*. Greater racquet tailed Drongo. 14ss. 32+30. Kashmir & Sri Lanka to SE Asia & Indonesia.
21. *Dicrurus remifer*. Lesser racquet tailed Drongo. 4ss. 26+50. Himalayas to Indonesia.
22. *Dicrurus waldenii*. Mayotte Drongo. 35. Mayotte.
23. *Dicrurus densus*. Wallacean Drongo. 5ss. 28. Wallacea.
24. *Dicrurus sumatranus*. Sumatran Drongo. 30. Sumatra.

1
2
3
4
5
6
JUV
7
8
9
10
23
11
12
20
21
13
14
15
16
24
22
19
17
18

CALLEIDAE, GRALLINIDAE, CRACTICIDAE New Zealand Wattlebirds, Mud nest builders, Australian Bell Magpies

Family 185. CALLAEIDAE. New Zealand Wattlebirds.

1. *Callaeas wilsoni.* North Island Kokako 38. North island, New Zealand.
2. *Callaeas cinerea* South Island Kokako. 38. South Island, New Zealand.
3. *Creadion/Philesturnus rufusater.* Saddleback. 25. North Island, New Zealand.
4. *C. / P. r. carunculatus.* Saddleback. 25. Stewart Is. & perhaps other Islands off South Island.
5. *Heteralocha acutirostris.* Huia. 45-48. North island, New Zealand (extinct since 1907.)

Juvenile of 4. Was formerly known as the 'Jackbird', and was wrongly considered a separate species.

Family 186. GRALLINIDAE. Mud nest builders.

1. *Grallina bruijni.* Torrent Lark. 20. New Guinea.
2. *Grallina cyanoleuca.* Magpie Lark. 26-30. Australia, New Guinea.
3. *Corcorax melanorhamphus.* White winged Chough. 46. E & SE Australia.
4. *Struthidea cinerea.* Apostle Bird. 31. N & E Australia.

Family 187. CRACTICIDAE (1). Australian Bell Magpies.

1. *Gymnorhina tibicea.* Black backed Magpie. 9ss. 38. Australia.
2. *Gymnorhina dorsalis.* Western Magpie. 38. W Australia.
3. *Gymnorhina hypoleuca.* White backed Magpie. 38. Victoria, Tasmania.

1
2
5
3
4
4 JUV
GRALLINIDAE
1
2
3
4
CRATICIDAE
1
2
3

CRACTICIDAE (2), PTILONORHYNCHIDAE (1) Butcherbird, Currawongs, Bowerbirds

4. *Cracticus cassicus*. Black headed / Hooded Butcherbird. 2ss. 32. New Guinea & adjacent islands.
5. *Cracticus louisiadensis*. White rumped Butcherbird. 29. Tagula Is.
6. *Cracticus mentalis*. Black backed / White throated Butcherbird. 2ss. 28. SW New Guinea, N Queensland.
7. *Cracticus nigrogularis*. Black throated / Pied Butcherbird. 3ss. 34. Australia.
8. *Cracticus quoyi*. Black Butcherbird. 3ss. 34. Australia, Tasmania.
9. *Cracticus torquatus* . Grey Butcherbird . 4ss. 24-30. Australia , Tasmania .
10. *Cracticus argenteus*. Silver backed Butcherbird. 24. N Territory, NW Australia.
11. *Strepera arguta*. Clinking Currawong. 45-50. Tasmania. (ss. of 14?)
12. *Strepera fuliginosa*. Black Currawong. 47. Tasmania.
13. *Strepera graculina*. Pied Currawong. 4ss. 46. E Australia, Lord Howe Is.
14. *Strepera versicolor*. Grey Currawong. 6ss. 45-50. SE & SW Australia.

Family 188. PTILONORHYNCHIDAE (1). Bowerbirds.

1. *Ailuroedus buccoides*. White eared Catbird. 4ss. 25. NW New Guinea, Papuan islands.
2. *Ailuroedus cinnamomeus*. Cinnamon crowned Catbird. 25. S New Guinea.
3. *Ailuroedus crassirostris*. Green Catbird. 31. SE Australia.
4. *Ailuroedus melanotis*. Spotted Catbird. 9ss. 29. NE Australia, New Guinea.
5. *Scenopoeetes dentirostris*. Tooth billed Catbird. 26. N Queensland.
6. *Archboldia papuensis*. Archbold's Bowerbird. 37. New Guinea.

6a. *Archboldia sanfordi*. Sanford's Bowerbird. 37. C New Guinea.

7. *Amblyornis flavifrons*. Yellow fronted Bowerbird. 24. NW New Guinea.
8. *Amblyornis inornatus*. Vogelkop Gardener Bowerbird. 25. NW New Guinea.

4
5
6
7
8 JUV
9
JUV
10
11
12
13
14
PTILONORHYNCHIDAE
1
2
3
4
5
8
6
6A
7

PTILONORYNCHIDAE (2), PARADISAEIDAE
Bowerbirds, Birds of Paradise

9. *Amblyornis Macgregoriae*. Macgregor's Bowerbird. 5ss. 26. New Guinea.
10. *Amblyornis subalaris*. Striped / Streaked Bowerbird. 22. SE New Guinea.
11. *Prionodura newtoniana*. (Australian) Golden Bowerbird. 23. Queensland.
12. *Sericulus/Xanthomelus aureus*. Golden Regent / New Guinea Golden Bowerbird. 2ss. 23. N New Guinea.
13. *Sericulus ardens*. Flame Bowerbird. 23. S New Guinea.
14. *Sericulus bakeri*. Fire maned / Beck's / Adelbert Regent Bowerbird. 27. N E New Guinea.
15. *Sericulus chrysocephalus*. Regent Bowerbird. 2ss. 25. Queensland, New South Wales.
16. *Ptilonorhynchus violaceus*. Satin Bowerbird. 2ss. 30. E Australia.
17. *Chlamydera cerviniventris*. Fawn breasted Bowerbird. 29. New Guinea to Cape York Peninsula.
18. *Chlamydera lauterbachi*. Yellow breasted Bowerbird. 27. C New Guinea.
19. incl. *C. L. uniformis* . Uniform / Lauterbach's Bowerbird. 27. NW S New Guinea.
20. *Chlamydera maculata*. Spotted Bowerbird. 27. Interior Australia.
21. *Chlamydera guttata*. Western Bowerbird. 27. WC Australia.
22. *Chlamydera nuchalis*. Great Bowerbird. 4ss. 36. N Australia.

Family 189. PARADISAEIDAE(1). Birds of Paradise.

1. *Loria/Cnemophilus loriae*. Loria's Bird of Paradise. 3ss. 22. New Guinea.
2. *Loboparadisea sericea*. Wattle billed / Yellow breasted Bird of Paradise. 2ss. 18. New Guinea.
3. *Cnemophilus sanguineus*. Sickle crested Bird of Paradise. 25. E New Guinea.
4. *Cnemophilus macgregorii*. Multicrested Birof Paradise. 25. SE New Guinea.
5. *Macgregoria pulchra*. Macgregor's Bird of Paradise. 2ss. 39. C & SE New Guinea.
6. *Lycocorax pyrrhopterus*. Paradise Crow / Brown winged Bird of Paradise. 3ss. 39. Moluccas.

9
10
11
12
13
14
15
16
17
18
19
20
21
22
PARADISAEIDAE
1
2
5
3
4
6

PARADISAEIDAE (2)
Birds of Paradise, Manucodes & Riflebirds

7. *Manucodia ater(atra)*. Glossy mantled Manucode. 3ss. 38. New Guinea, W Papuan Islands.
8. *Manucodia chalybatus*. Crinkle collared / Green breasted Manucode. 36. New Guinea.
9. *Manucodia comrii*. Curl crested Manucode. 2ss. 44. E Papuan Is.
10. *Manucodia jobiensis*. Jobi Manucode. 2ss. 33. N New Guinea, Japan.
11. *Phonygamnus(Manucodia)keraudrenii*. Trumpet Bird. 8ss. 31. New Guinea to N Australia.
12. *Ptiloris magnificus*. Magnificent Riflebird. 2ss. 33. New Guinea, Queensland.

12a. *Ptiloris intercedens* . Eastern Riflebird. 33. E New Guinea.

13. *Ptiloris paradiseus*. Paradise Riflebird. 26. S Queensland, New South Wales.
14. *Ptiloris victoriae*. Victoria Riflebird. 24. N Queensland.
15. *Semioptera wallacei*. Wallace's standard wing Bird of Paradise. 2ss. 25. Halmahera, Batjan.
16. *Seleucidis melenoleuca*. Twelve wired Bird of Paradise. 2ss. 34. New Guinea, Salawati.
17. *Paradigalla brevicauda*. Short tailed Paradigalla. 23. C New Guinea.
18. *Paradigalla carunculata*. Long tailed Paradigalla. 38. NW New Guinea.
19. *Drepanornis(Epimachus)albertisii*. Black billed sicklebill Bird of Paradise. 3ss. 36. New Guinea.
20. *Drepanornis bruijnii*. White billed sicklebill Bird of Paradise. 35. N New Guinea.

7
8
9
10
11
- 12 -
13
12A
- 14 -
-15-
- 16 -
17
18
- 19 -
- 20 -

PARADISAEIDAE (3)
Birds of Paradise & Astrapias

21. *Epimachus fastuosus*. Black sicklebill Bird of Paradise. 4ss. 110. New Guinea.
22. *Epimachus meyeri*. Brown sicklebill Bird of Paradise. 4ss. 100. New Guinea.
23. *Astrapia mayeri*. Ribbon tailed Astrapia. 135. C New Guinea.
24. *Astrapia nigra*. Arfak Astrapia. 76. NW New Guinea.
25. *Astrapia rothschildi*. Huon / Rothschild's Astrapia. 64. NE New Guinea.
26. *Astrapia splendidissima*. Splendid Astrapia. 3ss. 46. WC New Guinea.
27. *Astrapia stephaniae*. Princess Stephanie's Astrapia. 3ss. 84. New Guinea.

21
22
23
24
25
26
27

PARADISAEIDAE (4)
Birds of Paradise

28. *Lophorina superba*. Superb Bird of Paradise. 8ss.25. New Guinea.
29. *Parotia carolae*. Queen Carolas six wired Bird of Paradise. 6ss. 27. New Guinea.
30. *Parotia lawesi*. Lawes' Six wired (plumed) Bird of Paradise. 28. New Guinea.
31. *Parotia sefilata*. Arfak or Western Parotia. 33. W New Guinea.
32. *Parotia wahnesi*. Wahnes' Six wired Bird of Paradise. 43. Huon.
33. *Parotia helenae*. Eastern Parotia. 28. SE New Guinea.
34. *Pteridophora alberti*. King of Saxony Bird of Paradise. 3ss. 22. New Guinea.
35. *Cicinnurus regius*. King Bird of Paradise. 6ss. 16. New Guinea & adjacent Is.
36. *Diphyllodes (Cicinnurus)magnificus*. Magnificent Bird of Paradise. 4ss. 18. New Guinea & adjacent Is.
37. *Diphyllodes (Cicinnurus)respublica*. Wilson's / Waigan Bird of Paradise. 17. West Papuan islands.

28
(a)
(b)
29
- 30 -
31
- 33 -
32
34
35
36
37

Plate 362 Family 189.

PARADISAEIDAE (5)
Birds of Paradise

38. *Paradisaea apoda*. Greater Bird of Paradise. 2ss. 44. New Guinea, Aku I. (Intro. Tobago.)
39. *Paradisaea raggiana*. Count Raggi's Bird of Paradise. 5ss. 33. SE New Guinea.
40. *Paradisaea decora*. Goldie's Bird of Paradise. 32. D'Entrecasteaux Archipelago.
41. *Paradisaea guilielmi*. German emperor's Bird of Paradise. 29. E New Guinea.
42. *Paradisaea minor*. Lesser Bird of Paradise. 4ss. 32. NW New Guinea, Japen.
43. *Paradisaea rubra*. Red Bird of Paradise. 33. W Papuan Is.
44. *Paradisaea rudolphi*. Blue Bird of Paradise. 3ss. 30. SE New Guinea.

38
39
40
41
42
43
44

CORVIDAE (1)
Magpie Jays, Tree Pies, Magpies

Family 190 CORVIDAE (1). Magpie Jays, Tree Pies & Magpies

1. *Platylophus galericulatus*. Crested Malay / Shrike Jay. 3ss. 32. Malaysia, Indonesia.
2. *Platysmurus leucopterus*. White winged Black Magpie-Jay. 2ss. 35. Malaysia, Sumatra.
3. *Platysmurus aterrimus*. Black Magpie Jay. 35. Borneo.
4. *Dendrocitta vagabunda*. (Rufous / Indian Tree Pie 8ss. 50. India, SE Asia.
5. *Dendrocitta frontalis*. Black browed / Collared Tree Pie. 38. Himalayas.
6. *Dendrocitta formosae*. Grey / Himalayan Tree Pie. 8ss. 32. Himalayas, SE Asia.
7. *Dendrocitta leucogastra*. Southern / White bellied Tree Pie. 50. S India.
8. *Dendrocitta occipitalis*. Sumatran or Malaysian Tree Pie. 2ss. 50. Sumatra.
9. *Dendrocitta cinerascens*. Bornean Tree Pie. 50. Borneo.
10. *Dendrocitta bayleyi*. Andaman Tree Pie. 36. Andaman Is.
11. *Crypsirina cucullata*. Hooded Racquet tailed Tree Pie. 31. NC Burma.
12. *Crypsirina temia*. Bronzed Racquet tailed Tree Pie. 33. Burma to Java.
13. *Temnurus temnurus*. Notch tailed Tree Pie. 35. SE Asia.
14. *Urocissa whiteheadi*. White winged / Whitehead's Magpie. 2ss. 45. SE Asia.
15. *Urocissa erthrorhyncha*. Red billed Blue Magpie. 5ss. 67. Himalayas.
16. *Urocissa caerulea*. Formosan Blue Magpie. 68. Taiwan.
17. *Urocissa flavirostris*. Yellow billed Blue Magpie. 4ss. 64. Himalayas.
18. *Urocissa ornata*. Ceylon Magpie. 47. Sri Lanka.
19. *Cissa chinensis*. Green Magpie. 5ss. 42. SE Asia.
20. *Cissa poleuca*. Yellow breasted / Green Magpie. 5ss. 40. SE Asia.
21. *Cissa thalassina*. Short tailed Green Magpie. 2ss. 35. Indonesia.
22. *Cyanopica cyana*. Azure winged Magpie. 9ss. 34. E Asia, Spain, Portugal.
23. *Pica nuttalli*. Yellow billed Magpie. 40. W California.
24. *Pica pica*. (Black billed) Magpie. 13ss. 48. W USA, Palearctic to SE Asia.

1
2
3
4
5
6
7
8
9
10
11
12
13
14
15
16
17
18
19
20
21
22
23
24

CORVIDAE (2)
Jays

25. *Garrulus glandarius*. (European) Jay. 36ss. 33. Most of Palearctic.
26. incl. *G. g. brandtii*. Red headed Jay. 33. Russia, Siberia, Korea.
27. *G. g. bispecularis*. Sikkim / Red crowned Jay. 31. Himalayas, China, Taiwan.
28. *G. g. japonicus*. Japanese Jay. 31. Japan.
29. *G. g. leucotis*. Burmese / White faced Jay. Burma.
30. *G. g. atricapillus*. Persian Jay. 33. Middle East.
31. *G. g. cervicalis*. Tunisian Jay. 33. North Africa.
32. *Garrulus lanceolatus*. Eurasian Black throated Jay. 30. C Asia.
33. *Garrulus lidthi*. Lidth's Jay. 38. Ryukyu Is.
34. *Perisoreus canadensis*. Grey Jay. 9ss. 25. N America except SE USA.
35. *Perisoreus infaustus*. Siberian Jay. 10ss. 31. N Europe to Manchuria
36. *Perisoreus internigrans*. Sooty / Szechwan Grey Jay. 29. China.
37. *Cyanocitta cristata*. Blue Jay. 4ss. 28. S Canada, E USA.
38. *Cyanocitta stelleri*. Steller's Jay. 13ss. 29. W America, Alaska to C America.
39. *Cyanocitta ridgwayi*. Short crested Jay. 28. Central America.
40. *Aphelocoma coerulescens*. Scrub Jay. 17ss. 29. W USA, Florida, Mexico.
41. incl. *A. c. californica*. Long tailed Jay. 30. California, Mexico.
42 *A. c. woodhousei*. Texas Jay. 29. SW USA, Mexico.
43. *Aphelocoma ultramarina*. Mexican Jay. 7ss. 26. Arizona, Texas, Mexico.
44. *Aphelocoma unicolor*. Unicoloured Jay. 5ss. 31. Mexico, C America.
45. *Cyanolyca nana*. Dwarf Jay. 22. S Mexico.
46. *Cyanolyca pumilo*. Black throated Jay. 25. Mexico & C America.
47. *Cyanolyca mirabilis*. White throated Jay. 24. SW Mexico.
48. *Cyanolyca argentigula*. Silvery throated Jay. 25. Costa Rica, Panama.
49. *Cyanolyca cucullata*. Azure hooded Jay. 4ss. 28. Mexico to Panama.
50. *Cyanolyca pulchra*. Beautiful Jay. 27. Ecuador, Colombia.
51. *Cyanolyca viridicyana*. White collared Jay. 3ss. 32. Peru, Bolivia.
52. *Cyanolyca armillata*. Collared Jay. 3ss. 32. Venezuela to Ecuador.
53. *Cyanolyca turcosa*. Turquoise Jay. 32. Colombia, Peru.
54. *Cyanocorax dickeyi*. Tufted Jay. 37. W Mexico.
55. *Cyanocorax mysticalis*. White tailed Jay. 32. Ecuador, Peru.
56. *Cyanocorax cayanus*. Cayenne Jay. 32. Venezuela.
57. *Cyanocorax chrysops*. Plush crested Jay. 35. Brazil, Bolivia, Argentina.
58. *Cyanocorax cyanopogon*. White naped Jay. 35. E Brazil.

25
26
27
28
29
30
31
32
33
34
35
36
37
38
39
40
41
42
43
44
45
46
47
48
49
50
51
52
53
54
55
56
57
58

CORVIDAE (3)
Jays, Nutcrackers & Choughs

59. *Cyanocorax affinis*. Black chested Jay. 2ss. 34. N & C South America.
60. *Cyanocorax cyanomelas*. Purplish Jay. 32. Southern half of S America.
61. *Cyanocorax heilprini*. Azure naped Jay. 35. N South America.
62. *Cyanocorax violaceus*. Violaceous Jay. 2ss. 32. N South America.
63. *Cyanocorax caeruleus*. Azure Jay. 37. Brazil, Paraguay, Argentina.
64. *Cyanocorax cristatellus*. Curl crested Jay. 30. E C Brazil.
65. *Cyanocorax yncas*. Inca Jay. 6ss. 25. Colombia, Peru, Bolivia.
66. *Cyanocorax luxuosus*. Green Jay. 7ss. 24. Mexico & C America.
67. *Cissilopha beecheii*. Purplish backed Jay. 40. NW Mexico.
68. *Cissilopha sanblasiana*. San Blas / Black & blue Jay. 2ss. 32. SW Mexico.
69. *Cissilopha yucatanica*. Yucatan Jay. 2ss. 33. E Mexico & C America.
70. *Cissilopha melanocyanea*. Hartlaub's / Bushy crested Jay. 2ss. 30. C America.
71. *Psilorhinus morio*. Brown Jay. 5ss. 42. C America.
72. incl. *P. m. mexicanus*. White tipped Jay. 42. Mexico.
73. *Calocitta formosa*. Magpie Jay. 3ss. 60. Mexico to Costa Rica.
74. *Calocitta Colliei*. Collie's Magpie Jay. 60. W Mexico.
75. *Gymnorhinus cyanocephala*. Pinon Jay. 27. W USA, NW Mexico.
76. *Podoces biddulphi*. Biddulph's Ground Jay. 29. China.
77. *Podoces hendersoni*. Henderson's Ground Jay. 28. C Asian deserts.
78. *Podoces panderi*. Saxaul Grey / Pander's Ground Jay. 25. Russia, Turkestan.
79. *Podoces pleskei*. Pleske's / Persian Ground Jay. 25. E Iran.
80. *Pseudopodoces humilis*. Hume's Ground Jay. 20. China, Tibet, Sikkim.
81. *Nucifraga caryocatactes*. (Spotted) Nutcracker. 10ss. 32. Eurasia to Himalayas.
82. incl. *N. c. multipunctata*. Asian Nutcracker. 33. Central Asia.
83. *Nucifraga columbiana*. Clark's Nutcracker. 29. Western N America.
84. *Pyrrhocorax graculus*. Alpine / Yellow billed Chough. 2ss. 38. Eurasia.
85. *Pyrrhocorax pyrrhocorax*. (Red billed) Chough. 8ss. 40. Local, Eurasia.
86. *Ptilostomus afer*. Piapiac. 35. E to W Africa.
87. *Zavattarornis stresemanni*. Stresemann's Bush Crow. 27. S Ethiopia.

59
60
61
62
63
64
65
66
67
68
69
70
71
72
73
74
75
76
77
78
79
80
81
82
83
84
85
86
87

CORVIDAE (4)
Crows & Ravens

88. *Corvus monedula*. Jackdaw. 4ss. 33. Europe & N Africa to India.
89. *Corvus dauricus*. Daurian Jackdaw. 33. Siberia. Winters China & Japan.
90. *Corvus frugilegus*. Rook. 2ss. 47. Europe, N Africa to China.
91. *Corvus brachyrhynchos*. (American) Common Crow. 4ss. 43. N America.
92. *Corvus caurinus*. North western Crow. 36. Alaska to Washington coast.
93. *Corvus ossifragus*. Fish Crow. 37. E & S USA.
94. *Corvus sinaloae*. Sinaloa Crow. 35. Mexico Pacific coast.
95. *Corvus imparatus*. Mexican / Tamaulipas Crow. 34. Mexico E coast.
96. *Corvus leucognaphalus*. White necked Crow. 48. Hispaniola, Puerto Rico.
97. *Corvus nasicus*. Cuban Crow. 46. Cuba, Is. of Pines, Caicos Is.
98. *Corvus jamaicensis*. Jamaican Crow. 42. Jamaica.
99. *Corvus palmarum*. Palm Crow. 2ss. 43. Cuba, Hispaniola.
100. *Corvus splendens*. House Crow. 5ss. 43. India, SE Asia (intro. E Africa.)
101. *Corvus levaillantii*. Jungle Crow. 14ss. 49. S E Asia, Philippines.
102. *Corvus macrorhynchos*. Large billed Crow. 54. India, SE Asia, Philippines.
103. *Corvus enca*. Slender billed / Little Crow. 9ss. 45. SE Asia, Philippines.
104. *Corvus typicus*. Celebes or Piping Crow. 40. Sulawesi.
105. *Corvus unicolor*. Banggai Crow. 40. Banggai, Sula Is.
106. *Corvus florensis*. Flores Crow. 33. Flores, Lesser Sunda Is.
107. *Corvus validus*. Moluccan or Long billed Crow. 45. Halmahera, Moluccas.
108. *Corvus orru*. Torresian Crow. 4ss. 52. Australia, New Guinea, Moluccas.
109. *Corvus bennetti*. Small billed or Little Crow. 43. Australia.
110. *Corvus coronoides*. Australian Raven. 53. SE Australia.
111. *Corvus mellori*. South Australian or Little Raven. 50. SE Australia.
112. *Corvus boreus*. Relict Raven. 53. New South Wales.

112As. *Corvus tasmanicus*. Forest Raven. 2ss. 52. Tasmania, SE Australia.

88
89
90
91
92
93
94
95
96
97
98
99
100
101
102
103
104
105
106
107
108
112A
109
110
112
111

CORVIDAE (5)
Crows & Ravens

113. *Corvus woodfordi*. White billed Crow. 3ss. 40. Solomon Is.
114. *Corvus meeki*. Bougainville Crow. 40. Bougainville.
115. *Corvus fuscicapillus*. Brown headed Crow. 2ss. 45. New Guinea, Aru & Islands.
116. *Corvus tristis*. Bare faced / Grey Crow. 53. New Guinea & Islands.
117. *Corvus kubaryi*. Guam / Mariana Crow. 37. Guam, Rota.
118. *Corvus moneduloides*. New Caledonia Crow. 44. New Caledonia, Loyalty Is.
119. *Corvus (tropicus) hawaiiensis*. Hawaiian Crow. 47. Hawaii.
120. *Corvus Corone*. Carrion Crow, 6ss. 47. Eurasia.
121. incl. *C. C. cornix*. Hooded Crow. 47. NE Europe to central Asia.
122. *Corvus capensis*. Cape Rook. 43. Sudan to Angola & Cape.
123. *Corvus albus*. Pied Crow. 46. Africa South of Sahara.
124. *Corvus ruficollis*. Brown necked Raven. 2ss. 58. Cape Verde Is. & N Africa to Pakistan.
125. *Corvus edithae*. Dwarf Raven. 46. Somalia.
126. *Corvus cryptoleucus*. Chihuahuan / White necked Raven. 52 .Western USA, Mexico.
127. *Corvus torquatus*. Collared Crow. 50. Manchuria, China, Annam.
128. *Corvus corax*. Raven. 8ss 64. Holarctic region.
129. *Corvus rhipidurus*. Fan tailed Raven. 47. Middle East to Kenya.
130. *Corvus albicollis*. African white necked Raven. 56. E Africa to Cape.
131. *Corvus crassirostris*. Thick billed Raven. 64. E Africa.

113
114
115
116
117
118
119
120
121
122
123
124
125
126
127
128
129
130
131

INDEX

aalge, Uria 74
abbas, Thraupis 317
abbotti, Coracina 221
abbotti, Malacocincla 254
abbotti, Sula 11
abdimii, Ciconia 17
Abeillia 126
abeillei, Abeillia 126
abeillei, Arremon 311
abeillei, Coccothraustes 336
abeillei, Ictorus 328
abeillei, Orchesticus 314
aberdare, Cisticola 266
aberti, Pipilo 310
abingoni, Campethera 165
abnormis, Sasia 163
Abrosupus 264
aburri, Aburria 42
Aburria 42
abyssinica, Coracias 147
abyssinica, Hirundo 217
abyssinica, Zosterops 296
abyssinica, Asio 117
abyssinicus, Bucorvus 153
abyssinicus, Dendropicas 172
abyssinicus, Turdus 249
abyssinicus, Turtur 79
abyssinicus, Zosterops 296
acadicus, Aegolius 117
Acanthidops 307
Acanthis 334/34
Acanthisitta 214
Acanthiza 270
acauthizoides, Cittia 262
Acanthorhyndius 302
Acanthornis 271
accentor, Bradypterus 262
Accipter 32
accipitrinus, Deroptyus 104
Aceros, 150
Acestrura 134
Achaetops 263
achietae, Stactolaema 158
acitirostris, Stymphalornis 188
Acridotheres 352
Acrobatgrnis 184
Acrocephalus 262/63
Acrochordopus 205
acropternis 195
Acryllium 52
Actenoides 141
Actinodura 259
Actophilornis 62
acuminata, Calidris (Erolia) 67
acunhae, Nesospiza 307
acuta, Anas 23
acudicauda, Lonchura 340
acuticauda, Poephila 339
acuticaudata, Aratinga 100
acuticaudus, Apus 124
acuticaudus, Lamprotornis 350
acutipennis, Chordeiles 119
acutipennis, Pseudocolopteryx 203
acutirostris, Calandrilla 216
acutirostric, Heteralocha 356
Adamastor 7
adamsi, Montifringilla 343
adamsii, Gavia 5
adansonii, Excalfactoria 47
addita, Rhinomyias 273
adela, Oreotrochilus 130
adelaidae, Dendroica 322
adelaidae, Platyiercus 94
adelberti, Nectarinia 290
adeliae, Pygoscelis 4
Adelomyia 129
adolphinae, Myzomala 297
adorabilis, Paposia 127
adscitus, Platycercus 94
adsimiles, Dicrusrus 355
adspersus, Francolinus 45
adusta, Muscicapa 276
adusta, Roraimia 183
Aechmolophus 201
Aechmophorus 5
aedon, Acrocephalus 262
aÎdon, Troglodytes 237
Aegintha 339
aegithaloÔdes, Leptasthenura 180
Aegithalos 285
Aegithina 230
Aegolius 117
Aegotheles 118
Aegypius 30
Aegyptiaca, Alopchen 22
aegyptius, Caprimulgus 120
aegyptius, Pluvianus 68
aenea, Chloroceryle 138
aenea, Ducula 86
aenea, Glaucis 125
aeneocauda, Metallura 132
aeneum, Dicaeum 288
aeneus, Dicruruothera 294
aeneus, Molothrus 331
aenigma, Hemitriccus 202
aenigma, Idioptilon 202
aenigma, Sapayoa 207
aenobarbus, Pleruthius 259
Aepypodius 40
aequatorialis, Androdon 125
aequatorialis, Momotus 144
aequatorialis, Tachymarptis 124
aeguatorialis, Tangara 319
aequinoctialis, Acrocephalus 262
aequinoctialis, Buteogallus 34
aequinoctialis, Grothlypis 323
aequinoctialis, Procellaria 7
aereus, Ceuthinochares 108
Aerodramus 122
Aeronautes 124
Aerornis 123
aeruginosum, Dicaeum 288
aeruginosus, Circus 31
aeruginosus, Piculus 165
aestiva, Amazona 103
aestivalis, Aimophila 306
aethereus, Nyctibuis 118
aethereus, Phaeton 11
Aethia 74
aethiopica, Hirundo 217
aethiopicus, Laniarius 232
acthiopicus, Threskiornis 18
aethiops, Myrmecacichla 245
aerthiops, Thamnophilus 186
AÎthocorys 216
Aethopyga 294
afer, Euplectes 347
afer, Nilaus 231
afer, Parus 285
afer, Pternistis 45
afer, Ptilostomus 365
afer, Sphenoeacus 263
afer, Turtur 79
affine, Malacopteron 254
affinis, Apus 124
affinis, Arachnothera 294.
.
affinis, Aythya 25
affinis, Batrachostomus 118
affinis, Caprimulgus 121
affinis, Climacteris 287
affinis, Coccothraustes 336
PAGE 2
affinis, Cyanocorax 365
affinis, Dryoscopus 231
affinis, Emberiza 303
affinis, Empidonax 201
affinis, Euphonia 318
affinis, Garrulax 257
affinis, Hypsipetes 229
affinis, Lepidocalaptes 178
affinis, Megapidius 40
affinis, Melithreptus 299
affinis, Ninox 116
affinis, Penelopides 150
affinis, Phylloscopus 264
affinis, Sarothure 57
affinis, Seicercus 264
affinis, Suiriri 204
affinis, Turdoides 256
affinis, Veniliornis 172
afra, EupodotÔs 61
afra, Nectarinia 290
afra, Pytilia 337
Afribyx 63
africana, Actophilornis 62
africana, Mirafra 215
africana, Upupa 148
africana, Yerreauxia 163
africanoides, Mirafra 215
africanus, Bubo 114
africanus, Buphagus 352
africanus, Cursorius 68
africanus, Francolinus 45
africanus, Gyps 30
africanus, Phalacrocorax 12
africanus, Rhinoptilus 68
africanus, Spizaetus 37
Afropavo 51
Afrotis 61
agami, Agamia 15
Agamia 15
Agapornis 96
Agalaius 329
Agelastes 52
agile, Dicaeum 288
agilis, Amazona 103
agilisa, Anairetes 203
agilis, Geothlypis 323
agilis, Uromyias 203
Aglaeactis 130
Aglaiae Pachyramphus 210
Aglaiocercus 132
agraphia, Anairetes 203
agraphia, Uromyias 203
agricola, Acrocephalus 262
Agriocharis 52
Agriornis 196
aquimp, Motacilla 219
ahantensis, Grancolinus 45
Aidemosyne 340
aikeni, Junco 305
Ailuroedus 357
Aimophila 306
Aix 25
ajax, Cinclosoma 253
akahige, Erithagus 240
akool, Amaurornis 58

Alaemon 216
alai, Fulica 59
alario, Serinus 332
alaschanicus, Phoenicurus 242
Alauda 216
alaudina, Coryphistera 183
alaudinus, Phrygilus 306
alaudipes, Alaemon 216
alba, Ardea 15
alba, Cacatua 91
alba, Casmerodius 15
alba, Chionis 69
alba, Calidris (Crocethia) 67
alba, Motacilla 219
alba, Platalea 19
alba, Procnias 211
alba, Pterodroma 9
alba, Tyto 112
albatrus, Diomedea 6
albellus, Mergus 26
albeola, Bucephela 26
alberti, Crax 42
alberti, Menura 214
alberti, Prionops 231
alberti, Pteridophera 361
albertinae, Streptocitta 352
albertinum, Glaucidium 115
albertisi, Aegotheles 118
albertisi, Aegotheles 118
albertisi, Drepanornis 359
albertisii, Gymnophaps 87
albescens, Certhilauda 215
albescens, Synallaxis 180
albicapilla, Cossypha 241
albicapilla, Cranioleuca 181
albicapillas, Melithreptus 395
albicapillus, Spreo 350
albicauda, Agriornis, 196
albicauda, Elminia 279
albicauda, Miragra 215
albicaudata, Muscicapa 276
albicaudatus, Buteo 35
albiceps, Atlapetes 311
albiceps, Craniolenca 181
albiceps, Elaenia 204
albiceps, Psalidoprocne 217
albiceps, Vanellus 62
albicilla, Halcyon 141
albicilla, Haliaectus 29
albicilla, Mohoua 270
albicollis, Corvus 367
albicollis, Ficedula 274
albicollis, Leucochloris 128
albicollis, Leucopternis 34
albicollis, Merops 145
albicollis, Nyctidromus 119
albicollis, Pipilo 310
albicollis, Porzana 57
albicollis, Rhipidura 227
albicollis, Rhynchops 73
albicollis, Saltator 313
albicollis, Scelorchilus 195
albicollis, Streptocitta 352
albicollis, Turdus 251
albicollis, Xiphocalaptes 177
albicollis, Zonotrichia 305
albidinuchus, Lorius 88
aslbidus, Accipiter 32
albifacies, Geogrygon 81
albifacies, Myioborus 324
albifacies, Sceloglaux 115
albifacies, Pulsatrix 115
albifrons, Todirostrum 202
albifrons, Amazona 103
albifrons, Amblyospiza 343
albifrons, Conirostrum 321
albifrons, Donacospiza 307
albifrons, Ephthianura 271
albifrons, Henicophaps 79
albifrons, Muscisaxicola 196
albifrons, Myioborus 324
albifrons, Myrmecocichla 245
albifrons, Phylidonyris 302
albifrons, Pithys 192
albifrons, Platusteira 278
albifrons, Sterna 72
albigula, Buteo 35
albigula, Grallaria 193
albigula, Myzomela 297
albigule, Upercerthia 179
albigularis, Automolus 184
albigularis, Empidonex 201
albigularis, Falco 39
albigularis, Hirundo 217
albigularis, Laterallus 57
albigularis, Otus 113
albigularis, Phyllashephus 227
albigularis,Sclerurus 184
albigularis, Synallaxis 180
albilatera, Diglossa 321
albilinea, Tachycineta 217
albilineata, Meliphaja 298
albilora, Muscisexicola 196
albilora, Synallaxis 181
albiloris, Oriolus 353
albiloris, Polioptila 261
albinucha, Actophilornis 62
albinucha, Atlapetes 311
albinucha, Columba 76
albinucha, Ploceus 343
albinucha, Thryothorus 237
albinucha, Xenopsaris 199
albinectus, Illadopsis 254
albipectus, Pyrhura 101
albipennis, Penelope 41
albipennis, Petrophassa 79
albirostris, Bubalornis 341
albirostris, Galbula 154
albirostris, Onychognathus 349
albispecularis, Heteromyias 272
albistriata, Sterna 72
albistarsus, Ciccaba 116
albitorques, Columba 76
albitorques, Philemon 299
albiventer, Fluvicola 198
albiventer, Neochmia 339
albiventer, Phalacrocorax 12
albiventer, Pnoepyga 255
albiventer, Tachycineta 217
albiventre, Pellorneum 254
albiventris, Accipiter 33
albiventris, Brachypteryx 240
albiventris, Dacnis 320
albiventris, Halcyon 140
albiventris, Myiagra 280
albiventris, Myionnis 202
albiventris, Pachycephala 282
albiventris, Parus 285
albiventris, Trochocercus 279
albiventris, Zosterops 295
alboauricularis, Lichmera 297
albobrunneus, Campylorhynchus 236
albocinctus, Acridotheres 352
albocinctus, Turdus 250
albocoronata, Microchera 129
albocristata, Sericossypha 314
albocristatus, Berenicornis 150
albofasciata, Chersomanes 215
albofrenatus, Atlapetes 311
albofrontata, Gerygone 270
albogriseus, Pachyremphus 210
albogulare, Malacopteron 254
albogularis, Alroscopus 264
albogularis, Accipiter 33
albogularis, Anas 23
albogularis, Brachygalba 154
albogularis, Conopophila 302
albogularis, Contopus 200
albogularis, Francolinus 45
albogularis, Garrulax 257
albogularis, Melithreptus 299
albogularis, Otus 112
albogularis, Phalcoboenus 38
albogularis, Pygarrhichas 184
albogularis, Rhipidura 277
albogularis, Serinus 332
albogularis, Sporophila 308
albogularis, Tyrannus 198
albogularis, Zosterops 296
albolarvatus, Dendrocopos 172
albolimbata, Rhipidura 277
albolimbatus, Megalurus 262
albolineatus, Lepidocolaptes 178
alboniger, Oenanthe 246
alboniger, Spizaetus 37
albonotata, Halcyon 140
albonotata, Meliphaga 298
albonotata, Poecilodryas 272
albonotatus, Buteo 35
albonotatus, Crocias 260
albonotatus, Euplectes 347
albonotatus, Trochocercus 279
alboscapulatus, Malurus 269
albosignata, Eudyptula 4
albospecularis, Copsychus 242
albosquamatus, Picumnus 163
alboterminatus, Tockus 149
albotibiolis, Bycanistes 152
albovittatus, Coryphotriccus 199
albus, Lorvus 367
albus, Eudocimus 18
albus, Porphyrio 58
Alca 74
Alcedo 139
alchata, Pterocles 75
alcinus, Machaerhamphus 28
Alcippe 259/60
alcyon, Ceryle 138
aldabranus, Dicrurus 355
aldabranus, Nesillas 264
Alcadryas 283
alecto, Myiagra 280
alector, Crax 42
Alectoris 45
Alectroenas 85
Alectrurus 197
Alectura 40
Alethe 242
aleutica, Sterna 72
aleuticus, Ptychoramphus 74
alexandrae, Polytelis 94
alexandri, Apus 124
alexandri, Archilochus 133
alexandri, Psittacula 97
alexandrinus, Charadrius 63
alfredi, Bradypterus 262
alfredi, Otus 112
alfredi, Phyllastrephus 228
alice, Chlorostilbon 127
aliciae, Amazilia 130
alienus, Ploceus 343
alinae, Eriochemis 131
alinae, Nectarinia 290
alisteri, Cinclosoma 253
Alisterus 93
alius, Malaconotus 232
alixii, Clytoctantes 187
Alle 74
alle, Alle 74
alleni, Crallaria 193
alleni, Pipilo 310
alleni, Porphyrula 58
Allenia 239
alligator, Ptinilopus 84
Allocotopterus 207

alnorum, Empidonax 201
alopex, Falco 39
alopex, Mirafra 215
Alophoixus 228
Alopochelidon 217
Alopochen 22
alpestris, Eremophila 216
alphonsianus, Paradoxornis 261
alpina, Calidris 67
alpina, Enotia 67
alpina, Muscisaxicola 196
altaicus, Falco 39
altaieus, Tetraogallus 45
altera, Corapipo 207
althaea, Sylvia 263
alticola, Apalis 267
alticola, Charadrius 63
alticola, Junco 305
altifrons, Pluvialis 63
altiloquus, Vireo 326
altinostre, Chrysomma 256
altirostris, Moupinia 256
altirostris, Tyrdoides 256
aluco, Strix 117
amabilis, Amazilia 128
amabilis, Charmosyna 89
amabilis, Cotinga 208
amabilis, Loriculus 96
amabilis, Lorius 88
amabilis, Malurus 269
amabilis, Muscicapa 274
amabilis, Parus 285
Amadina 340
Amalocichla 250
Amandava 339
amandava, Amandava 339
amaurocephala, Nonnula 155
amaurocephalus, Hylophilus 326
amaurocephalus, Leptopogon 205
amaurochalinus, Turdus 251
Amaurocichla 265
Amaurolimnas 55
amauroptera, Pelargopsis 139
Amaurornis 58
Amaurospiza 309
amaurotis, Anabacerthia 183
amaurotis, Hypsipctes 229
Amazilia 128/29
amazilia, Amaziba 128
Amazona 103
amazone, Chloroceryle 138
Amazonetta 25
amazonica, Amaxona 103
amazonicus, Thamnophilus 186
amazonina, Hapalopsittaca 103
ambigua, Ara 98
ambigua, Carduelis 333
ambigua, Myrometherula 187
ambigua, Stachyris 285
ambiguus, Ramphastos 162
Amblyornis 357/58
Amblyospiza 343
Amblyramphus 330
amboinensis, Alisterus 93
amboinensis, Macropygia 78
ameliae, Macronyx 219
amelis, Collocalia 122
americana, Anas 23
americana, Aythya 25
americana, Certhia 298
americana, Chloroceryle 138
americana, Fulica 59
americana, Grus 54
americana, Mycteria 17
americana, Parala 322
americana, Recurvinostra 67
americana, Rhea 1
americana, Spiza 312
americana, Sporophila 308
americanus, Coccyzus 107
americanus, Daptrius 38
americanus, Numenius 63
amethysticollis, Heliangelus 131
amethystina, Calliphlox 134
amethystina, Nectarinia 290
amethystina, Phapitreron 82
amethystinus, Lampornis 129
amherstiae, Chrysolophus 51
amicta, Nyctyornis 145
ammodendri, Passer 342
Ammodramus 305
Ammomanes 216
Ammoperdix 45
amnicola, Locustella 262
amoena, Passerina 313
amoenus, Phyllascopus 264
Ampeliceps 352
ampelinus, Hypocolius 235
Ampelioides 209
Ampelion 209
amphichroa, Newtonia 276
Amphispiza 306
amsterdamensis, Diomedia 6
amuereusis, Falco 39
Amytornis 269
Anabacerthia 183
anabatina, Dendrocincla 176
anabatinus, Thamnistes 187
Anabazenops 183
anaethetus, Sterna 72
Anairetes 203
anais, Mino 352
analis, Catamenia 309
analis, Coracina 221
analis, Formicarius 192
analis, Iridosornis 318
analoga, Meliphaga 298
Anaplectes 346
Anarhynchus 64
Anas 23
Anastomus 17
anchietae, Anthreptes 290
anchietae, Buccandon 158
Ancistrops 183
andaecola, Upucerthia 179
andamanensis, Centropus 111
andamanensis, Dicrurus 355
andecola, Petrochelidon 217
andecolus, Aeronautes 124
andecolus, Apus 124
andicola, Agriornis 196
andicola, Grallaria 193
andicola, Leptasthenura 180
Andigena 161
andina, Gallinago 66
andina, Oxyura 26
andina, Recurvirostra 67
anbdinus, Phoenicoparrus 19
andium, Anas 23
andrei, Chaetura 123
andrei, Taeniotriccus 202
andrewsi, Frigata 13
andrewsi, Hirundo 217
Androdon 125
andromedae, Zoothera 248
Andropadus 226
Androphobus 253
anerythra, Pitta 212
angelae, Dendroica 322
angelinae, Otus 113
angolensis, Cisticola 266
angolensis, Dryoscopus 231
angolensis, Gypohierax 30
angolensis, Hirundo 217
angolensis, Mirafra 215
angolensis, Monticola 247
angolensis, Dryzoborus 309
angolensis, Pitta 212
angolensis, Ploceus 343
angolensis, Vraeginthus 338
anguitimeus, Eurocephalus 231
angulata, Gallinula 58
angusticauda, Cisticola 266
angustifrous, Psarocolius 327
angustipluma, Chaetoptila 301
angustirostris, Anas 24
angustirostris, Lepidocolaptes 178
angustirostris, Todus 144
Anhima 20
Anhinga 13
anhinga, Anhinga 13
ani, Crotophaga 109
Anisognathus 318
Anitibyx 62
ankoberensis, Scrinus 332
anna, Calypte 134
anna, Ciridops 325
annae, Dicaeum 288
annae, Psamathia 262
annamarulae, Melaenornis 273
annaea, Euphonia 318
annextans, Dicrurus 355
annextens, Heterophasia 260
annulosa, Poephila 339
annumbi, Anumbius 183
Anodorhynchus 98
anomala, Brachycope 346
anomala, Cossypha 242
anomala, Zosterops 295
Anomalophrys 63
Anomalospiza 347
anomalus, Eleothreptus 121
anomalus, Euplectes 346
anonyma, Cisticola 266
Anorrhinus 150
Anous 73
anoxanthus, Loxipasser 310
anselli, Centropus 110
Anser 21
anser, Anser 21
Anseranas 20
ansorgei, Andropadus 226
ansorgei, Cossypha 241
ansorgei, Nesocharis 337
ansorgei, Xenocopsychus 241
antarctica, Catharacta 69
antarctica, Geositta 179
antarctica, Pygoscelis 4
antarctica, Thalassoica 7
antarcticus, Anthus 219
antarcticus, Cinclodes 179
antarcticus, Lopholaimus 87
antarcticus, Rallus 55
Anthocephala 129
Anthochaera 302
anthoÔdes, Asthenes 182
anthonyi, Caprimulgres 121
anthongi, Dicaeum 288
anthopeplus, Polytelis 94
anthophilus, Phaethornis 125
Anthornis 302
Anthoscopus 285
anthracinus, Buteogallus 34
Anthracoceros 151
Anthracothorax 126
Anthreptes 290
Anthropoides 54
Anthus 219/20
antigore, Grus 54
antillarum, Myiarchus 200
antillarum, Sterna 72
antinorÔÔ, Psalidoprocne 217
antipodes, Megadyptes 4
antiquus, Synthliboramphus 74
antisianus, Pharomacrus 135
antisiensis, Cranioleuca 181
antoniae, Carpodectes 209
Anumbius 183
Anurolimnas 57
Anurophasis 45
Apalis 267
Apaloderma 137
Apalopteron 299
apertus, Atlapetes 311
Aphanolimnas 57
Aphanotriccus 201
Aphantochroa 129
Aphelocephala 270
Aphelocoma 364
Aphrastura 180
Aphriza 67
apiaster, Merops 145
apiata, Mirafra 215
apicalis, Acanthiza 270
apicalis, Moho 301
apicalis, Myiarchus 200
apicalis, Myiorchus 200
apicanda, Treron 83
apivorus, Pernis 28

Aplonis 348
Aplopelia 78
apoda, Paradisaea
apolinari, Cistotherus 236
apolites, Tnannus 198
apperti, Phyllastrophus 228
appromimous, Circus 31
apicaria, Pluvialis 63
Aprosmictus 93
Aptenodytes 4
Apteryx 1
Apus 124
apus, Apus 124
aquatica, Muscicapa 276
aquaticus, Rallus 55
Aquila 36
aquila, Eutoxeres 125
aquila, Fregata 60
aracari, Pteroglossus 160
Ara 98
arabs, Choristis 60
Arachnothera 294
aradus, Cyphonhinus 237
araea, Falco 39
araguayae, Serpophaga 203
Aramides 56
Aramidopsis 56
Aramus 54
ararauna, Ara 98
Aratinga 100
araycaba, Columba 76
arausiaca, Amazona 103
arborea, Dendrocygna 20
arborea, Lullula
arborea, Spizella
Arborophila 47
arcaei, Buthraupis 317
Arcanator 228
arcanus, Phylloscopus 264
arcanus, Ptilinopus 84
archboldi, Aegolethes 118
archoldi, Eurostopodus 119
archboldi, Newtonia 276
archboldi, Petroica 272
Archboldia 357
archeri, Buteo 35
archeri, Coscypha 241
archeri, Heteromirafra 215
Archilochus 133
archipelagus, Indicator 159
arctica Fratercula 74
arctice, Gavia 5
arctivus, PicoÔdes 172
arctitorquis, Pachycephala 282
arctoa, Leucosticte 334
arcuata, Dendrocygna 20
arcuata, Pipreola 209
acruata, Pitta 212
Andea 14
ardeno, Arborophila 47
ardens, Euphetes 347
ardeus, Harpactes 137
ardeus, Selasphorus 134
ardeus, Sericulus 358
Ardeola 14
ardeole, Dnomas 68
ardesiaca, Conopophega 194
ardesiaca, Egretta 15
ardesiaca, Fulica 59
ardesiaca, Melaenormis 273
ardesiaca, Rhopornis 190
ardesiaca, Sponophila 308
ardesiacus, Dysithemnus 187
ardosiaceus, Falco 39
Anenaria 66
arenarum, Sublegatus 204
arfaki, Oneocharis 289
arfaki, Oneopsittacus 89
arfakiana, Melanocheris 288
arfakianus, Acpypodius 40
arfakianus, Sericornis 271
argentatus, Ceyx 139
argentatus, Larus 69
argcutauris, Leiothrix 259
argentauris, Lichmera 297
argentca, Apalis 267
argenteus, Cracticus 357
argenticeps, Philemon 299
argentifrons, Seytalepus 195
argentigula, Cyanolyca 364
argentina, Columba 76
argoondah, Perdicula 47
argus, Argusianus 51
Angusianus 41
arguta, Strepera 357
Argya 256
argyrofenges, Tangara 319
argyrotis, Penelope 41
aridula, Cisticola 266
ariel, Fregata 13
ariel, Petrochelidon 217
aristotelis, Phelacrocorax 12
arizonae, Dendrocopus 174
armandii, Phyllosiopus 264
armeta, Merganetta 24
armatus, Anitibyx 62
armatus, Hoplopterus 62
armenicus, Larus 69
armenti, Molothrus 331
armillaris, Megalaima 156
armillata, Cyanolyca 364
armillata, Fulica 59
arminjoniana, Pterodroma 9
arnaudi, Pseudonigrita 342
arnoldi, Apalis 267
arnotti, Myrnecocichla 245
arossi, Macropygia 78
aroyae, Thamophilus 186
arquata, Cichladusa 242
arguata, Numenius 64
arquatrix, Columba 76
Arremon 311
Arremonops 311
arremonops, Oreothraupis 311
Arses 281
Artamella 235
Artamus 354
arthus, Tangara 319
Artomyias 276
aruensis, Meliphaga 298
arundinaceus, Acrocephalus 262
Arundinicola 198
arvensis, Alanda 216
ascaphus, Bubo 114
Ashbyia 271
ashi, Mirafra 215
asiatica, Megalaima 156
asiatica, Neetarinia 290
asiatica, Perdicula 47
asiatica, Zenaida 79
asiaticus, Caprimulgus 121
asiaticus, Charadsius 63
asiaticus, Ephippicrhynchus 17
Asio 17
asio, Otus
aspasia, Nectarinia 293
aspatha 144
assamica, Mirafra 215
assimilis, Atlapetes 311
assimilis, Chlorostilbon 127
assimilis, Circus
assimilis, Dendrocopos 172
assimilis, Malurus 269
assimilis, Myrmotherula 187
assimilis, Puffinus 8
assimilis, Tolmomyias 201
assimilis, Turdus 251
astec, Aratinga 100
asterios, Picamnus 163
Asthenes 182
Astrapia 360
astreans, Acestrura 134
astridd, Estrilda 338
astur, Eutriorchis 31
Asturina 35
Asyndesmus 171
atacamensis, Cinclodes 179
Atalotriccus 202
Atelornis 147
ater, Daptrius 38
ater, Haemotopus 62
ater, Manucodia 359
ater, Melipotes 301
ater, Merulaxis 195
ater, Molothrus 331
ater, Nesophylax 57
ater, Parus 285
ateralbus, Centropus 110
ateralbus, Monardia 281
aterrima, Pterodroma 9
aterrimus, Knipolegus 197
aterrimus, Phoeniculus 148
aterrimus, Platysmurus 363
aterrimus, Probosciger 90
Athene 116
athensis, Calandrella 216
athertoni,, Nyctyornis 145
atlanticus, Larus 69
Atlantisia 55
Atlapetes 311
atra, Afrotis 61
atra, Chalcopsitta 88
atra, Fulica 59
atra, Monasa 155
atra, Myiagra 280
atra, Porzana 57
atra, Pyriglena 190
atra, Rhipidura 277
atra, Tijuca 208
atrata, Carduelis 333
atrata, Cerotogymna 152
atrata, Leucosticte 334
astratus, Coragyps 27
astratus, Cygnus 20
atratus, Dendrocopos 172
atricapilla, Estrilda 338
atricapilla, Heteronetta 26
atricapilla, Lonchura 340
atricapilla, Sylvia 263
atricapilla, Zonotrichia 305
atricapilla, Zosterops 295
atricapillus, Accipiter 32
PAGE 7
atricapillus, Atlapetes 311
atricapillus, Donacobius 239
atricapillus, Garrulas 364
atricapillus, Herpsilochmas 189
atricapillus, Myiornis 202
atricapillus, Otus 112
atricapillus, Parus 285
atricapillus, Philydor 183
atricapillus, Virco 326
atricaudus, Myiobus 201
atriceps, Alcippe 259
atriceps, Carduelis 333
atriceps, Colinus 44
atriceps, Coracina 231
atriceps, Empidonex 201
atriceps, Hypergerus 267
atriceps, Phalecroconax 12
atriceps, Phsygilus 306
atriceps, Pycnonotus 226
atriceps, Thopocichla 256
atriceps, Saltator 313
atriceps, Zosterops 295
Atrichornis 214
atricilla, Larus 69
atricollis, Chrysophilus 164
atricollis, Enemomela 268
ztricollis, Ortygospiza 339
atricollis, Saltator 313
atricristatus, Parus 285
atrifrons, Odontophosus 44
atrifrons, Pluvialis 63
atrifrons, Zosterops 295
atrifusca, Aplonis 348
atrigularis, Napothera 255
atrigularis, Rhinomyias 273
atrimaxillaris, Habia 316
atripennis, Caprimulgus 121
atripennis, Dicrurus 355
atripennis, Phyllanthus 260
atripennis, Saltator 313
atrinostris, Oryzoborus 309
atrocaerulea, Hirundo 217
atrocaudata, Terpsiphone 279
atrochalybeia, Terpsiphone 279
atrococcineus Laniarius 232
atrodorsalis, Puffinus 8
atroflavus, Laniarius 232
atroflavus, Pogoniulus 158

atrogularis, Arborophila 47
atrogularis, Clytoctantes 187
atrogularis, Onthotomus 265
atrogularis, Prinia 265
atrogularis, Prosopeia 93
atrogularis, Prunella 239
atrogularis, Serinus 332
atrolularis, Spizella 306
atrogularis, Thryothorus 237
atrogularis, Turdus 250
atronitens, Xenopipo 207
atropileus, Hemispingus 314
atropurpurea, Xipholena 208
atropygialis, Poephila 339
atrothorax, Myrmeciza 191
atrosuperciliaris, Paradoxoinis 261
atroriolacea, Dives 330
atrovirens, Lalage 224
atrovirens, Psarocolius 327
Attagis 68
Atthis 134
atthis, Alcedo 139
Atticora 217
Attila 199
atyphus, Acrocephalus 262
aubryana, Gymnomyza 301
aucklandica, Anas 23
aucklandica, Coenocorypha 66
audax, Aphanotriccus 201
audax, Aquila 36
audeberti, Pachycoccyx 106
audouinii, Larus 69
audoboni, Dendroica 322
audubonii, Polyborus 38
auga, Meliphaga 298
Augasma 128
Augastes 133
augur, Buteo 35
auguralis, Buteo 35
augusti, Phaethornis 125
Aulacorhynchus 160
aura, Cathartes 27
aurantia, Stenna 72
aurantia, Tyto 112
aurantiaca, Pyrrhula 336
aurantiacus, Manacus 207
aurantiacus, Metopothrix 183
aurantiifrons, Hylophilus 326
aurantiifrons, Losiculus 96
aurantiifrons, Ptilinopus 84
aurantiigula, Macronyx 219
aurantiinostris, Arremon 311
aurantiinostris, Catharus 251
aurantiinostris, Ramphastos 162
aurantiinostirs, Saltator 313
aurantiiventris, Pachycephala 283
aurantiiventris, Trogon 135
aurantiivertex, Heterocercus 207
aurantioatrocristatus, Empidonomus 198
aurantium, Anthreptes 290
aurantius, Chaetops 241
aurantiusm Lanio 315
aurantius, Ploceus 343
aurantius, Turdus 251
aurata, Saroglossa 351
auratus, Chlorostilbon 127
auratus, Colaptes 164
auratus, Icterus 328
auratus, Oriolus 353
aurea, Aratinga 100
aurea, Jacamerops 154
aurea, Lalage 224
aurea, Pachycephala 282
aureata, Euphonia 318
aureliae, Haplophaedia 131
aureocincta, Buthraupis 317
aureodorsalis, Buthraupis 317
aureola, Emberiza 303
aureola, Pipra 206
aureola, Rhipidura 277
aureolimbatum, Dicaeum 288
aureonucha, Ploceus 343
aureopalliata, Amazona 104
aureopectus, Pipreola 209
aureoventris, Chlorostilbon 127
aureoventris, Pheucticus 312
aurescens, Polyplancta 129
aureus, Euplectes 347
aureus, Sericulus 358
auricapillus, Aratinga 100
auricapillus, Ictarus 328
auriceps, Cyanonamphas 95
auriceps, Deudrocopos 172
auriceps, Pharomacrus 135
auricollis, Ara 98
auricularis, Heterophesia 260
auricularis, Myiornis 202
auricularis, Piculus 165
auricularis, Puffinus 8
auriculata, Zenaida 79
aurifrons, Ammodramus 305
aurifrons, Bolborhynchus 101
aurifrons, Chloropsis 230
aurifrons, Ephthianura 271
aurifrons, Melanerpes 170
aurifrons, Myospiza 305
aurifrons, Neopelma 207
PAGE 8
aurifrons, Picumnus 163
aurigastu, Pyenonotus 226
Auriparus 285
Auripasser 342
aurita, Conopophaga 194
aurita, Heliothryx 133
aurita, Sporophila 308
aurita, Zenaida 79
auritum, Crossoptilon 48
auritus, Batrachostomus 118
auritus, Nettapus 25
auritus, Phalicrocorax 12
autirus, Podiceps 5
auriventris, Sicalis 308
aurocapillus, Seiurus 323
aurorae, Ducula 86
auroreus, Phoenicurus 242
aurovirens, Capito 156
aurulentus, Piculus 165
austeni, Garralax 257
australasia, Helcyon 141
australe, Dicaeum 288
australis, Acrocephalas 263
australis, Apteryx 1
australis, Aythya 25
australis, Choriotis 60
australis, Coturnix 47
australis, Eopsaltria 272
australis, Enemopterix 215
australis, Gallirallus 56
australis, Hyliota 268
australis, Lamprotornis 350
australis, Leucosticte 334
australis, Megalaima 156
australis, Mergus 26
australis, Oxyura 26
australis, Peltohyas 68
australis, Petroica 272
australis, Phalcoboenus 38
australis, Tchagra 231
australis, Treron 83
australis, Tyranniscus 204
australis, Vini 89
Automolus 184
automnalis, Amazona 103
autumnalis, Dendrocygna 20
avcrano, Procnias 211
Aviceda 28
Avocettula 126
avosetta, Recurvirostris 67
awokera, Picus 166
axillaris, Authreptes 290
axillaris, Aramides 56
axillaris, Euplectes 347
axillaris, Herpsilochmus 189
axillaris, Monarche 281
axillaris, Mynmotherala 187
axillaris, Pterodroma 9
aylmeri, Argya 256
aylmeri, Turdoides 256
aymara, Bolborhynchus 101
aymara, Metriopelia 80
ayresii, Cisticola 266
ayresii, Hieractus 37
ayresii, Sarothura 57
ayresii, spizactus 37
Aythya 25
azara, Pteroglossus 160
azurea, Cochoa 244
azurea, Coracina 221
azurea, Hypothymis 280
azurea, Sitta 286
azureocapilla, Myiagra 280
azureus, Alcedo 139
azureus, Ceyx 139
azureus, Eurystomus 147

Babax 257
baboecala, Bradyterus 262
bacchus, Ardeola 14
bachmani, Haematopus 62
bachmanii, Vermivora
badeigularis, Spelaeornis 255
badia, Ducula 86
badia, Halcyon 141
badiceps, Eremomela 268
badius, Accipitu 33
badius, Caprimulgus 121
badius, Molothnus 381
badius, Phodilas 112
badius, Ploceus 343
Baeopogon, 227
baeri, Asthenes 182
baeri, Aythya 25
baeri, Leucippus 128
baeri, Paroaria 312
baeri, Philyder 183
baeri, Poospiza 307
bactericatus, Acrocephalus 263
baglafecht, Ploceus 343
bahameasis, Anas 23
baileyi, Ammodramus 305
baileyi, Dendrocitta 363
baileyi, Xenospiza 305
bailleui, Loxioides 325
bailloni, Andigena 161
bailloni, Puffinus 8
bairdi, Junco 305
bairdi, Paroreomyza 325
bairdi, Vireo 326
bairdii, Acanthidops 307
bairdii, Ammodramus 305
bairdii, Enolia/Calidris 67
bairdii, Myiodynastes 199
bairdii, Prinia 265
bairdii, Trogon 136
bakeri, Ducula 86
bakeri, Sericulus 358
bakeri, Yuhina 260
bakkamoena, Otus 112
balaenarum, Sterna 72
Balaeniceps 17
balasiensis, Cypsiurus
Balearica 54
balfouri, Nectarinia 291
balicassius, Dicrurus 355
balli, Otus 112
balliviani, Odontopherus 44
ballmani, Malimbus 346
balstoni, Apus 124
bambla, Microcerculus 237
Bambusicola 47
bamendae, Apalis 267
bangsi, Grallaria 193
Bangsia 317
banksiana, Neolalage 272
banksii, Calyptoshyachus 90
bannermani, Nectarinia 291
bannermani, Ploceus 343
bannermani, Taucaco 105
banyumas, Niltava 275
baraui, Pterodroma 9

barbadensio Amazona 103
barbarus Laniarius 232
barbarus Otus 112
barbata Carduelis 333
barbata Cercotrichas 241
barbata Eythropygia 241t
barbata Penelope 41
barbata Perdix 46
barbatus Amytornis 269
barbatus Apul 124
barbatus Criniger 228
barbatus Dendrortyx 44
barbatus Gypaetus 30
barbatus Monarcha 281
barbatus Myiobias 201
barbatus Pyenonotus 226
barbirostris Myiarchus 200
baritula Diglossa 321
barnardi Platycercus 94
Barnardius 94
baroni Cranioleuca 181
baroni Metallura 132
barrabandi Pionopsitta 102
barrotti Bradypterus 262
barringeri Phlegopsis 193
barroti Heliothryx 133
bartelsi Spizaetus 37
bartletti Crypturellus 2
Bartramia 64
bartschi Collocalia 122
Baryphthengus 144
basalis Chalcites 107
basilanica Ficedula 274
basilanica Ptilocichla 255
Basileuterus 324
basilica Ducula 86
basilicus Basileuterus 324
Basilornis 352
bassana Sula 11
Batara 185
batasiensis Cypsiurus 124
bassana Sula 11
Batara 185
batasiensis Cypsiurus 124
batavica Touit 102
batesi Apus 124
batesi Caprimulgus 120
batesi Nectarinia 291
batesi Ploceus 343
batesi Terpsiphore 279
Bathmocercus 267
Batis 278
Batrachostomus 118
baudii Pitta 212
baudinii Calyptorhynchus 90
baumanni Phyllastrephus 227
beani Troglodytes 237
beaudouini Circaetus 31
beauharnaesii Pteroglossus 160
Bebrornis 264
beccarii Cochoa 244
beccarii Gallicolumba 81
beccarii Otus 113
beccarii Sericornis 271
becki Pseudohilwaria 9
becki Pterodroma
bedfordi Terpsiphone 279
beecheii Crosolopha 365
beema Motacilla 219
behni Myrmotherula 187
belcheri Larus 69
belcheri Pachyptila 7
beldingi Ammodramus 305
bildingi Grothlypis 323
beldingi Passerculus 305
belfordi Melidectes 301
bella Emblema 339
bella Goethalsia 128
belli Amphispiza 306
belli Basileuterus 324
bellicosa Hirundinea 201
bellicosa Pezites/Sturnella 330
bellicosus Polemaetus 37
belii Vireo 326
bellulus Margarornis 183
Belonopterus 62
bendeiri Toxostoma 238
bengalensis Bubo 114
bengalensis Centropus 110
bengalensis Graminicola 265
bengalensis Gyps 30
bengalensis Houbaropsis 61
bengalensis Sterna/Thalasseus 72
bengalus Uraeginthus 338
benghalense Dinopium 168
benghalensis Coracias 147
benghalensis Ploceus 344
benghalensis Rostratula 62
benjamini Urosticte 129
bennetti Casuarlus 1
bennetti Corvus 366
bennetti Aegotheles 118
bennetti Campethera 165
benschi Monias 53
bensoni Pseudocossyphus 247
Berenicornis 150
bergii Skina/Thalasseus 72
berigora Falco 39
berlepschi Acestrura 134
berlepschi Asthenes 182
berlepschi Crypturellus 3
berlepschi Dacnis 320
berlepschi Giallaria 193
berlepschi Pyrrhura 101
berlepschi Rhegmatorhina 192
berlepschi Sipia 190
berlepschi Thripophaga 182
Berlepschia 183
berliozi Apus 124
berliozi Serpophaga 203
bernardi Sakesphorus 185
bernicla Branta 21
bernieri Anas 23
bernieri Oriola 235
bernieri Threskiornis 18
bernsteini Centropus 110
bernsteini Sterna 73
bernsteinii Megapodius 40
bernsteinii Ptilinopus 84
berthelotii Anthus 219
bertrandi Ploceus 343
bertrandi Telophorus 233
beryllina Amazilia 128
beryllinus Loriculus 96
bewickii Cygnus 20
bewickii Thryomanes 236
bewsheri Turdus 249
biarcuatum Melozone 310
biarmicus Falco 39
biarmicus Panurus 261
Bias 278
Biatas 185
bicalcarata Galloperdix 47
bicalcarqatum Polyplectron 51
bicalcaratus Francolinus 45
bichenovii Poephila 339
bicincta Treron 83
bicinctus Charadrius 63
bicinctus Pterocles 75
bicolor Accipiter 33
bicolor Conirostrum
bicolor Coracina 221
bicolor Cyanophaia 127
bicolor Dendrocygna 20
bicolor Dicaeum 288
bicolor Ducula 86
biicolor Gymnopithys 192
bicolor Laniarius 232
bicolor Lonchura 340
bicolor Nigrita 337
bicolor Parus 285
bicolor Ploceus 343
bicolor Porzana 57
bicolor Rhyacornis 243
bicolor Speculipastor 350
bicolor Spreo 350
bicolor Tachycineta 217
bicolor Tiaris 309
bicolor Trichastoma 254
bicolor Turdoides 256
bicornis Buceros 153
biddulphi Podoces 365
bidentata Piranga 316
bidentatus Harpagus 28
bidentatus Lybius 158
bieti Garrulax 258
bifasciata Nectarinia 291
bifasciata Oenauthe 246
bifasciatus Psarocolius 327
bilineata Amphispiza 306
bilineata Polioptila 261
bilineatus Pogoniulus 158
bilopha Eremophila 216
bimaculata Melanocorypha 216
bimaculatus Peneothello 272
bimaculatus Pycnonotus 226
binotata Apalis 267
binotatus Caprimulgus 120
binotatus Veles 120
birostris Tockus 149
biscutata Streptoprocne 123
bishopi Catharopeza 323
bishopi Moho 301
bispecularis Garrulus 364
bistriatus Burhinus 68
bistrigiceps Acrocephalus 262
bitorquata Streptopelia 78
bitorquatus Pteroglossus 160
bitorquatus Rhinoptilus 68
bivittata Petroica 272
bivittatus Basileuterus 324
bivittatus Megalurulus 268
Biziura 26
blainvillii Peltops 280
blakei Grallaria 194
blakistoni Bubo 114
blanchoti Malaconotus 232
blanfordi Calandrella 216
blanfordi Montifeingilla 343
blanfordi Pychonotus 226
blasii Myzomela 297
Bleda 228
blewitti Athene 116
blighi Myiophoneus 247
blissetti Platysteira 278
blumenbachii Crax 42
blythii Onychognathus 349
blythii Tragopan 48
Blythipicus 175
boanensis Monarcha 281
bocagei Cossypha 241
bocagei Estrilda 338
bocagei Sheppardii 241
bocagei Telophorus 232
bocagii Ameurocichla 265
bocagii Nectarinia 291
bodessa Cisticola 266
boehmi Merops 145
boehmi Muscicapa 276
boehmi Neafrapus 123
boehmi Parisoma 268
bogdanowi Lanius 233
bogotensis Anthus 219
b¨hmi Mearnsia 123
b¨hmi Sarothrura 57
boiei Myzomela 298
Boissonneaua 131
boissonneautii Pseudocolaptes 183
bogeri Ploceus 343
bokharensis Parus 285
Bolbopsittacus 92
Bolborhynchus 101
boliviana Chiroxiphia 206
boliviana Poospiza 307
bolivianum Glaucidiam 114
bolivianus Attila 199
bolivianus Oreopsar 330
bolivianus Zimmerius 204
bollei Phoeniculus 148
bollii Columba 76
boltoni Aethopyga 294
bombus Acestrura 134
Bombycilla 235
bonana Icterus 328
bonapartei Coeligena 131
bonapartei Gymnobucco 158
bonapartei Nothocercus 2
bonariensis Molothrus 331
bonariensis Thraupis 317
Bonasa 43
bonasia Tetrastes 43
bonelli Phylloscopus 264
bonensis Hylocitrea 282
bonthaina Ficedula 274
boobook Ninox 116
boraquira Nothura 3
borbae Phlegopsis 193
borbae Picumnus 163
borbonica Phedina 217
borbonica Zosterops 296
borbonicus Hypsipetes 229
borealis Contopos 200
borealis Dendrocopos 173
borealis Numenius 64
borealis Phylloscopus 264
borealoides Phylloscopas 264
boreus Corvus 366
borin Sylvia 263
bornea Eos 88
Bostrychia 18

Botaurus 16
Botha 216
bottae Denauthe 246
botterii Aimophila 306
boucardi Amazilia 128
boucardi Crypturelleus 2
bougainvillei Halcyon 141
bougainvillei Melilestes 297
bougainvillei Stresemannia 297
bougainvillei Phalacrocorax 12
bougueri Urochroa 130
boulboul Turdus 250
bourbonnensis Terosiphone 279
bourcieri Phaethornis 125
bourcieri Eubucco 156
bourkii Neophema 95
bouroensis Oriolus 353
bouvieri Nectarinia 291
bouvieri Scotopelia 115
bouvreuil Sporophila 308
bouvronides Sporophila 309
boweri Colbericincla 284
boyciana Ciconia 17
boyeri Coracina 221
braccatus Moho 201
bracei Chlorostilbon 127
brachycope 346
brachydactyula Calandrella 216
brachydactyla Certhia 287
brachydactyla Petrolia 342
Brachygalba 154
brachylopha Lophonnis 127
brachyptera Cisticola 266
Brachypteracias 147
brachypterus Buteo 35
brachypterus Dasyornis 270
brachypterus Ploceus 344
brachypterus Tachyeres 22
Brachypterix 240
Brachyramphus 74
brachyshyncha Rhipidura 277
brachyshynchos Corvus 366
brachyshynchus Anser 21
brachyshynchus Oriolus 353
brachyura Camaroptera 267
brachyura Chaetura 123
brachyura Myrmotherula 187
brachyura Pitta 212
brachyura Poecilodryes 272
brachyura Sylvietta 268
brachyura Synallaxis 180
brachyurus Accipita 32
brachyurus Anthus 219
brachyurus Buteo 35
brachyurus Graydidascalus 103
brachyurus Idiopsar 307
brachyurus Micropternus 166
brachyurus Ramphocindus 239
bracteatus Dicrurus 355
bracteatus Nyctibius 118
bradfiddi Apus 124
bradfieldi Tockus 149
Bradornis 273
Bradypterus 262
brama Athene 116
brandti Leucosticte 334
brandtii Garralus 364
branickii Heliodoxa 130
branickii Leptosittaca 100
branickii Odontorchilus 236
branickii Theristicus 18
braustielleasis Phalacrocorax 12
Branta 21
brasiliana Cercomacra 190
brasiliana Hydropsalis 121
brasilianum Glaucidium 115
brasiliensis Amazona 103
brasiliensis Amazonetta 25
brasiliensis Tityra 240
brassi Philemon 300
brazzae Phedima 217
brehmeri Turtur 79
brehmii Monarcha 281
brehmii Psittacella 92
brenchleyi Ducula 86
bres Criniger 228
bresilius Ramphocelus 317
brevicauda Muscigulla 196
brevicauda Paradigalla 359
brevicaudata Camaroptera 267
brevicaudata Napothera 255
brevicauda Nesillas 264
brevipennis Acrocephalus 263
brevipennis Neochloe 326
brevipennis Vireo 326
brevipes Accipiter 33
brevipes Heteroscelas 65
brevipes Monticola 247
brevipes Pterodroma 9
brevirostris Brachyramphus 74
brevirostris Collocalia 122
brevirostris Crypturellus 2
brevirostris Larus 69
brevirostris Lugeusa 9
brevirostris Melithreptus 299
brevirostris Pericrocotus 225
brevirostris Pterodroma 9
brevirostris Rhynchocyclus 202
brevirostris Schoenicola 262
brevirostris Smicrornis 270
brevis Bycanistes 152
brevis Ramphastos 162
breweri Merops 145
breweri Spizella 306
brewsteri Siphonorhis 119
bredgesi Thamnophilus 186
bridgidae Hylexetastes 177
bridgesii Drymornis 177
brissonii Passerina 313
broadbenti Dasyornis 270
brodici Glaucidium 115
brookii Otus 112
Brotogeris 102
browni Monarcha 281
browni Reinwardtoena 79
browni Troglodytes 237
brucei Otus 112
bruijni Grallina 356
bruijnii Aepypodius 40
bruijnii Drepanornis 359
bruijnii Micropsitta 92
bruniceps Emberiza 303
brunnea Alcippe 259
brunnea Colluricincla 284
brunnea Nonnula 155
brunnea Speirops 296
brunneata Rhinomyias 273
brunneicapilla Aplonis 348
brunneicapillum Ornithion 205
brunneicapillus Campylorhynchus 236
brunneicauda Alcippe 259
brunneicauda Microeca 272
brunneicauda Nartonia 276
brunneiceps Hylophilus 326
brunneiceps Yuhima 260
brunneicollis Troglodytes 237
brunneinucha Atlapetes 311
brunneipectus Capito 156
brunneiventris Diglossa 321
brunneopectus Arborophila 47
brunneopygia Drymodes 240
brunnescens Cirticola 266
brunnescens Premnoplex 183
brunneus Dromaeocercus 264
brunneus Dioptrornis 273
brunneus Ezithacus 240
brunneus Melaenornis 273
brunneus Paradoxornis 261
brunneus Pycnonotus 226
brunnicephalus Larus 69
brunniceps Myioborus 324
brunnifrons Cettia 262
bryantae Philodice 133
Bubalornis 341
Bubo 114
bubo Bubo 114
Bubulcus 15
Buccanodon 158
buccinator Cygnus 20
Bucco 154
buccoides Ailuroedus 357
Bucephala 26
bucephalus Lanius 233
buceroides Philemon 300
Buceros 153
buchanani Emberiza 303
buchanani Prinia 265
buchanani Serinus 332
bucinator Bycanistes 152
buckleyi Columbina 80
buckleyi Micrastur 38
Bucorvus 153
budongoensis Phylloscopus 264
budytoides Stigmatura 203
buergersi Accipiter 32
buettikoferi Nectarinia 291
buffoni Circus 31
buffonii Chalybura 129
Bugeranus 54
Bulleri Diomedia 6
bulleri Larus 69
bulleri Puffinis 8
bullieus Cisticola 266
bullockii Icterus 328
bullockoides Merops 145
bulocki Merops 145
bulweri Lophura 49
Bulweria 9
bulwerii Bulweria 9
Buphagus 352
burchelli Pterocles 75
burcheltii Centropus 111
burchellii Neotis 60
Burhinus 68
burkii Seicercus 264
burmanoricus Sturnus 351
burmeisteri Acrochordops 205
burmeisteri Chunga 59
burnesii Prinia 265
burnieri Ploceus 345
burra Certhilauda 215
burrorianus Cathartes 27
burtoni Callcanthis 334
burtoni Serinus 332
buruensis Ficedula 274
buruensis Zosterops 295
buryi Parisoma 268
Busarellus 34
Butastur 34
Buteo 35
buteo Buteo 35
Buteogallus 34
Buthraupis 317
butleri Accipiter 33
butleri Strix 117
Butorides 14
Bycanistes 152

cabanisi Emberiza 303
cabanisi Knipolegus 197
cabanisi Lanius 233
cabanisi Melozore 310
cabanisi Phyllastrephus 227
cabanisi Pseudoniguta 342
cabanisi Synallaxis 180
cabanisi Taugara
Cabaret Acanthis 334
Cabot Tragopan 48
Cacatua 91
cacchinous Garrulax 257
cacchinous Herpetotheres 38
cacchinous Laras 69
Cacicus 328
Cacomantis 106
cactorum Aratiuga 100
cactorum Asthenes 182
cactorum Melaserpes 171
cactosum Isichopicus 171
caerulata Niltava 275
caerulatus Garrulax 257
caerulea Coua 109
caerulea Egretta 15

caerulea Halobaena 7
caerulea Passesina 313
caerulea Pitta 212
caerulea Polioptila 261
caerulea Unocissa 363
caeruleirostris Loxops 325
caeruleocapilla Pipra 206
caeruleocephalus Phoenicusus 242
caeruleoguisea Cosacina 221
caeruleogularis Aulacosamphus 160
caeruleogularis Lepidopyga 128
caerulesceus Auser 21
caerulesceus Dendroica 322
caerulesceus Dicrusus 355
caerulesceus Diglossopis 321
caerulesceus Estrilda 338
caerulesceus Eupetes 253
caerulesceus Eupodotis 61
caerulesceus Geranospiza 31
caerulesceus Melanotis 238
caerulesceus Miciohierax 38
caerulesceus Muscicapa 276
caerulesceus Passerina 313
caerulesceus Rallus 55
caerulesceus Spozophila 308
caerulesceus Thamnophilus 186
caerulesceus Theristicus 18
caerulesceus Cyanespes 320
caerulesceus Cyanocorax 365
caerulesceus Elanus 28
caerulesceus Myiophoneus 247
caerulesceus Pasus 285
caesar Poospiza 307
caesia Coracina 221
caesia Emberiza 303
caesius Thamnomanes 187
cafer Buceros 153
cafer Colaptes 164
cafer Cuculus 106
cafer Promerops 302
cafer Pycnonotus 226
caffer Acrocephalus 263
caffer Anthus 219
caffer Apus 124
caffra Cossypha 241
cafra Neotis 60
cahow Ptesodroma 9
caica Pionopsitta 102
caillantii Campethena 165
Cairina 25
cajanea Aramides 56
Calamanthus 270
Calamonastes 267
Calamospiza 305
calandra Embeiza 303
calandra Melanocorypha
Calandrella 216
Calcarius 304
calcicola Napothera 255
calcostitha Nectarinia 291
caledonica Coracina 221
caledonica Myiagra 280
caledonica Myzomele 298
caledonica Pachychephala 282
calidonicus Nycticorax 15
caledonicus Platycercus 94
Calendula 216
calendula Regulus 268
Calicalicus 235
Calidris 67
Caliechthrus 107
california Grococcyx 109
californianus Vultur 27
californica Aphelocoma 364
californica Lophortyx 44
californicum Glaucidium 115
californicus Larus 69
caligata Hippolais 263
Callacenthis 334
Callaeas 356
callainus Malurus 269
Callichelidon 217
calligyna Brachypteryx 240
calligyna Heinrichia 240
13
callinota Terenura 189
calliope Erithacus 240
calliope Stellula 134
calliparaea Chlorocrysa 319
Callipepla 44
Calliphlox 134
calliptera Pyrrhusa 101
callizonus Xenotriccus 201
Callocephalon 90
callonotus Veniliornis 172
callophrys Chlorophomia 319
callophrys Tangara 319
callopterus Piculus 165
Calochaetes 317
Calocitta 365
Caloenas 82
calolaena Lampornis 129
Calonectris 8
Caloperdix 47
calophrys Hemispingus 314
calopterum Todirostrum 202
calopterus Anamides 56
calopterus Mecocerculus 203
Calorhamphus 157
calorhynchus Aulacorhynchas 160
Calothorax 133
calthorpae Psittacula 97
calurus Grinigei 228
calva Trezon 83
calvus Aegypius 30
calvus Garrulax 258
calvus Geronticus 18
calvus Gymnobucco 158
calvus Sarcops 352
calorhynchus Phaenicophaeus 108
calorhynchus Rharephococcyx
Calypte 134
Calyptocichla 227
Calyptomena 176
Calyptophilus 315
Calyptorhynchus 90
Calyptura 209
Camarynchus 310
Camaroptera 267
cambodiane Astozophila 47
camelus Struthio 1
camerunensis Zoothera 249
camerunensis Anthus 220
camerunensis Bradypterus 262
camerunensis Francolinus 45
campanisona Chamaeza 192
campanisona Myzmothera 193
campbelli Malurus 269
campbelli Phalacrocorax 12
Campephaga 224
Campephilus 169-70
campestris Anthus 220
campestris Calamanthus 270
campestris Colaptes 164
campestris Eueornis 321
campestris Uropelia 80
campestroides Colaptes 164
Campethera 165
Campochaera 223
Camptorhynchus 26
Camptostorna 204
Campylopterus 126
Campylorhynchus 236
camurus Tockus 149
cana Agapornis 96
cana Tadorna 22
Canachites 43
canadensis Branta 21
canadensis Conachites 43
canadensis Caryothraustes 312
canadensis Grus 54
canadensis Perinsoreus 364
canadensis Sakesphorus 185
canadensis Sitta 286
canadensis Wilsonia 324
canagicus Anser 21
canaria Serinus 332
cancellata Tringa 65
cascrominus Platyshinchus 201
candei Marncus 207
candei Poecilurus 181
candicano Caprimnlgas 121
candida Amazitia 128
candida Mirafra 215
candidus Leuconerpes 170
canento Hemicixcus 174
canescens Eremomela 268
canicapilla Bledo 228
canicapilla Nigrita 337
canicapillus Serinus 332
canicapillus Dendrocopos 173
caniceps Apalis 267
caniceps Corduelis 333
caniceps Geogrygon 81
caniceps Junco 305
caniceps Chamaeza 192
caniceps Mylopagis 204
caniceps Prionops 231
caniceps Psittacula 97
canicollis Eupodotis 61
canicollis Ortalis 41
canicollis Serinus 332
canicularis Anatuiga 100
canifrons Gallicolumba 81
canifrons Spizixos 226
canigularis Chlorospirgus 314
caninde Aza 98
Canirallus 56
Canivettii Chlorostilbon 127
cannabina Acauthis 333
canningi Rallina 55
canora Tiaris 309
canorus Cuculus 106
canorus Garrulax 257
canorus Melierax 32
cantans Cisticola 266
cantans Lonchura 340
cantans Loxioides 325
cantator Hypocnemis 190
cantator Phylloscopus 264
cantator Gerygone 270
cantillaus Mirafra 215
cantillaus Sylvia 263
cantonensis Pericrocotus 225
cantoroides, Aplonis 348
canturians Cettia 262
canus Larus 69
canus Picus 166
canutus Calidrio 67
Capella 66
capellei Treron 83
capense Daption 7
capense Glaucidium 115
capensis Anas 24
capensis Asio 117
capensis Batis 278
capensis Buto 114
capensis Bucco 154
capensis Burhinus 68
capensis Corvus 367
capensis Emberiza 303
capensis Euplectes 347
capensis Francolinus 45
capensis Macronyx 219
capensis Microparra 62
capensis Motacilla 219
capensis Oena 79
capensis Pelargopsis 139
capensis Phalacrocorax 12
capensis Ploceus 343
capensis Pycnonotus 226
capensis Smithornis 176
capensis Sula 11
capensis Tyrnagra 284
capensis Tyto 112
capensis Zonotrichia 305
capicola Streptopelia 78
capillatus Phalacrocorax 12
capistrata Heterophasia 260
capistrata Muscisaxicola 196
capistrata Neosochasio 337
capistrata Oenanthe 246
capistratum Pellorneum 254
capistratus Campylorhynchus 236
capistratus Serinus 332
capitale Todirostrum 202
capitalis Aphanotriccus 201
capitalis Giallaria 194
capitalis Pezopetes 311

capitalis Ploceus 344
capitalis Stachysis 255
capitata Paroaria 312
Capito 156
capito Eopsaltria 272
capriata Saxicola 245
Caprimulgus 119-21
caprius Chrysococcyx 107
Capsiempis 203
capueira Odontophorus 44
carbo Cepphus 74
carbo Phalacrocorax 12
carbo Ramphocelus 317
carbonaria Cercomacra 190
carbonaria Diglossa 321
carbonarius Phsygilus 306
Cardellina 324
Cardinalis 312
cardinalis Cardinalis 312
cardinalis Chalcopsitta 88
cardinalis Myzomela 297
cardinalis Quelea 346
cardio Turdis 249
cardonai Myiobonus 324
Carduelis 333
carduelis Carduelis 333
Cariama 59
caribaea Columba 76
caribaea Fulica 59
caribaeus Contopus 200
caribaeus Visea 326
Caridonax 143
carinatum Electron 144
caripensis Steatornis 150
carmioli Chlorothraupis 315
carmioli Vireo 326
carneipes Puffinus 8
carnifex Phoenicircus 211
carnipes Coccothraustes 336
carola Ducula 86
carolae Parotia 361
caroli Anthoscopus 285
caroli Campethera 165
caroli Polyonymus 132
carolina Porzana 57
carolinae Cettia 262
carolinae Tanysiptera 143
carolinensis Caprimulgus 121
carolinensis Conuropsis 101
carolinensis Dumetella 238
carolinensis Parus 285
carolinensis Sitta 286
carolinus Euphagus 331
carolinus Melanerpes 179
carpalis Aimophila 306
carpalis Bradypterus 262
carpi Parus 285
carpococcyx 109
Carpodacus 334
Carpodectes 209
Carpornis 208
carrikeri Giallaria 194
carruthersi Cisticola 266
carteri Enermiornio 268
caruncalata Anthochaera 302
caruncalata Bostrychia 18
caruncalata Foulehaio 299
caruncalata Paradigalla 359
caruncalatus Bugeranus 54
carunculatus Creadion 356
carunculatus Phalacrocorax 12
carunculatus Phalcoboenus 38
caryocatactes Nucifraga 365
caryophyllacea Rhodenessa 24
Caryothraustes 312
cashmirensis Sitta 286
Casionnis 199
casiquiare Crypturellus 2
Casmerodius 15
caspia Sterna 72
caspius Tetraogallus 45
Cassiculus 328
cassicus Gracticus 357
Cassidix 331
cassidix Aceros 150
cassidix Meliphaga 298
cassini Chaetura 123
cassini Gymnostmops 327
cassini Leptotila 80
cassini Malimbus 346
cassini Muscicapa 276
cassini Neafrapus 123
cassini Psarocolius 327
cassini Veniliornis 172
cassinii Aimophila 306
cassinii Carpodacus 334
cassinii Mitrospingus 315
cassinii Vireo 326
castanea Alethe 242
castanea Anas 23
castanea Dendroica 322
castanea Hapaloptila 155
castanea Philepitta 213
castanea Pithys 192
castanea Platysfeira 278
castanea Sitta 286
castanea Synallaxis 181
castaneceps Alcippe 259
castaneiceps Anurolimnas 57
castaneiceps Conopophaga 194
castaneiceps Lysurus 311
castaneiceps Orthotomus 265
castaneiceps Phoeniculus 148
castaneiceps Ploceus 343
castaneicollis Francolinus 45
castaneiventris Amazilia 128
castaneiventris Aphelocephala 270
castaneiventris Cacomantis 106
castaneiventris Monarcha 281
castaneiventris Sporophila 308
castaneocapillus Myioborus 324
castaneocoronata Oligura 262
castaneocoronata Tesia 262
castaneothorax Lonchura 340
castaneoventris Delothraupis 318
castaneoventris Eulabeornis 56
castaneoventris Lampornis 129
castaneoventris Parus 286
castaneum Glaucidium 115
castaneus Bradypterus 262
castaneus Celeus 166
castaneus Pachyramphus 210
castaneus Pteroptochos 195
castaneus Thryothorus 237
castaniceps Seicercus 264
castaniceps Yuhina 260
castabilius Accipiter 52
castanonotum Glaucidium 115
castanonotus Eupetes 253
castanonotus Hypsipetes 229
castanops Ploceus 343
castanops Tyto 112
castanopterum Glaucidium 115
castanopterus Passer 342
castanota Turnix 53
castanotis Pteroglossus 160
castanotum Cinclosoma 253
castanotus Colius 135
castelnau Picumnes 163
castelnaudii Aglaeactis 130
castro Oceanodroma 10
castus Monarcha 281
Casuarius 1
casuarius Casuarius 1
Catamblyrhynchus 312
catamene Loriculus 96
Catamenia 309
Cataponera 250
Catharopeza 323
Cathartes 27
Catharus 251
Catherpes 236
cathpharius Dendrocopos 173
Catotrophorus 65
Catreus 50
caucasicus Tetraogallus 45
caudacuta Culicivora 203
caudacutus Ammodramus 305
caudacutus Hirundapus 122
caudacutus Sclerurius 184
caudata Chiroxipia 206
caudata Coracias 147
caudata Drymophila 189
caudatus Aegithalos 285
caudatus Bradypterus 262
caudatus Lamprotornis 350
caudatus Ptilogonys 235
caudatus Spelaeornis 255
caudatus Theristicus 18
caudatus Turdoides 256
caudifasciatus Tyrannus 198
caurensis Percnostola 191
caurinus Corvus 366
cauta Diomedea 6
cauta Hylacola 270
cayana Cotinga 208
cayana Dacnis 320
cayana Piaya 108
cayana Tangara 319
cayana Tityze 210
cayanensis Icterus 328
cayanensis Leptodon 28
cayanensis Myiozetetes 199
cayanus Cyanocorex 364
cayanus Hoploxypterus 63
cayennensis Caprimulgus 121
cayennensis Columba 76
cayennensis Euphonia 318
cayennensis Mesembrinitis 18
cayennensis Panyptila 124
cearae Conopophaga 194
cebuensis Copsychus 242
cebuensis Phylloscopus 264
cecilae Metriopelia 80
ceciliae Phylloscantes 203
cedronium Bombycilla 235
cela Cacicus 328
celaeno Rhodothraupis 312
celaenops Turdus 249
celata Vermivora 322
celebense Trichastoma 254
celebensis Acrocephalus 263
celebensis Basilornis 352
celebensis Caprimulgus 121
celebensis Ceatropis 110
celebensis Hirund Apus 122
celebensis Myza 301
celebensis Pernis 28
celebensis Scolopax 66
celebicum Dicaeum 289
Celeus 166
cenchroides Falco 39
centralasicus Caprimulgus 121
Centrocercus 43
Centropelme 5
Centropus 110/111
Cephaloptorus 211
Cephalopyrus 285
cephalotes Myiarchus 200
Cepphus 74
ceramensio Coracina 223
Ceratogymna 152
Ceratotriccus
Cercibis 19
Cercococcyx 106
Cercomacra 190
Cercomela 245
Cercotrichas 241
Cereposis 21
Cerorhinca 74
cerritus Manacus 207
Certhia 287
certhia Dendrocolaptes 177
Certhiaxis 181
Certhidea 310
Certhilauda 215
certhiola locustella 262
certhioides Upucerthia 179
Certhionyx 298
cerulea Dendroica 322
cerulea Procelstenna 73
cerverai Cyanolimnas 55
cerverai Ferminia 236

cervicalio Garrulus 364
cervicalis Pterodroma 9
Cervinicauda Myiagra 280
cerviniventris Bathmocercus 267
cerviniventris Chlamydera 358
cerviniventris Phyllastrephus 227
cerviniventris Pitohui 284
cerviniventris Poecilodryas 272
cervinus Acrocephalus 263
cervinus Anthus 220
Ceryle 138
cetti Cettia 262
Cettia 262
Ceuthmochares 108
ceylonensis Culicieapa 272
ceylonensis Himantopus 67
ceylonensis Zosterops 295
Ceyx 139
chabert Leptopterus 235
chacoensis Anthus 220
chacoensis Nothura 3
chacuru Nystalus 155
Chaetocercus 134
Chaetops 241
Chaetoptila 301
Chaetorhynchus 355
Chaetornis 355
Chaetura 123
Chaimarrornis 243
Chalcites 107
chalcomelas Nectarinia 291
chalconota Ducula 86
chalconotus Phalacrocorex 12
Chalcophaps 79
Chalcopsitta 88
chalcoptera Phaps 79
chalcopterus Cursorius 68
chalcopterus Pionus 103
chalcoptorus Rhinophilus 68
chalcospilos Turtur 79
Chalcostigma 132
Chalcurus 51
chalcurus Chalcurus 51
chalcurus Lamprotornis 350
chalcurus Ptilinopus 85
chalybaeus Lamprotornis 350
chalybatus Manucodia 359
chalybea Euphonia 318
chalybea Lophoznis 127
chalybea Nectarinia 291
chalybea Platysteira 278
chalybea Progne 217
chalybea Psalidoprocne 218
chalybeata Vidua 341
chalybeus Certropus 110
Chalybura 129
Chamaea 261
Chamaepetes 42
Chamaethlypis 323
Chamaeza 192
chapalensis Geothlypis 323
chapini Apalis 267
chapini Kupeornio 414
chapini Lioptilus 260
chapini Sylvietta 268
chaplini Lybius 158
chapmani Chaetura 123
chapmani Phylloscartes 203
Charadrius 63
chariessa Apalis 267
charitospiza 312
charlottae Hypsipetes 229
charltonii Tropicoperdix 47
Charmosyna 89
charmosyna Estrilda 338
Chasiempis 273
Chauna 20
Chaunoproctus 335
chavaria Chauna 20
cheela Spilornis 31
cheleînsis Calendrella 216
Chelectinia 28
chelicuti Halcyon 141
Chelidoptera 155
cheniana Mirafra 215
Chenonetta 25
Cheramoeca 217
cherina Cisticola 266
chermesina Myzomela 297
cherriei Cypseloides 123
cherriei Myzmotherula 187
cherriei Synallaxis 180
cherriei Thripophaga 182
cherrug Falco 39
Chersomanes 215
Chersophilus 216
Chettusia 62
chiapensis Campylarhynchus 236
chicquera Falco 39
chiguanco Turdus 251
chihi Plegadis 19
chilensis Accipita 33
chilensis Belonopterus 62
chilensis Catharacta 69
chilensis Phoenicopterus 19
chilensis Tangara 319
Chilia 179
chimachima Milvago 38
chimaera Uratelosnis 147
chimango Milvago 38
chimborazo Oneotrochilus 130
chinensis Cissa 363
chinensis Columba 78
chinensis Excalfactoria 47
chinensis Garrulax 257
chinensis Oniolus 353
chinensis Streptopelia 78
chiniane Cisticola 266
Chionis 69
chionogaster Accipiter 32
chionogaster Leucippus 128
chionopectus Amazilia 128
chionura Elvira 129
chiriri Brotogorus 102
chirindensis Apalio 267
chiriquensis Columba 76
chiriquensis Elaenia 204
chiriquensis Geothlypis 323
chiriquensis Geotrygon 81
chiriquensis Scytalopus 195
Chirocylla 210
Chiroxiphia 206
chirurgus Hydrophasianus 62
Chlamydera 358
Chlamydochaera 224
Chlamydotis 61
Chlidonias 72
Chloebia 340
Chloephaga 21
Chlorestes 127
chloricterus Orthogonys 315
chlorigaster Picus 166
chlorigula Andropadus 226
chlosis Acanthisitta 214
chlosis Anthus 220
chlosis Carduelis 333
chlosis Halcyon 141
chlosis Nicator 228
chlosis Piprites 207
chlosis Zosterops 295
chlorocephalus Oriolus 353
chlorocercus leucippus 128
chlorocercus Lorius
Chloroceryle 138
Chlorocharis 296
chlorochrysa 319
chlorocichla 227
chlorodrepanis 325
chlorolepidota Pipreola 209
chlorolepidotus Trichoglossus 88
chlorolophus Picus 166
chloromeros Pipra 206
chloronota Camaroptera 267
chloronota Gerygone 270
chloronotas Phylloscopus 264
chloronothos Zosterops 296
chloronotus Arremonops 311
chloronotus Guiriger 228
Chloropeta 263
chloropetoides Thamnosnio 265
chlorophaea Rhinostha 108
Chlorophanes 320
Chlorophonia 319
Chloropipo 207
chloropsis 230
chloropsis Melithreptus 299
chloroptera Ana 99
chloroptera Anatinga 100
chloroptera Myzomela 298
chloropterus Alisterus 93
chloropterus Lamprotornis 350
chloropus Galliuala 58
chloropus Tropicoperdix 47
chloropygria Nectarinia 291
chlororhynchos Diomedia 6
chlororhynchus Centripus 110
Chlorornis 314
Chlorosprigus 314
PAGE 17
Chlorostilbon 127
Chlorothraupis 315
Chlorotica Euphonia 318
Chlorurus 310
chlorurus Pipilo 310
chocoensis Venilioznis 172
chocoensis vireo 326
chocolatinus Melaenoznis 273
chocolatinus Spelaeornis 255
choliba Otus 112
choloensis Alethe 242
Chondestes 306
Chondrohierax 28
chopi Gnorimopsar 330
Chordeilis 119
Choriotis 60
christinae Aethopyga 294
chrysaea Stachysis 255
chrysaetos Aquila 36
chrysaeus Tarsiger 240
chrysater Icterus 328
chrysauchen Melanerpes 170
chrysia Giotrygon 81
chrysocephalum Neopelina 207
chrysocephalus Icterus 328
chrysocephalus Myiodynastes 199
chrysocephalus sericulus 358
chrysochloros Piculus 165
Chrysococcyx 107
Chrysocolaptes 175
chrysocome Eudyptes 4
chrysoconus Pogoniulus 158
chrysocorotaphum Todirostium 202
chrysogaster Basileuterus 324
chrysogaster Gerygone 270
chrysogaster Neophema 95
chrysogaster Pheucticus 312
chrysogenys Arachnothera 294
chrysogenys Melanerpes 170
chrysogenys Oreornis 299
chrysoÔdes Colaptes 164
Chrysolampis 126
chrysolaus Turdus 249
chrysolophum Neopelma 207
chrysolophus 51
chrysolophus Eudyptes 4
chrysomela Monarcha 281
chrysomelas Chrysothlypis 315
Chrysomma 256
chrysonotus Cacicus 328
chrysoparia Dendroica 322
chrysopasta Euphonia 318
chrysopeplus Pheucticus 312
chrysophrys Emberiza 303
chrysophrys Tangare 319
chrysopogon Megalaima 157
chrysops Cyanocorax 364
chrysops Lichenostornus 298
chrysops Meliphaga 298

chrysops Zimmerius 204
chrysoptera Anthochaera 302
chrysoptera Neositta 287
chrysoptera Vermivoza 322
chrysopterus Brotogesis 102
chrysopterus Cacicus 328
chrysopterus Masius 206
chrysopterygius Psephotus 94
Chrysoptilus 164
chrysopygia Oenanthe 246
chrysorrheum Dicaeum 289
chrysorrhoa Acanthiza 270
chrysorrhoa Eopsaltria 272
chrysostoma Diomedia 6
chrysostomus Neophema 95
Chrysothlypis 315
chrysotis Alcippe 259
chrysotis Tangara 319
chrysura Hylochasis 128
Chrysuronia 128
chthonia Gallaria 193
Chthonicola 270
chuana Mirafra 215
chubbi Cisticola 266
chukar Alectoris 45
Chunga 59
cia Emberiza 303
Ciccaba 116
cichladusa 242
Cichlherminia 251
Cichlocolaptes 184
Cichlornis 268
Cicinnurus 361
Ciconia 17
ciconia Ciconia 17
cinchoneti Conopias 198
Cinclidium 243
Cinclocerthia 239
Cinclodes 179
Cincloramphus 271
cinclorhynchus Monticola 247
Cinclosoma 253
Cinclus 236
cinclus cinclus 236
cincta Dichrozona 188
cincta Notiomystis 299
cincta Peophila 339
cincta Riparia 217
cincturus Ammomanes 126
cinctus Erythrogonys 63
cinctus Parus 285
cinctus Ptilonopus 84
cinctus Rhinoptilus 68
cinctus Rhynchortyx 44
cinctus Saltator 313
cineracea Ducula 86
cineracea Embriza 303
cineracea Myzomela 297
cineraceus Garrul 257
cineraceus Sturnus 351
cinerascens Aplonis 348
cinerascens Cercomacra 190
cinerascens Circaetus 31
cinerascens Dendrocitta 363
cinerascens Fraseria 273
cinerascens Melaenormis 273
cinerascens Monarcha 281
cinerascens Myiarchus 200
cinerascens Nothoprocta 3
cinerascens Parus 285
cinerascens Prinia 265
cinerascens Synallaxis 180
cinerea Alcippe 259
cinerea Apalis 267
cinerea Ardea 14
cinerea Batara 185
cinerea Calendrella 216
cinerea Callaeas 356
cinerea Coracina 221
cinerea Creatophona 351
cinerea Gallicrex 58
cinerea Gerygone 270
cinerea Glareola 68
cinerea Motacilla 219
cinerea Muscisaxicola 196
cinerea Mycteria 17
cinerea Pachycephala 282
cinerea Piezorhina 307
cinerea Poospiza
cinerea Procellaria 7
cinerea Serpophaga 203
cinerea Struthidea 356
cinerea Xolmis 196
cinerea Zoothera 248
cinerea Zosterops 296
cinereicapillus Spizixus 204
cinereicauda Lampornis 192
cinereiceps Alcippe 259
cinereiceps Malacocincla 254
cinereiceps Ontalis 41
cinereiceps Orthotomus 265
cinereiceps Oxylabes 227
cinereiceps Phyllastrephus 227
cinereiceps Phyllomyias 204
cinereicollis Basileuterus 324
cinereifrons Garrulex 257
cinereifrons Heteromyias 272
cinereigulare Oncostoma 202
cinereiventris Chaetura 123
cinereiventris Microbates 261
cinereocapilla Motacilla 219
cinereocapilla Prinia 265
cinereola Cisticola 266
cinereovinacea Euchistospiza 337
cinereum Coninostrum 321
cinereum Malacopteron 254
cinereum Todirostrum 202
cinereum Toxostorna 238
cinereus Artamus 354
cinereus Circaetus 31
cinereus Circus 31
cinereus Coccyzus 107
cinereus Contopus 200
cinereus Crypturellus 2
cinereus Microsarcops 62
cinereus Odontonchilus 236
cinereus Poliolimnas 37
cinereus Ptilogonys 235
cinereus Pycnopygius 199
cinereus Xenus 65
cinnamomea Certhiaxis 181
cinnamomea macropygia 78
cinnamomea Neopipo 207
cinnamomea Pyrrhomyias 201
cinnamomea Sporophila 308
cinnamomea Synallaxis 180
cinnamomea Tersiphone 279
cinnamomeipectus Hemitriccus 202
cinnamomeiventris Ochthoeca 197
cinnamomeiventris Thamnolaea 245
cinnamomeum Cinclosoma 253
cinnamomeus Acrociphalus 263
cinnamomeus Ailuroedus 357
cinnamomeus Anthus 220
cinnamomeus Attila 199
cinnamomeus Bradyptorus 262
cinnamomeus Crypturellus 2
cinnamomeus Hypocryptadis 296
cinnamomeus Ixobrychus 16
cinnamomeus Pachyramphus 210
cinnamomeus Pericrocotus 225
cinnamomeus Picumnus 163
cinnamomina Halcyon 141
cinnamominus Falco 39
Cinnycerthia 236
Cinnyricinclus 350
cioides Emberiza 303
Circaetus 31
circumcinetus Spiziapteryx 38
Circus 31
ciridops 325
ciris Passerina 313
cirlus Emberiza 303
cirratus Picumnus 163
cirrhata Luna 74
cirrhatus Spizaetus 37
cirrhocephalus Accipiter 32
cirrocephalus Larus 69
cirrochloris, Aphantochroa 129
Cissa 363
Cissilopha 365
Cissomela 302
Cissopis 314
Cisticola 266
Cistothorus 236
citrea Protonotaria 323
citreogularis Philemon 300
citreogularis Sericormis 271
citreola Motacilla 219
citreolaemus Ramphastos 162
citreolus Tregon 135
citrina Sicalis 308
citrina Wilsonia 324
citrina Zoothera 248
citrinella Emberiza 303
citrinella Serinus 332
citrinellus Atlapetes 311
citrinipectus Serinus 332
citriniventris Attila 199
Cittura 140
Cladorhynchus 67
clamans Baeopogon 227
clamans Spiloptila 265
Clamator 106
clamator Rhinoptynx 117
clamosa Rhipidura 277
clamosus Atrichornis 214
clamosus Cuculus 106
clanga Aquila 36
Clangula 26
clangula Bucephala 26
clappertoni Francolinus 45
clara Motacilla 219
clarae Anachnothera 294
Claravis 80
clarisse Heliangelus 131
clarkii Aechmophorus 5
clarkii Otus 112
clarus Caprinulgus 120
clathratus Trogon 135
claudi Glycichaera 297
cleaveri Illadopsis 254
clemenciae Lampornis 129
Cliptornis 299
Clibanornis 179
climacocerca Hydropsalis 121
Climacteris 287
climacurus Caprinalgus 120
clotibey Ramphocoris 216
clypeata Anas 24
Clytoceyx 140
Clytoctantes 187
Clytolaema 129
Clytomyias 269
Clytorhynchus 280
Clytospiza 337
Cnemophilus 358
Cnemoscopus 314
Cnemotriccus 201
Cnipodectes 201
coccinea Loxops 325
coccinea Vestiaria 325
coccineus Calochaetes 317
coccinigastra Nectarinia 291
Coccothraustes 336
coccothraustes Coccothraustes 336
Coccyzus 107
cochinchinensis Chloropsis 230
cochinchinensis Hirundapus 122
Cochlearius 15
cochlearius Cochlearuis 15
Cochoa 244
cockerelli Lichmera 297
cockerelli Philemon 300
cockerelli Rhipidura 277
cocoi Andea 14
codringtoni Vidua 341
coelebs Fringilla 332
coelestis Aglaiocercus 132
coelestis Forpus 102
PAGE 19
coelestis Hypothymis 280
coelicolor Grandala 243
Coeligena 131
coeligena Coeligena 131
Coenocerypha 66
Coereba
coeruleicinctis Aulacorhynachus 160
coeruleogularis Lepidopyga

128
coerulescens Alcedo 139
coerulescens Aphelocome 364
coerulescens Coracina 221
coerulescens Saltator 313
Colaptes 164
colchicus, Phasianus 50
colensoi Philacrocorax 12
Colibri 126
Colinus 44
Colius 135
collarvia Amazona 104
collaris Accipiter 33
collaris Anthreptes 290
collaris Aythya 25
collaris Charadrius 63
collaris Lanius 233
collaris Microbates 261
collaris Mirafra 215
collaris Prunella 239
collaris Sporophila 308
collaris Trogon 135
colliei Calocitta 365
Collocalia 122
colluricincla 284
collurico Lanius 233
colluroides Lanius 234
collybita Phylloscopus 264
colma Formicarius 192
colombianus Carduelis 333
colombica Thalurania 127
Colonia 197
colonus Colonia 197
colonus Rhinomyias 273
Colopterix 202
coloratus Myadestes 244
Colorhamphus 203
Coloria Erythrura 340
Colubris Anchilochus 133
Columba 76
Columba Cepphus 74
Columbarins Falco 39
columbiana Nucifrage 365
columbiana Otus 113
columbiana Porzana 57
columbiana Sicalis 308
columbianus Cygnus 20
columbianus Odontophorus 44
Columbigallina/Columbina 80
columboides Psittacula 97
cornata Hemiprocne 122
cornatus Berenicornis 150
comechingonus Cinclodes 179
comeri Pozphyionnis 58
comitata Muscicapa 276
communis Sylvia 263
comorensis Nectarinia 291
Compsothraupis 314
comptus Trogon 136
comrii Manucodia 359
concinens Acrocephalus 263
concinna Ducula 86
concinna Euphonia 318
concinna Glossopsitta 89
concinnus Aegithalos 285
concolor Amaurolimnas 55
concolor Amaurospiza 309
concolor Corytheixoides 105
concolor Dendrocolaptes 177
concolor Dicaeum 289
concolor Euplectea 347
concolor Falco 39
concolor Hirundis 217
concolor Macrosphenus
concolor Neospiza 333
concolor Xenospingus 307
conereta Halcyon 141
concreta Niltava 275
concreta Platysteira 278
concretus Caprimulgus 121
concretus Hemicircus 174
condamini Eutoxcres 125
condita Tijuca 208
confusa Pagodroma 7
congensis Afropavo 51
congensis Nectarinia 291
congica Riparia 217
Conioptilon 209
conirostris Arremonops 311
conirostris Calandrella 216
conirostris Geospiza 310
conirostris Indicator 159
Conirostrum 321
connivens Ninox 116
Conopias 198
Conopophaga 194
Conopophila 302
Conostroma 261
Conothraupis 314
conoveri Leptotila 80
conradii Coeligena 131
consobrinorum Zosterops 295
consobrinus Remiz 285
conspicillata Sylvia 263
conspicillata Zosterops 295
conspicillatus Basilenterus 324
conspicillatus Forpus 102
conspicillatus Paradoxornis 261
conspicillatus Pelecanus 11
constans Ducula 86
constantii Heliomaster 133
contaminatus Heliobletus 184
Contopus 200
contra Sturnus 351
Conuropsis 101
conversii Popelairia 127
convexus Anthacoceros 151
cookii Pterodroma 9
cooperi Otus 113
cooperii Accipiter 33
coprotheres Gyps 30
Copsychus 242
coquereli Coua 109
coquerellii Nectarinia 290
coqui Francolinus 45
cora Thaumastura 13
Coracias 147
Coracina 221/22
coracinus Entomodesteo 244
coracopsis 96
coracornis 283
cotagyps 27
coralensis Ptilinopus 85
corallirostris Hypisitta 235
Corapipo 206/7
corax Corvus 367
coraya Thryothorus 237
Corcorax 356
corensis Columba 76
corniculata Fratercula 74
corniculatus Philemon 300
cornix Convus 367
cornuta Anhima 20
cornuta Fulica 59
cornuta Heliactin 133
cornuta Pipra 206
cornutus Batrachostomus 118
cornutus Eunymphicus 95
coromanda Halcyon 141
coromandelianus Nettapus 25
coromandelica Cotwinix 47
coromandelicus Cursosicus 68
coromandus Bubo 114
coromandus Clamator 106
coronata Dendroica 322
coronata Hemiprocne 122
coronata Paroaria 312
coronata Thamnolace 245
coronata Xolmis 196
coronata Zeledonia 321
coronatus Ampeliceps 352
coronatus Anthracoceros 151
coronatus Basilenterus 324
coronatus Harpyhalioetus 34
coronatus Malimbus 346
coronatus Malurus 269
coronatus Onychorhyncluis 201
coronatus Phalacrocorex 12
coronatus Phylloscopus 264
coronatus Platyrinchus 201
coronatus Pterocles 75
coronatus Remiz 285
coronatus Stephanibyx 62
coronatus Stephanoaetus 37
coronatus Tachyphonus 316
corone Convus 367
coronoides Convus 366
coronulatus Ptilinopus 84
correndera Anthus 220
corrugatus aceros 150
corruscus Lamprotornis 350
ceruscans Colibri 126
coruscans Neodreparis 213
corvina Aplonis 348
corvina Corvinella 233
corvina Megalaima 157i
corvina Terpsiphone 279
Corvinella 233
Corvus 366/67
Corydon 176
Coryi Schizoeaca 180
Coryphaeus Cercotrichas 241
coryphaeus Pogoniulus 158
Coryphaspiza 312
Coryphistera 183
Coryphospingus 312
Coryphotriccus 199
Cosythaeola 105
corythaix Basilonnis 352
corythaix Tauraco 105
corythaixoides 105
corythopis 205
Coscoroba 20
coscoroba Coscoroba 20
Cosmopsarus 350
Cossypha 241
costae Calypte 134
costaricensis Geotrygon 81
costaricensis Touit 102
Cotinga 208
cotinga Cotinga 208
cotta Myiopagis 204
Coturnicops 57
Coturnix 47
coturnix Coturnix 47
Coua 109/110
couchii Tyrannus 198
couloni Ara 99
courseni Synallaxis 180
couitoisi Garralax 257
Cracticus 357
Cranioleuca 181/82
crassa Aplonis 348
crassa Napothera 255
crassirostris Ailwroedus 357
crassirostris Arachnothera 294
crassirostris Camarhynclus 310
crassirostris Carduelis 333
crassirostris Chalcitco 107
crassirostris Convus 367
crassirostris Cuculus 106
crassirostris Geositta 179
crassirostris Helcia 296
crassirostris Hemiparra 62
crassirostris Hypsipetes 229
crassirostris Larus 70
crassirostris Lysurus 311
crassirostris Oriolus 353
crassirostris Ozyzoborus 309
crassirostris Pachyptile 7
crassirostris Reinwardtoena 79
crassirostris Rhamphocharis 288
crassirostris Tyrannus 198
crassirostris Vireo 326
crassus Poicephalus 96
Crateroscelis 271
cratitia Meliphaga 298
craveri Brachyxamphus 74
Crax 42
Creadion 356
creagna Macropsalis 119
Creagrus 71
Creatophora 351
creatopus Puffinus 8
crecca Anas 23
Crecopsis 57
crenatus Anthus 220
crepitans Psophia 54
crestatus Eudyptes 4
Creurgops 315
Crex 57
crex Crex 57
Crinifer 105
crinifrons Aegotheles 118
Criniger 228
criniger Gallicolumba 81
criniger Hypsipetes 229
criniger Prinia 265
criniger Sctornis 229
crinitus Myiarchus 200
crispifrons Napothera 255
crispus Pelecanus 11
crissale Toxostroma 238
crispalis Pipilio 310
crispalis Vermivora 322
cristata Alcedo 139
cristata Calyptura 209
cristata Cariama 59
cristata Corythaeola 105

cristata Coua 109
cristata Cyanocitta 364
cristata Elaenia 204
cristata Fulica 59
cristata Galerida 216
cristata Goiira 82
cristata Gubernatrix 312
cristata Habia 316
cristata Lophostrix 113
cristata Lophotibis 19
cristata Prionops 231
cristata Pseudoseisura 183
cristata Rhegmatorhina 192
cristata Tadorna 22
cristatella Acthia 74
cristatellus Acridotheres 352
cristatellus Cyanocorax 365
cristatum Sphenostoma 253
cristatus Aegotheles 118
cristatus Colinus 44
cristatus Furnarius 180
cristatus Lanius 233
cristatus Orthorhynchus 126
cristatus Oxyruncus 205
cristatus Parus 285
cristatus Pavo 51
cristatus Pitohui 284
cristatus Podiceps 5
cristatus Sakeophorus 185
cristatus Tachyphorus 316
cristinae Threnetes 125
crocea Epthianura 271
Crocethia 67
Crocias 260
croconotus Icterus 328
crossleyi Atelornis 147
crossleyi Mystacornis 260
crossleyi Zoothera 249
Crossoptilon 48
crossoptilon Crossoptilon 48
Crotophaga 109
crudigularis Arborophile 47
cruenta Tchegra 231
curentata Myzomcla 297
curentata Pyrrhura 101
curentatum Dicceum 289
cruentatus Melanerpes 170
cruentus Ithaginis 48
cruentus Malaconotus 232
cruentus Oriolus 354
cruentus Rhodospingus 312
crumeniferus Leptoptilos 17
cruralis Cincloxamphus 271
cruziana Columbina 80
Crypsirina 363
crypta Ficedula 274
cryptoleuca Progne 217
cryptoleucus Corvus 367
cryptoleucus Peneothello 272
cryptoleucus Thamnophilus 186
cryptoluphus Lipangus 210
Cryptolybia 158
Cryptophaps 87
Cryptoplectron 47
Cyptospiza 337
Cryptosylvicola 268
cryptoxanthus Myiophobus 201
cryptoxanthus Poicephalus 96
Crypturellus 2
cryptus Cypseloides 123
cubanensis Caprimulgus 121
cubensis Tyrannus 198
cubla Dryoscopus 231
cucullata Andigena 161
cucullata Carduelis 333
cucullata Crypsirina 363
cucullata Cyanolyca 364
cucullata Grallaricula 193
cucullata Hirundo 217
cucullata Lonchura 340
cucullata Petroica 272
cucullataTangara 319
cucullatus Carpornis 208
cucullatus Charadrius 63
cucullatus Coryphospingus 312
cucullatus Icterus 328
cucullatus Mergus 26
cucullatus Orthotomus 265
cucullatus Ploceus 343
cuculoides Avideca 28
cuculoides Glaucidium 115
Cuculus 106
cujubi Aburria (Penelope) 42
Culicicapa 272
Culicivora 203
culicivorus Basileuterus 324
culik Selenidera 161
culminatus Corvus 366
culminatus Ramphastos 162
cumanensis Aburria (Pipile) 42
cumingi Lepidogrammus 108
cumingi Phoenicophaus 108
cumingi Megapodius 40
cuneata Geopelia 78
cunicularia Geositta 179
cunicularia Speotyto 116
cupido Tympanuchus 4
cuprea Nectarinia 291
cupreicaudus Centropus 110
cupreiceps Elvira 129
cupreocauda Lamprotornis 350
cupreoventris Eriocnemis 131
cupreus Chrysococcyx 107
cupripennis Aglacactis 130
Curaeus 330
curaeus Curaeus 330
curraca Sylvia 263
currucoides Sialia 244
cursor Coua 110
cursor Cursorius 68
Cursorius 68
curtata Cranioleuca 181
curucui rogon 136
curvipennis Campylopterus 126
curvirostra Loxia 336
curvirostra Treron 83
curvirostre Toxostoma 238
curvirostris Andropadus 226
curvirostris Certhilauda 215
curvirostris Limnornis 180
curvirostris Nothoprocta 3
curvirostris Ramphococcyx 108
curvirostris Vanga 235
Cutia 259
cuvieri Dryolimnas 55
cuvieri Falco 39
cuvieri Ramphostos 162
cuvieri Talegalla 40
cuvierii Phaeochroa 125
cyana Cyanopica 363
cyane Erithacus 240
cyanea Chlorophonia 319
cyanea Diglossopis 321
cyanea Passerina 313
cyanea Pitta 212
cyanea Platysteira 278
cyanecula Luscinia 240
cyaneoberylina Augasma 128
cyaneotincta Amazilia 129
cyaneovirens Erythrura 339
cyaneoviridis Callichelidon 217
Cyanerpes 320
cyanescens Galbula 154
cyanescens Terpsiphone 279
cyaneus Circus 31
cyaneus Cyanerpes 320
cyaneus Malurus 269
cyaniceps Rhipidura 277
cyanicollis Galbula 154
cyanicollis Tangara 319
Cyanicterus 317
cyanicterus Cyanicterus 317
cyanifirons Amazilia 128
cyanirostris Knipolegus 197
cyaniventer Tesia 262
cyaniventris Pycnonotus 226
cyanocampter Cossypha 241
cyanocephala Amazilia 129
cyanocephala Eudynamys 107
cyanocephala Gymnorhinus 365
cyanocephala Psittacula 97
cyanocephala Starnoenas 82
cyanocephala Tangara 319
cyanocephala Thraupis 317
cyanocephala Uraeginthus 338
cyanocephalus Euphagus 331
cyanocephalus Malurus 269
Cyanochen 22
Cyanocitta 364
Cyanocompsa 313
Cyanocorax 364/65
cyanogaster Coracias 147
cyanogaster Irena 230
cyanogenia Eos 38
cyanoides Passerina 313
cyanolaema Nectarinia 291
Cyanolanius 235
cyanoleuca Grallina 356
cyanoleuca Halycon 141
cyanoleuca Myiagna 280
cyanoleuca Notiochelidon 217
Cyanolimnas 55
Cyanoloseus 100
Cyanolyca 364
cyanomelana Cyanoptila 274
cyanomelas Cyanocorax 365
cyanolmelas Phoeniculus 148
cyanomelas Trochocercus 279
cyano pectus Ceyx 139
cyanopectus Sternoclyta 130
Cyanophaia 127
Cyanopica 363
cyanophrys Eupherusa 129
cyanopis Columbina 80
cyanopogon Chloropsis 230
cyanopogon Cyanocorax 364
Cyanopsitta 98
cyanoptera Anas 24
cyanoptera Brotogeris 102
cyanoptera Tangara 319
cyanoptera Thraupis 317
cyanopterus Artamus 354
cyanopterus Cyanochen 22
cyanopterus Pterophares 130
Cyanoptila 274
cyanopus Agelaius 329
cyanopygius Forpus 102
Cyanoramphus 95
cyanotis Cittura 140
cyanotis Entomyzon 299
cyanotis Tangara 319
cyanouroptera Minla 259
cyanoventris Halcyon 141
cyanoventris Tangara 319
cyanura Amazilia 129
cyanurus Erithacus 240
cyanurus Poittinus 92
cyanurus Tarsiger 240
cyanus Hylocharis 128
cyanus Parus 285
cyanus Peneothello 272
Cyclahis 326
Cyclorrhynchus 74
cygnoides Anser 21
Cygnus 20
cygnus Cygnus 20
cylindricus Bycanistes 152
Cymtilaimus 185
Cymbirhynchus 176
Cynanthus 127
cyornithopsis Erithacus 241
Cyphorhinus 237
cypriaca Oenanthe 246
Cypseloides 123
Cypsiurus 124
Cypsnagra 314
Cyrtonyx 44

dabberei Penelope 41
Dacelo 140
dachilleae Nannopscittaca 102
Dacnis 320
dacotiae Saxicola 245
dactylatra Sula 11
Dactylortyx 44
dahli Rhipidura 277
dalhousiae Psarisomus 176
damarensis Mirafra 215
damerensis Phoeniculus 148
dambo Cisticola 266
damii Xenopirostris 235
dammermani Myzomela 297
Damophila 128
danae Tanysiptera 143

danjoui Jabouilleia 254
dannefaerdi Petroica 272
Daphoenositta 287
Daption 7
Daptrius 38
darjellensis Dendrocopos 173
darnaudii Trachyphonus 159
darwinii Nothura 3
Dasyornis 270
dasypus Delichon 217
daubentoni Crax 42
dauma Zoothera 248
daurica Hirundo 217
dauricae Perdix 46
dauwrica Muscicapa 276
dauwricas Corvus 366
davidi Arborophila 47
davidi Garrulax 257
davidi Niltava 275
davidi Parus 285
davidi Strix 117
davidiana Montifungilla 343
davidianus Paradoxornis 261
davisoni Phylloscopus 264
davisoni Pseudibis 18
dayi Capito 156
dayi Elaenia 204
dea Galbula 154
debilis Phyllastnephus 227
decaecto Streptopelia 78
decipiens Streptopelia 78
deckeni Tockus 149
Deconychura 177
decora Amazilia 128
decora Paradisaea 362
decorata Acestrura 134
deconatus Pterocles 75
decumanus Psarocolius 327
decurtatus Hylophilus 326
dedemi Rhipidura 277
defilippiana Pterodroma 9
defilippii Pezites 330
degodiensis Mirafra 215
deiroleucus Falco 39
delalandei Coua 110
delalandi Corythopis 205
delalandii Treron 83
delatrii Tachyphonus 316
delattrei Lophornis 127
delattrii Basileuterus 324
delawarensis Larus 70
delegorguei Columba 76
delegorguei Coturnix 47
delesserti Garrulax 257
Delichon 217
deliciosus Machaeropterus 207
Delothraupis 318
delpinae Colibri 126
Deltarhynchus 200
demersus, Spheniscus 4
demissa Crauioleuca 181
Dendragapus 43
Dendexetastes 177
Dendrocinela 176/77
Dendrocitta 363
Dendrocolaptes 177
dendrocolaptoides Clibanornis 179
Dendrocopos 172-174
Dendrocygna 20
Dendroica 322
Dendronanthus 219
Dendropicos 172
Dendrortyx 44
denhami Neotis 60
deningeri Lichmera 297
dennistormi Stachysis 255
densus Dicrurus 355
dentata Creurgops 315
dentata Petronia 342
denti Sylvietta 268
dentirostris Scenopoeetes 357
derbianus Aulacorhynchus 160
derbianus Oreophasis 42
derbianus Orthotomus 265
derbyana Psittacula 97
derbyi Eriochemis
Deroptyus 104
deserti Ammomanes 216
deserti Oenanthe 246
deserticola Sylvia 263
desgodinsi Heterophasia 260
desmaresti Tangara 319
desmarestii Psittacularistris 92
desmursii Sylviorthorhynchus 180
desolata Pachyptila 7
deva Galerida 216
devillei Drymophila 189
devillei Pyrrhura 101
diabolicus Eurostopodus 119
diadema Catamblyrhynchus 312
diadema Charmosyna 89
diadema Ochthoeca 197
diademata Alethe 242
diademata Yuhina 260
diadematum Tricholaema 158
diadematus Euplectes 347
diadematus Stephanophorus 318
dialeucos Odontophorus 44
diana Cinclidium 243
diardi Diardigallus 49
diardi Rhopodytes 108
Diardigallus 49
diardi Harpactes 137
diazi Anas 23
Dicaeum 288/89
Dichroa Aplonis 348
dichroa Cossypha 241
dichrous Parus 285
dichrous Pitohui 284
Dichrozona 188
dickeyi Cyanocorax 364
dickinsoni Falco 39
dicolorus Ramphastos 162
dicrocephalus Ploceus
Dicrurus 355
Didunculus 82
dieffenbachii Rallus 55
diemenensis Philemon 300
difficilis Empidonax 201
difficilis Geospiza 310
difficilis Phylloscartes 203
diffusus Passer 342
Diglossa 321
Diglossopis 321
dignissima Grallaria 194
dignus Venilornis
dilectissima Touit 102
dilutye Rhipidura 277
dimidiata Hirundo 217
dimidiata Pomarca 273
dimidiatus Philydor 183
dimidiatus Ramphocelus 317
dimorpha Batis 278
dimorpha Egretta 15
dimorpha Urogleux 116
dinellianus Pseudocolopteryx 203
dinemelli Dinemellia 341
Dinemellia 341
Dinopium 168
disdon Harpagus 28
Diomedia 6
diomedia Calonectris
diophthalma Opopsitta 92
diops Batis 278
diops Halcyon 141
diops Hemitriccus 202
diphone Cettia 262
Diphyllodes 361
discolor Certhia 287
discolor Cisticola 266
discolor Dendroica 322
discolor Lathamus 95
discolor Leptosomus 146
discors Anas 24
Discosura 127
discurus Prioniturus 92
disjuncta Myrmeciza 191
dispar Coracina 223
dissimilis Turdus 249
dissita Cranioleuca 182
distincta Cisticola 266
Diuca 307
diuca Diuca 307
divaricatus Pericrocotus 225
Dives 330
dives Dives 330
dives Helopezus 193
dixoni Zoothera 248
dodsoni Pycnonotus 226
dohertyi Coracina 223
dohertyi Lophozosterops 296
dohertyi Pitta 212
dohertyi Ptilinopus 84
doyertyi Telophonus 232
dohertyi Zoothera 248
dohrni Horizorhinus 260
dohrnii Ramphodon 125
dolei Palmeria 325
doliatus Thamnophilus 186
Dolichonyx 331
Dolospingus 309
domesticus Passer 342
domicella Hirundo 217
domicellus Lorius 88
domicola Hirundo 217
dominica Dendroica 322
dominica Oxyura 26
dominica Pluvialis 63
dominicana Paroaria 312
dominicana Xolmis 196
dominicanus Larus 70
dominicensis Carduelis 333
dominicensis Icterus 328
dominicensis Progne 217
dominicensis Tyrannus 198
dominicus Anthracothorax 126
dominicus Dulus 235
dominicus Tachybaptus 5
Donacobius 239
Donacospiza 307
donaldsoni Caprimulgus 120
donaldsoni Plocepasser 342
donaldsoni Serinus 332
dorae Dendrocopos 173
donbignyi Asthenes 182
PAGE 24dorbygnianus Picumnus 163
doriae Megatriorchis 32
Doricha 133
dorotheae Amytornis 269
dorsale Ramphomicron 132
dorsale Toxostoma 238
dorsalis Automolus 184
dorsalis Gerygone 270
dorsalis Gymnorhina 356
dorsalis Lanius 234
dorsalis Mimus 238
dorsalis Phacellodomus 182
dorsalis Phrygilus 306
dorsomaculatus Herpsilochmus 189
dorsomaculatus Ploceus 343
dorsostriatus Serinus 332
dorsti Cisticola 266
Doryfera 125
dougallii Sterna 72
douglasii Lophertyx 44
dowii Tangara 319
Drepanis 325
Drepanoptila 85
Drepanornis 359
Dromaeocercus 264
Dromaius 1
Dromas 68
Dromococcyx 109
drownei Rhipidura 277
dryas Catharus 251
Drymocichla 267
Drymodes 240
Drymophila 189
Drymornis 177
Dryocopus 169
Dryolimnas 55
Dryoscopus 231
Dryotriorchis 31
dubia Alcippe 260
dubia Cercomela 245
dubium Scissirostrum 352
dubius Charadrius 63
dubius Hieraactus 37
dubius Leptoptilos 17
dubius Lybius 158
dubius Pyrocephalus 198
Dubusia 318
duchaillui Buccanodon 158
duchaillui Pogoniulus 158
Ducula 86/87
ducorps Cacatua 91
dufresniana Amazona 104
dugendi Herpsilochmus 189
duidae Atlapetes 311
duidae Campylopterus 126
duidae Crypturellas 2
duidae Diglossa 321
duidae Emberizoides 308
duivenbodei Chalcopsitta 88
dulcis Malurus 269
Dulus 235
dumasi Zoothera 248
dumetaria Upucerthia 179
Dumetella 238

Dumetia 236
dumetoria Ficedula 274
dumetorum Acrocephalus 263
dumicola Polioptila 261
dumontii Mino 352
dunni Eremalanda 216
dupetithouarsii Ptilinopus 84
Dupetor 16
duponti Chersophilus 216
dupontii Tilmatura 125
dussumierei Nectarinia 291
duvaucelii Harpactes 137
duvaucelii Hoplopterus 63
duyvenbodei Aethopyga 294
dybowskii Euschistospiza 338
Dysithamnus 187
Dysmorodrepanis 325

earlei Turdoides 256
eatoni Anas 23
ecaudatus Myiornis 202
ecaudatus Terathopius 31
ecaudatus Rallus 55
echo Psittacula 97
Eclectus 93
Ectopistes
edithae Corvus 367
Edithornis 56
edolioides Melaenornis 273
edouardi Guttera 52
eduardi Tylas 229
edward Amazilia 129
edwardsi Buthraupis 317
edwardsi Hierophasis 49
edwardsii Carpodacus 334
edwardsii Psittaculirostris 92
egertoni Actinodura 259
egregia Chaetura 123
egregia Crecopsis 57
egregia Pyrrhura 101
Egretta 15
eichhorni Myzomela 297
eichhorni Philemon 300
eidos Apalis 267
eisentranti Meligromon 159
eisenmanni Thryothorus 237
elacus Dendropicos 172
Elaenia 204
Elanoides 28
Elanus 28
elaphra Collocalia 122
elata Ceratogymna 152
elatus Tyrannulus 205
Electron 144
elegans Celeus 166
elegans Emberiza 303
elegans Eudromia 3
elegans Laniisoma 208
elagans Lanius 233
elegans Leptopoecile 268
elegans Malecrus 269
elegans Melanopareia 195
elegans Neophema 95
elegans Otus 112
elegans Parus 285
elegans Phaps 79
elegans Pitta 213
elegans Platycercus 94
elegans Rallus 55
elegans Sarothrusa 57
elegans Sterna 72
elegans Trogon 136
elegans Xiphorhynchus 177
elegantior Cranioleuca 181
elegantissima Euphonia 318
eleonorae Falco 39
Eleothreptus 121
elgini Spilornis 31
elgonensis Francolinus 46
eliciae Hylocharis 128
elisabeth Myadestes 244
elisabeth Lamprotornis 350
eliza Doricha 133
ellioti Atthis 132
ellioti Syzinaticus 50
ellioti Tanysiptera 143
elliotii Garrulax 257
elliotii Mesopicus 174
elliotii Pitta 212
ellisianus Hemignathus 325
Elminia 279
elphinstonii Columba 76
eludens Giallaria 194
Elvira 129
Emeriza 303
Emberizoides 308
Embernagra 308
Emblema 339
emiensis Phylloscopus 264
emiliae Chlonocharis 296
emiliana Macropygia 78
eminentissima Foudia 346
emini Cisticola 266
emini Ploceus 343
eminibey Sonella 342
emphanum Polyplectron 51
Empidonax 201
Empidonomus 198
enarratus Caprinulgus 120
enca Convus 366
engauensis Otus 113
Enicognathus 101
enicura Doricha 133
Enicurus 243
enigma Halcyon 141
Enodes 352
Ensifera 131
ensifera Ensifera 131
ensipennis Campyloptorus 126
Entomodestes 244
Entomyzon 299
Entotriccus 197
enucleator Pinicola 335
Eolophus 90
Eophona 336
Eopsaltria 272
Eos 88
eos Carpodacus 334
epauletta Pyrrhoplectes 336
Ephippiorhynchus 17
Ephthianura 271
epichlora Urolais 265
epilepidota Napothera 255
Epimachus 360
episcopus Ciconia 17
episcopus Thraupis 317
epomidis Centropus 111
epomophora Diomedia 6
epops Upupa 148
epulata Muscicapa 276
eques Myzomela 297
erckolii Francolinus 45
Eremalauda 216
Eremiornis 268
eremita Diomedia 6
eremita Geronticus 18
eremita Megapodius 40
eremita Nesocichla 249
Eremobius 179
Eremomela 268
Eremophila 216
Eremopteryx 215
Ereunetes 67
Ergaticus 324
Eriocnemis 131
Erithacus 240/41
erithacus Ceyx 139
erithacus Psittacus 96
erithronoton Dinopium 168
erlangeri Calendrella 216
Erolia 67
erythaca Pyrrhula 336
erythrauchen Accipiter 32
erythrinus Carpodacus 334
erythrocephala Amadina 340
erythrocephala Myzomela 297
erythrocephala Pipra 206
erythrocephala Piranga 316
erythrocephala Pyrrhula 336
erythrocephalus Garrulax 257
erythrocephalus Harpactes 137
erythrocephalus Hylocryptus 184
erythrocephalus Melanerpes 171
erythrocephalus Trachyphonus 159
erythrocerca Nectarinia 291
Erythrocercus 279
erythrocercus Philyder 183
erythrochlamus Certhilauda 215
erythrocnemis Pomatorhinus 254
erythrogaster Laniarius 232
erythrogaster Malimbus 346
erythrogaster Phoenicurus 243
erythrogaster Pitta 212
erythrogenys Aratinga 100
erythrogenys Microhierax 38
erythrogenys Pomatorhinus 254
Erythrogonys 63
erythroleuca Corallaria 194
erythrolophus Tauraco 105
erythromelas Myzomela 297
erythromelas Periporphysus 312
erythronemius Accipiter 32
erythronota Zoothera 248
erythronotos Estrilda 338
erythronotos Myrmotherula 188
erythronotes Dinopium 168
erythronotos Philydor 183
erythronotos Phoenicur 243
erythrophris Enodes 352
erythrophryx Poospiza 307
erythmophthalma Netta 25
erythrophthalmus Coccyzus 107
erythrophthalmus Houppifer 49
erythrophthalmus Phacellodormus 182
erythrophthalmus Pipilo 310
erythrophthalmus Pycnonotus 226
erythropheura Ptiloprora 300
erythropleura Zosterops 295
erythrops Cisticola 266
erythrops Climacteris 287
ereythrops Cranioleuca 181
erythrops Myiagra 280
erythrops Neocrex 57
erythrops Odontophorus 44
erythrops Quelca 346
erythroptera Gallicolumba 81
erythroptera Mirafra 215
erythroptera Ortalis 41
erythroptera Phlegopsis 193
erythroptera Prinia 265
erythroptera Stachyris 255
erythropterus Aprosmictus 93
erthropterus Philyder 183
erythrophthalmos Pycnonotus 226
erythrophthalmus Coccyzus 107
erythropus Accipiter 32
erythropus Anser 21
erythropus Crypturellus 2
erythropus Tainga 65
Erythropygia 241
erythropygia Pinerocorys 215
erythropygius Myiotheretes 196
erythropygius Pericrocotus 225
erythropygius Picus 166
erythropygius Pteroglossus 160
erythropygius Sturnus 351
erythropygius Xiphorhynchus 177
erythropygius Morococcyx 109
erythrorhamphus Halcyon 143
erythrorhyncha Anas 24
erythrorhyncha Coturnix 47
erythrorhyncha Urocissa 363
erythrorhynchos Dicaeum 289

erythrorhynchos Pelicanus 11
erythrorhynchum Cryptoplectron 47
erythrorhynchus Buphagus 352
erythrorhynchus Tockus 149
erythrostictus Monarcha 281
Erythrothlypis 315
erythrothorax Stiphrornis 241
erythrothorax Synallaxis 181
erythrotic Grallaria 194
Erythrotriorchis 32
Erythrura 339/40
erythrura Myrmotherula 188
erythrurus Terenotriccus 201
Esacus 68
esculenta Collocalia 122
estella Oreotrochilus 130
estherae Serinus 332
Estrilda 338
ethologus Periorocotus 225
Eubacco 156
euchlorus Auripasser 342
euchrysea Kalochilidon 217
Eucometis 315
eucosma Charitospiza 312
Eudocimus 18
Eudromia 3
Eudromias 64
Eudynamys 107
Eudyptes 4
Edyptula 4
Eugenes 130
eugeniae Ptilinopus 84
Eugerygone 270
Eugralla 195
Eulabeornis 56
Eulacestoma 282
Eulampis 126
eulesi Coccyzus 107
euleri Empidonax 201
Eulidia 134
eulophotes Egretta 15
eulophotes Lophotriccus 202
Eumamota 144
Eumyias 276
Euornis 321
eunomas Turdus 250
Eunymphicus 95
euophrys Thryotherus 237
euops Aratinga 100
eupatria Psittacula 97
Eupetes 253
Eupetomena 126
Euphagus 331
Eupherusa 129
Euphonia 318
Euphlectes 346/47
Eupodotis 61
eupogon Metallura 132
eurythmus Ixobrychus 16
eurizonoÔdes Rallina 55
Eurocephalus 231
europaea Sitta 286
europaeus Caprimulgus 120
Eurostopodus 119
Eurycoros 235
eurycricota Zosterops 296
eurygnatha Sterna 72
Eurylaimus 176
eurynome Phaethornis 125
Eurynorhynchus 67
euryptera Opisthroposa 132
Euryptila 267
Eurypyga 59
eurystomina Pseudochelidon 217
Eurystomus 147
euryura Rhipidura 277
euryzona Alcedo 139
Euscarthmus 203
Euschistospiza 337
eutel 194
Euthlypis 324
eutilotus Pycnonotus 226
Eutoxeres 125
Eutrichomyias 280
Eutriorchis 31
evelynae Calliphlox 134
evelynae Philodice 134
everetti Aceros 150
everetti Arachnothera 294
everetti Dicaeum 289
everetti Hypsipetes 229
everetti Monarcha 281
everetti Turnix 53
everetti Urosphena 262
everetti Yuhina 260
usa 129
eximia Megalaima 157
eximium Dicaeum 288
eximius Caprimulgus 120
eximius Phylloscartes 203
eximius Platycercus 94
eximius Vireolanius 326
exortis Heliangelus 131
explorator Monticola 247
explorator Zosterops 295
exquisita Pipra 206
exquisita Porzana 57
exsul Myrmeciza 191
exsul Psittacula 97
externa Pterodroma 9
exulaus Diomedea 6
exustus Pterocles 75
eytoni Dendrocygna 20
eytoni Xiphorhynchus 177

fabalis Anser 21
fagani Prunella 239
faiostricta Megalaima 157
falcata Anas 23
falcata Ptilocichla 255
falcatus Campylopterus 126
falcinellus Limicola 67
falcinellus Plegadis 19
Falcipennis 43
falcipennis Falcipennis 43
falcinostris Sporophila 308
falcinostris Xiphocolaptis 177
falcklandii Turdus 251
Falco 39
falcularius Campyloshempus 178
Falculea 235
Falcunculus 282
falkensteini Chlorocichla 227
falkensteini Nectarinia 293
falklandicus Charadsius 63
fallax Bulweria 9
fallax Ceyx 139
fallax Elaenia 204
fallax Glycichaera 297
fallax Leucippus 128
familiare Apalopteron 299
familiaris Acrocephalus 263
familiaris Cercomela 245
familiaris Certhia 287
familiaris Prinia 265
famosa Nectarinia 291
fanny Myatis 127
fannyi Thalurania 127
fanovanae Newtonic 276
farinosa Amazone 104
farquhari Halcyon 142
fasciata Amadina 340
fasciata Atticora 217
fasciata Chamaea 261
fasciata Columba 76
fasciata Neothraupis 314
fasciata Rallina 55
fasciato-ventris Thryothosus 237
fasciatum Tigrisoma 16
fasciatus Accipiter 33
fasciatus Campylorhynchus 236
fasciatus Harpactes 137
fasciatus Hieraaetus 37
fasciatus Laterallus 57
fasciatus Myiophobus 201
fasciatus Philortyz 44
fasciatus Phyllomyias 204
fasciatus Ramsayornis 302
fasciatus Tockus 149
fasciicauda Pipra 206
fasciinucha Falco 39
fasciiventer Parus 285
fascinaus Microeca 272
fasciogularis Meliphaga 298
fasciolata Crax 42
fasciolata Locustella 262
fasciolatus Calamonastes 267
fasciolatus Circaetus 31
fastuosa Tangara 319
fastuosus Epimachus 360
feadensis Aplonis 348
feae Pterodroma 9
feae Tardus 249
fetherstroni Phalcrocorax 13
fedoa Limosa 65
feldegg Motacilla 219
felix Thryothosus 237
femoralis Cinnyricinclus 350
femoralis Falco 39
femoralis Scytalopus 195
ferdinandi Cercomacra 190
feriata Malacocincla 254
ferina Aythya 25
Ferminia 236
fernandensis Sephanoides 131
fernandezianus Anairetes 203
fernandinae Nesoceleus 164
fernandinae Teretistris 324
ferox Myiarchus 200
ferrea Saxicola 245
ferreornostris Coccothraustes 335
ferrocyanea Myiagra 280
ferruginea Calidris 67
ferruginea Drymophila 189
ferruginea Gallicolomba 81
ferruginea Hirundinea 201
ferruginea Murcicapa 276
ferruginea Myrmeciza 191
ferruginea Oxyria 26
ferruginea Petrophassa 79
ferruginea Tadorna 22
ferrugineus Ericognathus 101
ferrugineifions Bollorhynchus 101
ferrugineipectus Giallaricula 193
ferrugineiventre Conirostrum 321
ferrugineus Ericognethus 101
ferrugineus Lamarius 232
ferruginosa Lonchura 340
ferruginosus Pomatoshinus 254
ferridus Caprimulgus 120
festiva Amazona 104
festivus Chrysocolaptes 175
Ficedula 274
ficedulina Zosterops 296
figulus Furnarius 180
filicauda Pipra 206
fimbriata Amazilia 129
fimbriata Coracina 221
fimbriatum Callocephalon 90
fimlaysoni Pycnonotus 226
finschi Amazona 104
finschi Aratiuga 100
finschi Euphonia 318
finschi Francolinus 45
finschi Haematopus 62
Finschia 270
finschii Cruniges 228
finschii Ducula 86
finschii Micropsitta 92
finschii Neocossyphus 244
finschii Oenanthe 246
finschii Psittacula 97
finschii Stizorhina 244
finschii Zasceops 295
fischeri Agaposius 96
fischeri Dioptrornis 273
fischeri Leucotreron 84
fischeri Melaenornis 273
fischeri Nectarinia 293
fischeri Phyllastrephus 227
fischeri Ptilinopus 84
fischeri Somateria 24
fischeri Spreo 350
fischeri Tauraco 105
fischeri Vidua 341
fischeri Zoothera 249
fisheri Ammodramus 305
fistulatos Bycanistes 152
flagrans Aethopyga 294
flammea Acanthis 334
flammea Parorcomyza 325
flammeolus Otus 113
flammeus Pericrocotus 225

flammiceps Cephalopyrus 285
flammigerus Ramphocelus 317
flammula Selasphorus 134
flammulata Asthenes 182
flammulata Megabyas 278
flammulatus Deltarhynchus 200
flammulatus Hemitriccus 202
flammulatus Thripadectes 184
PAGE 28
flava Campephaga 224
flava Meliphaga 298
flava Motacilla 219
flava Piranga 316
flava Zosterops 295
flavala Hypsipetes 229
flaveola Capsiempis 203
flaveola Coereba 321
flaveola Sicalis 308
flaveolus Barileuterus 324
flaveolus Criniger 228
flaveolus Passer 342
flaveolus Platycercus 94
flavescens Boissonneaua 131
flavescens Celeus 166
flavescens Empidonax 201
flavescens Meliphaga 298
flavescens Smicronnis 270
flavibuecale Tricholaerna 158
flavicans Foudia 346
flavicans Lichmera 297
flavicans Macrosphemis 268
flavicans Myiophobus 201
flavicans Prinia 265
flavicans Prionitusus 92
falvicans Trichoglossus 88
flavicapilla Chloropipo 207
flaviceps Atlapetes 311
flaviceps Auripasus 285
flaviceps Loxioides 325
flavicollis Chlorocichla 227
flavicollis Hemithraupis 315
flavicollis Ixobrychus 16
flavicollis Macronous 256
flalvicollis Macronyx 219
flalvicollis Meliphaga 298
flavicollis Yuhiua 260
flavicrisalis Eremomela 268
flavida Apalis 267
flavida Gerygone 270
flavifrons Amblyornis 357
flavifrons Anthoscopus 285
flavifrons Megalaima 157
flavifrons Melanerpes 171
flavifrons Pachyciphala 282
flavifrons Vireo 326
flavifrons Zosterops 295
flavigaster Anachnothera 294
flavigaster Hyliota 268
flavigaster Microeca 272
flavigaster Xiphorhynchus 177
flavigula Manorina 302
flavigula Piculus 165
flavigula Serinus 332
flavigularis Apalis 267
flavigularis Chlorospingus 314
flavigularis Chrysococcyx 107
flavigularis Platusinchus 201
flavinucha Muscisaxicola 196
flavinucha Picus
flavinucha Anisognathus 318
flavipectus Parus 285
flavipennis Chloropsis 230
flavipes Hylophilus 326
flavipes Ketupa 114
flavipes Malimbus 346
flavipes Notiochelidon 217
flavipes Platalea 19
flavipes Tringa 65
flaviprymna Lonchura 340
flavipunctatum Tricholaema 158
flavirictus Meliphaga 298
flavirostra Limnocorax 56
flavirostris Acanthis 333
flavirostris Anairetes 203
flavirostris Anas 23
flavirostris Arremon 311
flavirostris Chlorophoria 319
flavirostris Columba 76
flavirostris Grallaricula 193
flavirostris Humblotia 276
flavirostris Monasa 155
flavirostris Paradoxomis 261
flavirostris Philbalura 208
flavirostris Pteroglossus 160
flavirostris Rynchops 73
flavirostris Tockus 149
flavirostris Urocissa 363
flaviscapis Pteruthius 259
flavissima Motacilla 219
flaviventer Decris 320
flaviventer Machaerirhynchus 280
flaviventer Meliphaga 298
flaviventer Porzana 57
flaviventris Embresiza 303
flaviventris Empidonax 201
flaviventris Eopsaltria 272
flaviventris Motacilla 219
flaviventris Phylloscastes 203
flaviventris Prinia 265
flaviventris Pseudocolopteryx 265
flaviventris Serinus 332
flaviventris Sphecotheres 354
flaviventris Tolmomyias 201
flaviventex Heterocercus 207
flaviventex Myioborus 324
flaviventex Myiopagis 204
flaviventex Serinus 332
flavocinctus Oriolus 353
flavogaster Elaenia 204
flavogrisea Pachycare 282
flavolateralis Gerygone 270
flavolivacea Cettia 262
flavostriatus Phyllastrephus 228
flavovelata Geothylpis 323
flavovirens Chlorospingus 314
flavovirens Phylloscartes 203
flavovirescens Microeca 272
flavoviridis Neomixis 255
flavoviridis Trichoglossas 88
flavoviridis Vireo 326
flavus Celeus 166
flavus Xanthopsax 329
floccosas Pycroptilus 270
florensis Convus 366
floriceps Anthocephale 129
florida Tangara 319
floris Treson 83
florisaga 126
flosculus Loriculus 96
fluminea Poszena 57
fluminensis Myrmothesula 187
fluviatilis Locustella 262
fluviatilis Muscisaxicola 196
Fluvicola 197
fluvicola Petrochelidon 217
foersteri Henicophaps 79
foersteri Melidectes 301
foetidus Gymnodesus 211
fonsecai Acrobatornis 184
forbesi Curaeus 330
forbesi Leptodon 28
forbesi Lochura 340
forbesi Rallicula 55
forficatus Tyrannus 198
forficatus Dicrurus 355
forficatus Elanoides 28
Formacarius 192
Formicivora 189
formicivora Myrmecocichla 245
PAGE 29
formicivorus Melanerpes 170
formosa Amandava 339
formosa Anas 23
formosa Calocitta 365
formosa Eudromia 3
formosa Geothlypis 323
formosa Pipreda 209
formosa Sitta 286
formosa Dendrocitta 363
formosae Treron 83
formosus Garrulax 257
formosus Ptilinopus 84
formosus Spelacornis 255
fornsi Teretistris 324
Forpus 102
forsteni Ducula 86
forsteni Meropogon 145
forsteni Oriolus 353
forsteri Aptenodytes 4
forsteri Sterna 72
fortipes Cettia 262
fortis Coracina
fortis Geospiza 310
fortis Myrmeciza 191
fossii Caprimulgus 120
Foudia 346
Foulchaio 299
fraeratus Caprimulgus 120
francescae Gianatellus 324
francesii Accipiter 33
franciae Amazilia 129
francica Collocalia 122
franciscanus Euplectes 347
franciscanus Xiphocolaptes 177
Francolinus 45/46
francolinus Francolinus 45
franklinii Megalaima 157
frantzii Catharus 251
frantzii Elaenia 204
frantzii Pteroglossus 161
frantzii Semnornis 156
fraseri Anthreptes 290
fraseri Basileuterus 324
fraseri Neocossyphus 244
fraseri Oreomanes 321
fraseri Stizorhina 244
Fraseria 273
frater Monarcha 281
frater Onychognathus 349
Fratercula 74
fratum Batis 278
Frederickena 185
freethii Huiratione 325
Fregata 13
Fregetta 10
Fregilupus 351
fremautlii Pseudalaemon 216
frenata Geotrygon 81
frenta Meliphaga 298
frenata Nectarinia 292
frentatus Chaetops 241
freycinet Megapodius 40
freycineti Myiagra 280
fringillaris calandulla 216
fringillarius Microhierax 38
fringillinus Parus 285
fringilloides Dolospingus 309
fringilloides Lonchura 340
frontale Cinclidium 243
frontalis Anarhynchus 64
frontalis Dendrocitta 363
frontalis Hemispingus 314
frontalis Muscisaxicola 196
frontalis Nonnula 155
frontalis Ochthoeca 197
frontalis Onthotomus 265
frontalis Phoenicurus 243
frontalis Pipreola 209
frontalis Pyerhula 101
frontalis Sericornis 271
frontalis Serinus 332
frontalis Sitta 286
frontalis Sporophila 309
frontalis Sporopipes 343
frontalis Synallaxis 181
frontalis Venitionnis 172
frontatua Tricholaema 158
frontatus Falcunculus 282

frugilegus Convus 366
frugivorus Calyptophilus 315
fruticeti Phrygilus 306
fucata Alopochildon 217
fucata Emberiza 303
fuciphaga Collocalia 122
fucosa Tangara 319
fuelleborni Alethe 242
fuertesi Hapalopsittaca 103
fuertesi Icterus 329
fugax Cuculus 106
fulgens Eugenes 130
fulgida Halcyon 141
fulgidus Onychognathus 349
fulgidus Pharomacrus 135
fulgidus Psittichas 93
Fulica 59
fulica Heliornis 59
fulicarius Phalaropus 68
fulicata Saxicoloides
fuliginiceps Leptasthenura 180
fuliginosa Antomyisa 276
fuliginosa Dendrocincla 176
fuliginosa Geospiza 310
fuliginosa Nectarinia 291
fuliginosa Nesofiegatta 10
fuliginosa Passerells 305
fuliginosa Petrochelidon 217
fuliginosa Rhipidura 277
fuliginosa Schizoeaca 180
fuliginosa Strepera 357
fuliginosa Tiaris 309
fuliginosa Zonotrichia 305
fuliginosus Aegithales 285
fuliginosus Calamanthus 270
fuliginosus Caloramphus 157
fuliginosus Haematopus 62
fuliginosus Larus 70
fuliginosus Oneostruthus 339
fuliginosus Otus 112
fuliginosus Pitylus 313
fuliginosus Rhyacornis 243
fuligiventer Phylloscopus 264
fuligula Aythya 25
fuligula Hirundo 217
Fulmarus 7
fulva Petrochelidon 217
fulva Pluvialis 63
fulvescens Illadopsis 254
fulvescens Phyllastrephus 227
fulvescens Picumnus 163
fulvescens Prunella 239
fulvescens Strix 117
fulvicapilla Cisticola 266
fulvicanda Phaeothlypis 324
fulviceps Atlapetes 311
fulvicollis Treron 83
fulvicrissa Euphonia 318
fulvifrons Empidonax 201
fulvifrons Paradoxornis 261
fulvigula Anas 23
fulvigula Timeliopsis 297
fulvipectus Rhynchocyclus 202
fulviventris Grallaria 193
fulviventris Myrmotherula 188
PAGE 30
fulviventris Phyllastrephus 228
fulviventris Turdus 251
fulvogularis Melacoptila 155
fulvus Gyps 30
fulvus Lario 315
fulvus Mulleripicus 168
fulvus Phaeton
fulvus Turdoides 256
fumicolor Ochthoeca 197
fumifrons Todirostrum 202
fumigatus Contopus 200
fumigatus Cypseloides 123
fumigatus Melitopes 301
fumigatus Myiotheretes 196
fumigatus Turdus 251
fumigatus Veniliornis 172
funebris Halcyon 141
funebris Laniarius 232
funebris Mulleripicus 168
funerea Drepanis 325
funerea Vidua 341
funereus Aegotius 117
funereus Calyptorhynchus 90
funereus Onyzoborus 309
funereus Parus 285
furcata Cranioleuca 181
furcata Micropanyptila 121
furcata Oceanodroma 10
furcata Thalurania 127
furcatus Anthus 220
furcatus Coratotriccus 202
furcatus Hemitriccus 202
furcifer Heliomester 133
Furnarius 180
fusca Allinia 239
fusca Aplonis 348
fusca Casiornis 199
fusca Cercomela 245
fusca Dendroica 322
fusca Diomedia 6
fusca Gerygone 270
fusca Iodopleura 209
fusca Malacoptila 155
fusca Melanitta 26
fusca Meliphaga 298
fusca Nectarinia 291
fusca Porzana 57
fuscans Lonchura 340
fuscata Padda 340
fuscata Pseudeos 88
fuscata Sterna 72
fuscater Turdus 252
fuscatus Cnemotriccus 201
fuscatus Margarops 239
fuscatus Phylloscopus 264
fuscescens Catharus 251
fuscescens Dendiopicos 172
fuscescens Phalacrocorax 12
fuscicapilla Zostorops 295
fuscicapillus Corvus 367
fuscicapillus Philemon 300
fuscicauda Habia 316
fuscicauda Ramphotrigon 202
fusciceps Thripophaga 182
fuscicollis Calidris (Enolia) 67
fuscicollis Phalacrocorax 12
fuscigularis Apalis 267
fuscipennis Dicrurus 355
fuscipennis Philydor 183
fuscirostris Talegalla 40
fuscocapillum Pellorneum 254
fuscocinereus Lipaugus 210
fuscocrissa Ortygospiza 339
fusconotus Niguita 337
fuscoolivaceus Atlapites 311
fuscorufa Rhipidura 277
fuscorufa Syanallaxis 181
fuscorufus Myiotheretes 196
fuscus Acrocephalus 352
fuscus Anabazenops 183
fuscus Artames 354
fuscus Cinclodes 179
fuscus Larus 70
fuscus Lepidocolaptes 178
fuscus Melanstrodilus 126
fuscus Melidectes 301
fuscus Picumnus 163
fuscus Pionus 103
fuscus Pipolo 310
fuscus Telidromas 195
fytchii Bambusicola 47

gabar Melierax 32
gabela Prionops 231
gabela Sheppardia 241
gabonensis Dendropicos 172
gabonensis Ortygospiza 339
gatonicus Anthreptes 290
gaimardi Phalacrocorax 12
gainardii Myiopagis 204
galactotes Cercotrichas 241
galactotes Cisticola 266
galapagoensis Buteo 35
galapagoensis Zenaida 79
galatea Tanysiptera 143
Galbalcyrhynchus 154
galbanus Garrulax 257
Galbula 154
galbula Galbula 154
galbula Icterus 328
galbula Ploceus 343
galeata Ducula 86
galeata Hyiagra 280
galeata Pipra 206
galeatus Basilornis 352
galeatus Clopterix 202
galeatus Dryocopus 169
galericulata Aix 25
galericulatus Platylophus 363
Galerida 216
galerita Cacatua 91
galeritus Anorrhinus 150
galgulus Loriculus 96
gatinieri Parophasma 260
Gallardoi Podiceps 5
Gallicolumba 81/82
Gallicrex 58
gallicus Circaetus 31
gallinacea Irediparra 62
Gallinago 66
gallingo Capella 66
Gallinula 56-58
Gallirallus 55-56
gallopavo Meleagris 52
Galloperdix 47
Gallus 50
gallus Gallus 50
gambagae Muscicapa 276
gambeli Parus 286
gambelii Lophortyx 44
gambensis Dryoscopus 231
gambensis Plectropterus 26
gambieri Halcyon 141
gampsonyx 28
Gampsorhynchus 259
garleppi Poospiza 307
garnotii Pelecanoides 10
Garritornis 254
Garrodia 10
garrula Orbalis 41
Garrulax 257
Garrulus 364
garrulus Bombycilla 235
garrulus Coracias 147
garrulus Lorius 88
garzetta Egretta 15
gaudichaud Dacelo 140
Gavia 5
gava Puffinus 8
gayaquilensis Phloeoceastes 169
gayi Atlagis 68
guyi Phrygilus 306
Gecinulus 168
geelvinkiana Micropsitta 92
geelvinkianum Dicaeum 288
genei Drymophila 189
genei Larus 70
genibarbis Myadestes 244
genibarbis Thryothorus 237
Gennaeus 49
gentilis Accipiter 32
Geobates 179
Geococcyx 109
Geocolaptes 164
geoffroyi Geoffroyus 92
geoffroyi Neomorphus 109
geoffroyi Schistes 133
Geoffroyus 92
Geomolia 247
Geopelia 78
Geopsittacus 95
georgiana Eopsaltria 272
georgiana Zonotrichia

georgianus Phalacrocorax 12
georgica Anas 23
georgicus Pelecanoides 10
Geositta 179
Geospiza 310
Geothlypis 323
Geotrygon 81
Geranoaetus 34
Geranospica 31
germanii Polyplectron 51
germani Collocalia 122
Geronticus 18
Gerygone 270
gibberifrons Anas 23
gibsoni Chlorostilbon 127

gierowii Euplectes 347
gigantea Fulica 59
gigantea Grallaria 194
gigantea Mellopitta 253
gigantea Pseudibis 18
giganteus Hirundapus 122giganteus Macronectes 7
gigas Collocalie 122
gigas Coua 110
gigas Elaenia 204
gigas Patagona 130
gigas Podilymbus 5
gilberti Kupeornis 260
gilberti Lioptilus 260
gilletti Mirafra 215
giloleusis Micrastur 38
gilviventris Xenicus 214
gilvus Mimus 238
gilvus Vireo 326
gingalensis Tockus 149
gingica Anborophila 47
ginginianus Acridotheres 352
githaginea Rhodopechys 334glabricollis Melanoptila 239
glacialis Fulmarus 7
glacialoides Fulmarus 7
gladiator Malaconotus 232
glandarius Clamator 106
glandarius Garrulus 364
Glareola 68
glareola Tringa 65
glauca Drylossopis 321
glaucesceus Larus 70
Glaucidium 115
glaucinus Myiophoneus 247
Glaucis 125
glaucocaerulea Passerina 313
glaucocolpa Thraupis 317
glaucoides Larus 70
glaucopis Thalurania 127
glaucopoides Eriocremis 131
glaucops Tyto 112
glaucurus Eurystomus 147
glaucus Anodorhynchus 98
glabulosa Crax 42
gloriosa Diglossa 321
gloriosissima Diglossa 321
Glossopsitta 89
glyceria Zodalia 132
Glycichaera 297
Glyphorhynchus 177
gnoma Glaucidium 115
Gnorimopsar 330
godeffroyi Halcyon 141
godeffroyi Monarcha 281
godifrida Claravis 80
godini Eriocremis 131
godlewski Anthus 220
godlewski Emberiza 303
godmani Euphonia 318
goeldii Myrmeciza 191
goeringi Brachygalba 154
goeringi Hemispingus 314
goertae Mesopicos 174
Goethalsia 128
goffixi Cacatua 91
goiavier Pycnonotus 226
goisagi Gorsachius 16
goisagi Nycticorax 16
golandi Ploceus 344
goldiei Trichoglossus 88
goldmani Grotrygon 81
Goldmania 128
goliath Ardea 14
goliath Centropus 111
goliath Ducula 86
gongonensis Passer 342
goodenorii Petroica 272
goodfellowi Ceyx 139
goodfellowi Lophozosterops 296
goodfellowi Regulus 268
goodfellow Rhinornyias 273
goodsoni Columba 76
gordoni Philemon 300
Gorsachius 15/16
goslingi Apalis 267
goudoti Lepidopyga 128
goudotii Chamaepetes 42
goughensis Rowettia 307
gouldi Euphonia 318
gouldi Zosterops 296
gouldiae Aethopyga 294
gouldiae Chloebia 340
gouldii Lophornis 127
gouldii Selenidera 161
gounellei Phaethornis 125
Goüra 82
goyderi Amytornis 269
graceannae Icterus 328
graciae Dendroica 332
gracilipes Zimmerius 204
gracilirostris Acrocephalus 263
gracilirostris Andropadus 226
gracilirostris Catharus 251
gracilirostris Chloropeta 263
gracilirostris Virco 326
gracilis Anas 23
gracilis Andropadus 226
gracilis Heterophasia 260
gracilis Meliphaga 298
gracilis Oceanites 10
gracilis Prinia 265
Gracula 352
graculina Certhia 399
graculina Strepera 357
graculus Pyrrhocorax 365
graduacauda Icterus 328
graeca Alectoris 45
Grafisia 349
Gallaria 193/94
grallaria Fregetta 10
Grallaricula 193
Grallina 356
gramineus Megalurus 262
gramineus Pooecetes 306
gramineus Tanygrathus 93
Graminicola 265
grammacus Chondestes 306
grammiceps Seicercus 264
grammiceps Stachyris 255
grammicus Celeus 166
grammicus Pseudoscops 117
granadensis Hemitriccus 202
granadensis Idioptilon 202
granadensis Myiozetetes 199
granadensis Picumnus 163
Granatellus 324
granatina Pitta 212
granatina Uraeginthus 338
Grandala 243
grandidieri Zoonavena 123
grandis Acridotheres 352
grandis Aplonis 348
grandis Bradypterus 262
grandis Hyphantornis 346
grandis Lonchura 340
grandis Motacilla 219
grandis Niltava 275
grandis Nyctibus 118
grandis Ploceus 344
grandis Rhabdornis 287
granti Phoeniculus 148
grantia Gecinulus 168
granulifrons Ptilinopus 84
grata Malia 260
graueri Bradypterus 262
graueri Coracina 221
graueri Pseudocalyptomena 176
Graueria 268
gravis Puffinus 8
Graydidasculus 103
grayi Ammomanes 216
grayi Hylocharis 128
grayi Melurus 269
grayi Turdus 252
grayi Zosterops 295
grayii Andeola 14
graysoni Mimodes 238
graysoni Turdus 252
graysonii Icterus 329
gregalis Eremomela 268
gregaria Chettusia 62
greyi Gallirallus 56
greyii Ptilinopus 84
grillii Centropus 111
grimwoodi Macronyx 219
grindiana Eupodatis 61
grisea Eremopterix 215
grisea Formicivora 189
grisea Myrmotherula 188
griseigena Podiceps 5
griscicapilla Lonchura 340
griseicapillus Sittasomus 177
grammicus Celeus 166
grammicus Pseudoscops 117
granadensis Hemitriccus 202
granadensis Idioptilon 202
granadensis Myiozetetes 199
granadensis Picumnus 163
Granatellus 324
granatina Pitta 212
granatina Uraeginthus 338
Grandala 243
grandidieri Zoonavena 123
grandis Acridotheres 352
grandis Aplonis 348
grandis Bradypterus 262
grandis Hyphantornis 346
grandis Lonchura 340
grandis Motacilla 219
grandis Niltava 275
grandis Nyctibus 118
grandis Ploceus 344
grandis Rhabdornis 287
granti Phoeniculus 148
grantia Gecinulus 168
granulifrons Ptilinopus 84
grata Malia 260
graueri Bradypterus 262
graueri Coracina 221
graueri Pseudocalyptomena 176
Graueria 268
gravis Puffinus 8
Graydidasculus 103
grayi Ammomanes 216
grayi Hylocharis 128
grayi Malurus 269
grayi Turdus 252
grayi Zosterops 295
grayii Ardeola 14
graysoni Mimodes 238
graysoni Turdus 252
graysonii Icterus 329
gregalis Eremomela 268
gregaria Chettusia 62
greyi Gallirallus 56
greyii Ptilinopus 84
grillii Centropus 111
grimwoodi Macronyx 219
grindiana Eupodatis 61
grisea Eremopterix 215
grisea Formicivora 189
grisea Myrmotherula 188
griseigena Podiceps 5
griscicapilla Lonchura 340
grtselcapullus Slttasomus 177
griseicauda Treton 83
griseiceps Accipiter 33
griseiceps Apalis 267
griseiceps Basileuterus 324
griseiceps Myrmeciza 191
griseiceps Pachycephala 283
griseiceps Phyllomyias 204
griseiceps Piprites 207
griseiceps Serpophaga 203
griseigula Timeliopsis 297
griseigularis Muscicapa 276
griseonota Pachycephala 282
griseonucha Grallaria 194
griseopyga Hirundo 217
griseostriatus Francolinus 46
griserotincta Zosterops 295
griseovirescens Zosterops 296
griseus Campylorhynchus 236
griseus Limnodromus 66
griseus Nyctibius 118
griseus Passer 342
griseus Puffinus 8
griseus Thryothorus 237
griseus Tockus 149
griseus Virco 326
grizimeki Threnetes 125
grossus Pitylus 313
grosvenori Cichlornis 268
Grus 54
grus Grus 54
grylle Cepphus 74
gryphus Vultur 27
Guadalcanaria 298
guainumbi Polytmus 128

guajana Pitta 212
gualaquizae Phylloscantes 203
guarana Aramus 54
guarayanus Thryothorus 237
guarouba Aratinga 100
guatemalae Otus 113
guatemalensis Phloeocaestes 169
guatemalensis Sclerurus 184
guatimalensis Gallaria 194
guatimozinus Psarocolius 327
gubernator Lanius 234
Gubernatrix 312
Gubernetes 197
guerinii Oxypogon 132
guianensis Morphnus 36
guianensis Polioptila 261
guimeti Klais 126
guinea Columba 76
guineensis Parus 285
Guira 109
guira Guira 109
guira Hemithraupis 315
Guiraca 313
guirahuro Pseudoleistes 330
guisei Ptiloprora 300
gujanensis Cyclarhis 326
guganensis Odontophorus 44
gujanensis Synallaxis 181
gularis Accipiter 32
gularis Aspatha 144
gularis Campylonhynchus 236
gularis Cuculus 106
gularis Egretta 15
gularis Eurystomus 147
gularis Francolinus 46
gularis Garrulex 257
gularis Halcyon 142
gularis Heliodoxa 130
gularis Icterus 328
gularis Macronous 256
gularis Melithreptus 299
gularis Merops 145
gularis Monticola 247
gularis Myrmotherula 188
gularis Nicator 228
gularis Paradoxornis 261
gularis Rhinomyias 273
gularis Serinus 332
gularis Synallaxis 181
gularis Tephrodornis 225
gularis Turdoides 256
gularis Yuhina 260
gulgula Alauda 216
gulielmi Poicephalus 96
gulielmitertii Opopsitta 92
gundlachi Accipiter 33
gundlachii Chordeiles 119
gundlachii Mimus 238
gundlachii Vireo 326
gunningi Sheppardia 241
gurneyi Aquila 36
gurneyi Mimizuku 113
gurneyi Pitta 212
gurneyi Pomerops 302
gurneyi Zoothera 249*gustavi Anthus* 220
gustavi Brotogeris 102
guttata Chlamydera 358
guttata Cichladusa 242
guttata Dendrocygna 20
guttata Emblema 339
guttata Myrmotherula 188
guttata Ortalis 41
guttata Poephila 339
guttata Tangara 319
guttata Zoothera 249
guttaticollis Paradoxornis 261
guttatum Toxostoma 238
guttatus Catharus 251
guttatus Eurostopodus 119
guttatus Hypoedaleus 185
guttatus Ixonotus 227
guttatus Monarcha 281
guttatus Odontophorus 44
guttatus Psiloramphus 195
guttatus Tinamus 2
guttatus Xiphorhynchus 178
Guttera 52
guttifer Accipiter 33
guttifer Caprimulgus 120
guttifer Picumnus 163
guttifer Pseudototanus 65
guttulata Syndactyla 183
guttuligera Premnornia Grallaria 194
guttulus Monarcha 281
gutturalis Anthus 220
gutturalis Atlapetes 311
gutturalis Cinclocerthia 239
gutturalis Corapipo 206
gutturalis Crateroscelis 271
gutturalis Habia 316
gutturalis Irania 242
gutturalis Myronotherula 188
gutturalis Neocichla 350
gutturalis Oreoica 282
gutturalis Pseudoseisura 183
gutturalis Pterocles 75
gutturalis Saxicola 245
gutturalis Sericornis 271
gutturalis Vermivora 322
gutturata Cranioleuca 181
guy Phaethornis 125
Gygio 73
Gymnobucco 158
gymnocephala Pityriasis 234
gymnocephalus Picathartes 260
Gymnochichla 191
Gymnocrex 56
Gymnoderus 211
Gymnoglaux 113
Gymnomystax 329
Gymnomyza 301
Gymnophaps 87
Gymnopithys 192
Gymnorhina 356
Gymnorhinus 365
Gymnostinops 327
Gypaetus 30
Gypohierax 30
Gypopsitta 103
Gyps 30
gyrola Tangara 319

haestii Apteryx 1
habessinica Nectarinia 291
Habia 316
Habropteryx 56
Habroptila 56
haemacephala Megalaima 157
haemastica Limosa 65
haematina Spermophaga 337
Haematoderus 211
haematodes Trichoglossus 88
haematogaster Phloeoceastes 169
haematogaster Psephotus 94
haematonota Myrmotherula 188
haematonotus Psephotus 94
Haematopus 62
haematopus Himantornis 56
haematopygus Aulacorhynchus 160
Haematortyx 47
Haematospiza 336
haematotis Pionopsitta 102
haematuropygia Cacatua 91
haemorrhous Cacicus 328
haesitata Cisticola 266
hagedash Bostrychia 18
hainana Niltava 275
PAGE 34
hainanus Phylloscopus 264
haitiensis Lophura 49
Halcyon 140-142
Haliacetus 29
haliactus Pandion 38
Haliastur 29
hallae Andropadus 226
halli Macronectes 7
halli Pomatostomus 254
Halobaena 7
Halocyptena 10
hamatus Rostrhamus 28
hamertoni Alaemon 216
hamiltoni Gennaeus 49
Hamirostia 29
hammondi Empidonax 201
handleyi Amozilia 129
Hapalopsittaca 103
Hapaloptila 155
haplochrous Accipiter 33
haplochrous Turdus 252
haplonota Crallaria 194
Haplophoedia 131
Haplospiza 307
hardwickii Capella 66
hardwickii Chloropsis 230
hardwickii Dendrocopus 173
hardyi Glaucidium 114
harmani Grossoptilon 48
harmonica Colluricincla 284
Harpactes 137
Harpagus 28
Harpia 36
Harpiprion 18
Harpyhaliactus 34
harpyga Harpia 36
Harpyopsis 36
harrisi Phalacrocosax 12
harrisii Aegotius 117
harterti Acestrura 134
harterti Batrachostomus 118
harterti Cameroptera 267
harterti Ficedula 274
harterti Phlogophilus 129
harterti Schizoeaca 180
harterti Upucerthia 179
hartlaubi Cereotrichus 241
hartlaubi Euplectes 347
hartlaubi Enancolinus 46
hartlaubi Otus 113
hartlaubi Tauraco 105
hartlaubi Tockus 149
hartlaubi Larus 71
hartlaubi Lissotis 61
hartlaubi Nectarinia 291
hartlaubi Pteronetta 25
hartlaubi Turdoides 256
harwoodi Francolinus 46
hasitata Pterodroma 9
hastata Aquila 36
hattamensis Pachycephalopsis 273
hauxwelli Myrmotherula 188
hauxwelli Turdus 251
hawaiiensis Convus 367
hebetior Myiagra 280
hecki Poephila 339
heermanni Larus 70
heilprini Cyanocorax 365
heinei Tangara 319
heinei Zoothera 248
heinrichi Cacomantis 106
heinrichi Cossypha 241
heinrichi Geomalia 247
Heinrichia 240
heinrothi Puffinus 8
Heleia 296
helinae Lalypte 134
helenae Hypothymis 280
helenae Paphosia 127
helinae Parotia 361
heliaca Aquila 36
Heliactin 133
Heliangelus 131
helianthea Coeligena 131
heliantheo Culicapa 272
helias Euiypyga 59
Helicolestes 28
heliobates Camarhynchus 310
Heliobletus 184
heliodor Acestrura 134
Heliodoxa 130
Heliomaster 133
Heliopais 59
heliosylus Zonerodius 16
Heliothryx 133
helleri Schizoeaca 180
helleri Turdus 249
hellmayri Anthus 220
hellmayri Cranioleuca 181
hellmayri Mecocerculus 203
hellmayri Synallaxis 181
Helmitheros 323
heloisa Atthis 134
hemichrysus Myiodynastes 199
Hemicircus 74
Hemignathus 325
hemilasius Butes 35
hemileucurus Campylopterus 126
hemileucuras Phlogophilus 129
hemileucus Lampornis 129
hemileucus Myrmochanes

190
hemimelaena Myrmeciza 191
Hemiparra 62
Hemiphaga 87
Hemipodius 53
Hemiprocne 122
Hemipus 225
Hemispingus 314
Hemitesia 268
Hemithraupis 315
Hemitriccus 202
hemixautha Microeca 272
hemprichii Larus 70
hemprichii Tockus 149
hendersoni Podoces 365
henicogrammus Accipiter 33
Henicopernis 28
Henicophaps 79
Henicorhina 237
henricae Cranioleuca 181
henrici Ficedula 274
henrici Garrulax 257
henrici Uragus 334
henricii Megalaima 157
henslowii Ammodramus 305
henstii Accipiter 32
heraldica Pterodroma 9
herberti Phylloscopus 264
herberti Stachyris 255
herbicola Emberizoides 308
hercules Alcedo 139
heroro Namibornis 241
herioti Niltava 275
herminieri Melanerpes 171
herodias Andea 14
Herpetotheres 38
Herpsilochmus 189
herrani Chalcostigma 132
Hesperiphona 336
Heteralocha 356
Heterocercus 207
heteroclitus Geoffroyus 92
heterolaemus Orthotomus 265
Heteromirafra 215
Heteromunia 340
PAGE 35
Heteromyias 272
Heteronetta 26
Heterophasia 260
heterophrys Cisticola 266
heteropogon Chalcostigma 132
Heteroscelus 65
Heterospingus 316
Heterospizias 34
hetoura Asthenes 182
heteruras Tanygnathus 93
heudi Paradoxornis 261
heuglini Cossypha 241
heuglini Oenanthe 246
heuglini Ploceus 344
heuglinii Neotis 60
heyi Ammoperdix 45
hiaticula Charadrius 63
hiternans Saxicola 245
Hieraaetus 37
Hierophasis 49
hildebrandti Francolinus 46
hildebrandti Spreo 350
himalayana Certhia 287
himalayana Prunella 239
himalayana Psittacula 97
himalayensis Dendrocopos 173
himalayensis Gyps 30
himalayensis Sitta 286
himalayensis Tetraogallus 45
Himantopus 67
himantopus Himantopus 67
himantopus Micropalama 67
Himantornis 56
Himatione 3265
hindei Turdoides 256
hindwoodi Meliphaga 298
Hippolais 263
hirstum Tricholaema 158
Hirundapus 122
hirundinacea Collocalia 122
hirundinacea Cypsnagra 314
hirundinacea Euphonia 318
hirundinacea Sterna 72
hirundinaceum Dicaeum 289
hirundinaceus Caprimalgus 121
hirundinaceus Hemipus 225
Hirundinca 201
hirundineus Merops 145
Hirundo 217/218
hirundo Sterna 72
hispanica Oenanthe 246
hispaniolensis Passer 342
hispaniolensis Poospiza 308
hispidus Phaethornis 125
histrio Eos 88
Histronicus 26
histrionicus Histrionicus 26
Histriophaps 79
histrionica Histriophaps 79
Histurgaps 342
hoazin Opisthocomus 52
hodgei Dnyocopus 169
hodgsoni Anthus 220
hodgsoni Batrachostomus 118
hodgsoni Niltava 275
hodgsoni Phoenicurus 243
hodgsoni Tickellia 264
hodgsoniae Perdix 46
hodgsonii Columba 76
hodgsonii Ficedula 274
hodgsonii Prinia 265
Hodgsonius 243
hoedtii Gallicolumba 81
hoematotis Pyrrhura 101
hoeschi Anthus 220
hoevelli Niltava 275
hoffmanni Pyrrhura 101
hoffmannii Melanerpes 170
hoffmannsi Dendrocolaptes 177
hoffmannsii Rhegnatorhina 192
holerythra Rhytipterna 199
hollandicus Nymphicus 91
holachlora Anatinga 100
holochlora Chloropipo 207
holochlorus Enythrocercus 279
holomelaena Psalidoprocne 217
holopolia Coracina 222
holosericea Drepanoptila 85
holosericeus Amblyramphus 330
holosericeus Cacicus 328
holosericeus Sericotes 126
holospilus Spilornis 31
holostictus Thripadectes 184
holsti Parus 286
hombroni Halcyon 141
homeyeri Pachycephala 282
homochroa Catamenia 309
homochroa Dendrocincla 176
homochroa Oceonodroma 10
homochrous Pachyramphus 210
hoogerwerfi Lophura 49
hopkei Carpodectes 209
Hoplopterus 62/63
Hoploxypterus 63
hordeaceus Euplectes 347
Horizorhinus 260
hornbyi Oceanodroma 10
hornemanni Acanthos 334
horsfieldi Zoothera 248
horsfieldii Myiophoneus 247
horsfieldii Pomatorhinus 254
hortensis Sylvia 263
hortulana Emberiza 303
hortulorum Turdies 249
horus Apus 124
hosii Calyptomena 176
hosii Oriolus 354
hottentota Anas 24
hottentotta Turnix 53
hottentottus Dicrurus 355
Houbaropsis 61
Houppifer 49
housei Amytornis 269
hova Mirafra 215
hovarum Zosterops 296
huallagae Aulacorhynchus 160
hudsoni Asthenes 182
hudsoni Entotriccus 197
hudsonicus Parus 286
huetii Touit 102
huhula Ciccada 116
humbloti Andea 14
humbloti Nectarinia 291
Humblotia 276
humboldti Spheniscus 4
humei Sphenocichla 255
humeralis Agelaius 3298
humeralis Aimophila 306
humeralis Ammodramus 305
humeralis Caryothraustes 312
humeralis Cossypha 241
humeralis Diglossa 321
humeralis Geopelia 78
humeralis Myospiza 305
humeralis Terenura 189
humiae Syrmaticus 50
humicola Asthenes 182
humilis 182
humilis Eupodotis 61
humilis Pseudopodoces 365
humilis Sericornis 271
humilis Yuhina 260
hunsteini Lonchura 340

hunteri Cisticola 266
hunteri Nectarinia 291
huttoni Ptilinopus 84
huttoni Puffinis 8
huttoni Vireo 326
hyacinthina Niltava 275
hyacinthinus Andorhynchus 98
hybrida Chlidonias 72
hybrida Chloephaga 21
hybrida Sterna 72
Hydrobates 10
hydrocharis Tanysiptera 143
hydrocorax Buceros 153
Hydrophasianus 62
Hydropsalis 119
hyemalis Clangula 26
hyemalis Junco 305
Hylacola 270
Hylexetastes 177
Hylia 268
Hyliota 268
hylobius Philydor 183
Hylocharis 128
Hylocichla 251
Hylocitrea 282
Hylocryptus 184
Hyloctistes 183
Hylomanes 144
Hylonympha 130
hylophila Strix 117
Hylophylus 326
Hylophylax 193
Hylorchilus 236
Hymenolaimus 24
Hymenops 197
hyogastra Ptilinopus 84
Hypargos 337
hyperboreus Anser 21
hyperboreus Larus 70
hyperboreus Plectophenax 304
Hypergenus 267
hypermetra Mirafre 215
hyperythra Arborophila 47
hyperythra Brachypteryx 240
hyperythra Dumetia 256
hyperythra Erythrura 340
hyperythra Ficedula 274
hyperythra Myrmeciza 191
hyperythra Pachycephala 282
hyperythra Rhipidura 277
hyperythrus Campylopterus 126
hyperythrus Dendrocopos 173
hyperythrus Erithacus 240
hyperythrus Odontophorus 44
Hyphantornis 344
Hypnelus 155
Hypochera 341
hypocherina Vidua 341
hypochlora Theluriana 127
hypochloris Phyllastrephus 227
hypochondria Poospiza 308

hypochondriacus Siptornopsis 182
hypochroma Sporophila 309
hypochryseus Vireo 326
Hypocnemis 190
Hypocnemoides 190
Hypocolius 235
Hypocryptadius 296
Hypoedaleus 185
hypoglauca Andigena 161
Hypogramma 290
hypogrammica Pytilia 337
hypogrammica Stachyris 255
hypogrammicum Hypogramma 290
hypoinochrous Lorius 88
hypolais Zosterops 295
hypoleuca Cissa 363
hypoleuca Ficedula 274
hypoleuca Grallaria 194
hypoleuca Gymnorhina 356
hypoleuca Poecilodryas 272
hypoleuca Pterodroma 9
hypoleuca Serpophage 203
hypoleucos Actitis 65
hypoleucos Falco 39
hypoleucos Pomatorhinus 254
hypoleucos Tringa 65
hypoleucum Dicaeum 289
hypoleucus Basileuterus 324
hypoleucus Brachyramphus 74
hypoleucus Capito 156
hypoleucus Melanotis 238
hypoleucus Sphecotheres 354
hypoleucus Turdoides 256
hypopolins Melanerpes 354
hypopyrra Laniocera 199
hypopyrrha Streptopelia 78
Hypopyrhus 330
Hypositta 235
hypospodia Synallaxis 181
hypospodium Todirostrum 202
hyposticuts Serinus 332
hypostictus Taphrospilus 128
Hypothymis 280
hypoxantha Gerygone 270
hypoxantha Hypochemis 190
hypoxantha Neodrepanis 213
hypoxantha Pachycephala 282
hypoxantha Pyrrhura 101
hypoxantha Rhipidura 277
hypoxantha Sporophila 309
hypoxantha Zosterops 295
hypoxanthus Hylophilus 326
hypoxanthus Plocues 344
Hypsipetes 229
hyrcanus Parus 285

iagoensis Passer 342
ianthimogaster Uraeginthus 338
ibadanensis Malimbus 346
Ibidonhyncha 67
Ibis 17
ibis Bubulcus 15
ibis Egretta 15
ibis Mycteria 17
ichthyaetus Ichthyophaga 29
ichthyaetus Larus 70
Ichthyophaga 29
Icteria 324
icterina Hippolais 263
icterinus Phyllastrephus 228
icterioides Coccothriaustes 336
icterocephala Tangara 319
icterocephalus Agelaius 329
icteronotus Ramphocelus 317
icterophrys Satrapa 198
icteropygialis Enemomela 268
icterorhynchus Francolinus 46
icterorhynchus Otus 113
icterotis Ognorhynchus 100
icterotis Platycercus 94
Icterus 328/29
icterus Icterus 328
Icthyophaga 29
Ictinaetus 36
PAGE 37
Ictinia 28
idae Andeola 14
idaliae Phaethornis 125
Idiopsar 307
Idiptilon 202
Ifita 253
igata Gerygone 270
igneiventris Nectarinia 293
igneus Pericrocotus 225
ignicapillus Regulus 286
ignicauda Aethopyga 294
igniferum Dicaecum 289
ignipectus Dicaeum 289
ignita Lophura 49
igniventris Anisogathus 318
ignobilis Thripadectes 184
ignobilis Turdus 252
ignotincta Miula 259
ignotus Basilenterus 324
iheringi Formicivora 189
iheringi Myrmotherula 188
iherminieri Puffinus 8
ijimae Phylloscopus 264
iliaca Passerina 305
iliaca Zonotrichia 305
iliacus Turdis 250
Ilicura 206
iliophum Oedistorna 297
Illadopsis 254
imberbe Camptostoma 204
imberbis Anomalospiza 347
imerinus Pseudocossyphus 2476
imitans Euphoria 318
imitator Accipiter 33
immaculata Pnoepysia 255
immaculata Prunella 239
immaculatus Celeus 166
immaculatus Enicurus 243
immaculatus Myrmeciza 191
immer Gavia 5
immunda Rhytipterna 199
immutatilis Diomedia 6
imparatus Convus 366
impejanus Lophophorus 48
impennis Pinguinus 74
imperatrix Heliodoxa 130
imperialis Amazona 104
imperialis Andea 14
imperialis Campephilus 175
imperialis Gallinago 66
imperialis Hierophasis 49
impetuani Emberiza 303
implicata Pachyaphala 282
importunus Andropadus 226
importunus Pycnonotus 226
improbus Zimmerius 204
imthurini Macroagelaius 330
inca Columbina 80
inca Larosterna 73
inca Ramphastos 162
Incana 265
incana Drymocichla 267
incana Incana 265
incana Lichmera 297
incanus Heteroscelus 65
Incaspiza 307
incerta Amalocichla 250
incerta Coracina 223
incerta Pterodroma 9
incerta Zosterops 295
incertus Pitohui 284
incognita Megalaima 157
inda Chloroceryle 138
indica Chalcophaps 79
indica Sypheotides 61
Indicator 159
indicator Baeopogon 227
indicator Indicator 159
indicus Anser 21
indicus Butastur 34
indicus Caprimulgus 121
indicus Colius 135
indicus Dendronanthus 219
indicus Erithacus 240
indicus Gyps 30
indicus Hypsipetes 229
indicus Lobivanellus 62
indicus Metopidius 62
indicus Pterocles 75
indigo Muscicapa 276
indigotica Diglossipis 321
indigoticus Scytalopus 195
indistincta Lichmera 297
indus Haliastur 29
inepta Megacrex 56
inerme Ornithion 205
inexpectata Collocalia 122
inexpectata Guadalcanaria 298
inexpectata Meliphaga 298
inexpectata Pterodroma 9
inexpectata Torreornis 306
inexpectatus Chlorostilbon 127
inexpectatus Tyto 112
Inezia 203
infaustus Cacomantis 106
infaustus Perisoreus 364
infelix Monarcha 281
infuscata Collocalia 122
infuscata Hemicopernis 28
infuscata Muscicapa 276
infuscata Synallaxis 181
infuscatus Automolus 184
infuscatus Bradornis 273
infuscatus Melaenornis 273
infuscatus Phimosus 18
infuscatus Turdus 252
ingens Otus 113
ingoufi Tinamotis 3
innominata Collocalia 122
innominatus Picumnus 163
innotata Aythya 25
inopinatus Chalcurus 51
inornata Acanthiza 270
inonnata Catamenia 309
inornata Columba 76
inornata Gerygone 270
inornata Inezia 203
inornata Pachycephala 282
inornata Pinaroloxias 310
inornata Prinia 265
inornata Tangara 319
inornata Thlypopsis 315
inornata Zosterops 295
inornatus Amblyornio 357
inornatus Caprimulgus 120
inornatus Chlorspingus 314
inornatus Hemitriccus 202
inornatus Houppiter 49
inornatus Idioptilon 202
inornatus Myiopholus 201
inornatus Myiozetetes 199
inornatus Parus 286
inornatus Philemon 300
inornatus Phylloscopus 264
inornatus Rhabdornis 287
inquieta Collocalia 122
inquieta Myiagra 280
inquieta Scotocerca 265
inquisitor Tityza 210
insciptus Pteroglossus 161
insignibarbis Lophornis 127
insignis Aegotheles 118
insignis Ardea 14
insignis Artamus 354
PAGE 38
insignis Clytomyias 269
insignis Habropteryx 56
insignis Panterpe 128
insignis Ploceus 344
insignis Polihierax 38
insignis Prodotiseus 159
insignis Rhinomyias 273
insignis Saxicola 245
insignis Thamnophilus 186
insolitus Ptilinopus 84
insulana Cossypha 241
insularis aplonis 348

insularis Arseo 281
insularis Gerygone 270
insularis Junco 305
insularis Myiophoneus 247
insularis Otus 113
insularis Passer 342
insularis Ptilinopus 84
insularis Sarothrura 57
insulata Sporophila 309
intercadens Ptilnornis 359
interjecta Vidua 341
intermedia Egretta 15
intermedia Pipreola 209
intermedia Psittacula 97
intermedia Sporophila 309
intermedius Plocens 344
internigrans Perisoreus 364
interpres Anenaria 66
interpres Zoothera 247
interstes Micrastur 38
involucris Ixohychus 16
Iodopleura 209
Iole 229
iouschistos Aegithalos 285
iozonus Ptilinopus 84
iphis Pomarea 273
iracunda Metallura 132
Iramia 242
iredalei Acanthiza 270
Irediparra 62
Irena 230
ireneae Otus 113
iriditorques Columba 77
Iridophanes 320
Iridosornis 318
iris Coeligena 131
iris Lamprotornis 350
iris Pipra 206
iris Pitta 212
iris Trichoglossus 88
irrorata Diomedia 6
irupero Xolmis 196
isaacsonii Eniscnemis 131
isabella Glareola 68
isabella Stiltia 68
isabellae Cossypha 241
isabellae Iodopleura 209
isabellae Oniolus 353
isabellina Amaurornis 58
isabillina Geositta 179
isabellina Oenanthe 245
isabellina Sylvietta 268
isabillinus Calamanthus 270
isidorei Garritornis 254
isidorei Pipra 206
isidoni Oroactus 37
islandica Acanthis 334
islandica Bucephola 26
Ispidina 139
isura Lophoictinia 29
italiae Passer 342
Ithaginis 48
itombwensis Muscicapa 276
ituriensis Batis 278
Ixobrychus 16
ixoides Pycnopygius 299
Ixonotus 227
Ixos 229

Jabiru 17
Jabouilleia 254
Jacamaralcyon 154
Jacamerops 154
Jacana 62
Jacana Jacana 62
jacarina Volatinia 308
jacksoni Apalis 267
jacksoni Cryptospiza 337
jacksoni Euplectco 347
jacksoni Francolinus 46
jacksoni Ploceus 344
jacksoni Tockus 149
jacobinus Clamator 106
jacquacu Penelope 41
jacquinoti Ninox 116
jacucaca Penelope 41
jacula Heliodoxa 130
jacutinga (Penelope) Aburria 42
jamaica Euphonia 318
jamaicensis Buteo 25
jamaicensis Corvus 366
jamaicensis Laterallus 57
jamaicensis Leptotila 80
jamaicensis Nyctibius 118
jamaicensis Oxyura 26
jamaicensis Turdas 252
jambu Ptilinopus 84
jamesi Phoenicoparrus 19
jamesi Tchagra 231
jamesoni Chubbia 66
jamesoni Platysteira 278
jandaya Aratinga 100
jankowskii Emberiza 303
janthina Columba 76
japonensis Grus 54
japonica Alanda 216
japonica Bombycilla 235
japonica Coturnix 47
japonica Zosterops 295
japonicus Garrulus 364
jardineii Turdoides 256
jardini Boissonneaua 131
jardini Cracticus 357
jardinii Glaucidium 115
javanense Dinopium 168
javanica Arborophila 47
javanica Dendrocygna 20
javanica Hirundo 217
javanica Lophozosterops 296
javanica Mirafra 215
javanica Rhipidura 277
javanicus Acridotheres 352
javanicus Charedrius 63
javanicus Eurylaimus 176
javanicus Leptoptilos 17
javanicus Phoenicophaes 108
javensis Batrachostomus 118
javensis Coracina 222
javensis Dryocopus 169
javensis Megalaima 157
jebelmarrae Lanius 233
jefferyi Chlamydochaera 224
jefferyi Pithecophaga 36
jelskii Iridosornis 318
jelskii silvicultrix 196
jelskii Upucerthia 179
jerdoni Aviceda 28
jerdoni Garrulex 257
jerdoni Saxicola 245
jobiensis Gallicolumba 81
jobiensis Manucodia 359
jobiensis Pitohui 284
jobiensis Talegalla 40
jocosus Camplorhnchus 236
jocosus Pycnonotus 226
johannae Doryfera 125
johannae Nectarinia 292
johannae Prionochilus 288
johannae Tangara 319
johannis Acanthis 333
johannis Hemitriccus 202
johannis Idioptilon 202
johannis Warsanglia 333
johnstoni Nectarinia 292
johnstoni Tauraco 105
johnstoniae Erithacus 240
johnstoniae Trichoglossus 88
jonquillaceus Aprosmictus 93
josefinae Charmosyna 89
josefinae Microcochlearius 202
jourdanii Chaetocercus 134
jouyi Columba 76
jubata Chenonetta 25
jubata Neochen 22
jubatus Rhynochetos 59
Jubula 113
jucunda Pipreola 209
jugger Falco 39
jugularis Brotogeris 102
jugularis Eulampsi 126
jugularis Meiglyptos 168
jugularis Myzomela 297
jugalaris Nectarinia 292
juliae Arachnothera 294
julianae Monarche 281
julie Damophila 128
julius Nothocercus 2
jumana Celeus 166
juncidis Cisticola 266
Junco 305
juninensis Muscisaxicola 196
junoniae Columba 76
Jynx 163

kaboboensis Apalis 267
kaempteri Hemitriccus 202
kaempteri Idioptilon 202
kaestneri Grallaria 193
Kakamega 254
kakamegae Andropadus 226
kalinowskii Nothoprocta 3
Kalochelidon 217
kamtschatschensis Larus 69
kandti Estrulda 338
karamojac Apalis 267
kasumba Harpactes 137
katangae Ploceus 345
katherina Acanthiza 270
kaupi Anses 281
Kaupifalco 34
kawalli Amazona 104
keartiandi Meliphaga 298
keayi Gallicolumba 81
keiensio Micropsitta 92
krlaarti Lonchura 340
kelleyi Macronous 256
kempi Macrosphenus 268
kennicottii Otus 112
Kenopia 255
kenricki Poeoptera 349
keraudrenii Phonygammus 359
kerearako Acrocephelus 263
keri Sericornis 271
kerriae Crypturellus 2
kessleri Turdus 250
Ketupa 114
ketupa Ketupa 114
kibalensis Zoothera 249
kieneri Melozone 310
kienerii Hieraaetus 37
kikuyuensis Zosterop 296
kilimensiis Estrilda 338
kilimensis Nectarinia 292
kinabuluensis Spilornis 31
kingi Acrocephalus 263
kingi Agalaiocercus 132
kioloides Mentocrex 56
kirhocephalus Pitohui 284
kirkil Veniliornis 172
kirtlandii Dendroica 322
kisserensis Philemon 300
kisuki Dendrocopus 173
klaas Chrysococcyx 107
klagesi Myrmotherula 188
Klais 126
kleinschmiddti Enythrura 339
klossi Spiloznis 31
Knipolegus 197
knudseni Himautopus 67
kochi Pitta 212
koeniswaldiana Pulsatrix 115
koepckeae Cacieus 328
koepckeae Otus 113
koepckeae Phaethornis 125
koliensis Serinus 332
kollari Poecilurus 181
kornadori Erithacus 240
kona Loxioides 325
kori choniotis 60
koslowi Babax 257
koslowi Emberiza 303
koslowi Prunella 239
kowaldi Ifrita 253
knameri Psittacula 97
knetschmeri Macrosphenus 268
kreyenborgi Falco 39
kriiperi Sitta 286
kubaryi Corvus 367
kubaryi Gallicolumba 82
kubargi Rhipidura 277
kuehni Myzomela 297
kuckni Zosterops 295
kuhli Leucopternis 34
kuhlii Vini 89
kulambangrae Zosterops 295
kumlieni Larus 70
kupeensio Telephorus 232
kupeornis 260

labredorides Tangara 319
labradonius Camptonhynchus 26
Lacedo 139
PAGE 40
lacernulata Ducula 86
lacernulata lelucopternis 34
lacertosa Woodfordia 296
lachrymosa Euthlypis 324
lachrymosus Xiphorhynchus 178
lacrymosum Tricholaema 158
lacrymosus Anisognathus 318

lactea Amozilia 129
lactea Glereola 68
lactea Polioptila 261
lacteus Bubo 114
laemosticta Myrmeciza 191
lacta Cercomacra 190
lacta Incaspiza 307
lactior Melithreptus 299
lactissima Chlorocichla 227
laetus Phylloscopus 264
lafargei Myzonela 297
lafayetii Gallus 50
Lafresnaya 130
lafresnayarus Tridiolimnes 55
lafresnayei Aegintha 230
lafresnayi Lafresnaya 130
lafresnayi Picumnus 163
lafresnayii Diglossa 321
lafresnayii Merops 145
lagdeni Malaconotus 232
Lagonosticta 338
Lagopus 43
lagopus Buteo 35
lagopus Lagopus 43
lagrandieri Megalaima 157
lais Cisticola 266
Lalage 224
lalandi Stephanoxis 126
lamberti Malurus 269
lamelligerus Anastomus 17
lamellipennis Xipholena 208
laminirostric Andigena 161
Lampornis 129
Lampribis 18
Lamprolaima 130
Lamprolia 268
Lampropsar 330
Lamprospiza 314
Lamprotornis 350
lanaiensis Myadestes 244
lanceolata Chiroxiphia 206
lanceolata Locustella 262
lanceolata Micromonacha 155
lanceolata Plectorhyncha 302
lanceolata Rhinocrypta 195
lanceolatus Babax 257
lanceolatus Garrulus 364
lanceolatus Spizaetos 37
landanae Lagonosticta 338
langbianis Crocias 260
langsdorff Popelairia 127
languida Hippolais 263
Laniarius 232
laniirostris Euphmia 318
Laniisoma 208
Lanio 315
Laniocera 199
lanioides Lipaugus 210
lanioides Pachycephala 282
Lanioturdus 231
Lanius 233/34
lausbergei Pericrocotus 225
lansbergi Coccyzus 107
lanyioni Phylloscartes 203
laperouse Megapodius 40
lapponica Limosa 65
lapponicus Calcarius 304
largipennis Campylopterus 126
Larosterna 72
Larus 69/70/71
larvata Aplopelia 78
larvata Coracina 222
larvata Lagonosticta 338
larvata Tangera 319
larvaticola Vidua 341
larvatus Oriolus 353
latebricola Scytalopus 195
lateralis Cisticola 266
lateralis Poospiza 308
lateralis Zosterops 296
laterallus 57
laterostrip Calyptonhynchus 90
lathami Alectura 40
lathami Calyptorhynchus 90
lathami Francolinus 46
lathami Melophus 303
Lathamus 95
Lathotriccus 201
laticincta Platysteira 278
latifrons Microhies 330
lembeyei Polioptial 2651
lemosi Cypseloides 123
lempiji Otus 112
lemprieri Niltava 275
Lemurestes 340
lendu Muscicapa 276
lentiginosus Botaurus 16
Leonardina 254
leoninus Macrosphenus 268
leontica Prinia 265
lepe Cisticola 266
lepidocolaptes 178
lepidogrammus 108
PAGE 41
lepidopyga 128
lepidus Ceyx 139
lepidus Hypergerus 267
Leptasthenura 180
Leptodon 28
leptogrammica Strix 117
Leptopoecile 268
Leptopegon 205
Leptopterus 235
Leptoptilus 17
leptorhynchus Enicognathus 101
Leptosittaca 100
Leptosomus 146
leptosomus Brachypteracias 147
Leptotila 80
Leptotriccus 203
lepturus Phaeton 11
lerchi Thalurania 127
Lerwa 45
lerwa Lerwa 45
Lesbia 132
leschenaulti Enicurus 243
leschenaulti Merops 145
leschenaultii Charadrius 63
leschenaultii Taccocua 108
lessoni Mayrernis 272
Lessonia 196
lessonii Pterodroma 9
letitiae Popelairia 127
lettii Jubula 13
leucaspis Gymnopithys 192
leucionensis Tanygnathus 93
Leucippus 128
leucoblepharus Basileuterus 324
leucocephala Amozona 104
leucocephala Arundinicola 198
leucocephala Cladorhynchus 67
leucocephala Columba 76
leucocephala Emberiza 303
leucocephala Halcyon 141
leucocephala Motacilla 219
leucocephala Mycteria 17
leucocephala Neositta 287
leucocephala Oxyura 26
leucocephalus Aceros 150
leucocephalus Chaimarrornis 243
leucocephalus Cinclus 236
leucocephalus Cladorhynchus 67
leucocephalus Colius 135
leucocephalus Halincetus 29
leucocephalus Himantopus 67
leucocephalus Hypsipctes 229
leucocephalus Lybius 158
leucocephalus Tachyeres 22
leucocephalus Turdoides 256
Leucochloris 128
leucogaster Alcedo 139
leucogaster Amazilia 129
leucogaster Centropus 110
leucogaster Cinnyricinclus 350
leucogasterCorythaixoides 105
leucoster Falcunculus 282
leucogaster Haliacetus 29
leucogaster Lepidocolaptes 178
leucogaster Pacliycephala 283
leucogaster Picumnus 163
leucogaster Pionites 102
leucogaster Sula 11
leucogastia Dendrocitta 363
leucogastia Galbula 154
lleucogastia Lonchura 340
leucogastia Ontalis 41
leucogastra Uropsila 237
leucogastroides Lonchura 340
leucogenis Anas 24
leucogenis Merganetta 24
leucogenys Aegithalos 285
leucogenys Conirostrum 321
leucogenys Myadestes 244
leucogenys Pycnonotus 226
leucogenys Pyrrhula 336
leucogeranus Grus 54
leucognaphalus Corvus 366
leucogrammica Ptilocichle 255
leucogrammicus Pycnonotus 227
leucolaema Serinus 332
leucolaemus Odontophorus 44
leucolaemus Piculus 165
leucolaima Pogonilus 158
leucolepis Phyllastrephus 227
leucolopha Tigrisoma 16
leucolophus Caliechthrus 107
leucolophus Garrulex 257
leucolophus Tauraco 105
leucolophus Tigriomnis 16
leucomela Columba 76
leucomela Lalage 224
leucomelaena Sylvia 263
leucomelana Tricholaema 158
leucomelas Calonectris 8
leucomelas Turdus 252
leucomystax Pogoniulus 158
leuconerpes 170
leuconota Columba 77
leuconota Pyriglena 190
leuconotos Anaplectes 346
leuconotus Malurcus 269
leuconotus Nycticorax 15
leuconotus Parus 286
leuconotus Thalassornis 20
leucoparcia Eremopterix 215
Leucopeza 324
leucophaea Climacteris 287
leucophace Collacalia 122
leucophaea Microeca 272
leucophaeus Dicrurus 355
leucophains Legatus 198
leucophrus Cichlocolaptes 184
leucophrys Anas 24
leucophrys Anthus 220
leucophrys Basileuterus 324
leucophrys Brachypteryx 240
leucophrys Cercotrichus 241
leucophrys Dendrortyx 44
leucophrys Henicorhina 237
leucophrys Mecocerculus 203
leucophrys Ochthoeca 197
leucophrys Rhipidera 277
leucophrys Sylvietta 268
leucophlrys Vireo 326
leucophrys Zonotrichia 305
leucophthalma Myrmotherulea 188
leucophthalmus Aratinga 100
leucophthalmus Automolus 184
leucophthalmus Larus 70
leucopis Atlapetes 311
leucopleurus Thescelocichla 227
leucopleurus Oneotrochilus 130
leucopodus Haematopus 62
leucopogon Colinus 44
leucopogon Phloeoceastes

170
leucopogon Prinia 265
leucopogon Thryothorus 237
lencops Platycichla 251
leucops Tregellasia 272
Leucopsar 351
leucopsis Aphelocephala 270
leucopsis Branta 21
leucopsis Sitta 286
leucoptera Chlidonias 72
leucoptera Fulica 59
leucoptera Henicorhina 237
leucoptera Loxia 336
PAGE 42
leucoptera Melanocorypha 216
leucoptera Neositta 287
leucoptera Piranga 316
leucoptera Psophia 54
leucoptera Pterodroma 9
leucoptera Pyniglena 190
leucoptera Sporophila 309
leucoptera Sterna 72
leucopternis 34
leucopterus Atlapetes 311
leucopterus Dendrocopos 173
leucopterus Larus 70
leucopterus Malurus 269
leucopterus Nyctibius 118
leucopterus Platysmurus 363
leucopterus Serinus 332
leucopteryx Icterus 328
leucopus Furnarius 180
leucopyga Lalage 224
leucopyga Nyctiprogne 119
leucopyga Oenanthe 246
leucopyga Tachycineta 217
leucopygia Coracina 222
leucopygia Halllcyon 141
leucopygialis Chaetura 123
leucopygialis Lalage 62
leucopygialis Raphidura 123
leucopygius Serinus 332
leucopygius Turdoides 256
leucopyrrhus Laterallus 57
leucoramphus Cacicus 328
leucorhoa Oceanodroma 10
leucorhynchus Artamus 354
leucorhynchus Laniarius 232
leucorodia Platalea 19
leucorrhoa Crapipo 207
leucorrhoa Tachycineta 217
leucorrhous Buteo 35
leucorhyphus Haliacetus 29
leucorhyphus Platyrinchus 201
leucosarcia 79
leucoscepus Francolinus 46
leucoscepus Pternistis 46
leucosoma Hirundo 217
leucosomus Accipiter 33
leucospila Rallicula 55
leucospodia Pseudelaenia 204
leucostephes Melidectes 301
leucosternum Cheramoeca 217
leucosticta Cereotrichas 241
leucosticta Henicorhina 237
leucosticta Lonchura 340
Leucosticte 334
leucostictus Bubro 114
leucostictus Eupetes 253
leucostigma Percnostola 191
leucostigma Rhagologus 282
leucothorax Lanio 315
leucothorax rhipidura 277
leucotis Entomodestes 244
leucotis Eremopterix 215
leucotis Galbalcyrhunchus 154
leucotis Garrulus 364
leucotis Hylocharis 128
leucotis Meliphaga 298
leucotis Melozone 310
leucotis Monarche 281
leucotis Otus 113
leucotis Phapitrereon 82
leucotis Poephila 339
leucotis Pycnonotus 226
leucotis Pyrrhura 101
leucotis Smilorhis 158
leucotis Stachynis 255
leucotis Tauraco 105
leucotis Thryothorus 237
leucotis Vincolanius 326
leucotos Dendrocopos 173
Leucotreron 84
leucura Chettusia 62
lencura Oenanthe 246
leucara Saxicola 245
leucura Tityra 210
leucurum Cinclidium 243
leucurus Elanus 28
leucurus Lagopus 43
leucurus Monarcha 281
leucurus Threnetes 125
leuphotes Aviceda 28
levaillantii Clamator 106
leveallantii Convus 366
levaittantii Francolinus 46
levalliantoides Francolinus 46
leveriana Cissopis 314
levigaster Gorygone 270
levraudi Laterallus 57
lewinii Melanerpes 171
lewinii Meliphaga 298
lewis Asyndesmus 171
leytensis Micromacronus 256
lherminieri Cichlherminia 151
lherminieri Puffinus 8
lhuysii lophophorus 48
liberatus Laniarius 232
libonyanus Turdus 249
Lichenostomus 298/9
Lichmera 297
lichtensteini Philydor 183
lichtensteinii Pterocles 75
lictor Pitangus 199
ldthi Garrulus 364
lignarius Denrocopos 173
lilianae Agapornis 96
lilianae Styinella 330
lilliae Lepidopyga 128
linae Picumnus 163
limbata Lichmera 297
Limicola 67
limicola Rallus 55
limnacetus Spizaetus 37
Limnocorex 57
Limnoctites 181
Limnodromus 66
Limnornis 180
Limnothlypis 323
Limosa 65
Limosa Limosa 65
linchi Collocalia 122
lincolni Melaspiza 305
lincolnii Zonotrichia 305
lindsayi Halcyon 141
lincaris Chiroxiphia 206
linearis Geotrygon 81
lineata acanthiza 270
lincata Conopophaga 194
lincata Coracina 222
lincata Dacuis 320
lincata Pytilia 337
lincata Sarothrura 57
lineatum Tigrisoma 16
lineatus Buteo 35
lineatus Cymbilaimus 185
lineatus Dryocopus 169
lineatus Garrulax 257
lineatus Millvus 29
lineifrons Grallaricula 193
lineiventris Anthus 220
lineola Bolbonhyncus 101
lineola Sporophila 309
linteatus Heterocercus 207
lintoni Myiophobus 201
Linurgus 333
Liocichla 259
Liophlus 260
Liosceles 195
Lipaugus 210
Lissotis 61
litae Piculus 165
litsipsirupa Turdus 249
littoralis Ochthornis 198
livens Larus 71
liventer Bictastur 34
livia Columba 77
livida Agrionnis 196
livingstonei Erythrocercus 279
livingstonii Tauraco 105
llaneae Cichlornis 268
lobata Biziura 26
lobata Campephage 224
lobatus (Lobipes) Phalaropus 6rax 38
latimeri Vireo 326
latirostre Todirostrum 202
latirostris Andropadus 226
latirostris Contopus 200
latirostris Cynanthus 127
latirostris Muscicapa 276
latirostris Psarocolius 327
latistriata Stachynis 256
latistriatus Anthus 220
latoucheonris 303
latrons Ducula 86
landabilis Icterus 328
laurae Coereba 31
laurae Phylloscopus 264
lauterbachi Chlamydera 358
lavinia Tangera 319
lavesii Parotia 361
lawrencii Empidonax 201
lawrencii Geotrygon 81
lawrencii Gymnoglaux 113
lawrencii Pseudocolaptes
lawrencii Turdus 252
layardi Megapodius 40
layardi Parisoma 268
layardi Ptilinopus 84
laysancusis Anas 23
lazuli Halcyon 141
leachi Mackenziaena 185
leachii Dacelo 140
leadbeateri Bucorvus 153
leadbeateri Cacatua 91
leadbeateri Heliodoxa 130
leari Anodorhynchus 98
lebuni Sicalis 308
leclanchori Ptilinopus 84
lechancherii Passerina
lecontei Ceyx 139
lecontei Toxostoma 238
leconteii Ammodramus 305
ledanti Sitta 286
Legatus 198
leguati Necropsar 351
Leiothrix 259
Leipoa 40
Leisteeisura 183
Lophotibis 19
Lophotis 61
Lophotriccus 202
Lophozosterops 296
Lophura 49
lorata Sterna 72
lorealis Anses 281
lorentzi Pachycephala 282
lorenenzii Phylloscopus 264
Loria 358
loniae Loria 358
lonicata Compsothraupis 314
loricata Grallaricula 193
loricata Myrmeciza 191
loricatus Celeus 166
loricatus Monarcha 281
Loriculus 96
Lorius 88
lory Lorius 88
lotemia Nectarinia 292
louisiadensis Cracticus 357
lovensis Ashlyia 271
loveridgei Nectarinia 292
lowei Alethe 242
lowei Sheppardia 242
lowery Xenoglaus 115
lowi Collocalia 122
Loxia 336
Loxigilla 310
Loxioides 325
Loxipasser 310
Loxops 325
loyca Sturnella 330
lubomirskii Piprcola 209
luciae Amazilia 129
luciae Vermivora 322
luciani Eriochemis 131
lucida Hirundo 217
lucidus Chalcites 107
lucidus Chrysocolaptes 175
lucidus Cyanerpes 320
lucidus Hemignathus 325
lucidus Phalacrocorax 12
lucifer Calothorax 133
luconensis Prionituras 92
luctuosa Ducula 86
luctuosa Sporophila 309

luctuosus Sakesphorus 185
luctuosus Tachyphonus 316
lodlowi Alcippe 259
ludovicae Doryfera 125
ludocivensis Nectarinia 290
ludoviciae Turdus 249
ludoviciana Piranga 316
ludovicianus Caprimulgus 120
ludovicianus Lanius 234
ludovicianus Pheyucticay 312
loduvicianus Thryothorus 237
ludwigii Dicrurus 355
ludocigii Nestis 60
lugeus Haplophaedia 131
lugeus Motacilla 219
lugeus Oenauthe 246
lugeus Parisoma 268
lugeus Sarothrura 57
lugeus Streptopelia 78
lugensa 9
lugentoides Oenanthe 246
lugubris Brachygalba 154
lugubris Celeus 166
lugubris Ceryle 138
lugubris Contopus 200
lugubris Dendropicos 172
lugubris Garrulax 258
lugubris Melampitta 253
lugubris Myrmoborus 190
lugubris Denanthe 246
lugubris Parus 286
lugubris Poeoptera 349
lugubris Speirops 296
lugubris Stephanibyx 63
lugubris Surniculus 107
l,hderi Laniarius 232
luizae Asthenes 182
Lululla 216
lumachellus Augustes 133
luminosus Heliangelus 131
lunata Sterna 73
lunatus Melithreptus 299
lunatus Serilophus 176
Lunda 74
lunulata Anthochaera 302
lunulata Galloperdix 47
lunulata Gymnopithys 192
lunulata Zoothera 248
lunulatus Bolbopsittacus 92
lunulatus Garrulax 258
Lurocalis 119
Luscinia 240
luscinia Acrocephalus 263
luscinia Luscinia 240
luscinia Microcerculus 237
luscinioides Locustella 262
lutca Leiothrix 259
lutea Sicalis 308
lutea Zosterops 295
luteicapilla Euphonia 318
luteifrons Nigrita 337
luteirostris Zosterops 295
luteiventris Myiodynastes 199
luteiventris Sicalis 308
luteiventris Tyrannopsis 198
luteocephala Sicalis 308
luteocephalus Heterocercus 207
luteola Sicalis 308
luteolus Ploceus 344
luteolus Pycnonotus 226
luteoschistaceus Accipiter 33
luteoventris Bradypterus 262
luteovirens Ptilinopus 84
luteoviridis Basilenterus 324
luteoviridis Pselliophorus 311
lutescens Anthus 220
lutetiae Coeligena 131
luteus Auripasser 342
luteus Paswser 342
lutosus Polyborus 38
luxuosus Cyanocorax 365
luzonica Anas 23
luzonica Gallicolumba 81
luzoniensis Copsychus 242
lyalli Traversia 214
Lybius 158
Lycocorax 358
Lymnocryptes 66
lynesi Apalis 267
lynesi Sarothura 57
lyra Uropsalis 121
Lyrurus 43
Lysurus 311

macao Ara 99
macclounii Lybius 159
maccoa Oxyura 26
macconnellii Mionectes 205
macconnellii Pipromorpha 205*macconnellii Synallaxis* 181
maccormickii Catharacta 69
macdonaldi Nesomimus 238
macei Ceracina 221
macei Dendrocopos 173
macgillivrayi Pseudobulwaria 9
macgillivrayi Pterodroma 9
macGregonia 358
macGregoriae Amblyornis 358
macGregorii Cnemophilus 358
macGrigoriae Niltava 275
Machaerirhynchus 280
Machaeropterus 207
Macheiramphus 28
Machetornis 198
machiki Zoothera 248
Mackenziaena 185
mackinlayi Macropygia 78
mackinnoni Lanius 234*macklotii Pitta* 212
macleayana Meliphaga 248
macleayii Halcyon 142
macloviana Muscisaxicola 196
Macroagelaius 330
macrocephala Petroica 272
Macrocephalon 40
macrocerca Hylonympha 130
macrocercus Dicrurus 355
macrocercus Eupetes 253
macrocercus Euplectes 347
macrodactyla Capella 66
macrodactyla Napothera 255
macrodactyla Oceanodroma 10
macrodactylus Bucco 154
Macrodipteryx 120
macrolopha Percnostola 191
macrolopha Pucrasia 50
Macronextes 7
Macronous 256
Macronyx 219
macronyx Pipilo 310
Macropsalis 119
macroptera Pterodroma 9
macropterus Vanellus 62
macropus Seytalopus 195
Macropygia 78§Ç.•Δ*Amacrorhyncha Dendrocincla* 176
macrorhyncha Saxicola 245
macrorhynchos Corvus 366
macrorhynchos Cymbirhynchus 176
macrorhynchos Notharchus 154
macrorhynchus Tauraco 105
macrorrhina Melidera 140
Macrosphenus 268
macrotis Eurostopodus 119
macroura Dendrortyx 44
macroura Eupetomena 126
macroura Thripophaga 182
macroura Vidua 341
macroura Senaidura 79
macrourus Accipiter 33
macrourus Circus 31
macrourus Colius 135
macrourus Euplectes 347
macrourus Urotriorchis 33
macrurus Caprimulgus 121
macularia Actitis 65
macularia Grallaria 193
maculata Chlamydera 358
maculata Cotinga 208
maculata Paroseomyza 325
maculata Stachyris 255
maculata Terenura 189
maculatum Todirostrum 202
maculatus Chalcites 107
maculatus Dendrocopos 173
maculatus Enicurus 243
maculatas Indicator 159
maculatas Myiodynastes 199
maculatus Nystalus 155
maculatus Pipilo 310
maculatus Prionochilus 288
maculatus Rollus 55
maculialatus Icterus 328
maculicauda Astheres 182
maculicauda Hypocnemoides 190
maculicaudus Caprimulgus 121
maculicoronatus Capito 156
maculipectus Rhipidura 277
maculipectus Thryothorus 237
maculipennis Larus 70
maculipennis Phylloscopus 264
maculirostris Muscisaxicola 196
maculirostris Selenidera 161
maculirostris Turdus 252
maculosa Campethera 165
maculosa Columba 77
maculosa Lalage 224
maculosa Nothura 3
maculosa Prinia 265
maculosa Turnix 53
maculosus Caprimulgus 121
maculosus Nyctibius 118
mada Gymnophaps 87
mada Prioniturus 92
madagarensis Margaropendix 46
madagaxariensis Accipiter 32
madagascariensis Alectroenas 85
madagascariensis Aviceda 28
madagascariensis Calicalicus 235
madagascariensis Caprimulgus 120
madagascariensis Ceyx 139
madagascariensis Foudia 346
madagascariensis Hypsipetes 229
madagascariensis Ispidina 139
madagascariensis Numenius 64
madagascariensis Oxylabes 260
madagascariensis Phyllastrephus 228
madagascariensis Porphysio 58
madagascariensis Rallus 55
Madagascarinus leptoptrus 235
Madanga 296
madaraszi Psittacella 92
madeira Pterodroma 9
maderaspatana Motacilla 219
maderaspatana Zosterops 296
maesi Garrulax 258
magellani Pelecanoides 10
magellanica Carduelis 333
magellanicus Campephilus 175
magellanicus Phalacrocorax 12
magellanicus Scytalopus 195
magellanicus Spheniscus 4
magentae Pterodroma 9
magicus Otus 113
magister Vireo 326
magna Alectoris 45
magna Aplonis 348

magna Arachnothera 294
magna Cyanecula 240
magna Macropygia 78
magna Sitta 286
magna Sturnella 330
magnifica Lophornis 127
magnifica Megaloprepia 84
magnificens Fregata 13
magnificus Calyptorhynchus 90
magnificus Diphyllodes 361
magnificus Gorsachias 15
magnificus Nycticorax 15
magnificus Ptilinopus 84
magnificus Ptiloris 359
magnirostre Malacopteron 254
magnirostris Burhinus 68
magnirostris Buteo 35
magnirostris Calendula 216
magnirostris Geospiza 310
magnirostris Gerygone 270
magnirostris Mimus 238
magnirostris Myiarchus 200
magnirostris Orthoramphus 68
magnirostris Phylloscopus 264
magnirostris Sericornis 271
magnolia Dendroica 322
magnum Malacopteron 254
magnus Sericornis 271
maguari Ciconia 17
mahali Plocepasser 342
mahrattensis Caprimulgus 121
mahrattensis Dendrocopos 173
maillardi Ciscus 31
maja Lonchuza 340
major Brachypteryx 240
major Bradypterus 262
major Cettia 262
major Crotophaga 109
major Cypseloides 123
major Dendrocopus 173
major Diglossa 321
major Pachyramphus 210
major Parus 286
major Podiceps 5
major Quiscalus 331
major Schiffornis 207
major Taraba 185
major Tinamus 2
major Ziphocolaptes 177
major Zoothera 248
makawar Pogoniulus 158
makirensis Phylloscopus 264
malabarica Galerida 216
malabarica Lobipluvia 63
malabarica Lonchura 340
malabaricus Anthracoceros 151
malabaricus Copsychus 242
malabaricus Sturnus 351
malacca Lonchura 340
malaccensis Hypsipetes 229
malaccensis Malacocinda 254
malacensis Anthreptes 290
malacensis Polyplectron 51
malachitacea Triclaria 104
malachurus Spipiturus 269
Malacocincla 254
Malaconotus 232/33
Malacopteron 254
Malacoptila 155
malacoptilus Rimator 255
malacorhynchos Hymenolaimus 24
Malacorhynchus 24
malaitae Myzomela 297
malaitae Rhipidura 277
malaris Phaethornis 125
malayanus Anthracocerus 151
malayanus Chalcites 107
malayensis Ictinaetus 36
malcoloni Turdoides 256
maldivarum Glareola 68
malco Macrocephalon 40
malherbi Cyanoramphus 95
malherbii Columba 77
Malia 260
malimbica Halcyon 142
Malimbicus Malimbus 346
Malimbus 345
mallee Stipiturus 269
malouinus Attagis 68
malura Drymophila 189
maluroides Spartonoica 180
Malurus 269
mana Paroreomyza 325
Manacus 207
manacus Manacus 207
manadensis Monarcha 281
manadensis Otus 113
manadensis Turacoena 78
mandellii Arborophila 47
Mandingoa 337
mangbettorum Psalidoprocne 217
mangle Aramides 56
mango Anthracothorax 126
manilata Ara 99
manillensis Caprimulgus 121
manilloe Penelopides 150
manipurensis Cryptoplectron 47
manipurensis Perdicula 47
manoensis Nectarinia 291
Manorina 302
mantananensis Otus 113
mantchuricum Crossoptilon 48
mantelli Notornis 58
Manucodia 359
manu Cerconeacra 190
manusi Tylo 112
manyar Ploceus 344
maracana Ara 99
marail Penelope 41
maranhaensis Phaethornis 125
maranonica Synallaxis 181
maranonicus Melanopareia 195
maranonicus Turdus 252
marcapatae Cranioleuca 181
marchei Anthracoceros 151
marchei Cleptornis 299
marchei Ptilinopus 84
margaretae Zoothera 248
margarethae Charmosyna 89
margarettae Phaethornis 125
margaritaceiventer Idioptilon 202
margaritae Batis 278
margaritae Conirostrum 321
margaritatus Hypargos 337
margaritatus Megastictus 186
margaritatus Trachyphonus 159
Margaroperdix 46
Margarops 239
Margarornis 183
marginalis Porzana 57
marginata Collocalia 122
marginata Zoothera 248
marginatus Charadrius 63
marginatus Microcerculus 237
marginatus Pachyramphus 210
mariae Bradypterus 262
mariae Megalurulus 268
mariae Nesillas 264
mariae Pteroglossus 160
marila Aythya 25
marina Pelagodroma 10
marinus Larus 70
mariguensis Bradornis 273
mariquensis Melaenornis 273
mariguensis Nectarinia 292
maritima (Erolia) Calidris 67
maritima Geositta 179
maritimus Ammodramus 305
markhami Oceanodroma 10
marmorata Napothera 255
marmoratus Brachyramphus 74
marshalli Otus 113
martii Baryphthengus 144
martinica Chaetura 123
martinica Elaenia 204
martinica Porphyrula 58
martius Dryocopus 169
marwitzi Lanius 233
masafuerae Aphrastura 180
Masius 206
massena Trogon 136
masukuensis Andropodus 226
mathewsi Cinclonamphus 271
matsudairae Oceanodroma 10
matthewsii Boissonneana 131
matthiae Rhipidura 277
maugaeus Chlorostilbon 127
mangei Dicaeum 289
mauretanicus Puffinus 8
maurei (Ereunetes) Calidris 67
maurus Circus 31
mavornata Aplonis 348
mavors Heliangelus 131
maxillosus Saltator 313
maxima Ceryle 138
maxima Collocalia 122
maxima Melanocorypha 216
maxima Melospiza 305
maxima Pitta 212
maxima Pteropodocys 221
maxima Sterna 73
maxima Zonotrichia 305
maximiliani Melanopareia 195
maximiliani Oryzoborus 309
maximiliani Pionus 103
maximus Artamus 354
maximus Garrulax 258
maximus Saltator 313
mayeri Astrapia 360
mayeri Columba 77
maynana Cotinga 208
mayottensis Zosterops 296
mayri Ptiloprora 300
mayri Rallicula 55
Mayrornis 272
mccallii Erythrocercus 279
mcclellandii Hypsipetes 229
mccownii Calcarius 304
mcgregori Coracina 222
mcilhennyi Conioptilon 209
mcleannari Phlogopsis 193
mcleodii Otophanes 119
mearnsi Collocalia 122
Mearnsia 123
mechowi Cercococcyx 106
Mecocerculus 203
media Capella 66
mediocris Nectarinia
medius Dendrocopos 173
meeki Charmosyna 39
meeki Corvus 367
meeki Microgoura 82
meeki Micropsitta 92
meeki Ninox 116
meeki Zosterops 295
meekiana Ptiloprora 300
Megabyas 278
megacephala Ramphotrigon 202
Megacrex 56
Megadyptes 4
megaensis Hirundo 217
megala Capella 66
Megalaima 156/57
Megaloprepia 84
megalopterus Campylorhynchus 236
megalopterus Phalcoboenus 38
megalorhynchos Tanygnathus 93
megalotis Otus 112
PAGE 47
megalura Leptoltila 80
Megalurulus 268
Megalurus 262
Megapodius 40

megapodius Pteroptochos 195
megarhyncha Colluricuicla 284
megarhyncha Halcyon 142
megarhyncha Pitta 212
megarhynchos Luscinia 240
megarhynchus Dicrurus 355
megarhynchus Melilestes 297
megarhynchus Rhamphomantis 106
Megarynchus 199
Megastictus 186
Megatriorchis 32
Megaxenops 184
meiffrenii Orbyxelos 53
Meiglyptes 168
melacoryphus Coccyzus 107
melaena Coracina 223
melaena Lonchura 340
melaena Myrmecocichla 245
Melaenornis 273
melambrotus Cathortes 27
Melampitta 253
Melamprosops 325
melanaria Cercomacra 190
melancholicus Tyrannus 198
Melanerpes 170
melania Oceanodroma 10
melaniae Lophornis 127
melanicterus Cacicus 328
melanicterus Pycnonotus 226
Melanitta 26
melanocephala Alectoris 45
melanocephala Apalis 267
melanocephala Ardea 14
melanocephala Arenaria 66
melanocephala Emberiza 304
melanocephala Manorina 302
melanocephala Myzomela 297
melanocephala Speirops 296
melanocephala Sylvia 263
melanocephala Trogon 135
melanocephophasis 45
melanoleucos Pycnonotus 226
melanoleucus Accipiter 32
melanoleucus Geranoactus 34
melanoleucus Microhierax 38
melanoleucus Spizostur 37
melanolophus Gorsachius 16
melanolophus Nycticorax 16
melanolophus Parus 286
melanonota Pipnaeidea 318
melanonotus Odontophorus 44
melanonotus Sakesphorus 185
melanonotus Touit 102
Melanopareia 195
Melanoperdix 46
melanopezus Automolus 184
melanophaius Laterallus 57
melanophris Diomedea 6
melanophrys Manorina 302
melanopis Schistochlamys 314
melanopis Theristicus 18
melanopogon Acrocephalus 263
melanopogon Hypocnemoides 190
melanops Centropus 110
melanops Charadrius 64
melanops Conopophaga 194
melanops Leucopternis 34
melanops Meliphaga 298
melanops Nyadestes 244
melanops Pachycephala 283
melanops Phleocryptes 180
melanops Philidonyris 302
melanops Porphyriops 57
melanops Sporophila 309
melanops Trichothraupis 316
melanops Turdoides 256
melanopsis Monarcha 281
melanoptera Chloephaga 21
melanoptera Coracina 222
melanoptera Metriopelia 80
melanopterus Lybius 159
melanopterus Stephanibyx 63
melanopterus Sturnus 351
Melanoptila 238
melanopygia Chaetura 123
melanopygia Telecanthura 123
melanoramphos Corcorax 356
melanorhyncha §Ç.•ΔAEudynamys 107
melanorhyncha Pelargopsis 139
melanorhynchus Thripadectes 184
melanorrhoa Chalybura 129
melanospila Ptilinopus 84
Melanospiza 310
melanosternon Hamirostra 29
melanosticta Rhegmatorhina 192
melanota Climacteris 287
melanota Pulsatrix 115
melanothorax Sakesphorus 185
melanothorax Stachyris 255
melanothorax Sylvia 263
Melanotis 238
melanotis Ailureodus 357
melanotis Anaplectes 346
melanotis Oriolus 353
melanotis Coryphaspiza 312
melanotis Estrilda 338
melanotis Hapalopsittaca 103
melanotis Hemispingus 314
melanotis Manorina 302
melanotis Nesomimus 238
melanotis Odontophorus 44
melanotis Psaltriparus 285
melanotis Pteruthius 259
melanotos (Enolia) Calidris 67
melanotos Sarkidiornis 25
Melanotrochilus 126
melanotus Malurus 269
melanotus Porphyrio 58
melanoxantha Phainoptila 235
melanoxanthum Dicaeum 289
melanozanthos Coccothraustes 336
melanura Anthornis 302
melanura (Cisticola) Apalis 267
melanura Cercomela 245
melanura Chilia 179
melanura Climacteris 287
melanura Pachycephala 283
melanura Polioptila 261
melanura Pyrrhura 101
melanurus Ceyx 139
melanurus Himantopus 67
melanurus Myiophoneus 247
melanurus Myrmoborus 190
melanurus Passer 342
melanurus Ramphocaenus 261
melanurus Trogon 136
melaschista Coracina 222
melba Apus 124
melba Pytilia 337
melba Tachymarptis 124
meleagrides Agelastes 52
Meleagris 52
Meliarchus 301
Melichneutes 159
Melidectes 301
Melidora 140
Melierax 32
Melignornon 159
Melilestes 297
melindae Anthus 220
Meliphaga 298/99
meliphilus Indicator 159
Melipotes 301
Melithreptus 299
melitophrys Vireolanius 326
melleri Anas 23
mellianus Oriolus 354
Mellisuga 134
mellisugus Chlorostilbon 127
mellivora Florisuga 126
mellori Corvus 366
Melocichla 263
melodia Melospiza
melodia Zonotrichia 305
melodus Charadrius 64
Melophus 303
Melopsittacus 95
Melopyrrha
meloryphus Euscarthmus 203
Melospiza 305
Melozone 310
melpoda Estrilda 338
membranaceus Malacorhynchus 24
menachensis Serinus 332
menachensis Turdus 249
menagei Gallicolumba 81
menbeki Centropus 110
menckei Monarcha 281
mendanae Acrocephalus 263
mendiculus Spheniscus 4
mendozae Pomarea 273
menetriesii Myrmotherula 188
meninting Alcedo 139
mennelli Serinus 332
menstruus Pionus 103
mentalis Artamus 354
mentalis Cracticus 357
mentalis Dysithamnus 187
mentalis Melocichla 263
mentalis Picus 167
mentalis Pipra 206
mentawi Otus 113
Mentocrex 56
Menura 214
mercenaria Amazona 104
mercierii Ptilinopus 84
Merganetta 24
mergauser Mergus 26
Mergus 26
meridae Cistothorus 236
meridionalis Buteogallus 34
meridionalis Himantopus 67
meridionalis Nestor 91
merillii Ptilinopus 84
merlini Saurothera 108
merlini Tropicoperdix 47
Meropogon 145
Merops 145
merula Dendrocincla 176
merula Turdus 250
Merulaxis 195
merulinus Cacomantis 106
merulinus Garrulax 258
meruloides Chamaeza 192
Mesembrinibis 18
mesochrysa Euphonia 318
Mesoenas 53
mesoleuca Conothraupis 314
mesoleuca Elaenia 204
mesomelas Icterus 329
Mesophoyx 15
Mesopicos 174
metabates Melierax 32
Metabolus 280
metallica Aplonis 348
metallicus Anthreptes 290
Metallura 132
metcalfii Zosterops 295
metopias Orthotomus 265
Metopidius 62
Metopothrix 183
Metropelia 80
mevesii Lamprotornis 350
mexicana Sialia 244
mexicana Tangara 319
mexicanum Tigrisoma 16
mexicanus Aechmolophus 201
mexicanus Carpodacus 335

mexicanus Cassidix 331
mexicanus Catharus 251
mexicanus Catherpes 236
mexicanus Cinclus 236
mexicanus Falco 39
mexicanus Gymnomystax 329
mexicanus Himantopus 67
mexicanus Momotus 144
PAGE 49
mexicanus Nyctibius 180
mexicanus Psilorhinus 365
mexicanus Quiscalus 331
mexicanus Salpinetes 236
mexicanus Sclerurus 184
mexicanus Todus 144
mexicanus Trogon 136
mexicanus Xenotriccus 201
meyeni Zosterops 295
meyerdeschauenseei Tangara 319
meyeri Acrocephalus 263
meyeri Chalcites 107
meyeri Epimachus 360
meyeri Pachycephala 282
meyeri Philemon 300
meyeri Poicephalus 96
meyerianus Accipiter 32
michleri Pittasoma 193
micraster Heliangelus 131
Micrastur 38
Micrathene 115
Microbates 261
Microcerculus 237
Microchera 129
Microcochlearius 202
Microdynamis 107
Microeca 272
Microgoura 82
Microhierax 38
Microligea 324
Micromacronus 256
micromegas Nesoebites 163
Micromonacha 155
Micropalama 67
Micropanyptila 124
Microparra 62
Micropsitta 92
microptera Agriornis 196
microptera Rollandia 5
Micropternus 166
micropterus Cuculus 106
micropterus Podiceps 5
Micropygia 57
Microrhopias 188
microrhyncha Amazilia 129
microrhyncha Gygis 73
microrhyncha Bredornis 273
microrhynchum Ramphomicron 132
microhynchus Melaenornis
Microsarcops 62
microsoma Halocyptena 10
Microstilbon 133
micrura Myrmia 134
migraus Milvus 29
migratoria Ectopistes 79
migratorius Coccothraustes 336
migratorius Turdus 252
mikado Syrmaticus 50
mikettae Vireolanius 326
milaujensis Andropadus 226
milanjensis Pychonotus 226
miles Lobibyx 63
militaris Ara 99
militaris Haematoderus 211
militaris Ilicura 206
militaris Leistes 330
militaris Pexites 330
milleri Grallaria 194
milleri Polytmus 128
milleri Xenops 184
milleti Garrulax 258
milo Centropus 111
Milvago 38
Milvus 29
milvu Milvus 29
mimikae Miliphaga 298
Mimizuku 113
Mimocichla 252
Mimodes 238
Mimus 238
mindanensis Coracina 223
mindanensis Ptilocichla 255
mindorensis Ducula 86
mindorensis Otus 112
mindorensis Penelopides 150
mineaceus Picus 167
miniatus Myioborus 324
miniatus Pericrocotus 225
minima Batis 278
minima Lymnocryptes 66
minima Mellisuga 134
minor Aplonis 348
minor Antamus 354
minor Batis 278
minor Chionis 69
minor Chordeiles 119
minor Climacteris 287
minor Coccyzus 107
minor Dendrocopos 173
minor Eudyptula 4
minor Fregata 13
minor Furnarius 180minor Hylophilus 326
minor Indicator 159
minor Lanius 234
minor Lybius 159
minor Mecocerculus 203
minor Myrmotherula 188
minor Nothura 3
minor Pachyramphus 210
minor Paradisaea 362
minor Phoeniconaias 19
minor Platalea 19
minor Pyrenestes 337
minor Rhinopomastus 148
minor Scolopax 66
minor Snethlagea 202
minor Zosterops 295
minula Sylvia 263
minulla Batis 278
minulla Nectarinia 292
minullus Accipiter 32
minuta (Erolia) Calidriss 347
minuta Colombina 80
minuta Euphonia 318
minuta Piaya 108
minuta Sporophila 309
minuta Tchagra 231
minuta Zosterops 295
minutilla (Erolia) Calidris 67
minutillus Chalcites 107
minutissimum Glaucidium 115
minutissimus Picumnus 163
minutus Anoiis 73
minutus Anthoscopus 285
minutus Ixobrychus 16
minutus Larus 71
minutus Numenius 64
minutus Xenops 184
Mionectes 205
mira Scolopax 66
mirabilis Ammodramus 305
mirabilis Cyanolyca 364
mirabilis Eriocnemis 131
mirabilis Loddigesia 133
Mirafra 215
miranda Basilornis 352
miranda Daphoenositta 287
mirandae Hemitriccus 202
mirandae Idioptilon 202
mirandollei Micrastur 38
mirificus Rallus 55
mirus Otus 112
Misocalius 107
mississippiensis Ictinia 28
mitchellii Philodice 133
mitcellii Phegornis 64
mitrata Aratinga 100
mitratus Garrulax 258
Mitrephanes 201
Mitrospingus 315
mitu Mitu 42
mitu Crax 42
monachus Artamus 354
monachus Centropus 111
monachus Myiopsitta 101
monachus Necrosyrtes 30
Monarcha 281
Monasa 155
monasa Aphanolimnas 57
mondetoura Claravis 80
monedula Corvus 366
moneduloides Corvus 367
mongolica Melanocorypha 216
mongolica Rhodopechys 334
mongolus Charadrius 64
monguilloti Carduelis 333
Monias 53
monileger Ficedula 274
monileger Garrulax 258
monileger Batrachostomus 118
monocerata Cerorhinca 74
monogrammicus Kaupifalco 34
monorhis Oceanodroma 10
monorthonyx Anurlegatus 204
montagnii Penelope 41
montana Agriornis 196
montana Alethe 242
montana Brachypteryx 240
montana Buthraupis 317
monthana Celtia 262
montana Coracina 222
montana Geotrygon 81
montana Lonchura 340
montana Meliphaga 298
montana Paroreomyza 325
montana Sheppardia 242
montana Zenoligea 324
montana Zosterops 295
montanella Prunella 239
montanellus Calamanthus 270
montani Anthracoceros 151
montanus Andropadus 226
montanus Cercococcyx 106
montanus Cettia 262
montanus Charadrius 64
montanus Dicrurus 355
montanus Oreoscoptes 238
montanus Parus 286
montanus Passer 342
montanus Peltops 280
montanus Pericrocotus 225
montanus Pomatorhinus 254
montanus Prioniturus 92
monteiri Clytospiza 337
monteiri Tockus 149
montezuma Psarocolius 327
montezumae Cyrtonyx 44
Monticola 247
monticola Lichmera 297
monticola Lonchura 340
monticola Megalaima 157
monticola Oenanthe 246
monticola Troglocytes 237
monticola Zoothera 248
monticolum Dicaeum 289
monticolus Caprimulgus 121
monticolus Parus 286
montieri Tribonyx 58
Montifringilla 343
montifringilla Fringilla 332
montis Seicercus 264
montium Paramythia 289
montivagus Aeronautes 124
moquini Haematopus 62
morcaui Apalis 267
moreaui Nectarinia 292
moreaui Orthotomus 267
moreirae Oreophylax 180
morenoi Metriopelia 80
morinellus Eudromias 64
morio Coracina 223
PAGE 51
morio Onychognathus 349
morio Psilorhinus 365
Morococcyx 109
morphnoides Hieraetus 37
Morphnus 36
morphoeus Monasa 155
morrisonia Alcippe 259
morrisoniana Actinodura 259
morrisonianus Garrulax 257
montierii Tribonyx 58
moschata Cairina 25
mosquera Eriocnemis 131
mosquitus Chrysolampis 126
Motacilla 219
motacilla Seiurus 323
motacilloides Herpsilochmus 189
motitensis Passer 342
motmot Ortalis 41
mouki Gerygone 270
Moupinia 256
mouroniensis Zosterops

296
moussieri Phoenicurus 243
mozambicus Serinus 332
muelleri Heleia 296
muelleri Merops 146
muelleri Rallus 55
mufumbiri Laniarius 232
mugimaki Ficedula 274
m,lleri Cranioleuca 181
mullerii Ducula 86
Mulleripicus 168
mulsanti Acestrura 134
multicolor Petroica 272
multicolor Saltatricula 312
multicolor Telophorus 232
multicolor Todus 144
multipunctata Nucifraga 365

multistriata Charmosyna 89
multistriatus Thamnophilus 186
munda Serpophaga 203
mundus Monarcha 281
munroi Dysmorodrepanis 325
mupinensis Turdus 250
muraria Tichodroma 287
murina Acanthiza 270
murina Agriornis 196
murina Apalis 267
murina Crateroscelis 271
murina Notiochelidon 217
murina Phaeomyias 204
murina Xolmis 196
murinus Thamnophilus 186
murphyi Zosterops 295
Muscicapa 276
muscicapinus Hylophilus 326
Muscigralla 196
Muscipipra 197
Muscisaxicola 196
Muscivera 198
musculus Anthoscopus 285
musculus Troglodytes 237
musica Euphonia 318
musicus Bias 278
Musophaga 105
musschenbroekii Neopsittacus 89
mustelina Certhiaxis 181
mustelina Hylochichla 251
mutata Terpsiphore 279
muticus Pavo 51
muttui Muscicapa 276
mutus Lagopus 43
Myadestes 244
myadestinus Myadestes 244
Mycerobas 336
Mycteria 17
Myiagra 280
Myiarchus 200
Myiobus 201
Myioborus 324
Myioccyx 139
Myiodynastes 199
Myiopagis 204
Myioparus 276
Myiophobus 201
Myiophoneus 247
Myiopsitta 101
Myiornis 202
Myiotheretes 196
Myiotriceus 201
Myiozetetes 199
myoptilus Apus 124
myotherinus Myrmoborus 190
Myristicivora 87
myristicivora Ducula 86
Myrmeciza 191
Myrmecocichla 245
myrmecophoneus Picus 167
Myrmia 134
Myrmoborus 190
Myrmochanes 190
Myrmochilus 188
Myrmornis 193
Myrmothera 193
Myrmotherula 187/88
Myrtis 134
mysolensis Aploris 348
mysorensis Zosterops 295
mysticalis Aethopyga 294
mysticalis Aimophila 306
mysticalis Cyanocorax 364
mysticalis Diglossa 321
mysticalis Malacoptila 155
mysticalis Thryothorus 237
mystacca Aplonis 348
mystacca Geotrygon 81
mystacca Hemiprocne 122
mystacca Sylvia 263
mystaccus Platyrinchus 201
mystacophanos Megalaima 157
Mystacornis 260
mysticalis Diglossa 321
mysticalis Eurostopodus 119
mysticalis Rhabhornis 287
Myza 301
Myzomela 297/98
Myzornis 260

nabouroup Onychognathus 349
nacunda
naevia Hylophylax 193
naevia Locustella 262
naevia Miafra 215
naevia Sclateria 191
naevia Tapera 109
naevia Zoothera 248
naevioides Hylophylax 193
naevius Ramphodon 125
naevosa Stictonetta 24
nagaensis Sitta 286
nahani Francolinus 46
naina Ptilinopus 84
nais Alcedo 139
namaqua Cisticola 266
PAGE 52
namaqua Pterocles 75
namaquus Thripias 174
Namibornis 241
nana Acanthiza 170
nan Anatinga 100
nan Cisticola 266
nana Cyanolyca 364
nana Grallericula 193
nana Lonchura 340
nana Sylvia 263
nana Turnix 53
Nandayus 100
Nannopsittaca 102
Nannopterum 12
nanum Glaucidium 115
nanus Accipiter 32
nanus Dendrocopos 173
nanus Ichtyaetus 29
nanus Pyrocephalus 198
nanus Spizaetus 37
nanus Taoniscus 3
nanus Vireo 326
napensis Stigmatura 203
Napothera 255
narcissina Ficedula 274
narcondami Aceros 151
narethae Psephotus 94
narina Apcloderma 137
Nasica 177
nasicus Convus 366
nasutus Tockus 149
natalensis Caprimulgus 120
natalensis Chloropeta 263
natalensis Cossypha 241
natalensis Francolinus 46
natalis Zosterops 295
nationi Atlapetes 311
nativitatis Puffinus 8
nattereri Anthus 220
nattereri Phaethornis 125
nattereri Pipra 206
nattereri Selenidera 161
nattereri Tachyphonus 316
nattererii Cotinga 208
naumanni Falco 39
naumanni Turdus 250
navitatis Puffinus 8
ndussumensis Criniger 228
Neafrapus 123
nebubouxii Sula 11
nebularia Tringa 65
nebulosa Rhipidura 27
nebuloas Strix 117
nebulosus Picumnus 163
necopinus Xiphorhynchus 178
Necropsar 351
Necrosyrtes 30
Nectarinia 290/93
nectarinoides Nectarinia 292
neergaardi Nectarinia 292
neglicta Pterodroma 9
neglecta Sturnella 330
neglectus Anthreptes 290
neglectus Phalacrocorax 12
neglectus Phylloscopus 264
nehrkorni Dicaeum 288
nehrkorni Neolesbia 128
nelicourvi Ploceus 344
nelsoni Ammodromus 305
nelsoni Geothlypis
nelsoni Vireo 326
nematura Lochmias 184
nemoricola Capella 66
nemoricola Leucosticte 334
Nemosia 315
nenday Nandayus 100
nengetta Fluvicola 197
Neochelidon 217
Neochen 22
Neochloe 326
Neochmia 339/40
Neocichla 350
Neocossyphus 244
Neocrex 57
Neoctantes 187
Neodrepanis 213
Neolalage 272
Neolesbia 128
Neolestes 229
Neomixis 255
Neomorphus 109
Neopelma 207
Neophema 95
Neophron 30
Neopipo 207
Neopsittacus 89
Neositta 287
Neospiza 307
Neothraupis 314
Neotis 60
neoxena Hirundo 217
neoxenus Trogon 135
Neoxolmis 196
Nephelormis 315
Nephoecetes 123
nereis Garrodia 10
nereis Sterna 73
Nesasio 177
Nesillas 264
nesiotis Porphyriornis 58
Nesocharis 337
Nesoclopeus 56
Nesoctities 163
Nesoenas 77
Nisofregetta 10
Nesomimus 238
Nesophylax 57
Nesopsar 329
Nesospingus 314
Nesospiza 307
Nesotriccus 200
Nestor 91
Netta 25
Nettapus 25
neumanni Centropus 110
neumanni Hemitesia 268
neumayer Sitta 286
nevermanni Lonchura 340
newelli Puffinus
newtoni Acrocephalus
newtoni Coracina 222
newtoni Falco 39
newtoni Lanius 233
Newtonia 276
newtoniana Prionodura 358
newtonii Necarinia 292
ngamieuse Glaucidium 115
niansae Apus
nicaragueusis Quiscalus 331
Nicator 228
nicefori Thryothorus 237
nicobarica Caloenas 82
nicobariensis Hypsipetes 229
nicobariensis Megapodius 40
nicolli Ploceus 345
nidipendulum Idioptilon 202
nidipendulus Hemitriccus 202
nieuwenhuisii Pycnonotus 226
niger Bubalornis 341
niger Capito 156
niger Certhionyx 298
niger Copsychus 242
niger Neoctantes 187
PAGE 53
niger Nephoecetes 123

niger Pachyramphus 210
niger Parus 286
niger Phalacrocorex 12
niger Phasidus 52
niger Quiscalus 330
niger Threnetres 125
nigerrina Lonchura 340
nigerrimus Knipolegus 197
nigerrimus Nesopar 329
nigerrimas Ploceus 344
nigra Astrapia 360
nigra Chlidonias 72
nigra Ciconia 17
nigra Coracopsis 96
nigra Ciax 42
nigra Geranospiza 31
nigra Lalage 224
nigra Melanitta 26
nigra Melanocharis 288
nigra Melanoperdix 46
nigra Melopyrrha 309
nigra Myrmococichla 245
nigra Penelopina 42
nigra Phylidonyris 302
nigra Pomarea 273
nigra Rynchops 73
nigra Sterna 72
nigrescens Ammodramus 305
nigrescens Apalis 267
nigrescens Caprimulgus 121
nigrescens Cercomacra 190
nigrescens Contopus 200
nigrescens Dendroica 322
nigrescens Pitohui 284
nigrescens Rheimardia 51
nigrescens Turdus 252
nigricans Cercomacra 190
nigricans Hirundo 217
nigricans Pinarocoryps 215
nigricans Pycnonotus 227
nigricans Rallus 55
nigricans Sayornis 197
nigricans Serpophega 203
nigricapillus Formicarius 192
nigricapillus Lioptilus 260
nigricapillus Thryothorus 237
nigriceps Anbropodus 226
nigriceps Apbalis 267
nigriceps Choristris 60
nigriceps Eremopterix 215
nigriceps Lonchura 340
nigriceps Orthotomus 265
nigriceps Ploceus 344
nigriceps Polioptila 261
nigriceps Saltator 313
nigriceps Serinus 332
nigricips Stachyris 255
nigniceps Terpsiphone 279
nigriceps Thamnophilus 186
nigriceps Todirostrum 202
nigriceps Turdus 252
nigriceps Veniliornis 172
nigricincta Aphelocephala 270
nigricollis anthracothorax 126
nigricollis Busarelhus 34
nigricollis Grus 54
nigricollis Lagonosticta 338
nigrocollis Phoenicurcus 211
nigricollis Ploceus 344
nigricollis Podiceps 5
nigricollis Sporophila 309
nigricollis Stachysis 255
nigricollis Sturnus 351
nigricollis Turnix 53
nigrifrons Monasa 155
nigrifrons Phylloscartes 203
nigrifrons Telophorus 232
nigrigenis Agapornis 96
nigrilore Dicaeum 289
nigriloris Cisticola 266
nigriloris Estrilda 338
nigrimcuta Yuhina 260
nigrimcutum Ploceus 344
nigripectus Machaerirhynchus 280
nigripennis Gallinago 66
nigripennis Oriolus 353
nigripennis Pterodroma 9
nigripes Dacnis 320
nigripes Dionaedia 6
nigrirostris Andigena 161
nigrirostris Columba 77
nigrirostris Cyclarhis 326
nigrirostris Macropygia 78
nigrirostris Phaethornis 125
nigriscapularis Caprimulgus 120
Nigrita 337
nigrita Hirundo 217
nigrita Myzomela 297
migrita Ochthoeca 197
nigritemporalis Nilaus 231
nigriventris Eupherusa 129
nigrivestis Eriocnemis 131
nigrohunnea Tyto 112
nigrocapillas Nothocercus 2
nigrocapillus Phyllomyias 204
nigrocapitata Stachyris 255
nigrocincta Tangara 319
nigrocinereus Thamophilus 186
nigrocinnamomea Rhipidura 277
nigrocristatus Anairetes 203
nigrocristatus Basileuterus 324
nigrocyanca Halcyon 142
nigrofumosus Cinclodes 179
nigrogularis Clytorhynchus 280
nigrogularis Colinus 44
nigrogularis Cracticus 357
nigrogularis Icterus 329
nigrogularis Phalacrocarax 12
nigrogularis Psophodes 253
nigrogularis Ramphocelus 317
nigrolincaba Ciccuba 116
nigrolutea Aegithina 230
nigromaculata Phlegopis 193
nigromitratus Trochocercus 279
nigropectus Biatas 185
nigropectus Eulacestoma 282
nigropunctatus Picumnus 163
nigrorufa Crateroscelis 271
nigrofufa Ficedula 274
nigrorufa Hirundo 217
nigrorufa Poospiza 308
nigrorafa Sporophila 309
nigrorufus Centropus 111
nigrorum Stachyris 255
nigrorum Zosterops 295
nigroventris Euplectes 347
nigrovirides Sericornis 271
nigroviridis Tangura 319
Nilaus 231
nilotica Sterna 73
Niltava 275
Ninox 116
nipalensis Aceros 151
nipalinsis Actinodura 259
nipalensis Acthopyga 294
nipalensis Alcippe 259
nipalensis Apus 124
nipalensis Aquila 36
nipalensis Bubo 114
nipalensis Carpodacus 335
nipalensis Certhia 287
nipalensis Cutia 259
nipalensis Delichon 217
PAGE 54
nipalensis Paradoxornis 261
nipalensis Pitta 213
nipalensis Pyrrhula 336
nipalensis Sapizactus 37
nipalensis Turdoides 256
nippon Nipponia 18
Nipponia 18
nisonia Sylvia 263
nisus Accipiter 32
nitens Lamprotornis 350
nitens Malimbus 346
nitens Phamopepla 235
nitens Psalidoprocne 217
nitens Trochocercus 279
nitida Asturina 35
nitidissima Chlorochrysa 319
nitidula Lagonosticta 338
nitidula Maningoa 337
nitidum Dicaeum 288
nitidus Carpodectres 209
nitidus Cyanerpes 320
nitidus Phylloscopus 264
nivalis Montifringilla 343
nivalis Plectrophenax 304
nivea (Procellarra) Pagodroma 7
niveicapilla Cossypha 2421
niveigularis Tyrannus 198
niveogularis Aegithalos 285
niveoguttatus Hypargos 337
nivosa Campethera 165
nivosus Charadrius 63
njombe Cisticola 266
noanamae Bucco 154
nobilis Ana 99
nobilis Chamaeza 192
nobilis Francolinus 46
nobilis Gallinago 66
nobilis Moho 301
nobilis Orconympha 133
nobilis Otidiphaps 82
noctis Loxigrilla 310
noctitherus Ceprimulgus 121
noctivagus Crypturellus 2
noctua Athene 116
noevia Coracias 147
neguchii Sapheopipo 174
Nonnula 155
nonnula Estrilada 338
nordmanni Glareola
norfolciensis Columba 76
notabilis Anisognathus 318
notabilis Lichmera 297
notabilis Nestor 91
notabilis Phylidonyris 302
notata Campethera 165
notata Carduelis 333
notata Coturnicops 57
notata Gerygone 270
notata Meliphaga 299
notata Nectarinia 292
notatus Chlonestes 127
notatus Elanus 28
notatus Phoeniculus 148
Nothercus 154
Nothocercus 2
Nothocrax 42
Nothoprocta 3
Nothura 3
Notiochelidon 217
Notiomystis 299
Notornis 58
notosticta Aimophila 306
nouhuysi Melidectes 301
nouhuysi Sericornis 271
novacapitalis Scytalopus 195
novaeguineae Chaetura 123
novaeguineae Dacelo 140
novaeguineae Harpyopsis 36
novaeguineae Mearnsia 123
novaeguineae Philemon 300
novaeguineae Toxorhamphus 297
novaeguineae Zosterops 295
novaehollandiae Accipiter 33
novaehollandiae Anhinga 13
novaehollandiae Ardea 14
novaehollandiae Cereopsis 21
novaehollandiae Coracina 222
novaehollandiae Dromains 1
novaehollandiae Larus 71
novaehollandiae Lobibyx 63
novaehollandiae Menura 214
novaehollandiae Phylidonyris 302
novaehollandiae Plotus 13
novaehollandiae Podiceps 5
novaehollandiae Recurvirostia 67
novaehollandiae Scythrops

107
novaehollandiae Tachybaptus 5
novaehollandiae Tyto 112
novaeseclandiae Anthus 220
novaeseelandiae Aythya 25
novaeseelandiae Charadrius 64
novaescelandiae Falco 39
novaeseelandiae Finschia 270
novaeseelandiae Hemiphega 87
novaeseelandiae Ninox 116
novaeseelandiae Prosthemadera 302
novaesi Philydor 183
novaezelandiae Coturnix 47
novaezelandiae Cyanonamphus 95
novaezelandiae Himantopus 67
novaezelandiae Ixobrychus 16
noveboraccusis Cotarnicips 57
noveboracensis Seirus 323
nuba Neotis 60
nubica Campethera 165
nutricoides Merops 146
nubicus Caprimalgus 120
nubicus Lanius 234
nubicus Merops 146
nuchalis Campylorhynchus 236
nuchalis Chlemydera 358
nuchalis Garrulax 257
nuchalis Glareola 68
nuchalis Grallaria 194
nuchalis Parus 286
nuchalis Sphyrapicus 171
Nucifraga 365
nudiceps Gymnocichla 191
nudicollis Procnias 211
nudigenis Turdus 252
nudigula Pachycephala 283
nudipes Otus 113
nuditarsus Collocalia 122
nagator Myiarchus 200
Numenius 64
Numida 52
nuna Lesbia 132
nuttalli Pica 363
nattalli Dendrocopus 174
nuttalli Phalaenoptilus 119
nuttingi Myiarchus 200
nuttingi Oryzoborus 309
nyassae Anthus 220
Nyctanossa 15
Nyctea 115
nycthemerus Gennaeus 49
Nyctibius 118
Nycticorax 15
nycticorax Nycticorax 15
Nyctioryphes 62
Nyctidromus 119
Nyctiphrynus 119
Nyctiprogne 119
Nyctiornis 145
nympha Pitta 212
nympha Tamysiptera 143
Nymphicus 91
nyroca Aythya 25
Nystalus 155

oatesi Pitta 213
obliensis Spizorys 216
oberholseri Empidonax 201
oberi Icterus 329
oberi Myiarchus 200
oberlaenderi Zoothera 249
obscura Elaenia 204
obscura Maozina 302
obscura Meliphaga 299
obscura Myrmotherula 188
obscura Myzomela 297
obscura Penelope 41
oscura Pipra 206
obscura Psalidoprocne 217
obscura Sporophila 309
obscura Tiaris 309
obscurior Sublegatus 204
obscurus Charadrius 64
obscurus Dendragapus 43
obscurus Erithocus 240
obscurus Hemignathus 325
obscurus Myadestes 244
obscurus Phaeornis 251
obscurus Tetraophasis 45
obscurus Turdus 250
obsoleta Cranioleuca 181
obsoleta Ptyonoprogne 217
obsoleta Rhodopechya 334
obseletum Camptostoma 204
obsoletum Dicaeum 288
obsoletus Crypturellus 2
obsoletus Dendocopos 174
obsoletus Hemitriccus 202
obsoletus Salpinetes 236
obsoletus Turdus 251
obsoletus Xiphorhynchus 178
obtusa Vidua 341
ocai Pipilo 310
occidentalis Aechmophorus 5
occidentalis Andea 14
occidentalis Catharus 251
occidentalis Dendipica 322
occidentalis Empidopax 201
occidentalis Geoopsittacus 95
occidentalis Larus 71
occidentalis Leucopternis 34
occidentalis Myadestes 244
occidentalis Pelecanus 11
occidentalis Strix 117
occidentalis Thamnomanes 187
occipitalis Aegypius 30
occipitalis Chlorophonia 319
occipitalis Dendrocitta 363
occipitalis Lophaetus 37
occipitalis Melozone 310
occipitalis Phylloscopus 264
occipitalis Podiceps 5
occipitalis Ptilonopus 85
occipitalis Yuhina 260
oceanica Ducula 87
oceanica Myiagra 280
oceanicus Oceanites 10
Oceanites 10
Oceanodroma 10
ocellata Agriocharis 52
ocellata Leipoa 40
ocellata Rheinardia 51
ocellata Strix 117
ocellata Turnix 53
ocellatum Toxostoma 239
ocellatus Cyrtonyx 44
ocellatus Garrulax 258
ocellatus Nyctiphrynus 119
ocellatus Podargus 118
ocellatus Xiphorhynchus 178
ochotensis Locustella 262
ochracea Loxops 325
ochracea Sasia 163
ochraceiceps Hylophilus 326
ochraceiceps Pomatorhinus 254
ochraceifrons Grallaricula 193
ochraceiventris Leptotila 80
ochraceiventris Myiophobus 201
ochraceus Contopus 200
ochraceus Criniger 228
ochraceus Troglodytes 237
ochrocephala Amazona 104
ochrocophala Mohoua 270
ochrogaster Alcedo 139
ochrogaster Estrilda 338
ochrogester Penelope 41
ochrogaster Phylidor 183
ochrolaemus Automolus 184
ochroleuca Grallaria 193
ochromalus Eurylaimus 176
ochromelas Melidectes 301
ochropectus Francolinus 46
ochiopyga Drymophila 189
ochruros Phoenicurus 243
Ochthocca 196/7
Ochthornis 198
ocista Collocalia 122
ocreata Fraseria 273
Ocreatus 132
ocreatus Malaenormis 273
ocrophus Triuga 65
octosetaceus Mergus 26
ocularis Glareola 68
ocularis Ploceus 344
ocularis Prunella 239
oculata |*Emblema* 339
oculea Caloperdix 47
oculeus Canirallus 56
Oculocincta 296
oculta Batis 278
Ocyceros 149
Ocyphaps 79
odiosa Ninox 116
odomae Metallura 132
Odontophorus 44
Odontorchilus 236
oedicnernus Burhinus 68
Oedistoma 297
oemodium Conostoma 261
Oena 79
Oenanthe 246
oenanthe Oenanthe 246
oenanthoides Ochthoeca 197
oenas Columba 77
oenochlamys Sitta 286
oenone Chrysuronia 128
oenops Columba 77
oglei Stachyris 255
Ognorhynehus 100
okinawae Rallus 55
olax Treron 83
oleaginea Psalidopracne 217
oleaginea Rukia 296
PAGE 56
oleagineus Mionectes 205
oleagineus Mitrospingus 315
Oligura 262
olivacea Amaurornis 58
olivacea Bostrychia 18
olivacea Carduelis 333
olivacea Certhidia 310
olivacea Chlerothraupis 315
olivacea Cryptolybia 158
olivacea Gerygone 270
olivacea Iole 229
olivacea Nectarinia 292
olivacea Pachycephala 282
olivacea Piranga 316
olivacea Rhinomyias 273
olivacea Stactoloema 158
olivacea Tiaris 309
olivacea Zosterops 296
olivaceiceps Andropadus 226
olivaceiceps Ploceus 344
olivaceotuscus Turdus 249
olivaceum Chalcostigma 132
olivaceum Oncostroma 202
olivaceus Criniger 228
olivaceus Geocolaptes 164
olivaceus Hyophilus 326
olivaceus Linurgus 333
olivaceus Mionectes 205
olivaceus Mitrephenes 201
olivaceus Phalacroconax 12
olivaceus Phylloscopus 264
olivaceus Picumnus 163
olivaceus Prionochilus 288
olivaceus Psophodes 253
olivaceus Rhynchocyclus 202
olivaceus Telophorus 233
olivaceus Turdus 249
olivaceus Vireo 326
olivascens Muscicapa 276
olivascens Sicalis 308
olivater Turdus 252
olivea Tesia 262
olivetorum Hippolais 263
oliviae Columba 77
olivieri Porzana 57
olivii Turnix 53
olivinus Cercococcyx 106
olor Cygnus 20
olrogi Cinclodes 179
omiensis Liocichla 259
omissa Foudia 346
omissa Niltava 275
Oncostoma 202

oneilli Nephelonnis 315
onocrotalus Pelecanus 11
onslowi Phalacrocorax 12
Onychognathus 349
Onychorhynchus 201
oorti Megalaina 157
opaca Aplonis 348
Ophrysia 47
ophthalmica Cacatua 91
ophthalmicus Chlorospingus 314
ophthalmicus Phylloscartes 203
Opisthocomus 52
opistholeuca Oenanthe 246
opisthomdes Puffinus 8
Opisthoprora 132
Opopsitta 92
Oporornis 323
oratrix Amazona 104
orbygnianus Thinocorus 68
orbitalis Phylloscartes 203
orbitatum Idioptilon 202
orbitutus Hemitriccus 202
orbygnesius Bolborhynchus 101
orcesi Pyrrhura 101
Orchesticus 314
ordii Notharcus 154
oneas Lessonia 196
oreas Picathartes 261
oreganus Junco 305
orenocensis Knipolegus 197
orenocensis Saltator 313
Oreocharis 289
Oreoica 282
Oreomares 321
Oreomystis 325
Oreonympha 133
Oreophasis 42
oreophilus Buteo 35
Oreopholus 64
Oreophylax 180
Oreopsar 330
Oreopsittacus 89
Oreornis 299
Oreortyx 44
Oreoscoptes 238
Oreoscopus 271
Oreostruthus 339
Oreothraupis 311
Oreotriccus 204
Oreotrochilus 130
oreskios Harpactes 137
orientalis Acrocephalus 263
orientalis Anthreptes 290
orientalis Antorophila 47
orientalis Batis 278
orientalis Collocalia 122
orientalis Emberiza 303
orientalis Eurystomus 147
orientalis Meliphaga 299
orientalis Merops 146
orientalis Psalidoprocne 217
orientalis Pterocles 75
orientalis Streptopelia 78
orientalis Vidua 341
Origma 271
orina Coeligena 131
orinus Acrocephalus 263
Oriola 235
oriolina Campephaga 224
Oriolus 353
oriolus Oriolus 353
oritis Nectarinia 292
Oritusus 306
orix Euplectes 347
ornata Lophornis 127
ornata Meliphaga 299
ornata Myrmotherula 188
ornata Nothoprocta 3
ornata Poozpiza 308
ornata Poozpiza 308
ornata Thlypopsis 315
ornata Thraupis 317
ornata Unocissa 363
ornatus Calcarius 304
ornatus Cephalopterus 211
ornatus Lamprotornis 350
ornatus Merops 146
ornatus Myioborus 324
ornatus Myiotriccus 201
ornatus Pardalotus 289
ornatus Ptilmopus 85
ornatus Spizaetus 37
ornatus Trichoglossus 88
Ornithion 205
Oroaetus 37
orostruthus Ancanotor 228
orostrutyus Phyllastrephus 228
orpheus Pachycephala 283
orrhophaeus Harpactes 157
orru Corvus 366
Ortalis 41
Orthogonys 315
PAGE 57
Orthoryx 253
orthonyx Acropternis 195
Orthorauphus 68
Orthorhynchus 126
Orthotomus 265
ortizi Incaspiza 307
ortoni Penelope 41
Ortygocichla 268
Ortygospiza 339
Ortyxelos 53
oryzivora Padda 340
oryzivora Scaphidura 331
oryzivorus Dolichonyx 331
Oryzoborus 309
osburni Virco 326
oscillans Rhinomyias 273
oscitans Anastomus 17
osculans Chalcites 107
osea Nectarinia 292
oseryi Psarocolius 327
osgoodi Tinamus 2
ossifragus Corvus 366
ostenta Coracina 223
ostralegus Haematopus 62
ostrinus Pyrenestes 337
Otidiphaps 82
otiosus Caprinulgus 121
Otis 60
Otophanes 119
ottonis Asthenes 182
Otus 112/13
otus Asio 117
oustaleti Anas 23
oustaleti Cinclodes 179
oustaleti Nectarinia 292
oustaleti Phylloscartes 203
ovampensis Accipiter 32
owenii Apteryx 1
owstoni Rallus 55
oxycerca Cercibis 19
Oxylabes 260
Oxypogon 12
oxyptera Anas 23
Oxyruncus 205
Oxyura 26
oxyura Treron 83

pabsti Cinclodes 179
Pachycare 282
Pachycephala 282
pachycephaloides Clytorhynchus 280
Pachycephalopsis 273
Pachycoccyx 106
Pachyptila 7
Pachyramphus 210
pachyrhyncha Rhynchopsitta 100
pachyrhynchus Eudyptes 4
pachyrhynchus Ploceus 345
pacifica Andea 14
poacifica Drepanis 325
pacifica Ducula 87
pacifica Gallinula 58
pacifica Gavia 5
pacifica Parendiastes 58
pacificus Apus 124
pacificus Larus 71
pacificus Parendiastes 58
pacificus Puffinus 8
pacificus Rallus 55
Padda 340
paena Cereotrichas 241
pagodarum Sturnus 351
Pagodroma 7
Pagophila 70
palauensis Rukia 296
palawense Malacopteron 254
palawensis Chloropsis 230
palawensis Collocalia 122
palawensis Hypsipetes 229
pallasi Emberiza 304
pallasii Cinclus 236
pallatangae Elaenia 204
pallesceus Neopelma 207
palliata Falculea 235
palliatus Cinclodes 179
palliatus Garrulas 258
palliatus Haematopus 62
palliatus Thamnophilus 186
pallida Cranioleuca 181
pallida Hippolais 263
pallida Leptotila 80*pallida Lonchura* 340
pallida Spizella 306
pallida Zosterops 296
pallidiceps Atlapetes 311
pallidiceps Columba 77
pallidiceps Urosphena 262
pallidicinctus Tympanuchus 43
pallidigaster Anthreptes 290
pallidinucha Atlapetes 311
pallidirostris Tockus 149
pallidiventar Lonchura 340
pallidiventris Anthus 220
pallidiventris Parus 285
pallidus Apus 124
pallidus Carmarhynchus 310
pallidus Ceyx 139
pallidus Criniger 228
pallidus Cuculus 106
pallidus Melaenornis 273
pallidus Picumnus 163
pallidus Pitohui 248
pallidus Turdus 249
pallipes Niltava 275
palliseri Bradypterus 262
palmarum Charmosyna 89
palmarum Corvus 366
palmarum Dendroica 322
palmarum Phaenicophilus 315
palmarum Thraupis 317
palmeri Loxioides 325
palmeri Phaeornis 251
palmeri Porzanula 55
palmeri Tangara 319
Palmeria 325
palpebralis Schizoeaca 180
palpebrata Diomedea 6
palpebrose Gerygone 270
palpebrosa Zosterops
paludicola Acrocephalus 263
paludicola Estrilda 338
paludicola Riparia 217
palumboides Columba 77
palumbus Columba 77
palustre Pellorneum 254
palustris Aerocephalus 263
palustris Cistothorus 236
palustris Megalurus 262
palustris Microligea 324
palustris Parus 286
palustris Quiscalus 331
palustris Sporophila 309
pamela Aglaeactis 130
pammelaena Myzomela 297
pammelaina Melaenormis 273
panamensis Malacoptila 155
panamensis Myiarchus 200
panamensis Scytalopus 195
panayensis Aplonis 348
panayensis Coraciua 222
panayensis Muscicapa 276
panderi Podoces 365
Pandion 38
panini Penelopides 150
Panterpe 128
Panurus 261
panychlora Ninnopsittaca 102
Panyptile 124
papa Sarcoramphus 27
Paphosia 127
papillosa Pseudibis 18
papou Charmosyna 89
papua Pygoscelis 4
papuana Erythrura 339
papuana Microeca 272
papuensis Archboldia 357
papuensis Artamus 355
papuensis Chaetorhynchus 355
papuensis Collocalia 122
papuensis Coracina 221
papuensis Eurostopodus 119
papuensis Neositta 287
papuensis Podargus 118
papuensis Sericornis 271
Parabuteo 34

Paradigalla 359
Paradisaea 362
paradisaea Vidua 341
paradisea AntropoÔdes 54
paradisea Sterna 73
paradiscus Dicrurus 355
paradiseus Ptiloris 359
paradisi Terpsiphone 279
paradoxa Anthochaera 302
paradoxa Eugralla 195
Paradoxornis 261
paradoxus Paradoxornis 261
paradoxus Syrrhaptes 75
paraguiae Capella 66
paramelanotos Calidris 67
Paramythia 289
parasiticus Stercorarius 69
Pardalotus 289
pardalotus Xiphorhynchus 178
parellina Passerina 313
Parendiastes 58
parens Cettia 268

parens Vitia 268
pareola Chitoxiphia 206
pariae Myioborus 324
parina Xenodacnis 320
Parisoma 268
parisorum Icterus 329
parkeri Glaucidium 115
parkeri Herpsilochmus 189
parkinsoni Procellaria 7
Parmoptila 337
parnaguae Megaxenops 184
Paroaria 312
parodii Hemispingus 314
Parophasma 260
Paroreomyza 325
Parotia 361
Parula 322
parulus Anairetes 203
Parus 285/86
parva Conopias 198
parva Ficedula 274
parva Microdynamys 107
parva Porphyrula 58
parva Porzana 57
parva Viridonia 325
parvirostris Chlorospingus 314
parvirostris Colorhamphus 203
parvirostris Crypturellus 2
parvirostris Elaenia 204
parvirostris Tetrao 43
parvula Colluricinola 284
parvula Coracina 223
parvulus Anthoscepus 285
parvulus Camarhynchus 310
parvulus Caprimulgus 121
parvulus Nesomimus 238
parvus Cypsiurus 124
parvus Zosterops 295
parzudakii Tangara 319
Passer 342
Passerculus 305
Passerella 305
Passerina 313
passerina Columbina 80
passerina Mirafra 215
passerina Spizella 306
passerinii Ramphocelus 317
passerinum Glaucidium 115
passerinus Cacomantis 106
passerinus Forpus 102
passerinus Veniliornis 172
pastazae Galbula 154
pastinator Cacatua 91
patachonicus Tachyeres 22
Patagona 130
patagonica Aptenodytes 4
patagonica Asthenes 182
patagonicus Cinclodes 179
patagonicus Mimus 238
patagonicus Phrygilus 306
patagonus Cyanoliseus 100
pauliani Otus 113
paulistus Phylloscartes 203
pauper Camarhynchus 310
pauxi Crax 42
Pavo 51
pavonicus Dromococcyx 109
pavonina Balearica 54
pavoninus Lophornis 127
pavoninus Pharomacrus 135
paykullii Porzana 57
peolii Erythrura 339
pectardens Erithacus 240
pectorale Dicacum 288
pectoralis Aphelocephala 270
pectoralis Caprimulgus 121
pectoralis Circaetus 31
pectoralis Cissomela 302
pectoralis Colinus 44
pectoralis Coracina 223
pectoralis Coturnix 47
pectoralis Erithacus 240
pectoralis Euphonia 318
pectoralis Garrulax 258
pectoralis Herpsilochmus 189
pectoralis Hylophilus 326
pectoralis Icterus 329
pectoralis Lonchura 340
pectoralis Notharchus 154
pectoralis Pachycephala 283
pectoralis Polystictus 203
pectoralis Prinia 265
pectoralis Rallus 55
pectoralis Thlypopsis 315
pecuarius Charadrius 64
Pedioecetes 43
Pedionomus 53
pekinensis Rhopophilus 265
pelagica Chaetura 123
pelagicus Haliaeetus 29
pelagicus Hydrobates 10
pelagicus Phalacrocorax 12
PAGE 59Pelegodroma 10
Pelargopsis 139
Pelecanoides 10
Pelecanus 11
pelegrinoides Falco 39
pelewensis Collocalia 122
pelewensis Halcyon 141
pelewensis Ptilinopus 85
peli Gymnobucco 158
peli Scotopelia 115
pelios Turdus 249
pella Topaza 130
Pellorneum 254
pelopus Anthus 220
peltata Platysteira 278
Peltohyas 68
Peltops 280
pelzelni Aplonis 348
pelzelni Elaenia 204
pelzelni Granatellus 324
pelzelni Myrmeciza 192
pelzelni Ploceus 345
pelzelni Pseudotriccus 202
pelzelni Podiceps 5
pelzelni Tachybaptus 5
pembae Nectarinia 292
pembaensis Otus 113
pembaensis Treron 83
penduliger Cephalopterus 211
pendulinus Remiz 285
Penelope 41
penelope Anas 23
Penelopides 150
Penelopina 42
Peneoenanthe 272
Peneothello 272*penicillata Eucometis* 315
penicillata Meliphaga 299
penicillatus Phalacrocorax 12
penicillatus Pycnonotus 227
pennata Pterochemia 1
pennatus Hieranetus 37
Pennula 55
pensylvanica Dendroica 323
Penthoceryx 106
pentlandii Nothoprocta 3
pentlandi Tinamotis 3
peposaca Netta 25
peracensis Alcippe 260
percivali Oriolus 353
percnopterus Neophron 30
Poercnostola 191
percussus Prionochilus 288
percussus Xiphidiopicus 174
perdicaria Nothoprocta 3
Perdicula 47
dita Hirundo 217
Perdix 46
perdix Perdix 46
peregrina Vermivora 322
peregrinoides Falco 39
peregrinus Falco 39
Pericrocotus 225
perijana Schizoeaca 180
Periporphyrus 312
Perisoreus 364
Perissocephalus 211
perkeo Batis 278
perlata Pyrrhura 101
perlata Rhipidura 277
perlatum Glaucidium 115
parlatus Ptilinopus 85
permista Campethera 165
Pernis 28
pernix Myiotheretes 196
peronii Charadrius 64
peronii Zoothera 248
perousii Ptilinopus 85
perquisitor Vireo 326
perreini Estrilda 338
perrotii Hylexetastes 177
persa Tauraco 105
persicus Merops 146
persicus Puffinus 8
personata Agapornis 96
personata Apalis 267
personata Coracina 222
personata Corythaixoides 105
personata Gerygone 270
personata Heliopais 59
personata Incaspiza 307
personata Poephila 339
personata Prosopeia 93
personata Rhipidura 277
personata Spizocorys 216
personatus Artamus 354
personatus Atlapetes 311
personatus Coccothraustes 336
personatus Pterocles 75
personatus Trogon 136
personus Turdus 251
perspicax Penelope 41
perspicillata Ducula 87
perspicillata Grallaria 193
perspicillata Hymenops 197
perspicillata Melanitta 26
perspicillata Malacocincla 254
perspicillata Pulsatrix 115
perspicillatus Garrulax 258
perspicillatus Phalacrocorax 13
perspicillatus Sericornis 271
perstriata Ptiloprora 300
pertinax Aratinga 100
pertinax Contopus 200
peruana Cinnycerthia 236
peruanum Glaucidium 114
perusianus Galbalcyrhynchus 154
peravianus Conopophaga 194
peruviana Geositta 179
peruviana Grallaricula 193
peruviana Rupicola 208
peruviana Sporophila 309
peruviana Tangara 320
peruviana Vini 89
perversa Ninox 116
petechia Dendroica 323
petenica Aimophila 306
peterseni Otus 113
petiti Campephaga 224
petiti Psalidoproene 217
petoensis Falco 39
Petrochelidon 217
Petroica 272
Petronia 342
petronia Petronia 342
Petrophassa 79
petrophila Neophema 95
petrophilus Falco 39
petrosus Anthus 220
petrosus Ptilopachus 47
Peucedramus 324
Pezites 330
Pezopetes 311
Pezoporus 95
Phacellodomus 182
Phaenicophaeus 108
Phaenicophilus 315
phaenicuroides Hodgsonius 243

phaeocephalus Alophoixus 228
phaeocephalus Criniger 228
phaeocephalus Cyphorhinus 237
phaeocephalus Myiarchus 200
phaeocercus Mitrephanes 201
Phaeochroa 125
PAGE 60
phaeochromus Oriolus 353
Phaeomyias 204
phaeonotus Jimco 305
phaeopus Numenius 64
phaeopygia Pterodroma 9
Phaeornis 251
Phaeothlypis 324
Phaeotriccus 197
Phaethornis 125
phaeton Neochmia 339
Phaetusa 72
Phainopepla 235
phainopeplus Campylopterus 126
Phaimoptila 235
phaionota Pachycephala 283
Phalacrocorax 12
Phalaenoptilus 119
Phalaropus 68
Phalcoboenus 38
phalerata Coeligena 131
Phapitreron 82
Phaps 79
pharetra Dendroica 323
Pharomacrus 135
phasiana Rhipidura 277
phasianella Macropugia 78
phasianellus Dromococcyx 109
phasianellus Pedioecetes 43
phasianus Centropus 111
Phasianus 50
Phasidus 52
phayrei Pitta 213
Phedina 217
Phegornis 64
phelpsi Cypseloides
Phelpsia 199
Pheucticus 312
Phibalura 208
Phigys 89
philadelphia Geothlypis 323
philadelphia Larus 71
philadelphicus Vireo 326
philbyi Alectoris 45
Philemon 299/300
Philentoma 280
Philepitta 213
Philetairus 342
philippae Sylvietta 268
philippensis Loriculus 96
philippensis Ninox 116
philippensis Pelecanus 11
philippensis Pseudoptynx 114
philippensis Rallus 55
philippensis Spizaetus 37
philippensis Sturnus 351
philippii Phaethornis 125
philippinensis Arachnothera 294
philippinensis Pachycephala 283
philippinus Hypsipetes 229
philippinus Merops 146
philippinus Ploceus 344
philippsi Tangara 319
phillipsi Dumetia 256
phillipsi Oenanthe 246
Philodice 133
Philomachus 67
philomela Microcerculus 237
philomelos Turdus 250
Philortyx 44
Philydor 183
Phimosus 18
Phlegopsis 193
Phleocryptes 180
Phloeoceastes 169/70
Phlogophilus 129
Phlogothraupis 317
Phodilus 112
phoebe Metallura 132
phoebe Sayornis 197
phoenicae Campephaga 224
phoenicea Liocichla 259
phoenicea Petroica 272
phoeniceus Agelaius 329
phoeniceus Cardinalis 312
Phoenicircus 211
phoenicius Tachyphonus 316
phoenicobia Tachornis 124
phoenicomitra Myiophobus 201
Phoeniconaias 19
Phoenioparrus 19
Phoenicophaus 108
phoenicoptera Ptyilia 337
phoenicoptera Treron 83
Phoenicopterus 19
phoenicotis Chlorochrysa 319
Phoeniculus 148
phoenicura Rhipidura 277
phoenicuroides Lanius 233
phoenicurus Amaurornis 58
phoenicurus Ammomanes 216
phoenicurus Eremobius 179
phoenicurus Phoenicurus 243
phoenicurus Pseudattila 199
phoeosoma Melamprosops 325
Pholidornis 268
Phonygammus 359
phryganophila Schoeniophylax 180
phrygia Xanthomyza 302
Phrygilus 306
Phylidonysis 302
Phyllanthus 260
Phyllastrephus 227/28
Phyllomyias 204
Phylloscartes 203
Phylloscopus 264
Phytotoma 205
Piaggiae Zoothera
Piaya 108
Pica 363
pica Fluvicola 198
pica Pica 363
picaoides Heterophasia 260
picata Andea 14
picata Oenauthe 246
Picathartes 261
picatus Hemipus 225
picazuro Columba 77
picina Chaetura 123
picina Mearnsia 123
pickeringii Ducula 87
Picoides 172/74
picta Chloephaga 21
picta Conopophila 302
picta Emblema 339
picta Ispidina 139
picta Oreortyx 44
picta Psittacella 92
picta Pyrrhura 101
pictum Todirostrum 202
picturata Streptopelia 78
pictus Calcarius 304
pictus Chrysolophus 51
pictus Myioborus 324
picui Columbina 80
Piculus 165
Picumnus 163
picumnus Climacteris 287
picumnus Dendrocolaptes 177
Picus 166/67
picus Xiphorhynchus 178
Piezorhina 307
pilaris Atalotriccus 202
PAGE 61
pilaris Turdus 250
pileata Halcyon 142
pileata Leptasthenura 180
pileata Nemosia 315
pileata Neositta 287
pileata Notiochelid 217
pileata Oenauthe 246
pileata Penelope 41
pileata Pionopsitta 102
pileata Timalia 256
pileatus Accipiter 33
pileatus Atlapetes 311
pileatus Chlorospingus 314
pileatus Coryphozpingus 312
pileatus Dryocopus 169
pileatus Herpsilochmus 189
pileatus Lophotriccus 202
pileatus Monarcha 281
pileatus Pilherodias 15
pileatus Piprites 207
Pilherodius 15
pinaiae Lophozosterops 296
Pinarocorys 215
Pinaroloxias 310
Pinarornis 241
Pinguinas 74
Pinicola 335
pinicola Zoothera 248
pinnatus Botaurus 16
pinon Ducula 87
pintadeanus Francolinus 46
pinus Carduelis 333
pinus Dendroica 323
pinus Vermivora 322
Pionites 102
Pionopsitta 102
Pionus 103
pipiens Cisticola 266
Pipile
pipile (Pipile) Aburria 42
Pipilo 310
pipixcan Larus 71
Pipra 206
pipra Lodopleura 209
pipra Pipra 206
Pipraeidea 318
Pipreola 209
Piprites 207
Pipromorpha 205
Piranga 316
piscator Crinifer 105
pistrinaria Ducula 87
pitangua Megarynchus 199
Pitangus 199
Pithecophaga 36
Pithys 192
Pitiayami Parula 322
pitius Colaptes 164
Pitohui 284
Pitta 212
Pittasoma 193
pittoides Atelornis 147
Pitylus 313
pityophila Dendroica 323
Pitiriasis 234
piurae Ochthoeca 197
placens Climacteris 287
polacens Poecilodryas 272
placentis Charmosyna 89
placida Geopelia 78
placidus Charadrius 64
placidus Phyllastrephus 227
plagiata Astrurina 35
plancus Polyborus 38
Platalea 19
platalea Anas 24
platenae Ficedula 274
platenae Gallicolumba 81
platenae Prioniturus 92
plateni Aramidopsis 56
plateni Pachycephala 282
plateni Prionochilus 288
plateni Stachyris 255
platensis cistothorus 236
platensis Embernagra 308
platensis Leptasthenura 180
platurus Anthreptes 290
platurus Prioniturus 92
Platycercus 94
platycercus Selasphorus 134
Platycichla 251
Platylophus 363
(Platypsaris 210)
platypterus Buteo 35
platyrhynchos Anas 23
platyrhynchos Platyrinchus 201
platyrhynchum Electron 144
Platyrinchus 201
platyrostris Dendrocolaptes 177
Platysmurus 363
Platysteira 278
Platyura Schoenicola 262
plebejus Phrygilus 306
plebejus Turdoides 256
plebejus Turdus 252
Plectorhyncha 302
Plectrophenax 304
Plectopterus 26
Plegadis 19
pleschanka Oenanthe 246
pleskei Locustella 262
pleskei Podoces 365
pleurostictus Thryothorus 237
plicatus Aceros 151
Plocepasser 342

Ploceus 343/45
plumata Prionops 231
plumbea Columba 77
plumbea Dendroica 323
plumbea Diglossa 321
plumbea Euphonia 318
plumbea Ictinia 28
plumbea Leucopternis 34
plumbea Polisptila 261
plumbea Ptiloprora 300
plumbea Sporophila 309
plumbeiceps Leptotila 80
plumbeiceps Phyllomyias 204
plumbeiceps Oreotriccus 204
plumbeiceps Todirostrum 202
plumbeitarsus Phylloscopus 264
plumbeiventris Gymnoerex 56
plumbeus Dysithamnus 187
plumbeus Micrastur 38
plumbeus Myioparus 276
plumbeus Turdus 252
plumbeus Vireo 326
plumifera Numida 52
plumifera Petrophassa 79
plumosus Pinarornis 241
plumosus Pycnonotus 227
plumula Meliphaga 299
pluricinctus Pteroglossus 160
pluto Myiagra 280
Pluvialis 63
pluvialis Piaya 108
Pluvianellus 64
Pluvianus 68
Pygaga 255
Podager 119
podargina Pyrroglaux 112
Podargus 118
Podica 59
Podiceps 5
PAGE 62
podiceps Podilymbus 5
Podilymbus 5
peodobe Cercotrichas 241
Podoces 365
poecilocercus Mecocerculus 203
poecilocercus Phaeotriccus 197
poecilochrous Buteo 35
Poecilodryas 272
poecilolaemus Dendropicos 172
poecilonota Hylophylax 193
poeciloptera Nesoclopeus 56
poecilopterus Geobates 179
poecilorhyncha Anas 23
poecilorhynchus Garrulax 257
poecilorrhoa Gryptophaps 87
poecilosterna Mirafra 215
poecilotis Moupinia 256
poecilotis Phylloscartes 203
poecilotis Pogonotriccus 203
Poecilotriccus 202
poecilurus Chalcites 107
poecilurus Knipolegus 197
Poecilurus 181
poensis Batis 278
poensis Bubo 114
poensis Laniarius 232
poensis Neocossyphus 244
poensis Phyllastrephus 228
poensis Sheppardia 241
Poeoptera 349
Poephila 339
Pogoniulus 158
Pogonochichla 241
Pogonotriccus 203
Poicephalus 96
Poiciloptilus Botaurus 16
poicilotis Hylophilus 326
poioicephala Alcippe 260
Polemaetus 37
Polihierax 38
poliocephala Alethe 242
poliocephala Chloephaga 21
poliocephala Ducula 87
poliocephala Geothlypis 323
poliocephala Ortalis 41
poliocephala Stachyris 255
poliocephalum Todirostrum 202
poliocephalus Accipiter 33
poliocephalus Caprimulgus 120
poliocephalus Cuculus 106
poliocephalus Phaenicophilus 315
poliocephalus Phyllastrephus 228
poliocephalus Phylloscopus 264
poliocephalus Podiceps 5
poliocephalus Porphyrio 58
poliocephalus Tolmomyias 201
poliocephalus Turdus 249
poliocerca Eupherusa 129
poliogaster Accipiter 33
poliogaster Caryothraustes 312
poliogastra Zosterops 296
poliogenys Niltava 275
poliogenys Seicercus 264
poliogenys Spermophaga 337
Poliolais 267
Poliolimnas 57
poliolopha Prionops 231
poliolophus Batrachostomus 118
polionota Leucopternis 34
poliopareia Estrilda 338
poliophrys Alethe 242
poliophrys Synallaxis 181
poliopleura Emberiza 304
polioptera Coracina 223
polioptera Cossypha 241
polioptera Sheppardia 241
poliopterus Melierax 32
poliopterus Toxorhamphus 297
Polioptila 261
poliosoma Pachycephalopsis 273
poliothorax Kakamega 254
poliothorax Trichastoma 254
poliotis Paradoxornis 261
Polioxolnis 196
polleni Xenopirostris 235
pollenii Columba 77
pollens Coracina 222
pollens Phloeoceastes 170
Polyboroides 31
Polyborus 38
polychopterus Pachyramphus 210
polychroa Prinia 265
polyglotta Hippolais 263
polyglottos Mimus 238
polygramma Meliphaga 299
Polyonymus 132
polyosoma Buteo 35
Polyplancta 129
Polyplectron 51
Polysticta 24
Polystictus 203
Polytelis 94
Polytmus 128
polytmus Trochilus 128
Pomarea 273
pomarina Aquila 36
pomarinus Stercorarius 69
Pomatorhinus 254
Pomatostomus 254
pompadora Treron 83
pondicerianus Francolinus 46
pondicerianus Tephrodornis 225
Pooecetes 306
poortmani Chlorostilbon 127
Poospiza 307
Popelairia 127
popelairia Popelairia 127
porphyraceus Ptilinopus 85
porphyreolophus Tauraco 405
porphyreus Ptilonopus 85
Porphyrio 58
porphyrio Porphyrio 58
Porphyriops 57
Porphyriornis 58
porphyrocephala Glossopsitta 89
porphyrocephala Iridosornis 318
Porphyrolaema 208
porphyrolaema Apalis 267
porphyrolaema Porphyrolaema 208
Porphyrospiza 313
Porphyrula 58
portoricensis Loxigilla 310
portoricensis Melanerpes 171
Porzana 57
porzana Porzana 57
Porzanula 55
powelli Turnis 53
praecox Thamnophilus 186
prasina Erythrura 340
prasina Hylia 268
prasinus Aulacorhynchus 160
pratensis Anthus 220
pratincola Glareola 68
preciosa Tangara 320
Premnoplex 183
Premnormis 183
presbytes Phylloscopus 264
pretiosa Claravis 80
pretorise Monticola 247
pretrei Amazona 104
pretrei Phaethornis 125
preussi Nectarinia 292
preussi Petrochelidon 217
preussi Ploceus 345
PAGE 63
prevostii Anthracothorax 126
prevostii Euryceros 235
prigoginae Caprimulgus 120
prigoginae Chlorocichla 227
prigoginae Nectarinia 290
prigoginae Phodilus 112
primigenis Aethopyga 294
princei Zoothera 249
princeps Accipter 33
princeps Ammodramus 305
princeps Halcyon 143
princeps Leucopternis 34
princeps Melidectes 301
princeps Passerculus 305
princeps Ploceus 345
principalis Campephilus 175
pringlii Dryoscopus 231
Prinia 265
priocephalus Pycnonotus 227
Prionochilus 288
Prionodura 358
Prionops 231
pririt Batis 278
pristoptera Psalidoproene 217
pritchardii Megapodius 40
Probosciger 90
Procellaria 7
Procelsterna 73
procerus Hemignathus 325
Procnias 211
procurvoides Campylorhamphus 178
Prodotiscus 159
Progne 217
progne Euplectes 347
promerophirhynchus Xiphocolaptes 177
Promerops 302
propinqua Geospiza 310
propinqua Synallaxis 181
propinquus Hypsipetes 229
proprium Dicaeum 289
proregulus Phylloscopus 264
Prosobonia 65
Prosopeia 93
Prosthemadera 302
prosthemelas Icterus 328
Protonotaria 323
provacator Foulchaio 299
Prunella 239
prunellei Coeligena 131
pryeri Megalurus 262
przewalskii Grallaria 194
przewalskii Paradoxornis 261
Psalidoprocne 217
Psaltria 285
psaltria Carduelis 333
Psaltriparus 285
Psamathia 262
psammocromius Euplectes 347

Psarisomus 176
Psarocolius 327
Pselliophorus 311
Psephotus 94
Pseudalaemon 216
Pseudattila 199
Pseudeos 88
Pseudelaenia 204
Pseudibis 18
Pseudobias 278
Pseudobulweria 9
Pseudocalyptomena 176
Pseudochelidon 217
Pseudocolaptes 183
Pseudocolopterys 203
Pseudocossypphus 246
Pseudodacnis 320
Pseudogyps 30
Pseudoleistes 330
Pseudonestor 325
Pseudonigrita 342
Pseudopodoces 365
Pseudoptynx 114
Pseudoscops 117
Pseudoseisura 183
Pseudototanus 65
Pseudotriccus 202
pseudozosterops Randia 265
psilolaemus Francolinus 46
Psilopogon 156
Psilorhamphus 195
Psilorhinus 365
psittacea Erythrura 339
psittacea Psittirostra 325
psittacea Treron 83
Psittacella 92
psittacula Camarhynchus 310
psittacula Cyclorrhynchus 74
Psittacula 97
Psittaculostris 92
Psittacus 96
Psitteuteles 88
Psittinus 92
Psittirostra 325
Psittrichas 93
Psophia 54
Psophodes 253
psythopompos Scytalopus 195
ptaritepur Crypturellus 2
pteneres Tachyeres 22
Pteridophora 361
Pternistis 45/46
Pterocles 75
Pterocnemia 1
Pterodroma 9
Pteroglossus 160
Pteronetta 25
Pterophanes 130
Pteropodocys 221
Pteroptochus 195
Pteruthius 259
Ptilinopus 84
Ptilocichla 255
ptilocnemis (Erolia) Calidris 67
ptilogenys Gracula 352
Ptilogonys 235
Ptilolaemus 150
Ptilonorhynchus 358
Ptilopachus 47
Ptiloprora 300
ptilorhynchus Pernis 28
Ptiloris 359
Ptiloscelys 63
Ptilostomus 365
ptilosus Macronous 256
Ptychoramphus 74
Ptyonoprogne 217
Ptyrticus 254
pubescens Dendrocopos 174
pucherani Campyloramphus 178
pucherani Guttera 52
pucherani Melanerpes 171
pucheranii Neomorphus 109
Pucrasia 50
puella Hypothymis 280
puella Irena 230
puellus Hylphilus 326
Puffinus 8
puffinus Puffinus 8
pugnax Philomachus 67
pujoli Anthreptes 290
pulchella Charmosyna 89
pulchella Heterophasia 260
pulchella Lacedo 139
pulchella Myzomela 297
pulchella Nectarinia 292
PAGE 64
pulchella Neophema 95
pulchella Ochthoeca 197
pulchella Prinia 265
pulchellum Todirostrum 202
pulchellus Caprimulgus 121
pulchellus Nettapus 25
pulchellus Ptilinopus 85
pulchellus Vireolanius 326
pulcher Calothorax 133
pulcher Myiophobus 201
pulcher Phylloscopus 264
pulcher Spreo 350
pulcherrima Aethopyga 294
pulcherrima Alectroenas 85
pulcherrima Megalaima 157
pulcherrima Tangara 320
pulcherrimus Carpodacus 335
pulcherrimus Malurus 269
pulcherrimus Psephotus 94
pulchra Apalis 267
pulchra Cyanolyca 364
pulchra Incaspiza 307
pulchra Macgregoria 358
pulchra Pionopsitta 102
pulchra Pipneola 209
pulchra Sarothrura 57
pulchricollis Columba 77
pulitzeri Macrosphenus 268
pullaria Agapornis 96
pullicauda Neopsittacus 89
pulpa Mirafra 215
Pulsatrix 115
pulverentula Peneonanthe 272
pulverentulus Mulleripicus 168
pulverentulus Porphyrio 58
pumilero Cyanolyca 364
pumilio Indicator 159
pumilus Bradornis 273
pumilus Coccyzus 107
pumilus Picumnus 163
puna Anas 24
punctata Anas 24
punctata Tangara 319
punctatum Cinclosoma 253
punctatus Falco 39
punctatus Megalurus 268
punctatus Pardalotus 289
punctatus Phalacrocorax 13
punctatus Thamnophilus 186
puncticeps Dysithamnus 187
punctifrons Anthoscopus 285
punctigula Chrysoptilus 164
punctulasta Hylophylax 193
punctulata Lonchura 340
punctulata Ninox 116
punctalatus Chlorospingus 314
punctuligera Campethera 165
punensis Asthenes 182
punensis Geositta 179
punensis Grallaria 193
punensis Phrygilus 306
punicea Xipholena 208
puniceus Carpodacus 335
puniceus Picus 167
purnelli Amytornis 269
purpurascens Vidua 341
purpurata Querula 311
purpurata Touit 102
purpuratus Ptilinopus 85
purpuratus Trachyphonus 159
purpurea Ardea 14
purpurea Cochoa 244
purpureicauda Metallura 132
Purpureicephalus 94
purpureiceps Lamprotornis 350
purpureiventris Nectarinia 293
purpurescens Penelope 41
purpureus Carpodacus 335
purpureus Lamprotornis 350
purpureus Phoeniculus 148
purpuropterus Lamprotornis 350
pusilla Acanthiza 270
pusilla Aethia 74
pusilla Coenocorypha 66
pusilla Emberiza 304
pusilla Eremomela 268
pusilla Glossopsitta 89
pusilla Pnoepyga 255
pusilla Porzana 57
pusilla Sitta 286
pusilla Spizella 306
pusilla Wilsonia 324
pusillus Campyloramphus 178
pusillus Ceyx 139
pusillus Chordeiles 119
pusillus (Ereunetes) Calidris 67
pusillus Lophospingus 307
pusillus Loriculus 96
pusillus Merops 146
pusillus Pnoepyga 255
pusillus Pogoniulus 158
pusillus Serinus 332
pusio Micropsitta 92
pustulatus Icterus 329
puveli Illadopsis 254
pycnonotus 226/27
Pycnoptilus 270
Pycnopygius 299
pycnopygius Achaetops 263
pycrofti Pterodroma 9
pygargus Circus 31
Pygarrhichas 184
Pygiptila 186
pygmaea Aethia 74
pygmaea Sitta 286
pygmaeum Dicaeum 289
pygmaeum Oedistoma 297
pygmaeus Melanerpes 171
pygmaeus Phalacrocorax 12
pygmaeus Picumnus 163
pygmeus Eurynorhynchus 67
pylzowi Urocychramus 334
pyra Topaza 130
Pyrenestes 337
pyrgita Petronia 342
pyrhopterum Philentoma 280
Pyriglena 190
pyrilia Pionopsitta 102
Pyrocephalus 198
pyrocephalus Machaeropterus 207
Pyroderus 211
pyrohypogaster Hypopyrrhus 330
pyrolophus Psilopogon 156
Pyrope 196
pyrope Xolmis 196
pyropygia Hylocharis 128
pyrrhocephalus Phoenicophaeus 108
Pyrrhocoma 315
Pyrrhocorex 365
pyrrhocorax Pyrrhocorax 315
pyrrhodes Philyder 183
pyrrhogaster Mesopicos 174
Pyrrholaemus 270
pyrrholenca Asthenes 182
Pyrrhomyias 201
pyrrhonota Petrochelidon 217
pyrrhonotus Passer 342
pyrrophia Granioleuca 182
pyrrhophrys Chlorophoria 319
Pyrrhoplectes 336
pyrrhops Hapalopsittaca 103
pyrrhops Stachyris 255
pyrrhoptera Alcippe 260
pyrrhoptera Philidonyris 302
phrrhopterum Illadopsis 254
pyrrhopterus Brotogesis 102
pyrrhopterus Lycocorax 358
pyrrhopygia Halcyon 142
pyrrhopygia Hylacola 270
pyrrhothorax Turnix 53

pyrrhotis Blythicipus 175
pyrrhoura Myzornis 260
Pyrrhula 336
pyrrhula Pyrrhula 336
pyrrhura 101
pyrrogenys Pellorneum
Pyrroglaux 113
pyrrophanus Cacomantis 106
pyrropygus Copsythus 242
Pytilia 337
ptyopsittacus Loxia 336

quadragintus Pardalotus 289
quadribrachys Alcedo 139
quadricinctus Pterocles 75
quadricolor Dicaeum 289
quadricolor Halcyon 142
quadricolor Telophorus 233
quadsiringata Cercotrichas 241
quastina Estrilda 338
Quelea 346
quelea Quelea 346
querquedula Anas 24
querula 211
querula Zonotrichia 305
querulus Cacomantis 106
quinquestriata Aimophila 306
quinticolor Capito 156
quinticolor Lonchura 340
quiscalina Campephaga 224
Quisculus 330/31
quiscula Quiscalus 194
quitensis Giallaria 194
quixensis Microzhopias 188
quoyi Cracticus 357

rabieri Picus 167
rabori Napothera 255
racheliae Malimbus 346
radiata Ducula 87
radiatum Glaucidium 115
radiatus Accipiter 32
radiatus Erythrotrioselus 32
radiatus Nystalus 155
radiatus Polybosoides 31
radiceus Carpococcyx 109
radiolatus Melanorpes 171
radiolosus Neomorphus 109
radjah Tadorna 22
rafflesii Dinopium 168
rafflesii Megalaima 157
raggiena Paradisea 362
raimondii Phytotoma 205
raimondii Sicalis
Rallicula 55
Rallina 55
ralloides Ardeola 14
ralloides Myadestes 244
Rallus 55
rama Hippolais 263
ramphastinus Semnorius 156
Ramphastes 162
Ramphocaenus 261
Ramphocinclus 239
Ramphocosis 216
Ramphodon 125
Ramphomicron 132
Ramphotrigon 202
ramsayi Actinodura 259
Ramsayornis 302
randi Muscicapa 276
Randia 265
randrianasoli Cryptosylvicola 268
ranfurlys Phalacrocoraz 12
ranivorus Circus 31
rapax Aquila 36
Raphidura 123
rara Lampribia 18
rara Phytotoma 205
raricola Vidua 341
rarotongensis Pulinopus 85
raveni Coracornis 283
raveni Pachycephala 283
ravidus Twidus 252
raytal Calendrella 216
razae Calendrelle 216
rectirostris Anthreptis 290
rectirostris Hylocryptus 184
rectirostris Limnoctites 181
rectunguis Centropus 111
Recurvirostra 67
recurvirostris Avocettula 126
recurvirostris Esacus 68
recurvirostris Halcyon 142
redivivum Toxostoma 239
reevei Turdus 252
reevesii Phasianus 50
regalis Buteo 35
regalis Heliangelus 131
regia Erythsura 339
regia Nectarinia 293
regia Platalea 19
regia Vidua 341
regina Ptilinopus 85
regius Cicinnuras 361
regius Cosmopsarus 350
reguloides Acanthiza 270
reguloides Anairetes 203
reguloides Phylloscopus 264
regulorum Balearica 54
Regulus 268
regulus Machaeroptesus 207
regulus Prodotiscus 159
regulus Regulus 268
rehsei Acrocephalus 263
reichardi Ploceus 344
reichardi Serinus 293
reichenbachi Nectarinia 293
reichenbachii Halcyon 141
reichenovii Cryptospiza 337
reichenowi Anthreptes 290
reichenowi Apus 124
reichenowi Nectarinia 293
reichenowi Numida 52
reichenowi Pitta 213
reichenowi Ploceus 343
reichenowi Serinus 332
reichenowi Streptopelia 78
PAGE 66
Reinarda 124
reinhardti Iridormis 318
reinwardt Megapodius 40
reinwardtii Harpactes 137
reinwardtii Selenidera 161
reinwardtii Turdoides 256
Reinwardtoena 79
reinwardtsi Reinwardtoena 79
reiseri Phyllomyias 204
relicta Amaurospiza 309
relictensis Turdus 250
relictus Larus 71
religiosa Gracula 352
remifer Dicrurus 355
Remiz 285
renauldi Carpococcyx 109
rendovae Zosterops 295
rennelliana Rhipidura 277
repressa Sterna 73
resplendeus Ptiloscelys 63
respublica Diphyllodes 361
restricta Cisticola 266
reticulata Eos 88
reticulata Meliphaga 299
retrocinctum Dicaeum 289
retrii Prionops 231
revoilii Merops 146
rex Balaeniceps 17
rex Clytoceyx 140
reyi Hemispingus 314
reynaudi Coua 110
Rhabdornis 287
Rhagologus 282
rhami Lamprolaima 129
Rhamphocharis 288
Rhamphococcyx 108
Rhamphomantis 106
Rhea 1
Rhegmatoshina 192
Rheinardia 51
rhinoceros Buceros 153
Rhinocrypta 195
Rhinomyias 273
Rhinoplax 153
Rhinopomatus 148
Rhinoptilus 68
Rhinoptynx 117
Rhinostha 108
Rhipidura 277
Rhipidurus Corvus 367
Rhizothera 46
Rhodinocichla 315
rhodocephala Pyrzhura 101
rhodochlamys Carpodacus 335
rhodochrous Carpodacus 335
rhodocorytha Amazona 104
rhodogaster Accipiter 32
rhodogastes Pysshura 101
rhodolaema Anthreptes 290
Rhodonessa 24
rhodopareia Lagonosticta 338
Rhodopechys 334
rhodopeplus Carpodacus 335
Rhodopis 133
rhodopyga Estrilda 338
Rhodospingus 312
Rhodostethia 71
Rhodothraupis 312
Rhopocichla 256
Rhopodytes 108
Rhopophilus 265
Rhopornis 190
Rhyacornis 243
Rhychocyclus 202
Rhynchophanes 304
Rhynchopsitta 100
Rhynchortyx 44
Rhynchospiza 306
Rhynchostruthus 333
rhynchotis Anas 24
Rhynchotus 3
Rhynochetos 59
Rhyticeros 150
Rhytipterna 199
richardi Anthus 220
richardsi Pachycephala 282
richardsii Monarcha 281
richardsii Ptilinopus 85
richardsoni Contopus 200
richardsoni Eubucco 156
richardsoni Melanospiza 310
richmondi Gerygone 270
ricketti Paradoxornis 261
ricketti Phylloscopus 264
ricordi Chlorostilbon 127
ridgwayi Aegolius 117
ridgwayi Buteo 35
ridgwayi Caprimulgus 121
ridgwayi Colinus 44
ridgwayi Cotinga 208
ridgwayi Cyanocitta 364
ridgwayi Nesotriccus 200
ridgwayi Plegadis 19
ridgwayi Stelgidopteryx 217
ridgwayi Thaluriana 127
ridibundus Larus 71
ridleyanba Elaenia 204
riedeli Eclectus 93
riedelii Tauysiptera 143
riefferii Chloronnis 314
riefferi Pipreola 209
rikeri Berlepschia 183
Rimatoz 255
rimatorae Acrocephalus 263
(*ringrie Uria* 74)
ricourii Chelictinia 28
Riparia 217
riparia Riparia 217
ripponi Liocichla 259
risoria Streptopelia 78
risoria Yetapa 197
Rissa 69/71
rivoli Ptilinopis 85
rivolii Piculus 165
rivularis Phaeothlypis 324
rixosis Machetornis 198
roberti Conopophaga 194
roberti Cossypha 241
robertsi Prinia 265
robinsori Myiophoneus 247
roboratus Otus 113
roborowskii Carpodacus 335
robusta Anachnothera 294
robusta Cisticola 266
robusta Coracina 221
robusta Grateroscelis 271
robustirostris Acathiza 270
robustus Eudyptes 4
robustus Melichneutes 159
robustus Phloeoceastes 170

robustus Poicephalus 96
rochussenii Scolopax 66
rockefilleri Nectarinia 293
rodericanus Brenbornis 264
rodinogaster Petroica 272
rodolphei Stachysis 255
rogersi Atlantisia 55
rogersi Collocalia 122
Rogibyx 63
rolland Podiceps 5
Rollandia Podiceps 5
rolleti Lybius 159
Rollulus
PAGE 67
roquettei Phylloscastes 203
roraimae Automolus 184
roraimae Herpsilochmus 189
roraimae Myiophobus 201
roratus Eclectus 93
Rosaimia 183
rosacea Ducula 87
rosaceus Aegithalos 285
rosea Petroica 272
rosea Rhodinocichla 315
roseata Psittacula 97
roseatus Anthus 220
roseicapilla Ptilinopus 85
roseicapillus Eulophus 90
roseicollis Agapornis 96
roseifrons Pyrrhura 101
roseigaster Trogon 136
rosenbergi Amazilia 129
rosenbergi Sipia 190
rosenbergii Gymnocrex 56
rosenbergii Myzomela 297
rosenbergii Tyto 112
roseogrisla Streptopelia 78
roseogularis Piranga 316
roseus Carpodacus 335
roseus Larus 71
roseus Pelecanus 11
roseus Pericrotus 225
roseus Phoenicopterus 19
roseus Sturnus 351
rositae Passerina 313
rossae Musophaga 105
rossii Anser 21
rostrata Acanthis 334
rostrata Geothlypis 323
rostrata Pseudobulwaria 9
rostrata Pterodroma 9
rostratus Passerculus 305
Rostratula 62
rostratum Trichastoma 254
rostratus Ammodramus 305
Rostrhamus 28
rothschildi Astrapia 360
rothschildi Buthraupis 317
rothschildi Cypseloides 123
rothschildi Heliangelus 131
rothschildi Leucopsar 351
rothschildi Serinus 332
rougetti Rallus 55
rourei Nemesia 315
rovianae Gullirallus 55
rovuma Francolinus 46
Rowettia 307
rowleyi Eutrichomyias 280
rubatra Myzomela 297
rubecula Erithacus 240
rubecula Myiagra 280
rubecula Nonnula 155
rubecula Poospiza 308
rubecula Scelorchilus 195
rubeculoides Niltava 275
rubeculoides Prunella 239
rubeculus Pomatostornus 254
ruber Ergaticus 324
ruber Eudocimus 18
ruber Laterallus 57
ruber Phacellodornus 182
ruber Phaethornis 125
ruber Phoenicopterus 19
ruber Sphyrapicus 171
rubesceus Anthus 220
rubesceus Gallicolumba 81
rubesceus Nectarinia 293
rubetia Neoxolmis 196
rubetia Saxicola 245
rubetra Xolmis 196
rubrianae Accipiter 33
rubica Habia 316
rubicilla Carpodacus 335
rubicilloides Carpodacus 335
rubicunda Grus 54
rubida Prunella 239
rubidiceps Chloephaga 21
rubidiventris Pasus 286
rubiensis Monarcha 281
rubiginosa Ortygocichla 268
rubiginosus Automolus 184
rubiginosus Blythipicus 175
rubiginosus Margarornis 183
rubiginosus Megalusulus 268
rubiginosus Piculus 165
rubiginosus Ploceus 345
rubiginosus Trichoglossus 88
rubiginosus Turdoides 256
rubinoides Heliodoxa 130
rubinus Pyrocephalus 198
rubra Crax 42
rubra Euresygone 270
rubra Foudia 346
rubra Paradisaea 362
rubra Piranga 316
rubra Rallicula 55
rubricapilla Megalaima 137
rubricapillus Melanerpes 171
rubricata Lagonostieta 338
rubricatus Pardalotus 289
rubricauda Clytolaema 129
rubricauda Phaeton 11
rubriceps Poospiza 308
rubriceps Malimbus 346
rubriceps Piranga 316
rubricera Ducula 87
rubricollis Charadrius 63
rubricollis Malimbus 346
rubricollis Phloeoceastes 170
rubricornus Melanerpes 171
rubrifacies Lybius 159
rubrifrons Cordellina 324
rubrifrons Heterospingus 316
rubrifrons Melanerpes 171
rubrifrons Parmoptila 337
rubrigaster Tachuris 203
rubrigularis Charmosyna 89
rubripes Anas 23
rubrirostris Arborophila 47
rubrirostris Cnemoscopus 314
rubritorques Anthreptes 290
rubritorquis Trichoglossis 88
rubrocanus Turdus 250
rubrocapilla Pipra 206
rubrocristata Ampelion 209
rubrogenys Ara 99
rubronotata Charmosyna 89
rubropygius Serilophus 176
ruckeri Threnetes 125
ruddi Apalis 267
ruddi Heteromisafra 215
rudis Ceryle 138
rudolphi Ninox 116
rudolphi Paradisaea 362
ruecki Niltava 275
rueppellii Gyps 20
rufa Alectoris 45
rufa Anhinga 13
rufa Casiornis 199
rufa Cisticola 266
rufa Climacteris 287
rufa Formicivora 189
rufa Lessonia 196
rufa Lophura 49
rufa Loxops 325
rufa Malacoptila 155
PAGE 68
rufa Mirafra 215
rufa Ninox 268
rufa Ortygocichla 268
rufa Sarothrusa 57
rufa Schetba 235
rufa Trichocichla 268
rufalbus Thryothosus 237
rufaxilla Leptofila 80
rufesceus Aerocephalus 263
rufesceus Aimophila 306
rufesceus Atrichornis 214
rufesceus Calandrelle 216
rufesceus Egretta 15
rufesceus Illadopsis 254
rufesceus Laniocera 199
rufesceus Megalurus 268
rufesceus Otus 112
rufesceus Parus 286
rufesceus Pelecanus 11
rufesceus Prinia 265
rufesceus Rhynchotus 3
rufesceus Sericornis 271
rufesceus Sylvietta 268
rufesceus Turdoides 257
rufibarba Estrilda 338
ruficapilla Alcippe 260
ruficapilla Cettia 268
ruficapilla Giallaria 194
ruficapilla Hemethraupis 315
ruficapilla Normula 155
ruficapilla Spermophaga 337
ruficapilla Sylvietta 268
ruficapilla Synallaxis 181
ruficapilla Vermivera 322
ruficapilla Vitia 268
ruficapillus Agelaius 329
ruficapillus Baryphthengus 144
ruficapillus Cheradrius 64
ruficapillus Enicurus 243
ruficapillus Phylloscopus 264
ruficapillus Schistochlamys 314
ruficapillus Thamnophilus 186
ruficauda Aimophila 306
ruficauda Chamaeza 192
ruficauda Cichladusa 242
ruficauda Cinclocerthia 239
ruficauda Galbula 154
ruficauda Gerygone 270
ruficauda Histurgops 342
ruficauda Muscicapa 276
ruficauda Myrmeciza 192
ruficauda Neochgmia 339
ruficauda Ortalis 41
ruficauda Ramphotrigon 202
ruficauda Rhinomyias 273
ruficauda Upucerthia 179
ruficaudatus Philydon 183
ruficeps Aimophila 306
ruficeps Chalcostigma 132
ruficeps Cisticola 266
ruficeps Coua 110
ruficeps Elaenia 204
ruficeps Erithacus 240
ruficeps Laniarius 232
ruficeps Macropygia 78
ruficeps Orthotornus 265
ruficeps Paradoxornis 261
ruficeps Pelloracum 254
ruficeps Poecilotriccus 202
ruficeps Pomatostornus 254
ruficeps Pseudotriccus 202
ruficeps Pyrrhocoma 315
ruficeps Stackyris 255
ruficeps Stipiturus 269
ruficeps Thlypopsis 315
ruficervix Tangara 320
ruficollaris Halcyon 142
ruficollis Automolus 184
ruficollis Branta 21
ruficollis Caprimulgus 120
ruficollis Chalcites 107
ruficollis Corvus 367
ruficollis (Erolia) Celidrus 67
ruficollis Garrulax 258
ruficollis Gerygone 270
ruficollis Halcyon 142
ruficollis Hypnelus 155
ruficollis Jynx 163
ruficollis Madanga 296
ruficollis Micrestus 38
ruficollis Montifringilla 343
ruficollis Myiagra 280
ruficollis Oreopholus 64
ruficollis Pomatashinus 254
ruficollis Sporophila 309
ruficollis Stelgidopteryx

217
ruficollis Tachybaptus 5
ruficollis Turdus 250
ruficrissa Unosticte 129
ruficrista Lophotis 61
rufidorsa Rhipidura 277
rufidorsalis Apalis 267
rufidorsum Ceyx 139
rufifrons Apalis 267
rufifrons Basileuterus 324
rufifrons Formicarius 192
rufifrons Fulica 59
rufifrons Garrulax 258
rufifrons Percnostola 191
rufifrons Phacillodemus 182
rufifrons Rhipidura 277
rufifrons Stachyrus 256
rufigaster Ducula 87
rufigastra Niltava 275
rufigena Caprimulgus 120
rufigenis Atlapetes 311
rufigenis Tangara 320
rufigula Dendexetastes 177
rufigula Ficedula 274
rufigula Gallicolumba 81
rufigula Gymnopithys 192
rufigula Petrochelidon 215
rufigula Tarigara 320
rufigulari Idioptilon 202
rufigularis Falco 39
rufigularis Hemitriccus 202
rufigularis Hypsipetes 229
rufigularis Piaya 108
rufigularis Sclerurus 184
rufilata Cisticola 266
rufimargriatis Herpsilochmus 189
rufina Netta 25
rufinucha Aleadryas 283
rufinucha Atlapetes 311
rufinucha Campyloshynchus 236
rufinucha Pachycephala 283
rufinus Buteo 35
rufipectoralis Ochthoeca 197
rufipectus Arborphila 47
rufipectus Formicasius 192
rufipectus Leptopogon 205
rufipectus Nepothera 255
rufipectus Spilornis 31
rufipennis Butastur 34
rufipennis Geositta 179
rufipennis Illadopsis 254
rufipennis Macropygia 78
rufipennis Nectarinia 293
rufipennis Neomorphus 109
rufipennis Petrophassa 79
rufipennis Polioxolmis 196
PAGE 69
rufipennis Xolmis 196
rufipes Strix 117
rufipileatus Automolus 184
rufitorques Accipeter 33
rufitorques Turdus 252
rufiventer Pteruthius 259
rufiventer Tachyphonus 316
rufiventer Terpsiphone 279
rufiventris Accipiter 32
rufiventris Andea 14
rufiventris Andeola 14
rufiventris Colluricincha 194
rufiventris Euphoria 318
rufiventris Eurocalis 199
rufiventris Mionectes 205
rufiventris Monticola 247
rufiventris Neoxolmis 196
rufiventris Pachycephala 283
rufiventris Parus 286
rufiventris Picumnus 163
rufiventris Poicephalus 96
rufiventris Prionops 231
rufiventris Ramphocaenus 261
rufiventris Rhipidura 277
rufiventris Saltator 313
rufiventris Turdus 252
rufiventex Iridosornis 318
rufiventex Muscisaxicola 196
rufiaxillasis Molothrus 331
rufobrunneus Servinus 332
rufobrunneus Thripadectes 184
rufociliatus Troglodytes 237
rufocinctus Kupeornis 260
rufocinctus Lioptilus 260
rufocinctus Passer 342
rufocinerea Grallaria 194
rufocinerea Terpsiphone 279
rufocinereus Monticola 247
rufocinnamomea Mirafra 215
rufocollaris Hirundo 218
rufocrussalis Melidictes 301
rufofuscus Buteo 35
rufogularis Alcippe 260
rufogularis Anthochaera 302
rufogularis Apalis 267
rufogularis Artosophila 47
rufogularis Conopophila 302
rufogularis Garrulax 258
rufogularis Pachycephala 283
rufolateralis Smithornis 176
rufolaratus Podiceps 5
rufolaratus Tachybaptus 5
rufomarginatus Euscarthrus 203
rufomerus Chalcites 107
rufonuchalis Parus 286
rufopallistus Turdus 252
rufopectus Podiceps 5
rufopectus Poliscephalus 5
rufopicta Lagonosticta 338
rufopictus Pternistis 46
rufopileatum Pittasorna 193
rufoscapulatus Plocepasser 342
rufosuperciliaris Hemispingus 314
rufosuperciliata Syndactyla 183
rufula Grallaria 194
rufulus Anthus 220
rufulus Gampsorhynchus 259
rufulus Troglodytes 237
rufum Conirostrum 321
rufum Toxostorna 239
rufus Attila 199
rufus Bathmocercus 267
rufus Campyloptorus 126
rufus Caprimulgus 121
rufus Cursorius 68
rufus Furnasius 180
rufus Neocossyphus 244
rufus Pachysemphus 210
rufus Philydor 183
rufus Selasphorus 134
rufus Tachyphonus 316
rufus Trogon 136
rufusater Creadion 356
rugieusis Metabolus 280
ruki Rukia 296
Rukia 296
rumicivorus Thinocerus 68
rupestris Chordeiles 119
rupestris Columba 77
rupestris Monticola 247
rupestris Ptyonoprogne 217
Rupicola 208
rupicola colaptes 164
rupicola Pyrrhura 101
rupicola Rupicola 208
rupicoloides Faleo 39
ruppeli Sylvia 263
ruppelli Eurocephalus 231
ruppellii Eupodotis 61
ruppellii Poicephalus 96
rushiae Pholidornis 268
ruspolii Tauraco 105
russatum Todirostrum 202
russatus Chalcites 107
russatus Chlorostilbon 127
rustica Emberiza 304
rustica Haplospiza 307
rustica Hirundo 217
rusticola Scolopex 66
rusticolus Falco 39
ruticilla Setophaga 324
rutila Amazilia 129
rutila Chactura 123
rutila Emberiza 304
rutila Phytotoma 205
rutilaus Passer 342
rutilaus Synallaxis 181
rutilaus Xenops 184
rutilus Cypscloides 123
rutilus Otus 113
rutilus Thryothorus 237
ruwenzorii Apalis 267
ruwenzorii Caprimulgus 120
ruweti Ploceus 348
Rhynchops 73

sabini Chaetura
sabini Dryoscopus 231
sabini Larus 71
sabini Raphidura 123
sabini Xema 71
sabota Mirafra 215
sacerdotum Monarcha 281
sacra Egretta 15
Sagittarius 27
sagittata Chthonicola 270
sagittatus Oriolus 353
sagittatus Otus 112
sagittinostris Viridonia 325
sakalava Ploceus 345
Sakesphorus 185
salamonis Gallicolumba 81
salangana Collocalia 122
salinarum Xolmis 196
sallaei Granatellus 324
sallei Cyrtonyx 44
PAGE 70
salmoni Brachygalba 154
salmoni Chrysothlypis 315
salmoni Tigrisoma 16
Salpinctes 236
Salpornis 287
Saltator 313
Saltatricula 312
saltris Melospiza 305
saltonis Zonotrichia 305
saltuarius Cryptusellus 2
salvadorii Cryptospiza 337
salvadorii Enemomela 268
salvadorii Onychagnathus 349
salvadorii Psittaculinostris 92
salvadorii Zosterops 295
salvini Caprimulgus 121
salvini Diomedia 6
salvini Gymnopithys 192
salvini Mitu 42
salvini Pachyptila 7
salvini Tumbezia 198
samarensis Orthotornus 265
samarensis Penelopides 150
samoensis Gymnomyza 301
samoensis Zosterops 295
sanblasiana Cissolopha 365
sancta Halcyon 142
sanctaecaterinae Otus 113
sanctaecrucis Gallicolumba 81
sanctaecrucis Zosterops 295
sanctae helenae Charadrius 64
sanctae mariae Cymbilaimus 185
sancti hieronymi Panyptila 124
sancti thomae Brotogesis 102
sancti thomae Ploceus 345
sandvicensis Branta 21
sandvicensis Sterna 73
sandwichensis Ammodramus 305
sandwichensis Chasiempis 273
sandwichensis Passerculus 305
sandwichensis Pennula 55
sandwichensis Ptesodroma 9
sanfordi Aschboldia 387
sanfordi Niltava 275
sangirensis Nectarinia

293
sanguinea Cacatua 91
sanguinea Himatione 325
sanguinea Rhodopechyo 334
sanguineus Cnemophilus 358
sanguineus Pteroglossus 160
sanguineus Venilornis 172
sanguiniceps Haematortyx 47
sanguinolenta Myzomela 298
sanguinolentum Dicaeum 289
sanguinolentus Rallus 55
sanguinolentus Ramphocelus 317
sannio Garrulax 256
sanctaeonicis Carduelis 333
santhomae Treson 83
santovestris Aplonis 348
Sapayoa 207
Sapheopipo 174
saphirina Geotrygon 81
sapphira Ficedala 274
sapphirina Hylocharis 128
Sappho 132
saracura Aramides 56
sarasinosum Myza 301
sarasinosum Phylloscopus 264
Sarchiophorus 63
Sarcogyps 30
Sarcops 352
Sarcoramphus 27
sarda Sylvia 263
Sarkidiornis 25
Saroglossa 351
Sarothrusa 57
Sasia 163
sasin Selasphorus 134
Strapa 198
satrapa Regulus 268
saturata Acthopyga 294
saturata Euphonia 318
saturata Scolopax 66
saturatius Upucesthia 179
saturatus Buteo 35
saturatus Caprimulgus 121
saturatus Cuculus 106
saturatus Platyrinchus 201
saturninus Dysithamnus 187
saturninus Mimno 238
saturninus Thamnomanes 187
saucerrottei Amazilia 129
saularis Copsychus 242
saundersi Larus 71
saundersi Sterna 73
saurophaga Halcyon 142
saurothera 108
savana Tyrannus 198
savannarum Ammodramus 305
savesi Aegolothes 118
savilei Lophotis 61
sawtelli Collocalia 122
saxatalis Aeronautes 124
saxatalis Monticola 247
Saxicola 245
saxicolina Geositta 179
Saxicoloides 246
saya Sayornis 197
sayaca Thraupis 317
Sayornis 197
scalasis Dendrocopos 174
scandeus Geospiza 310
scandeus Phyllastrephus 228
scandiaca Nyctea 115
scansor Sclerurus 184
Scaphidura 331
scapularis Alisterus 93
Scardafilla 80
Sceloglaux 115
Scelorchilus 195
Scenopoeetes 357
Scepomycter 267
schach Larius 234
schalowi Oenanthe 246
schalowi Tauraco 105
scheepmakeri Goura 82
scheffleri Glaucidium 115
Schetba 235
Schiffornis 207
schistacca Coracina 223
schistacea Leucopternis 84
schistacea Passerella 305
schistacea Percnostola 191
schistacea Sporophila 309
schistacea Zonotrichia 305
schistacea Zoothera 248
schistaceigula Polioptila 261
schistaceus Atlapetes 311
schistaceus Enicurus 243
schistaceus Mayornis 272
schistaceus Thamnophilus 186
Schistes 133
Schisticeps Abroscopus 264
schisticeps Coracina 223
schisticeps Phoenicurus 243
schisticeps Pomatoshinus 254
schisticolor Myrmotherula 188
schistisagus Larus 71
Schistochlamyo 314
schistogynus Thamnomares 187
Schizoeaca 180
schlegeli Arremon 311
schlegeli Eudyptes 4
PAGE 71
schlegeli Philepitta 213
schlegelii Cercomela 245
schegelii Francolinus 46
schegelii Pachycephala 282
schleiermacheri Polyplectron 51
schneidesi Pitta 213
schoeniclus Emberiza 304
Schoemicola 262
Schoeniophylax 180
schoenobaenus Acrocephalus 263
schombungkii Micropygia 57
Schoutedenapus 124
schoutedeni Apalis 267
schoutedeni Apus 124
schrankii Tangara 320
schreibersii Heliodoxa 130
schulerbirga Scytalopus 195
schulzi Dryocopus 169
Schulzii Cinclus 236
sch,tti Tauraco 105
schwarzi Phylloscopus 264
scintilla Selasphorus 134
scirpaccus Acrocephalus 263
Scissinostrum 352
scita Stenostira 268
sclateri Ampelion 209
sclateri Asthenes 182
sclateri Cacicus 328
sclateri Eudtypes 4
sclateri Hylophilus 326
sclateri leterus 329
sclateri lophophorus 48
sclateri Meliarchus 301
sclateri Myiarchus 200
sclateri Myrmothesula 188
sclateri Myzomela 298
sclateri Nonnula 155
sclateri Parus 286
sclateri Phyllonugias 204
sclateri Picumnus 163
sclateri Pseudocoloropteryx 203
sclateri Spizocosys 216
sclateri Thryothorus 237
Sclateria 191
sclateriana Amalocichla 250
Selerurus 184
scolopacea Eudynamys 107
scolopaceus Limnodromus 66
scolopaceus Pogoninlus 158
Scolopax 66
scopifrons Prionops 231
scops Otus 113
Scopus 17
scopulinus Larus 71
scoresbii Larus 71
scotica Loxia 336
scoticus Legopus 43
Scotocerca 265
scotocerca Cercomela 245
Scotopelia 115
scotops Enemomela 268
scotops Serinus 332
Scotornis 120
scouleri Erimcurus 243
seripta Petrophassa
scutatus Augastes 133
scutatus Malimbus 346
scutatus Poecilurus 181
scutatus Pysodesus 211
scutulata Cairina 25
scutulata Ninox 116
Scytalopus 195
Scythrops 107
sechellarum Copsychus 242
sechellarum Foudia 346
sechellensis Bebrornis 264
seebohmi Atlapetes 311
seebohmi Bradypterus 262
seebohmi Cettia 262
seebohmi Dromaeocercus 264
seebohmi Oenauthe 246
seductus Otus 113
sefilata Parotia 361
segmentata Uropsalis 121
segregata Muscicapa 276
Seicercus 264
seimundi Nectarinia 293
seimundi Treron 83
Seiurus 323
Sclasphorus 134
Seledon Tangara 320
Selenidera 161
Seleucides 359
seloputo Strix 117
Semeiophorus 120
semibadius Thryothorus 237
semibrunneus Hylophilus 326
semicincta Malacoptila 155
semicinerea Gramioleuca 182
semicinereus Hylophilus 326
semicollaris Aîrornis 123
semicollaris Nycticryphes 62
semifasciata Tityra 210
semifasciatus Tockus 149
semiflava Geothlypis 323
semiflava Zosterops 296
semiflavum Ornithion 205
semifuscus Chlorospingus 314
semilarvata Eos 88
semilarvatus Parus 286
Semioptera 359
semipalmatus Catoptrophorus 65
semipalmatus Charadrius 64
semipalmatus Limnodromus . 66
sèmipartitus Melaenornis 273
semiphumbea Leucopternis 34
semiphumbeus Rallus 55
semisubra Rhipidara 277
semisufa Cossypha 241
semisufa Hirundo 217
semisufa Thamnolaea 245
semirufus Atlapetes 311
semirufus Myiarchus 200
semitorquata Alcedo 139
semitorquata Ficedula 274
semitorquata Streptopelia 78
semitorquatus Lurocalis 119
semitorquatus Micrastur 38
semitorquatus Polihierax 38
semitorques Spizixos 226
seminornis 156
semperi Leucopeza 324
semperi Zosterops 295
senator Lanius 234
senegala Lasgonosticta 338
senegala Tchagra 231
senegaleusis Batis 278
senegaleusis Bushuius 68
senegaleusis Centropus 111
senegaleusis Dryoscopus 231
senegaleusis Ephippiechynchus 17
senegaleusis Eupodotis 61

senegaleusis Hirundo 217
senegaleusis Nectarinia 293
senegaleusis Otus 113
senegaleusis Podica 59
senegaleusis Streptopclia 78
senegaleusis Zosterops 296
senegallus Afribyx 63
senegallus Pterocles 75
senegaloides Halcyon 142
senegallus Poicephalus 96
senex Aîrornis 123
senex Sturnus 351
PAGE 72
senex Todirostrum 202
senicula Pipilo 310
senilis Myornis 195
senilo Pionus 103
seniloides Pionus 103
sephaena Francolinus 46
Sephanoides 131
sephanoides Sephanoides 131
sepiaria Malacocincla 154
sepium Orthotornus 265
septimus Batrachostornus 118
sepulcratis Cacomantis 106
serena Pipra 206
sericea Loboparadisea 358
sericea Nectarinia 293
sericeus Orthotornus 265
sericeus Sturnus 351
sericocaudatis Caprimulgus 121
Sericornis 271
Sericossypha 314
Sericotes 126
Sericulus 358
Serilophus 176
serina Calyptocichla 227
Serinus 332
serinus Serinus 332
serpentarius Sagittarius 27
Serpophaga 203
serrana Formicivora 189
serrana Upucerthia 179
serranus Larus 71
serranus Turdus 252
serrator Mergus 26
serrator Sula 11
serriana Cona 110
serripennis Stelgidopteryx 217
serrirostris Colibri 126
serva Cercomacra 190
setaria Leptasthenura 180
sethsmithi Muxicapa 276
setifrons Xenornis 187
Setophaga 324
Setornis 229
severa Ana 99
severa Mackenziaena 185
severus Falco 39
sewerzowi Testrastes 43
sganzini Alectroenas 85
sharpei Lelage 176
sharpei Macronyx 219
sharpei Monticola 247
sharpei Sheppardia 241
sharpei Smithornis 176
sharpei Terenura 189
sharpei Turdoides 256
sharpii Apalis 267
sharpii Bycanistes 152
sharpii Cinnyricinclus 350
sharpii Mirafra 215
shelleyi Aethopyga 294
shelleyi Bubo 114
shelleyi Cryptospiza 337
shelleyi Francolinnus 46
shelleyi Nectarinia 292
shelleyi Nesocharis 337
shelleyi Spreo 350
Sheppardia 241
shorii Dinopium 168
Sialia 244
sialis Sialia 244
siamensis Zosterops 295
sibilans Erithacus 240
sibilater Sirystes 198
sibilatrix Anas 23
sibilatrix Phacellodornus 182
sibilatrix Phylloscopus 264
sibilatrix Sysigma 15
sibisica Muscicapa 276
sibisica Zoothera 248
sibicus Uregus 334
Sicalis 308
sichuaneusis Phylloscopus 264
sicki Terenura 189
sidamoeusis Heteromirafra 215
sieboldii Treron 83
siemiradzk, Carduelis 333
siemsseni Latoucheornis 303
Sigelus 273
sigillatus Peneothello 272
signata Cercotrichus 241
signata Eremopterix 215
signatus Basileuterus 324
signatus Knipolegus 197
signatus Myiotheretes 196
siju Glaucidium 115
silens Melaenonis 273
silens sigelus 273
silvanus Zosterops 296
silvestris Edithornis 56
silvicola Otus 113
Silvicultrix 196/97
similis Anthus 220
similis Chloropeta 263
similis Myiozetetes 199
similis Saltator 313
simoni Selasphorus 134
Simoxenops 183
simplex Anthreptes 290
simplex Calamonastes 267
simplex Chlorocichla 227
simplex Geoffroyus 92
simplex Myrmothera 193
simplex Pachycephala 283
simplex Passer 342
simplex Phaetusa 72
simplex Piculus 165
simplex Pogoniulus 158
simplex Pseudotriccus 202
simplex Pycnonotus 227
simplex Rhytiptorna 199
simplex Sporophila 309
simplex Sterna 72
sinaloa Thryothorus 237
sinaloae Corvus 366
sinaloae Progne 217
sindianus Phylloscopus 264
sinense Chrysomma 256
sinensis Centropus 111
sinensis Ixobrychus 16
sinensis Pycnonotus 227
sinensis Sturnus 351
singaleusis Anthreptes 290
singularis Xenerpestes 183
sinica Carduelis 333
sintillata Chalcopsitta 88
sinuata Cercomela 245
sinuatus Cardinalis 312
sipahi Haematospiza 336
siparaja Aethopyga 294
Siphonorhis 119
Sipia 190
Siptornis 183
Siptornopsis 182
siquijorensis Hypsipetes 229
sirintarae Pseudochelidon 217
Sirystes 198
sissonii Thryomanes 236
Sitta 286
Sittasornus 177
citticolor Coninostrum 321
sittoides Diglossa 321
sj`stedti Columba 76
sj`stedti Glaucidium 115
PAGE 73
skua Catharacta 69
sladeni Gymnobucco 158
sladeniae Apus 124
sloetii Campochaera 223
smaragfdinea Augasma 128
Smicrornis 270
Smilorhis 158
Smithii Anas 24
smithii Hirundo 217
smithii Petrophassa 79
Smithornis 176
smyrneusis Halcyon 142
Snethlagea 202
sociabilis Rostshamus 28
socialis Pluvianellus 64
socialis Prinia 265
socius Phibetarius 342
socorroensis Pipilo 310
socotrana Emberiza 304
socotranus Rhynchostruthus 333
s`derstr`mi Erioenemis 131
soemmerring, Sysmatieus 50
sokokensis Anthus 220
solala Caprimulgus 120
solandri Pterodroma 9
solangiae Sitta 286
solaris Nectarinia 291
solaris Pericrocotus 225
solitaria Capella 66
solitaria Gallinago 66
solitaria Origma 271
solitaria Tringa 65
solitaris Ficedula
solitarius Buteo 35
solitarius Cacicus 328
solitarius Cuculus 106
solitarius Harpyhaliaetus 34
solitarius Monticola 247
solitarius Myiodynastes 199
solitarius Phigys 89
solitarius Tiramus 2
solitarius Vireo 326
soloensis Accipiter 33
solomonensis Gymnophaps 87
solomonensis Nesasio 117
solomonensis Ptilinopus 85
solomonis Ninox 116
solstitialis Troglodytes 237
somalica Calendrella 216
somalica Mirafra 215
somalica Prinia 265
somalicus Larius 234
somaliensis Andopadus 226
somaliensis Phoeniculus 148
Somateria 24
sonnerati Chloropsis 230
sonnerati Gallus
sonnerati Penthoceryx 106
sophiae Leptopoecile 268
sordida Cercomele 245
sordida Muscicapa 276
sordida Pitta 213
sordida Thlypopsis 315
sordidulus Contropus 200
sordidulus Cynanthus 127
sordidus Pionus 103
Sorella 342
sorghophilus Acrocephalus 263
sorocula Tyto 112
soror Batis 278
soror Pachycephala 283
soror Pitta 213
soui Crypturellus 2
souimanga Nectarinia 293
souleyetii Lepidocolaptes 178
souilei Actinodura 259
soumagnei Tyto 112
souzae Lanius 234
sovimanga Nectarinia 293
spadicca Galloperdix 47
spadiceus Attila 199
spadix Thryothorus 236
spaldingii Orthonyx 253
sparganura Sappho 132
sparsa Anas 23
Spartonoica 180
sparveriodes Cuculus 106
sparveroides Falco 39
sparverius Falco 39
spatulata Coracias 147
speciosa Andeola 14
speciosa Columba 77
speciosa Geothlypis 323
speciosa Heliangelus 131
speciosa Stachysis 256
speciosum Corirostrum 321
speciosus Odontophorus 44
spectabilis Celeus 166
spectabilis Dryotriorchis 31
spectabilis Elaenia 204
spectabilis Lonchura 340
spectabilis Selenidera 161
spectabilis Somateria 24
specularioides Anas 22
specularis Anas 25
speculifera Dinca 307
speculiferus Nesospingus 314
speculigera Conothraupis 314
Speculipastor 350
Speirops 296

spekei Ploceus 345
spekoides Ploceus 345
Spelaeornis 255
speluncae Scytalopus 195
spencei Heliangelus 131
Speotyto 116
sperata Nectarinia 293
Spermophaga 337
Sphecotheres 354
Spheniscus 4
sphenocercus Lanius 234
Sphenocichla 255
Sphenoeacus 263
Sphenostorna 253
Sphenura Treron 83
Sphenurus 83
sphenurus Haliastur 29
Sphyrapicus 171
spilocephale Ninox 116
spilocephalus Otus 112
spilodera Hirundo 217
spilodera Rhipidura 277
spilodera Sericonnis 271
spilogaster Hieraaetus 37
spilogaster Picumnus 163
spilogaster Veniliornis 172
Spilonota Ninox 116
spilontus Ciscus 31
spilonotus Laterallus 57
spilonotus Ploceus 343
spilonotus Salpornis 287
spiloptera Sasoglossa 351
spiloptera Zoothera 348
spilopterus Centropus 111
spilopterus laterallus 57
Spiloptila 265
Spilonnis 31
spihorrhoa Ducula 87
Spindalis 317
spinescens Carduelis 333
Spinicauda Aphrastura 180
spinicauda Chaetura 123
spinicollis Threskiornis 18
spinoides Carduelis 333
PAGE 74
spinoletta Anthus 220
spinolotus Parus 286
spinosa Jacana 62
spinosus Hoplopterus 63
spinus Carduelis 333
spirusus Clyphosynchus 177
spixi Synallaxis 181
spixii Ana 98
spixii Xiphonshynchus 178
Spiza 312
spiza Motacilla 392
Spizaetus 37
Spizastur 37
Spisella 306
Spiziaptoryx 38
Spizixos 226
Spizocerys 216
splendens Corvus 366
splendens Malurus 269
splendens Prosopeia 93
splendida Neophema 95
splendida Zosterops 295
splendidissima Astrapia 360
splendidus Lamprotornis 350
spodionota Myrmotherula 187
spodicops Hemitriccus 202
spodicops Idioptilon 202
spodioptila Terenura 189
spodiopygria Collocalia 122
spodiurus Pachynamphus 210
spodocephala Emberiza 504
spodocephalus Dendropicos 174
sponsa Anas 25
Sporphila 308/9
Sporopipes 343
spragueii Anthus 220
Spreo 350
spurius Leterus 329
spurius Purpureicephalus 94
squalidus Phaethornis 125
squamata Callipepla 44
squamata Drymophila 189
squamata Eos 88
squamata Lichmera 297
squamata Reinarda 124
squamata Rhipidura 277
squamatus Capito 156
squamatus Francolinus 46
squamatus Garrulax 258
squamatus Lepidocolaptes 178
squamatus Mergus 26
squamatus Picus 167
squamatus Pycnonotus 227
squameiceps Urosphena 262
squamiceps Lophozosterops 296
squamiceps Turdoides 257
squamifrons Oculocincta 296
squamiger Margasorius 183
squamiger Neomorphus 109
squamigora Brachypteracias 147
squamigera Giallaria 194
squamisgularis Heliangchus 131
squamipila Ninox 116
squammata Columbina 80
squammata Scardafilla 80
squamosa Columba 77
squamosa Myzmeciza 192
squamosus Heliomaster 133
squamulatus Picumnus 163
squamulatus Turdoides 257
Squatarola 63
squatarola Squatarola 63
Stachysis 255
Stactolaema 158
stagnatilis Tringa 65
Stagonopleura 339
stairi Gallicolumba 81
Stalkeri Tephrozosterops 296
stanleyi Chalcostigma 132
starki Enemalauda 216
Starnoenas 82
Steatornis 118
steeri Oriolus 353
steerii Centropus 111
steerii Eurylaimus 176
steerii Liocichla 259
steerii Pitta 213
Steganopus 68
steinbachi Asthenes 182
steindachneri Picumnus 163
stejnegeri Viridonia 325
Stelgidopteryx 217
stellaris Botaurus 16
stellaris Pygiptila 186
stellata Gavia 5
stellata Pogonocichla 241
stellatus Batrachostornus 118
stellatus Brachypteryx 240
stellatus Caprimulgus 120
stellatus Marganornis 183
stellatus Odontophorus 44
stelleri Cyanocitta 364
stelleri Polysticta 24
Stellula 134
Stenostira 268
stentoreus Acrocephalus 263
stenura Capella 66
stenura Chlorostilbon 127
stephani Chalcophaps 79
stephaniae Astrapia 360
Stephanibyx 62/63
Stephanoaetus 37
Stephenophorus 318
Stephanoxis 126
stepheni Vini 89
Stercorasius 69
Sterna 72/73
Sternoclyta 130
sterrhopteron Wetmoreethraupis 317
stewarti Emberiza 304
stictigula Modulatrix 242
stictocephalus Herpsilochmus 189
stictocephalus Pycnopygius 299
stictolaema Decorychura 177
stictolaema Halcyon 142
stictolopha Lophornis 127
Stictonetta 24
stictoptera Touit 102
stictopterus Mecocerculus 203
stictothorax Dysithamnus 187
stictothorax Mysmeciza 192
stictothorax Synallaxis 181
sticturus Iterpsilochmus 189
stierlingi Calamonastes 267
stierlingi Dendropicos 172
Stigmatura 203
stigmatus Loriculus 96
stiphrornis 241
Stipiturus 269
Stizorhina 244
stolidus Ano,s 73
stolidus Myiarchus 200
stolzmanni Aimophila
stolzmanni Chlorothraupis 315
stolzmanni Rhynchospiza 306
stolzmanni Tyranneutes 207
stolzmanni Urothraupis 311
storeri Cypseloides 123
stormi Ciconia 17
strenua Aratinga 100
strenua Ninox 116
strenua Zosterops 296
Strepera 357
strepera Anas 23
strepera Elaenia 204
strepitaus Garrulax 258
PAGE 75
strepitaus Phyllastrephus 228
Streptocitta 352
Streptopelia 78
streptophorus Fraucolinus 46
streptophorus Lipaugus 210
Streptopraone 123
stresemanni Ampelion 209
stresemanni Hylexetastes 177
stresemanni Merulaxis 195
stresemanni Zavattariornis 365
stresemanni Zosterops 295
Stresmannia 297
striata Aplonis 348
striata Andeola 14
striata Butorides 14
striata Coracina 223
striata Dendroica 323
striata Geopelia 78
striata Kenopia 255
striata Leptasthenura 180
striata Lonchura 340
striata Malacoptila 155
striata Muscicapa 276
striata Neositta 287
striata Stachysis 256
striata Sterna 73
striaticeps Dysithamnus 187
striaticeps Entotriccus 197
striaticeps Macronous 256
striaticeps Phacellodornus 182
striaticolle Idioptilon 202
striaticollis Alcippe 260
striaticollis Anabacerthia 183
striaticollis Hermitriccus 202
striaticollis Mionectes 205
striaticollis Myiotheretes 196
striaticollis Phacellodornus 182
striaticollis Siptornis 183
striatigula Neomixis 255
striatigularis Xiphoshynchus 178
striativentris Melanochasis 288
striatus Accipiter 32
striatus Chaetornis 262
striatus Colius 135
striatus Garrulax 258
striatus Melanerpes 171
striatus Pendalotus 289
striatus Pycnonotus 227
striatus Rallus 55

striatus Simoxenops 183
striatusTurdoides 257
stricklandi Dendrocopos 174
stricklandii Chubbia 66
stricklandii Copsychus 242
strigiceps Aimophila 306
strigilatus Ancistrops 183
strigilatus Myrmorchilus 188
strigirostris Didunculus 82
strigoides Podargus 118
Strigops 95
strigula Mixla 259
strigulogus Crypturellus 2
striolata Emberiza 304
striolata Hirundo 217
striolata Leptasthenura 180
striolata Stachysis 256
striolatus Nystalus 155
striolatus Serinus 332
Strix 117
strophianus Heliangelus 131
strophiata Ficedula 274
strophiata Prunella 239
strophium Odontophorus 44
struthersii Ibidoshyncha 67
Struthidea 356
Struthio 1
st thoma Brotogesis 102
st thomee Ploceus 345
stuarti Phaethornis 125
stuhlmanni Nectarinia 290
stuhlmanni Ploceus 343
stuhlmanni Poeoptera 349
sturmii Ixobrychus 16
sturninus Sturnus 351
Sturnus 351
stygia Lonchura 340
stygius Asio 117
suavissima Pipra 206
suahelicus Euplectes 347
suahelicus Passer 342
subaffubus Phylloscopus 264
subalaris lipaugus 288
subalaris Macroagelaius 330
subalaris Syndactyla 183
subalaris Turdus
subaureus Ploceus 345
subbrunneus Gripodectes 201
subbuteo Falco 39
subcaeruleum Parisoma 268
subcinnamomea Euryptila 267
subcorniculatus Philemon 300
subcristata Aviceda 28
subcistata serpophaga 203
subcylindricus Bycanistes 152
subflammulatus Knipolegus 197
subflava Amandava 339
subflava Inezia 203
subflava Prinia 265
subflayescono Ducula 86
subfrenata Meliphaga 299
subgularis Ptilinopus 85
subhimachalus Pinicola 335
subis Progne 217
Sublegatus 204
subminuta (Erolia) Calidris 67
submiger Falco 39
subochraceus Phaethornis 125
subpersonatus Ploceus 345
subplacens Myiopagis 204
subpudica Synallaxis 181
subrubra Ficedula 274
subruficapilla Cisticola 266
subruficollis Aceris 151
subruficollis Tryngites 67
subrufus Turdoides 257
substriata Prinia 265
substriata Pardalotus 289
subselphureus Pogoniulus 158
subtilis Buteogallus 34
subtilis Picumnus 163
subulata Urosphena 262
subulatus Hyloctistes 183
subulatus Garrulax 258
subrimacea Columba 77
subvirgatus Ammodramus 305
subviridis Phylloscopus 264
sueurii Lalage 224
Suiriri 204
suiriri Suiriri 204
sukatschewi Garralax 258
Sula 11
sula Sula 11
Sulaensis Rhipidura 277
sulcatus Rhipidura 277
sulcatus Anlacoshynchus 160
sulcirostris Crotophaga 109
sulcirostris Phalacrocorax 13
sulfuratus Ramphastos 162
sulfureopectus Telophorus 233
sulfuriventer Pachycephala 283
sulphurata Campephaga 224
sulphurata Emberiza 304
sulphuratus Pitangus 199
PAGE 76
sulphuratus Serinus 332
sulphurea Cacatua 91
sulphurea Garygone 270
sulphurea Tyrannopsis 198
sulphureipygius Myiobius 201
sulphureiventer Neopelma 207
sulphurescens Tolmomyias 201
sulpharifera Cranisleuca 182
sultanea Melanochlora 286
sumatrana Andea 14
sumatrana Bubo 114
sumatrana Niltava 275
sumatrana Sterna 73
sumatranus Corydon 176
sumatranus Dicrurus
sumatranus Rhopodytes 108
sumatranus Tanygnathus 93
sumichrasti Aimophila 306
sumichrasti Catherpes 236
sumichrasti Hylorchilus 236
sundara Niltava 275
sundevalli Andeola 14
sundevalli Butorides 14
sunensis Myrmotherula 188
sunia Otus 112
superba Lophorina 361
superba Nectarinia 293
superba Niltava 275
superba Pitta 213
superbus Ptilinopus 85
superbus Spreo 350
superciliaris Abroscopus 264
superciliaris Burhinus 68
superciliaris Camaroptera 267
superciliaris Drymodes 240
superciliaris Ficedula 274
superciliaris Hemispingus 314
superciliaris Leistes 330
superciliaris Leistes 330
superciliaris Leptopogon 205
superciliaris Lophozostexops 296
superciliaris Melanerpes 171
superciliaris Ninox 116
superciliaris Ontalis 41
superciliaris Penelope 41
superciliaris Petronia 342
superciliaris Phylloscantes 203
superciliaris Rhipidura 277
superciliaris Scytalopus 195
superciliaris Sterna 73
superciliaris Tesia 262
superciliaris Thryothorus 237
supercilairis Xiphirhynchus 254
superciliosa Anas 23
superciliosa Eumomota 144
superciliosa Ophrysia 47
superciiosa Poecilodryas 272
superciliosa Synallaxis 181
superciliosa Vermivora 322
superciliosa Woodfordia 296
superciliosus Acanthorhynchus 302
superciliosus Accipiter 33
superciliosus Anomalophrys 63
superciliosus Antamus 354
superciliosus Centropus 111
superciliosus Dasylophus 108
superciliosus Merops 146
superciliosus Oriturus 306
superciliosus Parus 286
superciliosus Phaethornis 125
superciliosus Phoeniciphaus 108
superciliosus Plocepasser 342
superciliosus Ploceus 345
superciliosus Pomatorhinus 254
superflua Rhipidura 277
surda Touit 102
susrinamensis Myrmotherula 188
surinamus Pachyramphus 210
surinamus Tachyphonus 316
Surnia 115
Surniculus 107
surrucura Trogon 136
suscitator Turnix 53
sutorius Orthotomus 265
svecicus Erithacus 240
syecicus Luscinia 240
swainsoni Buteo 35
swainsoni Myiarchus 200
swainsonii Chlorostilbon 127
swainsonii Gampsonyx 28
swainsonii Limnothlypis 323
swainsonii Passer 342
swainsonii Polytelis 94
swainsonii Pternistis 46
swainsonii Ramphastos 162
swainsonii Vireo 326
swalesi Turdus 252
swierstrai Francolinus 46
swinderniana Agapornis 96
swinhoii Hierophasis 49
swynnertoni Pogonocichla 241
swynnertoni Swynertonia 241
Swynnertonia 241
sybillae Lampornis 129
sylvanus Anthus 220
sylvatica Prinia 265
sylvatica Turnix 53
sylvaticus Bradypterus 262
sylvestris Tricholimnas 55
Sylvia 263-268
sylvia Tanysiptera 143
sylvia Todinostrum 202
sylviella Anthoscopus 285
sylvietta 268
sylviolus Leptotriccus 203
sylviolus Phylloscartes 203
sylviorthorhynchus 180
Sylviparus 286
symonsi Serinus 332
Synallaxis 180/81
Syndactyla 183
Synoicus 47
Synthliboramphus 74
Sypheotides 61
syriacus Dendrocopus 174
syriacus Serinus 332
Syrigma 15
syrinx Acrocephalus 263
Syrmaticus 50
syrmatophorus Phaethornis

125
Syrrhaptes
szalayi Oriolus 353
szechenyii Tetraophasis 45

tabuensis Perzana 57
tabuensis Prospoeia 93
tacurcunae Chlorospingus 314
tacazze Nectarinia
Taccocua 108
tachiro Accipiter 32
Tachornis 124
Tacharis 203
Tachybaptus 5
Tachycineta 217
Tachymarptis 124
Tachyphonus 316
taciturnus Arremon 311
taczanowskii Cinclodes 179
taczanowskii Leptopogon 205
taczanowskii Leucippus 128
taczanowskii Montifungilla 343
taczanowskii Kothoprocta 3
taczanowskii Podiceps 5
taczanowskius Sicalis 308
taczanowskius Bradypterus 262
Tadorna 22
tadorna Tadorna 22
tadornoides Tadorna 22
taeniata Dubusia 318
taeniatus Microcerculus 237
taeniatus Peucedramus 324
taeniolaema Campothera 165
taeniopterus Ploceus 345
Taeniopygia 339
Taeniotriccus 202
tahanensis Zosterops 295
tahapisi Emberiza 304
tahitica Hirundo 217
tahitiensis Numenius 64
tiatensis Urodynamis 107
taiti Aoeocephalus 263
taivanus Pycnonotus 227
takatsukasae Monarcha 281
talaseae Zoothera 248
talatala Nectarixia 293
talantensis Terpsiphone 279
Talegalla 40
talcapoti Columbina 80
tamaringensis Conirosteum 321
tamatia Bucco 154
tanagrinus Lampropser 330
tanganjicae Zoothera 249
Tangara 319/20
Tangavius 331
tangorum Acrocephalus 262
tanki Turnix 534
tannensis Ptilinopus 85
tanneri Troglodytes 237
Tanygnathus 93
Tanysiptera 143
tao Tinamus 2
Taoniscus 3
Tapera 109
tapera Progne 217
Taphrospilus 128
Taraba 185
taranta Agapornis 96
tarapacensis Pterocaemia 1
tarda Otis 60
tarnii Pteroptochos 195
Tarsiger 240
tasmanicus Corvus 366
tatanpa Crypturellus
tatei Premnoplex 183
Tauraco 105
taverni Spizella 306
Tchagra 231
tchagra Tchagra 231
tectes saxicola 245
tectus Notharchus 154
tectus Sarciophorus 63
teerinki Lonchura 340
teesa Butastus 34
tegimae Pericrocotus 225
teijsmanni Rhipidura 277
Telacanthura 123
telasco Sporophila 309
Teledromas 195
telescophthalmus Arses 281
Telmatodytes 236
Telophorus 232/33
temia Crypsirina 363
temminckii Coracias 147
temminckii Coracina 223
temminckii Cursorius 68
temminckii Dendrocopos 174
temminckii (Erolia) Calidris 67
temminckii Eurostopodus 119
temminckii Orthonyx 253
temminckii Picumnus 163
temminckii Tragopan 48
Temnurus 363
temnurus Temnurus 363
temnurus Trogon 136
temporalis Aegintha 339
temporalis Ploceus 345
temporalis Pomatostomus 254
tenebricosa Tyto 112
tenebrosa Chelidoptera 155
tenebrosa Gallinula 58
tenebrosa Gerygone 270
tenebrosa Pachycephala 283
tenebrosa Rhipidura 277
tenebrosus Phasianus 50
tenebrosus Phyllastrephus 228
tenebrosus Pitohui 284
tenebrosus Turdoides 257
tenella Neomixis 255
tenellipes Phylloscopus 264
tenellus Tmetothylacus 219
tener Loriculus 96
teneriffae Regulus 268
tenuirostris Acanthorhynchus 302
tenuirostris AnoÔs 73
tenuirostris Cacatua 91
tenuirostris Calidris 67
tenuirostris Coracina 223
tenuirostris Geositta 179
tenuirostris Inezia 203
tenuirostris Macropygia 78
tenuirostris Numenius 64
tenuirostris Onychognathus 349
tenuirostris Oriolus 353
tenuirostris Puffinus 8
tenuirostris Xenops 184
tenuirostris Zosterops 296
tephrocotis Leucosticte 334
Tephrodornis 225
tephrolaema Anthreptes 290
tephrolaemus Andropadus 226
tephrolaemus Pycronotus 226
Tephrolesbia 132
tephronota Sitta 286
tephronotum Glaucidium 115
tephronotus Lanius 234
tephronotus Turdus 249
tephropleurus Zosterops 295
Tephrozosterops 296
Terathopius 31
Terenotriccus 201
Terenura 189
Teretistris 324
Terpsiphone 279
terrae-reginae Collocalia 122
terrestris Phyllastrephus 228
terrestris Trugon 82
terrestris Zoothera 248
terrisii Rhynchopsitta 100
Tersina 321
Tesia 262
tessmanni Muscicapa 276
testacea Erolia 67
tethys Oceanodroma 10
tetiparia Zosterops 295
Tetrao 43
Tetraogallus 45
Tetraophasis 45
Tetrastes 43
tetrax Otis 60
tetrix Lynurus 43
PAGE 78
Textilis Amytornis 269
textrix Cisticola 266
teydea Fringilla 332
teysmanni Pachycephala 283
teysmanni Rhipidura 277
teysmannii Treron 83
thagus Pelecanus 11
Thalasseus 72
thalassina Cissa 363
thalassina Muscicapa 276
thalassina Tachycineta 217
thalessinus Colibri 126Thalassoica 7
Thalassornis 20
Thalurania 127
Thamnistes 187
Thamnolaea 247
Thamnomanes 187
Thamnophilus 186
Thamnornis 265
Thaumastura 133
Thayeri Larus 71
theklae Galerida 216
thenca Mimus 238
theomacha Ninox 116
theresae Montifringilla 343
thersiae Metallura 132
theresiae Polytmus 128
Theristicus 18
Thescelocichla 227
thibetanus Serinus 332
thilius Agelaius 329
Thinocorus 68
Thlypopsis 315
tholloni Myrmecocichla 245
thomensis Alcedo 139
thomensis Chaetura 123
thomensis Columba 76
thomensis Estrilde 338
thomensis Nectarinia 293
thomensis Zoonavera 123
thompsoni Hypsipetes 229
thoracica Apalis 267
thoracica Bambusicola 47
thoracica Poospiza 308
thoracica Stachyris 256
thoracicus Bradypterus 262
thoracicus Charadrius 64
thoracicus Cyphorhinus 237
thoracicus Dactylortyx 44
thoracicus Hylophilus 326
thoracicus Liosceles 195
thoracicus Prionochilus 288
thoracicus Thryothorus 237
Thraupis 317
Threnetes 125
threnothorax Rhipidura 277
Threskiornis 18
Thripadectes 184
Thripias 174
Thripophaga 182
thruppi Parus 285
Thryomanes 236
Thryorchilus 237
Thryothorus 237
thula Egretta 15
thumbergi Motacilla 219
thura Carpodacus 335
thryroideus Sphynapicus 171
Tiaris 309
tibetanus Syrrhaptes 75
tibetanus Tetraogallus 45
tibialis Lorius 88
tibialis Neochelidon 217
tibialis Pselliophorus 311
tibicen Gymnorhina 356
ticehursti Sylvia 263
Tichodroma 287
tickelli Pellorneum 254
Tickellia 264
tickelliae Niltava 275
tigrina Dendroica 323
tigrinus Lanius 234
Tigrisoma 16
Tijuca 208
Tilmatura 125
Timalia 256
Timeliopsis 297
timorensis Ficedula 274
timoriensis Megalurus 262
Tinamotis 3
Tinamus 2
tinnieus Cisticola 266
tinnunculus Falco 39
tiphia Aegithina 230
tirica Brotogeris 102

tithys Synallaxis 181
Tityra 210
Tmetothylacus 219
tobaci Amazilia 129
Tockus 149
toco Ramphastos 162
tocuyensis Arremonops 311
Todirostrum 202
Todopsis 269
Todus 144
todus Todus 144
togoensis Vidua 341
tolmiei Geothlypis 323
Tolmomyias 201
tombacea Galbula 154
tomentosa Crax 42
tonsa Platysteira 278
Topaza 130
torda Alca 74
Torgos 30
tormenti Microeca 272
torotono Halcyon 142
torquata Ceryle 138
torquata Chauna
torquata Corythopis 205
torquata Grafisia 349
torquata Melanopareis 195
torquata Myrmornis 193
torquata Pachycephala 283
torquata Poospiza 308
torquata Saxicola 245
torquata Streptocitta 352
torquatus Atlapetes 311
torquatus Celeus 166
torquatus Corvus 367
torquatus Cracticus 357
torquatus Lanisturdus 231
torquatus Lybius 159
torquatus Melidectes 301
torquatus Myioborus 324
torquatus Neolestes
torquatus Pedionomus 53
torquatus Phasianus 50
torquatus Pteroglossus 161
torquatus Rallus 55
torquatus Thamnophilus 186
torquatus Turdus
torqueola Arborophila 47
torqueola Spozophila 309
torquilla Synx 163
Torreornis 306
torridus Attila 199
torridus Furnarius 180
torridus Selasphorus 134
torringtoni Columba 77
totanus Tringa 65
PAGE 79
totta Serinus 332
Touit 102
toulou Centropus 111
toulsoni Apus 124
toussenelii Accipiter 32
townsendi Dendroica 323
townsendi Myadestes 244
townsendi Thalurania 127
toxopei Charmosyna 89
Toxoramphus 297
Toxostorna 238/39
tracheliotus Aegypius 30
Trachyphonus 159
tractrac Cercomela 245
Tragopan 48
traillii Empidonax 201
traillii Oriolus 354
tranquebarica Streptopelia 78
transfasciatus Crypturellus 3
traversi Petroica 272
Traversia 214
Tregallasia 272
Treron 83
triangularis Xiphorhynchus 178
Tribonyx 58
tricarunculata Procnias 211
trichas Geothlypis 323
Trichastoma 254
Trichocichla 268
Trichoglossus 88
Tricholaema 158
Tricholimnas 55
Trichopicus 171
Trichothraupis 316
trichroa Erythrura 339
Triclaria 104
tricollaris Charadrius 64
tricolor Agelaius 329
tricolor Alectrurus 197
tricolor Ara 99
tricolor Atlapetes 311
tricolor Egretta 15
tricolor Ephthianura 271
tricolor Erythrura 339
tricolor Ficedula 274
tricolor Lalage 224
tricolor Perissocephalus 211
tricolor Ploceus 345
tricolor Pycnonotus 226
tricolor Rallina 55
tricolor Rogibyx 63
tricolor (Steganopus) Phaleropus 68
tricolor Vanellus 63
tricolor Zonifer 63
tridactyla Jacamaralcyon 154
tridectylus Larus 71
tridactylus Picoides 174
trifasciatus Basileuterus 324
trifasciatus Carpodacus 335
trifasciatus Hemispingus 314
trifasciatus Nesomimus 238
Trigonoceps 30
trigonostigma Dicaeum 289
Tringa 65
trinitatis Euphonia 318
trinotatus Accipiter 33
tristigma Caprimulgus 120
tristigmata Gallicolumba 82
tristis Acridotheres 352
tristis Carduelis 333
tristis Corvus 367
tristis Meiglyptes 168
tristis Rhopodytes 108
tristissima Lonchura 340
tristrami Dicaeum 289
tristrami Emberiza 304
tristrami Myzomela 298
tristrami Oceanodroma 10
tristramii Onychograthus 349
tristriatus Basileuterus 324
tristriatus Serinus 322
triurus Mimus 238
trivialis Anthus 220
trivirgates Conopias 198
trivirgatus Accipiter 33
trivirgatus Monacha 281
trivirgatus Phylloscopus 264
trocaz Columba 77
trochileum Dicaeum 289
trochilirostris Campyloramphus 178
trochiloides Phylloscopus 264
Trochilus 128
trochilus Phylloscopus 264
Trochocercus 279
Troglodytes 237
troglodytes Cisticola 266
troglodytes Estrilda 338
troglodytes Troglodytes 237
troglodytoides Spelaeornis 255
Trogon 135/36
tropica Fregatta 10
tropicalis Mirafra 215
Tropicoperdix 47
tropicus Corvus 367
trudeani Sterna 73
Trugon 82
Tryngites 67
tasvoensis Nectarinia 293
tschudii Ampeloides 209
tuberculifer Myiarchus 200
tyberosa Crax 42
tucanus Tamphastos 162
tucinkae Eubucco 156
tucumana Amazona 104
tukki Meiglyptes 168
tullbergi Campethera 165
Tumbezia 198
tumultuosus Pionus 103
Turacoena 78
turatii Laniarius 232
turcosa Cyanolyca 364
turcosa Niltava 275
Turdina Chamaeza 192
turdina Dendrocincla 176
turdinus Campylorhynchus 236
turdinus Ptyrticus 254
turdinus Schiffornis 207
Turdoides 256/57
turdoides Cataponera 250
Turdus 249/52
turipavae Cichlornis 268
Turnagra 284
turneri Eremomela 268
Turnix 53
Turtus 79
turtus Pachyptila 7
turtus Streptopelia 78
tuta Halcyon 143
Tylas 229
Tylibyx 63
tympanistria Turtur 79
tympanistrigus Pycnonotus 227
Tympanuchus 43
typica Coracina 222
typica Nesillas 264
typicus Corvus 366
typus Polyboroides 31
Tyranneutes 207
tyrannina Cercomacra 190
tyrannina Dendrocincla 176
Tyranniscus 204
Tyrannopsis 198
Tyrannulus 205
tyrannulus Myiarchus 200
Tyrannusw 198
tyrannus Muscivora 198
tyrannus Spizaetus 37
tyrannus Tyrannus 198
tyrianthina Metallura 132
tyro Dacelo 140
tytleri Phylloscopus 264
Tyto 112
tzacati Amazilia 129

ucayalae Simoxenops 183
udzungwensis Xenoperlix 47
ugrensis Monarelia 281
ugiensis Zosterops 295
ultima Loxioides 325
ultima Pterodroma 9
ultramarina Aphelocoma 364
ultramarina Vini
ulula Surnia 115
umbellus Bonasa 43
umbra Otus 113
umbratilis Rhinomyias 273
umbretta Scopus 17
umbrina Colhuricincla 283
umbrinodorsalis Lagonosticta 338
umbrovirens Phylloscopus 264
unappendiculatus Casuarius 1
unchall Macropygia 78
uncinatus Chondrohierax 28
undata Sylvia 263
undatus Celeus 166
underwoodi Ocreatus 132
undulata Anas 23
undulata Capella 66
undulata Chlamydotis 61
undulata Philidonyris 302
undulatus Aceros 151
undulatus Crypturellus 3
undulatus Melopsittacus 95
undulatus Zebrilus 16
unduligera Frederickena 185
unicincta Columba 77
unicinctus Parabuteo 34
unicolor Aphelocoma 364
unicolor Apus 124
unicolor Chamaepetes 42
unicolor Chloropipo 207
unicolor Collocalia 122
unicolor Corvus 366
unicolor Cosmopsarus 350
unicolor Cyanoramphus 95
unicolor Haematopus 62
unicolor Haplospiza 307
unicolor Meliphaga 299
unicolor Mesoenas 53
unicolor Myadestes 244
unicolor Myrmotherula 188
unicolor Niltava 275
unicolor Paradoxornis 261

unicolor Phrygilus 306
unicolor Scytalopus 195
unicolor Sturnus 351
unicolor Thamnophilus 186
unicolor Turdus 250
unicornis Pauxi 42
uniformis Chalmydera 358
uniformis Chloropipo 207
unisufa Cinnycerthia 236
unisufa Synallaxis 181
unisufa Terpsiphone 279
unirufus Centropus 111
unirufus Lipaugus 210
Upucerthia 179
Upupa 148
Uraeginthus 338
Uragus 334
uralensis Strix 117
Uratelornis 147
urbica Delichon 217
Uria 74
urile Phalacrocorax 13
urinator Pelecanoides 10
Urochroa 130
urochrysia Chalybura 129
Urocissa 363
Urocynchramus 334
Orudynamis 107
urogallus Tetrao 43
Uroglaux 116
Urolais 265
Uromyias 203
Uropelia 80
urophasianus Centrocercus 43
Uropsalis 119
Uropsila 237
Uropygialis Acanthiza 270
uropygialis Cacicus 328
uropygialis Carduelis 333
uropygialis Chirocylla 210
yropygialis Melanerpes 170
uropygialis Phyllomyias 204
uropygialis Pitohui 284
uropygialis Sicalis 308
uropygialis Zosterops 295
Urosphena 262
urosticta Myrmotherula 188
Urosticte 129
urostictus Pycnonotus 227
Urothraupis 311
Urstriorchis 33
ursulae Nectarinia 293
urubambensis Asthenes 182
urubitinga Buteogallus 34
urumatum Nothocrax 42
usambiro Trachyphonus 159
usculatus Microcerculus 237
usheri Tripophaga 182
ussheri Chaetura 123
ussheri Muscicapa 276
ussheri Scotopelia 115
ussheri Telecanthum 123
usta Otus 113
usticollis Eremomela 268
ustulatus Catharus 251
ustulatus Microcerculus 237
aalensis Anthus 220
vagabunda Dendrocitta 363
vagans Cuculus 106
vaillantii Picus 167
vaillantii Trachyphonus 159
valida Prinia 265
validirostris Lanius 234
validirostris Melithreptus 299
validirostris Upucerthia 179
validus Chrysocalaptes 175
validus Corvus 366
PAGE 81
PAGE 81
validus Myiarchus 200
validus Pachyramphus 210
valisineria Aythya 25
vana Lonchura 340
vanderbilti Malacocincla 254
vanderbilti trichastoma 254
vanellus 62/63
vanellus Vanellus 63
Vanga 235
vanikorensis Collocalia 122
vanikorensis Myiagra 280
varia Grallaria 194
varia Mniotilta 322
varia Strix 117
varia Tangara 320
varia Turnix 53
variabilis Emberiza 304
variegata Mesoenas 53
variegata Sula 11
varoagata tadprma 22
variegaticeps Alcippee 260
variegaticeps Anabacerthia 183
variegatus Certhionyx 298
variegatus Crypturellus 3
variegatus Garrulax 258
variegatus Merops 146
variolosus Cacomantis 106
varius Cuculus 106
varius Fregilupus 351
varois Ga::is 5-
varius Parus 286
varius Phalacrocorax
varius Psephotus 94
varius Sphynapicus 171
varzeae Picumnus 163
vasa Coracopsis 96
vassali Garrulex 258
vassorii Tangara 320
vaughani Acrocephalus 263
vaughani Zosterops 296
vauxi Chaetura 123
velata Xolis 196
velata Philentoma 280
velatus Enicurus 243
velatus Ploceus 345
velia Tangara 320
vellalavella Zosterops 295
velox Accipiter 32
velox Geococcyx 109
velox Hemipodius 53
velox Turnix 53
venerata Gracula 352
venerata Halcyon 143
venezuelanus Phylloscantes 203
venezuelensis Diglossa 321
venezuelensis Myiarchus 200
Veniliornis 172
ventralis Accipiter 32
ventralis Amazona 104
ventralis Buteo 35
ventralis Phylloscartes 203
ventralis Tribonyx 58
venusta Chloropsis 230
venusta Dacnis 320
venusta Nectarinia 293
venusta Pitta 213
venustulus Parus 286
venustus Charadrius 64
venustus Granatellus 324
venustus Platycercus 94
veraguensis Anthracothorax 126
veraguensis Geotrygon 81
veredus Charadrius 64
vermiculatas Burhinus 68
vermiculatus Otus 113
vermivora 322
vermivorus Helmitheros 323
vernalis Loriculus 96
vernans Treron 83
veroxii Nectarinia 293
verrcauxi Corra 110
verreauxi Leptoptila 80
verreauxi Paradoxornis 261
Verreauxia 163
verreauxii Aquila 36
verreauxii Carpodacus 335
verrucosus Phalacrocorax 12
versicolor Amazilia 129
versicolor Amozona 104
versicolor Anas 24
versicolor Columba 77
versicolor Engaticus 324
versicolor Eubacco 156
versicolor Geotrygon 81
versicolor Lanio 315
versicolor Mayrornis 272
versicolor Meliphaga 299
versicolor Pachynamphus 210
versicolor Passerina 313
versicolor Phasianus 50
versicolor Pitta 213
versicolor Strepera 357
versicolor Trichoglossus 88
versicolourus Brotogeris 102
versteri Melanocharis 288
verticalis Creurgops 315
verticalis Enemopterix 215
verticalis Hemispingus 314
verticalis Monarcha 231
verticalis Nectarinia 293
verticalis Prioniturus 92
verticalis Tyrannus 198
vesper Rhodopis 133
vespertinus Coccothraustes 336
vespertinus Falco 39
Vestiaria 325
vestita Collocalia 122
vestita Eriocnemis 131
vetula Muscipipra 197
vetula Ortalis 41
vetula Saurothera 108
vexillarius Semeiophotus 120
vicarius Peneothello 272
vicina Meliphaga 299
vicinior Scytalopus 195
vicinior Vireo 326
victor Ptilinopus 85
victoria Goiira 82
victoriae Lamprolia 268
victoriae Lesbia 132
victoriae Ploceus 345
victoriae Ptiloris 359
victoriae Sitta 286
victorini Bradypterus 262
Vidua 341
viduata Dendrocygna 20
viduus Monarcha 281
vieilloti Lybrus 159
vieilloti Saurothera 108
vieilloti Sphecotheres 354
vigil Buceros 153
vigil Rhinoplax 153
vigorsii Eupodotis 61
viguieri Dacnis 320
vilasboasi Pipra 206
viliabambae Schizoeaca 180
vilissimus Zimmerius 204
villaconota Thryothorus 237
villanovae Xiphocalaptes 177
villaviscensio Campylopterus 126
villosa Sitta 286
villosus Dendrocopas 174
villosus Myiobius 201
vinacea Amazzona 104
vinacea Lagonosticta 338
vinacea Streptopelia 78
vinaceigula Egretta 15
vinaceus Carpodacus 335
vinaceus Otus 112
vincens Dicaeum 289
vindhiana Aquila 36
Vini 89
vinipectus Alcippe 260
vintsioides Alcedo 139
viola Heliangelus 131
violacea Euphonia 318
violocea Geotrygon 81
violacea Hyliota 268
violacea Geotrygon 81
violacea Musophaga 105
violacea Nectarinia 293
violacea Nyctanassa 15
violaceus Centropus 111
violaceus Cyanocorax 365
violaceus Ptilonorhynchus 358
violaceus Trogon 136
violiceps Amazilia 129
violiceps Goldmania 128
violifer Coeligena 131
vipio Grus 54
virata Lagonosticta 338
virens Andropadus 226
virens Contopus 200
virens Dendroica 323
virens Icteria 324
virens Megalaima 157
virens Pycnonotus 226
virens Sylvietta 268
virens Viridonia 325
virens Zosterops 296
virenticips Atlapetes 311
Vireo 326

vireo Nicator 228
Vireolanius 326
virescens Andeola 14
virescens Butorides 14
virescens Cacomantis 106
virescens Empidonax 201
virescens Hypsipetes 229
virescens Meliphaga 299
virescens Phyllomyias 204
virescens Phylloscartes 203
virescens Pseudoleistes 330
virescens Schiffornis 207
virescens Tyranneutes 207
virgata Aphriza 67
virgata Asthenes 182
virgata Ciccaba 116
virgata Sterna 73
virgaticeps Thripadectes 184
virgatus Accipiter 32
virgatus Garrulax 258
virgatus Sericornis 271
virginiae Vermivora 322
virginianus Bubo 114
virginianus Colinus 44
virgo Anthropoides 54
viridanum Todirostrum 202
viridanus Picus 167
viridesceus Hypsipetes 229
viridicata Myiopagis 204
viridicata Pyrrhura 101
viridicauda Amazilia 129
viridiceps Apalis 267
viridicollis Tangara 320
viridicyana Cyanolyca 364
viridicacies Erythrur 340
viridiflavus Zimmerius 204
viridifrons Amazilia 129
viridigaster Amazilia 129
viridifuscus Oriolus 353
viridigaster Amazilia 129
viridigenalis Amazona 104
viridigula Anthracothorax 126
viridipallens Lampornis 129
viridirostris Rhopodytes 108
viridis Androphobus 253
viridis Anthracothorax 126
viridis Calyptomena 176
viridis Centropus 111
viridis Cochoa 244
viridis Frederickena 185
viridis Gecinulus 168
viridis Gymnomyza 310
viridis Laterallus 57
viridis Leptopterus 235
viridis Megalaina 157
viridis Merops 146
viridis Neomixis 255
viridis Pachyramphus 210
viridis Picus 167
viridis Psarocolius 326
viridis Psophia 54
viridis Pteroglossus 161
viridis Ptilinopus 85
viridis Sphecotheres 354
viridis Telephorus 233
viridis Terpsiphone 279
viridis Tersina 321
viridis Trogon 136
viridissima Aegithina 230
viridissima Tangara 319
Viridonia 325
viscivrus Turdus 250
vitellina Dendroica 323
vitellinus Manacus 207
vitellinus Ploceus 345
vitellinus Ramphastos 162
Vitia 268
vitiensis Clytorhynchus 280
vitiensis Columba
vitiosus Lophotriccus 202
vitriolina Tangara 320
vittata Amazona 104
vittata Cruaeria 268
vittata Oxyura 26
vittata Pachyptila 7
vittata Petroica 272
vittata Sterna
vittatum Apaloderma 137
vittatus Lanius 234
vittatus Picus 167
vitticeps Chlorostilbon 127
vivida Niltova 275
vocifer Haliacetus 29
vociferans Lipangus 210
vociferans Tyrannus 198
vociferoides Haliacetus 29
vocifrus Caprinulgus 121
vociferus Charadrius 64
Volatinia 308
Vosea 301
vosseleri Bubo 114
vulcani Junco 305
vulcania Cettia 262
vulcanorum Collocalia 122
vulgaris Sturnus 351
vulnerata Myzomela 298
vulneratum Dicaeum 288
vulpina Cranioleuca 182
vulpinus Buteo 35
Vultur 27
vulturina Gypopsitta 103
vulturinum Acryllium 52

waalia Treron 83
waddelli Babax 257
wagleri Aratinga 100
wagleri Icterus 329
wagleri Ortalis 41
wagleri Psarocolius 327
wahlgergi Aquila 36
wahnesi Parotia 361
waiginensis Anas 24
wakensis Rallus 55
wakoloensis Myzomela 298
waldeni Aceros 150
walderi Actinodura 259
walderii Dicrurus 355
wallacei Megapodius 40
wallacei Semioptera 359
wallacei Zosterops 295
wallacii Aegotheles 118
wallacii Habroptila 56
wallacii Malurus 269
wallacii Ptilinopus 85
walleri Onychognathus 349
wallichii Catreus 50
wallicus Pezoporus 95
wardi Harpactes 137
wardi Pseudobias 278
wardii Zoothera 248
Warsanglia 333
warszewiczi Dives 330
watersi Sarothrura 57
waterstradti Prioniturus 92
wateronii Thalwrania 127
watkinsi Grallaria 194
watkinsi Incaspiza 307
watsonii Otus 113
wattersi Dendriocopos 173
webbianus Paradoxornis 261
weberi Trichoglossus 88
websteri Ceyx 139
widdellii Aratinga 100
wellsi Climacteris 287
wellsi Leptotila 80
westermanni Ficedula 274
westlandica Procellaria 7
wetmorei Buthraupis 317
wetmorei Rallus 55
Wetmorethraupis 317
weynsi Ploceus 345
whartoni Ducula 87
whiteheadi Calypromena 176
whiteheadi Harpactes 137
whiteheadi Otus 112
whiteheadi Sitta 286
whiteheadi Stachysis 256
whiteheadi Urocissa 363
whiteheadi Urosphena 262
whitei Amytornis 269
whitei Cyornis 302
whitei Falcunculus 282
whitelyi Caprimulgus 121
whitelyi Pipreola 209
whitemanensis Vosea 301
whitii Prospiza 308
whitneyi Cichlornis 268
whitneyi Micrathene 115
whitneyi Pomarea 273
whytii stactolaema 158
whytii serinus 332
whytii sylvietta 268
wickhami Erithacus 240
wilhelminae Charmosgna 89
wilhelminae Dicaeum 289
wilkinsi Nesospiza 307
willcocksi Indicator 159
williami Metallura 132
williamsi Mirafra 215
williamsi Zoothera 249
williamsoni Muscicapa 276
wilsoni Callaeaus 356
wilsoni Coeligena 131
wilsoni Hemignathus 325
wilsoni Vidua 341
Wilsonia 324
wilsonia Charadrius 64
winchelli Halcyon 143
winifredae Bathmocercus 267
winifredae Scepomycter 267
wolfi Aramides 56
wollweberi Parus 286
woodfordi Corvus 367
woodfordi Nesoclopeus 56
wordfordia 296
woodfordii Ciccaba 116
woodhousei Parmoptila 337
woodhouseii Aphelocema 364
woodi Leonardina 254
woodwardi Amytornis 269
woodwardi Colluricincla 284
woosnami Cisticola 266
worcesteri Turnix 53
wortheni Spizella 306
wrightii Empidonax 201
wumizusume Synthliboramphus 74
wyatti Asthenes 182
wyvilliana Anas 23

xanthocephala Tangara 320
Xanthocephalus 329
xanthocephalus Xanthocephalus 329
xanthoclorus Pteruthius 259
xanthochroa Zosterops 296
xanthocollis Petronia 342
xanthogaster Euphonia 318
xanthogastra Corduelis 333
xanthogastra Tangare 320
xanthogenys Pachysumphus 210
xanthogenys Parus 286
xanthogonys Heliodoxa 130
xanthogramma Melanodera 307
xantholaemus Pycnonotus 227
xantholophus Mesopicus 174
xantholora Amazona 104
Xanthomelus 358
xanthomus Agelaius 329
Xanthomyias 204
Xanthomyza 302
xanthonotus Indicator 159
xanthonotus Oriolus 353
xanthonura Gallicolumba 82
xanthophrys Oxylabes 228
xanthophrys Phyllastrephus 228
xanthophsys Pseudonestor 325
xanthophthalmus Agelarius 329
xanthophthalmus Hemispingus 314
xanthoprymna Oenanthe 246
xanthops Amazona 104
xanthops Foipus 102
xanthops Ploceus 345
xanthopsar 329
xanthopterus Dysithamnus 187
xanthopterus Ploceus 345
xanthopygaeus Picus 167
xanthopygius Heterospingus 316
xanthopygius Prionochilus 288
xanthopygius Serinus 332
xanthopygos Pycnonotus 226
xanthopygus Pardalotus 289
xanthoshynchus Chalcites 107
xanthornus Oriolus 353

xanthorrhous Pycnonotus 227
xanthoschistos Seicercus 264
Xanthotis 298/9
xantusii Hylocharis 128
xavieri Phyllastrephus 228
Xema 71
Xenerpestes 183
Xenicus 214
Xenocopsychyus 241
Xenodacuis 320
Xenoglaus 115
Xenolegia 324
Xenopipo 207
Xenopirostris 235
Xenops 184
Xenoperdix 47
Xenopsaris 199
xenopterus Laterallus 57
Xenornis 187
Xenospingus 307
Xenospiza 305
xenothorax Leptasthenura 180
Xenotriccus 201
Xenus 65
Xiphidopicus 174
Xiphidiopterus 55
Xiphidichynchus 254
Xiphocolaptes 177
Xipholena 208
Xiphorhynchus 177
Xolmis 196

yanacensis Leptasihemura 180
yapura Crypturellus 3
yarrellii Carduelis 333
yarrellii Eulidia 134
yarrellii Motacilla 219
yaruqui Phaethornis 125
yelkonan Puffinus 8
yeltoniensis Melanocorypha 216
yemenensis Acanthis 334
yersini Garrulax 258
yessoensis Emberiza 304
Yetapa 197
yncas Cyanocorax 365
yorki Philemon 300
youngi Halcyon 143
ypecaha Araneides 56
ypinanganus Emberizoides 308
ypsilophorus Synoicus 47
yucatanensis Amazilia 129
yucatanensis Myiarchus 200
yucatanica Cissilopha 365
yucatanicus Campylorhynchus 236
yucatanicus Otophanes 119
Yuhina 260
yurnanensis Sitta 286
yuracares Psarocolius 327

zambesiae Prodotiscus 159
zambesianus Cercotrichus 241
zantholeuca Yuhina 260
zanthopygia Ficedula 274
zappeyi Paradoxornis 261
Zavattariornis 365
Zebrilus 16
zeelandicus Cyanoramphus 95
zeledoni Acrochordopus 205
zeledoni Chlorospingus 314
zeledoni Phyllomyias 205
zeledoni Thryothorus 237
Zeledonia 321
zelichi Sporophila 309
Zenaida 79
Zenaidura 79
zenkeri Melignomon 159
zeylanica Megalaima 157
zeylanicus Pycnonotus 227
zeylonensis Ketupa 114
zeylonica Nectarinia 294
zeylonus Telophorus 233
zimmeri Synallaxis 181
zimmermanni Sterna 72
Zodalia 132
zoeae Ducula 87
zombae Lybius 159
zonaris Streptoprocne
zonarius Platycercus 94
zonatus Campylorhynchus 236
Zonerodius 16
Zonibyx 64
zoniventris Falco 39
zonothorax Micrastur 38
Zonotrichia 305
zonurus Crinifer 105
zoonavena 122/23
Zoothera 248/49
Zosterops 295
zosterops Hemitriccus 202
zosterops Idioptilon 202
zosterops Phyllastrephus 227